Intermediate Algebra:
An Applied Approach

5th EDITION

Intermediate Algebra: An Applied Approach

Richard N. Aufmann
Palomar College, California

Vernon C. Barker
Palomar College, California

Joanne S. Lockwood
Plymouth State College, New Hampshire

HOUGHTON MIFFLIN COMPANY
Boston   New York

Senior Sponsoring Editor: *Maureen O'Connor*
Senior Associate Editor: *Dawn Nuttall*
Editorial Assistant: *John Brister*
Senior Project Editor: *Nancy Blodget*
Editorial Assistant: *Patricia English*
Senior Production/Design Coordinator: *Carol Merrigan*
Senior Manufacturing Coordinator: *Marie Barnes*
Marketing Manager: *Ros Kane*

Cover design: Harold Burch Designs, NYC

Cover image: Y. Akimoto, © Photonica

Printed in the U.S.A.

Library of Congress Catalog Card Number: 98-71980

ISBN
Text: 0-395-90707-1
Instructor's Annotated Edition: 0-395-92322-0

123456789-WC-02-01-00-99-98

Contents

Preface   xiii

To the Student   xxi

Index of Applications   xxiii

1 Review of Real Numbers   1

Section 1.1   Introduction to Real Numbers   3
Objective A   To use inequality and absolute value symbols with real numbers   3
Objective B   To write sets using the roster method and set-builder notation   6
Objective C   To perform operations on sets and write sets in interval notation   8

Section 1.2   Operations on Rational Numbers   17
Objective A   To add, subtract, multiply, and divide integers   17
Objective B   To add, subtract, multiply, and divide rational numbers   19
Objective C   To evaluate exponential expressions   21
Objective D   To use the Order of Operations Agreement   22

Section 1.3   Variable Expressions   29
Objective A   To use and identify the properties of the real numbers   29
Objective B   To evaluate a variable expression   31
Objective C   To simplify a variable expression   32

Section 1.4   Verbal Expressions and Variable Expressions   37
Objective A   To translate a verbal expression into a variable expression   37
Objective B   To solve application problems   40

Focus on Problem Solving: *Polya's Four-Step Process 43* ● Projects and Group Activities: *Water Displacement 45* ● Chapter Summary 46 ● Chapter Review 47 ● Chapter Test 49

2 First-Degree Equations and Inequalities   51

Section 2.1   Solving First-Degree Equations   53
Objective A   To solve an equation using the Addition or the Multiplication Property of Equations   53
Objective B   To solve an equation using both the Addition and the Multiplication Properties of Equations   56
Objective C   To solve an equation containing parentheses   57
Objective D   To solve a literal equation for one of the variables   58

Section 2.2   Applications: Puzzle Problems   63
Objective A   To solve integer problems   63
Objective B   To solve coin and stamp problems   65

Section 2.3   Applications: Mixture and Uniform Motion Problems   69
Objective A   To solve value mixture problems   69
Objective B   To solve percent mixture problems   71
Objective C   To solve uniform motion problems   73

Section 2.4   First-Degree Inequalities   79
  Objective A   *To solve an inequality in one variable*   79
  Objective B   *To solve a compound inequality*   82
  Objective C   *To solve application problems*   84

Section 2.5   Absolute Value Equations and Inequalities   **91**
  Objective A   *To solve an absolute value equation*   91
  Objective B   *To solve an absolute value inequality*   93
  Objective C   *To solve application problems*   95

Focus on Problem Solving: *Understand the Problem 101* ● Projects and Group Activities: *Venn Diagrams 102* ● Chapter Summary 103 ● Chapter Review 105 ● Chapter Test 107 ● Cumulative Review 109

3   Linear Functions and Inequalities in Two Variables   111

Section 3.1   The Rectangular Coordinate System   113
  Objective A   *To graph points in a rectangular coordinate system*   113
  Objective B   *To find the length and midpoint of a line segment*   115
  Objective C   *To graph a scatter diagram*   117

Section 3.2   Introduction to Functions   123
  Objective A   *To evaluate a function*   123

Section 3.3   Linear Functions   133
  Objective A   *To graph a linear function*   133
  Objective B   *To graph an equation of the form $Ax + By = C$*   135
  Objective C   *To find the x- and the y-intercept of a straight line*   138
  Objective D   *To solve application problems*   140

Section 3.4   Slope of a Straight Line   147
  Objective A   *To find the slope of a line given two points*   147
  Objective B   *To graph a line given a point and the slope*   151

Section 3.5   Finding Equations of Lines   157
  Objective A   *To find the equation of a line given a point and the slope*   157
  Objective B   *To find the equation of a line given two points*   158
  Objective C   *To solve application problems*   160

Section 3.6   Parallel and Perpendicular Lines   165
  Objective A   *To find parallel and perpendicular lines*   165

Section 3.7   Inequalities in Two Variables   171
  Objective A   *To graph the solution set of an inequality in two variables*   171

Focus on Problem Solving: *Find a Pattern 175* ● Projects and Group Activities: *Evaluating a Function with a Graphing Calculator 176* ● *Introduction to Graphing Calculators 176* ● Chapter Summary 177 ● Chapter Review 179 ● Chapter Test 181 ● Cumulative Review 183

4   Systems of Linear Equations and Inequalities   185

Section 4.1   Solving Systems of Linear Equations by Graphing and by the Substitution Method   187

Objective A   To solve a system of linear equations by graphing   187
Objective B   To solve a system of linear equations by the substitution method   189
Objective C   To solve investment problems   191

Section 4.2   **Solving Systems of Linear Equations by the Addition Method**   **197**
Objective A   To solve a system of two linear equations in two variables by the addition method   197
Objective B   To solve a system of three linear equations in three variables by the addition method   200

Section 4.3   **Solving Systems of Equations by Using Determinants**   **209**
Objective A   To evaluate a determinant   209
Objective B   To solve a system of equations by using Cramer's Rule   212

Section 4.4   **Application Problems**   **217**
Objective A   To solve rate-of-wind or rate-of-current problems   217
Objective B   To solve application problems   218

Section 4.5   **Solving Systems of Linear Inequalities**   **225**
Objective A   To graph the solution set of a system of linear inequalities   225

Focus on Problem Solving: *Solve an Easier Problem 229* • **Projects and Group Activities:** *Using a Graphing Calculator to Solve a System of Equations 230* • *Solving a First-Degree Equation with a Graphing Calculator 231* • **Chapter Summary 232** • **Chapter Review 233** • **Chapter Test 235** • **Cumulative Review 237**

5   Polynomials   239

Section 5.1   **Exponential Expressions**   **241**
Objective A   To multiply monomials   241
Objective B   To divide monomials and simplify expressions with negative exponents   243
Objective C   To write a number using scientific notation   247
Objective D   To solve application problems   248

Section 5.2   **Introduction to Polynomials**   **253**
Objective A   To evaluate polynomial functions   253
Objective B   To add or subtract polynomials   256

Section 5.3   **Multiplication of Polynomials**   **261**
Objective A   To multiply a polynomial by a monomial   261
Objective B   To multiply two polynomials   262
Objective C   To multiply polynomials that have special products   264
Objective D   To solve application problems   265

Section 5.4   **Division of Polynomials**   **271**
Objective A   To divide polynomials   271
Objective B   To divide polynomials by using synthetic division   273
Objective C   To evaluate a polynomial using synthetic division   275

Section 5.5   **Factoring Polynomials**   **281**
Objective A   To factor a monomial from a polynomial   281
Objective B   To factor by grouping   282
Objective C   To factor a trinomial of the form $x^2 + bx + c$ 283
Objective D   To factor $ax^2 + bx + c$ 285

Section 5.6   Special Factoring   293
  Objective A   *To factor the difference of two perfect squares or a perfect-square trinomial*   293
  Objective B   *To factor the sum or the difference of two perfect cubes*   295
  Objective C   *To factor a trinomial that is quadratic in form*   296
  Objective D   *To factor completely*   297

Section 5.7   Solving Equations by Factoring   303
  Objective A   *To solve an equation by factoring*   303
  Objective B   *To solve application problems*   304

  Focus on Problem Solving: *Find a Counterexample 307* ● Projects and Group Activities: *Reverse Polish Notation 308* ● *Pythagorean Triples 309* ● Chapter Summary 309 ● Chapter Review 311 ● Chapter Test 313 ● Cumulative Review 315

6 **Rational Expressions**   **317**

Section 6.1   Multiplication and Division of Rational Expressions   319
  Objective A   *To simplify a rational expression*   319
  Objective B   *To multiply rational expressions*   322
  Objective C   *To divide rational expressions*   323

Section 6.2   Addition and Subtraction of Rational Expressions   329
  Objective A   *To rewrite rational expressions in terms of a common denominator*   329
  Objective B   *To add or subtract rational expressions*   331

Section 6.3   Complex Fractions   337
  Objective A   *To simplify a complex fraction*   337

Section 6.4   Ratio and Proportion   341
  Objective A   *To solve a proportion*   341
  Objective B   *To solve application problems*   342

Section 6.5   Rational Equations   345
  Objective A   *To solve a fractional equation*   345
  Objective B   *To solve work problems*   347
  Objective C   *To solve uniform motion problems*   349

Section 6.6   Variation   355
  Objective A   *To solve variation problems*   355

  Focus on Problem Solving: *Implication 361* ● Projects and Group Activities: *Continued Fractions 362* ● *Graphing Rational Expressions 363* ● *Graphing Variation Expressions 363* ● Chapter Summary 364 ● Chapter Review 365 ● Chapter Test 367 ● Cumulative Review 369

7 **Exponents and Radicals**   **371**

Section 7.1   Rational Exponents and Radical Expressions   373
  Objective A   *To simplify expressions with rational exponents*   373
  Objective B   *To write exponential expressions as radical expressions and to write radical expressions as exponential expressions*   375

Objective C   *To simplify expressions of the form* $\sqrt[n]{a^n}$ 377

Section 7.2   **Operations on Radical Expressions**   **383**
    Objective A   *To simplify radical expressions*   383
    Objective B   *To add or subtract radical expressions*   384
    Objective C   *To multiply radical expressions*   385
    Objective D   *To divide radical expressions*   387

Section 7.3   **Complex Numbers**   **393**
    Objective A   *To simplify a complex number*   393
    Objective B   *To add or subtract complex numbers*   394
    Objective C   *To multiply complex numbers*   395
    Objective D   *To divide complex numbers*   398

Section 7.4   **Solving Equations Containing Radical Expressions**   **401**
    Objective A   *To solve a radical equation*   401
    Objective B   *To solve application problems*   403

Focus on Problem Solving: *Another Look at Polya's Four-Step Process 407* • **Projects and Group Activities:** *Complex Numbers 408* • *Solving Radical Equations with a Graphing Calculator 409* • **Chapter Summary 410** • **Chapter Review 411** • **Chapter Test 413** • **Cumulative Review 415**

8   **Quadratic Equations**   **417**

Section 8.1   **Solving Quadratic Equations by Factoring or by Taking Square Roots**   **419**
    Objective A   *To solve a quadratic equation by factoring*   419
    Objective B   *To write a quadratic equation given its solutions*   420
    Objective C   *To solve a quadratic equation by taking square roots*   421

Section 8.2   **Solving Quadratic Equations by Completing the Square**   **427**
    Objective A   *To solve a quadratic equation by completing the square*   427

Section 8.3   **Solving Quadratic Equations by Using the Quadratic Formula**   **433**
    Objective A   *To solve a quadratic equation by using the quadratic formula*   433

Section 8.4   **Solving Equations That Are Reducible to Quadratic Equations**   **439**
    Objective A   *To solve an equation that is quadratic in form*   439
    Objective B   *To solve a radical equation that is reducible to a quadratic equation*   440
    Objective C   *To solve a fractional equation that is reducible to a quadratic equation*   442

Section 8.5   **Quadratic Inequalities and Rational Inequalities**   **445**
    Objective A   *To solve a nonlinear inequality*   445

Section 8.6   **Applications of Quadratic Equations**   **449**
    Objective A   *To solve application problems*   449

Focus on Problem Solving: *Inductive and Deductive Reasoning 453* • **Projects and Group Activities:** *Completing the Square 454* • *Using a Graphing Calculator to Solve a Quadratic Equation 455* • *Solving Nonlinear Inequalities Using a Graphing Calculator 456* • **Chapter Summary 456** • **Chapter Review 457** • **Chapter Test 459** • **Cumulative Review 461**

9 **Functions and Relations**   **463**

Section 9.1   Properties of Quadratic Functions   **465**
Objective A   To graph a quadratic function   465
Objective B   To find the x-intercepts of a parabola   468
Objective C   To find the minimum or maximum of a quadratic function   471
Objective D   To solve application problems   472

Section 9.2   Graphs of Functions   **479**
Objective A   To graph functions   479

Section 9.3   Algebra of Functions   **485**
Objective A   To perform operations on functions   485
Objective B   To find the composition of two functions   487

Section 9.4   One-to-One and Inverse Functions   **491**
Objective A   To determine whether a function is one-to-one   491
Objective B   To find the inverse of a function   492

Focus on Problem Solving: *Proof in Mathematics 499* ● **Projects and Group Activities:** *Properties of Polynomials 500* ● *The Greatest-Integer Function 500* ● *Finding the Maximum or Minimum of a Function Using a Graphing Calculator 501* ● **Chapter Summary 502** ● **Chapter Review 503** ● **Chapter Test 505** ● **Cumulative Review 507**

10 **Exponential and Logarithmic Functions**   **509**

Section 10.1   Exponential Functions   **511**
Objective A   To evaluate an exponential function   511
Objective B   To graph an exponential function   513

Section 10.2   Introduction to Logarithms   **519**
Objective A   To write equivalent exponential and logarithmic equations   519
Objective B   To use the Properties of Logarithms to simplify expressions containing logarithms   521
Objective C   To use the change-of-base formula   524

Section 10.3   Graphs of Logarithmic Functions   **529**
Objective A   To graph a logarithmic function   529

Section 10.4   Solving Exponential and Logarithmic Equations   **533**
Objective A   To solve an exponential equation   533
Objective B   To solve a logarithmic equation   535

Section 10.5   Applications of Exponential and Logarithmic Functions   **539**
Objective A   To solve application problems   539

Focus on Problem Solving: *Proof by Contradiction 547* ● **Projects and Group Activities:** *Fractals 548* ● *Graphing Logarithmic Functions Using a Graphing Calculator 549* ● **Chapter Summary 550** ● **Chapter Review 551** ● **Chapter Test 553** ● **Cumulative Review 555**

11 Conic Sections 557

Section 11.1   The Parabola   559
     Objective A   To graph a parabola   559

Section 11.2   The Circle   565
     Objective A   To find the equation of a circle and then graph the circle   565
     Objective B   To write the equation of a circle in standard form   567

Section 11.3   The Ellipse and the Hyperbola   571
     Objective A   To graph an ellipse with center at the origin   571
     Objective B   To graph a hyperbola with center at the origin   573

Section 11.4   Solving Nonlinear Systems of Equations   577
     Objective A   To solve a nonlinear system of equations   577

Section 11.5   Quadratic Inequalities and Systems of Inequalities   583
     Objective A   To graph the solution set of a quadratic inequality in two variables   583
     Objective B   To graph the solution set of a nonlinear system of inequalities   585

Focus on Problem Solving: *Use a Variety of Problem-Solving Techniques 591* ● Projects and Group Activities: *Finding the Proper Dosage 592* ● *Graphing Conic Sections Using a Graphing Utility 593* ● Chapter Summary 594 ● Chapter Review 595 ● Chapter Test 597 ● Cumulative Review 599

12 Sequences and Series 601

Section 12.1   Introduction to Sequences and Series   603
     Objective A   To write the terms of a sequence   603
     Objective B   To find the sum of a series   604

Section 12.2   Arithmetic Sequences and Series   609
     Objective A   To find the nth term of an arithmetic sequence   609
     Objective B   To find the sum of an arithmetic series   611
     Objective C   To solve application problems   612

Section 12.3   Geometric Sequences and Series   615
     Objective A   To find the nth term of a geometric sequence   615
     Objective B   To find the sum of a finite geometric series   617
     Objective C   To find the sum of an infinite geometric series   619
     Objective D   To solve application problems   622

Section 12.4   Binomial Expansions   625
     Objective A   To expand $(a + b)^n$ 625

Focus on Problem Solving: *Forming Negations 631* ● Projects and Group Activities: *ISBN and UPC Numbers 632* ● Chapter Summary 634 ● Chapter Review 635 ● Chapter Test 637 ● Cumulative Review 639

Final Exam 641

Appendix   647
Guidelines for Using Graphing Calculators   647
Proof of the Formula for the Sum of n Terms of an Arithmetic Series   655
Table of Symbols   655
Proofs of Logarithmic Properties   656
Proof of the Formula for the Sum of n Terms of a Geometric Series   656
Table of Measurement Abbreviations   657

Solutions to You Try It   S1

Answers to Odd-Numbered Exercises   A1

Glossary   G1

Index   I1

Preface

The fifth edition of *Intermediate Algebra: An Applied Approach* provides mathematically sound and comprehensive coverage of the topics considered essential in an intermediate algebra course. The text has been designed not only to meet the needs of the traditional college student but also to serve the needs of returning students whose mathematical proficiency may have declined during years away from formal education.

In this new edition of *Intermediate Algebra: An Applied Approach,* we have continued to integrate some of the approaches suggested by AMATYC. Each chapter begins with a mathematical vignette in which there may be a historical note, an application, or a curiosity related to mathematics. At the end of each section there are "Applying the Concepts" exercises, which include writing, synthesis, critical thinking, and challenge problems. Each chapter ends with a "Focus on Problem Solving," which introduces students to problem-solving strategies. This is followed by "Projects and Group Activities," which can be used for cooperative learning activities.

INSTRUCTIONAL FEATURES

Interactive Approach

Intermediate Algebra: An Applied Approach uses an interactive style that provides a student with an opportunity to try a skill as it is presented. Each section is divided into objectives, and every objective contains one or more sets of matched-pair examples. The first example in each set is worked out; the second example, called "You Try It," is for the student to work. By solving this problem, the student practices concepts as they are presented in the text. There are complete worked-out solutions to these examples in an appendix at the end of the book. By comparing their solution to the solution in the appendix, students are able to obtain immediate feedback on and reinforcement of the concept.

Emphasis on Problem-Solving Strategies

Intermediate Algebra: An Applied Approach features a carefully developed approach to problem solving that emphasizes developing strategies to solve problems. Students are encouraged to develop their own strategies, to draw diagrams, and to write strategies as part of their solution to a problem. In each case, model strategies are presented as guides for students to follow as they attempt the "You Try It" problem. Having students provide strategies is a natural way to incorporate writing into the math curriculum.

Emphasis on Applications

The traditional approach to teaching algebra covers only the straightforward manipulation of numbers and variables and thereby fails to teach students the practical value of algebra. By contrast, *Intermediate Algebra: An Applied Approach* contains an extensive collection of contemporary application problems. Wherever appropriate, the last objective of a section presents applications that require the student to use the skills covered in that section to solve practical problems. This carefully integrated applied approach generates student awareness of the value of algebra as a real-life tool.

Completely Integrated Learning System Organized by Objectives

Each chapter begins with a list of the learning objectives included within that chapter. Each of the objectives is then restated in the chapter to remind the student of the current topic of discussion. The same objectives that organize the text are also used as the structure for exercises, testing programs, and the Computer

Tutor. For each objective in the text, there is a corresponding computer tutorial and a corresponding set of test questions.

AN INTERACTIVE APPROACH

Instructors have long realized the need for a text that requires students to use a skill as it is being taught. *Intermediate Algebra: An Applied Approach* uses an interactive technique that meets this need. Every objective, including the one shown below, contains at least one pair of examples. One of the examples is worked. The second example in the pair (You Try It) is not worked so that students may "interact" with the text by solving it. To provide immediate feedback, a complete worked-out solution to this example is provided in the Solutions Section at the end of the book. The benefit of this interactive style is that students can immediately determine whether a new skill has been learned before attempting a homework assignment or moving on to the next skill.

An explanatory passage begins each objective.

Paired examples follow the explanatory passage.

The interactive key is the You Try It in each pair. It has not been worked, so that the student may practice the skill, referring to the worked example at the left if necessary.

Reference to the Solutions Section allows the student to check full solutions immediately.

AN EMPHASIS ON APPLICATIONS

The traditional teaching approach neglects the difficulties that students have in making the transition from arithmetic to algebra. One of the most troublesome and uncomfortable transitions for the student is from concrete arithmetic to symbolic algebra. *Intermediate Algebra: An Applied Approach* recognizes the formidable task the student faces by introducing variables in a very natural way—through applications of mathematics. A secondary benefit of this approach is that the student becomes aware of the value of algebra as a real-life tool.

The solution of an application problem in *Intermediate Algebra: An Applied Approach* is always accompanied by two parts: **Strategy** and **Solution**. The strategy is a written description of the steps that are necessary to solve the problem; the solution is the implementation of the strategy. This format provides students with a structure for problem solving. It also encourages students to write strategies for solving problems, which, in turn, fosters organizing problem-solving strategies in a logical way.

A strategy, which the student may use in solving an application problem, is stated.

The strategy is used in the solution of the worked example.

Students are encouraged to write a strategy for the application problem they solve.

96   Chapter 2 / First-Degree Equations and Inequalities

Example 8
The diameter of a piston for an automobile is $3\frac{5}{16}$ in. with a tolerance of $\frac{1}{64}$ in. Find the lower and upper limits of the diameter of the piston.

You Try It 8
A machinist must make a bushing that has a tolerance of 0.003 in. The diameter of the bushing is 2.55 in. Find the lower and upper limits of the diameter of the bushing.

Strategy
To find the lower and upper limits of the diameter of the piston, let d represent the diameter of the piston, T the tolerance, and L the lower and upper limits of the diameter. Solve the absolute value inequality $|L - d| \leq T$ for L.

Your strategy

Solution
$$|L - d| \leq T$$
$$\left| L - 3\frac{5}{16} \right| \leq \frac{1}{64}$$
$$-\frac{1}{64} \leq L - 3\frac{5}{16} \leq \frac{1}{64}$$
$$-\frac{1}{64} + 3\frac{5}{16} \leq L - 3\frac{5}{16} + 3\frac{5}{16} \leq \frac{1}{64} + 3\frac{5}{16}$$
$$3\frac{19}{64} \leq L \leq 3\frac{21}{64}$$

The lower and upper limits of the diameter of the piston are $3\frac{19}{64}$ in. and $3\frac{21}{64}$ in.

Your solution

Solution on p. S6

OBJECTIVE-SPECIFIC APPROACH

Many mathematics texts are not organized in a manner that facilitates management of learning. Typically, students are left to wander through a maze of apparently unrelated lessons, exercise sets, and tests. *Intermediate Algebra: An Applied Approach* solves this problem by organizing all lessons, exercise sets, computer tutorials, and tests around a carefully constructed hierarchy of objectives. The advantage of this objective-by-objective organization is that it enables the student who is uncertain at any step in the learning process to refer easily to the original presentation and review that material.

The Objective-Specific Approach also gives the instructor greater control over the management of student progress. The Computerized Test Generator and the printed Test Bank are organized by the same objectives as the text. These references are provided with the answers to the test items, thereby allowing the instructor to quickly determine those objectives on which a student may need additional instruction.

The Computer Tutor is also organized around the objectives of the text. As a result, supplemental instruction is available for any objectives that are troublesome for a student.

An objective statement names the topic of each lesson.

2.5 Absolute Value Equations and Inequalities

Objective A   *To solve an absolute value equation* .... **CT**

The exercise sets correspond to the objectives in the text.

2.5 Exercises

· ·

Objective A

Solve.

1. $|x| = 7$ **2.** $|a| = 2$ **3.** $|b| = 4$ **4.** $|c| = 12$

The answers to the odd-numbered exercises are provided in the Answer Section.

SECTION 2.5

1. 7 and -7 **3.** 4 and -4 **5.** 6 and -6 **7.** 7 and -7 **9.** There is no solution.   **11.** There is no solution.

13. -5 and 1   **15.** 2 and 8   **17.** 2   **19.** There is no solution.   **21.** 3 and $-\frac{3}{2}$ **23.** $\frac{3}{2}$ **25.** There is no solution.

27. -3 and 7   **29.** $-\frac{10}{3}$ and 2   **31.** 3 and 1   **33.** $\frac{3}{2}$ **35.** There is no solution.   **37.** $-\frac{1}{6}$ and $\frac{11}{6}$

The answers to the Chapter Review Exercises, the Chapter Test, and the Cumulative Review Exercises show the objective to study if the student incorrectly answers the exercise.

CHAPTER REVIEW

1. 6 [2.1B]   **2.** $\left\{x \mid x > \frac{5}{3}\right\}$ [2.4A]   **3.** $L = \frac{P - 2W}{2}$ [2.1D]   **4.** -9 [2.1A]   **5.** $\left\{x \mid -3 < x < \frac{4}{3}\right\}$ [2.4B]

6. $-\frac{40}{7}$ [2.1B]   **7.** $-\frac{2}{3}$ [2.1A]   **8.** -1 and 9 [2.5A]   **9.** $\{x \mid 1 < x < 4\}$ [2.5B]   **10.** $-\frac{9}{19}$ [2.1C]

11. $\frac{26}{17}$ [2.1C]   **12.** $\{x \mid x > 2 \text{ or } x < -2\}$ [2.4B]   **13.** $\left\{x \mid x \geq 2 \text{ or } x \leq \frac{1}{2}\right\}$ [2.5B]   **14.** $C = R - Pn$ [2.1D]

CHAPTER TEST

1. -2 [2.1A]   **2.** $-\frac{1}{8}$ [2.1A]   **3.** $\frac{5}{6}$ [2.1A]   **4.** 4 [2.1B]   **5.** $\frac{32}{3}$ [2.1B]   **6.** $-\frac{1}{5}$ [2.1B]   **7.** 1 [2.1C]

8. $R = \frac{E - Ir}{I}$ [2.1D]   **9.** $\frac{12}{7}$ [2.1C]   **10.** $\{x \mid x \leq -3\}$ [2.4A]   **11.** $\{x \mid x > -1\}$ [2.4A]   **12.** $\{x \mid x > 2\}$ [2.4B]

CUMULATIVE REVIEW

1. -11 [1.2A]   **2.** -108 [1.2C]   **3.** 3 [1.2D]   **4.** -64 [1.2D]   **5.** -8 [1.3B]   **6.** 1 [1.3B]

7. Commutative Property of Addition [1.3A]   **8.** $(3n + 6) + 3n; 6n + 6$ [1.4A]   **9.** $B = \frac{Fc}{ev}$ [2.1D]

10. $25y$ [1.3C]   **11.** $\{-4, 0\}$ [1.1C]   **12.** $-5\,-4\,-3\,-2\,-1\ 0\ 1\ 2\ 3\ 4\ 5$ [1.1C]   **13.** $y = \frac{-Ax - C}{B}$ [2.1D]

ADDITIONAL LEARNING AIDS

Chapter Opener

The Chapter Opener relates a historical, contemporary, or interesting note about mathematics or its application.

Focus on Problem Solving

At the end of each chapter there is a Focus on Problem Solving, the purpose of which is to introduce the student to various successful problem-solving strategies. Each Focus consists of a problem and an appropriate strategy to solve the problem. Strategies such as guessing, trying to solve a simpler but similar problem, drawing a diagram, and looking for patterns are some of the techniques that are demonstrated.

Projects and Group Activities

The Projects and Group Activities feature can be used as extra credit or cooperative learning activities. The projects cover various aspects of mathematics including use of calculators, extended applications, and additional problem-solving strategies.

Chapter Summaries

At the end of each chapter there is a Chapter Summary that includes Key Words and Essential Rules that were covered in the chapter. These chapter summaries provide a single point of reference as the student prepares for a test.

Study Skills

The To the Student preface provides suggestions for using this text and approaches to creating good study habits. Students are referred to this preface at appropriate places in the text.

Computer Tutor

This state-of-the-art Tutor is a networkable, interactive, algorithmically driven software package. Features include full-color graphics, a glossary, extensive hints, animated solution steps, and a comprehensive class management system. Written by the authors, the Tutor and the text are in the same voice.

Glossary

A Glossary at the end of the book includes definitions of terms used in the text.

Margin Notes

There are three types of margin notes in the student text. *Point of Interest* notes feature interesting sidelights of the topic being discussed. The *Take Note* feature warns students that a procedure may be particularly involved or reminds students that there are certain checks of their work that should be performed. *Calculator Notes* provide suggestions for using a calculator in certain situations. In addition, there are *Instructor Notes* that are printed only in the Instructor's Annotated Edition. These notes provide suggestions for presenting the material or related material that can be used in class.

Index of Applications

The Index of Applications illustrates the power and scope of mathematics and its application. This may help some students see the benefits of mathematics as a tool that is used in everyday experiences.

EXERCISES

End-of-Section Exercises

Intermediate Algebra: An Applied Approach contains more than 6000 exercises. At the end of each section there are exercise sets that are keyed to the corresponding learning objectives. The exercises are carefully developed to ensure that students can apply the concepts in the section to a variety of problem situations. Data Analysis exercises are identified by ⬤ . Calculator exercises are identified by ▦ .

Applying the Concepts Exercises

The End-of-Section Exercises are followed by Applying the Concepts Exercises. These sections contain a variety of exercise types, including:

- challenge problems
- problems that require the student to determine if a statement is always true, sometimes true, or never true
- problems that ask students to determine incorrect procedures

Writing Exercises

Within the Applying the Concepts Exercises, there are Writing Exercises denoted by ✏ . These exercises ask students to write about a topic in the section or to research and report on a related topic.

Chapter Review Exercises

Review Exercises are found at the end of each chapter. These exercises are selected to help the student integrate all of the topics presented in the chapter. The answers to all Review Exercises are given in the Answer Section at the end of the book. Along with the answer, there is a reference to the objective that pertains to each exercise.

Chapter Test Exercises

The Chapter Test Exercises are designed to simulate a possible test of the material in the chapter. The answers to all Chapter Test Exercises are given in the Answer Section at the end of the book. Along with the answer, there is a reference to the objective that pertains to each exercise.

Cumulative Review Exercises

Cumulative Review Exercises, which appear at the end of each chapter (beginning with Chapter 2), help students maintain skills learned in previous chapters. The answers to all Cumulative Review Exercises are given in the Answer Section. Along with the answer, there is a reference to the objective that pertains to each exercise.

NEW TO THIS EDITION

The sequence of chapters has been slightly changed so as to allow a better pedagogical organization. The chapter on Rational Expressions, which requires a lot of factoring, is now Chapter 6, and immediately follows Chapter 5, Polynomials, in which factoring is introduced. The chapter on Exponents and Radicals is now Chapter 7, which lends support to the material on quadratic equations immediately following in Chapter 8.

Investment problems have been moved to Chapter 4, Systems of Equations and Inequalities.

We have added some problems that have too much data, thereby requiring the student to select the information needed to solve the problem.

For some exercises, not enough information is given to reach a single answer. Thus, there is more than one answer that satisfies the conditions of the problem.

The skill development exercises were thoroughly reviewed to ensure that there was adequate representation of various problem types. As a result of this review, we have changed or replaced some drill exercises to include problem types that were missing.

Many of the application problems were changed to reflect current data and trends. New application problems were added to demonstrate to students the variety of problems that require mathematical analysis.

Career notes were added to the chapter opener pages to illustrate to students the diverse ways in which mathematics is used in the workplace.

We have more than doubled the number of projects and group activities. Some of these projects have suggested Internet sites so that the student may continue to explore a topic.

In response to suggestions by users, the Chapter Review Exercises are no longer categorized by section. Thus there are no organizational clues to students as to the type of skill needed to solve an exercise. The answers to all Chapter Review Exercises are in the Answer Section. Along with the answer, there is a reference to the objective that pertains to each exercise.

SUPPLEMENTS FOR THE INSTRUCTOR

Instructor's Annotated Edition

The Instructor's Annotated Edition is an exact replica of the student text except that answers to all exercises are given in the text. Also, there are *Instructor Notes* in the margin that offer suggestions for presenting the material in that objective.

Instructor's Resource Manual with Chapter Tests

The Instructor's Resource Manual contains the printed Chapter Tests, which are the first of three sources of testing material. Eight printed tests—four free-response and four multiple-choice—are provided for each chapter. In addition, there are Cumulative Tests after Chapters 3, 6, 9, and 12, and a Final Exam. The Instructor's Resource Manual also includes suggestions for course sequencing and outlines for the answers to the Writing Exercises.

Computerized Test Generator

The Computerized Test Generator is the second source of testing material. The database contains more than 2000 test items. The Test Generator is designed to provide an unlimited number of tests for each chapter, cumulative chapter tests, and a final exam. It is available for Microsoft Windows® and the Macintosh. Both versions provide **on-line testing** and **gradebook** functions.

Printed Test Bank

The printed Test Bank, the third component of the testing material, is a print-out of all items in the Computerized Test Generator. Instructors who do not have access to a computer can use the Test Bank to select items to include on a test being prepared by hand.

Solutions Manual

The Solutions Manual contains worked-out solutions for all end-of-section exercises, Chapter Review Exercises, Chapter Test Exercises, Cumulative Review Exercises, and the Final Exam.

SUPPLEMENTS FOR THE STUDENT

Student Solutions Manual

The Student Solutions Manual contains the complete solutions to all odd-numbered exercises in the text.

Computer Tutor

The content of this interactive, state-of-the-art tutorial software was written by the authors and is in the same voice as the text. The Tutor supports every topic in the text. Problems are algorithmically generated, solution steps are animated, lessons and problems are presented in a colorful, lively manner, and an integrated classroom management system tracks and reports student performance. Features include:

- assessment
- free-response problems
- ability to repeat same problem type
- ability to print problems
- syllabus customization
- ability to bookmark

The Computer Tutor can be used in several ways: (1) to cover material the student missed because of absence; (2) to reinforce instruction on a concept that the student has not yet mastered; (3) to review material in preparation for exams.

This networkable Tutor is available on CD-ROM or floppy disk for Windows. There is also a version available for the Macintosh. The Tutor is free to any school upon adoption of this text; however, students can purchase a copy of the Tutor on floppy disk for home use.

Within each section of the book, a computer icon **CT** appears next to each objective. The icon serves as a reminder that there is a Computer Tutor lesson corresponding to that objective.

Videotapes

Within each section of the text, a videotape icon appears next to an objective for which there is a corresponding video. The icon contains the reference number of the appropriate video. Each video topic is motivated through an application, and the necessary mathematics to solve that problem are then presented.

ACKNOWLEDGMENTS

We sincerely wish to thank the following reviewers, who reviewed the manuscript in various stages of development, for their valuable contributions:

Susan P. Bradley, *Angelina College, TX;* **James Brasel,** *Philips Community College, AR;* **Annalisa Ebanks,** *Jefferson Community College, KY;* **Hugh Griffith,** *Victor Valley College, CA;* **R. L. Howard,** *Coconino Community College, AZ;* **Ilhan A. Izmirli,** *Strayer College, Washington, DC;* **Sarah Jackman,** *Richland College, TX;* **Brian Jackson,** *Connors State College, OK;* **Harvey Leboff,** *Mass Bay Community College, MA;* **Jaclyn LeFebvre,** *Illinois Central College;* **Chip D. Nava,** *Pueblo Community College, CO;* **Kathryn Pletsch,** *Antelope Valley College, CA;* **Hassan Saffari,** *University of Kentucky/Prestonsburg College;* **John Searcy;** **Marsha Self,** *El Paso Community College, TX;* **John Wardigo,** *Bloomsburg University, PA;* **Don W. Williams,** *Brazosport College, TX.*

Special thanks to **Dan Clegg** of *Palomar College* for some of the new application problems.

To the Student

Take an active role in the learning process.

Do the homework.

Attend class regularly.

Participate in class.

Use the features of the text.

   Read the objective statement.

   Read the objective material.

   Study the in-text examples.

Use the boxed examples.

1. Study the example on the left.

2. Solve the You Try It example.

3. Check your work against the solution in the back of the book.

Do the exercises.

Check your answers to the odd-numbered exercises.

Read the Chapter Summary.

Do the Chapter Review exercises.

Many students feel that they will never understand math, while others appear to do very well with little effort. Oftentimes what makes the difference is that successful students take an active role in the learning process.

Learning mathematics requires your *active* participation. Although doing homework is one way you can actively participate, it is not the only way. First, you must attend class regularly and become an active participant. Second, you must become actively involved with the textbook.

Intermediate Algebra: An Applied Approach was written and designed with you in mind as a participant. Here are some suggestions on how to use the features of this textbook.

There are 12 chapters in this text. Each chapter is divided into sections, and each section is subdivided into learning objectives. Each learning objective is labeled with a letter from A to D.

First, read each objective statement carefully so you will understand the learning goal that is being presented. Next, read the objective material carefully, being sure to note each bold word. These words indicate important concepts that you should familiarize yourself with. Study carefully each in-text example (denoted by an orange arrow), noting the techniques and strategies used to solve the example.

You will then come to the key learning feature of this text, the *boxed examples*. These examples have been designed to assist you in a very specific way. Notice that in each example box, the example on the left is completely worked out and the You Try It example on the right is not. *You* are expected to work the right-hand example (in the space provided) in order to immediately test your understanding of the material you have just studied.

You should study the worked-out example carefully by working through each step presented. This allows you to focus on each step and reinforces the technique for solving that type of problem. You can then use the worked-out example as a model for solving similar problems.

Next, try to solve the You Try It example using the problem-solving techniques that you have just studied. When you have completed your solution, check your work by turning to the page in the Appendix where the complete solution can be found. The page number on which the solution appears is printed at the bottom of the example box in the right-hand corner. By checking your solution, you will know immediately whether or not you fully understand the skill you just studied.

When you have completed studying an objective, do the exercises in the exercise set that correspond with that objective. The exercises are labeled with the same letter as the objective. Math is a subject that needs to be learned in small sections and practiced continually in order to be mastered. Doing all of the exercises in each exercise set will help you to master the problem-solving techniques necessary for success. As you work through the exercises for an objective, check your answers to the odd-numbered exercises with those in the back of the book.

After completing a chapter, read the Chapter Summary. This summary highlights the important topics covered in the chapter. Following the Chapter Summary are a Chapter Review, a Chapter Test, and a Cumulative Review (beginning with Chapter 2). Doing the review exercises is an important way of testing your understanding of the chapter. The answer to each review exercise is given at the back

Check your answers.

Restudy objectives you missed.

of the book. Each answer to the Chapter Test and Cumulative Review is followed by a reference that tells which objective that exercise was taken from. For example, (4.2B) means Section 4.2, Objective B. After checking your answers, restudy any objective that you missed. It may be very helpful to retry some of the exercises for that objective to reinforce your problem-solving techniques.

Do the Chapter Test.

The Chapter Test should be used to prepare for an exam. We suggest that you try the Chapter Test a few days before your actual exam. Take the test in a quiet place and try to complete the test in the same amount of time you will be allowed for your exam. When taking the Chapter Test, practice the strategies of successful test takers: 1) scan the entire test to get a feel for the questions; 2) read the directions carefully; 3) work the problems that are easiest for you first; and, perhaps most importantly, 4) try to stay calm.

Check your answers.

Restudy objectives you missed.

When you have completed the Chapter Test, check your answers. If you missed a question, review the material in that objective and rework some of the exercises from that objective. This will strengthen your ability to perform the skills in that objective.

The Cumulative Review allows you to refresh the skills you have learned in previous chapters. This is very important in mathematics. By consistently reviewing previous material, you will retain the skills already learned as you build new ones.

Remember, to be successful: attend class regularly; read the textbook carefully; actively participate in class; work with your textbook using the You Try It examples for immediate feedback and reinforcement of each skill; do all of the homework assignments; review constantly; and work carefully.

Index of Applications

Age Problems, 224
The Airline Industry, 129
Animal Science, 143
Architecture, 344
The Arts, 477, 614, 640
Astronomy, 41, 252, 312
Athletics, 132
Automotive Industry, 48, 122

Business, 358, 359, 452, 477, 614, 638

Carpentry, 42
Cartography, 366
Chemistry, 121
Coin Problems, 66, 68, 106, 110, 184, 220, 222, 223, 224, 238
Commissions, 89, 106
Compensation, 238, 359, 614
Computers, 344
Computer Science, 248
Conservation, 343, 438
Construction, 180, 343, 358, 403, 412, 452, 472, 477
Consumer Credit, 40
Consumerism, 84, 88, 89, 90, 108, 110, 144, 154, 342, 556
Criminology, 344

Demography, 517, 518
Depreciation, 150, 182, 184, 462
Discount, 155

Education, 84, 90, 106, 182, 366, 498, 532, 542, 544, 641
Elections, 370
Electronics, 100, 358, 360, 366, 368
Employment, 164, 344
Energy, 122
Entertainment, 406
Exponential Decay, 543, 552, 554, 624, 636, 638, 640

Fund Raising, 344

Geography, 451
Geometry, 40, 42, 48, 84, 88, 170, 224, 265, 266, 269, 270, 292, 304, 306, 312, 314, 359, 406, 450, 451, 458, 460, 462, 478, 504, 506, 570, 641
Government, 252

Health, 614
Health Care, 164

Industry, 132
Interior Decorating, 344, 368
Investments, 42, 192, 195, 196, 220, 224, 234, 236, 416, 542, 543, 552, 556, 622, 641, 642

Labor, 140
Light, 544, 646
Lotteries, 344, 612

Manufacturing, 128, 144, 160, 163, 180, 477
Markup, 155
Mathematics, 39, 41, 48, 50, 64, 67, 68, 84, 88, 90, 106, 108, 110, 156, 306, 312, 316, 354, 370, 458
Measurement, 252, 314
Mechanics, 96, 99, 100, 106, 108, 110, 360, 462, 600
Media, 153, 343
Medicine, 344, 357
Mining, 472
Mixtures, 42, 70, 72, 75, 76, 77, 78, 106, 108, 110, 184, 222, 223, 234, 236, 238, 316, 370, 508, 556, 600, 640
Motion Problems, 40, 74, 77, 78, 106, 108, 110, 144, 153, 154, 180, 184, 218, 221, 222, 252, 316, 350, 353, 354, 360, 366,

368, 370, 416, 452, 458, 518, 538, 600, 645, 646
Music, 508
The Music Industry, 164

Nutrition, 118

pH Problems, 542, 544
Physics, 42, 131, 132, 248, 251, 252, 260, 306, 312, 314, 340, 357, 358, 359, 360, 366, 404, 405, 406, 412, 414, 416, 432, 451, 452, 472, 477, 508, 518, 538, 556, 612, 614, 622, 624, 640, 646
Physiology, 140
Power, 94, 131, 412

Rate-of-Wind and Rate-of-Current Problems, 218, 221, 222, 234, 236, 238, 350, 354, 370, 450, 452, 460, 556, 600, 640, 646
Real Estate, 129, 624, 646
Recreation, 42
Richter Scale, 542, 522, 552

Salaries, 636
Shipping, 127, 129, 344, 498
Social Science, 40, 42, 343, 622
Sound, 552
Sports, 118, 432, 477
Stamp Problems, 66, 68, 108, 416
Stock Market, 342, 641

Taxes, 150
Telecommunications, 41, 154
Temperature, 89, 132, 160, 636
Tolerance, 96, 99, 100, 106, 108, 110, 238, 462

Wages, 143, 163, 624
Work Problems, 348, 352, 353, 366, 368, 370, 452, 458, 508, 640

Introductory Algebra:
An Applied Approach

1

Review of Real Numbers

The job of a flight engineer is to assist the pilot and copilot of a large aircraft in checking the equipment on a plane before takeoff, to operate certain navigational devices during flight, to record performance levels, and to report any mechanical problems to the pilot. Airlines look for candidates who have completed at least two years of college, including courses in mathematics and science.

Objectives

Section 1.1

To use inequality and absolute value symbols with real numbers

To write sets using the roster method and set-builder notation

To perform operations on sets and write sets in interval notation

Section 1.2

To add, subtract, multiply, and divide integers

To add, subtract, multiply, and divide rational numbers

To evaluate exponential expressions

To use the Order of Operations Agreement

Section 1.3

To use and identify the properties of the real numbers

To evaluate a variable expression

To simplify a variable expression

Section 1.4

To translate a verbal expression into a variable expression

To solve application problems

Early Egyptian Number System

The early Egyptian type of picture writing shown at the left is known as hieroglyphics.

The Egyptian hieroglyphic method of representing numbers differs from our modern version in an important way. For the hieroglyphic number, the symbol indicated the value. For example, the symbol ∩ meant 10. The symbol was repeated to get larger values.

The markings below represent the number 743. Each vertical stroke represents 1, each ∩ represents 10, and each ⟨ represents 100.

There are 3 ones, 4 tens, and 7 hundreds, representing the number 743.

In our system, the position of a number is important. The number 5 in 356 means 5 tens; but the number 5 in 3517 means 5 hundreds. Our system is called a positional number system.

Consider the hieroglyphic number below. Note that the ∩ is missing. For the early Egyptians, when a certain group of ten was not needed, it was just omitted.

There are 4 ones and 5 hundreds. Thus the number 504 is represented by this group of markings.

In a positional system of notation like ours, a zero is used to show that a certain group of ten is not needed. This may seem like a fairly simple idea, but it was not until near the 14th century that a zero was introduced into the number system.

1.1 Introduction to Real Numbers

Objective A   ***To use inequality and absolute value symbols with real numbers*** .... 1 CT

It seems to be a human characteristic to put similar items in the same place. For instance, an astronomer places stars in *constellations* and a geologist divides the history of the earth into *eras.*

Mathematicians likewise place objects with similar properties in *sets.* A **set** is a collection of objects. The objects are called **elements** of the set. Sets are denoted by placing braces around the elements in the set.

The numbers that we use to count things, such as the number of books in a library or the number of CDs sold by a record store, have similar characteristics. These numbers are called the *natural numbers.*

Natural numbers = {1, 2, 3, 4, 5, 6, 7, 8, 9, 10, 11, . . .}

Each natural number is a *prime* number or a *composite* number. **A prime number** is a natural number greater than 1 that is divisible (evenly) only by itself and 1. For example, 2, 3, 5, 7, 11, and 13 are the first 6 prime numbers. A natural number that is not a prime number is a **composite number.** The numbers 4, 6, 8, and 9 are the first four composite numbers.

The natural numbers do not have a symbol to denote the concept of none, for instance, the number of trees taller than 1000 feet. The *whole numbers* include zero and the natural numbers.

Whole numbers = {0, 1, 2, 3, 4, 5, 6, 7, 8, . . .}

The whole numbers alone do not provide all the numbers that are useful in applications. For instance, a meteorologist needs numbers below zero and above zero.

Integers = {. . . , −5, −4, −3, −2, −1, 0, 1, 2, 3, 4, 5, . . .}

The integers . . . , −5, −4, −3, −2, −1 are **negative integers.** The integers 1, 2, 3, 4, 5, . . . are **positive integers.** Note that the natural numbers and the positive integers are the same set of numbers. The integer zero is neither a positive nor a negative integer.

Still other numbers are necessary to solve the variety of application problems that exist. For instance, a landscape architect may need to purchase irrigation pipe that has a diameter of $\frac{5}{8}$ in. The numbers that include fractions are called *rational numbers.*

Rational numbers = $\left\{ \dfrac{p}{q}, \text{ where } p \text{ and } q \text{ are integers and } q \neq 0 \right\}$

Examples of rational numbers include $\frac{2}{3}$, $-\frac{9}{2}$, and $\frac{5}{1}$. Note that $\frac{5}{1} = 5$ so all integers are rational numbers. The number $\frac{4}{\pi}$ is not a rational number because π is not an integer.

A rational number written as a fraction can be written in decimal notation by dividing the numerator by the denominator.

➡ Write $\frac{3}{8}$ as a decimal.

Divide 3 by 8.

```
    0.375
8)3.000
  -2 4
  ─────
    60
   -56
   ────
    40
   -40
   ────
     0
```
← This is a terminating decimal.

← The remainder is zero.

$$\frac{3}{8} = 0.375$$

➡ Write $\frac{2}{15}$ as a decimal.

Divide 2 by 15.

```
    0.133
15)2.000
  -1 5
  ─────
    50
   -45
   ────
    50
   -45
   ────
     5
```
← This is a repeating decimal.

← The remainder is never zero.

$$\frac{2}{15} = 0.1\overline{3}$$

• The bar over 3 indicates this digit repeats.

Some numbers cannot be written as terminating or repeating decimals, for example, $0.01001000100001\ldots$, $\sqrt{7} \approx 2.6457513$, and $\pi \approx 3.1415927$. These numbers have decimal representations that neither terminate nor repeat. They are called **irrational numbers.** The rational numbers and the irrational numbers taken together are the *real numbers.*

Real numbers = {rational numbers and irrational numbers}

The relationship among sets of numbers is shown in the figure below.

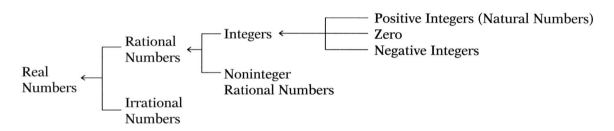

The **graph of a real number** is made by placing a heavy dot on a number line directly above the number. The graphs of some real numbers are shown below.

Consider the following sentences:

A restaurant's chef prepared a dinner and served *it* to the customers.
A maple tree was planted and *it* grew two feet in one year.

In the first sentence, "it" means dinner; in the second sentence, "it" means tree. In language, this word can stand for many different objects. Similarly, in mathematics, a letter of the alphabet can be used to stand for some number. A letter used in this way is called a **variable.**

It is convenient to use a variable to represent or stand for any one of the elements of a set. For instance, the statement "x is an *element of* the set {0, 2, 4, 6}" means that x can be replaced by 0, 2, 4, or 6. The set {0, 2, 4, 6} is called the **domain** of the variable.

The symbol for "is an element of" is ∈; the symbol for "is not an element of" is ∉. For example,

$$2 \in \{0, 2, 4, 6\} \qquad 6 \in \{0, 2, 4, 6\} \qquad 7 \notin \{0, 2, 4, 6\}$$

Variables are used in the next definition.

Definition of Inequality Symbols

If a and b are two real numbers and a is to the left of b on the number line, then a is **less than** b. This is written $a < b$.

If a and b are two real numbers and a is to the right of b on the number line, then a is **greater than** b. This is written $a > b$.

Here are some examples.

$$5 < 9 \qquad -4 > -10 \qquad \pi < \sqrt{17} \qquad 0 > -\frac{2}{3}$$

The inequality symbols ≤ (less than or equal) and ≥ (greater than or equal) are also important. Note the examples below.

$$4 \leq 5 \quad \text{is a true statement because } 4 < 5.$$
$$5 \leq 5 \quad \text{is a true statement because } 5 = 5.$$

The numbers 5 and −5 are the same distance from zero but on opposite sides of zero. The numbers 5 and −5 are called **additive inverses** or **opposites** of each other.

The additive inverse (or opposite) of 5 is −5. The additive inverse of −5 is 5. The symbol for additive inverse is −.

$-(2)$ means the additive inverse of *positive* 2. $\qquad\qquad -(2) = -2$

$-(-5)$ means the additive inverse of *negative* 5. $\qquad\qquad -(-5) = 5$

The **absolute value** of a number is its distance from zero on the number line. The symbol for absolute value is $|\ \ |$.

Note from the figure above that the distance from 0 to 5 is 5. Therefore, $|5| = 5$. That figure also shows that the distance from 0 to −5 is 5. Therefore, $|-5| = 5$.

Absolute Value

The absolute value of a positive number is the number itself. The absolute value of a negative number is the opposite of the negative number. The absolute value of zero is zero.

➡ Evaluate: $-|-12|$

$$-|-12| = -12 \qquad$$ • The absolute value sign does not affect the negative sign *in front* of the absolute value sign.

Example 1

Let $y \in \{-7, 0, 6\}$. For which values of y is the inequality $y < 4$ a true statement?

Solution

Replace y by each of the elements of the set and determine whether the inequality is true.

$$y < 4$$
$$-7 < 4 \quad \text{True}$$
$$0 < 4 \quad \text{True}$$
$$6 < 4 \quad \text{False}$$

The inequality is true for -7 and 0.

You Try It 1

Let $z \in \{-10, -5, 6\}$. For which values of z is the inequality $z > -5$ a true statement?

Your solution

Example 2

Let $y \in \{-12, 0, 4\}$.
a. Determine $-y$, the additive inverse of y, for each element of the set.
b. Evaluate $|y|$ for each element of the set.

Solution

a. Replace y in $-y$ by each element of the set and determine the value of the expression.

$$-y$$
$$-(-12) = 12$$
$$-(0) = 0 \qquad \bullet \; \text{0 is neither positive}$$
$$\qquad\qquad\qquad \text{nor negative.}$$
$$-(4) = -4$$

b. Replace y in $|y|$ by each element of the set and determine the value of the expression.

$$|y|$$
$$|-12| = 12$$
$$|0| = 0$$
$$|4| = 4$$

You Try It 2

Let $d \in \{-11, 0, 8\}$.
a. Determine $-d$, the additive inverse of d, for each element of the set.
b. Evaluate $|d|$ for each element of the set.

Your solution

Solutions on p. S1

Objective B   *To write sets using the roster method and set-builder notation*   CT

The **roster method** of writing a set encloses the list of the elements of the set in braces. The set of whole numbers, written $\{0, 1, 2, 3, 4, \ldots\}$, and the set of natural numbers, written $\{1, 2, 3, 4, \ldots\}$, are **infinite sets.** The pattern of numbers continues without end. It is impossible to list all the elements of an infinite set.

The set of even natural numbers less than 10 is written {2, 4, 6, 8}. This is an example of a **finite set;** all the elements of the set can be listed.

The set that contains no elements is called the **empty set,** or **null set,** and is symbolized by $\varnothing$ or { }. The set of trees over 1000 feet tall is the empty set.

⮕ Use the roster method to write the set of whole numbers less than 5.

{0, 1, 2, 3, 4}   • Recall that the whole numbers include 0.

A second method of representing a set is **set-builder notation.** Set-builder notation can be used to describe almost any set, but it is especially useful when writing infinite sets. In set-builder notation, the set of integers greater than −3 is written

$$\{x \mid x > -3, \; x \in \text{integers}\}$$

The set of all x such that $x > -3$ and x is an element of the integers.

This is an infinite set. It is impossible to list all the elements of the set, but the set can be described using set-builder notation.

The set of real numbers less than 5 is written

$$\{x \mid x < 5, x \in \text{real numbers}\}$$

and is read "the set of all x such that x is less than 5 and x is an element of the real numbers."

⮕ Use set-builder notation to write the set of integers greater than 20.

$$\{x \mid x > 20, x \in \text{integers}\}$$

Example 3
Use the roster method to write the set of positive integers less than or equal to 7.

Solution
{1, 2, 3, 4, 5, 6, 7}

Example 4
Use set-builder notation to write the set of integers less than −9.

Solution
$\{x \mid x < -9, x \in \text{integers}\}$

You Try It 3
Use the roster method to write the set of negative integers greater than −6.

Your solution

You Try It 4
Use set-builder notation to write the set of whole numbers greater than or equal to 15.

Your solution

Solutions on p. S1

Objective C   **To perform operations on sets and write sets in interval notation** ....

Just as operations such as addition and multiplication are performed on real numbers, operations are performed on sets. Two operations performed on sets are *union* and *intersection*.

Union of Two Sets

The **union** of two sets, written $A \cup B$, is the set of all elements that belong to either set A **or** set B. In set-builder notation, this is written

$$A \cup B = \{x \mid x \in A \quad \text{or} \quad x \in B\}$$

Given $A = \{2, 3, 4\}$ and $B = \{0, 1, 2, 3\}$, the union of A and B contains all the elements that belong to either A or B. The elements that belong to both sets are listed only once.

$$A \cup B = \{0, 1, 2, 3, 4\}$$

Intersection of Two Sets

The **intersection** of two sets, written $A \cap B$, is the set of all elements that are common to both set A **and** set B. In set-builder notation, this is written

$$A \cap B = \{x \mid x \in A \quad \text{and} \quad x \in B\}$$

POINT OF INTEREST

The symbols $\in$, $\cup$, and $\cap$ were first used by Giuseppe Peano in *Arithmetices Principia, Nova Exposita* (The Principle of Mathematics, a New Method of Exposition), published in 1889. The purpose of this book was to deduce the principles of mathematics from pure logic.

Given $A = \{2, 3, 4\}$ and $B = \{0, 1, 2, 3\}$, the intersection of A and B contains all the elements that are common to both A and B.

$$A \cap B = \{2, 3\}$$

➡ Given $A = \{2, 3, 5, 7\}$ and $B = \{0, 1, 2, 3, 4\}$, find $A \cup B$ and $A \cap B$.

$A \cup B = \{0, 1, 2, 3, 4, 5, 7\}$ • List the elements of each set. The elements that belong to both sets are listed only once.

$A \cap B = \{2, 3\}$ • List the elements that are common to both A and B.

Set-builder notation and the inequality symbols $>$, $<$, $\geq$, and $\leq$ are used to describe infinite sets of real numbers. These sets can also be graphed on the real number line.

The graph of $\{x \mid x > -2, x \in \text{real numbers}\}$ is shown below. The set is the real numbers greater than -2. The parenthesis on the graph indicates that -2 is not included in the set.

The graph of $\{x \mid x \geq -2, x \in \text{real numbers}\}$ is shown below. The set is the real numbers greater than or equal to -2. The bracket at -2 indicates that -2 is included in the set.

In many cases, we will assume that real numbers are being used and omit "$x \in$ real numbers" from set-builder notation. For instance, the above set is written $\{x \mid x \geq -2\}$.

➡ Graph $\{x \mid x \leq 3\}$.

- Draw a bracket at 3 to indicate that 3 is in the set. Draw a solid line to the left of 3.

The union of two sets is the set of all elements belonging to either one or the other of the two sets. The set $\{x \mid x \leq -1\} \cup \{x \mid x > 3\}$ is the set of real numbers that are either less than or equal to -1 or greater than 3.

The set is written $\{x \mid x \leq -1 \text{ or } x > 3\}$.

The set $\{x \mid x > 2\} \cup \{x \mid x > 4\}$ is the set of real numbers that are either greater than 2 or greater than 4.

The set is written $\{x \mid x > 2\}$.

➡ Graph $\{x \mid x > 1\} \cup \{x \mid x < -4\}$.

- The graph includes all the numbers that are either greater than 1 or less than -4.

The intersection of two sets is the set that contains the elements common to both sets. The set $\{x \mid x > -2\} \cap \{x \mid x < 5\}$ is the set of real numbers that are greater than -2 and less than 5.

The set can be written $\{x \mid x > -2 \text{ and } x < 5\}$. However, it is more commonly written $\{x \mid -2 < x < 5\}$.

The set $\{x \mid x < 4\} \cap \{x \mid x < 5\}$ is the set of real numbers that are less than 4 and less than 5.

The set is written $\{x \mid x < 4\}$.

➡ Graph $\{x \mid x < 0\} \cap \{x \mid x > -3\}$.

* The set is $\{x \mid -3 < x < 0\}$.

Some sets can also be expressed using **interval notation.** For example, the interval notation $(-3, 2]$ indicates the interval of all real numbers greater than -3 and less than or equal to 2. As on the graph of a set, the left parenthesis indicates that -3 is not included in the set. The right bracket indicates that 2 is included in the set.

An interval is said to be **closed** if it includes both endpoints; it is **open** if it does not include either endpoint. An interval is **half-open** if one endpoint is included and the other is not. In each example given below, -3 and 2 are the **endpoints** of the interval. In each case, the set notation, the interval notation, and the graph of the set are shown.

$\{x \mid -3 < x < 2\}$	$(-3, 2)$ Open interval	
$\{x \mid -3 \leq x \leq 2\}$	$[-3, 2]$ Closed interval	
$\{x \mid -3 \leq x < 2\}$	$[-3, 2)$ Half-open interval	
$\{x \mid -3 < x \leq 2\}$	$(-3, 2]$ Half-open interval	

To indicate an interval that extends forever in one or both directions using interval notation, we use the **infinity symbol** ∞ or the **negative infinity symbol** $-\infty$. The infinity symbol is not a number; it is simply a notation to indicate that the interval is unlimited. In interval notation, a parenthesis is always used to the right of an infinity symbol or to the left of a negative infinity symbol, as shown in the following examples.

$\{x \mid x > 1\}$	$(1, \infty)$	
$\{x \mid x \geq 1\}$	$[1, \infty)$	
$\{x \mid x < 1\}$	$(-\infty, 1)$	
$\{x \mid x \leq 1\}$	$(-\infty, 1]$	
$\{x \mid -\infty < x < \infty\}$	$(-\infty, \infty)$	

⇒ Graph $(-2, 5)$.

• The graph is all the numbers that are greater than -2 and less than 5.

Example 5
Given $A = \{0, 2, 4, 6, 8, 10\}$ and $B = \{0, 3, 6, 9\}$, find $A \cup B$.

Solution
$A \cup B = \{0, 2, 3, 4, 6, 8, 9, 10\}$

You Try It 5
Given $C = \{1, 5, 9, 13, 17\}$ and $D = \{3, 5, 7, 9, 11\}$, find $C \cup D$.

Your solution

Example 6
Given $A = \{x \mid x \in$ natural numbers$\}$ and $B = \{x \mid x \in$ negative integers$\}$, find $A \cap B$.

Solution
$A \cap B = \varnothing$ • There are no natural numbers that are also negative integers.

You Try It 6
Given $E = \{x \mid x \in$ odd integers$\}$ and $F = \{x \mid x \in$ even integers$\}$, find $E \cap F$.

Your solution

Example 7
Graph $\{x \mid x \geq 3\}$.

Solution
Draw a bracket at 3 to indicate that 3 is in the set. Draw a solid line to the right of 3.

You Try It 7
Graph $\{x \mid x < 0\}$.

Your solution

Example 8
Graph $\{x \mid x > -1\} \cup \{x \mid x < 2\}$.

Solution
This is the set of real numbers greater than -1 *or* less than 2. Any real number satisfies this condition. The graph is the entire real number line.

You Try It 8
Graph $\{x \mid x < -2\} \cup \{x \mid x > -1\}$.

Your solution

Solutions on p. S1

Example 9

Graph $\{x \mid x < 3\} \cap \{x \mid x \geq -1\}$.

Solution

This is the set of real numbers greater than or equal to -1 *and* less than 3.

$$\overset{\longleftarrow \;|\;|\;|\;|\;(\!|\;|\;|\;)\;|\;|\;\longrightarrow}{\underset{-5\;-4\;-3\;-2\;-1\;\;0\;\;1\;\;2\;\;3\;\;4\;\;5}{}}$$

You Try It 9

Graph $\{x \mid x < 1\} \cap \{x \mid x > -3\}$.

Your solution

$$\overset{\longleftarrow \;|\;|\;|\;|\;|\;|\;|\;|\;|\;|\;|\;\longrightarrow}{\underset{-5\;-4\;-3\;-2\;-1\;\;0\;\;1\;\;2\;\;3\;\;4\;\;5}{}}$$

Example 10

Write each set in interval notation.
a. $\{x \mid x > 3\}$
b. $\{x \mid -2 < x \leq 4\}$

Solution

a. The set $\{x \mid x > 3\}$ is the numbers greater than 3. In interval notation, this is written $(3, \infty)$.
b. The set $\{x \mid -2 < x \leq 4\}$ is the numbers greater than -2 and less than or equal to 4. In interval notation, this is written $(-2, 4]$.

You Try It 10

Write each set in interval notation.
a. $\{x \mid x < -1\}$
b. $\{x \mid -2 \leq x < 4\}$

Your solution

Example 11

Write each set in set-builder notation.
a. $(-\infty, 4]$
b. $[-3, 0]$

Solution

a. $(-\infty, 4]$ is the numbers less than or equal to 4. In set-builder notation, this is written $\{x \mid x \leq 4\}$.
b. $[-3, 0]$ is the numbers greater than or equal to -3 and less than or equal to 0. In set-builder notation, this is written $\{x \mid -3 \leq x \leq 0\}$.

You Try It 11

Write each set in set-builder notation.
a. $(3, \infty)$
b. $(-4, 1]$

Your solution

Example 12

Graph $(-2, 2]$.

Solution

Draw a parenthesis at -2 to show it is not in the set. Draw a bracket at 2 to show it is in the set. Draw a solid line between -2 and 2.

$$\overset{\longleftarrow \;|\;|\;|\;(\!|\;|\;|\;]\;|\;|\;|\;\longrightarrow}{\underset{-5\;-4\;-3\;-2\;-1\;\;0\;\;1\;\;2\;\;3\;\;4\;\;5}{}}$$

You Try It 12

Graph $[-2, \infty)$.

Your solution

$$\overset{\longleftarrow \;|\;|\;|\;|\;|\;|\;|\;|\;|\;|\;|\;\longrightarrow}{\underset{-5\;-4\;-3\;-2\;-1\;\;0\;\;1\;\;2\;\;3\;\;4\;\;5}{}}$$

Solutions on p. S1

1.1 Exercises

. . . .

TAKE NOTE

To the Student (in the front of the book, following the Preface) discusses the exercise sets in this textbook.

Objective A

Determine which of the numbers are **a.** integers, **b.** rational numbers, **c.** irrational numbers, **d.** real numbers. List all that apply.

1. $-\dfrac{15}{2}, 0, -3, \pi, 2.\overline{33}, 4.232232223\ldots, \dfrac{\sqrt{5}}{4}, \sqrt{7}$

2. $-17, 0.3412, \dfrac{3}{\pi}, -1.010010001\ldots, \dfrac{27}{91}, 6.1\overline{2}$

Find the additive inverse of each of the following.

3. 27

4. -3

5. $\dfrac{3}{4}$

6. $\sqrt{17}$

7. 0

8. $-\pi$

9. $-\sqrt{33}$

10. -1.23

11. -91

12. $-\dfrac{2}{3}$

Solve.

13. Let $x \in \{-3, 0, 7\}$. For which values of x is $x < 5$ true?

14. Let $z \in \{-4, -1, 4\}$. For which values of z is $z > -2$ true?

15. Let $y \in \{-6, -4, 7\}$. For which values of y is $y > -4$ true?

16. Let $x \in \{-6, -3, 3\}$. For which values of x is $x < -3$ true?

17. Let $w \in \{-2, -1, 0, 1\}$. For which values of w is $w \le -1$ true?

18. Let $p \in \{-10, -5, 0, 5\}$. For which values of p is $p \ge 0$ true?

19. Let $b \in \{-9, 0, 9\}$. Evaluate $-b$ for each element of the set.

20. Let $a \in \{-3, -2, 0\}$. Evaluate $-a$ for each element of the set.

21. Let $c \in \{-4, 0, 4\}$. Evaluate $|c|$ for each element of the set.

22. Let $q \in \{-3, 0, 7\}$. Evaluate $|q|$ for each element of the set.

23. Let $m \in \{-6, -2, 0, 1, 4\}$. Evaluate $-|m|$ for each element of the set.

24. Let $x \in \{-5, -3, 0, 2, 5\}$. Evaluate $-|x|$ for each element of the set.

Objective B

Use the roster method to write the set.

25. the integers between −3 and 5

26. the integers between −4 and 0

27. the even natural numbers less than 14

28. the odd natural numbers less than 14

29. the positive-integer multiples of 3 that are less than or equal to 30

30. the negative-integer multiples of 4 that are greater than or equal to −20

31. the negative-integer multiples of 5 that are greater than or equal to −35

32. the positive-integer multiples of 6 that are less than or equal to 36

Use set-builder notation to write the set.

33. the integers greater than 4

34. the integers less than −2

35. the real numbers greater than or equal to −2

36. the real numbers less than or equal to 2

37. the real numbers between 0 and 1

38. the real numbers between −2 and 5

39. the real numbers between 1 and 4, inclusive

40. the real numbers between 0 and 2, inclusive

Objective C

Find $A \cup B$.

41. $A = \{1, 4, 9\}, B = \{2, 4, 6\}$

42. $A = \{-1, 0, 1\}, B = \{0, 1, 2\}$

43. $A = \{2, 3, 5, 8\}, B = \{9, 10\}$

44. $A = \{1, 3, 5, 7\}, B = \{2, 4, 6, 8\}$

45. $A = \{-4, -2, 0, 2, 4\}, B = \{0, 4, 8\}$

46. $A = \{-3, -2, -1\}, B = \{-2, -1, 0, 1\}$

47. $A = \{1, 2, 3, 4, 5\}, B = \{3, 4, 5\}$

48. $A = \{2, 4\}, B = \{0, 1, 2, 3, 4, 5\}$

Find $A \cap B$.

49. $A = \{6, 12, 18\}, B = \{3, 6, 9\}$

50. $A = \{-4, 0, 4\}, B = \{-2, 0, 2\}$

51. $A = \{1, 5, 10, 20\}, B = \{5, 10, 15, 20\}$

52. $A = \{1, 3, 5, 7, 9\}, B = \{1, 9\}$

53. $A = \{1, 2, 4, 8\}, B = \{3, 5, 6, 7\}$

54. $A = \{-3, -2, -1, 0\}, B = \{1, 2, 3, 4\}$

55. $A = \{2, 4, 6, 8, 10\}, B = \{4, 6\}$

56. $A = \{-9, -5, 0, 7\}, B = \{-7, -5, 0, 5, 7\}$

Graph.

57. $\{x \mid x < 2\}$

58. $\{x \mid x < -1\}$

59. $\{x \mid x \geq 1\}$

60. $\{x \mid x \leq -2\}$

61. $\{x \mid -1 < x < 5\}$

62. $\{x \mid 1 < x < 3\}$

63. $\{x \mid 0 \leq x \leq 3\}$

64. $\{x \mid -1 \leq x \leq 1\}$

65. $\{x \mid x > 1\} \cup \{x \mid x < -1\}$

66. $\{x \mid x \leq 2\} \cup \{x \mid x > 4\}$

67. $\{x \mid x \leq 2\} \cap \{x \mid x \geq 0\}$

68. $\{x \mid x > -1\} \cap \{x \mid x \leq 4\}$

69. $\{x \mid x > 1\} \cap \{x \mid x \geq -2\}$

70. $\{x \mid x < 4\} \cap \{x \mid x \leq 0\}$

71. $\{x \mid x > 2\} \cup \{x \mid x > 1\}$

72. $\{x \mid x < -2\} \cup \{x \mid x < -4\}$

Write each interval in set-builder notation.

73. $(0, 8)$ **74.** $(-2, 4)$ **75.** $[-5, 7]$ **76.** $[3, 4]$ **77.** $[-3, 6)$

78. $(4, 5]$ **79.** $(-\infty, 4]$ **80.** $(-\infty, -2)$ **81.** $(5, \infty)$ **82.** $[-2, \infty)$

Write each set of real numbers in interval notation.

83. $\{x \mid -2 < x < 4\}$ **84.** $\{x \mid 0 < x < 3\}$ **85.** $\{x \mid -1 \le x \le 5\}$ **86.** $\{x \mid 0 \le x \le 3\}$

87. $\{x \mid -\infty < x < 1\}$ **88.** $\{x \mid -\infty < x \le 6\}$ **89.** $\{x \mid -2 \le x < \infty\}$ **90.** $\{x \mid 3 \le x < \infty\}$

Graph.

91. $(-2, 5)$

$$\xleftarrow{\hspace{1em}} \begin{array}{cccccccccccc} & & & & & & & & & & & \\ -5 & -4 & -3 & -2 & -1 & 0 & 1 & 2 & 3 & 4 & 5 \end{array} \xrightarrow{\hspace{1em}}$$

92. $(0, 3)$

$$\xleftarrow{\hspace{1em}} \begin{array}{cccccccccccc} & & & & & & & & & & & \\ -5 & -4 & -3 & -2 & -1 & 0 & 1 & 2 & 3 & 4 & 5 \end{array} \xrightarrow{\hspace{1em}}$$

93. $[-1, 2]$

$$\xleftarrow{\hspace{1em}} \begin{array}{cccccccccccc} & & & & & & & & & & & \\ -5 & -4 & -3 & -2 & -1 & 0 & 1 & 2 & 3 & 4 & 5 \end{array} \xrightarrow{\hspace{1em}}$$

94. $[-3, 2]$

$$\xleftarrow{\hspace{1em}} \begin{array}{cccccccccccc} & & & & & & & & & & & \\ -5 & -4 & -3 & -2 & -1 & 0 & 1 & 2 & 3 & 4 & 5 \end{array} \xrightarrow{\hspace{1em}}$$

95. $(-\infty, 3]$

$$\xleftarrow{\hspace{1em}} \begin{array}{cccccccccccc} & & & & & & & & & & & \\ -5 & -4 & -3 & -2 & -1 & 0 & 1 & 2 & 3 & 4 & 5 \end{array} \xrightarrow{\hspace{1em}}$$

96. $(-\infty, -1)$

$$\xleftarrow{\hspace{1em}} \begin{array}{cccccccccccc} & & & & & & & & & & & \\ -5 & -4 & -3 & -2 & -1 & 0 & 1 & 2 & 3 & 4 & 5 \end{array} \xrightarrow{\hspace{1em}}$$

97. $[3, \infty)$

$$\xleftarrow{\hspace{1em}} \begin{array}{cccccccccccc} & & & & & & & & & & & \\ -5 & -4 & -3 & -2 & -1 & 0 & 1 & 2 & 3 & 4 & 5 \end{array} \xrightarrow{\hspace{1em}}$$

98. $[-2, \infty)$

$$\xleftarrow{\hspace{1em}} \begin{array}{cccccccccccc} & & & & & & & & & & & \\ -5 & -4 & -3 & -2 & -1 & 0 & 1 & 2 & 3 & 4 & 5 \end{array} \xrightarrow{\hspace{1em}}$$

APPLYING THE CONCEPTS

Let $R = \{\text{real numbers}\}$, $A = \{x \mid -1 \le x \le 1\}$, $B = \{x \mid 0 \le x \le 1\}$, $C = \{x \mid -1 \le x \le 0\}$, and $\varnothing$ be the empty set. Answer the following using R, A, B, C, or $\varnothing$.

99. $A \cup B$ **100.** $A \cup A$ **101.** $B \cap B$ **102.** $A \cup C$ **103.** $A \cap R$

104. $C \cap R$ **105.** $B \cup R$ **106.** $A \cup R$ **107.** $R \cup R$ **108.** $R \cap \varnothing$

109. The set $B \cap C$ cannot be expressed using R, A, B, C, or $\varnothing$. What real number is represented by $B \cap C$?

110. A student wrote $-3 > x > 5$ as the inequality that represents the real numbers less than -3 or greater than 5. Explain why this is incorrect.

1.2 Operations on Rational Numbers

Objective A   *To add, subtract, multiply, and divide integers* .... 1 CT

An understanding of the operations on integers is necessary to succeed in algebra. Let's review those properties, beginning with the sign rules for addition.

Rules for Addition of Real Numbers

To add numbers with the same sign, add the absolute values of the numbers. Then attach the sign of the addends.

To add numbers with different signs, find the absolute value of each number. Subtract the smaller of the two numbers from the larger. Then attach the sign of the number with the larger absolute value.

Add: **a.** $-65 + (-48)$ **b.** $27 + (-53)$

a. $-65 + (-48) = -113$

- The signs are the same. Add the absolute values of the numbers. Then attach the sign of the addends.

b. $27 + (-53)$
$|27| = 27$ $|-53| = 53$
$53 - 27 = 26$

$27 + (-53) = -26$

- The signs are different. Find the absolute value of each number.
- Subtract the smaller number from the larger.
- Because $|-53| > |27|$, attach the sign of -53.

Subtraction is defined as addition of the additive inverse.

Rule for Subtraction of Real Numbers

If a and b are real numbers, then $a - b = a + (-b)$.

Subtract: **a.** $48 - (-22)$ **b.** $-31 - 18$

a. $48 - (-22) = 48 + 22 = 70$ **b.** $-31 - 18 = -31 + (-18) = -49$

Opposite of -22 Opposite of 18

Simplify: $-3 - (-16) + (-12)$

$-3 - (-16) + (-12) = -3 + 16 + (-12)$

- Write subtraction as addition of the opposite.

$= 13 + (-12) = 1$

- Add from left to right.

The rules for multiplying real numbers are given below.

> **Rules for Multiplication of Real Numbers**
>
> The product of two numbers with the same sign is positive.
>
> The product of two numbers with different signs is negative.

⇨ Multiply: **a.** $-4(-9)$ **b.** $84(-4)$

   a. $-4(-9) = 36$ • The product of two numbers with the same sign is positive.

   b. $84(-4) = -336$ • The product of two numbers with different signs is negative.

The **multiplicative inverse** of a nonzero real number a is $\frac{1}{a}$. This number is also called the **reciprocal** of a. For instance, the reciprocal of 2 is $\frac{1}{2}$ and the reciprocal of $-\frac{3}{4}$ is $-\frac{4}{3}$. Division of real numbers is defined in terms of multiplication by the multiplicative inverse.

> **Rule for Division of Real Numbers**
>
> If a and b are real numbers and $b \neq 0$, then $a \div b = a \cdot \frac{1}{b}$.

Because division is defined in terms of multiplication, the rules for dividing real numbers are the same as the rules for multiplying.

⇨ Divide: **a.** $\dfrac{-54}{9}$ **b.** $(-21) \div (-7)$

   a. $\dfrac{-54}{9} = -6$ • The quotient of two numbers with different signs is negative.

   b. $(-21) \div (-7) = 3$ • The quotient of two numbers with the same sign is positive.

Note that $\frac{-12}{3} = -4$, $\frac{12}{-3} = -4$, and $-\frac{12}{3} = -4$. This suggests the following rule.

> If a and b are real numbers and $b \neq 0$, then $\dfrac{-a}{b} = \dfrac{a}{-b} = -\dfrac{a}{b}$.

⇨ Simplify: $-\dfrac{-63}{-9}$

   $-\dfrac{-63}{-9} = -7$

Properties of Zero and One in Division

• Zero divided by any number other than zero is zero.

$$\frac{0}{a} = 0, a \neq 0$$

• Division by zero is not defined.

To understand that division by zero is not permitted, suppose $\frac{4}{0} = n$, where n is some number. Because each division problem has a related multiplication problem, $\frac{4}{0} = n$ means $n \cdot 0 = 4$. But $n \cdot 0 = 4$ is impossible because any number times 0 is 0. Therefore, division by 0 is not defined.

• Any number other than zero divided by itself is 1.

$$\frac{a}{a} = 1, a \neq 0$$

• Any number divided by 1 is the number.

$$\frac{a}{1} = a$$

Example 1   Simplify: $-3 - (-5) - 9$

Solution $-3 - (-5) - 9 = -3 + 5 + (-9)$
$$= 2 + (-9) = -7$$

You Try It 1   Simplify: $6 - (-8) - 10$

Your solution

Example 2   Simplify: $-6|-5|(-15)$

Solution $-6|-5|(-15) = -6(5)(-15)$
$$= -30(-15) = 450$$

You Try It 2   Simplify: $12(-3)|-6|$

Your solution

Example 3   Simplify: $-\dfrac{36}{-3}$

Solution $-\dfrac{36}{-3} = -(-12) = 12$

You Try It 3   Simplify: $-\dfrac{28}{|-14|}$

Your solution

Solutions on p. S1

Objective B   To add, subtract, multiply, and divide rational numbers .... ⟨2⟩ CT

Recall that a rational number is one that can be written in the form $\frac{p}{q}$, where p and q are integers and $q \neq 0$. Examples of rational numbers are $-\frac{5}{9}$ and $\frac{12}{5}$. The number $\frac{9}{\sqrt{7}}$ is not a rational number because $\sqrt{7}$ is not an integer. All integers are rational numbers. Terminating and repeating decimals are also rational numbers.

➡ Add: $-12.34 + 9.059$

$12.340 - 9.059 = 3.281$

$-12.34 + 9.059 = -3.281$

• The signs are different. Subtract the absolute values of the numbers.

• Attach the sign of the number with the larger absolute value.

➡ Multiply: $(-0.23)(0.04)$

$(-0.23)(0.04) = -0.0092$ • The signs are different. The product is negative.

➡ Divide: $(-4.0764) \div (-1.72)$

$(-4.0764) \div (-1.72) = 2.37$ • The signs are the same. The quotient is positive.

To add or subtract rational numbers written as fractions, first rewrite the fractions as equivalent fractions with a common denominator. The common denominator is the **least common multiple** (LCM) of the denominators.

➡ Add: $\dfrac{5}{6} + \left(-\dfrac{7}{8}\right)$

$$\frac{5}{6} + \left(-\frac{7}{8}\right) = \frac{5}{6} \cdot \frac{4}{4} + \left(\frac{-7}{8} \cdot \frac{3}{3}\right)$$

• The common denominator is 24. Write each fraction in terms of the common denominator.

$$= \frac{20}{24} + \left(\frac{-21}{24}\right) = \frac{20 + (-21)}{24}$$

• Add the numerators. Place the sum over the common denominator.

$$= \frac{-1}{24} = -\frac{1}{24}$$

➡ Subtract: $-\dfrac{7}{15} - \left(-\dfrac{1}{6}\right)$

$$-\frac{7}{15} - \left(-\frac{1}{6}\right) = -\frac{7}{15} + \frac{1}{6}$$

• Write subtraction as addition of the opposite.

$$= \frac{-7}{15} \cdot \frac{2}{2} + \frac{1}{6} \cdot \frac{5}{5} = \frac{-14}{30} + \frac{5}{30}$$

• Write each fraction in terms of the common denominator, 30.

$$= \frac{-9}{30} = -\frac{3}{10}$$

• Add the numerators. Write the answer in simplest form.

The product of two fractions is the product of the numerators over the product of the denominators.

➡ Multiply: $-\dfrac{5}{12} \cdot \dfrac{8}{15}$

$$-\frac{5}{12} \cdot \frac{8}{15} = -\frac{5 \cdot 8}{12 \cdot 15} = -\frac{40}{180}$$

• The signs are different. The product is negative. Multiply the numerators and multiply the denominators.

$$= -\frac{20 \cdot 2}{20 \cdot 9} = -\frac{2}{9}$$

• Write the answer in simplest form.

In the last problem, the fraction was written in simplest form by dividing the numerator and denominator by 20, which is the largest integer that divides evenly into both 40 and 180. The number 20 is called the **greatest common factor** (GCF) of 40 and 180. To write a fraction in simplest form, divide the numerator and denominator by the GCF. If you have difficulty finding the GCF, try finding the prime factorization of the numerator and denominator and then divide by the common prime factors. For instance,

$$-\frac{5}{12} \cdot \frac{8}{15} = -\frac{\overset{1}{\cancel{5}} \cdot (2 \cdot \overset{1}{\cancel{2}} \cdot 2)}{(\underset{1}{\cancel{2}} \cdot \underset{1}{\cancel{2}} \cdot 3) \cdot (3 \cdot \cancel{5})} = -\frac{2}{9}$$

Division of Fractions

To divide two fractions, multiply by the reciprocal of the divisor.

$$\frac{a}{b} \div \frac{c}{d} = \frac{a}{b} \cdot \frac{d}{c}$$

➡ Divide: $\frac{3}{8} \div \frac{9}{16}$

$$\frac{3}{8} \div \frac{9}{16} = \frac{3}{8} \cdot \frac{16}{9} = \frac{48}{72} = \frac{2}{3}$$

• Multiply by the reciprocal of the divisor.
Write the answer in simplest form.

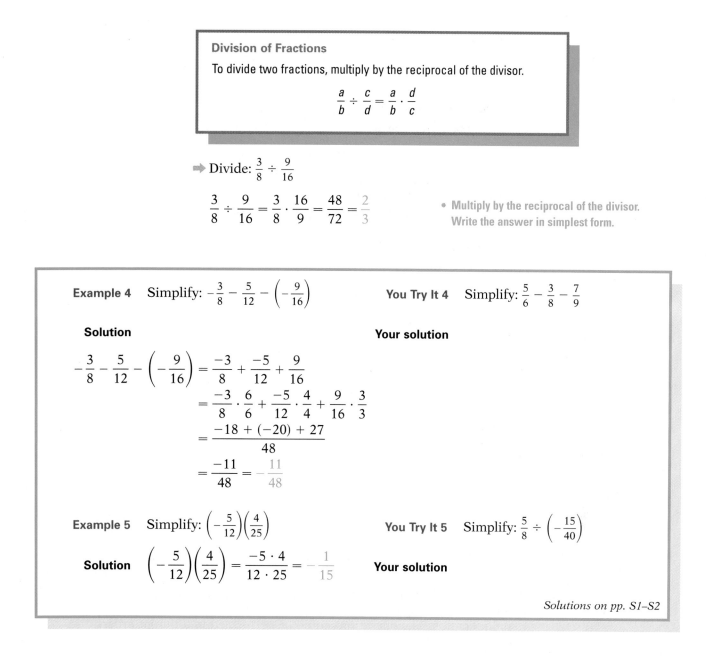

Example 4 Simplify: $-\frac{3}{8} - \frac{5}{12} - \left(-\frac{9}{16}\right)$

Solution

$$-\frac{3}{8} - \frac{5}{12} - \left(-\frac{9}{16}\right) = \frac{-3}{8} + \frac{-5}{12} + \frac{9}{16}$$

$$= \frac{-3}{8} \cdot \frac{6}{6} + \frac{-5}{12} \cdot \frac{4}{4} + \frac{9}{16} \cdot \frac{3}{3}$$

$$= \frac{-18 + (-20) + 27}{48}$$

$$= \frac{-11}{48} = -\frac{11}{48}$$

You Try It 4 Simplify: $\frac{5}{6} - \frac{3}{8} - \frac{7}{9}$

Your solution

Example 5 Simplify: $\left(-\frac{5}{12}\right)\left(\frac{4}{25}\right)$

Solution $\left(-\frac{5}{12}\right)\left(\frac{4}{25}\right) = \frac{-5 \cdot 4}{12 \cdot 25} = -\frac{1}{15}$

You Try It 5 Simplify: $\frac{5}{8} \div \left(-\frac{15}{40}\right)$

Your solution

Solutions on pp. S1–S2

Objective C   *To evaluate exponential expressions* .... 〔1〕 〔3〕 CT

Repeated multiplication of the same factor can be written using an exponent.

$2 \cdot 2 \cdot 2 \cdot 2 \cdot 2 \cdot 2 = 2^6 \leftarrow$ **Exponent**
↑——**Base**

$b \cdot b \cdot b \cdot b \cdot b = b^5 \leftarrow$ **Exponent**
↑——**Base**

The **exponent** indicates how many times the factor, called the **base**, occurs in the multiplication. The multiplication $2 \cdot 2 \cdot 2 \cdot 2 \cdot 2 \cdot 2$ is in **factored form.** The exponential expression 2^6 is in **exponential form.**

2^1 is read "the first power of two" or just "two."
2^2 is read "the second power of two" or "two squared."
2^3 is read "the third power of two" or "two cubed."
2^4 is read "the fourth power of two."
2^5 is read "the fifth power of two."
b^5 is read "the fifth power of b."

• Usually the exponent 1 is not written.

> ***n*th Power of *a***
>
> If *a* is a real number and *n* is a positive integer, the *n*th power of *a* is the product of *n* factors of *a*.
>
> $$a^n = \underbrace{a \cdot a \cdot a \cdots \cdot a}_{a \text{ as a factor } n \text{ times}}$$

TAKE NOTE

Examine the results of $(-3)^4$ and -3^4 very carefully. As another example, $(-2)^6 = 64$ but $-2^6 = -64$.

$5^3 = 5 \cdot 5 \cdot 5 = 125$

$(-3)^4 = (-3)(-3)(-3)(-3) = 81$

$-3^4 = -(3)^4 = -(3 \cdot 3 \cdot 3 \cdot 3) = -81$

Note the difference between $(-3)^4$ and -3^4. The placement of the parentheses is very important.

Example 6   Evaluate $(-2)^5$ and -5^2.

Solution

$(-2)^5 = (-2)(-2)(-2)(-2)(-2) = -32$

$-5^2 = -(5 \cdot 5) = -25$

You Try It 6   Evaluate -2^5 and $(-5)^2$.

Your solution

Example 7   Evaluate $\left(-\dfrac{3}{4}\right)^3$.

Solution $\left(-\dfrac{3}{4}\right)^3 = \left(-\dfrac{3}{4}\right)\left(-\dfrac{3}{4}\right)\left(-\dfrac{3}{4}\right)$

$\qquad\qquad = -\dfrac{3 \cdot 3 \cdot 3}{4 \cdot 4 \cdot 4} = -\dfrac{27}{64}$

You Try It 7   Evaluate $\left(\dfrac{2}{3}\right)^4$.

Your solution

Solutions on p. S2

Objective D   **To use the Order of Operations Agreement** ....

Suppose we wish to evaluate $16 + 4 \cdot 2$. There are two operations, addition and multiplication. The operations could be performed in different orders.

Multiply first. $16 + \underbrace{4 \cdot 2}$

Then add. $\underbrace{16 + 8}$

$\qquad\qquad 24$

Add first. $\underbrace{16 + 4} \cdot 2$

Then multiply. $\underbrace{20 \cdot 2}$

$\qquad\qquad 40$

Note that the answers are different. To avoid possibly getting more than one answer to the same problem, an *Order of Operations Agreement* is followed.

> **Order of Operations Agreement**
>
> ***Step 1*** Perform operations inside grouping symbols. Grouping symbols include parentheses ( ), brackets [ ], braces { }, the absolute value symbol, and the fraction bar.
>
> ***Step 2*** Simplify exponential expressions.
>
> ***Step 3*** Do multiplication and division as they occur from left to right.
>
> ***Step 4*** Do addition and subtraction as they occur from left to right.

➡️ Simplify: $8 - \dfrac{2 - 22}{4 + 1} \cdot 2^2$

$$8 - \dfrac{2 - 22}{4 + 1} \cdot 2^2 = 8 - \dfrac{-20}{5} \cdot 2^2$$
$$= 8 - \dfrac{-20}{5} \cdot 4$$
$$= 8 - (-4) \cdot 4$$
$$= 8 - (-16)$$
$$= 24$$

- The fraction bar is a grouping symbol. Perform the operations above and below the fraction bar.
- Simplify exponential expressions.

- Do multiplication and division as they occur from left to right.

- Do addition and subtraction as they occur from left to right.

One or more of the steps in the Order of Operations Agreement may not be needed. In that case, just proceed to the next step.

➡️ Simplify: $14 - [(25 - 9) \div 2]^2$

$$14 - [(25 - 9) \div 2]^2 = 14 - [16 \div 2]^2$$
$$= 14 - [8]^2$$
$$= 14 - 64$$
$$= -50$$

- Perform the operations inside grouping symbols.

- Simplify exponential expressions.

- Do addition and subtraction as they occur from left to right.

A **complex fraction** is a fraction whose numerator or denominator contains one or more fractions. Examples of complex fractions are shown at the right.

$$\dfrac{\dfrac{2}{3}}{-\dfrac{5}{2}}, \quad \dfrac{\dfrac{1}{7} + 5}{\dfrac{3}{4} - \dfrac{7}{8}} \quad \leftarrow \text{Main fraction bar}$$

When simplifying complex fractions, recall that $\dfrac{\dfrac{a}{b}}{\dfrac{c}{d}} = \dfrac{a}{b} \div \dfrac{c}{d} = \dfrac{a}{b} \cdot \dfrac{d}{c}$.

➡️ Simplify: $\dfrac{\dfrac{3}{4} - \dfrac{1}{3}}{\dfrac{1}{5} - 2}$

$$\dfrac{\dfrac{3}{4} - \dfrac{1}{3}}{\dfrac{1}{5} - 2} = \dfrac{\dfrac{9}{12} - \dfrac{4}{12}}{\dfrac{1}{5} - \dfrac{10}{5}} = \dfrac{\dfrac{5}{12}}{-\dfrac{9}{5}}$$
$$= \dfrac{5}{12}\left(-\dfrac{5}{9}\right)$$
$$= -\dfrac{25}{108}$$

- Perform the operations above and below the main fraction bar.

- Multiply the numerator of the complex fraction by the reciprocal of the denominator of the complex fraction.

Example 8

Simplify: $-3 \cdot 4^2 + [2 - 5(8 \div 2)]$

Solution

$-3 \cdot 4^2 + [2 - 5(8 \div 2)]$

$\quad = -3 \cdot 4^2 + [2 - 5(4)]$

$\quad = -3 \cdot 4^2 + [2 - 20]$

$\quad = -3 \cdot 4^2 + [-18]$

$\quad = -3 \cdot 16 + [-18]$

$\quad = -48 + [-18]$

$\quad = -66$

You Try It 8

Simplify: $-2\left[3 - 3^3 + \dfrac{16 + 2}{1 - 10}\right]$

Your solution

Example 9

Simplify: $\left(\dfrac{1}{2}\right)^3 - \left[\left(\dfrac{2}{3} + \dfrac{1}{4}\right) \div \dfrac{5}{6}\right]$

Solution

$\left(\dfrac{1}{2}\right)^3 - \left[\left(\dfrac{2}{3} + \dfrac{1}{4}\right) \div \dfrac{5}{6}\right] = \left(\dfrac{1}{2}\right)^3 - \left[\dfrac{11}{12} \div \dfrac{5}{6}\right]$

$\qquad\qquad = \left(\dfrac{1}{2}\right)^3 - \left[\dfrac{11}{12} \cdot \dfrac{6}{5}\right]$

$\qquad\qquad = \left(\dfrac{1}{2}\right)^3 - \dfrac{11}{10}$

$\qquad\qquad = \dfrac{1}{8} - \dfrac{11}{10}$

$\qquad\qquad = -\dfrac{39}{40}$

You Try It 9

Simplify: $\dfrac{1}{3} + \dfrac{5}{8} \div \dfrac{15}{16} - \dfrac{7}{12}$

Your solution

Example 10

Simplify: $9 \cdot \dfrac{\dfrac{5}{6} - 2}{\dfrac{3}{8}} \div \dfrac{7}{6}$

Solution

$9 \cdot \dfrac{\dfrac{5}{6} - 2}{\dfrac{3}{8}} \div \dfrac{7}{6} = 9 \cdot \dfrac{-\dfrac{7}{6}}{\dfrac{3}{8}} \div \dfrac{7}{6}$

$\qquad\qquad = 9 \cdot \left(-\dfrac{7}{6} \cdot \dfrac{8}{3}\right) \div \dfrac{7}{6}$

$\qquad\qquad = 9 \cdot \left(-\dfrac{28}{9}\right) \div \dfrac{7}{6}$

$\qquad\qquad = -28 \div \dfrac{7}{6}$

$\qquad\qquad = -28 \cdot \dfrac{6}{7}$

$\qquad\qquad = -24$

You Try It 10

Simplify: $\dfrac{11}{12} - \dfrac{\dfrac{5}{4}}{2 - \dfrac{7}{2}} \cdot \dfrac{3}{4}$

Your solution

Solutions on p. S2

1.2 Exercises

· ·

Objective A

Simplify.

1. $-18 + (-12)$

2. $-18 - 7$

3. $5 - 22$

4. $16 \cdot (-60)$

5. $3 \cdot 4 \cdot (-8)$

6. $18 \cdot 0 \cdot (-7)$

7. $18 \div (-3)$

8. $25 \div (-5)$

9. $-60 \div (-12)$

10. $(-9)(-2)(-3)(10)$

11. $-20(35)(-16)$

12. $54(19)(-82)$

13. $-271(-365)$

14. $|(-16)(10)|$

15. $|12(-8)|$

16. $|7 - 18|$

17. $|15 - (-8)|$

18. $|-16 - (-20)|$

19. $|-56 \div 8|$

20. $|81 \div (-9)|$

21. $|-153 \div (-9)|$

22. $|-4| - |-2|$

23. $-|-8| + |-4|$

24. $-|-16| - |24|$

25. $-30 + (-16) - 14 - 2$

26. $3 - (-2) + (-8) - 11$

27. $-2 + (-19) - 16 + 12$

28. $-6 + (-9) - 18 + 32$

29. $13 - |6 - 12|$

30. $-9 - |-7 - (-15)|$

31. $738 - 46 + (-105) - 219$

32. $-871 - (-387) - 132 - 460$

33. $-442 \div (-17)$

34. $621 \div (-23)$

35. $-4897 \div 59$

36. $-17|-5|$

Objective B

Simplify.

37. $\dfrac{7}{12} + \dfrac{5}{16}$

38. $\dfrac{3}{8} - \dfrac{5}{12}$

39. $-\dfrac{5}{9} - \dfrac{14}{15}$

40. $\dfrac{1}{2} + \dfrac{1}{7} - \dfrac{5}{8}$

41. $-\dfrac{1}{3} + \dfrac{5}{9} - \dfrac{7}{12}$

42. $\dfrac{1}{3} + \dfrac{19}{24} - \dfrac{7}{8}$

43. $\dfrac{2}{3} - \dfrac{5}{12} + \dfrac{5}{24}$

44. $-\dfrac{7}{10} + \dfrac{4}{5} + \dfrac{5}{6}$

45. $\dfrac{5}{8} - \dfrac{7}{12} + \dfrac{1}{2}$

46. $-\dfrac{1}{3} \cdot \dfrac{5}{8}$

47. $\left(\dfrac{6}{35}\right)\left(-\dfrac{5}{16}\right)$

48. $\dfrac{2}{3}\left(-\dfrac{9}{20}\right) \cdot \dfrac{5}{12}$

49. $-\dfrac{8}{15} \div \dfrac{4}{5}$

50. $-\dfrac{2}{3} \div \left(-\dfrac{6}{7}\right)$

51. $-\dfrac{11}{24} \div \dfrac{7}{12}$

52. $\dfrac{7}{9} \div \left(-\dfrac{14}{27}\right)$

53. $\left(-\dfrac{5}{12}\right)\left(\dfrac{4}{35}\right)\left(\dfrac{7}{8}\right)$

54. $\dfrac{6}{35}\left(-\dfrac{7}{40}\right)\left(-\dfrac{8}{21}\right)$

55. $-14.27 + 1.296$

56. $-0.4355 + 172.5$

57. $1.832 - 7.84$

58. $(3.52)(4.7)$

59. $(0.03)(10.5)(6.1)$

60. $(1.2)(3.1)(-6.4)$

61. $5.418 \div (-0.9)$

62. $-0.2645 \div (-0.023)$

63. $-0.4355 \div 0.065$

64. $-6.58 - 3.97 + 0.875$

Simplify. Round to the nearest hundredth.

65. $38.241 \div [-(-6.027)] - 7.453$

66. $-9.0508 - (-3.177) + 24.77$

67. $-287.3069 \div 0.1415$

68. $6472.3018 \div (-3.59)$

Objective C

Simplify.

69. 5^3

70. 3^4

71. -2^3

72. -4^3

73. $(-5)^3$

74. $(-8)^2$

75. $2^2 \cdot 3^4$

76. $4^2 \cdot 3^3$

77. $-2^2 \cdot 3^2$

78. $-3^2 \cdot 5^3$

79. $(-2)^3(-3)^2$

80. $(-4)^3(-2)^3$

81. $4 \cdot 2^3 \cdot 3^3$

82. $-4(-3)^2(4^2)$

83. $2^2 \cdot (-10)(-2)^2$

84. $-3(-2)^2(-5)$

85. $(-3)^3 \cdot 15 \cdot (-2)^4$

86. $-4 \cdot 2^2 \cdot 5^5$

87. $2^5 \cdot (-3)^4 \cdot 4^5$

88. $4^4(-3)^5(6)^2$

Objective D

Simplify.

89. $5 - 3(8 \div 4)^2$

90. $4^2 - (5 - 2)^2 \cdot 3$

91. $16 - \dfrac{2^2 - 5}{3^2 + 2}$

92. $\dfrac{4(5 - 2)}{4^2 - 2^2} \div 4$

93. $\dfrac{3 + \dfrac{2}{3}}{\dfrac{11}{16}}$

94. $\dfrac{\dfrac{11}{14}}{4 - \dfrac{6}{7}}$

95. $5[(2 - 4) \cdot 3 - 2]$

96. $2[(16 \div 8) - (-2)] + 4$

97. $16 - 4\left(\dfrac{8 - 2}{3 - 6}\right) \div \dfrac{1}{2}$

98. $25 \div 5\left(\dfrac{16 + 8}{-2^2 + 8}\right) - 5$

99. $6[3 - (-4 + 2) \div 2]$

100. $12 - 4[2 - (-3 + 5) - 8]$

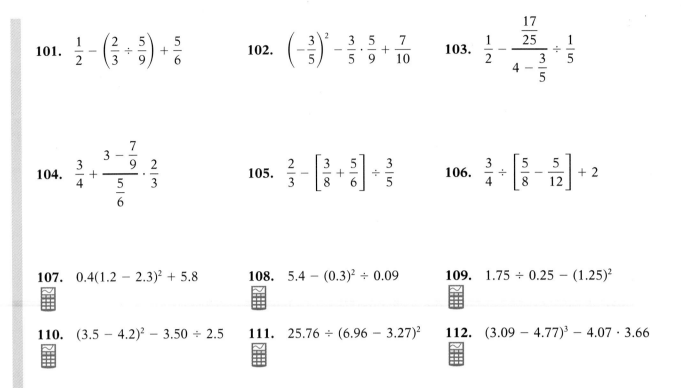

101. $\dfrac{1}{2} - \left(\dfrac{2}{3} \div \dfrac{5}{9}\right) + \dfrac{5}{6}$

102. $\left(-\dfrac{3}{5}\right)^2 - \dfrac{3}{5} \cdot \dfrac{5}{9} + \dfrac{7}{10}$

103. $\dfrac{1}{2} - \dfrac{\frac{17}{25}}{4 - \frac{3}{5}} \div \dfrac{1}{5}$

104. $\dfrac{3}{4} + \dfrac{3 - \frac{7}{9}}{\frac{5}{6}} \cdot \dfrac{2}{3}$

105. $\dfrac{2}{3} - \left[\dfrac{3}{8} + \dfrac{5}{6}\right] \div \dfrac{3}{5}$

106. $\dfrac{3}{4} \div \left[\dfrac{5}{8} - \dfrac{5}{12}\right] + 2$

107. $0.4(1.2 - 2.3)^2 + 5.8$

108. $5.4 - (0.3)^2 \div 0.09$

109. $1.75 \div 0.25 - (1.25)^2$

110. $(3.5 - 4.2)^2 - 3.50 \div 2.5$

111. $25.76 \div (6.96 - 3.27)^2$

112. $(3.09 - 4.77)^3 - 4.07 \cdot 3.66$

APPLYING THE CONCEPTS

113. A number that is its own additive inverse is _____ .

114. Which two numbers are their own multiplicative inverse?

115. Do all real numbers have a multiplicative inverse? If not, which ones do not have a multiplicative inverse?

116. What is the tens digit of 11^{22}?

117. What is the ones digit of 7^{18}?

118. What are the last two digits of 5^{33}?

119. What are the last three digits of 5^{234}?

120. Does $(2^3)^4 = 2^{(3^4)}$? If not, which expression is larger?

121. What is the Order of Operations Agreement for a^{b^c}? *Note:* Even calculators that normally follow the Order of Operations Agreement may not do so for this expression.

1.3 **Variable Expressions**

Objective A *To use and identify the properties of the real numbers* .... 4 CT

The properties of the real numbers describe the way operations on numbers can be performed. Following is a list of some of the real-number properties and an example of each property.

Properties of the Real Numbers

The Commutative Property of Addition

$$a + b = b + a$$

$3 + 2 = 2 + 3$
$5 = 5$

The Commutative Property of Multiplication

$$a \cdot b = b \cdot a$$

$(3)(-2) = (-2)(3)$
$-6 = -6$

The Associative Property of Addition

$$(a + b) + c = a + (b + c)$$

$(3 + 4) + 5 = 3 + (4 + 5)$
$7 + 5 = 3 + 9$
$12 = 12$

The Associative Property of Multiplication

$$(a \cdot b) \cdot c = a \cdot (b \cdot c)$$

$(3 \cdot 4) \cdot 5 = 3 \cdot (4 \cdot 5)$
$12 \cdot 5 = 3 \cdot 20$
$60 = 60$

The Addition Property of Zero

$$a + 0 = 0 + a = a$$

$3 + 0 = 0 + 3 = 3$

The Multiplication Property of Zero

$$a \cdot 0 = 0 \cdot a = 0$$

$3 \cdot 0 = 0 \cdot 3 = 0$

The Multiplication Property of One

$$a \cdot 1 = 1 \cdot a = a$$

$$5 \cdot 1 = 1 \cdot 5 = 5$$

The Inverse Property of Addition

$$a + (-a) = (-a) + a = 0$$

$$4 + (-4) = (-4) + 4 = 0$$

$-a$ is called the **additive inverse** of a. a is the additive inverse of $-a$. The sum of a number and its additive inverse is 0.

The Inverse Property of Multiplication

$$a \cdot \frac{1}{a} = \frac{1}{a} \cdot a = 1 \quad a \neq 0$$

$$(4)\left(\frac{1}{4}\right) = \left(\frac{1}{4}\right)(4) = 1$$

$\frac{1}{a}$ is called the **multiplicative inverse** of a. $\frac{1}{a}$ is also called the reciprocal of a. The product of a number and its multiplicative inverse is 1.

The Distributive Property

$$a(b + c) = ab + ac$$

$$3(4 + 5) = 3 \cdot 4 + 3 \cdot 5$$
$$3 \cdot 9 = 12 + 15$$
$$27 = 27$$

Example 1
Complete the statement by using the Commutative Property of Multiplication.

$$(x)\left(\frac{1}{4}\right) = (?)(x)$$

Solution

$$(x)\left(\frac{1}{4}\right) = \left(\frac{1}{4}\right)(x)$$

You Try It 1
Complete the statement by using the Inverse Property of Addition.
$$3x + ? = 0$$

Your solution

Example 2
Identify the property that justifies the statement: $3(x + 4) = 3x + 12$

Solution
The Distributive Property

You Try It 2
Identify the property that justifies the statement: $(a + 3b) + c = a + (3b + c)$

Your solution

Solutions on p. S2

Objective B   *To evaluate a variable expression* .... CT

An expression that contains one or more variables is a **variable expression.** The variable expression $6x^2y - 7x - z + 2$ contains **four terms:** $6x^2y$, $-7x$, $-z$, and 2. The first three terms are **variable terms.** The 2 is a **constant term.**

Each variable term is composed of a **numerical coefficient** and a **variable part.**

Variable Term	Numerical Coefficient	Variable Part
$6x^2y$	6	x^2y
$-7x$	-7	x
$-z$	-1	z

• A coefficient of 1 or -1 is usually not written.

➡ Evaluate $a^2 - (a - b^2c)$ when $a = -2$, $b = 3$, and $c = -4$.

Replace each variable with its value. Then use the Order of Operations Agreement to simplify the resulting numerical expression.

$a^2 - (a - b^2c)$

$$(-2)^2 - [(-2) - 3^2(-4)] = (-2)^2 - [(-2) - 9(-4)]$$

• $a = -2$, $b = 3$, $c = -4$

$$= (-2)^2 - [(-2) - (-36)]$$
$$= (-2)^2 - [34]$$
$$= 4 - 34$$
$$= -30$$

Example 3
Evaluate $2x^3 - 4(2y - 3z)$ when $x = 2$, $y = 3$, and $z = -2$.

Solution
$2x^3 - 4(2y - 3z)$
$$2(2)^3 - 4[2(3) - 3(-2)] = 2(2)^3 - 4[6 - (-6)]$$
$$= 2(2)^3 - 4[12]$$
$$= 2(8) - 4[12]$$
$$= 16 - 48 = -32$$

You Try It 3
Evaluate $-2x^2 + 3(4xy - z)$ when $x = -3$, $y = -1$, and $z = 2$.

Your solution

Example 4
Evaluate $3 - 2|3x - 2y^2|$ when $x = -1$ and $y = -2$.

Solution
$3 - 2|3x - 2y^2|$
$$3 - 2|3(-1) - 2(-2)^2| = 3 - 2|3(-1) - 2(4)|$$
$$= 3 - 2|(-3) - 8|$$
$$= 3 - 2|-11| = 3 - 2(11)$$
$$= 3 - 22 = -19$$

You Try It 4
Evaluate $2x - y|4x^2 - y^2|$ when $x = -2$ and $y = -6$.

Your solution

Solutions on p. S2

Objective C   *To simplify a variable expression* ··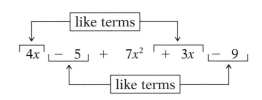

Like terms of a variable expression are the terms with the same variable part.

Constant terms are like terms.

$$4x - 5 + 7x^2 + 3x - 9$$

(like terms connecting $4x$ and $3x$, like terms connecting -5 and -9)

To simplify a variable expression, combine the like terms by using the Distributive Property. For instance,

$$7x + 4x = (7 + 4)x = 11x$$

Adding the coefficients of like terms is called **combining** like terms.

The Distributive Property is also used to remove parentheses from a variable expression so that like terms can be combined.

➡ Simplify: $3(x + 2y) + 2(4x - 3y)$

$3(x + 2y) + 2(4x - 3y)$

$= 3x + 6y + 8x - 6y$ • Use the Distributive Property.

$= (3x + 8x) + (6y - 6y)$ • Use the Commutative and Associative Properties of Addition to rearrange and group like terms.

$= 11x$ • Combine like terms.

➡ Simplify: $2 - 4[3x - 2(5x - 3)]$

$2 - 4[3x - 2(5x - 3)] = 2 - 4[3x - 10x + 6]$ • Use the Distributive Property to remove the inner parentheses.

$= 2 - 4[-7x + 6]$ • Combine like terms.

$= 2 + 28x - 24$ • Use the Distributive Property to remove the brackets.

$= 28x - 22$ • Combine like terms.

TAKE NOTE

To the Student (in the front of the book, following the Preface) explains how best to use the boxed examples in this text.

Example 5
Simplify: $7 + 3(4x - 7)$

Solution
$7 + 3(4x - 7)$
$= 7 + 12x - 21$ • The Order of Operations Agreement requires multiplication before addition.
$= 12x - 14$

You Try It 5
Simplify: $9 - 2(3y - 4) + 5y$

Your solution

Example 6
Simplify: $5 - 2(3x + y) - (x - 4)$

Solution
$5 - 2(3x + y) - (x - 4)$
$= 5 - 6x - 2y - x + 4$
$= -7x - 2y + 9$

You Try It 6
Simplify: $6z - 3(5 - 3z) + 5(2z - 3)$

Your solution

Solutions on p. S2

1.3 Exercises

· ·

Objective A

Use the given property of the real numbers to complete the statement.

1. The Commutative Property of Multiplication
$3 \cdot 4 = 4 \cdot ?$

2. The Commutative Property of Addition
$7 + 15 = ? + 7$

3. The Associative Property of Addition
$(3 + 4) + 5 = ? + (4 + 5)$

4. The Associative Property of Multiplication
$(3 \cdot 4) \cdot 5 = 3 \cdot (? \cdot 5)$

5. The Division Properties of Zero
$\dfrac{5}{?}$ is undefined.

6. The Multiplication Property of Zero
$5 \cdot ? = 0$

7. The Distributive Property
$3(x + 2) = 3x + ?$

8. The Distributive Property
$5(y + 4) = ? \cdot y + 20$

9. The Division Properties of Zero
$\dfrac{?}{-6} = 0$

10. The Inverse Property of Addition
$(x + y) + ? = 0$

11. The Inverse Property of Multiplication
$\dfrac{1}{mn}(mn) = ?$

12. The Multiplication Property of One
$? \cdot 1 = x$

13. The Associative Property of Multiplication
$2(3x) = ? \cdot x$

14. The Commutative Property of Addition
$ab + bc = bc + ?$

Identify the property that justifies the statement.

15. $\dfrac{0}{-5} = 0$

16. $-8 + 8 = 0$

17. $(-12)\left(-\dfrac{1}{12}\right) = 1$

18. $(3 \cdot 4) \cdot 2 = 2 \cdot (3 \cdot 4)$

Identify the property that justifies the statement.

19. $y + 0 = y$

20. $2x + (5y + 8) = (2x + 5y) + 8$

21. $\dfrac{-9}{0}$ is undefined.

22. $(x + y)z = xz + yz$

23. $6(x + y) = 6x + 6y$

24. $(-12y)(0) = 0$

25. $(ab)c = a(bc)$

26. $(x + y) + z = (y + x) + z$

Objective B

Evaluate the variable expression when $a = 2, b = 3, c = -1,$ and $d = -4.$

27. $ab + dc$

28. $2ab - 3dc$

29. $4cd \div a^2$

30. $b^2 - (d - c)^2$

31. $(b - 2a)^2 + c$

32. $(b - d)^2 \div (b - d)$

33. $(bc + a)^2 \div (d - b)$

34. $\dfrac{1}{3}b^3 - \dfrac{1}{4}d^3$

35. $\dfrac{1}{4}a^4 - \dfrac{1}{6}bc$

36. $2b^2 \div \dfrac{ad}{2}$

37. $\dfrac{3ac}{-4} - c^2$

38. $\dfrac{2d - 2a}{2bc}$

39. $\dfrac{3b - 5c}{3a - c}$

40. $\dfrac{2d - a}{b - 2c}$

41. $\dfrac{a - d}{b + c}$

42. $|a^2 + d|$

43. $-a|a + 2d|$

44. $d|b - 2d|$

45. $\dfrac{2a - 4d}{3b - c}$

46. $\dfrac{3d - b}{b - 2c}$

47. $-3d \div \left| \dfrac{ab - 4c}{2b + c} \right|$

48. $-2bc + \left| \dfrac{bc + d}{ab - c} \right|$

49. $2(d - b) \div (3a - c)$

50. $(d - 4a)^2 \div c^3$

51. $-d^2 - c^3 a$

52. $a^2 c - d^3$

53. $-d^3 + 4ac$

54. b^a

55. $4^{(a^2)}$

56. a^b

Objective C

Simplify.

57. $5x + 7x$

58. $3x + 10x$

59. $-8ab - 5ab$

60. $-2x + 5x - 7x$

61. $3x - 5x + 9x$

62. $-2a + 7b + 9a$

63. $5b - 8a - 12b$

64. $12 \left(\dfrac{1}{12} x \right)$

65. $\dfrac{1}{3}(3y)$

66. $-3(x - 2)$

67. $-5(x - 9)$

68. $(x + 2)5$

69. $-(x + y)$

70. $-(-x - y)$

71. $3(a - 5)$

72. $3(x - 2y) - 5$

73. $4x - 3(2y - 5)$

74. $-2a - 3(3a - 7)$

75. $3x - 2(5x - 7)$

76. $2x - 3(x - 2y)$

77. $3[a - 5(5 - 3a)]$

78. $5[-2 - 6(a - 5)]$

79. $3[x - 2(x + 2y)]$

80. $5[y - 3(y - 2x)]$

81. $-2(x - 3y) + 2(3y - 5x)$

82. $4(-a - 2b) - 2(3a - 5b)$

83. $5(3a - 2b) - 3(-6a + 5b)$

84. $-7(2a - b) + 2(-3b + a)$

85. $3x - 2[y - 2(x + 3[2x + 3y])]$

86. $2x - 4[x - 4(y - 2[5y + 3])]$

87. $4 - 2(7x - 2y) - 3(-2x + 3y)$

88. $3x + 8(x - 4) - 3(2x - y)$

89. $\dfrac{1}{3}[8x - 2(x - 12) + 3]$

90. $\dfrac{1}{4}[14x - 3(x - 8) - 7x]$

APPLYING THE CONCEPTS

In each of the following, it is possible that at least one of the properties of real numbers has been applied incorrectly. If the statement is incorrect, state the incorrect application of the properties of real numbers and correct the answer. If the statement is correct, state the property of real numbers that is being used.

91. $4(3y + 1) = 12y + 4$

92. $-4(5x - y) = -20x + 4y$

93. $2 + 3x = (2 + 3)x = 5x$

94. $6 - 6x = 0x = 0$

95. $2(3y) = (2 \cdot 3)(2y) = 12y$

96. $3a - 4b = 4b - 3a$

97. $-x^2 + y^2 = y^2 - x^2$

98. $x^4 \cdot \dfrac{1}{x^4} = 1, x \neq 0$

1.4 Verbal Expressions and Variable Expressions

Objective A *To translate a verbal expression into a variable expression* ...... 6 CT

One of the major skills required in applied mathematics is translating a verbal expression into a mathematical expression. Doing so requires recognizing the verbal phrases that translate into mathematical operations. Following is a partial list of the verbal phrases used to indicate the different mathematical operations.

Addition	more than	8 more than w	$w + 8$
	added to	x added to 9	$9 + x$
	the sum of	the sum of z and 9	$z + 9$
	the total of	the total of r and s	$r + s$
	increased by	x increased by 7	$x + 7$
Subtraction	less than	12 less than b	$b - 12$
	the difference between	the difference between x and 1	$x - 1$
	minus	z minus 7	$z - 7$
	decreased by	17 decreased by a	$17 - a$
Multiplication	times	negative 2 times c	$-2c$
	the product of	the product of x and y	xy
	multiplied by	3 multiplied by n	$3n$
	of	three-fourths of m	$\frac{3}{4}m$
	twice	twice d	$2d$
Division	divided by	v divided by 15	$\frac{v}{15}$
	the quotient of	the quotient of y and 3	$\frac{y}{3}$
	the ratio of	the ratio of x to 7	$\frac{x}{7}$
Power	the square of or the second power of	the square of x	x^2
	the cube of or the third power of	the cube of r	r^3
	the fifth power of	the fifth power of a	a^5

Translating a phrase that contains the word *sum, difference, product,* or *quotient* can sometimes cause a problem. In the examples at the right, note where the operation symbol is placed.

the *sum* of x and y $x + y$

the *difference* between x and y $x - y$

the *product* of x and y $x \cdot y$

the *quotient* of x and y $\dfrac{x}{y}$

➡ Translate "three times the sum of c and five" into a variable expression.

Identify words that indicate the mathematical operations.

3 times the sum of c and 5

Use the identified words to write the variable expression. Note that the phrase *times the sum of* requires parentheses.

$3(c + 5)$

➡ The sum of two numbers is thirty-seven. If x represents the smaller number, translate "twice the larger number" into a variable expression.

Write an expression for the larger number by subtracting the smaller number, x, from 37.

larger number: $37 - x$

Identify the words that indicate the mathematical operations.

twice the larger number

Use the identified words to write a variable expression.

$2(37 - x)$

➡ Translate "five less than twice the difference between a number and seven" into a variable expression. Then simplify.

Identify words that indicate the mathematical operations.

the unknown number: x

5 less than twice the difference between x and 7

Use the identified words to write the variable expression.

$2(x - 7) - 5$

Simplify the expression.

$2x - 14 - 5 = 2x - 19$

Example 1

Translate "the quotient of r and the sum of r and four" into a variable expression.

Solution

the <u>quotient of</u> r and the <u>sum of</u> r and four

$$\frac{r}{r + 4}$$

You Try It 1

Translate "twice x divided by the difference between x and seven" into a variable expression.

Your solution

Example 2

Translate "the sum of the square of y and six" into a variable expression.

Solution

the <u>sum of</u> the <u>square of</u> y and six

$y^2 + 6$

You Try It 2

Translate "the product of negative three and the square of d" into a variable expression.

Your solution

Example 3

The sum of two numbers is twenty-eight. Using x to represent the smaller number, translate "the sum of three times the larger number and the smaller number" into a variable expression. Then simplify.

Solution

The smaller number is x.
The larger number is $28 - x$.
the <u>sum of</u> three <u>times</u> the larger number and the smaller number

$3(28 - x) + x$ • **This is the variable expression.**

$84 - 3x + x$ • **Simplify.**

$84 - 2x$

You Try It 3

The sum of two numbers is sixteen. Using x to represent the smaller number, translate "the difference between twice the smaller number and the larger number" into a variable expression. Then simplify.

Your solution

Example 4

Translate "eight more than the product of four and the total of a number and twelve" into a variable expression. Then simplify.

Solution

Let the unknown number be x.
8 <u>more than</u> the <u>product</u> of 4 and the <u>total of</u> x and 12

$4(x + 12) + 8$ • **This is the variable expression.**

$4x + 48 + 8$ • **Simplify.**

$4x + 56$

You Try It 4

Translate "the difference between fourteen and the sum of a number and seven" into a variable expression. Then simplify.

Your solution

Solutions on p. S2

Objective B *To solve application problems* .... ((6)) [CT]

Many of the applications of mathematics require that you identify the unknown quantity, assign a variable to that quantity, and then attempt to express other unknowns in terms of that quantity.

➡ Ten gallons of paint were poured into two containers of different sizes. Express the amount of paint poured into the smaller container in terms of the amount poured into the larger container.

Assign a variable to the amount of paint poured into the larger container.

the number of gallons of paint poured into the larger container: g

Express the amount of paint in the smaller container in terms of g. (g gallons of paint were poured into the larger container.)

the number of gallons of paint poured into the smaller container: $10 - g$

Example 5
A cyclist is riding at a rate that is twice the speed of a runner. Express the speed of the cyclist in terms of the speed of the runner.

Solution
the speed of the runner: r
the speed of the cyclist is twice r: $2r$

You Try It 5
The length of the Carnival cruise ship *Destiny* is 56 ft more than the height of the Empire State Building. Express the length of *Destiny* in terms of the height of the Empire State Building.

Your solution

Example 6
The length of a rectangle is 2 ft more than 3 times the width. Express the length of the rectangle in terms of the width.

Solution
the width of the rectangle: w
the length is 2 more than 3 times w: $3w + 2$

You Try It 6
The depth of the deep end of a swimming pool is 2 ft more than twice the depth of the shallow end. Express the depth of the deep end in terms of the depth of the shallow end.

Your solution

Example 7
In a survey of listener preferences for AM or FM radio stations, one-third of the number of people surveyed preferred AM stations. Express the number of people who preferred AM stations in terms of the number of people surveyed.

Solution
the number of people surveyed: x
the number of people who preferred AM

stations: $\frac{1}{3}x$

You Try It 7
A customer's recent credit card bill showed that one-fourth of the total bill was for the cost of restaurant meals. Express the cost of restaurant meals in terms of the credit card bill.

Your solution

Solutions on p. S3

1.4 Exercises

. . . .

Objective A

Translate into a variable expression. Then simplify.

1. a number minus the sum of the number and two

2. a number decreased by the difference between five and the number

3. five times the product of eight and a number

4. a number increased by two-thirds of the number

5. the difference between seventeen times a number and twice the number

6. one-half of the total of six times a number and twenty-two

7. the difference between the square of a number and the total of twelve and the square of the number

8. eleven more than the square of a number added to the difference between the number and seventeen

9. the sum of five times a number and twelve added to the product of fifteen and the number

10. four less than twice the sum of a number and eleven

11. The sum of two numbers is fifteen. Using x to represent the smaller of the two numbers, translate "the sum of two more than the larger number and twice the smaller number" into a variable expression. Then simplify.

12. The sum of two numbers is twenty. Using x to represent the smaller of the two numbers, translate "the difference between two more than the larger number and twice the smaller number" into a variable expression. Then simplify.

13. The sum of two numbers is thirty-four. Using x to represent the larger of the two numbers, translate "the quotient of five times the smaller number and the difference between the larger number and three" into a variable expression.

14. The sum of two numbers is thirty-three. Using x to represent the larger of the two numbers, translate "the difference between six more than twice the larger number and the sum of the smaller number and three" into a variable expression. Then simplify.

Objective B   *Application Problems*

15. The distance from Earth to the sun is approximately 390 times the distance from Earth to the moon. Express the distance from Earth to the sun in terms of the distance from Earth to the moon.

16. According to *Time*, in 1996, there were 20 more U.S. patent applications involving the Internet than in 1995. Express the number of patent applications involving the Internet in 1996 in terms of the number in 1995.

17. A mixture of candy contains 3 lb more of milk chocolate than of caramel. Express the amount of milk chocolate in the mixture in terms of the amount of caramel in the mixture.

18. According to *USA Today* (December 1996), two-thirds of Americans say they have trouble paying their bills. Assuming this is correct, express the number of Americans who have trouble paying their bills in terms of the total number of Americans.

19. The length of an infrared ray is twice the length of an ultraviolet ray. Express the length of the infrared ray in terms of the ultraviolet ray.

20. The length of a rectangle is three more than twice the width. Express the length of the rectangle in terms of the width.

21. A financial advisor has invested $10,000 in two accounts. If one account contains x dollars, express the amount in the second account in terms of x.

22. A fishing line 3 feet long is cut into two pieces, one shorter than the other. Express the length of the shorter piece in terms of the length of the longer piece.

23. The measure of angle A of a triangle is twice the measure of angle B. The measure of angle C is twice the measure of angle A. Write expressions for angle A and angle C in terms of angle B.

24. A 12-foot board is cut into two pieces of different lengths. Express the length of the longer piece in terms of the length of the shorter piece.

APPLYING THE CONCEPTS

For each of the following, write a phrase that would translate into the given expression.

25. $2x + 3$ **26.** $5y - 4$ **27.** $2(x + 3)$ **28.** $5(y - 4)$

29. Translate each of the following into a variable expression. Each expression is part of a formula from the sciences, and its translation requires more than one variable.
   a. the product of one-half the acceleration due to gravity (g) and the time (t) squared
   b. the product of mass (m) and acceleration (a)
   c. the product of the area (A) and the square of the velocity (v)
   d. the square root of the quotient of the spring constant (k) and the mass (m)

Focus on Problem Solving

Polya's Four-Step Process

Your success in mathematics and your success in the workplace are heavily dependent on your ability to solve problems. One of the foremost mathematicians to study problem solving was George Polya (1887–1985). The basic structure that Polya advocated for problem solving has four steps, as outlined below.

1. Understand the Problem

You must have a clear understanding of the problem. To help you focus on understanding the problem, here are some questions to think about.

- Can you restate the problem in your own words?
- Can you determine what is known about these types of problems?
- Is there missing information that you need in order to solve the problem?
- Is there information given that is not needed?
- What is the goal?

2. Devise a Plan

Successful problem solvers use a variety of techniques when they attempt to solve a problem. Here are some frequently used strategies.

- Make a list of the known information.
- Make a list of information that is needed to solve the problem.
- Make a table or draw a diagram.
- Work backwards.
- Try to solve a similar but simpler problem.
- Research the problem to determine whether there are known techniques for solving problems of its kind.
- Try to determine whether some pattern exists.
- Write an equation.

3. Carry out the Plan

Once you have devised a plan, you must carry it out.

- Work carefully.
- Keep an accurate and neat record of all your attempts.
- Realize that some of your initial plans will not work and that you may have to return to Step 2 and devise another plan or modify your existing plan.

4. Review your Solution

Once you have found a solution, check the solution against the known facts.

- Ensure that the solution is consistent with the facts of the problem.
- Interpret the solution in the context of the problem.
- Ask yourself whether there are generalizations of the solution that could apply to other problems.
- Determine the strengths and weaknesses of your solution. For instance, is your solution only an approximation to the actual solution?
- Consider the possibility of alternative solutions.

We will use Polya's four-step process to solve the following problem.

1.5 in.

6 in.

1 in.

A large soft drink costs $1.25 at a college cafeteria. The dimensions of the cup are shown at the left. Suppose you don't put any ice in the cup. Determine the cost per ounce for the soft drink.

1. *Understand the problem.* We must determine the cost per ounce for the soda. To do this, we need the dimensions of the cup (which are given), the cost of the drink (given), and a formula for the volume of the cup (unknown). Also, because the dimensions are given in inches, the volume will be in cubic inches; we need a conversion factor that will convert cubic inches to fluid ounces.

2. *Devise a plan.* Consult a resource book that gives the volume of the figure, which is called a **frustrum.** The formula for the volume is

$$V = \frac{\pi h}{3}(r^2 + rR + R^2)$$

   where h is the height, r is the radius of the base, and R is the radius of the top. Also from a reference book, 1 in.³ ≈ 0.55 fl oz. The general plan is to calculate the volume, convert the answer to fluid ounces, and then divide the cost by the number of fluid ounces.

3. *Carry out the plan.* Using the information from the drawing, evaluate the formula for the volume.

$$V = \frac{6\pi}{3}[1^2 + 1(1.5) + 1.5^2] = 9.5\pi \approx 29.8451 \text{ in}^3$$

$$V \approx 29.8451(0.55) \approx 16.4148 \text{ fl oz} \qquad \bullet \text{ Convert to fluid ounces.}$$

$$\text{Cost per ounce} \approx \frac{1.25}{16.4148} \approx 0.07615 \qquad \bullet \text{ Divide the cost by the volume.}$$

   The cost of the soft drink is approximately 7.62 cents per ounce.

4. *Review the solution.* The cost of a 12-ounce can of soda from a vending machine is generally about 75¢. Therefore, the cost of canned soda is 75¢ ÷ 12 = 6.25¢ per ounce. This is consistent with our solution. This does not mean our solution is correct, but it does indicate that it is at least reasonable. Why might soda from a cafeteria be more expensive per ounce than soda from a vending machine?

   Is there an alternative way to obtain the solution? There are probably many, but one possibility is to get a measuring cup, pour the soft drink into it, and read the number of ounces. Name an advantage and a disadvantage of this method.

Use the four-step solution process for the following problems.

1. A cup dispenser next to a water cooler holds cups that have the shape of a right circular cone. The height of the cone is 4 in. and the radius of the circular top is 1.5 in. How many ounces of water can the cup hold?

2. Soft drink manufacturers do research into the preferences of consumers with regard to the look and feel and size of a soft drink can. Suppose that a manufacturer has determined that people want to have their hand reach around approximately 75% of the can. If this preference is to be achieved, how tall should the can be if it contains 12 oz of fluid? Assume the can is a right circular cylinder.

Projects and Group Activities

Water Displacement   When an object is placed in water, the object displaces an amount of water that is equal to the volume of the object.

➡ A sphere with a diameter of 4 in. is placed in a rectangular tank of water that is 6 in. long and 5 in. wide. How much does the water level rise? Round to the nearest hundredth.

$$V = \frac{4}{3}\pi r^3$$ • Use the formula for the volume of a sphere.

$$V = \frac{4}{3}\pi(2^3) = \frac{32}{3}\pi$$ • $r = \frac{1}{2}d = \frac{1}{2}(4) = 2$

5 in.

x

d = 4 in.

6 in.

Let x represent the amount of the rise in water level. The volume of the sphere will equal the volume displaced by the water. As shown at the left, this volume is the rectangular solid with width 5 in., length 6 in., and height x in.

$$V = LWH$$ • Use the formula for the volume of a rectangular solid.

$$\frac{32}{3}\pi = (6)(5)x$$ • Substitute $\frac{32}{3}\pi$ for V, 5 for W, and 6 for L.

$$\frac{32}{90}\pi = x$$ • The exact height that the water will fill is $\frac{32}{90}\pi$.

$$1.12 \approx x$$ • Use a calculator to find an approximation.

The water will rise approximately 1.12 in.

20 cm   30 cm

16 in.   20 in.

12 in.   12 in.

Figure 1   Figure 2   Figure 3

1. A cylinder with a 2-centimeter radius and a height of 10 cm is submerged in a tank of water that is 20 cm wide and 30 cm long (see Figure 1). How much does the water level rise? Round to the nearest hundredth.

2. A sphere with a radius of 6 in. is placed in a rectangular tank of water that is 16 in. wide and 20 in. long (see Figure 2). The sphere displaces water until two-thirds of the sphere is submerged. How much does the water level rise? Round to the nearest hundredth.

3. A chemist wants to know the density of a statue that weighs 15 lb. The statue is placed in a rectangular tank of water that is 12 in. long and 12 in. wide (see Figure 3). The water level rises 0.42 in. Find the density of the statue. Round to the nearest hundredth. (*Hint*: density = weight ÷ volume)

Chapter Summary

Key Words
The *integers* are ... $-4, -3, -2, -1, 0, 1, 2, 3, 4, ...$. The *negative integers* are $... -4, -3, -2, -1$. The *positive integers*, or *natural numbers*, are $1, 2, 3, 4, ...$. A *rational number* can be written in the form $\frac{a}{b}$, where a and b are integers and $b \neq 0$.

An *irrational number* has a decimal representation that never terminates or repeats. The rational numbers and the irrational numbers taken together are the *real numbers*.

The *additive inverse* of a number is the opposite of the number. The *multiplicative inverse* of a number is the reciprocal of the number. The *absolute value* of a number is its distance from zero on the number line.

A *set* is a collection of objects. The objects are called the *elements* of the set. The *roster method* of writing sets encloses a list of the elements in braces. *Set-builder notation* makes use of a variable and a certain property that only elements of that set possess. Sets of real numbers are also expressed using *interval notation*.

The *union* of two sets, written $A \cup B$, is the set that contains all the elements of A and all the elements of B. The *intersection* of two sets, written $A \cap B$, is the set that contains the elements that are common to both A and B.

The expression a^n is in *exponential form*, where a is the base and n is the exponent.

A *variable expression* is an expression that contains one or more variables. The *terms* of a variable expression are the addends of the expression. A *variable term* is composed of a numerical coefficient and a variable part.

Essential Rules
To add numbers with the same sign, add the absolute values of the numbers; then attach the sign of the addends. **To add numbers with different signs,** find the difference between the absolute values of the numbers; then attach the sign of the addend with the larger absolute value.

To subtract two integers, add the opposite of the second number to the first number.

The product or quotient of two numbers with the same sign is positive. **The product or quotient of two numbers with different signs** is negative.

Commutative Property of Addition	$a + b = b + a$
Commutative Property of Multiplication	$a \cdot b = b \cdot a$
Associative Property of Addition	$(a + b) + c = a + (b + c)$
Associative Property of Multiplication	$(a \cdot b) \cdot c = a \cdot (b \cdot c)$
Addition Property of Zero	$a + 0 = a$ or $0 + a = a$
Multiplication Property of Zero	$a \cdot 0 = 0$ or $0 \cdot a = 0$
Multiplication Property of One	$a \cdot 1 = a$ or $1 \cdot a = a$
Inverse Property of Addition	$a + (-a) = -a + a = 0$
Inverse Property of Multiplication	If $a \neq 0$, $a \cdot \dfrac{1}{a} = \dfrac{1}{a} \cdot a = 1$.
Distributive Property	$a(b + c) = ab + ac$
Division Properties of Zero and One	If $a \neq 0$, $0 \div a = 0$ and $a \div a = 1$.
	$a \div 1 = a$
	$a \div 0$ is undefined.

The Order of Operations Agreement

Step 1 Perform all operations inside grouping symbols.

Step 2 Simplify exponential expressions.

Step 3 Do multiplication and division as they occur from left to right.

Step 4 Do addition and subtraction as they occur from left to right.

Chapter Review

1. Use the roster method to write the set of integers between -3 and 4.

2. Find $A \cap B$ given $A = \{0, 1, 2, 3\}$ and $B = \{2, 3, 4, 5\}$.

3. Graph $(-2, 4]$.

   ```
   ←+—+—+—+—+—+—+—+—+—+—+→
    -5 -4 -3 -2 -1  0  1  2  3  4  5
   ```

4. Identify the property that justifies the statement.
   $2(3x) = (2 \cdot 3)x$

5. Simplify: $-4.07 + 2.3 - 1.07$

6. Evaluate $(a - 2b^2) \div ab$ when $a = 4$ and $b = -3$.

7. Simplify: $-2 \cdot (4^2) \cdot (-3)^2$

8. Simplify: $4y - 3[x - 2(3 - 2x) - 4y]$

9. Find the additive inverse of $-\dfrac{3}{4}$.

10. Use set-builder notation to write the set of real numbers less than -3.

11. Graph $\{x \mid x < 1\}$.

    ```
    ←+—+—+—+—+—+—+—+—+—+—+→
     -5 -4 -3 -2 -1  0  1  2  3  4  5
    ```

12. Simplify: $-10 - (-3) - 8$

13. Simplify: $-\dfrac{2}{3} + \dfrac{3}{5} - \dfrac{1}{6}$

14. Use the Associative Property of Addition to complete the statement.
    $3 + (4 + y) = (3 + \,?\,) + y$

15. Simplify: $-\dfrac{3}{8} \div \dfrac{3}{5}$

16. Let $x \in \{-4, -2, 0, 2\}$. For what values of x is $x > -1$ true?

17. Evaluate $2a^2 - \dfrac{3b}{a}$ when $a = -3$ and $b = 2$.

18. Simplify: $18 - |-12 + 8|$

19. Simplify: $20 \div \dfrac{3^2 - 2^2}{3^2 + 2^2}$

20. Graph $[-3, \infty)$.

21. Find $A \cup B$ given $A = \{1, 3, 5, 7\}$ and $B = \{2, 4, 6, 8\}$.

22. Simplify: $-204 \div (-17)$

23. Write $[-2, 3]$ in set-builder notation.

24. Simplify: $\dfrac{3}{5}\left(-\dfrac{10}{21}\right)\left(-\dfrac{7}{15}\right)$

25. Use the Distributive Property to complete the statement.
$6x - 21y = ?(2x - 7y)$

26. Graph $\{x \mid x \leq -3\} \cup \{x \mid x > 0\}$.

27. Simplify: $-2(x - 3) + 4(2 - x)$

28. Let $p \in \{-4, 0, 7\}$. Evaluate $-|p|$ for each element of the set.

29. Identify the property that justifies the statement.
$-4 + 4 = 0$

30. Simplify: $-3.286 \div (-1.06)$

31. Translate and simplify "twelve minus the quotient of three more than a number and the number."

32. The sum of two numbers is forty. Using x to represent the smaller of the two numbers, translate "the sum of twice the smaller number and five more than the larger number" into a variable expression. Then simplify.

33. The length of a rectangle is three feet less than three times the width. Express the length of the rectangle in terms of the width.

34. According to *USA Today*, in the first quarter of 1997, Ford Motor Company sold 341,602 more vehicles than Chrysler Corporation did. Express the number of vehicles sold by Chrysler Corporation in the first quarter of 1997 in terms of the number of vehicles sold by Ford Motor Company during that period.

Chapter Test

1. Simplify: $(-2)(-3)(-5)$

2. Find $A \cap B$ given $A = \{1, 3, 5, 7\}$ and $B = \{5, 7, 9, 11\}$.

3. Simplify: $(-2)^3(-3)^2$

4. Graph $(-\infty, 1]$.

    $$-5 \;-4 \;-3 \;-2 \;-1 \;\; 0 \;\; 1 \;\; 2 \;\; 3 \;\; 4 \;\; 5$$

5. Find $A \cap B$ given $A = \{-3, -2, -1, 0, 1, 2, 3\}$ and $B = \{-1, 0, 1\}$.

6. Evaluate $(a - b)^2 \div (2b + 1)$ when $a = 2$ and $b = -3$.

7. Simplify: $\left| -3 - (-5) \right|$

8. Simplify: $2x - 4[2 - 3(x + 4y) - 2]$

9. Find the additive inverse of -12.

10. Simplify: $-5^2 \cdot 4$

11. Graph $\{x \,|\, x < 3\} \cap \{x \,|\, x > -2\}$.

    $$-5 \;-4 \;-3 \;-2 \;-1 \;\; 0 \;\; 1 \;\; 2 \;\; 3 \;\; 4 \;\; 5$$

12. Simplify: $2 - (-12) + 3 - 5$

13. Simplify: $\dfrac{2}{3} - \dfrac{5}{12} + \dfrac{4}{9}$

14. Use the Commutative Property of Addition to complete the statement.
    $(3 + 4) + 2 = (? + 3) + 2$

15. Simplify: $-\dfrac{2}{3}\left(\dfrac{9}{15}\right)\left(\dfrac{10}{27}\right)$

16. Let $x \in \{-5, 3, 7\}$. For what values of x is $x < -1$ true?

17. Evaluate $\dfrac{b^2 - c^2}{a - 2c}$ when $a = 2$, $b = 3$, and $c = -1$.

18. Simplify: $-180 \div 12$

19. Simplify: $12 - 4\left(\dfrac{5^2 - 1}{3}\right) \div 16$

20. Graph $(3, \infty)$.

21. Find $A \cup B$ given $A = \{1, 3, 5, 7\}$ and $B = \{2, 3, 4, 5\}$.

22. Simplify: $3x - 2(x - y) - 3(y - 4x)$

23. Simplify: $8 - 4(2 - 3)^2 \div 2$

24. Simplify: $\dfrac{3}{5}\left(-\dfrac{10}{21}\right)\left(-\dfrac{7}{15}\right)$

25. Identify the property that justifies the statement.
$-2(x + y) = -2x - 2y$

26. Graph $\{x \,|\, x \le 3\} \cup \{x \,|\, x < -2\}$.

27. Simplify: $4.27 - 6.98 + 1.3$

28. Find $A \cup B$ given $A = \{-2, -1, 0, 1, 2, 3\}$ and $B = \{-1, 0, 1\}$.

29. Translate and simplify "thirteen decreased by the product of three less than a number and nine."

30. The sum of two numbers is nine. Using x to represent the larger of the two numbers, translate "the difference between one more than the larger number and twice the smaller number" into a variable expression. Then simplify.

2

First-Degree Equations and Inequalities

Accountants are responsible for preparing and analyzing financial reports. Many *public accountants* work within an accounting firm. *Management accountants* generally work for large companies and handle their financial records. *Government accountants* examine records of either government agencies or private firms whose business is regulated by the government. All accountants work with equations. The fundamental accounting equation is Assets = Liabilities + Owner's Equity.

Objectives

Section 2.1
To solve an equation using the Addition or the Multiplication Property of Equations
To solve an equation using both the Addition and the Multiplication Properties of Equations
To solve an equation containing parentheses
To solve a literal equation for one of the variables

Section 2.2
To solve integer problems
To solve coin and stamp problems

Section 2.3
To solve value mixture problems
To solve percent mixture problems
To solve uniform motion problems

Section 2.4
To solve an inequality in one variable
To solve a compound inequality
To solve application problems

Section 2.5
To solve an absolute value equation
To solve an absolute value inequality
To solve application problems

Moscow Papyrus

Most of the early history of mathematics can be traced to the Egyptians and Babylonians. This early work began around 3000 B.C. The Babylonians used clay tablets and a type of writing called *cuneiform* (wedge-shape) to record their thoughts and discoveries. Here are the symbols for 10, 1, and subtraction.

Simple groupings of these symbols were used to represent numbers less than 60. The numbers 32 and 28 are shown below.

To make records, the Egyptians used papyrus, a plant reed dried and pounded thin, and hieratic writing that was derived from hieroglyphics. A number of papyrus documents have been discovered over the years. One particularly famous one is called the Moscow Papyrus, which dates from 1850 B.C. It is approximately 18 feet long and 3 inches wide and contains 25 problems.

The Moscow Papyrus dealt with solving practical problems related to geometry, food preparation, and grain allotments. Here is one of the problems:

> The width of a rectangle is $\frac{3}{4}$ the length,
>
> and the area is 12.
> Find the dimensions of the rectangle.

You might recognize this as a type of problem you have solved before. Word problems are very old indeed. This one is around 3900 years old.

2.1 Solving First-Degree Equations

Objective A *To solve an equation using the Addition or the Multiplication Property of Equations* .... (7) CT

An **equation** expresses the equality of two mathematical expressions. The expressions can be either numerical or variable expressions.

$$2 + 8 = 10$$
$$x + 8 = 11$$ } Equations
$$x^2 + 2y = 7$$

The equation at the right is a **conditional equation.** The equation is true if the variable is replaced by 3. The equation is false if the variable is replaced by 4. A conditional equation is true for at least one value of the variable.

$x + 2 = 5$ A conditional equation

$3 + 2 = 5$ A true equation
$4 + 2 = 5$ A false equation

The replacement values of the variable that will make an equation true are called the **roots** or the **solutions** of the equation. The solution of the equation $x + 2 = 5$ is 3 because $3 + 2 = 5$ is a true equation.

The equation at the right is an **identity.** Any replacement for x will result in a true equation.

$x + 2 = x + 2$

The equation at the right has no solution because there is no number that equals itself plus one. Any replacement value for x will result in a false equation. This equation is a **contradiction.**

$x = x + 1$

Each of the equations at the right is a **first-degree equation in one variable.** All variables have an exponent of 1.

$x + 2 = 12$
$3y - 2 = 5y$
$3(a + 2) = 14a$

To **solve** an equation means to find a root or solution of the equation. The simplest equation to solve is an equation of the form *variable = constant*, because the constant is the solution. If $x = 3$, then 3 is the solution of the equation, because $3 = 3$ is a true equation.

Equivalent equations are equations that have the same solution. For instance, $x + 4 = 6$ and $x = 2$ are equivalent equations because the solution of each equation is 2. In solving an equation, the goal is to produce *simpler* but equivalent equations until you reach the goal of *variable = constant*. The Addition Property of Equations can be used to rewrite an equation in this form.

The Addition Property of Equations

If *a*, *b*, and *c* are algebraic expressions, then the equation $a = b$ has the same solutions as the equation $a + c = b + c$.

The Addition Property of Equations states that the same quantity can be added to each side of an equation without changing the solution of the equation. This property is used to remove a term from one side of the equation by adding the opposite of that term to each side of the equation.

➡ Solve: $x - 3 = 7$

$$x - 3 = 7$$
$$x - 3 + 3 = 7 + 3$$ • Add 3 to each side of the equation.
$$x + 0 = 10$$ • Simplify.
$$x = 10$$ • The equation is in the form variable = constant.

Check:

$$\frac{x - 3 = 7}{10 - 3 \mid 7}$$ • Check the solution. Replace *x* with 10.
$$7 = 7$$ • When simplified, the left side of the equation equals the right

The solution is 10.   side. Therefore, 10 is the correct solution of the equation.

Because subtraction is defined in terms of addition, the Addition Property of Equations enables us to subtract the same number from each side of an equation.

➡ Solve: $x + \dfrac{7}{12} = \dfrac{1}{2}$

$$x + \frac{7}{12} = \frac{1}{2}$$

$$x + \frac{7}{12} - \frac{7}{12} = \frac{1}{2} - \frac{7}{12}$$ • Subtract $\frac{7}{12}$ from each side of the equation.

$$x + 0 = \frac{6}{12} - \frac{7}{12}$$ • Simplify.

$$x = -\frac{1}{12}$$

The solution is $-\dfrac{1}{12}$.

The Multiplication Property of Equations is also used to produce equivalent equations.

> **The Multiplication Property of Equations**
>
> If *a*, *b*, and *c* are algebraic expressions and $c \neq 0$, then the equation $a = b$ has the same solution as the equation $ac = bc$.

This property states that each side of an equation can be multiplied by the same nonzero number without changing the solution of the equation.

Recall that the goal of solving an equation is to rewrite the equation in the form *variable = constant*. The Multiplication Property of Equations is used to rewrite an equation in this form by multiplying each side by the reciprocal of the coefficient.

➡ Solve: $-\dfrac{3}{4}x = 12$

$$-\frac{3}{4}x = 12$$

$$\left(-\frac{4}{3}\right)\left(-\frac{3}{4}\right)x = \left(-\frac{4}{3}\right)12$$ • Multiply each side of the equation by $-\frac{4}{3}$, the reciprocal of $-\frac{3}{4}$.

$$1x = -16$$ • Simplify.
$$x = -16$$

The solution is -16.

Because division is defined in terms of multiplication, the Multiplication Property of Equations enables us to divide each side of an equation by the same nonzero quantity.

➡ Solve: $-5x = 9$

Multiply each side of the equation by the reciprocal of -5. This is equivalent to dividing each side of the equation by -5.

$$-5x = 9$$
$$\frac{-5x}{-5} = \frac{9}{-5}$$ • Divide each side of the equation by -5.

$$1x = -\frac{9}{5}$$ • Simplify.

$$x = -\frac{9}{5}$$

The solution is $-\frac{9}{5}$. You should check the solution.

When using the Multiplication Property of Equations, it is usually easier to multiply each side of the equation by the reciprocal of the coefficient when the coefficient is a fraction. Divide each side of the equation by the coefficient when the coefficient is an integer or a decimal.

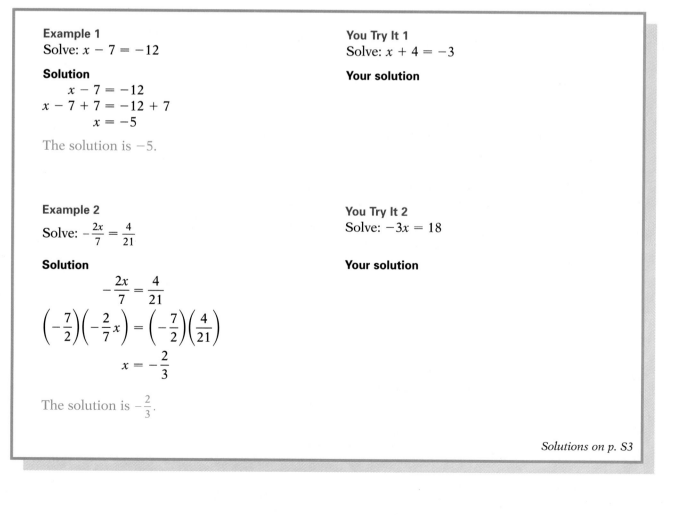

Example 1
Solve: $x - 7 = -12$

Solution
$$x - 7 = -12$$
$$x - 7 + 7 = -12 + 7$$
$$x = -5$$

The solution is -5.

You Try It 1
Solve: $x + 4 = -3$

Your solution

Example 2
Solve: $-\frac{2x}{7} = \frac{4}{21}$

Solution
$$-\frac{2x}{7} = \frac{4}{21}$$
$$\left(-\frac{7}{2}\right)\left(-\frac{2}{7}x\right) = \left(-\frac{7}{2}\right)\left(\frac{4}{21}\right)$$
$$x = -\frac{2}{3}$$

The solution is $-\frac{2}{3}$.

You Try It 2
Solve: $-3x = 18$

Your solution

Solutions on p. S3

Objective B   **To solve an equation using both the Addition and the Multiplication Properties of Equations** ··· ⟨ 7 ⟩ CT

In solving an equation, it is often necessary to apply both the Addition and the Multiplication Properties of Equations.

➡ Solve: $4x - 3 + 2x = 8 + 9x - 12$

$$4x - 3 + 2x = 8 + 9x - 12$$
$$6x - 3 = -4 + 9x$$

• Simplify each side of the equation by combining like terms.

$$6x - 3 - 9x = -4 + 9x - 9x$$
$$-3x - 3 = -4$$

• Subtract $9x$ from each side of the equation. Then simplify.

$$-3x - 3 + 3 = -4 + 3$$
$$-3x = -1$$

• Add 3 to each side of the equation. Then simplify.

$$\frac{-3x}{-3} = \frac{-1}{-3}$$

• Divide each side of the equation by the coefficient -3. Then simplify.

$$x = \frac{1}{3}$$

TAKE NOTE

You should always check your work by substituting your answer into the original equation and simplifying the resulting numerical expressions. If the left and right sides are equal, your answer is the solution of the equation.

Check:

$$\begin{array}{c|c} \hline 4x - 3 + 2x = 8 + 9x - 12 \\ \hline 4\left(\dfrac{1}{3}\right) - 3 + 2\left(\dfrac{1}{3}\right) & 8 + 9\left(\dfrac{1}{3}\right) - 12 \\ \dfrac{4}{3} - 3 + \dfrac{2}{3} & 8 + 3 - 12 \\ -\dfrac{5}{3} + \dfrac{2}{3} & 11 - 12 \\ -1 = -1 \end{array}$$

The solution is $\dfrac{1}{3}$.

Example 3
Solve: $3x - 5 = x + 2 - 7x$

Solution
$$3x - 5 = x + 2 - 7x$$
$$3x - 5 = -6x + 2$$
$$3x - 5 + 6x = -6x + 2 + 6x$$
$$9x - 5 = 2$$
$$9x - 5 + 5 = 2 + 5$$
$$9x = 7$$
$$\frac{9x}{9} = \frac{7}{9}$$
$$x = \frac{7}{9}$$

The solution is $\dfrac{7}{9}$.

You Try It 3
Solve: $6x - 5 - 3x = 14 - 5x$

Your solution

Solution on p. S3

Objective C   **To solve an equation containing parentheses** .... 🎞 CT

When an equation contains parentheses, one of the steps required in solving the equation involves using the Distributive Property.

➡ Solve: $3(x - 2) + 3 = 2(6 - x)$

$$3(x - 2) + 3 = 2(6 - x)$$
$$3x - 6 + 3 = 12 - 2x$$
$$3x - 3 = 12 - 2x$$

- Use the Distributive Property to remove parentheses. Then simplify.

$$3x - 3 + 2x = 12 - 2x + 2x$$
$$5x - 3 = 12$$

- Add 2*x* to each side of the equation.

$$5x - 3 + 3 = 12 + 3$$
$$5x = 15$$

- Add 3 to each side of the equation.

$$\frac{5x}{5} = \frac{15}{5}$$
$$x = 3$$

- Divide each side of the equation by the coefficient 5.

The solution is 3.

To solve an equation containing fractions, first clear the denominators by multiplying each side of the equation by the least common multiple (LCM) of the denominators.

➡ Solve: $\frac{x}{2} - \frac{7}{9} = \frac{x}{6} + \frac{2}{3}$

Find the LCM of the denominators. The LCM of 2, 9, 6, and 3 is 18.

$$\frac{x}{2} - \frac{7}{9} = \frac{x}{6} + \frac{2}{3}$$

$$18\left(\frac{x}{2} - \frac{7}{9}\right) = 18\left(\frac{x}{6} + \frac{2}{3}\right)$$

- Multiply each side of the equation by the LCM of the denominators.

$$\frac{18x}{2} - \frac{18 \cdot 7}{9} = \frac{18x}{6} + \frac{18 \cdot 2}{3}$$

- Use the Distributive Property to remove parentheses. Then simplify.

$$9x - 14 = 3x + 12$$

$$6x - 14 = 12$$

- Subtract 3*x* from each side of the equation. Then simplify.

$$6x = 26$$

- Add 14 to each side of the equation. Then simplify.

$$\frac{6x}{6} = \frac{26}{6}$$

- Divide each side of the equation by the coefficient of *x*. Then simplify.

$$x = \frac{13}{3}$$

The solution is $\frac{13}{3}$.

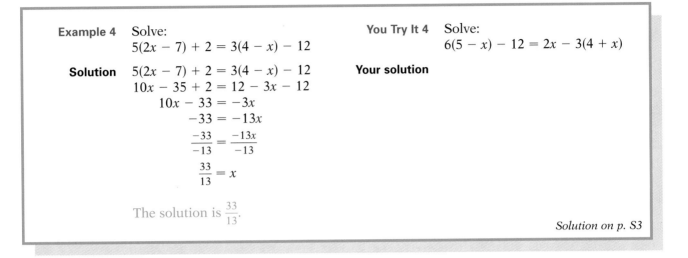

Example 4   Solve:
$$5(2x - 7) + 2 = 3(4 - x) - 12$$

Solution
$$5(2x - 7) + 2 = 3(4 - x) - 12$$
$$10x - 35 + 2 = 12 - 3x - 12$$
$$10x - 33 = -3x$$
$$-33 = -13x$$
$$\frac{-33}{-13} = \frac{-13x}{-13}$$
$$\frac{33}{13} = x$$

The solution is $\frac{33}{13}$.

You Try It 4   Solve:
$$6(5 - x) - 12 = 2x - 3(4 + x)$$

Your solution

Solution on p. S3

Objective D   To solve a literal equation for one of the variables .... [7] CT

A **literal equation** is an equation that contains more than one variable. Some examples are shown at the right.

$$3x - 2y = 4$$
$$v^2 = v_0^2 + 2as$$

Formulas are used to express a relationship among physical quantities. A **formula** is a literal equation that states rules about measurement. Examples are shown at the right.

$$s = vt - 16t^2 \quad \text{(Physics)}$$
$$c^2 = a^2 + b^2 \quad \text{(Geometry)}$$
$$I = P(1 + r)^n \quad \text{(Business)}$$

The Addition and Multiplication Properties of Equations can be used to solve a literal equation for one of the variables. The goal is to rewrite the equation so that the variable being solved for is alone on one side of the equation and all the other numbers and variables are on the other side.

⇒ Solve $A = P + Prt$ for t.

$$A = P + Prt$$
$$A - P = Prt$$
• Subtract P from each side of the equation.
$$\frac{A - P}{Pr} = \frac{Prt}{Pr}$$
• Divide each side of the equation by Pr.
$$\frac{A - P}{Pr} = t$$

Example 5

Solve $C = \frac{5}{9}(F - 32)$ for F.

Solution

$$C = \frac{5}{9}(F - 32)$$

$$\frac{9}{5}C = \frac{9}{5} \cdot \frac{5}{9}(F - 32)$$

$$\frac{9}{5}C = F - 32$$

$$\frac{9}{5}C + 32 = F$$

You Try It 5

Solve $S = C - rC$ for r.

Your solution

Solution on p. S3

2.1 Exercises

. . . .

Objective A

Solve and check.

1. $x - 2 = 7$

2. $x - 8 = 4$

3. $a + 3 = -7$

4. $a + 5 = -2$

5. $b - 3 = -5$

6. $10 + m = 2$

7. $-7 = x + 8$

8. $-12 = x - 3$

9. $3x = 12$

10. $8x = 4$

11. $-3x = 2$

12. $-5a = 7$

13. $-\dfrac{3}{2} + x = \dfrac{4}{3}$

14. $\dfrac{2}{7} + x = \dfrac{17}{21}$

15. $x + \dfrac{2}{3} = \dfrac{5}{6}$

16. $\dfrac{5}{8} - y = \dfrac{3}{4}$

17. $\dfrac{2}{3}y = 5$

18. $\dfrac{3}{5}y = 12$

19. $-\dfrac{5}{8}x = \dfrac{4}{5}$

20. $-\dfrac{5}{12}x = \dfrac{7}{16}$

21. $-\dfrac{3b}{5} = -\dfrac{3}{5}$

22. $-\dfrac{7b}{12} = \dfrac{7}{8}$

23. $-\dfrac{2}{3}x = -\dfrac{5}{8}$

24. $-\dfrac{3}{4}x = -\dfrac{4}{7}$

25. $-\dfrac{5}{8}x = 40$

26. $\dfrac{2}{7}y = -8$

27. $-\dfrac{5}{6}y = -\dfrac{25}{36}$

28. $-\dfrac{15}{24}x = -\dfrac{10}{27}$

Objective B

Solve and check.

29. $3x + 5x = 12$

30. $2x - 7x = 15$

31. $2x - 4 = 12$

32. $5x + 9 = 6$

33. $3y - 5y = 0$

34. $2y - 9 = -9$

35. $4x - 6 = 3x$

36. $2a - 7 = 5a$

37. $7x + 12 = 9x$

38. $3x - 12 = 5x$

39. $4x + 2 = 4x$

40. $3m - 7 = 3m$

41. $2x + 2 = 3x + 5$

42. $7x - 9 = 3 - 4x$

43. $2 - 3t = 3t - 4$

44. $7 - 5t = 2t - 9$

45. $3b - 2b = 4 - 2b$

46. $3x - 5 = 6 - 9x$

47. $3x + 7 = 3 + 7x$

48. $\dfrac{5}{8}b - 3 = 12$

49. $\dfrac{1}{3} - 2b = 3$

Objective C

Solve and check.

50. $2x + 2(x + 1) = 10$

51. $2x + 3(x - 5) = 15$

52. $2(a - 3) = 2(4 - 2a)$

53. $5(2 - b) = -3(b - 3)$

54. $3 - 2(y - 3) = 4y - 7$

55. $3(y - 5) - 5y = 2y + 9$

56. $2(3x - 2) - 5x = 3 - 2x$

57. $4 - 3x = 7x - 2(3 - x)$

58. $8 - 5(4 - 3x) = 2(4 - x) - 8x$

59. $-3x - 2(4 + 5x) = 14 - 3(2x - 3)$

60. $3[2 - 3(y - 2)] = 12$

61. $3y = 2[5 - 3(2 - y)]$

62. $4[3 + 5(3 - x) + 2x] = 6 - 2x$

63. $2[4 + 2(5 - x) - 2x] = 4x - 7$

64. $3[4 - 2(a - 2)] = 3(2 - 4a)$

65. $2[3 - 2(z + 4)] = 3(4 - z)$

66. $-3(x - 2) = 2[x - 4(x - 2) + x]$

67. $3[x - (2 - x) - 2x] = 3(4 - x)$

68. $\dfrac{2}{9}t - \dfrac{5}{6} = \dfrac{1}{12}t$

69. $\dfrac{3}{4}t - \dfrac{7}{12}t = 1$

70. $\dfrac{2}{3}x - \dfrac{5}{6}x - 3 = \dfrac{1}{2}x - 5$

71. $\dfrac{1}{2}x - \dfrac{3}{4}x + \dfrac{5}{8} = \dfrac{3}{2}x - \dfrac{5}{2}$

72. $\dfrac{5 - 2x}{5} + \dfrac{x - 4}{10} = \dfrac{3}{10}$

73. $\dfrac{2x - 5}{12} - \dfrac{3 - x}{6} = \dfrac{11}{12}$

74. $\dfrac{x - 2}{4} - \dfrac{x + 5}{6} = \dfrac{5x - 2}{9}$

75. $\dfrac{2x - 1}{4} + \dfrac{3x + 4}{8} = \dfrac{1 - 4x}{12}$

76. If $5x - 7 = 2x + 2$, evaluate $7x + 4$.

77. If $3x - 5 = 9x + 4$, evaluate $6x - 3$.

78. If $2x - 5(x + 1) = 7$, evaluate $x^2 - 1$.

79. If $3(2x + 1) = 5 - 2(x - 2)$, evaluate $2x^2 + 1$.

80. If $4 - 3(2x + 3) = 5 - 4x$, evaluate $x^2 - 2x$.

81. If $5 - 2(4x - 1) = 3x + 7$, evaluate $x^4 - x^2$.

Objective D

Solve the formula for the given variable.

82. $I = Prt;\ r$ (Business)

83. $C = 2\pi r;\ r$ (Geometry)

84. $PV = nRT;\ R$ (Chemistry)

85. $A = \dfrac{1}{2}bh;\ h$ (Geometry)

86. $V = \dfrac{1}{3}\pi r^2 h;\ h$ (Geometry)

87. $I = \dfrac{100M}{C};\ M$ (Intelligence Quotient)

88. $P = 2L + 2W;\ W$ (Geometry)

89. $A = P + Prt;\ r$ (Business)

90. $s = V_0 t - 16t^2; V_0$ (Physics)   **91.** $s = \dfrac{1}{2}(a + b + c); c$ (Geometry)

92. $F = \dfrac{9}{5}C + 32; C$ (Temperature Conversion)   **93.** $S = 2\pi r^2 + 2\pi rh; h$ (Geometry)

94. $A = \dfrac{1}{2}h(b_1 + b_2); b_2$ (Geometry)   **95.** $P = \dfrac{R - C}{n}; R$ (Business)

96. $a_n = a_1 + (n - 1)d; d$ (Mathematics)   **97.** $S = 2WH + 2WL + 2LH; H$ (Geometry)

APPLYING THE CONCEPTS

98. Explain the difference between a variable expression and an equation.

99. The following is offered as the solution of $5x + 15 = 2x + 3(2x + 5)$.

$$5x + 15 = 2x + 3(2x + 5)$$
$$5x + 15 = 2x + 6x + 15$$
$$5x + 15 = 8x + 15$$
$$5x + 15 - 15 = 8x + 15 - 15$$

- Use the Distributive Property.
- Combine like terms.
- Subtract 15 from each side of the equation.

$$5x = 8x$$
$$\dfrac{5x}{x} = \dfrac{8x}{x}$$

- Divide each side of the equation by x.

$$5 = 8$$

Because $5 = 8$ is not a true equation, the equation has no solution.

If this is correct, so state. If not, explain why it is not correct and supply the correct answer.

100. In your own words, explain the Addition Property of Equations.

101. In your own words, explain the Multiplication Property of Equations.

102. Why, when the Multiplication Property of Equations is used, must the quantity that multiplies each side of the equation not be zero?

2.2 Applications: Puzzle Problems

Objective A *To solve integer problems* ································· CT

An equation states that two mathematical expressions are equal. Therefore, to translate a sentence into an equation requires recognition of the words or phrases that mean "equals." A partial list of these phrases includes "is," "is equal to," "amounts to," and "represents."

Once the sentence is translated into an equation, the equation can be solved by rewriting it in the form *variable = constant*.

Recall that an **even integer** is an integer that is divisible by 2. An **odd integer** is an integer that is not divisible by 2.

Consecutive integers are integers that follow one another in order. Examples of consecutive integers are shown at the right. (Assume that the variable n represents an integer.)

$$8, 9, 10$$
$$-3, -2, -1$$
$$n, n + 1, n + 2$$

Examples of **consecutive even integers** are shown at the right. (Assume that the variable n represents an even integer.)

$$16, 18, 20$$
$$-6, -4, -2$$
$$n, n + 2, n + 4$$

Examples of **consecutive odd integers** are shown at the right. (Assume that the variable n represents an odd integer.)

$$11, 13, 15$$
$$-23, -21, -19$$
$$n, n + 2, n + 4$$

➡ The sum of three consecutive even integers is seventy-eight. Find the integers.

> **Strategy for Solving an Integer Problem**
>
> 1. Let a variable represent one of the integers. Express each of the other integers in terms of that variable. Remember that for consecutive integer problems, consecutive integers differ by 1. Consecutive even or consecutive odd integers differ by 2.

First even integer: n • Represent three consecutive even integers.
Second even integer: $n + 2$
Third even integer: $n + 4$

> 2. Determine the relationship among the integers.

$$n + (n + 2) + (n + 4) = 78$$ • The sum of the three even integers is 78.
$$3n + 6 = 78$$
$$3n = 72$$
$$n = 24$$ • The first integer is 24.

$$n + 2 = 24 + 2 = 26$$ • Find the second and third integers.
$$n + 4 = 24 + 4 = 28$$

The three consecutive even integers are 24, 26, and 28.

Example 1

One number is four more than another number. The sum of the two numbers is sixty-six. Find the two numbers.

Strategy

- The smaller number: n
  The larger number: $n + 4$
- The sum of the numbers is 66.

$$n + (n + 4) = 66$$

Solution

$$n + (n + 4) = 66$$
$$2n + 4 = 66$$
$$2n = 62$$
$$n = 31$$

$$n + 4 = 31 + 4 = 35$$

The numbers are 31 and 35.

You Try It 1

The sum of three numbers is eighty-one. The second number is twice the first number, and the third number is three less than four times the first number. Find the numbers.

Your strategy

Your solution

Example 2

Five times the first of three consecutive even integers is five more than the product of four and the third integer. Find the integers.

Strategy

- First even integer: n
  Second even integer: $n + 2$
  Third even integer: $n + 4$
- Five times the first integer equals five more than the product of four and the third integer.

$$5n = 4(n + 4) + 5$$

Solution

$$5n = 4(n + 4) + 5$$
$$5n = 4n + 16 + 5$$
$$5n = 4n + 21$$
$$n = 21$$

Because 21 is not an even integer, there is no solution.

You Try It 2

Find three consecutive odd integers such that three times the sum of the first two integers is ten more than the product of the third integer and four.

Your strategy

Your solution

Solutions on p. S3

Objective B   *To solve coin and stamp problems* .... (8) CT

In solving problems dealing with coins or stamps of different values, it is necessary to represent the value of the coins or stamps in the same unit of money. The unit of money is frequently cents. For example,

The value of five 8¢ stamps is 5 · 8, or 40 cents.
The value of four 20¢ stamps is 4 · 20, or 80 cents.
The value of n 10¢ stamps is n · 10, or $10n$ cents.

➡ A collection of stamps consists of 5¢, 13¢, and 18¢ stamps. The number of 13¢ stamps is two more than three times the number of 5¢ stamps. The number of 18¢ stamps is five less than the number of 13¢ stamps. The total value of all the stamps is $1.68. Find the number of 18¢ stamps.

> **Strategy for Solving a Stamp Problem**
>
> 1. For each denomination of stamp, write a numerical or variable expression for the number of stamps, the value of the stamp, and the total value of the stamps in cents. The results can be recorded in a table.

The number of 5¢ stamps: x
The number of 13¢ stamps: $3x + 2$
The number of 18¢ stamps: $(3x + 2) - 5 = 3x - 3$

Stamp	Number of Stamps	·	Value of Stamp in Cents	=	Total Value in Cents
5¢	x	·	5	=	$5x$
13¢	$3x + 2$	·	13	=	$13(3x + 2)$
18¢	$3x - 3$	·	18	=	$18(3x - 3)$

> 2. Determine the relationship between the total values of the stamps. Use the fact that the sum of the total values of each denomination of stamp is equal to the total value of all the stamps.

The sum of the total values of each denomination of stamp is equal to the total value of all the stamps (168 cents)

$$5x + 13(3x + 2) + 18(3x - 3) = 168$$
$$5x + 39x + 26 + 54x - 54 = 168$$
$$98x - 28 = 168$$
$$98x = 196$$
$$x = 2$$

• The sum of the total values equals 168.

The number of 18¢ stamps is $3x - 3$. Replace x by 2 and evaluate.

$$3x - 3 = 3(2) - 3 = 3$$

There are three 18¢ stamps in the collection.

Some of the problems in Section 4 of the chapter "Review of Real Numbers" involved using one variable to describe two numbers whose sum was known. For example, given that the sum of two numbers is 12, we let one of the two numbers be x. Then the other number is $12 - x$. Note that the sum of these two numbers, $x + 12 - x$, equals 12.

In Example 3 below, we are told that there are only nickels and dimes in a coin bank, and that there is a total of twenty-two coins. This means that the sum of the number of nickels and the number of dimes is 22. Let the number of nickels be x. Then the number of dimes is $22 - x$. (If you let the number of dimes be x and the number of nickels be $22 - x$, the solution to the problem will be the same.)

Example 3

A coin bank contains $1.80 in nickels and dimes; in all, there are twenty-two coins in the bank. Find the number of nickels and the number of dimes in the bank.

You Try It 3

A collection of stamps contains 3¢, 10¢, and 15¢ stamps. The number of 10¢ stamps is two more than twice the number of 3¢ stamps. There are three times as many 15¢ stamps as there are 3¢ stamps. The total value of the stamps is $1.56. Find the number of 15¢ stamps.

Strategy

• Number of nickels: x
  Number of dimes: $22 - x$

Coin	Number	Value	Total Value
Nickel	x	5	$5x$
Dime	$22 - x$	10	$10(22 - x)$

Your strategy

• The sum of the total values of each denomination of coin equals the total value of all the coins (180 cents)

$$5x + 10(22 - x) = 180$$

Solution

$$5x + 10(22 - x) = 180$$
$$5x + 220 - 10x = 180$$
$$-5x + 220 = 180$$
$$-5x = -40$$
$$x = 8$$

$$22 - x = 22 - 8 = 14$$

The bank contains 8 nickels and 14 dimes.

Your solution

Solution on p. S4

2.2 Exercises

· ·

Objective A   *Application Problems*

1. What number must be added to the numerator of $\frac{3}{10}$ to produce the fraction $\frac{4}{5}$?

2. What number must be added to the numerator of $\frac{5}{12}$ to produce the fraction $\frac{2}{3}$?

3. The sum of two integers is ten. Three times the larger integer is three less than eight times the smaller integer. Find the integers.

4. The sum of two integers is thirty. Eight times the smaller integer is six more than five times the larger integer. Find the integers.

5. One integer is eight less than another integer. The sum of the two integers is fifty. Find the integers.

6. One integer is four more than another integer. The sum of the integers is twenty-six. Find the integers.

7. The sum of three numbers is one hundred twenty-three. The second number is two more than twice the first number. The third number is five less than the product of three and the first number. Find the three numbers.

8. The sum of three numbers is forty-two. The second number is twice the first number, and the third number is three less than the second number. Find the three numbers.

9. The sum of three consecutive integers is negative fifty-seven. Find the integers.

10. The sum of three consecutive integers is one hundred twenty-nine. Find the integers.

11. Five times the smallest of three consecutive odd integers is ten more than twice the largest. Find the integers.

12. Find three consecutive even integers such that twice the sum of the first and third integers is twenty-one more than the second integer.

13. Find three consecutive odd integers such that three times the middle integer is seven more than the sum of the first and third integers.

14. Find three consecutive even integers such that four times the sum of the first and third integers is twenty less than six times the middle integer.

Objective B   *Application Problems*

15. A collection of fifty-three coins has a value of $3.70. The collection contains only nickels and dimes. Find the number of dimes in the collection.

16. A collection of twenty-two coins has a value of $4.75. The collection contains dimes and quarters. Find the number of quarters in the collection.

17. A coin bank contains twenty-two coins in nickels, dimes, and quarters. There are four times as many dimes as quarters. The value of the coins is $2.30. How many dimes are in the bank?

18. A coin collection contains nickels, dimes, and quarters. There are twice as many dimes as quarters and seven more nickels than dimes. The total value of all the coins is $2.00. How many quarters are in the collection?

19. A stamp collector has some 15¢ stamps and some 20¢ stamps. The number of 15¢ stamps is eight less than three times the number of 20¢ stamps. The total value is $4. Find the number of each type of stamp in the collection.

20. An office has some 20¢ stamps and some 28¢ stamps. All together the office has 140 stamps for a total value of $31.20. How many of each type of stamp does the office have?

21. A stamp collection consists of 3¢, 8¢, and 13¢ stamps. The number of 8¢ stamps is three less than twice the number of 3¢ stamps. The number of 13¢ stamps is twice the number of 8¢ stamps. The total value of all the stamps is $2.53. Find the number of 3¢ stamps in the collection.

22. An account executive bought 330 stamps for $79.50. The purchase included 15¢ stamps, 20¢ stamps, and 40¢ stamps. The number of 20¢ stamps is four times the number of 15¢ stamps. How many 40¢ stamps were purchased?

23. A stamp collector has 8¢, 13¢, and 18¢ stamps. The collector has twice as many 8¢ stamps as 18¢ stamps. There are three more 13¢ than 18¢ stamps. The total value of the stamps in the collection is $3.68. Find the number of 18¢ stamps in the collection.

24. A stamp collection consists of 3¢, 12¢, and 15¢ stamps. The number of 3¢ stamps is five times the number of 12¢ stamps. The number of 15¢ stamps is four less than the number of 12¢ stamps. The total value of the stamps in the collection is $3.18. Find the number of 15¢ stamps in the collection.

APPLYING THE CONCEPTS

25. Find three consecutive odd integers such that the product of the second and third minus the product of the first and second is 42.

26. The sum of the digits of a three-digit number is six. The tens digit is one less than the units digit, and the number is twelve more than one hundred times the hundreds digit. Find the number.

2.3 Applications: Mixture and Uniform Motion Problems

Objective A *To solve value mixture problems* .... ◁ 9 ▷ CT

A **value mixture problem** involves combining two ingredients that have different prices into a single blend. For example, a coffee manufacturer may blend two types of coffee into a single blend.

The solution of a value mixture problem is based on the equation $AC = V$, where A is the amount of the ingredient, C is the cost per unit of the ingredient, and V is the value of the ingredient.

⇒ How many pounds of peanuts that cost $2.25 per pound must be mixed with 40 lb of cashews that cost $6.00 per pound to make a mixture that costs $3.50 per pound?

> **Strategy for Solving a Value Mixture Problem**
>
> 1. For each ingredient in the mixture, write a numerical or variable expression for the amount of the ingredient used, the unit cost of the ingredient, and the value of the amount used. For the mixture, write a numerical or variable expression for the amount, the unit cost of the mixture, and the value of the amount. The results can be recorded in a table.

Pounds of peanuts: x
Pounds of cashews: 40
Pounds of mixture: $x + 40$

	Amount (A)	·	Unit Cost (C)	=	Value (V)
Peanuts	x	·	$2.25	=	$2.25x$
Cashews	40	·	$6.00	=	6.00(40)
Mixture	$x + 40$	·	$3.50	=	3.50($x + 40$)

> 2. Determine how the values of the ingredients are related. Use the fact that the sum of the values of all the ingredients taken separately is equal to the value of the mixture.

The sum of the values of the peanuts and the cashews is equal to the value of the mixture.

$$2.25x + 6.00(40) = 3.50(x + 40)$$ • Value of cashews plus value of peanuts equals value of mixture.
$$2.25x + 240 = 3.50x + 140$$
$$-1.25x + 240 = 140$$
$$-1.25x = -100$$
$$x = 80$$

The mixture must contain 80 lb of peanuts.

Example 1

How many ounces of a gold alloy that costs $320 per ounce must be mixed with 100 oz of an alloy that costs $100 per ounce to make a mixture that costs $160 per ounce?

x oz

100 oz

You Try It 1

A butcher combined hamburger that costs $3.00 per pound with hamburger that costs $1.80 per pound. How many pounds of each were used to make a 75-pound mixture costing $2.20 per pound?

Strategy

- Ounces of $320 gold alloy: x
  Ounces of $100 gold alloy: 100
  Ounces of $160 mixture: $x + 100$

	Amount	Cost	Value
$320 alloy	x	320	$320x$
$100 alloy	100	100	$100(100)$
Mixture	$x + 100$	160	$160(x + 100)$

- The sum of the values before mixing equals the value after mixing.

  $320x + 100(100) = 160(x + 100)$

Your strategy

Solution

$$320x + 100(100) = 160(x + 100)$$
$$320x + 10{,}000 = 160x + 16{,}000$$
$$160x + 10{,}000 = 16{,}000$$
$$160x = 6000$$
$$x = 37.5$$

The mixture must contain 37.5 oz of the $320 gold alloy.

Your solution

Solution on p. S4

Objective B ***To solve percent mixture problems*** .... (9) [CT]

The amount of a substance in a solution or alloy can be given as a percent of the total solution or alloy. For example, in a 10% hydrogen peroxide solution, 10% of the total solution is hydrogen peroxide. The remaining 90% is water.

The solution of a percent mixture problem is based on the equation $Ar = Q$, where A is the amount of solution or alloy, r is the percent of concentration, and Q is the quantity of a substance in the solution or alloy.

⇒ A chemist mixes an 11% acid solution with a 4% acid solution. How many milliliters of each solution should the chemist use to make a 700-milliliter solution that is 6% acid?

Strategy for Solving a Percent Mixture Problem

1. For each solution, use the equation $Ar = Q$. Write a numerical or variable expression for the amount of solution, the percent of concentration, and the quantity of the substance in the solution. The results can be recorded in a table.

Amount of 11% solution: x
Amount of 4% solution: $700 - x$
Amount of 6% mixture: 700

	Amount of Solution (A)	·	Percent of Concentration (r)	=	Quantity of Substance (Q)
11% solution	x	·	0.11	=	$0.11x$
4% solution	$700 - x$	·	0.04	=	$0.04(700 - x)$
6% solution	700	·	0.06	=	$0.06(700)$

2. Determine how the quantities of the substance in each solution are related. Use the fact that the sum of the quantities of the substances being mixed is equal to the quantity of the substance after mixing.

The sum of the quantities of the substance in the 11% solution and the 4% solution is equal to the quantity of the substance in the 6% solution.

$0.11x + 0.04(700 - x) = 0.06(700)$ • Quantity in 11% solution plus quantity in 4% solution equals quantity in 6% solution.

$$0.11x + 28 - 0.04x = 42$$
$$0.07x + 28 = 42$$
$$0.07x = 14$$
$$x = 200$$

The amount of 4% solution is $700 - x$. Replace x by 200 and evaluate.

$$700 - x = 700 - 200 = 500 \qquad • \ x = 200$$

The chemist should use 200 ml of the 11% solution and 500 ml of the 4% solution.

Example 2

How many grams of pure acid must be added to 60 g of an 8% acid solution to make a 20% acid solution?

You Try It 2

A butcher has some hamburger that is 22% fat and some that is 12% fat. How many pounds of each should be mixed to make 80 lb of hamburger that is 18% fat?

Strategy

Grams of pure acid: x

60 g of 8% acid + x g of 100% acid = $(60 + x)$ g of 20% acid

Your strategy

	Amount	Percent	Quantity
Pure Acid (100%)	x	1.00	x
8%	60	0.08	0.08(60)
20%	$60 + x$	0.20	0.20(60 + x)

The sum of the quantities before mixing equals the quantity after mixing.

$x + 0.08(60) = 0.20(60 + x)$

Solution

$$x + 0.08(60) = 0.20(60 + x)$$
$$x + 4.8 = 12 + 0.20x$$
$$0.8x + 4.8 = 12$$
$$0.8x = 7.2$$
$$x = 9$$

To make the 20% acid solution, 9 g of pure acid must be used.

Your solution

Solution on p. S4

Objective C *To solve uniform motion problems* .... (9) CT

A car that travels constantly in a straight line at 55 mph is in uniform motion. **Uniform motion** means that the speed of an object does not change.

The solution of a uniform motion problem is based on the equation $rt = d$, where r is the rate of travel, t is the time spent traveling, and d is the distance traveled.

⇒ An executive has an appointment 785 mi from the office. The executive takes a helicopter from the office to the airport and a plane from the airport to the business appointment. The helicopter averages 70 mph and the plane averages 500 mph. The total time spent traveling is 2 h. Find the distance from the executive's office to the airport.

> **Strategy for Solving a Uniform Motion Problem**
>
> 1. For each object, write a numerical or variable expression for the distance, rate, and time. The results can be recorded in a table. It may also help to draw a diagram.

├— 70 t —┼— 500 (2 – t) —┤
Office   Airport   Appointment
├——————— 785 ———————┤

Unknown time in the helicopter: t
Time in the plane: $2 - t$

	Rate (r)	·	Time (t)	=	Distance (d)
Helicopter	70	·	t	=	$70t$
Plane	500	·	$2 - t$	=	$500(2 - t)$

> 2. Determine how the distances traveled by each object are related. For example, the total distance traveled by both objects may be known, or it may be known that the two objects traveled the same distance.

The total distance traveled is 785 mi.

$$70t + 500(2 - t) = 785$$ • Distance by helicopter plus distance by plane equals 785.

$$70t + 1000 - 500t = 785$$
$$-430t + 1000 = 785$$
$$-430t = -215$$
$$t = 0.5$$

The time spent traveling from the office to the airport in the helicopter is 0.5 h. To find the distance between these two points, substitute the values of r and t into the equation $rt = d$.

$$rt = d$$
$$70 \cdot 0.5 = d$$ • $r = 70;\ t = 0.5$
$$35 = d$$

The distance from the office to the airport is 35 mi.

Example 3

A long-distance runner started a course running at an average speed of 6 mph. One and one-half hours later, a cyclist traveled the same course at an average speed of 12 mph. How long after the runner started did the cyclist overtake the runner?

You Try It 3

Two small planes start from the same point and fly in opposite directions. The first plane is flying 30 mph faster than the second plane. In 4 h the planes are 1160 mi apart. Find the rate of each plane.

Strategy

Your strategy

Unknown time for the cyclist: t
Time for the runner: $t + 1.5$

	Rate	Time	Distance
Runner	6	$t + 1.5$	$6(t + 1.5)$
Cyclist	12	t	$12t$

The runner and the cyclist travel the same distance. Therefore the distances are equal.

$6(t + 1.5) = 12t$

Solution

$$6(t + 1.5) = 12t$$
$$6t + 9 = 12t$$
$$9 = 6t$$
$$\frac{3}{2} = t$$

The cyclist traveled for 1.5 h.

$t + 1.5 = 1.5 + 1.5 = 3$

The cyclist overtook the runner 3 h after the runner started.

Your solution

Solution on p. S4

2.3 Exercises

Objective A   *Application Problems*

1. Forty pounds of cashews costing $5.60 per pound were mixed with 100 lb of peanuts costing $1.89 per pound. Find the cost of the resulting mixture.

2. A coffee merchant combines coffee costing $6 per pound with coffee costing $3.50 per pound. How many pounds of each should be used to make 25 lb of a blend costing $5.25 per pound?

3. Adult tickets for a play cost $5.00 and children's tickets cost $2.00. For one performance, 460 tickets were sold. Receipts for the performance were $1880. Find the number of adult tickets sold.

4. Tickets for a school play sold for $2.50 for each adult and $1.00 for each child. The total receipts for 113 tickets sold were $221. Find the number of adult tickets sold.

5. A breakfast cook mixes 5 L of pure maple syrup that costs $9.50 per liter with imitation maple syrup that costs $4.00 per liter. How much imitation maple syrup is needed to make a mixture that costs $5.00 per liter?

6. To make a flour mixture, a miller combined soybeans that cost $8.50 per bushel with wheat that cost $4.50 per bushel. How many bushels of each were used to make a mixture of 1000 bushels costing $5.50 per bushel?

7. A goldsmith combined pure gold that cost $400 per ounce with an alloy of gold that cost $150 per ounce. How many ounces of each were used to make 50 oz of gold alloy costing $250 per ounce?

8. A silversmith combined pure silver that cost $5.20 per ounce with 50 oz of a silver alloy that cost $2.80 per ounce. How many ounces of the pure silver were used to make an alloy of silver costing $4.40 per ounce?

9. A tea mixture was made from 40 lb of tea costing $5.40 per pound and 60 lb of tea costing $3.25 per pound. Find the cost of the tea mixture.

10. Find the cost per ounce of a sunscreen made from 100 oz of lotion that cost $3.46 per ounce and 60 oz of lotion that cost $12.50 per ounce.

11. The owner of a fruit stand combined cranberry juice that cost $4.60 per gallon with 50 gal of apple juice that cost $2.24 per gallon. How much cranberry juice was used to make the cranapple juice if the mixture cost $3.00 per gallon? Round to the nearest tenth.

12. Walnuts that cost $4.05 per kilogram were mixed with cashews that cost $7.25 per kilogram. How many kilograms of each were used to make a 50-kilogram mixture costing $6.25 per kilogram? Round to the nearest tenth.

Objective B   *Application Problems*

13. How many pounds of a 15% aluminum alloy must be mixed with 500 lb of a 22% aluminum alloy to make a 20% aluminum alloy?

14. A hospital staff mixed a 75% disinfectant solution with a 25% disinfectant solution. How many liters of each were used to make 20 L of a 40% disinfectant solution?

15. Rubbing alcohol is typically diluted with water to 70% strength. If you need 3.5 oz of 45% rubbing alcohol, how many ounces of 70% rubbing alcohol and how much water should you combine?

16. A silversmith mixed 25 g of a 70% silver alloy with 50 g of a 15% silver alloy. What is the percent concentration of the resulting alloy?

17. How many ounces of pure water must be added to 75 oz of an 8% salt solution to make a 5% salt solution?

18. How many quarts of water must be added to 5 qt of an 80% antifreeze solution to make a 50% antifreeze solution?

19. How many milliliters of alcohol must be added to 200 ml of a 25% iodine solution to make a 10% iodine solution?

20. A butcher has some hamburger that is 21% fat and some that is 15% fat. How many pounds of each should be mixed to make 84 lb of hamburger that is 17% fat?

21. Many fruit drinks are actually only 5% real fruit juice. If you let 2 oz of water evaporate from 12 oz of a drink that is 5% fruit juice, what is the percent concentration of the result?

22. How much water must be evaporated from 6 qt of a 50% antifreeze solution to produce a 75% solution?

23. A car radiator contains 12 qt of a 40% antifreeze solution. How many quarts will have to be replaced with pure antifreeze if the resulting solution is to be 60% antifreeze?

Objective C   Application Problems

24. A car traveling at 56 mph overtakes a cyclist who, traveling at 14 mph, had a 1.5-hour head start. How far from the starting point does the car overtake the cyclist?

25. A helicopter traveling 130 mph overtakes a speeding car traveling 80 mph. The car had a 0.5-hour head start. How far from the starting point does the helicopter overtake the car?

26. Two planes are 1620 mi apart and are traveling toward each other. One plane is traveling 120 mph faster than the other plane. The planes meet in 1.5 h. Find the speed of each plane.

27. Two cars are 310 mi apart and are traveling toward each other. One car travels 8 mph faster than the other car. The cars meet in 2.5 h. Find the speed of each car.

28. A ferry leaves a harbor and travels to a resort island at an average speed of 20 mph. On the return trip, the ferry travels at an average speed of 12 mph because of fog. The total time for the trip is 5 h. How far is the island from the harbor?

29. A commuter plane provides transportation from an international airport to the surrounding cities. One commuter plane averaged 250 mph flying to a city and 150 mph returning to the international airport. The total flying time was 4 h. Find the distance between the two airports.

30. A student rode a bicycle to the repair shop and then walked home. The student averaged 12 mph riding to the shop and 3 mph walking home. The round trip took 1 h. How far is it from the student's home to the repair shop?

31. A passenger train leaves a depot 1.5 h after a freight train leaves the same depot. The passenger train is traveling 18 mph faster than the freight train. Find the rate of each train if the passenger train overtakes the freight train in 2.5 h.

32. A plane leaves an airport at 3 P.M. At 4 P.M. another plane leaves the same airport traveling in the same direction at a speed 150 mph faster than that of the first plane. Four hours after the first plane takes off, the second plane is 250 mi ahead of the first plane. How far does the second plane travel?

33. A jogger and a cyclist set out at 9 A.M. from the same point headed in the same direction. The average speed of the cyclist is four times the average speed of the jogger. In 2 h, the cyclist is 33 mi ahead of the jogger. How far did the cyclist ride?

APPLYING THE CONCEPTS

34. **a.** If a parade 2 mi long is proceeding at 3 mph, how long will it take a runner jogging at 6 mph to travel from the front of the parade to the end of the parade?
   b. If a parade 2 mi long is proceeding at 3 mph, how long will it take a runner jogging at 6 mph to travel from the end of the parade to the start of the parade?

35. The concentration of gold in an alloy is measured in karats, which indicate how many parts out of 24 are pure gold. For example, 1 karat is $\frac{1}{24}$ pure gold. What amount of 12 karat gold should be mixed with 3 oz of 24 karat gold to create 14 karat gold, the most commonly used alloy?

36. A student jogs 100 yd at a rate of 8 mph and jogs back at a rate of 6 mph. Does it seem reasonable that the average rate is 7 mph? Why or why not? Support your answer.

37. Two cars are headed directly toward each other at rates of 40 mph and 60 mph. How many miles apart are they 2 min before impact?

38. **a.** A radiator contains 6 qt of a 25% antifreeze solution. How much should be removed and replaced with pure antifreeze to yield a 33% solution?
   b. A radiator contains 6 qt of a 25% antifreeze solution. How much should be removed and replaced with pure antifreeze to yield a 60% solution?

39. Two birds start flying, at the same time and at the same rate, from the tops of two towers that are 50 ft apart. One tower is 30 ft high, and the other tower is 40 ft high. At exactly the same time, the two birds reach a grass seed on the ground. How far is the grass seed from the base of the 40-foot tower? (This problem appeared in a math text written around A.D. 1200.)

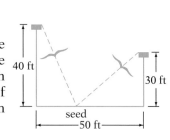

2.4 First-Degree Inequalities

Objective A   *To solve an inequality in one variable* .... (10) [CT]

The **solution set of an inequality** is a set of numbers, each element of which, when substituted for the variable, results in a true inequality.

The inequality at the right is true if the variable is replaced
by (for instance) 3, -1.98, or $\frac{2}{3}$.

$$x - 1 < 4$$
$$3 - 1 < 4$$
$$-1.98 - 1 < 4$$
$$\frac{2}{3} - 1 < 4$$

There are many values of the variable x that will make the inequality $x - 1 < 4$ true. The solution set of the inequality is any number less than 5. The solution set can be written in set-builder notation as $\{x \mid x < 5\}$.

The graph of the solution set of
$x - 1 < 4$ is shown at the right.

When solving an inequality, we use the Addition and Multiplication Properties of Inequalities to rewrite the inequality in the form *variable < constant* or in the form *variable > constant*.

**The Addition Property
of Inequalities**

If $a > b$, then $a + c > b + c$.
If $a < b$, then $a + c < b + c$.

The Addition Property of Inequalities states that the same number can be added to each side of an inequality without changing the solution set of the inequality. This property is also true for an inequality that contains the symbol $\leq$ or $\geq$.

The Addition Property of Inequalities is used to remove a term from one side of an inequality by adding the additive inverse of that term to each side of the inequality. Because subtraction is defined in terms of addition, the same number can be subtracted from each side of an inequality without changing the solution set of the inequality.

➡ Solve: $x + 2 \geq 4$

$$x + 2 \geq 4$$
$$x + 2 - 2 \geq 4 - 2 \qquad \text{• Subtract 2 from each side of the inequality.}$$
$$x \geq 2 \qquad \text{• Simplify.}$$

The solution set is $\{x \mid x \geq 2\}$.

➡ Solve: $3x - 4 < 2x - 1$

$$3x - 4 < 2x - 1$$

$$3x - 4 - 2x < 2x - 1 - 2x$$ • Subtract $2x$ from each side of the inequality.

$$x - 4 < -1$$

$$x - 4 + 4 < -1 + 4$$ • Add 4 to each side of the inequality.

$$x < 3$$

The solution set is $\{x \mid x < 3\}$.

The Multiplication Property of Inequalities is used to remove a coefficient from one side of an inequality by multiplying each side of the inequality by the reciprocal of the coefficient.

The Multiplication Property of Inequalities

Rule 1   If $a > b$ and $c > 0$, then $ac > bc$.
         If $a < b$ and $c > 0$, then $ac < bc$.

Rule 2   If $a > b$ and $c < 0$, then $ac < bc$.
         If $a < b$ and $c < 0$, then $ac > bc$.

Here are some examples of this property.

	Rule 1			**Rule 2**	
$3 > 2$		$2 < 5$	$3 > 2$		$2 < 5$
$3(4) > 2(4)$		$2(4) < 5(4)$	$3(-4) < 2(-4)$		$2(-4) > 5(-4)$
$12 > 8$		$8 < 20$	$-12 < -8$		$-8 > -20$

Rule 1 states that when each side of an inequality is multiplied by a positive number, the inequality symbol remains the same. However, Rule 2 states that when each side of an inequality is multiplied by a negative number, the inequality symbol must be reversed. Because division is defined in terms of multiplication, when each side of an inequality is divided by a *positive* number, the inequality symbol remains the same. But when each side of an inequality is divided by a *negative* number, the inequality symbol must be reversed.

The Multiplication Property of Inequalities is also true for the symbols $\leq$ and $\geq$.

TAKE NOTE

Each side of the inequality is divided *by* a negative number; the inequality symbol must be reversed.

➡ Solve: $-3x > 9$

$$-3x > 9$$

$$\frac{-3x}{-3} < \frac{9}{-3}$$ • Divide each side of the inequality by the coefficient -3. Because -3 is a negative number, the inequality symbol must be reversed.

$$x < -3$$

The solution set is $\{x \mid x < -3\}$.

➡ Solve: $3x + 2 < -4$

$3x + 2 < -4$

$3x < -6$ • Subtract 2 from each side of the inequality.

$\dfrac{3x}{3} < \dfrac{-6}{3}$ • Divide each side of the inequality by the coefficient 3.

$x < -2$

The solution set is $\{x \,|\, x < -2\}$.

➡ Solve: $2x - 9 > 4x + 5$

$2x - 9 > 4x + 5$

$-2x - 9 > 5$ • Subtract 4x from each side of the inequality.

$-2x > 14$ • Add 9 to each side of the inequality.

$\dfrac{-2x}{-2} < \dfrac{14}{-2}$ • Divide each side of the inequality by the coefficient -2. Reverse the inequality symbol.

$x < -7$

The solution set is $\{x \,|\, x < -7\}$.

➡ Solve: $5(x - 2) \geq 9x - 3(2x - 4)$

$5(x - 2) \geq 9x - 3(2x - 4)$

$5x - 10 \geq 9x - 6x + 12$ • Use the Distributive Property to remove parentheses.

$5x - 10 \geq 3x + 12$

$2x - 10 \geq 12$ • Subtract 3x from each side of the inequality.

$2x \geq 22$ • Add 10 to each side of the inequality.

$\dfrac{2x}{2} \geq \dfrac{22}{2}$ • Divide each side of the inequality by the coefficient 2.

$x \geq 11$

The solution set is $\{x \,|\, x \geq 11\}$.

Example 1
Solve: $x + 3 > 4x + 6$

Solution
$x + 3 > 4x + 6$
$-3x + 3 > 6$ • Subtract 4x from each side.
$-3x > 3$ • Subtract 3 from each side.
$\dfrac{-3x}{-3} < \dfrac{3}{-3}$ • Divide each side by -3.
$x < -1$

The solution set is $\{x \,|\, x < -1\}$.

You Try It 1
Solve: $2x - 1 < 6x + 7$

Your solution

Solution on p. S5

Example 2   Solve:
$$3x - 5 \le 3 - 2(3x + 1)$$

Solution
$$3x - 5 \le 3 - 2(3x + 1)$$
$$3x - 5 \le 3 - 6x - 2$$
$$3x - 5 \le 1 - 6x$$
$$9x - 5 \le 1$$
$$9x \le 6$$
$$\frac{9x}{9} \le \frac{6}{9}$$
$$x \le \frac{2}{3}$$
$$\left\{ x \,\middle|\, x \le \frac{2}{3} \right\}$$

You Try It 2   Solve:
$$5x - 2 \le 4 - 3(x - 2)$$

Your solution

Solution on p. S5

Objective B   ***To solve a compound inequality*** ···

A **compound inequality** is formed by joining two inequalities with a connective word such as "and" or "or." The inequalities at the right are compound inequalities.

$$2x < 4 \text{ and } 3x - 2 > -8$$

$$2x + 3 > 5 \text{ or } x + 2 < 5$$

The solution set of a compound inequality with the connective word *and* is the set of all elements that appear in the solution sets of both inequalities. Therefore, it is the intersection of the solution sets of the two inequalities.

➡ Solve: $2x < 6$ and $3x + 2 > -4$

$$\begin{array}{lll} 2x < 6 & \text{and} & 3x + 2 > -4 \\ x < 3 & & 3x > -6 \\ \{x \,|\, x < 3\} & & x > -2 \\ & & \{x \,|\, x > -2\} \end{array}$$

• Solve each inequality.

The solution set of a compound inequality with *and* is the intersection of the solution sets of the two inequalities.

$$\{x \,|\, x < 3\} \cap \{x \,|\, x > -2\} = \{x \,|\, -2 < x < 3\}$$

➡ Solve: $-3 < 2x + 1 < 5$

This inequality is equivalent to the compound inequality shown at the right.

$$-3 < 2x + 1 \text{ and } 2x + 1 < 5$$

$$\begin{array}{ll} -3 < 2x + 1 & \text{and } 2x + 1 < 5 \\ -4 < 2x & 2x < 4 \\ -2 < x & x < 2 \\ \{x \,|\, x > -2\} & \{x \,|\, x < 2\} \end{array}$$

• Solve each inequality.

The solution of a compound inequality with *and* is the intersection of the solution sets of the two inequalities.

$$\{x \,|\, x > -2\} \cap \{x \,|\, x < 2\} = \{x \,|\, -2 < x < 2\}$$

There is an alternative method for solving the inequality in the last example.

➡ Solve: $-3 < 2x + 1 < 5$

$$-3 < 2x + 1 < 5$$
$$-3 - 1 < 2x + 1 - 1 < 5 - 1$$
$$-4 < 2x < 4$$
$$\frac{-4}{2} < \frac{2x}{2} < \frac{4}{2}$$
$$-2 < x < 2$$

- Subtract 1 from each of the three parts of the inequality.

- Divide each of the three parts of the inequality by the coefficient 2.

The solution set is $\{x \mid -2 < x < 2\}$.

The solution set of a compound inequality with the connective word *or* is the union of the solution sets of the two inequalities.

➡ Solve: $2x + 3 > 7$ or $4x - 1 < 3$

$$2x + 3 > 7 \quad \text{or} \quad 4x - 1 < 3$$
$$2x > 4 \qquad\qquad 4x < 4$$
$$x > 2 \qquad\qquad x < 1$$
$$\{x \mid x > 2\} \qquad \{x \mid x < 1\}$$

- Solve each inequality.

Find the union of the solution sets.

$$\{x \mid x > 2\} \cup \{x \mid x < 1\} = \{x \mid x > 2 \ \text{or} \ x < 1\}$$

Example 3
Solve: $1 < 3x - 5 < 4$

Solution
$$1 < 3x - 5 < 4$$
$$1 + 5 < 3x - 5 + 5 < 4 + 5$$
$$6 < 3x < 9$$
$$\frac{6}{3} < \frac{3x}{3} < \frac{9}{3}$$
$$2 < x < 3$$
$$\{x \mid 2 < x < 3\}$$

You Try It 3
Solve: $-2 \le 5x + 3 \le 13$

Your solution

Example 4
Solve: $11 - 2x > -3$ and $7 - 3x < 4$

Solution
$$11 - 2x > -3 \quad \text{and} \quad 7 - 3x < 4$$
$$-2x > -14 \qquad\qquad -3x < -3$$
$$x < 7 \qquad\qquad x > 1$$
$$\{x \mid x < 7\} \qquad\qquad \{x \mid x > 1\}$$
$$\{x \mid x < 7\} \cap \{x \mid x > 1\} = \{x \mid 1 < x < 7\}$$

You Try It 4
Solve: $2 - 3x > 11$ or $5 + 2x > 7$

Your solution

Solutions on p. S5

Objective C *To solve application problems* ·································

Example 5
A cellular phone company advertises two pricing plans. The first is $19.95 per month with 20 free minutes and $.39 per minute thereafter. The second is $23.95 per month with 20 free minutes and $.30 per minute thereafter. How many minutes can you talk per month for the first plan to cost less than the second?

Strategy
To find the number of minutes, write and solve an inequality using N to represent the number of minutes. Then $N - 20$ is the number of minutes for which you are charged after the first free 20 min.

Solution

$$\text{Cost of first plan} < \text{cost of second plan}$$
$$19.95 + 0.39(N - 20) < 23.95 + 0.30(N - 20)$$
$$19.95 + 0.39N - 7.8 < 23.95 + 0.30N - 6$$
$$12.15 + 0.39N < 17.95 + 0.30N$$
$$12.15 + 0.09N < 17.95$$
$$0.09N < 5.8$$
$$N < 64.\overline{4}$$

The first plan costs less if you talk less than 65 min.

Example 6
Find three consecutive positive odd integers whose sum is between 27 and 51.

Strategy
To find the three integers, write and solve a compound inequality using x to represent the first odd integer.

Solution

$$\begin{matrix}\text{Lower limit} \\ \text{of the sum}\end{matrix} < \text{sum} < \begin{matrix}\text{upper limit} \\ \text{of the sum}\end{matrix}$$
$$27 < x + (x + 2) + (x + 4) < 51$$
$$27 < 3x + 6 < 51$$
$$27 - 6 < 3x + 6 - 6 < 51 - 6$$
$$21 < 3x < 45$$
$$\frac{21}{3} < \frac{3x}{3} < \frac{45}{3}$$
$$7 < x < 15$$

The three odd integers are 9, 11, and 13; or 11, 13, and 15; or 13, 15, and 17.

You Try It 5
The base of a triangle is 12 in. and the height is $(x + 2)$ in. Express as an integer the maximum height of the triangle when the area is less than 50 in².

Your strategy

Your solution

You Try It 6
An average score of 80 to 89 in a history course receives a B. Luisa Montez has grades of 72, 94, 83, and 70 on four exams. Find the range of scores on the fifth exam that will give Luisa a B for the course.

Your strategy

Your solution

Solutions on p. S5

2.4 Exercises

· ·

Objective A

Solve.

1. $x - 3 < 2$

2. $x + 4 \geq 2$

3. $4x \leq 8$

4. $6x > 12$

5. $-2x > 8$

6. $-3x \leq -9$

7. $3x - 1 > 2x + 2$

8. $5x + 2 \geq 4x - 1$

9. $2x - 1 > 7$

10. $3x + 2 < 8$

11. $5x - 2 \leq 8$

12. $4x + 3 \leq -1$

13. $6x + 3 > 4x - 1$

14. $7x + 4 < 2x - 6$

15. $8x + 1 \geq 2x + 13$

16. $5x - 4 < 2x + 5$

17. $4 - 3x < 10$

18. $2 - 5x > 7$

19. $7 - 2x \geq 1$

20. $3 - 5x \leq 18$

21. $-3 - 4x > -11$

22. $-2 - x < 7$

23. $4x - 2 < x - 11$

24. $6x + 5 \leq x - 10$

25. $x + 7 \geq 4x - 8$

26. $3x + 1 \leq 7x - 15$

27. $3x + 2 \leq 7x + 4$

28. $3x - 5 \geq -2x + 5$

29. $\dfrac{3}{5}x - 2 < \dfrac{3}{10} - x$

30. $\dfrac{5}{6}x - \dfrac{1}{6} < x - 4$

31. $\dfrac{2}{3}x - \dfrac{3}{2} < \dfrac{7}{6} - \dfrac{1}{3}x$

32. $\dfrac{7}{12}x - \dfrac{3}{2} < \dfrac{2}{3}x + \dfrac{5}{6}$

33. $\dfrac{1}{2}x - \dfrac{3}{4} < \dfrac{7}{4}x - 2$

34. $6 - 2(x - 4) \le 2x + 10$

35. $4(2x - 1) > 3x - 2(3x - 5)$

36. $2(1 - 3x) - 4 > 10 + 3(1 - x)$

37. $2 - 5(x + 1) \ge 3(x - 1) - 8$

38. $7 + 2(4 - x) < 9 - 3(6 + x)$

39. $3(4x + 3) \le 7 - 4(x - 2)$

40. $2 - 2(7 - 2x) < 3(3 - x)$

41. $3 + 2(x + 5) \ge x + 5(x + 1) + 1$

42. $10 - 13(2 - x) < 5(3x - 2)$

43. $3 - 4(x + 2) \le 6 + 4(2x + 1)$

44. $3x - 2(3x - 5) \le 2 - 5(x - 4)$

45. $12 - 2(3x - 2) \ge 5x - 2(5 - x)$

Objective B

Solve.

46. $3x < 6$ and $x + 2 > 1$

47. $x - 3 \le 1$ and $2x \ge -4$

48. $x + 2 \ge 5$ or $3x \le 3$

49. $2x < 6$ or $x - 4 > 1$

50. $-2x > -8$ and $-3x < 6$

51. $\dfrac{1}{2}x > -2$ and $5x < 10$

52. $\frac{1}{3}x < -1$ or $2x > 0$

53. $\frac{2}{3}x > 4$ or $2x < -8$

54. $x + 4 \geq 5$ and $2x \geq 6$

55. $3x < -9$ and $x - 2 < 2$

56. $-5x > 10$ and $x + 1 > 6$

57. $7x < 14$ and $1 - x < 4$

58. $2x - 3 > 1$ and $3x - 1 < 2$

59. $4x + 1 < 5$ and $4x + 7 > -1$

60. $3x + 7 < 10$ or $2x - 1 > 5$

61. $6x - 2 < -14$ or $5x + 1 > 11$

62. $-5 < 3x + 4 < 16$

63. $5 < 4x - 3 < 21$

64. $0 < 2x - 6 < 4$

65. $-2 < 3x + 7 < 1$

66. $4x - 1 > 11$ or $4x - 1 \leq -11$

67. $3x - 5 > 10$ or $3x - 5 < -10$

68. $2x - 3 \geq 5$ and $3x - 1 > 11$

69. $6x - 2 < 5$ or $7x - 5 < 16$

70. $9x - 2 < 7$ and $3x - 5 > 10$

71. $8x + 2 \leq -14$ and $4x - 2 > 10$

72. $3x - 11 < 4$ or $4x + 9 \geq 1$

73. $5x + 12 \geq 2$ or $7x - 1 \leq 13$

74. $-6 \leq 5x + 14 \leq 24$

75. $3 \leq 7x - 14 \leq 31$

76. $3 - 2x > 7$ and $5x + 2 > -18$

77. $1 - 3x < 16$ and $1 - 3x > -16$

78. $5 - 4x > 21$ or $7x - 2 > 19$

79. $6x + 5 < -1$ or $1 - 2x < 7$

80. $3 - 7x \leq 31$ and $5 - 4x > 1$

81. $9 - x \geq 7$ and $9 - 2x < 3$

Objective C *Application Problems*

82. Five times the difference between a number and two is greater than the quotient of two times the number and three. Find the smallest integer that will satisfy the inequality.

83. Two times the difference between a number and eight is less than or equal to five times the sum of the number and four. Find the smallest number that will satisfy the inequality.

84. The length of a rectangle is two feet more than four times the width. Express as an integer the maximum width of the rectangle when the perimeter is less than thirty-four feet.

85. The length of a rectangle is five centimeters less than twice the width. Express as an integer the maximum width of the rectangle when the perimeter is less than sixty centimeters.

86. In 1997, the computer service America Online offered its customers a rate of $19.95 per month for unlimited use or $4.95 per month with 3 free hours plus $2.50 for each hour thereafter. How many hours can you use this service per month if the second plan costs you less than the first?

87. TopPage advertises local paging service for $6.95 per month for up to 400 pages, and $.10 per page thereafter. A competitor advertises service for $3.95 per month for up to 400 pages and $.15 per page thereafter. For what number of pages per month is the TopPage plan less expensive?

88. Suppose PayRite Rental Cars rents compact cars for $32 per day with unlimited mileage and Otto Rentals offers compact cars for $19.99 per day but charges $.19 for each mile beyond 100 mi driven per day. You want to rent a car for one week. How many miles can you drive during the week if Otto Rentals is to be less expensive than PayRite?

89. During a weekday, to call a city 40 mi away from a certain pay phone costs $.70 for the first 3 min and $.15 for each additional minute. If you use a calling card, there is a $.35 fee and then the rates are $.196 for the first minute and $.126 for each additional minute. How long must a call be if it is cheaper to pay with coins rather than a calling card?

90. The temperature range for a week was between 14°F and 77°F. Find the temperature range in Celsius degrees. $F = \frac{9}{5}C + 32$

91. The temperature range for a week in a mountain town was between 0°C and 30°C. Find the temperature range in Fahrenheit degrees. $C = \frac{5(F - 32)}{9}$

92. You are a sales account executive earning $1200 per month plus 6% commission on the amount of sales. Your goal is to earn a minimum of $6000 per month. What amount of sales will enable you to earn $6000 or more per month?

93. George Stoia earns $1000 per month plus 5% commission on the amount of sales. George's goal is to earn a minimum of $3200 per month. What amount of sales will enable George to earn $3200 or more per month?

94. Heritage National Bank offers two different checking accounts. The first charges $3 per month, and $.50 per check after the first 10 checks. The second account charges $8 per month with unlimited check writing. How many checks can be written per month if the first account is less expensive than the second account?

95. Glendale Federal Bank offers a checking account to small businesses. The charge is $8 per month plus $.12 per check after the first 100 checks. A competitor is offering an account for $5 per month plus $.15 per check after the first 100 checks. If a business chooses the first account, how many checks does the business write monthly if it is assumed that the first account will cost less than the competitor's account?

96. An average score of 90 or above in a history class receives an A grade. You have grades of 95, 89, and 81 on three exams. Find the range of scores on the fourth exam that will give you an A grade for the course.

97. An average of 70 to 79 in a mathematics class receives a C grade. A student has grades of 56, 91, 83, and 62 on four tests. Find the range of scores on the fifth test that will give the student a C for the course.

98. Find four consecutive integers whose sum is between 62 and 78.

99. Find three consecutive even integers whose sum is between 30 and 51.

APPLYING THE CONCEPTS

100. Determine whether the following statements are always true, sometimes true, or never true.
  a. If $a > b$, then $-a < -b$.
  b. If $a < b$ and $a \neq 0$, $b \neq 0$, then $\dfrac{1}{a} < \dfrac{1}{b}$.
  c. When dividing both sides of an inequality by an integer, we must reverse the inequality symbol.
  d. If $a < 1$, then $a^2 < a$.
  e. If $a < b < 0$ and $c < d < 0$, then $ac > bd$.

101. The following is offered as the solution of $2 + 3(2x - 4) < 6x + 5$.

$$2 + 3(2x - 4) < 6x + 5$$
$$2 + 6x - 12 < 6x + 5 \qquad \bullet \text{ Use the Distributive Property.}$$
$$6x - 10 < 6x + 5 \qquad \bullet \text{ Simplify.}$$
$$6x - 6x - 10 < 6x - 6x + 5 \qquad \bullet \text{ Subtract } 6x \text{ from each side.}$$
$$-10 < 5$$

Because $-10 < 5$ is a true inequality, the solution set is all real numbers.

If this is correct, so state. If it is not correct, explain the incorrect step and supply the correct answer.

2.5 Absolute Value Equations and Inequalities

Objective A   *To solve an absolute value equation* ....

The **absolute value** of a number is its distance from zero on the number line. Distance is always a positive number or zero. Therefore, the absolute value of a number is always a positive number or zero.

The distance from 0 to 3 or from 0 to −3 is 3 units.

$$|3| = 3 \qquad\qquad |-3| = 3$$

Absolute value can be used to represent the distance between any two points on the number line. The **distance between two points** on the number line is the absolute value of the difference between the coordinates of the two points.

The distance between point a and point b is given by $|b - a|$.

The distance between 4 and −3 on the number line is 7 units. Note that the order in which the coordinates are subtracted does not affect the distance.

$$\begin{aligned} \text{Distance} &= |-3 - 4| \qquad & \text{Distance} &= |4 - (-3)| \\ &= |-7| & &= |7| \\ &= 7 & &= 7 \end{aligned}$$

For any two numbers a and b, $|b - a| = |a - b|$.

An equation containing an absolute value symbol is called an **absolute value equation.** Here are three examples.

$$|x| = 3 \qquad\qquad |x + 2| = 8 \qquad\qquad |3x - 4| = 5x - 9$$

> **Solution of an Absolute Value Equation**
>
> If $a \geq 0$ and $|x| = a$, then $x = a$ or $x = -a$.

For instance, given $|x| = 3$, then $x = 3$ or $x = -3$ because $|3| = 3$ and $|-3| = 3$. We can solve this equation as follows:

$$|x| = 3$$
$$x = 3 \qquad x = -3$$

● Remove the absolute value sign from $|x|$ and let x equal 3 and the opposite of 3.

Check:

$$\begin{array}{c|c} |x| = 3 & |x| = 3 \\ \hline |3| \mid 3 & |-3| \mid 3 \\ 3 = 3 & 3 = 3 \end{array}$$

The solutions are 3 and −3.

⇒ Solve: $|x + 2| = 8$

$$|x + 2| = 8$$
$$x + 2 = 8 \qquad x + 2 = -8$$
$$x = 6 \qquad x = -10$$

- Remove the absolute value sign and rewrite as two equations.
- Solve each equation.

Check:

$|x + 2| = 8$		$|x + 2| = 8$	
$|6 + 2|$	8	$|-10 + 2|$	8
$|8|$	8	$|-8|$	8
	$8 = 8$		$8 = 8$

The solutions are 6 and −10.

⇒ Solve: $|5 - 3x| - 8 = -4$

$$|5 - 3x| - 8 = -4$$
$$|5 - 3x| = 4$$
$$5 - 3x = 4 \qquad 5 - 3x = -4$$

$$-3x = -1 \qquad -3x = -9$$
$$x = \frac{1}{3} \qquad x = 3$$

- Solve for the absolute value.
- Remove the absolute value sign and rewrite as two equations.
- Solve each equation.

Check:

$|5 - 3x| - 8 = -4$		$|5 - 3x| - 8 = -4$	
$\left|5 - 3\left(\frac{1}{3}\right)\right| - 8$	-4	$|5 - 3(3)| - 8$	4
$|5 - 1| - 8$	-4	$|5 - 9| - 8$	-4
$4 - 8$	-4	$4 - 8$	-4
	$-4 = -4$		$-4 = -4$

The solutions are $\frac{1}{3}$ and 3.

Example 1
Solve: $|2 - x| = 12$

Solution

$$|2 - x| = 12$$
$$2 - x = 12 \qquad 2 - x = -12$$
$$-x = 10 \qquad -x = -14$$
$$x = -10 \qquad x = 14$$

The solutions are −10 and 14.

You Try It 1
Solve: $|2x - 3| = 5$

Your solution

Example 2
Solve: $|2x| = -4$

Solution
$$|2x| = -4$$

There is no solution to this equation because the absolute value of a number must be nonnegative.

You Try It 2
Solve: $|x - 3| = -2$

Your solution

Solutions on p. S5

Example 3

Solve: $3 - |2x - 4| = -5$

Solution

$$3 - |2x - 4| = -5$$
$$-|2x - 4| = -8$$
$$|2x - 4| = 8$$

$2x - 4 = 8$	$2x - 4 = -8$
$2x = 12$	$2x = -4$
$x = 6$	$x = -2$

The solutions are 6 and −2.

You Try It 3

Solve: $5 - |3x + 5| = 3$

Your solution

Solution on p. S5

Objective B   To solve an absolute value inequality ....

Recall that absolute value represents the distance between two points. For example, the solutions of the absolute value equation $|x - 1| = 3$ are the numbers whose distance from 1 is 3. Therefore the solutions are −2 and 4.

The solutions of the absolute value inequality $|x - 1| < 3$ are the numbers whose distance from 1 is less than 3. Therefore, the solutions are the numbers greater than −2 and less than 4. The solution set is $\{x \mid -2 < x < 4\}$.

Distance less than 3   Distance less than 3

−5 −4 −3 −2 −1 0 1 2 3 4 5

To solve an absolute value inequality of the form $|ax + b| < c$, solve the equivalent compound inequality $-c < ax + b < c$.

➡ Solve: $|3x - 1| < 5$

$$|3x - 1| < 5$$
$$-5 < 3x - 1 < 5$$
$$-5 + 1 < 3x - 1 + 1 < 5 + 1$$
$$-4 < 3x < 6$$
$$\frac{-4}{3} < \frac{3x}{3} < \frac{6}{3}$$
$$-\frac{4}{3} < x < 2$$

• Solve the equivalent compound inequality.

The solution set is $\left\{x \mid -\dfrac{4}{3} < x < 2\right\}$.

The solutions of the absolute value inequality $|x + 1| > 2$ are the numbers whose distance from −1 is greater than 2. Therefore, the solutions are the numbers that are less than −3 or greater than 1. The solution set of $|x + 1| > 2$ is $\{x \mid x < -3 \text{ or } x > 1\}$.

Distance greater than 2   Distance greater than 2

−5 −4 −3 −2 −1 0 1 2 3 4 5

To solve an absolute value inequality of the form $|ax + b| > c$, solve the equivalent compound inequality $ax + b < -c$ or $ax + b > c$.

⇒ Solve: $|3 - 2x| > 1$

$$3 - 2x < -1 \quad \text{or} \quad 3 - 2x > 1$$
$$-2x < -4 \qquad\qquad -2x > -2$$
$$x > 2 \qquad\qquad\quad x < 1 \qquad\qquad \text{• Solve each inequality.}$$
$$\{x \mid x > 2\} \qquad\qquad \{x \mid x < 1\}$$

The solution of a compound inequality with *or* is the union of the solution sets of the two inequalities.

$$\{x \mid x > 2\} \cup \{x \mid x < 1\} = \{x \mid x > 2 \text{ or } x < 1\}$$

The rules for solving these absolute value inequalities are summarized below.

Solutions of Absolute Value Inequalities

To solve an absolute value inequality of the form $|ax + b| < c$, solve the equivalent compound inequality $-c < ax + b < c$.

To solve an absolute value inequality of the form $|ax + b| > c$, solve the equivalent compound inequality $ax + b < -c$ or $ax + b > c$.

Example 4   Solve: $|4x - 3| < 5$

Solution   Solve the equivalent compound inequality.

$$-5 < 4x - 3 < 5$$
$$-5 + 3 < 4x - 3 + 3 < 5 + 3$$
$$-2 < 4x < 8$$
$$\frac{-2}{4} < \frac{4x}{4} < \frac{8}{4}$$
$$-\frac{1}{2} < x < 2$$
$$\left\{ x \,\middle|\, -\frac{1}{2} < x < 2 \right\}$$

You Try It 4   Solve: $|3x + 2| < 8$

Your solution

Example 5   Solve: $|x - 3| < 0$

Solution   The absolute value of a number is greater than or equal to zero. Therefore, the solution set of $|x - 3| < 0$ is the empty set.

You Try It 5   Solve: $|3x - 7| < 0$

Your solution

Solutions on p. S6

Example 6   Solve: $|x + 4| > -2$

Solution   The absolute value of a number is greater than or equal to zero. Therefore, the solution set of $|x + 4| > -2$ is the set of real numbers.

You Try It 6   Solve: $|2x + 7| \geq -1$

Your solution

Example 7   Solve: $|2x - 1| > 7$

Solution   Solve the equivalent compound inequality.

$2x - 1 < -7$ or $2x - 1 > 7$
$2x < -6$ $2x > 8$
$x < -3$ $x > 4$
$\{x \mid x < -3\}$ $\{x \mid x > 4\}$
$\{x \mid x < -3\} \cup \{x \mid x > 4\}$
    $= \{x \mid x < -3 \text{ or } x > 4\}$

You Try It 7   Solve: $|5x + 3| > 8$

Your solution

Solutions on p. S6

Objective C   *To solve application problems* .... CT

The **tolerance** of a component, or part, is the acceptable amount by which the component may vary from a given measurement. For example, the diameter of a piston may vary from the given measurement of 9 cm by 0.001 cm. This is written 9 cm ± 0.001 cm and is read "9 centimeters plus or minus 0.001 centimeter." The maximum diameter, or **upper limit,** of the piston is 9 cm + 0.001 cm = 9.001 cm. The minimum diameter, or **lower limit,** is 9 cm − 0.001 cm = 8.999 cm.

The lower and upper limits of the diameter of the piston could also be found by solving the absolute value inequality $|d - 9| \leq 0.001$, where d is the diameter of the piston.

$$|d - 9| \leq 0.001$$
$$-0.001 \leq d - 9 \leq 0.001$$
$$-0.001 + 9 \leq d - 9 + 9 \leq 0.001 + 9$$
$$8.999 \leq d \leq 9.001$$

The lower and upper limits of the diameter of the piston are 8.999 cm and 9.001 cm.

Example 8

The diameter of a piston for an automobile is $3\frac{5}{16}$ in. with a tolerance of $\frac{1}{64}$ in. Find the lower and upper limits of the diameter of the piston.

You Try It 8

A machinist must make a bushing that has a tolerance of 0.003 in. The diameter of the bushing is 2.55 in. Find the lower and upper limits of the diameter of the bushing.

Strategy

To find the lower and upper limits of the diameter of the piston, let d represent the diameter of the piston, T the tolerance, and L the lower and upper limits of the diameter. Solve the absolute value inequality $|L - d| \leq T$ for L.

Your strategy

Solution

$$|L - d| \leq T$$

$$\left| L - 3\frac{5}{16} \right| \leq \frac{1}{64}$$

$$-\frac{1}{64} \leq L - 3\frac{5}{16} \leq \frac{1}{64}$$

$$-\frac{1}{64} + 3\frac{5}{16} \leq L - 3\frac{5}{16} + 3\frac{5}{16} \leq \frac{1}{64} + 3\frac{5}{16}$$

$$3\frac{19}{64} \leq L \leq 3\frac{21}{64}$$

The lower and upper limits of the diameter of the piston are $3\frac{19}{64}$ in. and $3\frac{21}{64}$ in.

Your solution

Solution on p. S6

2.5 Exercises

· ·

Objective A

Solve.

1. $|x| = 7$

2. $|a| = 2$

3. $|b| = 4$

4. $|c| = 12$

5. $|-y| = 6$

6. $|-t| = 3$

7. $|-a| = 7$

8. $|-x| = 3$

9. $|x| = -4$

10. $|y| = -3$

11. $|-t| = -3$

12. $|-y| = -2$

13. $|x + 2| = 3$

14. $|x + 5| = 2$

15. $|y - 5| = 3$

16. $|y - 8| = 4$

17. $|a - 2| = 0$

18. $|a + 7| = 0$

19. $|x - 2| = -4$

20. $|x + 8| = -2$

21. $|3 - 4x| = 9$

22. $|2 - 5x| = 3$

23. $|2x - 3| = 0$

24. $|5x + 5| = 0$

25. $|3x - 2| = -4$

26. $|2x + 5| = -2$

27. $|x - 2| - 2 = 3$

28. $|x - 9| - 3 = 2$

29. $|3a + 2| - 4 = 4$

30. $|2a + 9| + 4 = 5$

31. $|2 - y| + 3 = 4$

32. $|8 - y| - 3 = 1$

33. $|2x - 3| + 3 = 3$

34. $|4x - 7| - 5 = -5$

35. $|2x - 3| + 4 = -4$

36. $|3x - 2| + 1 = -1$

37. $|6x - 5| - 2 = 4$

38. $|4b + 3| - 2 = 7$

39. $|3t + 2| + 3 = 4$

40. $|5x - 2| + 5 = 7$

41. $3 - |x - 4| = 5$

42. $2 - |x - 5| = 4$

43. $8 - |2x - 3| = 5$

44. $8 - |3x + 2| = 3$

45. $|2 - 3x| + 7 = 2$

46. $|1 - 5a| + 2 = 3$

47. $|8 - 3x| - 3 = 2$

48. $|6 - 5b| - 4 = 3$

49. $|2x - 8| + 12 = 2$

50. $|3x - 4| + 8 = 3$

51. $2 + |3x - 4| = 5$

52. $5 + |2x + 1| = 8$

53. $5 - |2x + 1| = 5$

54. $3 - |5x + 3| = 3$

55. $6 - |2x + 4| = 3$

56. $8 - |3x - 2| = 5$

57. $8 - |1 - 3x| = -1$

58. $3 - |3 - 5x| = -2$

59. $5 + |2 - x| = 3$

60. $6 + |3 - 2x| = 2$

Objective B

61. $|x| > 3$

62. $|x| < 5$

63. $|x + 1| > 2$

64. $|x - 2| > 1$

65. $|x - 5| \leq 1$

66. $|x - 4| \leq 3$

67. $|2 - x| \geq 3$

68. $|3 - x| \geq 2$

69. $|2x + 1| < 5$

70. $|3x - 2| < 4$

71. $|5x + 2| > 12$

72. $|7x - 1| > 13$

73. $|4x - 3| \le -2$

74. $|5x + 1| \le -4$

75. $|2x + 7| > -5$

76. $|3x - 1| > -4$

77. $|4 - 3x| \ge 5$

78. $|7 - 2x| > 9$

79. $|5 - 4x| \le 13$

80. $|3 - 7x| < 17$

81. $|6 - 3x| \le 0$

82. $|10 - 5x| \ge 0$

83. $|2 - 9x| > 20$

84. $|5x - 1| < 16$

85. $|2x - 3| + 2 < 8$

86. $|3x - 5| + 1 < 7$

87. $|2 - 5x| - 4 > -2$

88. $|4 - 2x| - 9 > -3$

89. $8 - |2x - 5| < 3$

90. $12 - |3x - 4| > 7$

Objective C *Application Problems*

91. The diameter of a bushing is 1.75 in. The bushing has a tolerance of 0.008 in. Find the lower and upper limits of the diameter of the bushing.

1.75 in.

92. A machinist must make a bushing that has a tolerance of 0.004 in. The diameter of the bushing is 3.48 in. Find the lower and upper limits of the diameter of the bushing.

93. An electric motor is designed to run on 220 volts plus or minus 25 volts. Find the lower and upper limits of voltage on which the motor will run.

94. A power strip is utilized on a computer to prevent the loss of programming by electrical surges. The power strip is designed to allow 110 volts plus or minus 16.5 volts. Find the lower and upper limits of voltage to the computer.

95. A piston rod for an automobile is $9\frac{5}{8}$ in. long with a tolerance of $\frac{1}{32}$ in. Find the lower and upper limits of the length of the piston rod.

96. A piston rod for an automobile is $9\frac{3}{8}$ in. long with a tolerance of $\frac{1}{64}$ in. Find the lower and upper limits of the length of the piston rod.

The tolerance of the resistors used in electronics is given as a percent. Use your calculator for the following exercises.

97. Find the lower and upper limits of a 29,000-ohm resistor with a 2% tolerance.

98. Find the lower and upper limits of a 15,000-ohm resistor with a 10% tolerance.

99. Find the lower and upper limits of a 25,000-ohm resistor with a 5% tolerance.

100. Find the lower and upper limits of a 56-ohm resistor with a 5% tolerance.

APPLYING THE CONCEPTS

101. For what values of the variable is the equation true? Write the solution set in set-builder notation.
   a. $|x + 3| = x + 3$ **b.** $|a - 4| = 4 - a$

102. Write an absolute value inequality to represent all real numbers within 5 units of 2.

103. Replace the question mark with $\leq$, $\geq$, or $=$.
   a. $|x + y|\ ?\ |x| + |y|$ **b.** $|x - y|\ ?\ |x| - |y|$

   c. $||x| - |y||\ ?\ |x| - |y|$ **d.** $\left|\dfrac{x}{y}\right|\ ?\ \dfrac{|x|}{|y|},\ y \neq 0$

   e. $|xy|\ ?\ |x||y|$

Focus on Problem Solving

Understand the Problem
The first of the four steps that Polya advocated to solve problems is to *understand the problem*. This aspect of problem solving is frequently not given enough attention. There are various exercises that you can try to achieve a good understanding of a problem. Some of these are stated in the Focus on Problem Solving in the chapter entitled "Review of Real Numbers" and are reviewed here.

- Try to restate the problem in your own words.
- Determine what is known about this type of problem.
- Determine what information is given.
- Determine what information is unknown.
- Determine whether any of the information given is unnecessary.
- Determine the goal.

To illustrate this aspect of problem solving, consider the following famous ancient limerick.

> As I was going to St. Ives,
> I met a man with seven wives;
> Each wife had seven sacks,
> Each sack had seven cats,
> Each cat had seven kits:
> Kits, cats, sacks, and wives,
> How many were there going to St. Ives?

To answer the question in the limerick, we will ask and answer some of the questions listed above.

1. What is the goal?

The goal is to determine how many were going to St. Ives. (We know this from reading the last line of the limerick.)

2. What information is necessary and what information is unnecessary?

The first line indicates that the poet was going to St. Ives. The next five lines describe a man the poet *met* on the way. This information is irrelevant.

The answer to the question, then, is 1. Only the poet was going to St. Ives.

There are many other examples of the importance, in problem solving, of recognizing *irrelevant information*. One that frequently makes the college circuit is posed in the form of a test. The first line of a 100-question test states, "Read the entire test before you begin." The last line of the test reads, "Choose any *one* question to answer." Many people ignore the information given in the first line and just begin the test, only to find out much later that they did a lot more work than necessary.

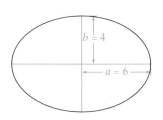

To illustrate another aspect of Polya's first step in the problem-solving process, consider the problem of finding the area of the oval-shaped region (called an *ellipse*) shown in the diagram at the left. This problem can be solved by doing some research to determine *what information is known about this type of problem*. Mathematicians have found a formula for the area of an ellipse. That formula is $A = \pi ab$, where a and b are as shown in the diagram. Therefore, $A = \pi(6)(4) = 24\pi \approx 75.40$ square units. Without the formula, this problem is difficult to solve. With the formula, it is fairly easy.

For each of the following problems, examine the problem in terms of the first step in Polya's problem-solving method. *Do not solve the problem.*

1. Johanna spent one-third of her allowance on a book. She then spent $5.00 for a sandwich and iced tea. The cost of the iced tea was one-fifth the cost of the sandwich. Find the cost of the iced tea.

2. A flight from Los Angeles to Boston took 6 h. What was the average speed of the plane?

3. A major league baseball is approximately 5 in. in diameter and is covered with cowhide. Approximately how much cowhide is used to cover 10 baseballs?

4. How many donuts are in seven baker's dozen?

5. The smallest prime number is 2. Twice the difference between the eighth and the seventh prime numbers is two more than the smallest prime number. How large is the smallest prime number?

Projects and Group Activities

Venn Diagrams   Diagrams can be very useful when working with sets. The set diagrams shown below are called **Venn diagrams.**

In the Venn diagram at the right, the rectangle represents the set U, and the circles A and B represent subsets of set U. The common area of the two circles represents the intersection of A and B.

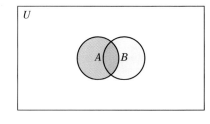

This Venn diagram represents the set $U = \{1, 2, 3, 4, 5, 6, 7, 8\}$. The sets $A = \{2, 3, 4, 5\}$ and $B = \{4, 5, 6, 7\}$ are subsets of U. Note that 1 and 8 are in set U but not in A or B. The numbers 4 and 5 are in both set A and set B.

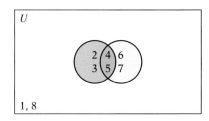

Sixty-five students at a small college enrolled in the following courses.

39 enrolled in English.
26 enrolled in mathematics.
35 enrolled in history.
19 enrolled in English and history.
11 enrolled in English and
mathematics.
9 enrolled in mathematics and
history.
2 enrolled in all three courses.

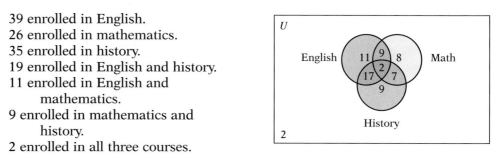

The Venn diagram is shown above. The diagram was drawn by placing the 2 students in the intersection of all three courses. Since 9 students took history and mathematics and 2 students are already in the intersection of history and mathematics, then 7 more students are placed in the intersection of history and mathematics. Continue in this manner until all information is used.

Complete the following.

1. Use the Venn diagram above that shows course enrollments.
   a. How many students enrolled only in English and mathematics?
   b. How many students enrolled in English but did not enroll in mathematics or history?
   c. How many students did not enroll in any of the three courses?

2. Sketch the Venn diagram for $U = \{1, 2, 3, 4, 5, 6, 7, 8\}$, $A = \{2, 3, 4, 5, 6\}$, $B = \{4, 5, 6, 7, 8\}$, and $C = \{4, 5\}$.

3. A busload of 50 scouts stopped at a fast-food restaurant and ordered hamburgers. The scouts could have pickles, or tomatoes, or lettuce on their hamburgers.

   31 ordered pickles.
   36 ordered tomatoes.
   31 ordered lettuce.
   21 ordered pickles and tomatoes.
   24 ordered tomatoes and lettuce.
   22 ordered pickles and lettuce.
   17 ordered all three.

   a. How many scouts ordered a hamburger with pickles only?
   b. How many scouts ordered a hamburger with lettuce and tomatoes without the pickles?
   c. How many scouts ordered a hamburger without pickles, tomatoes, or lettuce?

Chapter Summary

Key Words   An *equation* expresses the equality of two mathematical expressions. A *solution,* or *root,* of an equation is a replacement value for the variable that will make the equation true. To *solve an equation* means to find its solutions.

A *contradiction* is an equation for which no value of the variable produces a true equation. A *conditional equation* is one that is true for at least one value of the variable but not all values of the variable. An *identity* is an equation that is true for all values of the variable.

An equation of the form $ax + b = c$, $a \neq 0$, is called a *first-degree equation*.

Equivalent equations are equations that have the same solution.

A *literal equation* is an equation that contains more than one variable.

A *value mixture problem* involves combining into a single blend two ingredients that have different prices. A *percent mixture problem* involves combining into a single blend two solutions that contain different amounts of a substance.

Uniform motion means that the speed of an object does not change.

The *solution set of an inequality* is a set of numbers, each element of which, when substituted for the variable, results in a true inequality.

A *compound inequality* is formed by joining two inequalities with a connective word such as "and" or "or."

The *absolute value* of a number is its distance from zero on the number line. An *absolute value equation* contains an absolute value symbol.

Essential Rules

Addition Property of Equations	If $a = b$, then $a + c = b + c$.
Multiplication Property of Equations	If $a = b$ and $c \neq 0$, then $ac = bc$.
Addition Property of Inequalities	If $a > b$, then $a + c > b + c$. If $a < b$, then $a + c < b + c$.
Multiplication Property of Inequalities	**Rule 1** If $a > b$ and $c > 0$, then $ac > bc$. If $a < b$ and $c > 0$, then $ac < bc$. **Rule 2** If $a > b$ and $c < 0$, then $ac < bc$. If $a < b$ and $c < 0$, then $ac > bc$.
Consecutive Integers	$n, n + 1, n + 2, \ldots$
Consecutive Even Integers	$n, n + 2, n + 4, \ldots$
Consecutive Odd Integers	$n, n + 2, n + 4, \ldots$
Coin (or Stamp) Equation	$\dfrac{\text{Number}}{\text{of coins}} \times \dfrac{\text{value of}}{\text{coin in cents}} = \dfrac{\text{total value}}{\text{in cents}}$
Value Mixture Equation	Value $=$ amount $\times$ unit cost $V = AC$
Percent Mixture Equation	Quantity $=$ amount $\times \dfrac{\text{percent}}{\text{concentration}}$ $Q = Ar$
Uniform Motion Equation	Distance $=$ rate $\times$ time $d = rt$
Solution of an Absolute Value Equation	If $a \geq 0$ and $|x| = a$, then $x = a$ or $x = -a$.

To solve an absolute value inequality of the form $|ax + b| < c$, solve the equivalent compound inequality $-c < ax + b < c$.

To solve an absolute value inequality of the form $|ax + b| > c$, solve the equivalent compound inequality $ax + b < -c$ or $ax + b > c$.

Chapter Review

1. Solve: $3t - 3 + 2t = 7t - 15$

2. Solve: $3x - 7 > -2$

3. Solve $P = 2L + 2W$ for L.

4. Solve: $x + 4 = -5$

5. Solve: $3x < 4$ and $x + 2 > -1$

6. Solve: $\frac{3}{5}x - 3 = 2x + 5$

7. Solve: $-\frac{2}{3}x = \frac{4}{9}$

8. Solve: $|x - 4| - 8 = -3$

9. Solve: $|2x - 5| < 3$

10. Solve: $\frac{2x - 3}{3} + 2 = \frac{2 - 3x}{5}$

11. Solve: $2(a - 3) = 5(4 - 3a)$

12. Solve: $5x - 2 > 8$ or $3x + 2 < -4$

13. Solve: $|4x - 5| \geq 3$

14. Solve $P = \frac{R - C}{n}$ for C.

15. Solve: $\frac{1}{2}x - \frac{5}{8} = \frac{3}{4}x + \frac{3}{2}$

16. Solve: $6 + |3x - 3| = 2$

17. Solve: $3x - 2 > x - 4$ or $7x - 5 < 3x + 3$

18. Solve: $2x - (3 - 2x) = 4 - 3(4 - 2x)$

19. A grocer mixed apple juice that costs $3.20 per gallon with 40 gal of cranberry juice that costs $5.50 per gallon. How much apple juice was used to make cranapple juice costing $4.20 per gallon?

20. A sales executive earns $800 per month plus 4% commission on the amount of sales. The executive's goal is to earn $3000 per month. What amount of sales will enable the executive to earn $3000 or more per month?

21. A coin collection contains thirty coins in nickels, dimes, and quarters. There are three more dimes than nickels. The value of the coins is $3.55. Find the number of quarters in the collection.

22. The diameter of a bushing is 2.75 in. The bushing has a tolerance of 0.003 in. Find the lower and upper limits of the diameter of the bushing.

23. The sum of two integers is twenty. Five times the smaller integer is two more than twice the larger integer. Find the two integers.

24. An average score of 80 to 90 in a psychology class receives a B grade. A student has grades of 92, 66, 72, and 88 on four tests. Find the range of scores on the fifth test that will give the student a B for the course.

25. Two planes are 1680 mi apart and are traveling toward each other. One plane is traveling 80 mph faster than the other plane. The planes meet in 1.75 h. Find the speed of each plane.

26. An alloy containing 30% tin is mixed with an alloy containing 70% tin. How many pounds of each were used to make 500 lb of an alloy containing 40% tin?

27. A piston rod for an automobile is $10\frac{3}{8}$ in. long with a tolerance of $\frac{1}{32}$ in. Find the lower and upper limits of the length of the piston rod.

Chapter Test

1. Solve: $x - 2 = -4$

2. Solve: $b + \dfrac{3}{4} = \dfrac{5}{8}$

3. Solve: $-\dfrac{3}{4}y = -\dfrac{5}{8}$

4. Solve: $3x - 5 = 7$

5. Solve: $\dfrac{3}{4}y - 2 = 6$

6. Solve: $2x - 3 - 5x = 8 + 2x - 10$

7. Solve: $2[a - (2 - 3a) - 4] = a - 5$

8. Solve $E = IR + Ir$ for R.

9. Solve: $\dfrac{2x + 1}{3} - \dfrac{3x + 4}{6} = \dfrac{5x - 9}{9}$

10. Solve: $3x - 2 \geq 6x + 7$

11. Solve: $4 - 3(x + 2) < 2(2x + 3) - 1$

12. Solve: $4x - 1 > 5$ or $2 - 3x < 8$

13. Solve: $4 - 3x \geq 7$ and $2x + 3 \geq 7$

14. Solve: $|3 - 5x| = 12$

15. Solve: $2 - |2x - 5| = -7$

16. Solve: $|3x - 5| \leq 4$

17. Solve: $|4x - 3| > 5$

18. Gambelli Agency rents cars for $12 a day and 10¢ for every mile driven. McDougal Rental rents cars for $24 a day with unlimited mileage. How many miles a day can you drive a Gambelli Agency car if it is to cost you less than a McDougal Rental car?

19. A machinist must make a bushing that has a tolerance of 0.002 in. The diameter of the bushing is 2.65 in. Find the lower and upper limits of the diameter of the bushing.

20. The sum of two integers is fifteen. Eight times the smaller integer is one less than three times the larger integer. Find the integers.

21. A stamp collection contains 11¢, 15¢, and 24¢ stamps. There are twice as many 11¢ stamps as 15¢ stamps. There are thirty stamps in all, with a value of $4.40. How many 24¢ stamps are in the collection?

22. A butcher combines 100 lb of hamburger that costs $1.60 per pound with 60 lb of hamburger that costs $3.20 per pound. Find the cost of the hamburger mixture.

23. A jogger runs a distance at a speed of 8 mph and returns the same distance running at a speed of 6 mph. Find the total distance that the jogger ran if the total time running was one hour and forty-five minutes.

24. Two trains are 250 mi apart and are traveling toward each other. One train is traveling 5 mph faster than the other train. The trains pass each other in 2 h. Find the speed of each train.

25. How many ounces of pure water must be added to 60 oz of an 8% salt solution to make a 3% salt solution?

Cumulative Review

1. Simplify: $-4 - (-3) - 8 + (-2)$

2. Simplify: $-2^2 \cdot 3^3$

3. Simplify: $4 - (2 - 5)^2 \div 3 + 2$

4. Simplify: $4 \div \dfrac{\frac{3}{8} - 1}{5} \cdot 2$

5. Evaluate $2a^2 - (b - c)^2$ when $a = 2$, $b = 3$, and $c = -1$.

6. Evaluate $\dfrac{a - b^2}{b - c}$ when $a = 2$, $b = -3$, and $c = 4$.

7. Identify the property that justifies the statement.
   $(2x + 3y) + 2 = (3y + 2x) + 2$

8. Translate and simplify "the sum of three times a number and six added to the product of three and a number."

9. Solve $F = \dfrac{evB}{c}$ for B.

10. Simplify: $5[y - 2(3 - 2y) + 6]$

11. Find $A \cap B$, given $A = \{-4, -2, 0, 2\}$ and $B = \{-4, 0, 4, 8\}$.

12. Graph the solution set of $\{x \mid x \le 3\} \cap \{x \mid x > -1\}$.

13. Solve $Ax + By + C = 0$ for y.

14. Solve: $-\dfrac{5}{6}b = -\dfrac{5}{12}$

15. Solve: $2x + 5 = 5x + 2$

16. Solve: $\dfrac{5}{12}x - 3 = 7$

17. Solve: $2[3 - 2(3 - 2x)] = 2(3 + x)$

18. Solve: $3[2x - 3(4 - x)] = 2(1 - 2x)$

19. Solve: $\dfrac{1}{2}y - \dfrac{2}{3}y + \dfrac{5}{12} = \dfrac{3}{4}y - \dfrac{1}{2}$

20. Solve: $\dfrac{3x - 1}{4} - \dfrac{4x - 1}{12} = \dfrac{3 + 5x}{8}$

21. Solve: $3 - 2(2x - 1) \geq 3(2x - 2) + 1$

22. Solve: $3x + 2 \leq 5$ and $x + 5 > 1$

23. Solve: $|3 - 2x| = 5$

24. Solve: $3 - |2x - 3| = -8$

25. Solve: $|3x - 1| > 5$

26. Solve: $|2x - 4| < 8$

27. A bank offers two types of checking accounts. One account has a charge of $5 per month plus 4¢ for each check. The second account has a charge of $2 per month plus 10¢ for each check. How many checks can a customer who has the second type of account write if it is to cost the customer less than the first type of account?

28. Four times the sum of the first and third of three consecutive odd integers is one less than seven times the middle integer. Find the first integer.

29. A coin purse contains dimes and quarters. The number of dimes is five less than twice the number of quarters. The total value of the coins is $4.00. Find the number of dimes in the coin purse.

30. A silversmith combined pure silver that costs $8.50 per ounce with 100 oz of a silver alloy that costs $4.00 per ounce. How many ounces of pure silver were used to make an alloy of silver costing $6.00 per ounce?

31. Two planes are 1400 mi apart and are traveling toward each other. One plane is traveling 120 mph faster than the other plane. The planes meet in 2.5 h. Find the speed of the slower plane.

32. The diameter of a bushing is 2.45 in. The bushing has a tolerance of 0.001 in. Find the lower and upper limits of the diameter of the bushing.

33. How many liters of a 12% acid solution must be mixed with 4 L of a 5% acid solution to make an 8% acid solution?

3

Linear Functions and Inequalities in Two Variables

Petroleum technicians measure and record physical and geologic conditions in oil or gas wells from instruments lowered into wells. They also perform a chemical analysis of the mud from wells to determine petroleum and mineral content. By measuring the rate at which oil or gas is being pumped from a well, the technician can estimate the useful life of the well. Rates are one of the topics of this chapter.

Objectives

Section 3.1
To graph points in a rectangular coordinate system
To find the length and midpoint of a line segment
To graph a scatter diagram

Section 3.2
To evaluate a function

Section 3.3
To graph a linear function
To graph an equation of the form $Ax + By = C$
To find the x- and the y-intercept of a straight line
To solve application problems

Section 3.4
To find the slope of a line given two points
To graph a line given a point and the slope

Section 3.5
To find the equation of a line given a point and the slope
To find the equation of a line given two points
To solve application problems

Section 3.6
To find parallel and perpendicular lines

Section 3.7
To graph the solution set of an inequality in two variables

Brachistochrone Problems

Consider the diagram at the right.
What curve should be drawn so that a
ball allowed to roll along the curve will travel
from *A* to *B* in the shortest time?

At first thought, one might conjecture that a straight
line should connect the two points, since that shape is
the shortest *distance* between the two points. Actually,
however, the answer is half of one arch of an inverted
cycloid.

A cycloid is shown below as the graph in blue. One way
to draw this curve is to think of a wheel rolling along a
straight line without slipping. Then a point on
the rim of the wheel traces a cycloid.

There are many applications of the idea of finding the
shortest time between two points. As the above problem
illustrates, the path of shortest time is not necessarily the
path of shortest distance. Problems involving paths of
shortest time are called *brachistochrone* problems.

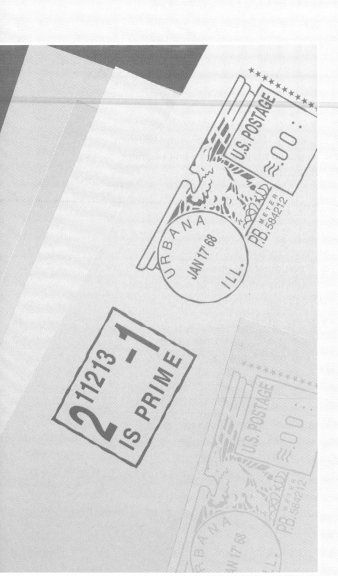

3.1 The Rectangular Coordinate System

Objective A *To graph points in a rectangular coordinate system* ....

Before the 15th century, geometry and algebra were considered separate branches of mathematics. That all changed when René Descartes, a French mathematician who lived from 1596 to 1650, founded **analytic geometry.** In this geometry, a *coordinate system* is used to study relationships between variables.

A **rectangular coordinate system** is formed by two number lines, one horizontal and one vertical, that intersect at the zero point of each line. The point of intersection is called the **origin.** The two lines are called **coordinate axes,** or simply **axes.**

The axes determine a **plane,** which can be thought of as a large, flat sheet of paper. The two axes divide the plane into four regions called **quadrants.** The quadrants are numbered counterclockwise from I to IV.

Each point in the plane can be identified by a pair of numbers called an **ordered pair.** The first number of the pair measures a horizontal distance and is called the **abscissa.** The second number of the pair measures a vertical distance and is called the **ordinate.** The **coordinates** of the point are the numbers in the ordered pair associated with the point. The abscissa is also called the **first coordinate** of the ordered pair, and the ordinate is also called the **second coordinate** of the ordered pair.

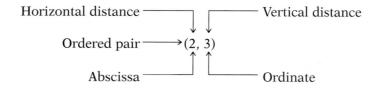

To **graph** or **plot** an ordered pair in the plane, place a dot at the location given by the ordered pair. The **graph of an ordered pair** is the dot drawn at the coordinates of the point in the plane. The points whose coordinates are (3, 4) and (−2.5, −3) are graphed in the figure at the right.

The points whose coordinates are $(3, -1)$ and $(-1, 3)$ are graphed at the right. Note that the graphs are in different locations. The *order* of the coordinates of an ordered pair is important.

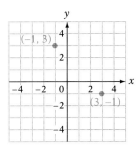

When drawing a rectangular coordinate system, we often label the horizontal axis x and the vertical axis y. In this case, the coordinate system is called an **xy-coordinate system.** The coordinates of the points are given by ordered pairs (x, y), where the abscissa is called the **x-coordinate** and the ordinate is called the **y-coordinate.**

The *xy*-coordinate system is used to graph equations in *two variables*. Examples of equations in two variables are shown at the right.

$$y = 3x + 7$$
$$y = x^2 - 4x + 3$$
$$x^2 + y^2 = 25$$
$$x = \frac{y}{y^2 + 4}$$

A **solution of an equation in two variables** is an ordered pair (x, y) whose coordinates make the equation a true statement.

➡ Is the ordered pair $(-3, 7)$ a solution of the equation $y = -2x + 1$?

$$y = -2x + 1$$

7	$-2(-3) + 1$
7	$6 + 1$

$7 = 7$

Yes, the ordered pair $(-3, 7)$ is a solution of the equation.

- Replace *x* by -3 and *y* by 7.
- Simplify.
- Compare the results. If the resulting equation is a true statement, the ordered pair is a solution of the equation. If it is not a true statement, the ordered pair is not a solution of the equation.

Besides the ordered pair $(-3, 7)$, there are many other ordered-pair solutions of the equation $y = -2x + 1$. For example, $(-5, 11)$, $(0, 1)$, $\left(-\frac{3}{2}, 4\right)$, and $(4, -7)$ are also solutions of the equation.

In general, an equation in two variables has an infinite number of solutions. By choosing any value of x and substituting that value into the equation, we can calculate a corresponding value of y. The resulting ordered-pair solution (x, y) of the equation can be graphed in a rectangular coordinate system.

⇒ Graph the solutions (x, y) of $y = x^2 - 1$ when x equals $-2, -1, 0, 1,$ and 2.

Substitute each value of x into the equation and solve for y. Then graph the resulting ordered pairs. It is convenient to record the ordered-pair solutions in a table similar to the one shown below.

x	$y = x^2 - 1$	y	(x, y)
-2	$y = (-2)^2 - 1$	3	$(-2, 3)$
-1	$y = (-1)^2 - 1$	0	$(-1, 0)$
0	$y = 0^2 - 1$	-1	$(0, -1)$
1	$y = 1^2 - 1$	0	$(1, 0)$
2	$y = 2^2 - 1$	3	$(2, 3)$

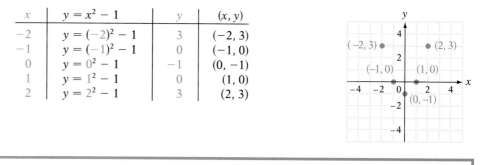

Example 1

Determine the ordered-pair solution of

$y = \dfrac{x}{x - 2}$ corresponding to $x = 4$.

Solution

Replace x by 4 and solve for y.

$$y = \frac{4}{4 - 2} = \frac{4}{2} = 2$$

The ordered-pair solution is $(4, 2)$.

You Try It 1

Determine the ordered-pair solution of

$y = \dfrac{3x}{x + 1}$ corresponding to $x = -2$.

Your solution

Example 2

Graph the ordered-pair solutions of
$y = x^2 - x$ when $x = -1, 0, 1,$ and 2.

Solution

x	y
-1	2
0	0
1	0
2	2

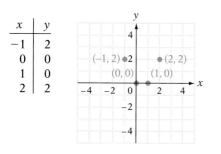

You Try It 2

Graph the ordered-pair solutions of
$y = |x + 1|$ when $x = -3, -2, -1, 0,$ and 1.

Your solution

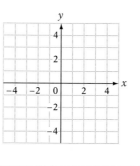

Solutions on p. S6

Objective B   *To find the length and midpoint of a line segment* .... **CT**

The distance between two points in an xy-coordinate system can be calculated by using the Pythagorean Theorem.

POINT OF INTEREST

Although Pythagoras (c. 550 B.C.) is given credit for this theorem, a clay tablet called Plimpton 322 shows that the Babylonians knew the theorem 1000 years before Pythagoras!

Pythagorean Theorem

If a and b are the lengths of the legs of a right triangle and c is the length of the hypotenuse, then $a^2 + b^2 = c^2$.

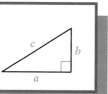

Consider the two points and the right triangle shown at the right. The vertical distance between $P_1(x_1, y_1)$ and $P_2(x_2, y_2)$ is $|y_2 - y_1|$.

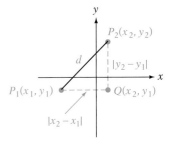

The horizontal distance between the points $P_1(x_1, y_1)$ and $P_2(x_2, y_2)$ is $|x_2 - x_1|$.

The quantity d^2 is calculated by applying the Pythagorean Theorem to the right triangle.

$$d^2 = |x_2 - x_1|^2 + |y_2 - y_1|^2$$
$$d^2 = (x_2 - x_1)^2 + (y_2 - y_1)^2$$

The distance d is the square root of d^2.

$$d = \sqrt{(x_2 - x_1)^2 + (y_2 - y_1)^2}$$

Because $(x_2 - x_1)^2 = (x_1 - x_2)^2$ and $(y_2 - y_1)^2 = (y_1 - y_2)^2$, the distance formula is usually written in the following form.

The Distance Formula

If $P_1(x_1, y_1)$ and $P_2(x_2, y_2)$ are two points in the plane, then the distance d between the two points is given by

$$d = \sqrt{(x_1 - x_2)^2 + (y_1 - y_2)^2}.$$

The midpoint of a line segment is equidistant from its endpoints. The coordinates of the midpoint of the line segment P_1P_2 are (x_m, y_m). The intersection of the horizontal line segment through P_1 and the vertical line segment through P_2 is Q, with coordinates (x_2, y_1).

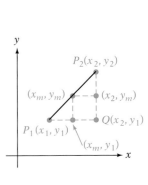

The x-coordinate x_m of the midpoint of the line segment P_1P_2 is the same as the x-coordinate of the midpoint of the line segment P_1Q. It is the average of the x-coordinates of the points P_1 and P_2.

$$x_m = \frac{x_1 + x_2}{2}$$

Similarly, the y-coordinate y_m of the midpoint of the line segment P_1P_2 is the same as the y-coordinate of the midpoint of the line segment P_2Q. It is the average of the y-coordinates of the points P_1 and P_2.

$$y_m = \frac{y_1 + y_2}{2}$$

> **The Midpoint Formula**
>
> If $P_1(x_1, y_1)$ and $P_2(x_2, y_2)$ are the endpoints of a line segment, then the coordinates of the midpoint (x_m, y_m) of the line segment are given by
>
> $$x_m = \frac{x_1 + x_2}{2} \quad \text{and} \quad y_m = \frac{y_1 + y_2}{2}$$

Example 3

Find the distance (to the nearest hundredth) between the points whose coordinates are $(-3, 2)$ and $(4, -1)$.

Solution

$(x_1, y_1) = (-3, 2); (x_2, y_2) = (4, -1)$

$d = \sqrt{(x_1 - x_2)^2 + (y_1 - y_2)^2}$

$ = \sqrt{(-3 - 4)^2 + [2 - (-1)]^2}$

$ = \sqrt{(-7)^2 + 3^2} = \sqrt{49 + 9}$

$ = \sqrt{58} \approx 7.62$

You Try It 3

Find the distance (to the nearest hundredth) between the points whose coordinates are $(5, -2)$ and $(-4, 3)$.

Your solution

Example 4

Find the coordinates of the midpoint of the line segment with endpoints $(-5, 4)$ and $(-3, 7)$.

Solution

$(x_1, y_1) = (-5, 4); (x_2, y_2) = (-3, 7)$

$x_m = \dfrac{x_1 + x_2}{2} \qquad y_m = \dfrac{y_1 + y_2}{2}$

$ = \dfrac{-5 + (-3)}{2} \qquad = \dfrac{4 + 7}{2}$

$ = -4 \qquad\qquad = \dfrac{11}{2}$

The midpoint is $\left(-4, \dfrac{11}{2}\right)$.

You Try It 4

Find the coordinates of the midpoint of the line segment with endpoints $(-3, -5)$ and $(-2, 3)$.

Your solution

Solutions on p. S6

Objective C **To graph a scatter diagram** .... CT

Discovering a relationship between two variables is an important task in the study of mathematics. These relationships occur in many forms and in a wide variety of applications. Here are some examples.

- A botanist wants to know the relationship between the number of bushels of wheat yielded per acre and the amount of watering per acre.

- An environmental scientist wants to know the relationship between the incidence of skin cancer and the amount of ozone in the atmosphere.

- A business analyst wants to know the relationship between the price of a product and the number of products that are sold at that price.

A researcher may investigate the relationship between two variables by means of *regression analysis,* which is a branch of statistics. The study of the relationship between the two variables may begin with a **scatter diagram,** which is a graph of the ordered pairs of the known data.

The following table shows randomly selected data from the participants 40 years old and older and their times (in minutes) for the 1997 Boston Marathon.

Age (x)	55	46	53	40	40	44	54	44	41	50
Time (y)	254	204	243	194	281	197	238	300	232	216

TAKE NOTE

The jagged portion of the horizontal axis in the figure at the right indicates that the numbers between 0 and 40 are missing.

The scatter diagram for these data is shown at the right. Each ordered pair represents the age and time for a participant. For instance, the ordered pair (53, 243) indicates that a 53-year-old participant ran the marathon in 243 min.

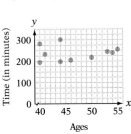

Example 5

The grams of sugar and the grams of fiber in a 1-ounce serving of six breakfast cereals are shown in the table below.

	Sugar (x)	Fiber (y)
Wheaties	4	3
Rice Krispies	3	0
Total	5	3
Life	6	2
Kix	3	1
Grape-Nuts	7	5

Draw a scatter diagram of these data.

Strategy

To draw a scatter diagram:

- Draw a coordinate grid with the horizontal axis representing the grams of sugar and the vertical axis the grams of fiber.
- Graph the ordered pairs (4, 3), (3, 0), (5, 3), (6, 2), (3, 1), and (7, 5).

Solution

You Try It 5

The number of yards gained and the number of points scored for six games of the Green Bay Packers are shown in the scatter diagram below. How many points did Green Bay score when it gained 275 yd?

Your strategy

Your solution

Solution on p. S7

3.1 Exercises

Objective A

1. Graph the ordered pairs $(1, -1)$, $(2, 0)$, $(3, 2)$, and $(-1, 4)$.

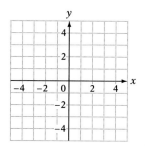

2. Graph the ordered pairs $(-1, -3)$, $(0, -4)$, $(0, 4)$, and $(3, -2)$.

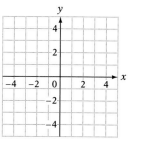

3. Find the coordinates of each of the points.

4. Find the coordinates of each of the points.

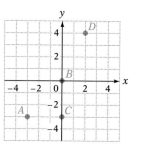

5. Draw a line through all points with an abscissa of 2.

6. Draw a line through all points with an abscissa of -3.

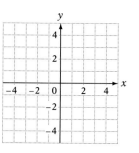

7. Draw a line through all points with an ordinate of -3.

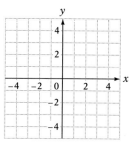

8. Draw a line through all points with an ordinate of 4.

9. Graph the ordered-pair solutions of $y = x^2$ when $x = -2, -1, 0, 1$, and 2.

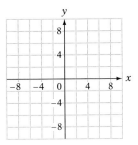

10. Graph the ordered-pair solutions of $y = -x^2 + 1$ when $x = -2, -1, 0, 1$, and 2.

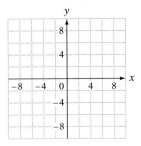

11. Graph the ordered-pair solutions of $y = |x + 1|$ when $x = -5, -3, 0, 3$, and 5.

12. Graph the ordered-pair solutions of $y = -2|x|$ when $x = -3, -1, 0, 1$, and 3.

13. Graph the ordered-pair solutions of $y = -x^2 + 2$ when $x = -2, -1, 0, 1$, and 2.

14. Graph the ordered-pair solutions of $y = -x^2 + 4$ when $x = -3, -1, 0, 1$, and 3.

15. Graph the ordered-pair solutions of $y = x^3 - 2$ when $x = -1, 0, 1$, and 2.

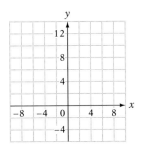

16. Graph the ordered-pair solutions of $y = -x^3 + 1$ when $x = -1, 0, 1$, and $\frac{3}{2}$.

Objective B

Find the length (to the nearest hundredth) and midpoint of the line segment between the given points.

17. $P_1(3, 5)$ and $P_2(5, 1)$

18. $P_1(-2, 3)$ and $P_2(4, -1)$

19. $P_1(0, 3)$ and $P_2(-2, 4)$

20. $P_1(6, -1)$ and $P_2(-3, -2)$

21. $P_1(-3, -5)$ and $P_2(2, -4)$

22. $P_1(-7, -5)$ and $P_2(-2, -1)$

23. $P_1(5, -2)$ and $P_2(-2, 5)$

24. $P_1(3, -6)$ and $P_2(6, 0)$

25. $P_1(5, -5)$ and $P_2(2, -5)$

26. $P_1(-2, -3)$ and $P_2(-2, 5)$

27. $P_1\left(\dfrac{3}{2}, -\dfrac{4}{3}\right)$ and $P_2\left(-\dfrac{1}{2}, \dfrac{7}{3}\right)$

28. $P_1(4.5, -6.3)$ and $P_2(-1.7, -4.5)$

Objective C

Solve.

29. The temperature of a chemical reaction is measured at intervals of 10 min and recorded in the scatter diagram at the right.
a. Find the temperature of the reaction after 20 min.
b. After how many minutes is the temperature 160°F?

The jagged line means that the numbers between 0 and 140 are missing.

30. The amount of a substance that can be dissolved in a fixed amount of water usually increases as the temperature of the water increases. Cerium selenate, however, does not behave in this manner. The graph at the right shows the number of grams of cerium selenate that will dissolve in 100 mg of water for various temperatures, in degrees Celsius.
a. Determine the temperature at which 25 g of cerium selenate will dissolve.
b. Determine the number of grams of cerium selenate that will dissolve when the temperature is 80°C.

31. Past experience by executives of a car company shows that the profit of a dealership will depend on the total income of all the residents of the town in which the dealership is located. The table below shows the profit of several dealerships and the total income of the towns. Draw the scatter diagram for these data.

Profit (thousands of $)	65	85	81	77	89	69
Total Income (billions of $)	2.2	2.6	2.5	2.4	2.7	2.3

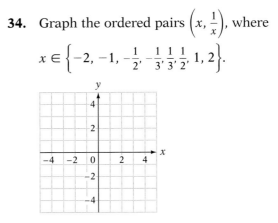

32. A power company suggests that a larger power plant can produce energy more efficiently and therefore at lower cost to consumers. The table below shows the output and average cost for power plants of various sizes. Draw the scatter diagram for these data.

Output (millions of watts)	0.7	2.2	2.6	3.2	2.8	3.5
Average Cost (in dollars)	6.9	6.5	6.3	6.4	6.5	6.1

APPLYING THE CONCEPTS

33. Graph the ordered pairs (x, x^2), where $x \in \{-2, -1, 0, 1, 2\}$.

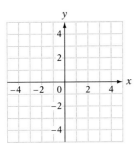

34. Graph the ordered pairs $\left(x, \frac{1}{x}\right)$, where

$$x \in \left\{-2, -1, -\frac{1}{2}, -\frac{1}{3}, \frac{1}{3}, \frac{1}{2}, 1, 2\right\}.$$

35. Describe the graph of all the ordered pairs (x, y) that are 5 units from the origin.

36. Consider two distinct fixed points in the plane. Describe the graph of all the points (x, y) that are equidistant from these fixed points.

37. Draw a line passing through every point whose abscissa equals its ordinate.

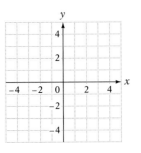

38. Draw a line passing through every point whose ordinate is the additive inverse of its abscissa.

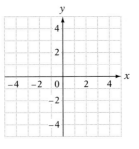

3.2   Introduction to Functions

Objective A   *To evaluate a function* ··

In mathematics and its applications, there are many times when it is necessary to investigate a relationship between two quantities. Here is a financial application: Consider a person who is planning to finance the purchase of a car. If the current interest rate for a five-year loan is 9%, the equation that describes the relationship between the amount that is borrowed B and the monthly payment P is $P = 0.020758B$.

For each amount the purchaser may borrow (B), there is a certain monthly payment (P). The relationship between the amount borrowed and the payment can be recorded as ordered pairs, where the first coordinate is the amount borrowed and the second coordinate is the monthly payment. Some of these ordered pairs are shown at the right.

$$0.020758B = P$$

(5000, 103.79)
(6000, 124.55)
(7000, 145.31)
(8000, 166.06)

A relationship between two quantities is not always given by an equation. The table at the right describes a grading scale that defines a relationship between a score on a test and a letter grade. For each score, the table assigns only one letter grade. The ordered pair (84, B) indicates that a score of 84 receives a letter grade of B.

Score	Grade
90–100	A
80–89	B
70–79	C
60–69	D
0–59	F

The graph at the right also shows a relationship between two quantities. It is a graph of the viscosity V of SAE 40 motor oil at various temperatures T. Ordered pairs can be approximated from the graph. The ordered pair (120, 250) indicates that the viscosity of the oil at 120°F is 250 units.

In each of these examples, there is a rule (an equation, a table, or a graph) that determines a certain set of ordered pairs.

> **Definition of Relation**
>
> A **relation** is a set of ordered pairs.

Here are some of the ordered pairs for the relations given above.

Relation	Some of the Ordered Pairs of the Relation
Car Payment	(2500, 51.90), (3750, 77.84), (4396, 91.25)
Grading Scale	(78, C), (98, A), (70, C), (81, B), (94, A)
Oil Viscosity	(100, 500), (120, 250), (130, 200), (150, 180)

These three relations are actually a special type of relation called a function. Functions play an important role in mathematics and its applications.

Definition of Function

A **function** is a relation in which no two ordered pairs have the same first coordinate and different second coordinates.

Although functions defined by tables or graphs have important applications, a major focus of this text is functions defined by equations in two variables.

The "square" function, which pairs each real number with its square, can be defined by the equation

$$y = x^2$$

Given a value of x, the value of y is the square of x. For instance, given $x = 3$, then $y = 9$. Because the value of y *depends* on the value of x, y is called the **dependent variable** and x is called the **independent variable.** Some of the ordered pairs of the square function are $(3, 9)$, $(-2, 4)$, $(0, 0)$, $(-3, 9)$, and $\left(\frac{1}{2}, \frac{1}{4}\right)$. In each case, the second coordinate is the square of the first coordinate. The ordered pairs of the square function are (x, y), where x is any real number and $y = x^2$. By substituting x^2 for y in (x, y), we can also write the ordered pairs (x, x^2).

Not every equation in two variables, however, defines a function. For instance,

$$y^2 = x^2 + 9$$

is not an equation that defines a function. Because

$$5^2 = 4^2 + 9 \quad \text{and} \quad (-5)^2 = 4^2 + 9$$

the ordered pairs $(4, 5)$ and $(4, -5)$ are both solutions of the equation. Consequently, there are two ordered pairs that have the same first coordinate, 4, but *different* second coordinates, 5 and -5; the equation does not define a function. The phrase "y is a function of x," or a similar phrase with different variables, is used to describe those equations in two variables that define functions.

Functional notation is used for those equations that define functions. Just as x is commonly used as a variable, the letter f is commonly used to name a function.

The square function is written in functional notation as follows:

The value of the function. This is the number that is paired with x.

$$f(x) = x^2$$

The name of the function is f.   An algebraic expression that defines the relationship between the dependent and independent variables.

The symbol $f(x)$ is read "the *value* of f at x" or "f of x."

It is important to note that $f(x)$ does not mean f times x. The symbol $f(x)$ is the **value of the function** and represents the value of the dependent variable for a given value of the independent variable. We often write $y = f(x)$ to emphasize the relationship between the independent variable, x, and the dependent variable, y. Remember that y and $f(x)$ are different symbols for the same number.

The letters used to represent a function are somewhat arbitrary. Each of the equations below represents the same function.

$$\left.\begin{array}{l} f(x) = x^2 \\ s(t) = t^2 \\ P(v) = v^2 \end{array}\right\} \quad \text{These equations represent the same function.}$$

The process of determining $f(x)$ for a given value of x is called **evaluating the function.** For instance, to evaluate $f(x) = x^2$ when $x = 4$, replace x by 4 and simplify.

$$f(x) = x^2$$
$$f(4) = 4^2 = 16 \qquad \bullet \text{ Replace } x \text{ by 4.}$$

The *value* of the function, $f(4)$, is 16 when $x = 4$. An ordered pair of the function is (4, 16).

➡ Evaluate $g(t) = 3t^2 - 5t + 1$ when $t = -2$.

$$g(t) = 3t^2 - 5t + 1$$
$$g(-2) = 3(-2)^2 - 5(-2) + 1 \qquad \bullet \text{ Replace } t \text{ by } -2.$$
$$= 3(4) + 10 + 1 = 23 \qquad \bullet \text{ Simplify.}$$

The value of the function is 23 when $t = -2$.

It is possible to evaluate a function for a variable expression.

➡ Evaluate $P(z) = 3z - 7$ when $z = 3 + h$.

$$P(z) = 3z - 7$$
$$P(3 + h) = 3(3 + h) - 7 \qquad \bullet \text{ Replace } z \text{ by } 3 + h.$$
$$= 9 + 3h - 7 \qquad \bullet \text{ Simplify.}$$
$$= 3h + 2$$

The **domain** of a function is the set of the first coordinates of all the ordered pairs of the function. The **range** is the set of the second coordinates of all the ordered pairs of the function.

For the function defined by the ordered pairs

$$\{(2, 3), (4, 5), (6, 7), (8, 9)\}$$

the domain is {2, 4, 6, 8} and the range is {3, 5, 7, 9}.

When a function is given by an equation, the domain of the function is all real numbers for which the function evaluates to a real number. For instance:

- The domain of $f(x) = x^2$ is all real numbers, because each real number can be squared.
- The domain of $g(x) = \dfrac{1}{x - 2}$ is all real numbers except 2, because when $x = 2$, $g(2) = \dfrac{1}{2 - 2} = \dfrac{1}{0}$, which is not a real number.

The domain of the grading scale function is the set of whole numbers from 0 to 100. In set-builder notation, this is written $\{x \mid 0 \le x \le 100, x \in \text{whole numbers}\}$. The range is $\{A, B, C, D, F\}$.

Score	Grade
90–100	A
80–89	B
70–79	C
60–69	D
0–59	F

Example 1
Given $p(r) = 5r^3 - 6r - 2$, find $p(-3)$.

Solution
$$p(r) = 5r^3 - 6r - 2$$
$$p(-3) = 5(-3)^3 - 6(-3) - 2$$
$$= 5(-27) + 18 - 2$$
$$= -135 + 18 - 2 = -119$$

You Try It 1
Evaluate $G(x) = \dfrac{3x}{x+1}$ when $x = -2$.

Your solution

Example 2
Find the domain and range of the function $\{(2, 3), (4, 6), (6, 8), (10, 6)\}$.

Solution
Domain: $\{2, 4, 6, 10\}$; Range: $\{3, 6, 8\}$

You Try It 2
Find the domain and range of the function $\{(-1, 5), (3, 5), (4, 5), (6, 5)\}$.

Your solution

Example 3
Find the range of $f(x) = x^2 - 1$ if the domain is $\{-2, -1, 0, 1, 2\}$.

Solution
To find the range, evaluate the function at each element of the domain.

$$f(x) = x^2 - 1$$
$$f(-2) = (-2)^2 - 1 = 4 - 1 = 3$$
$$f(-1) = (-1)^2 - 1 = 1 - 1 = 0$$
$$f(0) = 0^2 - 1 = 0 - 1 = -1$$
$$f(1) = 1^2 - 1 = 1 - 1 = 0$$
$$f(2) = 2^2 - 1 = 4 - 1 = 3$$

The range is $\{-1, 0, 3\}$. Note that 0 and 3 are listed only once.

You Try It 3
Find the range of $h(z) = 3z + 1$ if the domain is $\left\{0, \dfrac{1}{3}, \dfrac{2}{3}, 1\right\}$.

Your solution

Example 4
What is the domain of $f(x) = 2x^2 - 7x + 1$?

Solution
Because $2x^2 - 7x + 1$ evaluates to a real number for any value of x, the domain of the function is all real numbers.

You Try It 4
What value is excluded from the domain of
$$f(x) = \dfrac{2}{x - 5}?$$

Your solution

Solutions on p. S7

3.2 Exercises

Objective A

State which of the following relations are functions.

1. {(0, 0), (2, 4), (3, 6), (4, 8), (5, 10)}

2. {(1, 3), (3, 5), (5, 7), (7, 9)}

3. {(−2, −1), (−4, −5), (0, −1), (3, 5)}

4. {(−3, −1), (−1, −1), (0, 1), (2, 6)}

5. {(−2, 3), (−1, 3), (0, −3), (1, 3), (2, 3)}

6. {(0, 0), (1, 0), (2, 0), (3, 0), (4, 0)}

7. {(1, 1), (4, 2), (9, 3), (1, −1), (4, −2)}

8. {(3, 1), (3, 2), (3, 3), (3, 4)}

Solve.

9. The table at the right shows the cost in 1997 to send an overnight package using United Parcel Service.
   a. Does this table define a function?
   b. Given $x = 2.75$ lb, find y.

Weight in pounds (x)	Cost (y)
$0 < x \le 1$	$18.00
$1 < x \le 2$	$20.25
$2 < x \le 3$	$22.25
$3 < x \le 4$	$24.25
$4 < x \le 5$	$26.25

10. The table at the right shows the cost in 1997 to send an "Express Mail" package using the U.S. Postal Service.
   a. Does this table define a function?
   b. Given $x = 0.5$ lb, find y.

Weight in pounds (x)	Cost (y)
$0 < x \le 0.5$	$9.95
$0.5 < x \le 2$	$14.00
$2 < x \le 3$	$16.15
$3 < x \le 4$	$18.30
$4 < x \le 5$	$20.45

Given $f(x) = 5x - 4$, evaluate:

11. $f(3)$

12. $f(-2)$

13. $f(0)$

14. $f(-1)$

Given $G(t) = 4 - 3t$, evaluate:

15. $G(0)$

16. $G(-3)$

17. $G(-2)$

18. $G(4)$

Given $q(r) = r^2 - 4$, evaluate:

19. $q(3)$

20. $q(4)$

21. $q(-2)$

22. $q(-5)$

Given $F(x) = x^2 + 3x - 4$, evaluate:

23. $F(4)$ **24.** $F(-4)$ **25.** $F(-3)$ **26.** $F(-6)$

Given $H(p) = \dfrac{3p}{p+2}$, evaluate:

27. $H(1)$ **28.** $H(-3)$ **29.** $H(t)$ **30.** $H(v)$

Given $s(t) = t^3 - 3t + 4$, evaluate:

31. $s(-1)$ **32.** $s(2)$ **33.** $s(a)$ **34.** $s(w)$

35. Given $P(x) = 4x + 7$, write $P(-2 + h) - P(-2)$ in simplest form.

36. Given $G(t) = 9 - 2t$, write $G(-3 + h) - G(-3)$ in simplest form.

37. Given $f(z) = 8 - 3z$, write $f(-3 + h) - f(-3)$ in simplest form.

38. Given $M(n) = 5 - 2n$, write $M(-6 + h) - M(-6)$ in simplest form.

39. Game Engineering has just completed the programming and testing for a new computer game. The cost to manufacture and package the game depends on the number of units Game Engineering plans to sell. The table at the right shows the cost per game for packaging various quantities. Evaluate this function when
a. $x = 7000$ **b.** $x = 20,000$

Number of Games Manufactured	Cost to Manufacture One Game
$0 < x \le 2500$	$6.00
$2500 < x \le 5000$	$5.50
$5000 < x \le 10{,}000$	$4.75
$10{,}000 < x \le 20{,}000$	$4.00
$20{,}000 < x \le 40{,}000$	$3.00

40. Airport administrators have a tendency to price airport parking at a rate that discourages people from using the parking lot for long periods of time. The rate structure for an airport is given in the table at the right. Evaluate this function when
    a. $t = 2.5$ h   **b.** $t = 7$ h

Hours Parked	Cost
$0 < t \le 1$	$1.00
$1 < t \le 2$	$3.00
$2 < t \le 4$	$6.50
$4 < t \le 7$	$10.00
$7 < t \le 12$	$14.00

41. A real estate appraiser charges a fee that depends on the estimated value, V, of the property. A table giving the fees charged for various estimated values of the real estate appears at the right. Evaluate this function when
    a. $V = \$5,000,000$ **b.** $V = \$767,000$

Value of Property	Appraisal Fee
$V < 100,000$	$350
$100,000 \le V < 500,000$	$525
$500,000 \le V < 1,000,000$	$950
$1,000,000 \le V < 5,000,000$	$2500
$5,000,000 \le V < 10,000,000$	$3000

42. The cost to mail a package by Federal Express depends on the weight, w, of the package. A table of the costs for selected weights is given at the right. Evaluate this function when
    a. $w = 2$ lb 3 oz   **b.** $w = 1.9$ lb

Weight (lb)	Cost
$0 < w < 1$	$16.75
$1 \le w < 2$	$18.50
$2 \le w < 3$	$20.25
$3 \le w < 4$	$22.00
$4 \le w < 5$	$23.75

Find the domain and range of the function.

43. $\{(1, 1), (2, 4), (3, 7), (4, 10), (5, 13)\}$

44. $\{(2, 6), (4, 18), (6, 38), (8, 66), (10, 102)\}$

45. $\{(0, 1), (2, 2), (4, 3), (6, 4)\}$

46. $\{(0, 1), (1, 2), (4, 3), (9, 4)\}$

47. $\{(1, 0), (3, 0), (5, 0), (7, 0), (9, 0)\}$

48. $\{(-2, -4), (2, 4), (-1, 1), (1, 1), (-3, 9), (3, 9)\}$

49. $\{(0, 0), (1, 1), (-1, 1), (2, 2), (-2, 2)\}$

50. $\{(0, -5), (5, 0), (10, 5), (15, 10)\}$

51. $\{(-2, -3), (-1, 6), (0, 7), (2, 3), (1, 9)\}$

52. $\{(-8, 0), (-4, 2), (-2, 4), (0, -4), (4, 4)\}$

What values are excluded from the domain of the function?

53. $f(x) = \dfrac{1}{x - 1}$

54. $g(x) = \dfrac{1}{x + 4}$

55. $h(x) = \dfrac{x + 3}{x + 8}$

56. $F(x) = \dfrac{2x - 5}{x - 4}$

57. $f(x) = 3x + 2$

58. $g(x) = 4 - 2x$

59. $G(x) = x^2 + 1$

60. $H(x) = \dfrac{1}{2}x^2$

61. $f(x) = \dfrac{x - 1}{x}$

62. $g(x) = \dfrac{2x + 5}{7}$

63. $H(x) = x^2 - x + 1$

64. $f(x) = 3x^2 + x + 4$

65. $f(x) = \dfrac{2x - 5}{3}$

66. $g(x) = \dfrac{3 - 5x}{5}$

67. $H(x) = \dfrac{x - 2}{x + 2}$

68. $h(x) = \dfrac{3 - x}{6 - x}$

69. $f(x) = \dfrac{x - 2}{2}$

70. $G(x) = \dfrac{2}{x - 2}$

Find the range of the function defined by each equation and the given domain.

71. $f(x) = 4x - 3$; domain = $\{0, 1, 2, 3\}$

72. $G(x) = 3 - 5x$; domain = $\{-2, -1, 0, 1, 2\}$

73. $g(x) = 5x - 8$; domain = $\{-3, -1, 0, 1, 3\}$

74. $h(x) = 3x - 7$; domain = $\{-4, -2, 0, 2, 4\}$

75. $h(x) = x^2$; domain = $\{-2, -1, 0, 1, 2\}$

76. $H(x) = 1 - x^2$; domain = $\{-2, -1, 0, 1, 2\}$

77. $f(x) = 2x^2 - 2x + 2$;
domain = $\{-4, -2, 0, 4\}$

78. $G(x) = -2x^2 + 5x - 2$;
domain = $\{-3, -1, 0, 1, 3\}$

79. $H(x) = \dfrac{5}{1-x}$; domain = $\{-2, 0, 2\}$

80. $g(x) = \dfrac{4}{4-x}$; domain = $\{-5, 0, 3\}$

81. $f(x) = \dfrac{2}{x-4}$; domain = $\{-2, 0, 2, 6\}$

82. $g(x) = \dfrac{x}{3-x}$; domain = $\{-2, -1, 0, 1, 2\}$

83. $H(x) = 2 - 3x - x^2$; domain = $\{-5, 0, 5\}$

84. $G(x) = 4 - 3x - x^3$; domain = $\{-3, 0, 3\}$

APPLYING THE CONCEPTS

85. Explain the words *relation* and *function*. Include in your explanation how the meanings of the two words differ.

86. Give a real-world example of a relation that is not a function. Is it possible to give an example of a function that is not a relation? If so, give one. If not, explain why it is not possible.

87. Find the set of ordered pairs (x, y) determined by the equation $y = x^3$, where $x \in \{-2, -1, 0, 1, 2\}$. Does the set of ordered pairs define a function? Why or why not?

88. Find the set of ordered pairs (x, y) determined by the equation $|y| = x$, where $x \in \{0, 1, 2, 3\}$. Does the set of ordered pairs define a function? Why or why not?

89. The distance, s (in feet), a car will skid on a certain road surface after the brakes are applied is a function of the car's velocity, v (in miles per hour). The function can be approximated by $s = f(v) = 0.017v^2$. How far will a car skid after its brakes are applied if it is traveling 60 mph?

90. The power a windmill can generate is a function of the velocity of the wind. The function can be approximated by $P = f(v) = 0.015v^3$, where P is the power in watts and v is the velocity of the wind in meters per second. How much power will be produced by a windmill when the velocity of the wind is 15 m/s?

Each of the following graphs defines a function. Evaluate the function by estimating the ordinate (which is the value of the function) for the given value of *t*.

91. The graph at the right shows the speed, *v*, in feet per second that a parachutist is falling during the first 20 s after jumping out of a plane. Estimate the speed at which the parachutist is falling when

a. *t* = 5 s   **b.** *t* = 15 s

92. The graph at the right shows what an industrial psychologist has determined to be the average percent score, *P*, for an employee taking a performance test *t* weeks after training begins. Estimate the score an employee would receive on this test when

a. *t* = 4 weeks   **b.** *t* = 10 weeks

93. The graph at the right shows the temperature, *T*, in degrees Fahrenheit of a can of cola *t* hours after it is placed in a refrigerator. Use the graph to estimate the temperature of the cola when

a. *t* = 5 h   **b.** *t* = 15 h

94. The graph at the right shows the decrease in the heart rate, *r*, of a runner (in beats per minute) *t* minutes after the completion of a race. Use the graph to estimate the heart rate of a runner when

a. *t* = 5 min   **b.** *t* = 20 min

3.3 Linear Functions

Objective A   *To graph a linear function* .... [11] [12] [CT]

Recall that the ordered pairs of a function can be written as $(x, f(x))$ or (x, y). The **graph of a function** is a graph of the ordered pairs (x, y) that belong to the function. Certain functions have characteristic graphs. A function that can be written in the form $f(x) = mx + b$ (or $y = mx + b$) is called a **linear function** because its graph is a straight line.

Examples of linear functions are shown at the right. Note that the exponent on each variable is 1.

$$f(x) = 2x + 5 \qquad (m = 2, b = 5)$$
$$P(t) = 3t - 2 \qquad (m = 3, b = -2)$$
$$y = -2x \qquad (m = -2, b = 0)$$
$$y = -\frac{2}{3}x + 1 \qquad \left(m = -\frac{2}{3}, b = 1\right)$$
$$g(z) = z - 2 \qquad (m = 1, b = -2)$$

The equation $y = x^2 + 4x + 3$ is not a linear function because it includes a term with a variable squared. The equation $f(x) = \dfrac{3}{x - 2}$ is not a linear function because a variable occurs in the denominator. Another example of an equation that is not a linear function is $y = \sqrt{x} + 4$; this equation contains a variable within a radical and so is not a linear function.

Consider $f(x) = 2x + 1$. Evaluating the linear function when $x = -2, -1, 0, 1,$ and 2 produces some of the ordered pairs of the function. It is convenient to record the results in a table similar to the one at the right. The graph of the ordered pairs is shown in the leftmost figure below.

x	$f(x) = 2x + 1$	y	(x, y)
-2	$2(-2) + 1$	-3	$(-2, -3)$
-1	$2(-1) + 1$	-1	$(-1, -1)$
0	$2(0) + 1$	1	$(0, 1)$
1	$2(1) + 1$	3	$(1, 3)$
2	$2(2) + 1$	5	$(2, 5)$

Evaluating the function when x is not an integer produces more ordered pairs to graph, such as $\left(-\frac{5}{2}, -4\right)$ and $\left(\frac{3}{2}, 4\right)$, as shown in the middle figure below. Evaluating the function for still other values of x would result in more and more ordered pairs being graphed. The result would be so many dots that the graph would look like the straight line shown in the rightmost figure, which is the graph of $f(x) = 2x + 1$.

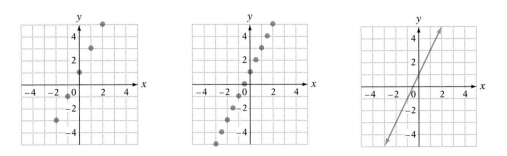

No matter what value of x is chosen, $2x + 1$ is a real number. This means the domain of $f(x) = 2x + 1$ is all real numbers. Therefore, we can use any real number when evaluating the function. Normally, however, values such as π or $\sqrt{5}$ are not used because it is difficult to graph the resulting ordered pairs.

Note from the graph of $f(x) = 2x + 1$ shown at the right that $(-1.5, -2)$ and $(3, 7)$ are the coordinates of points on the graph and that $f(-1.5) = -2$ and $f(3) = 7$. Note also that the point whose coordinates are $(2, 1)$ is not a point on the graph and that $f(2) \neq 1$. Every point on the graph is an ordered pair that belongs to the function, and every ordered pair that belongs to the function corresponds to a point on the graph.

Whether an equation is written as $f(x) = mx + b$ or as $y = mx + b$, the equation represents a linear function, and the graph of the equation is a straight line.

Because the graph of a linear function is a straight line, and a straight line is determined by two points, the graph of a linear function can be drawn by finding only two of the ordered pairs of the function. However, it is recommended that you find at least *three* ordered pairs to ensure accuracy.

⇒ Graph: $f(x) = -\dfrac{1}{2}x + 3$

x	$y = f(x)$
-4	5
0	3
2	2

● Find at least three ordered pairs. When the coefficient of x is a fraction, choose values of x that will simplify the evaluations. The ordered pairs can be displayed in a table.

● Graph the ordered pairs and draw a line through the points.

Example 1   Graph: $f(x) = -\dfrac{3}{2}x - 3$

Solution

x	$y = f(x)$
0	-3
-2	0
-4	3

You Try It 1   Graph: $f(x) = \dfrac{3}{5}x - 4$

Your solution

Solution on p. S7

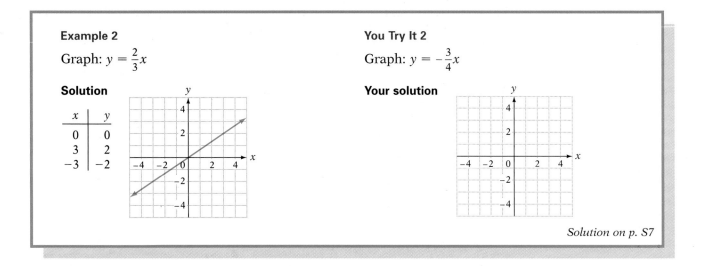

Example 2

Graph: $y = \dfrac{2}{3}x$

Solution

x	y
0	0
3	2
-3	-2

You Try It 2

Graph: $y = -\dfrac{3}{4}x$

Your solution

Solution on p. S7

Objective B   **To graph an equation of the form $Ax + By = C$** ....

An equation of the form $Ax + By = C$, where A, B, and C are constants, is also a *linear equation in two variables*. This equation can be written in the form $y = mx + b$.

➡ Write $4x - 3y = 6$ in the form $y = mx + b$.

$$4x - 3y = 6$$
$$-3y = -4x + 6$$ • Subtract $4x$ from each side of the equation.
$$y = \frac{4}{3}x - 2$$ • Divide each side of the equation by -3. This is the form
$$y = mx + b.\ m = \frac{4}{3},\ b = -2$$

To graph an equation of the form $Ax + By = C$, first solve the equation for y. Then follow the same procedure used for graphing an equation of the form $y = mx + b$.

➡ Graph: $3x + 2y = 6$

$$3x + 2y = 6$$
$$2y = -3x + 6$$ • Solve the equation for y.
$$y = -\frac{3}{2}x + 3$$

x	y
0	3
2	0
4	-3

• Find at least three solutions.

• Graph the ordered pairs in a rectangular coordinate system. Draw a straight line through the points.

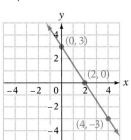

An equation in which one of the variables is missing has a graph that is either a horizontal or a vertical line.

The equation $y = -2$ can be written

$$0 \cdot x + y = -2$$

Because $0 \cdot x = 0$ for all values of x, y is always -2 for every value of x.

Some of the possible ordered pairs are given in the table below. The graph is shown at the right.

x	y
-2	-2
0	-2
3	-2

Graph of $y = b$

The graph of $y = b$ is a horizontal line passing through the point $(0, b)$.

The equation $y = -2$ represents a function. Some of the ordered pairs of this function are $(-2, -2)$, $(0, -2)$, and $(3, -2)$. In functional notation we would write $f(x) = -2$. This function is an example of a constant function. No matter what value of x is selected, $f(x) = -2$.

Definition of the Constant Function

A function given by $f(x) = b$, where b is a constant, is a **constant function**. The graph of the constant function is a horizontal line passing through $(0, b)$.

For each value in the domain of a constant function, the value of the function is the same (constant). For instance, if $f(x) = 4$, then $f(2) = 4$, $f(3) = 4$, $f(\sqrt{3}) = 4$, $f(\pi) = 4$, and so on. The value of $f(x)$ is 4 for all values of x.

➡ Graph: $y + 4 = 0$

Solve for y.
$y + 4 = 0$
$y = -4$

The graph of $y = -4$ is a horizontal line passing through $(0, -4)$.

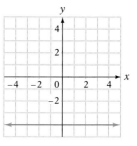

➡ Evaluate $P(t) = -7$ when $t = 6$.

$P(t) = -7$

$P(6) = -7$

• The value of the constant function is the same for all values of the variable.

For the equation $y = -2$, the coefficient of x was zero. For the equation $x = 2$, the coefficient of y is zero. For instance, the equation $x = 2$ can be written

$$x + 0 \cdot y = 2$$

No matter what value of y is chosen, $0 \cdot y = 0$ and therefore x is always 2.

Some of the possible ordered pairs are given in the table below. The graph is shown at the right.

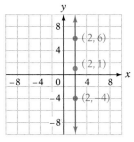

x	y
2	6
2	1
2	-4

Graph of $x = a$

The graph of $x = a$ is a vertical line passing through the point $(a, 0)$.

TAKE NOTE

The equation $y = b$ represents a function. The equation $x = a$ does *not* represent a function. Remember, not all equations represent functions.

Recall that a function is a set of ordered pairs in which no two ordered pairs have the same first coordinate and different second coordinates. Because $(2, 6)$, $(2, 1)$, and $(2, -4)$ are ordered pairs belonging to the equation $x = 2$, this equation does not represent a function, and the graph is not the graph of a function.

Example 3

Graph: $5x + 3y = 9$

Solution

Solve the equation for y.

$5x + 3y = 9$

$\qquad 3y = -5x + 9$

$\qquad y = -\dfrac{5}{3}x + 3$

x	y
0	3
3	-2

You Try It 3

Graph: $-3x + 2y = 4$

Your solution

Solution on p. S7

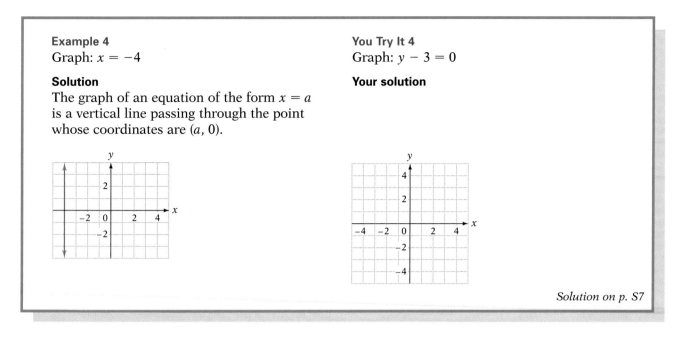

Example 4

Graph: $x = -4$

Solution

The graph of an equation of the form $x = a$ is a vertical line passing through the point whose coordinates are $(a, 0)$.

You Try It 4

Graph: $y - 3 = 0$

Your solution

Solution on p. S7

Objective C   To find the x- and the y-intercept of a straight line ....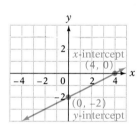

The graph of the equation $x - 2y = 4$ is shown at the right. The graph crosses the x-axis at the point $(4, 0)$. This point is called the **x-intercept.** The graph also crosses the y-axis at the point $(0, -2)$. This point is called the **y-intercept.**

➡ Find the x- and y-intercepts of the graph of the equation $3x + 4y = -12$.

TAKE NOTE

The x-intercept occurs when $y = 0$.

The y-intercept occurs when $x = 0$.

To find the x-intercept, let $y = 0$. (Any point on the x-axis has y-coordinate 0.)

$$3x + 4y = -12$$
$$3x + 4(0) = -12$$
$$3x = -12$$
$$x = -4$$

The x-intercept is $(-4, 0)$.

To find the y-intercept, let $x = 0$. (Any point on the y-axis has x-coordinate 0.)

$$3x + 4y = -12$$
$$3(0) + 4y = -12$$
$$4y = -12$$
$$y = -3$$

The y-intercept is $(0, -3)$.

TAKE NOTE

Note that the y-coordinate of the y-intercept $(0, 7)$ has the same value as the constant term of $y = \frac{2}{3}x + 7$.

As shown below, this is always true:

$$y = mx + b$$
$$y = m(0) + b$$
$$y = b$$

Thus, the y-intercept is $(0, b)$.

➡ Find the y-intercept of $y = \frac{2}{3}x + 7$.

$$y = \frac{2}{3}x + 7$$

$$y = \frac{2}{3}(0) + 7 \qquad \bullet \text{ To find the } y\text{-intercept, let } x = 0.$$

$$y = 7$$

The y-intercept is $(0, 7)$.

For any equation of the form $y = mx + b$, the y-intercept is $(0, b)$.

A linear equation can be graphed by finding the *x*- and *y*-intercepts and then drawing a line through the two points.

⇒ Graph $3x - 2y = 6$ by using the *x*- and *y*-intercepts.

$$3x - 2y = 6$$
$$3x - 2(0) = 6$$
$$3x = 6$$
$$x = 2$$

* To find the *x*-intercept, let $y = 0$. Then solve for *x*.

$$3x - 2y = 6$$
$$3(0) - 2y = 6$$
$$-2y = 6$$
$$y = -3$$

* To find the *y*-intercept, let $x = 0$. Then solve for *y*.

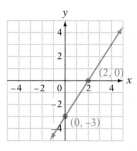

The *x*-intercept is (2, 0). The *y*-intercept is (0, −3).

Example 5
Graph $4x - y = 4$ by using the *x*- and *y*-intercepts.

Solution

x-intercept:

$$4x - y = 4$$
$$4x - 0 = 4$$
$$4x = 4$$
$$x = 1$$
$$(1, 0)$$

y-intercept:

$$4x - y = 4$$
$$4(0) - y = 4$$
$$-y = 4$$
$$y = -4$$
$$(0, -4)$$

You Try It 5
Graph $3x - y = 2$ by using the *x*- and *y*-intercepts.

Your solution

Example 6
Graph $y = \frac{2}{3}x - 2$ by using the *x*- and *y*-intercepts.

Solution

x-intercept:

$$y = \frac{2}{3}x - 2$$
$$0 = \frac{2}{3}x - 2$$
$$-\frac{2}{3}x = -2$$
$$x = 3$$
$$(3, 0)$$

y-intercept:

$$(0, b)$$
$$b = -2$$
$$(0, -2)$$

You Try It 6
Graph $y = \frac{1}{4}x + 1$ by using the *x*- and *y*-intercepts.

Your solution

Solutions on p. S7

Objective D **To solve application problems** .... (11) [CT]

There are a variety of applications of linear functions.

→ The heart rate, *R*, after *t* minutes for a person taking a brisk walk can be approximated by the equation $R = 2t + 72$.
  a. Graph this equation for $0 \le t \le 12$. (*Note:* In many applications, the domain of the variable is given such that the equation makes sense. For instance, it would not be sensible to have values of *t* that are less than 0. This would indicate negative time! The number 12 is somewhat arbitrary, but after 12 min most people's heart rates would level off and a linear function would no longer apply.)
  b. The point whose coordinates are (5, 82) is on the graph. Write a sentence that describes the meaning of this ordered pair.

a.

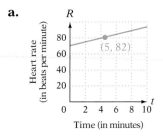

b. The point whose coordinates are (5, 82) means that after 5 min the person's heart rate is 82 beats per minute.

Example 7

A telephone repair technician charges $45 plus $1 per minute to repair defective wiring in a home or apartment. The equation that describes the total cost, *C*, to have defective wiring repaired is given by $C = t + 45$, where *t* is the number of minutes the technician works. Graph this equation for $0 \le t \le 60$. The point whose coordinates are (15, 60) is on this graph. Write a sentence that describes the meaning of this ordered pair.

Solution

The ordered pair (15, 60) means that it costs $60 for the technician to work 15 min.

You Try It 7

The height *h* (in inches) of a person and the length *L* (in inches) of that person's stride while walking are related. The equation $h = \frac{3}{4}L + 50$ approximates that relationship. Graph this equation for $15 \le L \le 40$. The point whose coordinates are (32, 74) is on this graph. Write a sentence that describes the meaning of this ordered pair.

Your solution

Solution on p.S8

3.3 Exercises

Objective A

Graph.

1. $y = 3x - 4$

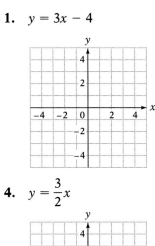

2. $y = -2x + 3$

3. $y = -\dfrac{2}{3}x$

4. $y = \dfrac{3}{2}x$

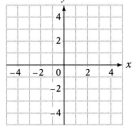

5. $y = \dfrac{2}{3}x - 4$

6. $y = \dfrac{3}{4}x + 2$

7. $y = -\dfrac{1}{3}x + 2$

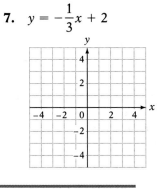

8. $y = -\dfrac{3}{2}x - 3$

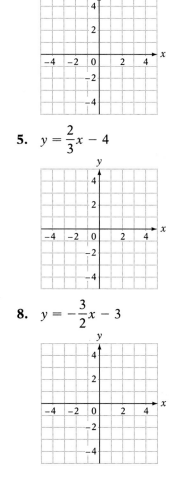

9. $y = \dfrac{3}{5}x - 1$

Objective B

Graph.

10. $2x - y = 3$

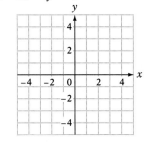

11. $2x + y = -3$

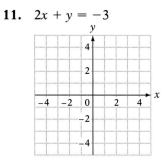

12. $2x + 5y = 10$

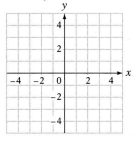

13. $x - 4y = 8$

14. $y = -2$

15. $y = \dfrac{1}{3}x$

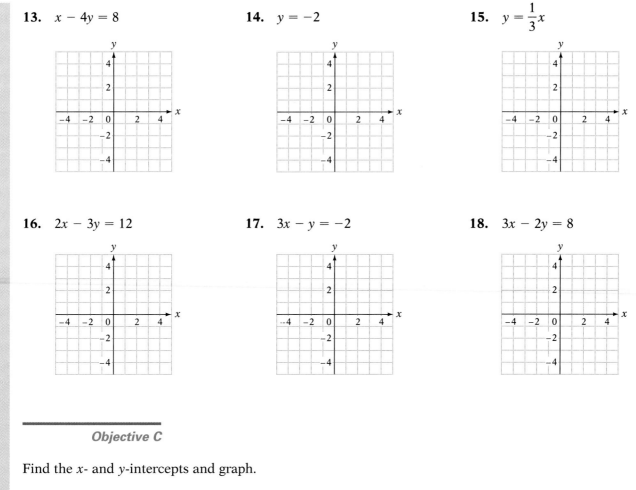

16. $2x - 3y = 12$

17. $3x - y = -2$

18. $3x - 2y = 8$

Objective C

Find the x- and y-intercepts and graph.

19. $x - 2y = -4$

20. $3x + y = 3$

21. $2x - 3y = 9$

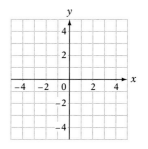

22. $4x - 2y = 5$

23. $2x - y = 4$

24. $2x + y = 3$

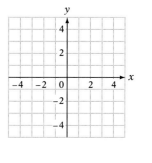

25. $3x + 2y = 5$

26. $4x - 3y = 8$

27. $3x + 2y = 4$

28. $2x - 3y = 4$

29. $3x - 5y = 9$

30. $4x - 3y = 6$

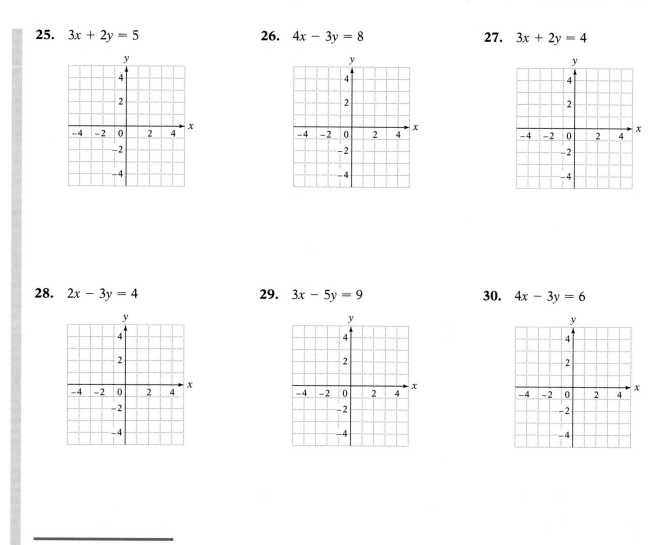

Objective D   *Application Problems*

31. Marlys receives $11 per hour as a mathematics tutor. The equation that describes Marlys's wages is $W = 11t$, where t is the number of hours she spends tutoring. Graph this equation for $0 \le t \le 20$. The ordered pair (15, 165) is on the graph. Write a sentence that describes the meaning of this ordered pair.

32. A bee beats its wings approximately 100 times per second. The equation that describes the total number of times a bee beats its wings is given by $B = 100t$. Graph this equation for $0 \le t \le 60$. The ordered pair (35, 3500) is on this graph. Write a sentence that describes the meaning of this ordered pair.

33. The Rattler roller coaster at Fiesta, in San Antonio, Texas, has a maximum speed of approximately 110 ft/s. The equation that describes the total number of feet traveled by the roller coaster in t seconds at this speed is given by $D = 110t$. Graph this equation for $0 \leq t \leq 10$. The point (5, 550) is on this graph. Write a sentence that describes the meaning of this ordered pair.

34. The monthly cost for receiving messages from a telephone answering service is $8.00 plus $.20 a message. The equation that describes the cost is $C = 0.20n + 8.00$, where n is the number of messages received. Graph this equation for $0 \leq n \leq 40$. The point (32, 14.40) is on the graph. Write a sentence that describes the meaning of this ordered pair.

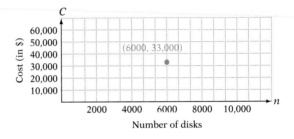

35. The cost of manufacturing compact disks is $3000 for startup and $5 per disk. The equation that describes the cost of manufacturing n compact disks is $C = 5n + 3000$. Graph this equation for $0 \leq n \leq 10,000$. The point (6000, 33,000) is on the graph. Write a sentence that describes the meaning of this ordered pair.

36. The cost of manufacturing skis is $5000 for startup and $80 per pair of skis manufactured. The equation that describes the cost of manufacturing n pairs of skis is $C = 80n + 5000$. Graph this equation for $0 \leq n \leq 2000$. The point (50, 9000) is on the graph. Write a sentence that describes the meaning of this ordered pair.

APPLYING THE CONCEPTS

37. Explain what the graph of an equation represents.

38. Explain how to graph the equation of a straight line by plotting points.

39. Explain how to graph the equation of a straight line by using its x- and y-intercepts.

40. Explain why you cannot graph the equation $4x + 3y = 0$ by using just its intercepts.

Use a graphing calculator to draw the graph of each of the following equations. (The Projects in Mathematics at the end of this chapter describes how to use a graphing calculator to draw the graph of a linear function.)

41. $f(x) = 1.2x + 2.3$

42. $f(x) = 2.4x + 0.5$

43. $y = -0.5x - 1.25$

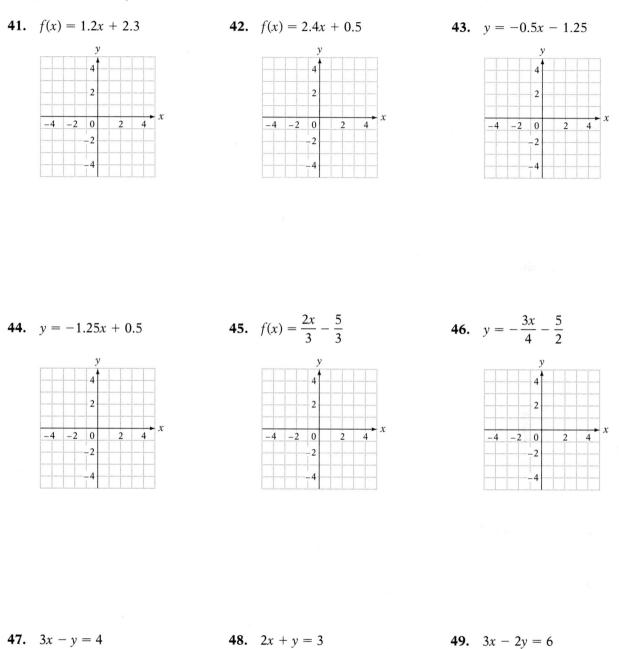

44. $y = -1.25x + 0.5$

45. $f(x) = \dfrac{2x}{3} - \dfrac{5}{3}$

46. $y = -\dfrac{3x}{4} - \dfrac{5}{2}$

47. $3x - y = 4$

48. $2x + y = 3$

49. $3x - 2y = 6$

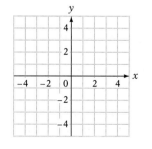

50. $x + 3y = 6$

51. $4x + 3y = 12$

52. $5x - 2y = 10$

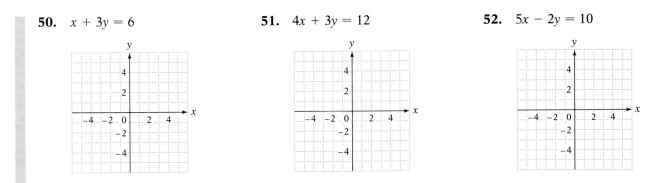

An equation of the form $\dfrac{x}{a} + \dfrac{y}{b} = 1$, where $a \neq 0$ and $b \neq 0$, is called the intercept form of a straight line because $(a, 0)$ and $(0, b)$ are the x- and y-intercepts of the graph of the equation. Graph each of the following.

53. $\dfrac{x}{2} + \dfrac{y}{3} = 1$

54. $\dfrac{x}{3} + \dfrac{y}{5} = 1$

55. $\dfrac{x}{3} - \dfrac{y}{2} = 1$

56. $\dfrac{x}{4} - \dfrac{y}{2} = 1$

57. $-\dfrac{x}{2} + \dfrac{y}{2} = 1$

58. $-\dfrac{x}{4} - \dfrac{y}{2} = 1$

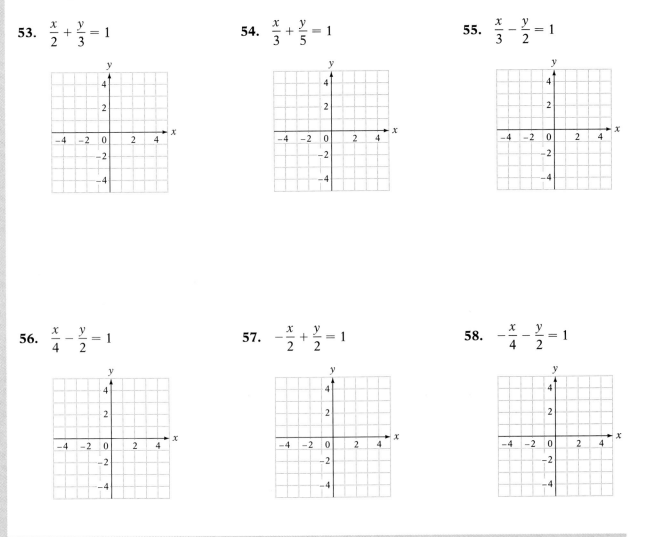

3.4 Slope of a Straight Line

Objective A   *To find the slope of a line given two points* .... (13) [CT]

The graphs of $y = 3x + 2$ and $y = \frac{2}{3}x + 2$ are shown at the left. Each graph crosses the y-axis at the point $(0, 2)$, but the graphs have different slants. The **slope** of a line is a measure of the slant of the line. The symbol for slope is m.

The slope of a line containing two points is the ratio of the change in the y values between the two points to the change in the x values. The line containing the points whose coordinates are $(-1, -3)$ and $(5, 2)$ is shown below.

The change in the y values is the difference between the y-coordinates of the two points.

$$\text{Change in } y = 2 - (-3) = 5$$

The change in the x values is the difference between the x-coordinates of the two points.

$$\text{Change in } x = 5 - (-1) = 6$$

The slope of the line between the two points is the ratio of the change in y to the change in x.

$$\text{Slope} = m = \frac{\text{change in } y}{\text{change in } x} = \frac{5}{6} \qquad m = \frac{2 - (-3)}{5 - (-1)} = \frac{5}{6}$$

In general, if $P_1(x_1, y_1)$ and $P_2(x_2, y_2)$ are two points on a line, then

$$\text{Change in } y = y_2 - y_1 \qquad \text{Change in } x = x_2 - x_1$$

Using these ideas, we can state a formula for slope.

Slope Formula

The slope of the line containing the two points $P_1(x_1, y_1)$ and $P_2(x_2, y_2)$ is given by

$$m = \frac{y_2 - y_1}{x_2 - x_1}, \; x_1 \neq x_2$$

Frequently, the Greek letter Δ is used to designate the change in a variable. Using this notation, we can write the equations for the change in y and change in x as follows:

$$\text{Change in } y = \Delta y = y_2 - y_1 \qquad \text{Change in } x = \Delta x = x_2 - x_1$$

With this notation, the slope formula is written $m = \dfrac{\Delta y}{\Delta x}$.

⇒ Find the slope of the line containing the points whose coordinates are $(-2, 0)$ and $(4, 5)$.

Let $P_1 = (-2, 0)$ and $P_2 = (4, 5)$. (It does not matter which point is named P_1 or P_2; the slope will be the same.)

$$m = \frac{y_2 - y_1}{x_2 - x_1} = \frac{5 - 0}{4 - (-2)} = \frac{5}{6}$$

A line that slants upward to the right always has a **positive slope**.

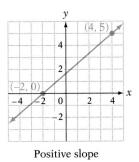

Positive slope

⇒ Find the slope of the line containing the points whose coordinates are $(-3, 4)$ and $(4, 2)$.

Let $P_1 = (-3, 4)$ and $P_2 = (4, 2)$.

$$m = \frac{y_2 - y_1}{x_2 - x_1} = \frac{2 - 4}{4 - (-3)} = \frac{-2}{7} = -\frac{2}{7}$$

A line that slants downward to the right always has a **negative slope**.

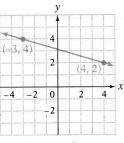

Negative slope

⇒ Find the slope of the line containing the points whose coordinates are $(-2, 2)$ and $(4, 2)$.

Let $P_1 = (-2, 2)$ and $P_2 = (4, 2)$.

$$m = \frac{y_2 - y_1}{x_2 - x_1} = \frac{2 - 2}{4 - (-2)} = \frac{0}{6} = 0$$

A horizontal line has **zero slope**.

Zero slope

⇒ Find the slope of the line containing the points whose coordinates are $(1, -2)$ and $(1, 3)$.

Let $P_1 = (1, -2)$ and $P_2 = (1, 3)$.

$$m = \frac{y_2 - y_1}{x_2 - x_1} = \frac{3 - (-2)}{1 - 1} = \frac{5}{0} \quad \text{Not a real number}$$

The slope of a vertical line is **undefined**.

Undefined

There are many applications of slope. Here are two possibilities.

The first record for the one-mile run was recorded in 1865 in England. Richard Webster ran the mile in 4 min 36.5 s. His average speed was approximately 19 feet per second. The graph at the right shows the distance he ran during that run. From the graph, note that after 60 s (1 min) he had traveled 1140 ft and that after 180 s (3 min) he had traveled 3420 ft. The slope of the line between these two points is

$$m = \frac{3420 - 1140}{180 - 60} = \frac{2280}{120} = 19$$

Note that the slope of the line is the same as Webster's average speed, 19 feet per second. Average speed is related to slope.

Here is another example, this one related to economics.

During the 1980s the value of a 1957 Chevrolet increased dramatically to around $26,000 by 1990. Since then, however, the value has been decreasing at a rate of approximately $3500 per year. The graph at the right shows the value of the car for the years 1990 through 1994. From the graph, note that the value of the car in 1991 was $22,500 and that its value in 1993 was $15,500. The slope of the line between these two points is

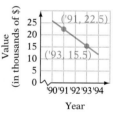

$$m = \frac{15,500 - 22,500}{1993 - 1991} = \frac{-7000}{2} = -3500$$

Note that if we interpret negative slope as decreasing, then the slope of the line is the same as the rate at which the value of the car is decreasing, $3500 per year.

In general, any quantity that is expressed by using the word *per* is represented mathematically as slope. In the first example, the slope was 19 feet per second. In the second example, the slope was −$3500 per year.

Example 1

Find the slope of the line containing the points $(2, -5)$ and $(-4, 2)$.

Solution

Let $P_1 = (2, -5)$ and $P_2 = (-4, 2)$.

$$m = \frac{y_2 - y_1}{x_2 - x_1} = \frac{2 - (-5)}{-4 - 2} = \frac{7}{-6}$$

The slope is $-\frac{7}{6}$.

You Try It 1

Find the slope of the line containing the points $(4, -3)$ and $(2, 7)$.

Your solution

Example 2

Find the slope of the line containing the points $(-3, 4)$ and $(5, 4)$.

Solution

Let $P_1 = (-3, 4)$ and $P_2 = (5, 4)$.

$$m = \frac{y_2 - y_1}{x_2 - x_1}$$

$$= \frac{4 - 4}{5 - (-3)}$$

$$= \frac{0}{8} = 0$$

The slope of the line is zero.

You Try It 2

Find the slope of the line containing the points $(6, -1)$ and $(6, 7)$.

Your solution

Example 3

The graph below shows the relationship between the cost of an item and the sales tax. Find the slope of the line between the two points shown on the graph. Write a sentence that states the meaning of the slope.

Solution

$$m = \frac{5.25 - 3.50}{75 - 50}$$

$$= \frac{1.75}{25}$$

$$= 0.07$$

A slope of 0.07 means that the sales tax is $.07 per dollar.

You Try It 3

The graph below shows the decrease in the value of a printing press for a period of 6 years. Find the slope of the line between the two points shown on the graph. Write a sentence that states the meaning of the slope.

Your solution

Solutions on p. S8

Objective B   ***To graph a line given a point and the slope*** ....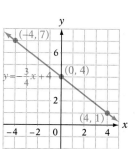

The graph of the equation $y = -\frac{3}{4}x + 4$ is shown at the right. The points $(-4, 7)$ and $(4, 1)$ are on the graph. The slope of the line is

$$m = \frac{7 - 1}{-4 - 4} = \frac{6}{-8} = -\frac{3}{4}$$

Note that the slope of the line has the same value as the coefficient of x. The y-intercept is $(0, 4)$.

> **Slope-Intercept Formula**
>
> The equation $y = mx + b$ is called the **slope-intercept** form of a straight line. The slope of the line is m, the coefficient of x. The y-intercept is $(0, b)$.

When the equation of a straight line is in the form $y = mx + b$, the graph can be drawn by using the slope and y-intercept. First locate the y-intercept. Use the slope to find a second point on the line. Then draw a line through the two points.

➡ Graph $y = \frac{5}{3}x - 4$ by using the slope and y-intercept.

The slope is the coefficient of x:

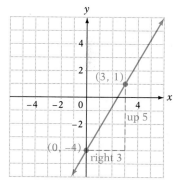

$$m = \frac{5}{3} = \frac{\text{change in } y}{\text{change in } x}$$

The y-intercept is $(0, -4)$.

Beginning at the y-intercept $(0, -4)$, move right 3 units (change in x) and then up 5 units (change in y).

The point whose coordinates are $(3, 1)$ is a second point on the graph. Draw a line through the points $(0, -4)$ and $(3, 1)$.

➡ Graph $x + 2y = 4$ by using the slope and y-intercept.

Solve the equation for y.

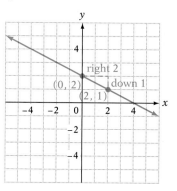

$$x + 2y = 4$$
$$2y = -x + 4$$
$$y = -\frac{1}{2}x + 2 \qquad • \ m = -\frac{1}{2},$$

$$\text{\textit{y}-intercept} = (0, 2).$$

Beginning at the y-intercept $(0, 2)$, move right 2 units (change in x) and then down 1 unit (change in y).

The point whose coordinates are $(2, 1)$ is a second point on the graph. Draw a line through the points $(0, 2)$ and $(2, 1)$.

The graph of a line can be drawn when any point on the line and the slope of the line are given.

⇒ Graph the line that passes through the point $(-4, -4)$ and has slope 2.

When the slope is an integer, write it as a fraction with denominator 1.

$$m = 2 = \frac{2}{1} = \frac{\text{change in } y}{\text{change in } x}$$

Locate $(-4, -4)$ in the coordinate plane. Beginning at that point, move right 1 unit (change in x) and then up 2 units (change in y).

The point whose coordinates are $(-3, -2)$ is a second point on the graph. Draw a line through the points $(-4, -4)$ and $(-3, -2)$.

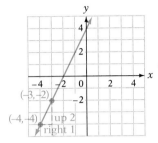

TAKE NOTE

This example differs from the other two in that a point other than the y-intercept is used. In this case, start at the given point.

Example 4   Graph $y = -\frac{3}{2}x + 4$ by using the slope and y-intercept.

Solution $m = -\frac{3}{2} = \frac{-3}{2}$

y-intercept $= (0, 4)$

You Try It 4   Graph $2x + 3y = 6$ by using the slope and y-intercept.

Your solution

Example 5   Graph the line that passes through the point $(-2, 3)$ and has slope $-\frac{4}{3}$.

Solution $(x_1, y_1) = (-2, 3)$

$m = -\frac{4}{3} = \frac{-4}{3}$

You Try It 5   Graph the line that passes through the point $(-3, -2)$ and has slope 3.

Your solution

Solutions on p. S8

3.4 Exercises

· ·

Objective A

Find the slope of the line containing the points.

1. $P_1(1, 3), P_2(3, 1)$

2. $P_1(2, 3), P_2(5, 1)$

3. $P_1(-1, 4), P_2(2, 5)$

4. $P_1(3, -2), P_2(1, 4)$

5. $P_1(-1, 3), P_2(-4, 5)$

6. $P_1(-1, -2), P_2(-3, 2)$

7. $P_1(0, 3), P_2(4, 0)$

8. $P_1(-2, 0), P_2(0, 3)$

9. $P_1(2, 4), P_2(2, -2)$

10. $P_1(4, 1), P_2(4, -3)$

11. $P_1(2, 5), P_2(-3, -2)$

12. $P_1(4, 1), P_2(-1, -2)$

13. $P_1(2, 3), P_2(-1, 3)$

14. $P_1(3, 4), P_2(0, 4)$

15. $P_1(0, 4), P_2(-2, 5)$

16. $P_1(-2, 3), P_2(-2, 5)$

17. $P_1(-3, -1), P_2(-3, 4)$

18. $P_1(-2, -5), P_2(-4, -1)$

19. The graph below shows the relationship between the distance traveled by a motorist and the time of travel. Find the slope of the line between the two points shown on the graph. Write a sentence that states the meaning of the slope.

20. The graph below shows the number of people subscribing to a sports magazine whose popularity is increasing. Find the slope of the line between the two points shown on the graph. What is the meaning of the slope?

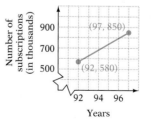

21. The average number of gallons of bottled water sold per person in the United States from 1978 to 1996 can be approximated by the linear function graphed below. Find the slope of the line between the two points shown on the graph. What is the meaning of the slope? Source: *Time Magazine 9/8/97*

22. The graph below shows the number of channels a cable company has offered its subscribers during different years. Find the slope of the line between the two points shown on the graph. What is the meaning of the slope?

23. The graph below shows the relationship between the distance and the time for the 5000-meter run for the world record by Said Aouita in 1987. Find the slope of the line between the two points shown on the graph. Write a sentence that states the meaning of the slope.

24. The graph below shows the relationship between the distance and the time for the 10,000-meter run for the world record by Arturo Barrios in 1989. Find the slope of the line between the two points shown on the graph. Write a sentence that states the meaning of the slope.

Objective B

Graph by using the slope and the *y*-intercept.

25. $y = \dfrac{1}{2}x + 2$ **26.** $y = \dfrac{2}{3}x - 3$ **27.** $y = -\dfrac{3}{2}x$

28. $y = \dfrac{3}{4}x$ **29.** $y = -\dfrac{1}{2}x + 2$ **30.** $y = \dfrac{2}{3}x - 1$

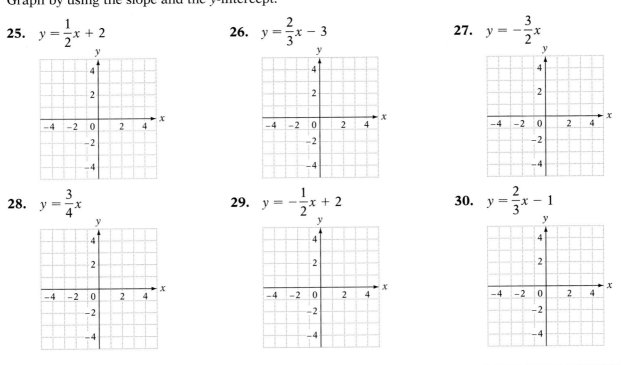

31. $x - 3y = 3$ **32.** $3x + 2y = 8$ **33.** $4x + y = 2$

34. Graph the line that passes through the point $(-1, -3)$ and has slope $\frac{4}{3}$.

35. Graph the line that passes through the point $(-2, -3)$ and has slope $\frac{5}{4}$.

    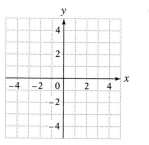

36. Graph the line that passes through the point $(-3, 0)$ and has slope -3.

37. Graph the line that passes through the point $(2, 0)$ and has slope -1.

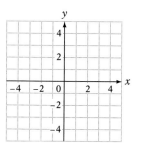

APPLYING THE CONCEPTS

38. The sale price of an item is a function, s, of the original price, p, where $s(p) = 0.80p$. If an item's original price is $200, what is the sale price of the item?

39. The markup on an item is a function, m, of its cost, c, where $m(c) = 0.25c$. If the cost of an item is $150, what is the markup on the item?

40. Let $f(x)$ be the digit in the xth decimal place of the repeating digit $0.\overline{387}$. For example, $f(3) = 7$ because 7 is the digit in the third decimal place. Find $f(14)$.

41. Let $f(x)$ be the digit in the xth decimal place of the repeating digit $0.\overline{018}$. For example, $f(1) = 0$ because 0 is the digit in the first decimal place. Find $f(21)$.

Complete the following sentences.

42. If a line has a slope of 2, then the value of y <u>increases/decreases</u> by _____ as the value of x increases by 1.

43. If a line has a slope of -3, then the value of y <u>increases/decreases</u> by _____ as the value of x increases by 1.

44. If a line has a slope of -2, then the value of y <u>increases/decreases</u> by _____ as the value of x decreases by 1.

45. If a line has a slope of 3, then the value of y <u>increases/decreases</u> by _____ as the value of x decreases by 1.

46. If a line has a slope of $\frac{1}{2}$, then the value of y <u>increases/decreases</u> by _____ as the value of x increases by 1.

47. If a line has a slope of $-\frac{2}{3}$, then the value of y <u>increases/decreases</u> by _____ as the value of x increases by 1.

48. Explain how to graph the equation of a straight line by using its slope and a point on the line.

49. Explain why $y = mx + b$ is called the slope-intercept form of the equation of a straight line.

50. Explain how you can use the slope of a line to determine whether three given points lie on the same line. Then use your procedure to determine whether each of the following sets of points lie on the same line.
a. $(2, 5), (-1, -1), (3, 7)$ **b.** $(-1, 5), (0, 3), (-3, 4)$

Determine the value of k such that the points whose coordinates are given below lie on the same line.

51. $(3, 2), (4, 6), (5, k)$

52. $(-2, 3), (1, 0), (k, 2)$

53. $(k, 1), (0, -1), (2, -2)$

54. $(4, -1), (3, -4), (k, k)$

3.5 Finding Equations of Lines

Objective A   *To find the equation of a line given a point and the slope* .... (14) [CT]

When the slope of a line and a point on the line are known, the equation of the line can be determined. If the particular point is the y-intercept, use the slope-intercept form, $y = mx + b$, to find the equation.

⇒ Find the equation of the line that contains the point $(0, 3)$ and has slope $\frac{1}{2}$.

The known point is the y-intercept, $(0, 3)$.

$y = mx + b$ • Use the slope-intercept form.

$y = \frac{1}{2}x + 3$ • Replace m with $\frac{1}{2}$, the given slope.

Replace b with 3, the y-coordinate of the y-intercept.

The equation of the line is $y = \frac{1}{2}x + 3$.

One method of finding the equation of a line when the slope and *any* point on the line are known involves using the *point-slope* formula. This formula is derived from the formula for the slope of a line as follows.

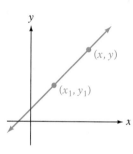

Let (x_1, y_1) be the given point on the line, and let (x, y) be any other point on the line. See the graph at the left.

$\dfrac{y - y_1}{x - x_1} = m$ • Use the formula for the slope of a line.

$\dfrac{y - y_1}{x - x_1}(x - x_1) = m(x - x_1)$ • Multiply each side by $(x - x_1)$.

$y - y_1 = m(x - x_1)$ • Simplify.

Point-Slope Formula

Let m be the slope of a line, and let (x_1, y_1) be the coordinates of a point on the line. The equation of the line can be found from the **point-slope formula:**

$$y - y_1 = m(x - x_1)$$

⇒ Find the equation of the line that contains the point whose coordinates are $(4, -1)$ and has slope $-\frac{3}{4}$.

$y - y_1 = m(x - x_1)$ • Use the point-slope formula.

$y - (-1) = \left(-\dfrac{3}{4}\right)(x - 4)$ • $m = -\dfrac{3}{4}$, $(x_1, y_1) = (4, -1)$

$y + 1 = -\dfrac{3}{4}x + 3$ • Simplify.

$y = -\dfrac{3}{4}x + 2$ • Write the equation in the form $y = mx + b$.

The equation of the line is $y = -\dfrac{3}{4}x + 2$.

⇒ Find the equation of the line that passes through the point whose coordinates are (4, 3) and whose slope is undefined.

Because the slope is undefined, the point-slope formula cannot be used to find the equation. Instead, recall that when the slope is undefined, the line is vertical and that the equation of a vertical line is $x = a$, where a is the x-coordinate of the x-intercept. Because the line is vertical and passes through (4, 3), the x-intercept is (4, 0). The equation of the line is $x = 4$.

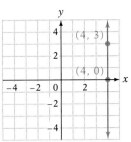

Example 1

Find the equation of the line that contains the point (3, 0) and has slope −4.

Solution

$m = -4 \qquad (x_1, y_1) = (3, 0)$

$y - y_1 = m(x - x_1)$
$y - 0 = -4(x - 3)$
$\qquad y = -4x + 12$

The equation of the line is $y = -4x + 12$.

You Try It 1

Find the equation of the line that contains the point (−3, −2) and has slope $-\dfrac{1}{3}$.

Your solution

Example 2

Find the equation of the line that contains the point (−2, 4) and has slope 2.

Solution

$m = 2 \qquad (x_1, y_1) = (-2, 4)$

$y - y_1 = m(x - x_1)$
$y - 4 = 2[x - (-2)]$
$y - 4 = 2(x + 2)$
$y - 4 = 2x + 4$
$\qquad y = 2x + 8$

The equation of the line is $y = 2x + 8$.

You Try It 2

Find the equation of the line that contains the point (4, −3) and has slope −3.

Your solution

Solutions on p. S8

Objective B   *To find the equation of a line given two points* ....

The point-slope formula and the formula for slope are used to find the equation of a line when two points are known.

➡ Find the equation of the line containing the points (3, 2) and (−5, 6).

To use the point-slope formula, we must know the slope. Use the formula for slope to determine the slope of the line between the two given points. Let $(x_1, y_1) = (3, 2)$ and $(x_2, y_2) = (−5, 6)$.

$$m = \frac{y_2 - y_1}{x_2 - x_1} = \frac{6 - 2}{-5 - 3} = \frac{4}{-8} = -\frac{1}{2}$$

Now use the point-slope formula with $m = -\frac{1}{2}$ and $(x_1, y_1) = (3, 2)$.

$$y - y_1 = m(x - x_1)$$ • Use the point-slope formula.

$$y - 2 = \left(-\frac{1}{2}\right)(x - 3)$$ • $m = -\frac{1}{2}, (x_1, y_1) = (3, 2)$

$$y - 2 = -\frac{1}{2}x + \frac{3}{2}$$ • Simplify.

$$y = -\frac{1}{2}x + \frac{7}{2}$$ The equation of the line is $y = -\frac{1}{2}x + \frac{7}{2}$.

Example 3

Find the equation of the line containing the points (2, 3) and (4, 1).

Solution

Let $(x_1, y_1) = (2, 3)$ and $(x_2, y_2) = (4, 1)$.

$$m = \frac{y_2 - y_1}{x_2 - x_1} = \frac{1 - 3}{4 - 2} = \frac{-2}{2} = -1$$

$$y - y_1 = m(x - x_1)$$
$$y - 3 = -1(x - 2)$$
$$y - 3 = -x + 2$$
$$y = -x + 5$$

The equation of the line is $y = -x + 5$.

You Try It 3

Find the equation of the line containing the points (2, 0) and (5, 3).

Your solution

Example 4

Find the equation of the line containing the points (2, −3) and (2, 5).

Solution

Let $(x_1, y_1) = (2, −3)$ and $(x_2, y_2) = (2, 5)$.

$$m = \frac{y_2 - y_1}{x_2 - x_1} = \frac{5 - (-3)}{2 - 2} = \frac{8}{0}$$

The slope is undefined, so the graph of the line is vertical.

The equation of the line is $x = 2$.

You Try It 4

Find the equation of the line containing the points (2, 3) and (−5, 3).

Your solution

Solutions on p. S8

Objective C **To solve application problems** ....

Linear functions can be used to model a variety of applications in science and business. For each application, data are collected and the independent and dependent variables are selected. Then a linear function is determined that models the data.

Example 5

Suppose a manufacturer has determined that at a price of $115, consumers will purchase 1 million portable CD players and that at a price of $90, consumers will purchase 1.25 million portable CD players. Describe this situation with a linear function. Use this function to predict how many portable CD players consumers will purchase if the price is $80.

Strategy

- Select the independent and dependent variables. Because you are trying to determine the number of CD players, that quantity is the *dependent* variable, y. The price of CD players is the *independent* variable, x.
- From the given data, two ordered pairs are (115, 1) and (90, 1.25). (The ordinates are in millions of units.) Use these ordered pairs to determine the linear function.

Solution

Let $(x_1, y_1) = (115, 1)$ and $(x_2, y_2) = (90, 1.25)$.

$$m = \frac{y_2 - y_1}{x_2 - x_1} = \frac{1.25 - 1}{90 - 115} = -\frac{0.25}{25} = -0.01$$

$$y - y_1 = m(x - x_1)$$

$$y - 1 = -0.01(x - 115)$$

$$y = -0.01x + 2.15$$

The linear function is $f(x) = -0.01x + 2.15$. Evaluate this function when $x = 80$ to predict how many CD players consumers will purchase if the price is $80.

$$f(80) = -0.01(80) + 2.15 = 1.35$$

Consumers will purchase 1.35 million CD players at a price of $80.

You Try It 5

Gabriel Daniel Fahrenheit invented the mercury thermometer in 1717. In terms of readings on this thermometer, water freezes at 32°F and boils at 212°F. In 1742 Anders Celsius invented the Celsius temperature scale. On this scale, water freezes at 0°C and boils at 100°C. Determine a linear function that can be used to predict the Celsius temperature when the Fahrenheit temperature is known.

Your strategy

Your solution

Solution on p. S9

3.5 Exercises

Objective A

Find the equation of the line that contains the given point and has the given slope.

1. Point $(0, 5)$, $m = 2$

2. Point $(0, 3)$, $m = 1$

3. Point $(2, 3)$, $m = \frac{1}{2}$

4. Point $(5, 1)$, $m = \frac{2}{3}$

5. Point $(-1, 4)$, $m = \frac{5}{4}$

6. Point $(-2, 1)$, $m = \frac{3}{2}$

7. Point $(3, 0)$, $m = -\frac{5}{3}$

8. Point $(-2, 0)$, $m = \frac{3}{2}$

9. Point $(2, 3)$, $m = -3$

10. Point $(1, 5)$, $m = -\frac{4}{5}$

11. Point $(-1, 7)$, $m = -3$

12. Point $(-2, 4)$, $m = -4$

13. Point $(-1, -3)$, $m = \frac{2}{3}$

14. Point $(-2, -4)$, $m = \frac{1}{4}$

15. Point $(0, 0)$, $m = \frac{1}{2}$

16. Point $(0, 0)$, $m = \frac{3}{4}$

17. Point $(2, -3)$, $m = 3$

18. Point $(4, -5)$, $m = 2$

19. Point $(3, 5)$, $m = -\frac{2}{3}$

20. Point $(5, 1)$, $m = -\frac{4}{5}$

21. Point $(0, -3)$, $m = -1$

22. Point $(2, 0)$, $m = \frac{5}{6}$

23. Point $(1, -4)$, $m = \frac{7}{5}$

24. Point $(3, 5)$, $m = -\frac{3}{7}$

25. Point $(4, -1)$, $m = -\frac{2}{5}$ **26.** Point $(-3, 5)$, $m = -\frac{1}{4}$ **27.** Point $(3, -4)$, slope is undefined

28. Point $(-2, 5)$, slope is undefined **29.** Point $(-2, -5)$, $m = -\frac{5}{4}$ **30.** Point $(-3, -2)$, $m = -\frac{2}{3}$

31. Point $(-2, -3)$, $m = 0$ **32.** Point $(-3, -2)$, $m = 0$ **33.** Point $(4, -5)$, $m = -2$

34. Point $(-3, 5)$, $m = 3$ **35.** Point $(-5, -1)$, slope is undefined **36.** Point $(0, 4)$, slope is undefined

---

Objective B

Find the equation of the line that contains the given points.

37. $P_1(0, 2)$, $P_2(3, 5)$ **38.** $P_1(0, 4)$, $P_2(1, 5)$ **39.** $P_1(0, -3)$, $P_2(-4, 5)$

40. $P_1(0, -2)$, $P_2(-3, 4)$ **41.** $P_1(2, 3)$, $P_2(5, 5)$ **42.** $P_1(4, 1)$, $P_2(6, 3)$

43. $P_1(-1, 3)$, $P_2(2, 4)$ **44.** $P_1(-1, 1)$, $P_2(4, 4)$ **45.** $P_1(-1, -2)$, $P_2(3, 4)$

46. $P_1(-3, -1)$, $P_2(2, 4)$ **47.** $P_1(0, 3)$, $P_2(2, 0)$ **48.** $P_1(0, 4)$, $P_2(2, 0)$

49. $P_1(-3, -1)$, $P_2(2, -1)$ **50.** $P_1(-3, -5)$, $P_2(4, -5)$ **51.** $P_1(-2, -3)$, $P_2(-1, -2)$

52. $P_1(4, 1), P_2(3, -2)$ **53.** $P_1(-2, 3), P_2(2, -1)$ **54.** $P_1(3, 1), P_2(-3, -2)$

55. $P_1(2, 3), P_2(5, -5)$ **56.** $P_1(7, 2), P_2(4, 4)$ **57.** $P_1(2, 0), P_2(0, -1)$

58. $P_1(0, 4), P_2(-2, 0)$ **59.** $P_1(3, -4), P_2(-2, -4)$ **60.** $P_1(-3, 3), P_2(-2, 3)$

61. $P_1(0, 0), P_2(4, 3)$ **62.** $P_1(2, -5), P_2(0, 0)$ **63.** $P_1(2, -1), P_2(-1, 3)$

64. $P_1(3, -5), P_2(-2, 1)$ **65.** $P_1(-2, 5), P_2(-2, -5)$ **66.** $P_1(3, 2), P_2(3, -4)$

67. $P_1(2, 1), P_2(-2, -3)$ **68.** $P_1(-3, -2), P_2(1, -4)$ **69.** $P_1(-4, -3), P_2(2, 5)$

70. $P_1(4, 5), P_2(-4, 3)$ **71.** $P_1(0, 3), P_2(3, 0)$ **72.** $P_1(1, -3), P_2(-2, 4)$

Objective C   *Application Problems*

73. According to the Bureau of Labor Statistics, the average hourly wage in the United States has increased from approximately $7.80 in 1990 to $12.50 in 1998. Determine a linear function that will predict the average hourly wage for a given year. Use this model to determine the average hourly wage, to the nearest cent, in 1995.

74. The manufacturer of graphing calculators determined that 10,000 calculators per week would be sold at a price of $95. At a price of $90, it was estimated that 12,000 calculators would be sold. Determine a linear function to predict the number of calculators that would be sold at a given price. Use this model to predict the number of calculators per week that would be sold at a price of $75.

75. Data provided by the job placement center at a college show that the number of jobs in the residential health care field will increase from approximately 600,000 in 1994 to 1,100,000 in 2005. Determine a linear function that will predict the number of residential health care jobs for a given year. Round values to the nearest integer. Use this model to determine the number of residential health care jobs in 2000.

76. According to record industry statistics, approximately $37.75 was spent per person in the United States for music CDs in 1991. It is expected that by 2001, the amount spent per person will increase to $71.60. Determine a linear function that will predict the amount a person will spend for music CDs for a given year. Use this model to determine the amount a person will spend for music CDs, to the nearest cent, in 1999.

APPLYING THE CONCEPTS

77. Explain the similarities and differences between the point-slope formula and the slope-intercept form of a straight line.

78. Explain why the point-slope formula cannot be used to find the equation of a line that is parallel to the y-axis.

79. Refer to Example 5 in this section for each of the following.
   a. Explain the meaning of the slope of the graph of the linear function.
   b. Explain the meaning of the y-intercept.
   c. Explain the meaning of the x-intercept.

80. If $y = mx + b$, where m is a given constant, how does the graph of this equation change as the value of b changes?

81. What is the x-intercept of the graph of $y = mx + b$?

82. A line contains the points $(-3, 6)$ and $(6, 0)$. Find the coordinates of three other points that are on this line.

83. A line contains the points $(4, -1)$ and $(2, 1)$. Find the coordinates of three other points that are on this line.

84. Given that f is a linear function for which $f(1) = 3$ and $f(-1) = 5$, determine $f(4)$.

85. Given that f is a linear function for which $f(-3) = 2$ and $f(2) = 7$, determine $f(0)$.

86. Find the equation of the line that passes through the midpoint of the line segment between $P_1(2, 5)$ and $P_2(-4, 1)$ and has slope -2.

3.6   Parallel and Perpendicular Lines

Objective A   *To find parallel and perpendicular lines* .... ⟨13⟩ CT

Two lines that have the same slope do not intersect and are called **parallel lines.**

The slope of each of the lines at the right is $\frac{2}{3}$.

The lines are parallel.

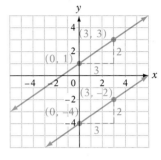

Slopes of Parallel Lines

Two nonvertical lines with slopes of m_1 and m_2 are parallel if and only if $m_1 = m_2$. Any two vertical lines are parallel.

➡ Is the line containing the points $(-2, 1)$ and $(-5, -1)$ parallel to the line that contains the points $(1, 0)$ and $(4, 2)$?

$$m_1 = \frac{-1 - 1}{-5 - (-2)} = \frac{-2}{-3} = \frac{2}{3}$$ • Find the slope of the line through $(-2, 1)$ and $(-5, -1)$.

$$m_2 = \frac{2 - 0}{4 - 1} = \frac{2}{3}$$ • Find the slope of the line through $(1, 0)$ and $(4, 2)$.

Because $m_1 = m_2$, the lines are parallel.

➡ Find the equation of the line that contains the point $(2, 3)$ and is parallel to the line $y = \frac{1}{2}x - 4$.

The slope of the given line is $\frac{1}{2}$. Because parallel lines have the same slope, the slope of the unknown line is also $\frac{1}{2}$.

$$y - y_1 = m(x - x_1)$$ • Use the point-slope formula.

$$y - 3 = \frac{1}{2}(x - 2)$$ • $m = \frac{1}{2}, (x_1, y_1) = (2, 3)$

$$y - 3 = \frac{1}{2}x - 1$$ • Simplify.

$$y = \frac{1}{2}x + 2$$ • Write the equation in the form $y = mx + b$.

The equation of the line is $y = \frac{1}{2}x + 2$.

⇒ Find the equation of the line that contains the point $(-1, 4)$ and is parallel to the line $2x - 3y = 5$.

Because the lines are parallel, the slope of the unknown line is the same as the slope of the given line. Solve $2x - 3y = 5$ for y and determine its slope.

$$2x - 3y = 5$$
$$-3y = -2x + 5$$
$$y = \frac{2}{3}x - \frac{5}{3}$$

The slope of the given line is $\frac{2}{3}$. Because the lines are parallel, this is the slope of the unknown line. Use the point-slope formula to determine the equation.

$$y - y_1 = m(x - x_1)$$ • Use the point-slope formula.

$$y - 4 = \frac{2}{3}[x - (-1)]$$ • $m = \frac{2}{3}$, $(x_1, y_1) = (-1, 4)$

$$y - 4 = \frac{2}{3}x + \frac{2}{3}$$ • Simplify.

$$y = \frac{2}{3}x + \frac{14}{3}$$ • Write the equation in the form $y = mx + b$.

The equation of the line is $y = \frac{2}{3}x + \frac{14}{3}$.

Two lines that intersect at right angles are **perpendicular lines.**

Any horizontal line is perpendicular to any vertical line. For example, $x = 3$ is perpendicular to $y = -2$.

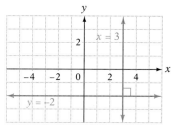

Slopes of Perpendicular Lines

If m_1 and m_2 are the slopes of two lines, neither of which is vertical, then the lines are perpendicular if and only if $m_1 \cdot m_2 = -1$.

A vertical line is perpendicular to a horizontal line.

Solving $m_1 \cdot m_2 = -1$ for m_1 gives $m_1 = -\dfrac{1}{m_2}$. This last equation states that the slopes of perpendicular lines are *negative reciprocals* of each other.

⇒ Is the line that contains the points $(4, 2)$ and $(-2, 5)$ perpendicular to the line that contains the points $(-4, 3)$ and $(-3, 5)$?

$$m_1 = \frac{5 - 2}{-2 - 4} = \frac{3}{-6} = -\frac{1}{2}$$ • Find the slope of the line through $(4, 2)$ and $(-2, 5)$.

$$m_2 = \frac{5 - 3}{-3 - (-4)} = \frac{2}{1} = 2$$ • Find the slope of the line through $(-4, 3)$ and $(-3, 5)$.

$$m_1 \cdot m_2 = -\frac{1}{2}(2) = -1$$ • Find the product of the two slopes.

Because $m_1 \cdot m_2 = -1$, the lines are perpendicular.

➡ Are the graphs of the lines whose equations are $3x + 4y = 8$ and $8x + 6y = 5$ perpendicular?

To determine whether the lines are perpendicular, solve each equation for y and find the slope of each line. Then use the equation $m_1 \cdot m_2 = -1$.

$$3x + 4y = 8 \qquad\qquad\qquad 8x + 6y = 5$$
$$4y = -3x + 8 \qquad\qquad\qquad 6y = -8x + 5$$
$$y = -\frac{3}{4}x + 2 \qquad\qquad\qquad y = -\frac{4}{3}x + \frac{5}{6}$$

$$m_1 = -\frac{3}{4} \qquad\qquad\qquad\qquad m_2 = -\frac{4}{3}$$

$$m_1 \cdot m_2 = \left(-\frac{3}{4}\right)\left(-\frac{4}{3}\right) = 1$$

Because $m_1 \cdot m_2 = 1 \neq -1$, the lines are not perpendicular.

➡ Find the equation of the line that contains the point $(-2, 1)$ and is perpendicular to the line $y = -\frac{2}{3}x + 2$.

The slope of the given line is $-\frac{2}{3}$. The slope of the line perpendicular to the given line is the negative reciprocal of $-\frac{2}{3}$, which is $\frac{3}{2}$. Substitute this slope and the coordinates of the given point, $(-2, 1)$, into the point-slope formula.

$$y - y_1 = m(x - x_1)$$ • The point-slope formula

$$y - 1 = \frac{3}{2}[x - (-2)]$$ • $m = \frac{3}{2}, (x_1, y_1) = (-2, 1)$

$$y - 1 = \frac{3}{2}x + 3$$ • Simplify.

$$y = \frac{3}{2}x + 4$$ • Write the equation in the form $y = mx + b$.

The equation of the perpendicular line is $y = \frac{3}{2}x + 4$.

➡ Find the equation of the line that contains the point $(3, -4)$ and is perpendicular to the line $2x - y = -3$.

$$2x - y = -3$$ • Determine the slope of the given line by
$$-y = -2x - 3$$ solving the equation for y.
$$y = 2x + 3$$ • The slope is 2.

The slope of the line perpendicular to the given line is $-\frac{1}{2}$, the negative reciprocal of 2. Now use the point-slope formula to find the equation of the line.

$$y - y_1 = m(x - x_1)$$ • The point-slope formula

$$y - (-4) = -\frac{1}{2}(x - 3)$$ • $m = -\frac{1}{2}, (x_1, y_1) = (3, -4)$

$$y + 4 = -\frac{1}{2}x + \frac{3}{2}$$ • Simplify.

$$y = -\frac{1}{2}x - \frac{5}{2}$$ • Write the equation in the form $y = mx + b$.

The equation of the perpendicular line is $y = -\frac{1}{2}x - \frac{5}{2}$.

Example 1

Is the line that contains the points $(-4, 2)$ and $(1, 6)$ parallel to the line that contains the points $(2, -4)$ and $(7, 0)$?

Solution

$$m_1 = \frac{6 - 2}{1 - (-4)} = \frac{4}{5}$$

$$m_2 = \frac{0 - (-4)}{7 - 2} = \frac{4}{5}$$

$$m_1 = m_2 = \frac{4}{5}$$

The lines are parallel.

You Try It 1

Is the line that contains the points $(-2, -3)$ and $(7, 1)$ perpendicular to the line that contains the points $(4, 1)$ and $(6, -5)$?

Your solution

Example 2

Are the lines $4x - y = -2$ and $x + 4y = -12$ perpendicular?

Solution

$$4x - y = -2$$
$$-y = -4x - 2$$
$$y = 4x + 2$$
$$m_1 = 4$$

$$x + 4y = -12$$
$$4y = -x - 12$$
$$y = -\frac{1}{4}x - 3$$
$$m_2 = -\frac{1}{4}$$

$$m_1 \cdot m_2 = 4\left(-\frac{1}{4}\right) = -1$$

The lines are perpendicular.

You Try It 2

Are the lines $5x + 2y = 2$ and $5x + 2y = -6$ parallel?

Your solution

Example 3

Find the equation of the line that contains the point $(3, -1)$ and is parallel to the line $3x - 2y = 4$.

Solution

$$3x - 2y = 4$$
$$-2y = -3x + 4$$
$$y = \frac{3}{2}x - 2 \qquad \bullet \; m = \frac{3}{2}$$

$$y - y_1 = m(x - x_1)$$
$$y - (-1) = \frac{3}{2}(x - 3)$$
$$y + 1 = \frac{3}{2}x - \frac{9}{2}$$
$$y = \frac{3}{2}x - \frac{11}{2}$$

The equation of the line is $y = \frac{3}{2}x - \frac{11}{2}$.

You Try It 3

Find the equation of the line that contains the point $(-2, 2)$ and is perpendicular to the line $x - 4y = 3$.

Your solution

Solutions on p. S9

3.6 Exercises

Objective A

1. Is the line $x = -2$ perpendicular to the line $y = 3$?

2. Is the line $y = \frac{1}{2}$ perpendicular to the line $y = -4$?

3. Is the line $x = -3$ parallel to the line $y = \frac{1}{3}$?

4. Is the line $x = 4$ parallel to the line $x = -4$?

5. Is the line $y = \frac{2}{3}x - 4$ parallel to the line $y = -\frac{3}{2}x - 4$?

6. Is the line $y = -2x + \frac{2}{3}$ parallel to the line $y = -2x + 3$?

7. Is the line $y = \frac{4}{3}x - 2$ perpendicular to the line $y = -\frac{3}{4}x + 2$?

8. Is the line $y = \frac{1}{2}x + \frac{3}{2}$ perpendicular to the line $y = -\frac{1}{2}x + \frac{3}{2}$?

9. Are the lines $2x + 3y = 2$ and $2x + 3y = -4$ parallel?

10. Are the lines $2x - 4y = 3$ and $2x + 4y = -3$ parallel?

11. Are the lines $x - 4y = 2$ and $4x + y = 8$ perpendicular?

12. Are the lines $4x - 3y = 2$ and $4x + 3y = -7$ perpendicular?

13. Is the line that contains the points $(3, 2)$ and $(1, 6)$ parallel to the line that contains the points $(-1, 3)$ and $(-1, -1)$?

14. Is the line that contains the points $(4, -3)$ and $(2, 5)$ parallel to the line that contains the points $(-2, -3)$ and $(-4, 1)$?

15. Is the line that contains the points $(-3, 2)$ and $(4, -1)$ perpendicular to the line that contains the points $(1, 3)$ and $(-2, -4)$?

16. Is the line that contains the points $(-1, 2)$ and $(3, 4)$ perpendicular to the line that contains the points $(-1, 3)$ and $(-4, 1)$?

17. Is the line that contains the points $(-5, 0)$ and $(0, 2)$ parallel to the line that contains the points $(5, 1)$ and $(0, -1)$?

18. Is the line that contains the points $(3, 5)$ and $(-3, 3)$ perpendicular to the line that contains the points $(2, -5)$ and $(-4, 4)$?

19. Find the equation of the line containing the point $(-2, -4)$ and parallel to the line $2x - 3y = 2$.

20. Find the equation of the line containing the point $(3, 2)$ and parallel to the line $3x + y = -3$.

21. Find the equation of the line containing the point $(4, 1)$ and perpendicular to the line $y = -3x + 4$.

22. Find the equation of the line containing the point $(2, -5)$ and perpendicular to the line $y = \frac{5}{2}x - 4$.

23. Find the equation of the line containing the point $(-1, -3)$ and perpendicular to the line $3x - 5y = 2$.

24. Find the equation of the line containing the point $(-1, 3)$ and perpendicular to the line $2x + 4y = -1$.

APPLYING THE CONCEPTS

25. Explain how to determine whether the graphs of two lines are parallel.

26. Explain how to determine whether the graphs of two lines are perpendicular.

27. If the graphs of $A_1x + B_1y = C_1$ and $A_2x + B_2y = C_2$ are perpendicular, express $\frac{A_1}{B_1}$ in terms of A_2 and B_2.

28. If the graphs of $A_1x + B_1y = C_1$ and $A_2x + B_2y = C_2$ are parallel, express $\frac{A_1}{B_1}$ in terms of A_2 and B_2.

29. The graphs of $y = -\frac{1}{2}x + 2$ and $y = \frac{2}{3}x - 5$ intersect at the point whose coordinates are $(6, -1)$. Find the equation of a line whose graph intersects the graphs of the given lines to form a right triangle. (*Hint:* There is more than one answer to this question.)

30. A theorem from geometry states that a line passing through the center of a circle and through a point P on the circle is perpendicular to the tangent line at P. (See the figure at the right.) If the coordinates of P are $(5, 4)$ and the coordinates of C are $(3, 2)$, what is the equation of the tangent line?

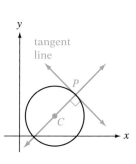

31. Find the x- and y-intercepts of the tangent line in Exercise 30.

3.7 Inequalities in Two Variables

Objective A   ***To graph the solution set of an inequality in two variables*** ......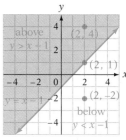

The graph of the linear equation $y = x - 1$ separates the plane into three sets: the set of points on the line, the set of points above the line, and the set of points below the line.

The point whose coordinates are $(2, 1)$ is a solution of $y = x - 1$ and is a point on the line.

The point whose coordinates are $(2, 4)$ is a solution of $y > x - 1$ and is a point above the line.

The point whose coordinates are $(2, -2)$ is a solution of $y < x - 1$ and is a point below the line.

The set of points on the line are the solutions of the equation $y = x - 1$. The set of points above the line are the solutions of the inequality $y > x - 1$. These points form a **half-plane.** The set of points below the line are solutions of the inequality $y < x - 1$. These points also form a half-plane.

An inequality of the form $y > mx + b$ or $Ax + By > C$ is a **linear inequality in two variables.** (The inequality symbol could be replaced by $\geq$, $<$, or $\leq$.) The solution set of a linear inequality in two variables is a half-plane.

The following illustrates the procedure for graphing the solution set of a linear inequality in two variables.

➡ Graph the solution set of $3x - 4y < 12$.

$$3x - 4y < 12$$
$$-4y < -3x + 12$$
$$y > \frac{3}{4}x - 3$$

• Solve the inequality for *y*.

Change the inequality $y > \frac{3}{4}x - 3$ to the equality $y = \frac{3}{4}x - 3$, and graph the line.

If the inequality contains $\leq$ or $\geq$, the line belongs to the solution set and is shown by a *solid line*. If the inequality contains $<$ or $>$, the line is not part of the solution set and is shown by a *dotted line*.

If the inequality contains $>$ or $\geq$, shade the upper half-plane. If the inequality contains $<$ or $\leq$, shade the lower half-plane.

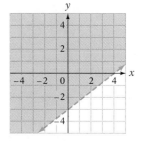

As a check, use the ordered pair $(0, 0)$ to determine whether the correct region of the plane has been shaded. If $(0, 0)$ is a solution of the inequality, then $(0, 0)$ should be in the shaded region. If $(0, 0)$ is not a solution of the inequality, then $(0, 0)$ should not be in the shaded region. In the above example, $(0, 0)$ is in the shaded region, and $(0, 0)$ is a solution of the inequality. Therefore, the solution set is drawn correctly.

If the line passes through the point (0, 0), another point, such as (0, 1), must be used as a check.

From the graph of $y > \frac{3}{4}x - 3$, note that for a given value of x, more than one value of y can be paired with that value of x. For instance, (4, 1), (4, 3), (5, 1), and $\left(5, \frac{9}{4}\right)$ are all ordered pairs that belong to the graph. Because there are ordered pairs with the same first component and different second components, the inequality does not represent a function. The inequality is a relation but not a function.

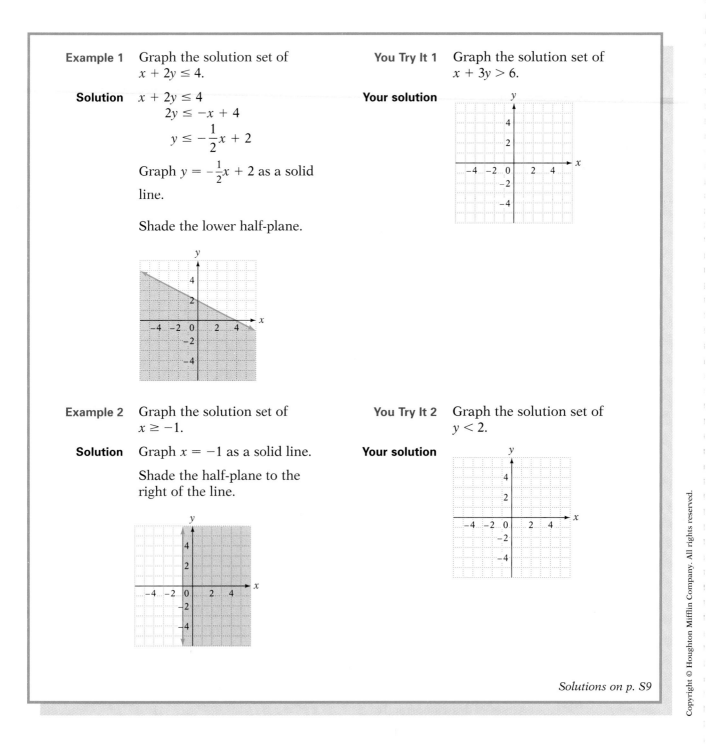

Example 1   Graph the solution set of
$x + 2y \le 4$.

Solution $x + 2y \le 4$
$\qquad 2y \le -x + 4$
$\qquad y \le -\frac{1}{2}x + 2$

Graph $y = -\frac{1}{2}x + 2$ as a solid line.

Shade the lower half-plane.

You Try It 1   Graph the solution set of
$x + 3y > 6$.

Your solution

Example 2   Graph the solution set of
$x \ge -1$.

Solution   Graph $x = -1$ as a solid line.

Shade the half-plane to the right of the line.

You Try It 2   Graph the solution set of
$y < 2$.

Your solution

Solutions on p. S9

3.7 Exercises

Objective A

Graph the solution set.

1. $3x - 2y \geq 6$

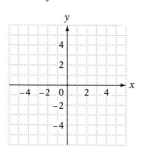

2. $4x - 3y \leq 12$

3. $x + 3y < 4$

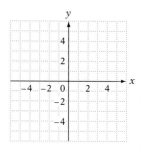

4. $3x - 5y > 15$

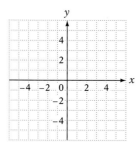

5. $4x - 5y > 10$

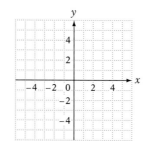

6. $4x + 3y < 9$

7. $x + 3y < 6$

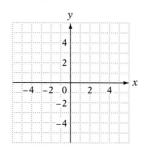

8. $2x - 5y \leq 10$

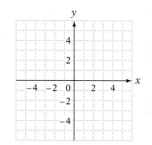

9. $2x + 3y \geq 6$

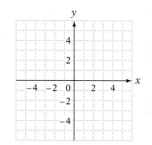

10. $3x + 2y < 4$

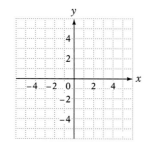

11. $-x + 2y > -8$

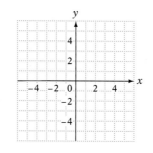

12. $-3x + 2y > 2$

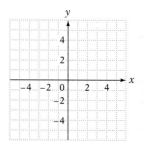

13. $y - 4 < 0$

14. $x + 2 \geq 0$

15. $6x + 5y < 15$

16. $3x - 5y < 10$

17. $-5x + 3y \geq -12$

18. $3x + 4y \geq 12$

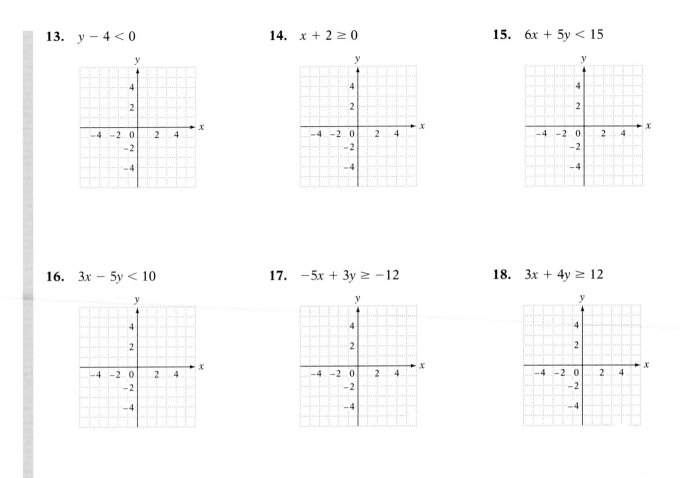

APPLYING THE CONCEPTS

19. Does the inequality $y < 3x - 1$ represent a function? Explain your answer.

20. Does the inequality $y \geq -2x - 4$ represent a function? Explain your answer.

21. Are there any points whose coordinates satisfy both $y \leq x + 3$ and $y \geq -\frac{1}{2}x + 1$? If so, give the coordinates of three such points. If not, explain why not.

22. Are there any points whose coordinates satisfy both $y \leq x - 1$ and $y \geq x + 2$? If so, give the coordinates of three such points. If not, explain why not.

Focus on Problem Solving

Find a Pattern   Polya's four recommended problem-solving steps are stated below.

1. Understand the problem.   **3.** Carry out the plan.

2. Devise a plan.   **4.** Review your solution.

One of the several ways of devising a plan is first to try to find a pattern. Karl Friedrich Gauss supposedly used this method to solve a problem that was given to his math class when he was in elementary school. As the story goes, his teacher wanted to grade some papers while the class worked on a math problem. The problem given to the class was to find the sum

$$1 + 2 + 3 + 4 + \cdots + 100$$

Gauss quickly solved the problem by seeing a pattern. Here is what he saw.

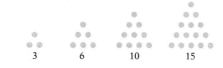

Note that

$1 + 100 = 101$
$2 + 99 = 101$
$3 + 98 = 101$
$4 + 97 = 101$

Gauss noted that there were 50 sums of 101. Therefore, the sum of the first 100 natural numbers is

$$1 + 2 + 3 + 4 + \cdots + 97 + 98 + 99 + 100 = 50(101) = 5050$$

Try to solve the following problems by finding a pattern.

1. Find the sum $2 + 4 + 6 + \cdots + 96 + 98 + 100$.

2. Find the sum $1 + 3 + 5 + \cdots + 97 + 99 + 101$.

3. Find another method of finding the sum $1 + 3 + 5 + \cdots + 97 + 99 + 101$ given in the previous exercise.

4. Find the sum $\dfrac{1}{1 \cdot 2} + \dfrac{1}{2 \cdot 3} + \dfrac{1}{3 \cdot 4} + \cdots + \dfrac{1}{49 \cdot 50}$.

Hint: $\dfrac{1}{1 \cdot 2} = \dfrac{1}{2}, \dfrac{1}{1 \cdot 2} + \dfrac{1}{2 \cdot 3} = \dfrac{2}{3}, \dfrac{1}{1 \cdot 2} + \dfrac{1}{2 \cdot 3} + \dfrac{1}{3 \cdot 4} = \dfrac{3}{4}$

5. A *figurative number* is a number that can be represented by arranging that number of dots in rows to form a geometric figure such as a triangle, square, pentagon, or hexagon. For instance, the first four *triangular* numbers, 3, 6, 10, and 15, are given (and shown) below. What are the next two triangular numbers?

3   6   10   15

6. The following problem shows that checking a few cases does not always result in a conjecture that is true for *all* cases. Select any two points on a circle and draw a *chord* (see drawing in the left margin), the line connecting the points. The chord divides the circle into 2 regions. Now select 3 different points and draw chords connecting each of the three points with every other point. The chords divide the circle into 4 regions. Now select 4 points and connect each of the points with every other point. Make a conjecture as to the relationship between the number of regions and the number of points on the circle. Does your conjecture work for 5 points? 6 points?

2 points, 2 regions   3 points, 4 regions

4 points, 8 regions   5 points, ? regions

Projects and Group Activities

Evaluating a Function with a Graphing Calculator

You can use a graphing calculator to evaluate some functions. We will give the keystrokes to evaluate $f(x) = 3x^2 + 2x - 1$ when $x = -2$ for three different calculators.[1] If you try these keystrokes, you should get 7 as the value of the function.

TI-83	*SHARP EL-9600*	*Casio CFX-9850G*
Y= CLEAR 3 X,T,θ,n △ 2 + 2 X,T,θ,n − 1 2nd QUIT (−) 2 STO ▶ X,T,θ,n ENTER VARS ▶ 1 1 ENTER	Y= CL 3 X/θ/T/n aᵇ ▶ 2 + 2 X/θ/T/n − 1 ×÷ (−) 2 STO X/θ/T/n ENTER VARS ENTER ENTER 1 ENTER	MENU 5 F2 F1 3 X,θ,T △ 2 + 2 X,θ,T − 1 EXE MENU 1 (−) 2 → X,θ,T EXE VARS F4 F1 1 EXE

Introduction to Graphing Calculators

Calculator Screen

There are a variety of computer programs and calculators that can graph an equation. A computer or graphing calculator screen is divided into pixels. Depending on the computer or calculator, there are approximately 6000 to 790,000 pixels available on the screen. The greater the number of pixels, the smoother the graph will appear. A portion of a screen is shown at the left. Each little rectangle represents one pixel.

A graphing calculator draws a graph in a manner similar to the way we have shown in this chapter. Values of x are chosen and ordered pairs calculated. Then a graph is drawn through those points by illuminating pixels (an abbreviation for "picture element") on the screen.

Graphing utilities can display only a portion of the xy-plane, called a window. The window [Xmin, Xmax] by [Ymin, Ymax] consists of those points (x, y) that satisfy both of the following:

$$\text{Xmin} \le x \le \text{Xmax} \text{ and } \text{Ymin} \le y \le \text{Ymax}$$

The user sets these values before a graph is drawn.

The numbers Xscl and Yscl are the distances between the tick marks that are drawn on the x- and y-axes. If you do not want tick marks on the axes, set Xscl = 0 and Yscl = 0.

The graph at the right is a portion of the graph of $y = \frac{1}{2}x + 1$, as it was drawn with a graphing calculator. The window is

Xmin = −4.7, Xmax = 4.7
Ymin = −3.1, Ymax = 3.1
Xscl = 1 and Yscl = 1

Using interval notation, this is shown as [−4.7, 4.7] by [−3.1, 3.1].

[1]There are other methods of evaluating functions. This is just one option.

The window $[-4.7, 4.7]$ by $[-3.1, 3.1]$ gives "nice" coordinates in the sense that each time the ▶ or the ◀ is pressed, the change in x is 0.1. The reason for this is that the horizontal distance from the middle of the first pixel to the middle of the last pixel is 94 units. By using Xmin $= -4.7$ and Xmax $= 4.7$, we have[1]

$$\text{Change in } x = \frac{\text{Xmax} - \text{Xmin}}{94} = \frac{4.7 - (-4.7)}{94} = \frac{9.4}{94} = 0.1$$

Similarly, the vertical distance from the middle of the first pixel to the last pixel is 62 units. Therefore, using Ymin $= -3.1$ and Ymax $= 3.1$ will give nice coordinates in the vertical direction.

Graph each of the following by using a graphing calculator.

1. $y = 2x + 1$ — For $2x$, you may enter $2 \times x$ or just $2x$. The times sign $\times$ is not necessary on many graphing calculators.

2. $y = -x + 2$ — Many calculators use the $(-)$ key to enter a negative sign.

3. $3x + 2y = 6$ — Solve for y. Then enter the equation.

4. $y = 50x$ — You must adjust the viewing window. Try the window given by $[-4.7, 4.7]$ by $[-250, 250]$ with Yscl $= 50$.

5. $y = \frac{2}{3}x - 3$ — You may enter $\frac{2}{3}x$ as $2x/3$ or $(2/3)x$. Although entering $2/3x$ works on some calculators, it is not recommended.

6. $4x + 3y = 75$ — You must adjust the viewing window.

Chapter Summary

Key Words   A *function* is a set of ordered pairs in which no two ordered pairs that have the same first coordinate have different second coordinates.

Functional notation is used for those equations that represent functions. For the equation $y = f(x)$, x is the *independent variable* and y is the *dependent variable*.

The *domain* of a function is the set of first coordinates of all the ordered pairs of the function.

The *range* of a function is the set of second coordinates of all the ordered pairs of the function.

A *linear function* is one that can be expressed in the form $f(x) = mx + b$.

The *graph of a function* is the graph of the ordered pairs that belong to the function.

---

[1]Some calculators have screen widths of 126 pixels. For those calculators, use Xmin $= -6.3$ and Xmax $= 6.3$ to obtain nice coordinates.

The point at which a graph crosses the x-axis is called the *x-intercept.*

The point at which a graph crosses the y-axis is called the *y-intercept.*

An equation of the form $Ax + By = C$ is a *linear equation in two variables.*

The *graph of a linear function* is a straight line.

The *slope* of a line is a measure of the slant, or tilt, of the line. The symbol for slope is m.

A line that slants upward to the right has a *positive slope.*

A line that slants downward to the right has a *negative slope.*

A horizontal line has *zero slope.*

The slope of a vertical line is *undefined.*

Two lines that have the same slope do not intersect and are called *parallel lines.*

Two lines that intersect at right angles are called *perpendicular lines.*

An inequality of the form $y > mx + b$ or $Ax + By > C$ is a *linear inequality in two variables.* (The symbol > could be replaced by ≥, <, or ≤.)

The solution set of an inequality in two variables is a *half-plane.*

Essential Rules   *Pythagorean Theorem*
$a^2 + b^2 = c^2$

Distance Formula
$d = \sqrt{(x_1 - x_2)^2 + (y_1 - y_2)^2}$

Midpoint Formula
$\left(\dfrac{x_1 + x_2}{2}, \dfrac{y_1 + y_2}{2} \right)$

Slope of a Straight Line
$m = \dfrac{y_2 - y_1}{x_2 - x_1}, x_1 \neq x_2$

Slope-Intercept Formula
$y = mx + b$

Point-Slope Form of a Straight Line
$y - y_1 = m(x - x_1)$

Slopes of Parallel Lines
$m_1 = m_2$

Slopes of Perpendicular Lines
$m_1 \cdot m_2 = -1$

Chapter Review

1. Determine the ordered-pair solution of $y = \dfrac{x}{x-2}$ that corresponds to $x = 4$.

2. Given $P(x) = 3x + 4$, evaluate $P(-2)$ and $P(a)$.

3. Graph the ordered-pair solutions of $y = 2x^2 - 5$ when $x = -2, -1, 0, 1,$ and 2.

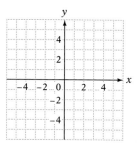

4. Draw a line through all the points with an abscissa of -3.

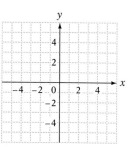

5. Find the range of $f(x) = x^2 + x - 1$ if the domain is $\{-2, -1, 0, 1, 2\}$.

6. Find the domain and range of the function $\{(-1, 0), (0, 2), (1, 2), (5, 4)\}$.

7. Find the midpoint and the length (to the nearest hundredth) of the line segment with endpoints $(-2, 4)$ and $(3, 5)$.

8. What value of x is excluded from the domain of $f(x) = \dfrac{x}{x+4}$?

9. Find the x- and y-intercepts and graph $y = -\dfrac{2}{3}x - 2$.

10. Graph $3x + 2y = -6$ by using the x- and y-intercepts.

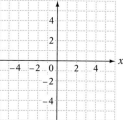

11. Graph: $y = -2x + 2$

12. Graph: $4x - 3y = 12$

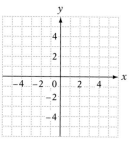

13. Find the slope of the line that contains the ordered pairs $(3, -2)$ and $(-1, 2)$.

14. Find the equation of the line that contains the ordered pair $(-3, 4)$ and has slope $\dfrac{5}{2}$.

15. Graph the solution set of $y \geq 2x - 3$.

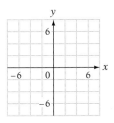

16. Graph the solution set of $3x - 2y \leq 6$.

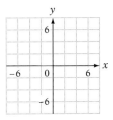

17. Find the equation of the line that contains the ordered pairs $(-2, 4)$ and $(4, -3)$.

18. Find the equation of the line that contains the ordered pair $(-2, -4)$ and is parallel to the graph of $4x - 2y = 7$.

19. Graph the line that passes through the point whose coordinates are $(-1, 4)$ and has slope $-\frac{1}{3}$.

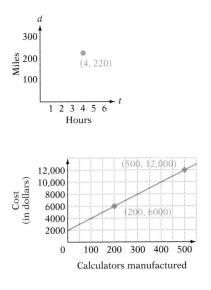

20. Find the equation of the line that contains the ordered pair $(3, -2)$ and is parallel to the graph of $y = -3x + 4$.

21. Find the equation of the line that contains the ordered pair $(2, 5)$ and is perpendicular to the graph of the line $y = -\frac{2}{3}x + 6$.

22. A car is traveling at 55 mph. The equation that describes the distance traveled is $d = 55t$. Graph this equation for $0 \leq t \leq 6$. The point whose coordinates are $(4, 220)$ is on the graph. Write a sentence that explains the meaning of this ordered pair.

23. The graph at the right shows the relationship between the cost of manufacturing calculators and the number of calculators manufactured. Find the slope of the line between the two points shown on the graph. Write a sentence that explains the meaning of the slope of this line.

24. A building contractor estimates that the cost to build a new home is $25,000 plus $80 for each square foot of floor space. Determine a linear function that will give the cost to build a house that contains a given number of square feet. Use the model to determine the cost to build a house that contains 2000 ft².

Chapter Test

1. Graph the ordered-pair solutions of $P(s) = 2 - x^2$ when $x = -2, -1, 0, 1,$ and 2.

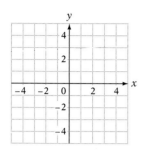

2. Find the ordered-pair solution of $y = 2x + 6$ that corresponds to $x = -3$.

3. Graph: $y = \dfrac{2}{3}x - 4$

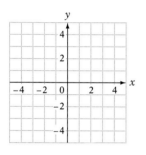

4. Graph: $2x + 3y = -3$

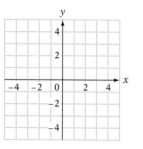

5. Find the equation of the vertical line that contains the point $(-2, 3)$.

6. Find the midpoint and length (to the nearest hundredth) of the line segment with endpoints $(4, 2)$ and $(-5, 8)$.

7. Find the slope of the line that contains the points $(-2, 3)$ and $(4, 2)$.

8. Given $P(x) = 3x^2 - 2x + 1$, evaluate $P(2)$.

9. Graph $2x - 3y = 6$ by using the x- and the y-intercepts.

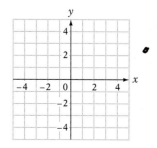

10. Graph the line that passes through the point $(-2, 3)$ and has slope $-\dfrac{3}{2}$.

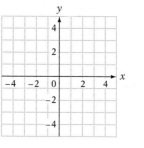

11. Find the equation of the line that contains the point $(-5, 2)$ and has slope $\frac{2}{5}$.

12. What value of x is excluded from the domain of $f(x) = \frac{2x + 1}{x}$?

13. Find the equation of the line that contains the points $(3, -4)$ and $(-2, 3)$.

14. Find the equation of the horizontal line that contains the point $(4, -3)$.

15. Find the domain and range of the function $\{(-4, 2), (-2, 2), (0, 0), (3, 5)\}$.

16. Find the equation of the line that contains the point $(1, 2)$ and is parallel to the line $y = -\frac{3}{2}x - 6$.

17. Find the equation of the line that contains the point $(-2, -3)$ and is perpendicular to the line $y = -\frac{1}{2}x - 3$.

18. Graph the solution set of $3x - 4y > 8$.

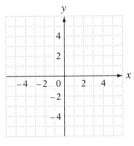

19. The graph below shows the relationship between the cost of a rental house and the depreciation allowed for income tax purposes. Find the slope between the two points shown on the graph. Write a sentence that states the meaning of the slope.

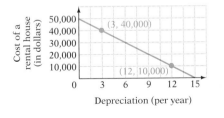

20. The director of a baseball school estimates that 100 students will enroll if the tuition is $250. For each $20 increase in tuition, six fewer students will enroll. Determine a linear function that will predict the number of students who will enroll at a given tuition. Use this model to predict enrollment when the tuition is $300.

Cumulative Review

1. Identify the property that justifies the statement $(x + y) \cdot 2 = 2 \cdot (x + y)$.

2. Solve: $3 - \frac{x}{2} = \frac{3}{4}$

3. Solve:
$2[y - 2(3 - y) + 4] = 4 - 3y$

4. Solve:
$\frac{1 - 3x}{2} + \frac{7x - 2}{6} = \frac{4x + 2}{9}$

5. Solve:
$x - 3 < -4$ or $2x + 2 > 3$

6. Solve:
$8 - |2x - 1| = 4$

7. Solve: $|3x - 5| < 5$

8. Simplify: $4 - 2(4 - 5)^3 + 2$

9. Evaluate $(a - b)^2 \div (ab)$ when $a = 4$ and $b = -2$.

10. Graph: $\{x \,|\, x < -2\} \cup \{x \,|\, x > 0\}$

11. Solve $P = \frac{R - C}{n}$ for C.

12. Solve $2x + 3y = 6$ for x.

13. Solve: $3x - 1 < 4$ and $x - 2 > 2$

14. Given $P(x) = x^2 + 5$, evaluate $P(-3)$.

15. Find the ordered-pair solution of $y = -\frac{5}{4}x + 3$ that corresponds to $x = -8$.

16. Find the slope of the line that contains the points $(-1, 3)$ and $(3, -4)$.

17. Find the equation of the line that contains the point $(-1, 5)$ and has slope $\frac{3}{2}$.

18. Find the equation of the line that contains the points $(4, -2)$ and $(0, 3)$.

19. Find the equation of the line that contains the point (2, 4) and is parallel to the line $y = -\frac{3}{2}x + 2$.

20. Find the equation of the line that contains the point (4, 0) and is perpendicular to the line $3x - 2y = 5$.

21. A coin purse contains 17 coins with a value of $1.60. The purse contains nickels, dimes, and quarters. There are four times as many nickels as quarters. Find the number of dimes in the purse.

22. Two planes are 1800 mi apart and are traveling toward each other. One plane is traveling twice as fast as the other plane. The planes meet in 3 h. Find the speed of each plane.

23. A grocer combines coffee costing $9.00 per pound with coffee costing $6.00 per pound. How many pounds of each should be used to make 60 pounds of a blend costing $8.00 per pound?

24. Graph $3x - 5y = 15$ by using the x- and y-intercepts.

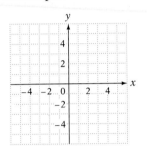

25. Graph the line that passes through the point $(-3, 1)$ and has slope $-\frac{3}{2}$.

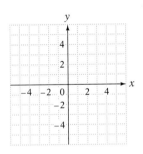

26. Graph the inequality $3x - 2y \geq 6$.

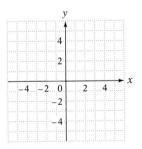

27. The relationship between the cost of a truck and the depreciation allowed for income tax purposes is shown in the graph at the right. Write the equation for the line that represents the depreciated value of the truck. Write a sentence that explains the meaning of the slope in the context of this exercise.

4

Systems of Linear Equations and Inequalities

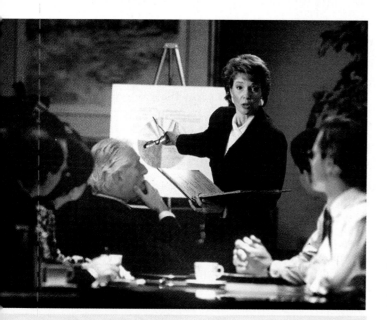

A budget analyst provides advice and technical assistance in the preparation of annual budgets. Managers and department heads submit proposed operating and financial plans to the budget analyst for review. These plans outline proposed program increases or new products, estimated costs and expenses, and capital expenditures needed to finance these programs. To analyze the different needs of each department or division requires solving large systems of equations.

Objectives

Section 4.1
To solve a system of linear equations by graphing
To solve a system of linear equations by the substitution method
To solve investment problems

Section 4.2
To solve a system of two linear equations in two variables by the addition method
To solve a system of three linear equations in three variables by the addition method

Section 4.3
To evaluate a determinant
To solve a system of equations by using Cramer's Rule

Section 4.4
To solve rate-of-wind or rate-of-current problems
To solve application problems

Section 4.5
To graph the solution set of a system of linear inequalities

Analytic Geometry

Euclid's geometry (the plane geometry that is still taught in high school) was developed around 300 B.C. Euclid's approach depends on a synthetic proof—a proof based on pure logic.

Algebra is the science of solving equations. As early as the 3rd century, equations were solved by trial and error. However, the appropriate terminology and symbols of operation were not fully developed until the 17th century.

Analytic geometry is the combining of algebraic methods with geometric concepts. The development of analytic geometry in the 17th century is attributed to Descartes.

The development of analytic geometry depended on the invention of a system of coordinates in which any point in the plane could be represented by an ordered pair of numbers. This invention allowed lines and curves (such as the conic sections) to be represented and described by algebraic equations.

Some equations are quite simple and have a simple graph. For example, the graph of the equation $y = 2x - 3$ is a line.

Other graphs are quite complicated and have complicated equations. The graph of the Mandelbrot set, which is shown at the left, is very complicated. The graph is called a fractal.

4.1 Solving Systems of Linear Equations by Graphing and by the Substitution Method

Objective A   ***To solve a system of linear equations by graphing*** .... ▢15▢ ▢CT▢

A **system of equations** is two or more equations considered together. The system at the right is a system of two linear equations in two variables. The graphs of the equations are straight lines.

$$3x + 4y = 7$$
$$2x - 3y = 6$$

A **solution of a system of equations in two variables** is an ordered pair that is a solution of each equation of the system.

➡ Is $(3, -2)$ a solution of the system
$$2x - 3y = 12$$
$$5x + 2y = 11?$$

$2x - 3y = 12$		$5x + 2y = 11$	
$2(3) - 3(-2)$	12	$5(3) + 2(-2)$	11
$6 - (-6)$		$15 + (-4)$	
	$12 = 12$		$11 = 11$

• **Replace *x* by 3 and *y* by −2.**

Yes, because $(3, -2)$ is a solution of each equation, it is a solution of the system of equations.

A solution of a system of linear equations can be found by graphing the lines of the system on the same coordinate axes. The point of intersection of the lines is the ordered pair that lies on both lines. It is the solution of the system of equations.

➡ Solve by graphing: $x + 2y = 4$
$$2x + y = -1$$

Graph each line.

Find the point of intersection.

The ordered pair $(-2, 3)$ lies on each line.

The solution is $(-2, 3)$.

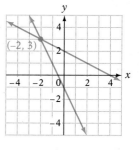

When the graphs of a system of equations intersect at only one point, the system of equations is called an **independent system of equations.**

➡ Solve by graphing: $2x + 3y = 6$
$$4x + 6y = -12$$

Graph each line.

The lines are parallel and therefore do not intersect. The system of equations has no solution.

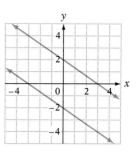

When a system of equations has no solution, it is called an **inconsistent system of equations.**

➡ Solve by graphing: $x - 2y = 4$
$2x - 4y = 8$

Graph each line.

The two equations represent the same line. This is a **dependent system of equations.** When a system of two equations is dependent, solve (if necessary) one of the equations of the system for y. The solutions of the dependent system are $(x, mx + b)$, where $y = mx + b$. For this system,

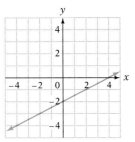

$$x - 2y = 4$$
$$-2y = -x + 4$$
$$y = \frac{1}{2}x - 2$$

The solutions are the ordered pairs $\left(x, \frac{1}{2}x - 2\right)$.

TAKE NOTE

Keep in mind the difference between independent, dependent, and inconsistent systems of equations. You should be able to express your understanding of these terms by using graphs.

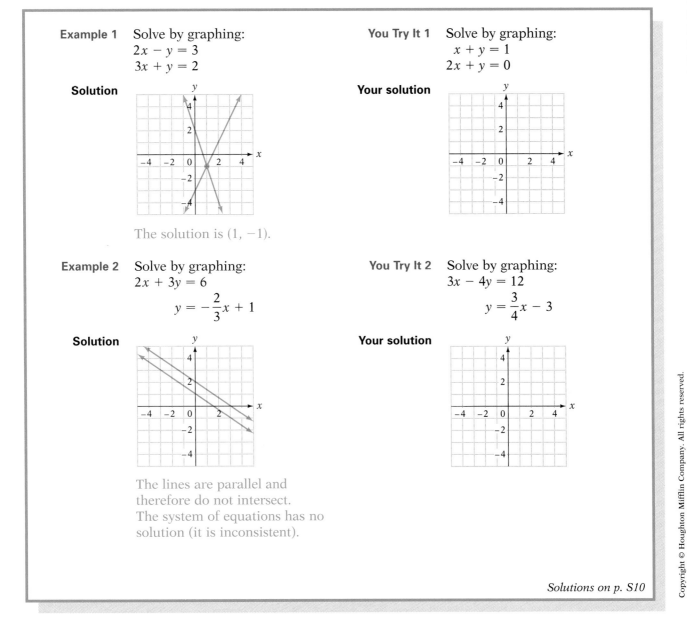

Example 1 Solve by graphing:
$2x - y = 3$
$3x + y = 2$

Solution

The solution is $(1, -1)$.

You Try It 1 Solve by graphing:
$x + y = 1$
$2x + y = 0$

Your solution

Example 2 Solve by graphing:
$2x + 3y = 6$

$$y = -\frac{2}{3}x + 1$$

Solution

The lines are parallel and therefore do not intersect. The system of equations has no solution (it is inconsistent).

You Try It 2 Solve by graphing:
$3x - 4y = 12$

$$y = \frac{3}{4}x - 3$$

Your solution

Solutions on p. S10

Objective B   *To solve a system of linear equations by the*
substitution method .... (16) CT

A graphical solution of a system of equations is based on approximating the coordinates of a point of intersection. An algebraic method called the **substitution method** can be used to find an exact solution of a system of equations. To use the substitution method, we must write one of the equations of the system in terms of x or in terms of y.

➡ Solve by the substitution method: (1) $3x + y = 5$
(2) $4x + 5y = 3$

$$3x + y = 5$$
(3) $\qquad y = -3x + 5 \qquad$ • This is Equation (3).

Substitute $-3x + 5$ for y in Equation (2). Then solve for x.

$$4x + 5y = 3 \qquad$$ • This is Equation (2).
$$4x + 5(-3x + 5) = 3 \qquad$$ • From Equation (3), because $y = -3x + 5$, substitute $-3x + 5$ for y.

$$4x - 15x + 25 = 3 \qquad$$ • Solve for x.
$$-11x + 25 = 3$$
$$-11x = -22$$
$$x = 2$$

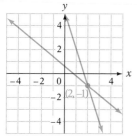

Now substitute the value of x into Equation (3) and solve for y.

$$y = -3x + 5 \qquad$$ • This is Equation (3).
$$y = -3(2) + 5 \qquad$$ • Substitute 2 for x.
$$y = -6 + 5 = -1$$

The solution is the ordered pair $(2, -1)$.

The graph of the system of equations is shown at the left. Note that the graphs intersect at the point whose coordinates are $(2, -1)$, the solution of the system of equations.

Example 3   Solve by substitution:
(1) $3x - 2y = 4$
(2) $-x + 4y = -3$

Solution   Solve Equation (2) for x.
$$-x + 4y = -3$$
$$-x = -4y - 3$$
$$x = 4y + 3 \quad$$ • Equation (3)

Substitute $4y + 3$ for x in Equation (1).

$$3x - 2y = 4 \quad$$ • Equation (1)
$$3(4y + 3) - 2y = 4 \quad$$ • $x = 4y + 3$
$$12y + 9 - 2y = 4$$
$$10y + 9 = 4$$
$$10y = -5$$
$$y = -\frac{5}{10} = -\frac{1}{2}$$

Substitute the value of y into Equation (3).

$$x = 4y + 3 \quad$$ • Equation (3)
$$= 4\left(-\frac{1}{2}\right) + 3 \quad$$ • $y = -\frac{1}{2}$
$$= -2 + 3 = 1$$

The solution is $\left(1, -\frac{1}{2}\right)$.

You Try It 3   Solve by substitution:
$$3x - y = 3$$
$$6x + 3y = -4$$

Your solution

Solution on p. S10

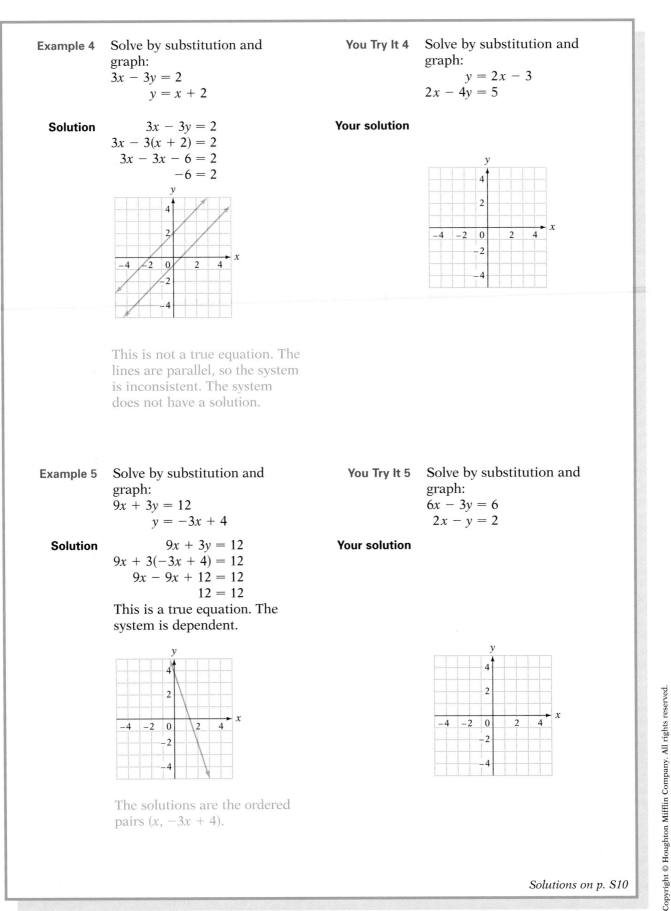

Example 4 Solve by substitution and graph:

$3x - 3y = 2$

$y = x + 2$

Solution

$3x - 3y = 2$

$3x - 3(x + 2) = 2$

$3x - 3x - 6 = 2$

$-6 = 2$

This is not a true equation. The lines are parallel, so the system is inconsistent. The system does not have a solution.

You Try It 4 Solve by substitution and graph:

$y = 2x - 3$

$2x - 4y = 5$

Your solution

Example 5 Solve by substitution and graph:

$9x + 3y = 12$

$y = -3x + 4$

Solution

$9x + 3y = 12$

$9x + 3(-3x + 4) = 12$

$9x - 9x + 12 = 12$

$12 = 12$

This is a true equation. The system is dependent.

The solutions are the ordered pairs $(x, -3x + 4)$.

You Try It 5 Solve by substitution and graph:

$6x - 3y = 6$

$2x - y = 2$

Your solution

Solutions on p. S10

Objective C **To solve investment problems** ....

The annual simple interest that an investment earns is given by the equation $Pr = I$, where P is the principal, or the amount invested, r is the simple interest rate, and I is the simple interest.

For instance, if you invest \$500 at a simple interest rate of 5%, then the interest earned after one year is calculated as follows.

$$Pr = I$$
$$500(0.05) = I$$ • Replace *P* by 500 and *r* by 0.05 (5%).
$$25 = I$$ • Simplify.

The amount of interest earned was \$25.

➡ You have a total of \$5000 to invest in two simple interest accounts. On one account, the money market fund, the annual simple interest rate is 3.5%. On the second account, the bond fund, the annual simple interest rate is 7.5%. If you earn \$245 per year from these two investments, how much do you have invested in each account?

> **Strategy for Solving Simple-Interest Investment Problems**
>
> 1. For each amount invested, use the equation $Pr = I$. Write a numerical or variable expression for the principal, the interest rate, and the interest earned.

Amount invested at 3.5%: x
Amount invested at 7.5%: y

	Principal, P	$\cdot$	Interest rate, r	$=$	Interest earned, I
Amount at 3.5%	x	$\cdot$	0.035	$=$	$0.035x$
Amount at 7.5%	y	$\cdot$	0.075	$=$	$0.075y$

> 2. Write a system of equations. One equation will express the relationship between the amounts invested. The second equation will express the relationship between the amounts of interest earned by the investments.

The total amount invested is \$5000: $x + y = 5000$
The total annual interest earned is \$245: $0.035x + 0.075y = 245$
Solve the system of equations.
(1) $x + y = 5000$
(2) $0.035x + 0.075y = 245$
Solve Equation (1) for y and substitute into Equation (2).
(3) $y = -x + 5000$
$$0.035x + 0.075(-x + 5000) = 245$$
$$0.035x - 0.075x + 375 = 245$$
$$-0.04x = -130$$
$$x = 3250$$
Substitute the value of x into Equation (3) and solve for y.
$$y = -x + 5000$$
$$y = -3250 + 5000 = 1750$$
The amount invested at 3.5% is \$3250. The amount invested at 7.5% is \$1750.

Example 6

An investment of $4000 is made at an annual simple interest rate of 4.9%. How much additional money must be invested at an annual simple interest rate of 7.4% so that the total interest earned is 6.4% of the total investment?

You Try It 6

An investment club invested $13,600 into two simple interest accounts. On one account, the annual simple interest rate is 4.2%. On the other, the annual simple interest rate is 6%. How much should be invested in each account so that both accounts earn the same annual interest?

Strategy

- Amount invested at 4.9%: 4000
  Amount invested at 7.4%: x
  Amount invested at 6.4%: y

	Principal	Rate	Interest
Amount at 4.9%	4000	0.049	0.049(4000)
Amount at 7.4%	x	0.074	0.074x
Amount at 6.4%	y	0.064	0.064y

- The amount invested at 6.4% (y) is $4000 more than the amount invested at 7.4% (x):
  $y = x + 4000$

  The sum of the interest earned at 4.9% and the interest earned at 7.4% equals the interest earned at 6.4%:
  $0.049(4000) + 0.074x = 0.064y$

Your strategy

Solution

$$y = x + 4000 \quad (1)$$
$$0.049(4000) + 0.074x = 0.064y \quad (2)$$

Replace y in Equation (2) by $x + 4000$ from Equation (1). Then solve for x.

$$0.049(4000) + 0.074x = 0.064(x + 4000)$$
$$196 + 0.074x = 0.064x + 256$$
$$0.01x = 60$$
$$x = 6000$$

$6000 must be invested at an annual simple interest rate of 7.4%.

Your solution

Solution on p. S11

4.1 Exercises

. . . .

Objective A

Solve by graphing.

1. $x + y = 2$
   $x - y = 4$

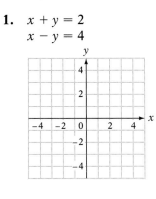

2. $x + y = 1$
   $3x - y = -5$

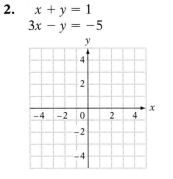

3. $x - y = -2$
   $x + 2y = 10$

4. $2x - y = 5$
   $3x + y = 5$

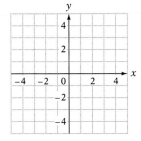

5. $3x - 2y = 6$
   $y = 3$

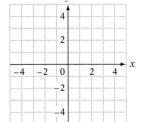

6. $x = 4$
   $3x - 2y = 4$

7. $x = 4$
   $y = -1$

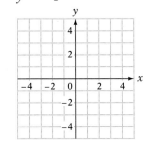

8. $x + 2 = 0$
   $y - 1 = 0$

9. $2x + y = 3$
   $x - 2 = 0$

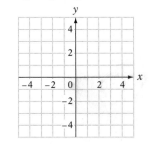

10. $x - 3y = 6$
    $y + 3 = 0$

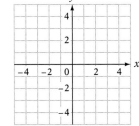

11. $x - y = 6$
    $x + y = 2$

12. $2x + y = 2$
    $-x + y = 5$

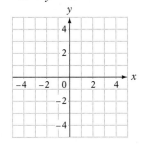

13. $y = x - 5$
$2x + y = 4$

14. $2x - 5y = 4$
$y = x + 1$

15. $y = \dfrac{1}{2}x - 2$
$x - 2y = 8$

16. $2x + 3y = 6$
$y = -\dfrac{2}{3}x + 1$

17. $2x - 5y = 10$
$y = \dfrac{2}{5}x - 2$

18. $3x - 2y = 6$
$y = \dfrac{3}{2}x - 3$

19. $3x - 4y = 12$
$5x + 4y = -12$

20. $2x - 3y = 6$
$2x - 5y = 10$

21. $2x - 3y = 2$
$5x + 4y = 5$

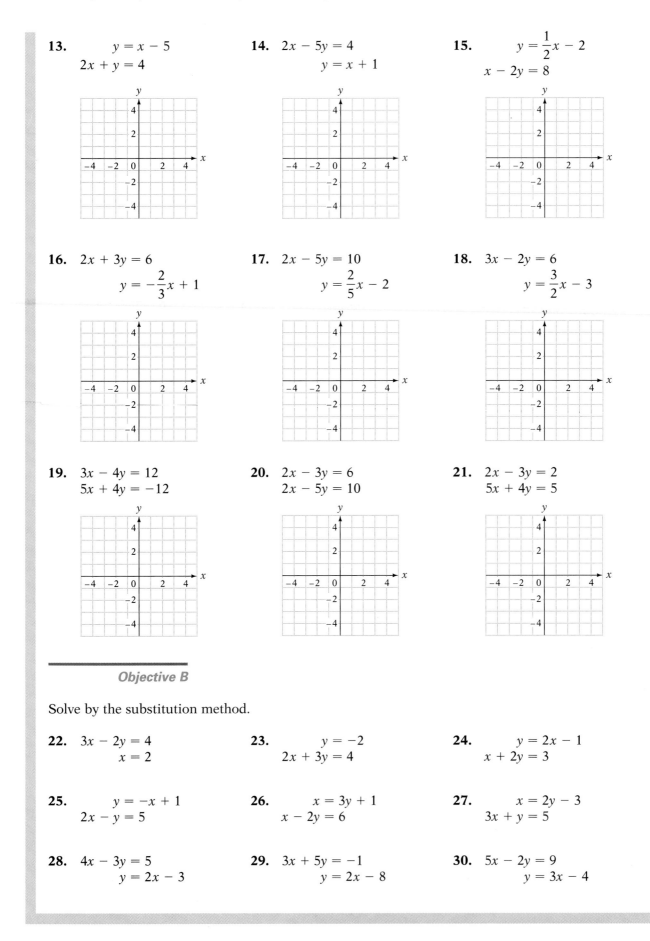

Objective B

Solve by the substitution method.

22. $3x - 2y = 4$
$x = 2$

23. $y = -2$
$2x + 3y = 4$

24. $y = 2x - 1$
$x + 2y = 3$

25. $y = -x + 1$
$2x - y = 5$

26. $x = 3y + 1$
$x - 2y = 6$

27. $x = 2y - 3$
$3x + y = 5$

28. $4x - 3y = 5$
$y = 2x - 3$

29. $3x + 5y = -1$
$y = 2x - 8$

30. $5x - 2y = 9$
$y = 3x - 4$

31. $4x - 3y = 2$
$\quad\quad y = 2x + 1$

32. $\quad\quad x = 2y + 4$
$\quad 4x + 3y = -17$

33. $3x - 2y = -11$
$\quad\quad x = 2y - 9$

34. $5x + 4y = -1$
$\quad\quad y = 2 - 2x$

35. $3x + 2y = 4$
$\quad\quad y = 1 - 2x$

36. $2x - 5y = -9$
$\quad\quad y = 9 - 2x$

37. $5x + 2y = 15$
$\quad\quad x = 6 - y$

38. $7x - 3y = 3$
$\quad\quad x = 2y + 2$

39. $3x - 4y = 6$
$\quad\quad x = 3y + 2$

40. $2x + 2y = 7$
$\quad\quad y = 4x + 1$

41. $3x + 7y = -5$
$\quad\quad y = 6x - 5$

42. $\quad 3x + y = 5$
$\quad 2x + 3y = 8$

43. $\quad 3x - y = 10$
$\quad 6x - 2y = 5$

44. $6x - 4y = 3$
$\quad 3x - 2y = 9$

45. $3x + 4y = 14$
$\quad 2x + y = 1$

46. $5x + 3y = 8$
$\quad 3x + y = 8$

47. $3x + 5y = 0$
$\quad\quad x - 4y = 0$

48. $2x - 7y = 0$
$\quad 3x + y = 0$

49. $2x - 4y = 16$
$\quad -x + 2y = -8$

50. $3x - 12y = -24$
$\quad\quad -x + 4y = 8$

51. $y = 3x + 2$
$\quad y = 2x + 3$

52. $y = 3x - 7$
$\quad y = 2x - 5$

53. $y = 3x + 1$
$\quad y = 6x - 1$

54. $y = 2x - 3$
$\quad y = 4x - 4$

Objective C *Application Problems*

55. The Community Relief Charity Group is earning 3.5% simple interest on the $2800 it invested in a savings account. It earns 4.2% simple interest on an insured bond fund. The annual interest earned from both accounts is $329. How much is invested in the insured bond fund?

56. Two investments earn an annual income of $575. One investment earns an annual simple interest rate of 8.5%, and the other investment earns an annual simple interest rate of 6.4%. The total amount invested is $8000. How much is invested in each account?

57. An investment club invested $6000 at an annual simple interest rate of 4.0%. How much additional money must be invested at an annual simple interest rate of 6.5% so that the total annual interest earned will be 5% of the total investment?

58. A small company invested $30,000 by putting part of it into a savings account that earned 3.2% annual simple interest and the remainder in a risky stock fund that earned 12.6% annual simple interest. If the company earned $1665 annually from the investments, how much was in each account?

59. An account executive divided $42,000 between two simple interest accounts. On the tax-free account the annual simple interest rate is 3.5%, and on the money market fund the annual simple interest rate is 4.5%. How much should be invested in each account so that both accounts earn the same annual interest?

60. The Ridge Investment Club placed $33,000 into two simple interest accounts. On one account, the annual simple interest rate is 6.5%. On the other, the annual simple interest rate is 4.5%. How much should be invested in each account so that both accounts earn the same annual interest?

61. The Cross Creek Investment Club has $20,000 to invest. The members of the club decided to invest $16,000 of their money in two bond funds. The first, a mutual bond fund, earns annual simple interest of 4.5%. The second account, a corporate bond fund, earns 8% annual simple interest. If the members earned $1070 from these two accounts, how much was invested in the mutual bond fund?

62. Cabin Financial Service Group recommends that a client purchase for $10,000 a corporate bond that earns 5% annual simple interest. How much additional money must be placed in U.S. government securities that earn a simple interest rate of 3.5% so that the total annual interest earned from the two investments is 4% of the total investment?

APPLYING THE CONCEPTS

Use a graphing calculator to estimate solutions to the following systems of equations. See the Projects and Group Activities on page 230 for assistance.

63. $y = -\dfrac{1}{2}x + 2$

$y = 2x - 1$

64. $y = \sqrt{2}x - 1$

$y = -\sqrt{3}x + 1$

65. $y = \pi x - \dfrac{2}{3}$

$y = -x + \dfrac{\pi}{2}$

66. How is a solution of a system of equations in two variables represented?

67. For a system of two linear equations in two variables, explain, in geometric terms, each of the following: dependent system of equations, inconsistent system of equations, independent system of equations.

68. Explain how to determine whether a linear system of equations in two variables is dependent, independent, or inconsistent without graphing or solving the system of equations.

4.2 Solving Systems of Linear Equations by the Addition Method

Objective A   *To solve a system of two linear equations in two variables by the addition method* .... (16) CT

The **addition method** is an alternative method for solving a system of equations. This method is based on the Addition Property of Equations. Use the addition method when it is not convenient to solve one equation for one variable in terms of another variable.

Note for the system of equations at the right the effect of adding Equation (2) to Equation (1). Because $-3y$ and $3y$ are additive inverses, adding the equations results in an equation with only one variable.

$$(1)\ 5x - 3y = 14$$
$$(2)\ 2x + 3y = -7$$
$$7x + 0y = 7$$
$$7x = 7$$

The solution of the resulting equation is the first component of the ordered-pair solution of the system.

$$7x = 7$$
$$x = 1$$

The second component is found by substituting the value of x into Equation (1) or (2) and then solving for y. Equation (1) is used here.

$$(1)\quad 5x - 3y = 14$$
$$5(1) - 3y = 14$$
$$5 - 3y = 14$$
$$-3y = 9$$
$$y = -3$$

The solution is $(1, -3)$.

POINT OF INTEREST

There are records of Babylonian mathematicians solving systems of equations 3600 years ago. Here is a system of equations from that time (in our modern notation):

$$\frac{2}{3}x = \frac{1}{2}y + 500$$
$$x + y = 1800$$

We say *modern notation* for many reasons. Foremost is the fact that using variables did not become widespread until the 17th century. There are many other reasons, however. The equals sign had not been invented, 2 and 3 did not look like they do today, and zero had not even been considered as a possible number.

Sometimes each equation of the system of equations must be multiplied by a constant so that the coefficients of one of the variable terms are opposites.

➡ Solve by the addition method: (1) $3x + 4y = 2$
                                    (2) $2x + 5y = -1$

To eliminate x, multiply Equation (1) by 2 and Equation (2) by -3. Note at the right how the constants are chosen.

$$2(3x + 4y) = 2 \cdot 2$$
$$-3(2x + 5y) = -3(-1)$$

- The negative is used so that the coefficients will be opposites.

$$6x + 8y = 4$$
$$\underline{-6x - 15y = 3}$$
$$-7y = 7$$
$$y = -1$$

- 2 times Equation (1).
- -3 times Equation (2).
- Add the equations.
- Solve for y.

Substitute the value of y into Equation (1) or Equation (2) and solve for x. Equation (1) will be used here.

$$(1)\quad 3x + 4y = 2$$
$$3x + 4(-1) = 2$$
$$3x - 4 = 2$$
$$3x = 6$$
$$x = 2$$

- Substitute -1 for y.
- Solve for x.

The solution is $(2, -1)$.

➡ Solve by the addition method: (1) $\frac{2}{3}x + \frac{1}{2}y = 4$

                                            (2) $\frac{1}{4}x - \frac{3}{8}y = -\frac{3}{4}$

Clear fractions. Multiply each equation by the LCM of the denominators.

$$6\left(\frac{2}{3}x + \frac{1}{2}y\right) = 6(4)$$

$$8\left(\frac{1}{4}x - \frac{3}{8}y\right) = 8\left(-\frac{3}{4}\right)$$

$$\begin{aligned} 4x + 3y &= 24 \\ 2x - 3y &= -6 \\ \hline 6x &= 18 \\ x &= 3 \end{aligned}$$

• Eliminate y. Add the equations. Then solve for x.

$$\frac{2}{3}x + \frac{1}{2}y = 4$$

• This is Equation (1).

$$\frac{2}{3}(3) + \frac{1}{2}y = 4$$

• Substitute $x = 3$ into Equation (1) and solve for y.

$$2 + \frac{1}{2}y = 4$$

$$\frac{1}{2}y = 2$$

$$y = 4$$

The solution is (3, 4).

➡ Solve by the addition method: (1) $2x - y = 3$
                                               (2) $4x - 2y = 6$

Eliminate y. Multiply Equation (1) by -2.

(1) $-2(2x - y) = -2(3)$ • -2 times Equation (1).
(3) $-4x + 2y = -6$ • This is Equation (3).

Add Equation (3) to Equation (2).

$$\begin{aligned} (2) \quad 4x - 2y &= 6 \\ (3) \quad -4x + 2y &= -6 \\ \hline 0 &= 0 \end{aligned}$$

The equation $0 = 0$ indicates that the system of equations is dependent. This means that the graphs of the two lines are the same. Therefore, the solutions of the system of equations are the ordered-pair solutions of the equation of the line. Solve Equation (1) for y.

$$\begin{aligned} 2x - y &= 3 \\ -y &= -2x + 3 \\ y &= 2x - 3 \end{aligned}$$

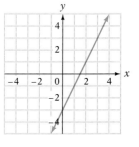

The ordered-pair solutions are (x, y), where $y = 2x - 3$. These ordered pairs are usually written $(x, 2x - 3)$, where $2x - 3$ is substituted for y.

Example 1   Solve by the addition method:
(1) $3x - 2y = 2x + 5$
(2) $2x + 3y = -4$

Solution   Write Equation (1) in the form
$Ax + By = C$.

$$3x - 2y = 2x + 5$$
$$x - 2y = 5$$

Solve the system:

$$x - 2y = 5$$
$$2x + 3y = -4$$

Eliminate x.

$$-2(x - 2y) = -2(5)$$
$$2x + 3y = -4$$

$$-2x + 4y = -10$$
$$2x + 3y = -4$$

Add the equations.

$$7y = -14$$
$$y = -2$$

Replace y in Equation (2).

$$2x + 3y = -4$$
$$2x + 3(-2) = -4$$
$$2x - 6 = -4$$
$$2x = 2$$
$$x = 1$$

The solution is $(1, -2)$.

You Try It 1   Solve by the addition method:
$2x + 5y = 6$
$3x - 2y = 6x + 2$

Your solution

Example 2   Solve by the addition method:
(1) $4x - 8y = 36$
(2) $3x - 6y = 27$

Solution   Eliminate x.

$$3(4x - 8y) = 3(36)$$
$$-4(3x - 6y) = -4(27)$$

$$12x - 24y = 108$$
$$-12x + 24y = -108$$

Add the equations.

$$0 = 0$$

The system of equations is
dependent. The solutions are
the ordered pairs
$\left(x, \dfrac{1}{2}x - \dfrac{9}{2}\right)$.

You Try It 2   Solve by the addition method:
$2x + y = 5$
$4x + 2y = 6$

Your solution

Solutions on p. S11

Objective B **To solve a system of three linear equations in three variables by the addition method** ....

An equation of the form $Ax + By + Cz = D$, where A, B, C, and D are constants, is a **linear equation in three variables.** Examples of these equations are shown at the right. The graph of a linear equation in three variables is a plane.

$$2x + 4y - 3z = 7$$
$$x - 6y + z = -3$$

Graphing an equation in three variables requires a third coordinate axis perpendicular to the xy-plane. The third axis is commonly called the z-axis. The result is a three-dimensional coordinate system called the xyz-coordinate system. To help visualize a three-dimensional coordinate system, think of a corner of a room: the floor is the xy-plane, one wall is the yz-plane, and the other wall is the xz-plane. A three-dimensional coordinate system is shown at the right.

Graphing an ordered triple requires three moves, the first in the direction of the x-axis, the second in the direction of the y-axis, and the third in the direction of the z-axis. The graph of the points $(-4, 2, 3)$ and $(3, 4, -2)$ is shown at the right.

The graph of a linear equation in three variables is a plane. That is, if all the solutions of a linear equation in three variables were plotted in an xyz-coordinate system, the graph would look like a large piece of paper extending infinitely. The graph of $x + y + z = 3$ is shown at the right.

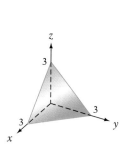

There are different ways in which three planes can be oriented in an *xyz*-coordinate system. The systems of equations represented by the planes below are inconsistent.

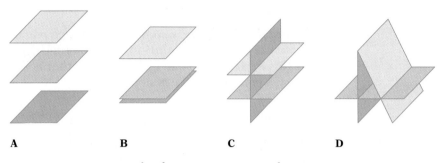

Graphs of Inconsistent Systems of Equations

For a system of three equations in three variables to have a solution, the graphs of the planes must intersect at a single point, they must intersect along a common line, or all equations must have a graph that is the same plane. These situations are shown in the figures below.

The three planes shown in Figure E intersect at a point. A system of equations represented by planes that intersect at a point is independent.

E

An Independent System
of Equations

The planes shown in Figures F and G intersect along a common line. The system of equations represented by the planes in Figure H has a graph that is the same plane. The systems of equations represented by the graphs below are dependent.

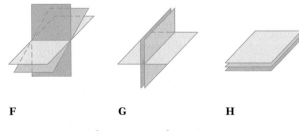

Dependent Systems of Equations

Just as a solution of an equation in two variables is an ordered pair (x, y), a **solution of an equation in three variables** is an ordered triple (x, y, z). For example, $(2, 1, -3)$ is a solution of the equation $2x - y - 2z = 9$. The ordered triple $(1, 3, 2)$ is not a solution.

A **system of linear equations in three variables** is shown at the right. A **solution of a system of equations in three variables** is an ordered triple that is a solution of each equation of the system.

$$x - 2y + z = 6$$
$$3x + y - 2z = 2$$
$$2x - 3y + 5z = 1$$

A system of linear equations in three variables can be solved by using the addition method. First, eliminate one variable from any two of the given equations. Then eliminate the same variable from any other two equations. The result will be a system of two equations in two variables. Solve this system by the addition method.

➡ Solve: (1) $x + 4y - z = 10$
  (2) $3x + 2y + z = 4$
  (3) $2x - 3y + 2z = -7$

Eliminate z from Equations (1) and (2) by adding the two equations.

$$x + 4y - z = 10$$
$$3x + 2y + z = 4$$
(4) $4x + 6y = 14$ • Add the equations.

Eliminate z from Equations (1) and (3). Multiply Equation (1) by 2 and add to Equation (3).

$$2x + 8y - 2z = 20$$ • 2 times Equation (1).
$$2x - 3y + 2z = -7$$ • This is Equation (3).
(5) $4x + 5y = 13$ • Add the equations.

Using Equations (4) and (5), solve the system of two equations in two variables.

(4) $4x + 6y = 14$
(5) $4x + 5y = 13$

Eliminate x. Multiply Equation (5) by -1 and add to Equation (4).

$$4x + 6y = 14$$ • This is Equation (4).
$$-4x - 5y = -13$$ • -1 times Equation (5).
$$y = 1$$ • Add the equations.

Substitute the value of y into Equation (4) or Equation (5) and solve for x. Equation (4) is used here.

$$4x + 6y = 14$$ • This is Equation (4).
$$4x + 6(1) = 14$$ • $y = 1$
$$4x = 8$$ • Solve for x.
$$x = 2$$

Substitute the value of y and the value of x into one of the equations in the original system. Equation (2) is used here.

$$3x + 2y + z = 4$$
$$3(2) + 2(1) + z = 4$$ • $x = 2, y = 1$
$$6 + 2 + z = 4$$
$$8 + z = 4$$
$$z = -4$$

The solution is $(2, 1, -4)$.

➡ Solve: (1) $2x - 3y - z = 1$
　　　(2) $x + 4y + 3z = 2$
　　　(3) $4x - 6y - 2z = 5$

Eliminate x from Equations (1) and (2).

$2x - 3y - z = 1$ 　　　• This is Equation (1).
$-2x - 8y - 6z = -4$ 　• -2 times Equation (2).
　$-11y - 7z = -3$ 　• Add the equations.

Eliminate x from Equations (1) and (3).

$-4x + 6y + 2z = -2$ 　• -2 times Equation (1).
$4x - 6y - 2z = 5$ 　　• This is Equation (3).
　　　$0 = 3$ 　　　• Add the equations.

The equation $0 = 3$ is not a true equation. The system of equations is inconsistent and therefore has no solution.

➡ Solve: (1)　　$3x - z = -1$
　　　(2)　　$2y - 3z = 10$
　　　(3)　$x + 3y - z = 7$

Eliminate x from Equations (1) and (3). Multiply Equation (3) by -3 and add to Equation (1).

　　　$3x - z = -1$ 　　• This is Equation (1).
　$-3x - 9y + 3z = -21$ 　• -3 times Equation (3).
(4)　　$-9y + 2z = -22$ 　• Add the equations.

Use Equations (2) and (4) to form a system of equations in two variables.

(2)　　$2y - 3z = 10$
(4)　$-9y + 2z = -22$

Eliminate z. Multiply Equation (2) by 2 and Equation (4) by 3.

$4y - 6z = 20$ 　　　• 2 times Equation (2).
$-27y + 6z = -66$ 　• 3 times Equation (4).
　$-23y = -46$ 　　• Add the equations.
　　$y = 2$ 　　　• Solve for y.

Substitute the value of y into Equation (2) or Equation (4) and solve for z. Equation (2) is used here.

(2)　　$2y - 3z = 10$ 　• This is Equation (2).
　　$2(2) - 3z = 10$ 　• $y = 2$
　　$4 - 3z = 10$ 　　• Solve for z.
　　　$-3z = 6$
　　　$z = -2$

Substitute the value of z into Equation (1) and solve for x.

(1)　　$3x - z = -1$ 　　• This is Equation (1).
　$3x - (-2) = -1$ 　　• $z = -2$
　　$3x + 2 = -1$ 　　• Solve for x.
　　　$3x = -3$
　　　$x = -1$

The solution is $(-1, 2, -2)$.

Example 3   Solve: (1) $3x - y + 2z = 1$
             (2) $2x + 3y + 3z = 4$
             (3) $x + y - 4z = -9$

You Try It 3   Solve: $x - y + z = 6$
             $2x + 3y - z = 1$
             $x + 2y + 2z = 5$

Solution   Eliminate y. Add
Equations (1) and (3).

$$3x - y + 2z = 1$$
$$x + y - 4z = -9$$
$$4x - 2z = -8$$

Multiply each side of the
equation by $\frac{1}{2}$.

(4) $2x - z = -4$

Multiply Equation (1) by 3 and
add to Equation (2).

$$9x - 3y + 6z = 3$$
$$2x + 3y + 3z = 4$$
(5) $11x + 9z = 7$

Solve the system of two
equations.

(4) $2x - z = -4$
(5) $11x + 9z = 7$

Multiply Equation (4) by 9 and
add to Equation (5).

$$18x - 9z = -36$$
$$11x + 9z = 7$$
$$29x = -29$$
$$x = -1$$

Replace x by -1 in
Equation (4).

$$2x - z = -4$$
$$2(-1) - z = -4$$
$$-2 - z = -4$$
$$-z = -2$$
$$z = 2$$

Replace x by -1 and z by 2 in
Equation (3).

$$x + y - 4z = -9$$
$$-1 + y - 4(2) = -9$$
$$-9 + y = -9$$
$$y = 0$$

The solution is $(-1, 0, 2)$.

Your solution

Solution on p. S11

4.2 Exercises

· ·

Objective A

Solve by the addition method.

1. $x - y = 5$
$x + y = 7$

2. $x + y = 1$
$2x - y = 5$

3. $3x + y = 4$
$x + y = 2$

4. $x - 3y = 4$
$x + 5y = -4$

5. $3x + y = 7$
$x + 2y = 4$

6. $x - 2y = 7$
$3x - 2y = 9$

7. $2x + 3y = -1$
$x + 5y = 3$

8. $x + 5y = 7$
$2x + 7y = 8$

9. $3x - y = 4$
$6x - 2y = 8$

10. $x - 2y = -3$
$-2x + 4y = 6$

11. $2x + 5y = 9$
$4x - 7y = -16$

12. $8x - 3y = 21$
$4x + 5y = -9$

13. $4x - 6y = 5$
$2x - 3y = 7$

14. $3x + 6y = 7$
$2x + 4y = 5$

15. $3x - 5y = 7$
$x - 2y = 3$

16. $3x + 4y = 25$
$2x + y = 10$

17. $x + 3y = 7$
$-2x + 3y = 22$

18. $2x - 3y = 14$
$5x - 6y = 32$

19. $3x + 2y = 16$
$2x - 3y = -11$

20. $2x - 5y = 13$
$5x + 3y = 17$

21. $4x + 4y = 5$
$2x - 8y = -5$

22. $3x + 7y = 16$
$4x - 3y = 9$

23. $5x + 4y = 0$
$3x + 7y = 0$

24. $3x - 4y = 0$
$4x - 7y = 0$

25. $5x + 2y = 1$
$2x + 3y = 7$

26. $3x + 5y = 16$
$5x - 7y = -4$

27. $3x - 6y = 6$
$9x - 3y = 8$

28. $\dfrac{2}{3}x - \dfrac{1}{2}y = 3$
$\dfrac{1}{3}x - \dfrac{1}{4}y = \dfrac{3}{2}$

29. $\dfrac{3}{4}x + \dfrac{1}{3}y = -\dfrac{1}{2}$
$\dfrac{1}{2}x - \dfrac{5}{6}y = -\dfrac{7}{2}$

30. $\dfrac{2}{5}x - \dfrac{1}{3}y = 1$
$\dfrac{3}{5}x + \dfrac{2}{3}y = 5$

31. $\dfrac{5x}{6} + \dfrac{y}{3} = \dfrac{4}{3}$
$\dfrac{2x}{3} - \dfrac{y}{2} = \dfrac{11}{6}$

32. $\dfrac{3x}{4} + \dfrac{2y}{5} = -\dfrac{3}{20}$
$\dfrac{3x}{2} - \dfrac{y}{4} = \dfrac{3}{4}$

33. $\dfrac{2x}{5} - \dfrac{y}{2} = \dfrac{13}{2}$
$\dfrac{3x}{4} - \dfrac{y}{5} = \dfrac{17}{2}$

34. $\dfrac{x}{2} + \dfrac{y}{3} = \dfrac{5}{12}$
$\dfrac{x}{2} - \dfrac{y}{3} = \dfrac{1}{12}$

35. $\dfrac{3x}{2} - \dfrac{y}{4} = -\dfrac{11}{12}$
$\dfrac{x}{3} - y = -\dfrac{5}{6}$

36. $\dfrac{3x}{4} - \dfrac{2y}{3} = 0$
$\dfrac{5x}{4} - \dfrac{y}{3} = \dfrac{7}{12}$

37. $4x - 5y = 3y + 4$
$2x + 3y = 2x + 1$

38. $5x - 2y = 8x - 1$
$2x + 7y = 4y + 9$

39. $2x + 5y = 5x + 1$
$3x - 2y = 3y + 3$

40. $4x - 8y = 5$
$8x + 2y = 1$

41. $5x + 2y = 2x + 1$
$2x - 3y = 3x + 2$

42. $3x + 3y = y + 1$
$x + 3y = 9 - x$

Objective B

Solve by the addition method.

43. $x + 2y - z = 1$
$2x - y + z = 6$
$x + 3y - z = 2$

44. $x + 3y + z = 6$
$3x + y - z = -2$
$2x + 2y - z = 1$

45. $2x - y + 2z = 7$
$x + y + z = 2$
$3x - y + z = 6$

46. $x - 2y + z = 6$
$x + 3y + z = 16$
$3x - y - z = 12$

47. $3x + y = 5$
$3y - z = 2$
$x + z = 5$

48. $2y + z = 7$
$2x - z = 3$
$x - y = 3$

49. $x - y + z = 1$
$2x + 3y - z = 3$
$-x + 2y - 4z = 4$

50. $2x + y - 3z = 7$
$x - 2y + 3z = 1$
$3x + 4y - 3z = 13$

51. $2x + 3z = 5$
$3y + 2z = 3$
$3x + 4y = -10$

52. $3x + 4z = 5$
$2y + 3z = 2$
$2x - 5y = 8$

53. $2x + 4y - 2z = 3$
$x + 3y + 4z = 1$
$x + 2y - z = 4$

54. $x - 3y + 2z = 1$
$x - 2y + 3z = 5$
$2x - 6y + 4z = 3$

55. $2x + y - z = 5$
$x + 3y + z = 14$
$3x - y + 2z = 1$

56. $3x - y - 2z = 11$
$2x + y - 2z = 11$
$x + 3y - z = 8$

57. $3x + y - 2z = 2$
$x + 2y + 3z = 13$
$2x - 2y + 5z = 6$

58. $4x + 5y + z = 6$
$2x - y + 2z = 11$
$x + 2y + 2z = 6$

59. $2x - y + z = 6$
$3x + 2y + z = 4$
$x - 2y + 3z = 12$

60. $3x + 2y - 3z = 8$
$2x + 3y + 2z = 10$
$x + y - z = 2$

61. $3x - 2y + 3z = -4$
  $2x + y - 3z = 2$
  $3x + 4y + 5z = 8$

62. $3x - 3y + 4z = 6$
  $4x - 5y + 2z = 10$
  $x - 2y + 3z = 4$

63. $3x - y + 2z = 2$
  $4x + 2y - 7z = 0$
  $2x + 3y - 5z = 7$

64. $2x + 2y + 3z = 13$
  $-3x + 4y - z = 5$
  $5x - 3y + z = 2$

65. $2x - 3y + 7z = 0$
  $x + 4y - 4z = -2$
  $3x + 2y + 5z = 1$

66. $5x + 3y - z = 5$
  $3x - 2y + 4z = 13$
  $4x + 3y + 5z = 22$

APPLYING THE CONCEPTS

67. Explain, graphically, the following situations when they are related to a system of three linear equations in three variables.
  a. The system of equations has no solution.
  b. The system of equations has exactly one solution.
  c. The system of equations has infinitely many solutions.

68. Describe the graph of each of the following equations in an *xyz*-coordinate system.
  a. $x = 3$
  b. $y = 4$
  c. $z = 2$
  d. $y = x$

The following are not linear systems of equations. However, they can be solved by using a modification of the addition method. Solve each system of equations.

69. $\dfrac{1}{x} - \dfrac{2}{y} = 3$
  $\dfrac{2}{x} + \dfrac{3}{y} = -1$

70. $\dfrac{1}{x} + \dfrac{2}{y} = 3$
  $\dfrac{1}{x} - \dfrac{3}{y} = -2$

71. $\dfrac{3}{x} + \dfrac{2}{y} = 1$
  $\dfrac{2}{x} + \dfrac{4}{y} = -2$

72. $\dfrac{3}{x} - \dfrac{5}{y} = -\dfrac{3}{2}$
  $\dfrac{1}{x} - \dfrac{2}{y} = -\dfrac{2}{3}$

73. For Exercise 69, solve each equation of the system for *y*. Then use a graphing calculator to verify the solution you determined algebraically. Note that the graphs are not straight lines.

74. For Exercise 70, solve each equation of the system for *y*. Then use a graphing calculator to verify the solution you determined algebraically. Note that the graphs are not straight lines.

Solving Systems of Equations by Using Determinants

Objective A *To evaluate a determinant* .... CT

A **matrix** is a rectangular array of numbers. Each number in the matrix is called an **element** of the matrix. The matrix at the right, with three rows and four columns, is called a 3×4 (read "3 by 4") matrix.

$$A = \begin{pmatrix} 1 & -3 & 2 & 4 \\ 0 & 4 & -3 & 2 \\ 6 & -5 & 4 & -1 \end{pmatrix}$$

A matrix of m rows and n columns is said to be of **order $m \times n$.** The matrix above has order 3×4. The notation a_{ij} refers to the element of a matrix in the ith row and the jth column. For matrix A, $a_{23} = -3$, $a_{31} = 6$, and $a_{13} = 2$.

A **square matrix** is one that has the same number of rows as columns. A 2×2 matrix and a 3×3 matrix are shown at the right.

$$\begin{pmatrix} -1 & 3 \\ 5 & 2 \end{pmatrix} \qquad \begin{pmatrix} 4 & 0 & 1 \\ 5 & -3 & 7 \\ 2 & 1 & 4 \end{pmatrix}$$

Associated with every square matrix is a number called its **determinant.**

Determinant of a 2 × 2 Matrix

The **determinant** of a 2×2 matrix $\begin{pmatrix} a_{11} & a_{12} \\ a_{21} & a_{22} \end{pmatrix}$ is written $\begin{vmatrix} a_{11} & a_{12} \\ a_{21} & a_{22} \end{vmatrix}$. The value of this determinant is given by the formula

$$\begin{vmatrix} a_{11} & a_{12} \\ a_{21} & a_{22} \end{vmatrix} = a_{11} a_{22} - a_{12} a_{21}$$

➡ Find the value of the determinant $\begin{vmatrix} 3 & 4 \\ -1 & 2 \end{vmatrix}$.

$$\begin{vmatrix} 3 & 4 \\ -1 & 2 \end{vmatrix} = 3 \cdot 2 - 4(-1) = 6 - (-4) = 10$$

The value of the determinant is 10.

For a square matrix whose order is 3×3 or greater, the value of the determinant of that matrix is found by using 2×2 determinants.

The **minor of an element** in a 3×3 determinant is the 2×2 determinant that is obtained by eliminating the row and column that contain that element.

➡ Find the minor of -3 for the determinant $\begin{vmatrix} 2 & -3 & 4 \\ 0 & 4 & 8 \\ -1 & 3 & 6 \end{vmatrix}$.

The minor of -3 is the 2×2 determinant created by eliminating the row and column that contain -3.

Eliminate the row and column as shown: $\begin{vmatrix} 2 & -3 & 4 \\ 0 & 4 & 8 \\ -1 & 3 & 6 \end{vmatrix}$

The minor of -3 is $\begin{vmatrix} 0 & 8 \\ -1 & 6 \end{vmatrix}$.

Copyright © Houghton Mifflin Company. All rights reserved.

TAKE NOTE

The only difference between the cofactor and the minor is one of sign. The definition at the right can be stated symbolically as follows: If C_{ij} is the cofactor and M_{ij} is the minor of the matrix element a_{ij}, then $C_{ij} = (-1)^{i+j} M_{ij}$. If $i + j$ is an even number, then $(-1)^{i+j} = 1$ and $C_{ij} = M_{ij}$. If $i + j$ is an odd number, then $(-1)^{i+j} = -1$ and $C_{ij} = -M_{ij}$.

Cofactor of an Element of a Matrix

The **cofactor** of an element of a matrix is $(-1)^{i+j}$ times the minor of that element, where i is the row number of the element and j is the column number of the element.

⇒ For the determinant $\begin{vmatrix} 3 & -2 & 1 \\ 2 & -5 & -4 \\ 0 & 3 & 1 \end{vmatrix}$, find the cofactor of -2 and of -5.

Because -2 is in the first row and the second column, $i = 1$ and $j = 2$. Thus $(-1)^{i+j} = (-1)^{1+2} = (-1)^3 = -1$. The cofactor of -2 is $(-1)\begin{vmatrix} 2 & -4 \\ 0 & 1 \end{vmatrix}$.

Because -5 is in the second row and the second column, $i = 2$ and $j = 2$.

Thus $(-1)^{i+j} = (-1)^{2+2} = (-1)^4 = 1$. The cofactor of -5 is $1 \cdot \begin{vmatrix} 3 & 1 \\ 0 & 1 \end{vmatrix}$.

Note from this example that the cofactor of an element is -1 times the minor of that element or 1 times the minor of that element, depending on whether the sum $i + j$ is an odd or even integer.

The value of a 3×3 or larger determinant can be found by **expanding by cofactors** of *any* row or any column. The result of expanding by cofactors using the first row of a 3×3 matrix is shown below.

$$\begin{vmatrix} a_{11} & a_{12} & a_{13} \\ a_{21} & a_{22} & a_{23} \\ a_{31} & a_{32} & a_{33} \end{vmatrix} = a_{11}(-1)^{1+1}\begin{vmatrix} a_{22} & a_{23} \\ a_{32} & a_{33} \end{vmatrix} + a_{12}(-1)^{1+2}\begin{vmatrix} a_{21} & a_{23} \\ a_{31} & a_{33} \end{vmatrix} + a_{13}(-1)^{1+3}\begin{vmatrix} a_{21} & a_{22} \\ a_{31} & a_{32} \end{vmatrix}$$

$$= a_{11}\begin{vmatrix} a_{22} & a_{23} \\ a_{32} & a_{33} \end{vmatrix} - a_{12}\begin{vmatrix} a_{21} & a_{23} \\ a_{31} & a_{33} \end{vmatrix} + a_{13}\begin{vmatrix} a_{21} & a_{22} \\ a_{31} & a_{32} \end{vmatrix}$$

⇒ Find the value of the determinant $\begin{vmatrix} 2 & -3 & 2 \\ 1 & 3 & -1 \\ 0 & -2 & 2 \end{vmatrix}$.

Expand by cofactors of the first row.

$$\begin{vmatrix} 2 & -3 & 2 \\ 1 & 3 & -1 \\ 0 & -2 & 2 \end{vmatrix} = 2\begin{vmatrix} 3 & -1 \\ -2 & 2 \end{vmatrix} - (-3)\begin{vmatrix} 1 & -1 \\ 0 & 2 \end{vmatrix} + 2\begin{vmatrix} 1 & 3 \\ 0 & -2 \end{vmatrix}$$

$$= 2(6 - 2) - (-3)(2 - 0) + 2(-2 - 0)$$
$$= 2(4) - (-3)(2) + 2(-2) = 8 - (-6) + (-4) = 10$$

To illustrate a statement made earlier, the value of this determinant will now be found by expanding by cofactors using the second column.

$$\begin{vmatrix} 2 & -3 & 2 \\ 1 & 3 & -1 \\ 0 & -2 & 2 \end{vmatrix} = -3(-1)^{1+2}\begin{vmatrix} 1 & -1 \\ 0 & 2 \end{vmatrix} + 3(-1)^{2+2}\begin{vmatrix} 2 & 2 \\ 0 & 2 \end{vmatrix} + (-2)(-1)^{3+2}\begin{vmatrix} 2 & 2 \\ 1 & -1 \end{vmatrix}$$

$$= -3(-1)\begin{vmatrix} 1 & -1 \\ 0 & 2 \end{vmatrix} + 3(1)\begin{vmatrix} 2 & 2 \\ 0 & 2 \end{vmatrix} + (-2)(-1)\begin{vmatrix} 2 & 2 \\ 1 & -1 \end{vmatrix}$$

$$= 3(2 - 0) + 3(4 - 0) + 2(-2 - 2)$$
$$= 3(2) + 3(4) + 2(-4) = 6 + 12 + (-8) = 10$$

Note that the value of the determinant is the same whether the first row or the second column is used to expand by cofactors. *Any row or column* can be used to evaluate a determinant by expanding by cofactors.

Example 1

Find the value of $\begin{vmatrix} 3 & -2 \\ 6 & -4 \end{vmatrix}$.

Solution

$\begin{vmatrix} 3 & -2 \\ 6 & -4 \end{vmatrix} = 3(-4) - (-2)(6) = -12 + 12 = 0$

The value of the determinant is 0.

You Try It 1

Find the value of $\begin{vmatrix} -1 & -4 \\ 3 & -5 \end{vmatrix}$.

Your solution

Example 2

Find the value of $\begin{vmatrix} -2 & 3 & 1 \\ 4 & -2 & 0 \\ 1 & -2 & 3 \end{vmatrix}$.

Solution
Expand by cofactors of the first row.

$\begin{vmatrix} -2 & 3 & 1 \\ 4 & -2 & 0 \\ 1 & -2 & 3 \end{vmatrix}$

$= -2 \begin{vmatrix} -2 & 0 \\ -2 & 3 \end{vmatrix} - 3 \begin{vmatrix} 4 & 0 \\ 1 & 3 \end{vmatrix} + 1 \begin{vmatrix} 4 & -2 \\ 1 & -2 \end{vmatrix}$

$= -2(-6 - 0) - 3(12 - 0) + 1(-8 + 2)$

$= -2(-6) - 3(12) + 1(-6)$

$= 12 - 36 - 6$

$= -30$

The value of the determinant is -30.

You Try It 2

Find the value of $\begin{vmatrix} 1 & 4 & -2 \\ 3 & 1 & 1 \\ 0 & -2 & 2 \end{vmatrix}$.

Your solution

Example 3

Find the value of $\begin{vmatrix} 0 & -2 & 1 \\ 1 & 4 & 1 \\ 2 & -3 & 4 \end{vmatrix}$.

Solution

$\begin{vmatrix} 0 & -2 & 1 \\ 1 & 4 & 1 \\ 2 & -3 & 4 \end{vmatrix}$

$= 0 \begin{vmatrix} 4 & 1 \\ -3 & 4 \end{vmatrix} - (-2) \begin{vmatrix} 1 & 1 \\ 2 & 4 \end{vmatrix} + 1 \begin{vmatrix} 1 & 4 \\ 2 & -3 \end{vmatrix}$

$= 0 - (-2)(4 - 2) + 1(-3 - 8)$

$= 2(2) + 1(-11)$

$= 4 - 11$

$= -7$

The value of the determinant is -7.

You Try It 3

Find the value of $\begin{vmatrix} 3 & -2 & 0 \\ 1 & 4 & 2 \\ -2 & 1 & 3 \end{vmatrix}$.

Your solution

Solutions on p. S12

Objective B **To solve a system of equations by using Cramer's Rule** .... CT

The connection between determinants and systems of equations can be understood by solving a general system of linear equations.

Solve: (1) $a_1 x + b_1 y = c_1$
(2) $a_2 x + b_2 y = c_2$

Eliminate y. Multiply Equation (1) by b_2 and Equation (2) by $-b_1$.

$a_1 b_2 x + b_1 b_2 y = c_1 b_2$ • b_2 times Equation (1).
$-a_2 b_1 x - b_1 b_2 y = -c_2 b_1$ • $-b_1$ times Equation (2).

Add the equations.

$a_1 b_2 x - a_2 b_1 x = c_1 b_2 - c_2 b_1$

$(a_1 b_2 - a_2 b_1)x = c_1 b_2 - c_2 b_1$ • Solve for x, assuming $a_1 b_2 - a_2 b_1 \neq 0$.

$$x = \frac{c_1 b_2 - c_2 b_1}{a_1 b_2 - a_2 b_1}$$

The denominator $a_1 b_2 - a_2 b_1$ is the determinant of the coefficients of x and y. This is called the **coefficient determinant**.

$$a_1 b_2 - a_2 b_1 = \begin{vmatrix} a_1 & b_1 \\ a_2 & b_2 \end{vmatrix}$$

coefficients of x ⟶
coefficients of y ⟶

The numerator $c_1 b_2 - c_2 b_1$ is the determinant obtained by replacing the first column in the coefficient determinant by the constants c_1 and c_2. This is called a **numerator determinant**.

$$c_1 b_2 - c_2 b_1 = \begin{vmatrix} c_1 & b_1 \\ c_2 & b_2 \end{vmatrix}$$

constants of ⟶
the equations

Following a similar procedure and eliminating x, it is possible also to express the y-component of the solution in determinant form. These results are summarized in Cramer's Rule.

POINT OF INTEREST

Cramer's Rule is named after Gabriel Cramer, who used it in a book he published in 1750. However, this rule was published in 1683 by the Japanese mathematician Seki Kown. That publication occurred seven years before Cramer's birth.

Cramer's Rule

The solution of the system of equations $\begin{aligned} a_1 x + b_1 y = c_1 \\ a_2 x + b_2 y = c_2 \end{aligned}$ is given by

$x = \dfrac{D_x}{D}$ and $y = \dfrac{D_y}{D}$, where $D = \begin{vmatrix} a_1 & b_1 \\ a_2 & b_2 \end{vmatrix}$, $D_x = \begin{vmatrix} c_1 & b_1 \\ c_2 & b_2 \end{vmatrix}$,

$D_y = \begin{vmatrix} a_1 & c_1 \\ a_2 & c_2 \end{vmatrix}$, and $D \neq 0$.

➡ Solve by using Cramer's Rule: $3x - 2y = 1$
$2x + 5y = 3$

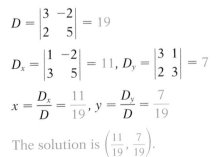

$D = \begin{vmatrix} 3 & -2 \\ 2 & 5 \end{vmatrix} = 19$ • Find the value of the coefficient determinant.

$D_x = \begin{vmatrix} 1 & -2 \\ 3 & 5 \end{vmatrix} = 11$, $D_y = \begin{vmatrix} 3 & 1 \\ 2 & 3 \end{vmatrix} = 7$ • Find the value of each of the numerator determinants.

$x = \dfrac{D_x}{D} = \dfrac{11}{19}$, $y = \dfrac{D_y}{D} = \dfrac{7}{19}$ • Use Cramer's Rule to write the solution.

The solution is $\left(\dfrac{11}{19}, \dfrac{7}{19} \right)$.

A procedure similar to that followed for two equations in two variables can be used to extend Cramer's Rule to three equations in three variables.

Cramer's Rule for a System of Three Equations in Three Variables

The solution of the system of equations
$$a_1x + b_1y + c_1z = d_1$$
$$a_2x + b_2y + c_2z = d_2$$
$$a_3x + b_3y + c_3z = d_3$$

is given by $x = \dfrac{D_x}{D}$, $y = \dfrac{D_y}{D}$, and $z = \dfrac{D_z}{D}$, where

$$D = \begin{vmatrix} a_1 & b_1 & c_1 \\ a_2 & b_2 & c_2 \\ a_3 & b_3 & c_3 \end{vmatrix}, \quad D_x = \begin{vmatrix} d_1 & b_1 & c_1 \\ d_2 & b_2 & c_2 \\ d_3 & b_3 & c_3 \end{vmatrix}, \quad D_y = \begin{vmatrix} a_1 & d_1 & c_1 \\ a_2 & d_2 & c_2 \\ a_3 & d_3 & c_3 \end{vmatrix}, \quad D_z = \begin{vmatrix} a_1 & b_1 & d_1 \\ a_2 & b_2 & d_2 \\ a_3 & b_3 & d_3 \end{vmatrix}, \text{ and } D \neq 0.$$

➡ Solve by using Cramer's Rule:
$$2x - y + z = 1$$
$$x + 3y - 2z = -2$$
$$3x + y + 3z = 4$$

Find the value of the coefficient determinant.

$$D = \begin{vmatrix} 2 & -1 & 1 \\ 1 & 3 & -2 \\ 3 & 1 & 3 \end{vmatrix} = 2\begin{vmatrix} 3 & -2 \\ 1 & 3 \end{vmatrix} - (-1)\begin{vmatrix} 1 & -2 \\ 3 & 3 \end{vmatrix} + 1\begin{vmatrix} 1 & 3 \\ 3 & 1 \end{vmatrix}$$
$$= 2(11) + 1(9) + 1(-8)$$
$$= 23$$

Find the value of each of the numerator determinants.

$$D_x = \begin{vmatrix} 1 & -1 & 1 \\ -2 & 3 & -2 \\ 4 & 1 & 3 \end{vmatrix} = 1\begin{vmatrix} 3 & -2 \\ 1 & 3 \end{vmatrix} - (-1)\begin{vmatrix} -2 & -2 \\ 4 & 3 \end{vmatrix} + 1\begin{vmatrix} -2 & 3 \\ 4 & 1 \end{vmatrix}$$
$$= 1(11) + 1(2) + 1(-14)$$
$$= -1$$

$$D_y = \begin{vmatrix} 2 & 1 & 1 \\ 1 & -2 & -2 \\ 3 & 4 & 3 \end{vmatrix} = 2\begin{vmatrix} -2 & -2 \\ 4 & 3 \end{vmatrix} - 1\begin{vmatrix} 1 & -2 \\ 3 & 3 \end{vmatrix} + 1\begin{vmatrix} 1 & -2 \\ 3 & 4 \end{vmatrix}$$
$$= 2(2) - 1(9) + 1(10)$$
$$= 5$$

$$D_z = \begin{vmatrix} 2 & -1 & 1 \\ 1 & 3 & -2 \\ 3 & 1 & 4 \end{vmatrix} = 2\begin{vmatrix} 3 & -2 \\ 1 & 4 \end{vmatrix} - (-1)\begin{vmatrix} 1 & -2 \\ 3 & 4 \end{vmatrix} + 1\begin{vmatrix} 1 & 3 \\ 3 & 1 \end{vmatrix}$$
$$= 2(14) + 1(10) + 1(-8)$$
$$= 30$$

Use Cramer's Rule to write the solution.

$$x = \frac{D_x}{D} = \frac{-1}{23}, \qquad y = \frac{D_y}{D} = \frac{5}{23}, \qquad z = \frac{D_z}{D} = \frac{30}{23}$$

The solution is $\left(-\dfrac{1}{23}, \dfrac{5}{23}, \dfrac{30}{23}\right)$.

Example 4
Solve by using Cramer's Rule.
$6x - 9y = 5$
$4x - 6y = 4$

Solution

$$D = \begin{vmatrix} 6 & -9 \\ 4 & -6 \end{vmatrix} = 0$$

Because $D = 0$, $\dfrac{D_x}{D}$ is undefined. Therefore,
the system is dependent or inconsistent.

You Try It 4
Solve by using Cramer's Rule.
$3x - y = 4$
$6x - 2y = 5$

Your solution

Example 5
Solve by using Cramer's Rule.
$3x - y + z = 5$
$x + 2y - 2z = -3$
$2x + 3y + z = 4$

Solution

$$D = \begin{vmatrix} 3 & -1 & 1 \\ 1 & 2 & -2 \\ 2 & 3 & 1 \end{vmatrix} = 28,$$

$$D_x = \begin{vmatrix} 5 & -1 & 1 \\ -3 & 2 & -2 \\ 4 & 3 & 1 \end{vmatrix} = 28,$$

$$D_y = \begin{vmatrix} 3 & 5 & 1 \\ 1 & -3 & -2 \\ 2 & 4 & 1 \end{vmatrix} = 0,$$

$$D_z = \begin{vmatrix} 3 & -1 & 5 \\ 1 & 2 & -3 \\ 2 & 3 & 4 \end{vmatrix} = 56$$

$$x = \frac{D_x}{D} = \frac{28}{28} = 1, \; y = \frac{D_y}{D} = \frac{0}{28} = 0,$$

$$z = \frac{D_z}{D} = \frac{56}{28} = 2$$

The solution is $(1, 0, 2)$.

You Try It 5
Solve by using Cramer's Rule.
$2x - y + z = -1$
$3x + 2y - z = 3$
$x + 3y + z = -2$

Your solution

Solutions on p. S12

4.3 Exercises

· ·

Objective A

Evaluate the determinant.

1. $\begin{vmatrix} 2 & -1 \\ 3 & 4 \end{vmatrix}$

2. $\begin{vmatrix} 5 & 1 \\ -1 & 2 \end{vmatrix}$

3. $\begin{vmatrix} 6 & -2 \\ -3 & 4 \end{vmatrix}$

4. $\begin{vmatrix} -3 & 5 \\ 1 & 7 \end{vmatrix}$

5. $\begin{vmatrix} 3 & 6 \\ 2 & 4 \end{vmatrix}$

6. $\begin{vmatrix} 5 & -10 \\ 1 & -2 \end{vmatrix}$

7. $\begin{vmatrix} 1 & -1 & 2 \\ 3 & 2 & 1 \\ 1 & 0 & 4 \end{vmatrix}$

8. $\begin{vmatrix} 4 & 1 & 3 \\ 2 & -2 & 1 \\ 3 & 1 & 2 \end{vmatrix}$

9. $\begin{vmatrix} 3 & -1 & 2 \\ 0 & 1 & 2 \\ 3 & 2 & -2 \end{vmatrix}$

10. $\begin{vmatrix} 4 & 5 & -2 \\ 3 & -1 & 5 \\ 2 & 1 & 4 \end{vmatrix}$

11. $\begin{vmatrix} 4 & 2 & 6 \\ -2 & 1 & 1 \\ 2 & 1 & 3 \end{vmatrix}$

12. $\begin{vmatrix} 3 & 6 & -3 \\ 4 & -1 & 6 \\ -1 & -2 & 3 \end{vmatrix}$

Objective B

Solve by using Cramer's Rule.

13. $2x - 5y = 26$
    $5x + 3y = 3$

14. $3x + 7y = 15$
    $2x + 5y = 11$

15. $x - 4y = 8$
    $3x + 7y = 5$

16. $5x + 2y = -5$
    $3x + 4y = 11$

17. $2x + 3y = 4$
    $6x - 12y = -5$

18. $5x + 4y = 3$
    $15x - 8y = -21$

19. $2x + 5y = 6$
    $6x - 2y = 1$

20. $7x + 3y = 4$
    $5x - 4y = 9$

21. $-2x + 3y = 7$
    $4x - 6y = 9$

22. $9x + 6y = 7$
    $3x + 2y = 4$

23. $2x - 5y = -2$
    $3x - 7y = -3$

24. $8x + 7y = -3$
    $2x + 2y = 5$

25.
$$2x - y + 3z = 9$$
$$x + 4y + 4z = 5$$
$$3x + 2y + 2z = 5$$

26.
$$3x - 2y + z = 2$$
$$2x + 3y + 2z = -6$$
$$3x - y + z = 0$$

27.
$$3x - y + z = 11$$
$$x + 4y - 2z = -12$$
$$2x + 2y - z = -3$$

28.
$$x + 2y + 3z = 8$$
$$2x - 3y + z = 5$$
$$3x - 4y + 2z = 9$$

29.
$$4x - 2y + 6z = 1$$
$$3x + 4y + 2z = 1$$
$$2x - y + 3z = 2$$

30.
$$x - 3y + 2z = 1$$
$$2x + y - 2z = 3$$
$$3x - 9y + 6z = -3$$

APPLYING THE CONCEPTS

31. Determine whether the following statements are always true, sometimes true, or never true.

a. The determinant of a matrix is a positive number.

b. A determinant can be evaluated by expanding about any row or column of the matrix.

c. Cramer's Rule can be used to solve a system of linear equations in three variables.

32. Show that $\begin{vmatrix} a & b \\ c & d \end{vmatrix} = - \begin{vmatrix} c & d \\ a & b \end{vmatrix}$.

Solve the following systems of equations by using Cramer's Rule and a calculator.

33.
$$3x - 7y + z = 2$$
$$x + y - z = -1$$
$$-x + 2y + 3z = 0$$

34.
$$3x + 2y - z = 1$$
$$x - 4y - 5z = 2$$
$$3x + 4y + z = 1$$

35.
$$x + 2y + 3z = 1$$
$$4x + 5y + 6z = 2$$
$$7x + 8y + 9z = 3$$

4.4   Application Problems

Objective A   *To solve rate-of-wind or rate-of-current problems* .... (18) CT

Motion problems that involve an object moving with or against a wind or current normally require two variables to solve.

A motorboat traveling with the current can go 24 mi in 2 h. Against the current it takes 3 h to go the same distance. Find the rate of the motorboat in calm water and the rate of the current.

> **Strategy for Solving Rate-of-Wind or Rate-of-Current Problems**
>
> 1. Choose one variable to represent the rate of the object in calm conditions and a second variable to represent the rate of the wind or current. Using these variables, express the rate of the object with and against the wind or current. Use the equation $rt = d$ to write expressions for the distance traveled by the object. The results can be recorded in a table.

Rate of the boat in calm water: x
Rate of the current: y

	Rate	·	Time	=	Distance
With the current	$x + y$	·	2	=	$2(x + y)$
Against the current	$x - y$	·	3	=	$3(x - y)$

> 2. Determine how the expressions for distance are related.

The distance traveled with the current is 24 mi: $2(x + y) = 24$
The distance traveled against the current is 24 mi: $3(x - y) = 24$

Solve the system of equations.

$$2(x + y) = 24 \xrightarrow{\text{Multiply by } \frac{1}{2}} \frac{1}{2} \cdot 2(x + y) = \frac{1}{2} \cdot 24 \longrightarrow x + y = 12$$

$$3(x - y) = 24 \xrightarrow{\text{Multiply by } \frac{1}{3}} \frac{1}{3} \cdot 3(x - y) = \frac{1}{3} \cdot 24 \longrightarrow x - y = 8$$

$$2x = 20$$
$$x = 10$$

• Add the equations.

Replace x by 10 in the equation $x + y = 12$.
Solve for y.

$$x + y = 12$$
$$10 + y = 12$$

The rate of the boat in calm water is 10 mph. $y = 2$
The rate of the current is 2 mph.

Example 1

Flying with the wind, a plane flew 1000 mi in 5 h. Flying against the wind, the plane could fly only 500 mi in the same amount of time. Find the rate of the plane in calm air and the rate of the wind.

Strategy

• Rate of the plane in still air: p
  Rate of the wind: w

	Rate	Time	Distance
With wind	$p + w$	5	$5(p + w)$
Against wind	$p - w$	5	$5(p - w)$

• The distance traveled with the wind is 1000 mi.
  The distance traveled against the wind is 500 mi.

$5(p + w) = 1000$
$5(p - w) = 500$

Solution

$5(p + w) = 1000 \qquad \dfrac{1}{5} \cdot 5(p + w) = \dfrac{1}{5} \cdot 1000$

$5(p - w) = 500 \qquad \dfrac{1}{5} \cdot 5(p - w) = \dfrac{1}{5} \cdot 500$

$$p + w = 200$$
$$p - w = 100$$
$$2p = 300$$
$$p = 150$$

$p + w = 200$
$150 + w = 200$
$w = 50$

The rate of the plane in calm air is 150 mph.
The rate of the wind is 50 mph.

You Try It 1

A rowing team rowing with the current traveled 18 mi in 2 h. Against the current, the team rowed 10 mi in 2 h. Find the rate of the rowing team in calm water and the rate of the current.

Your strategy

Your solution

Solution on p. S12

Objective B   *To solve application problems* .... (18) CT

The application problems in this section are varieties of problems solved earlier in the text. Each of the strategies for the problems in this section will result in a system of equations.

A store owner purchased twenty 60-watt light bulbs and 30 fluorescent bulbs for a total cost of $40. A second purchase, at the same prices, included thirty 60-watt light bulbs and 10 fluorescent bulbs for a total cost of $25. Find the cost of a 60-watt bulb and that of a fluorescent bulb.

> **Strategy for Solving Application Problems**
>
> 1. Choose a variable to represent each of the unknown quantities. Write numerical or variable expressions for all the remaining quantities. These results may be recorded in tables, one for each condition.

Cost of 60-watt bulb: b
Cost of fluorescent bulb: f

First purchase

	Amount	·	Unit Cost	=	Value
60-watt	20	·	b	=	$20b$
Fluorescent	30	·	f	=	$30f$

Second purchase

	Amount	·	Unit Cost	=	Value
60-watt	30	·	b	=	$30b$
Fluorescent	10	·	f	=	$10f$

> 2. Determine a system of equations. The strategies presented in Chapter 2 can be used to determine the relationships among the expressions in the tables. Each table will give one equation of the system of equations.

The total of the first purchase was $40: $20b + 30f = 40$
The total of the second purchase was $25: $30b + 10f = 25$

Solve the system of equations: (1) $20b + 30f = 40$
(2) $30b + 10f = 25$

$$60b + 90f = 120$$
$$-60b - 20f = -50$$
$$70f = 70$$
$$f = 1$$

• 3 times Equation (1).
• −2 times Equation (2).

Replace f by 1 in Equation (1) and solve for b.

$$20b + 30f = 40$$
$$20b + 30(1) = 40$$
$$20b + 30 = 40$$
$$20b = 10$$
$$b = 0.5$$

The cost of a 60-watt bulb was $.50.
The cost of a fluorescent bulb was $1.00.

Some application problems may require more than two variables, as shown in Example 2 and You Try It 2 on the next page.

Example 2

An investor has a total of $20,000 deposited in three different accounts, which earn annual interest rates of 9%, 7%, and 5%. The amount deposited in the 9% account is twice the amount in the 7% account. If the total annual interest earned for the three accounts is $1300, how much is invested in each account?

You Try It 2

A coin bank contains only nickels, dimes, and quarters. The value of the 19 coins in the bank is $2. If there are twice as many nickels as dimes, find the number of each type of coin in the bank.

Strategy

• Amount invested at 9%: x
Amount invested at 7%: y
Amount invested at 5%: z

Your strategy

	Principal	Rate	Interest
Amount at 9%	x	0.09	$0.09x$
Amount at 7%	y	0.07	$0.07y$
Amount at 5%	z	0.05	$0.05z$

• The amount invested at 9% (x) is twice the amount invested at 7% (y): $x = 2y$
The sum of the interest earned for all three accounts is $1300:
$0.09x + 0.07y + 0.05z = 1300$
The total amount invested is $20,000:
$x + y + z = 20,000$

Solution

(1) $\qquad\qquad\quad x = 2y$
(2) $\quad 0.09x + 0.07y + 0.05z = 1300$
(3) $\qquad\qquad x + y + z = 20,000$

Solve the system of equations. Substitute $2y$ for x in Equation (2) and Equation (3).

$0.09(2y) + 0.07y + 0.05z = 1300$
$\qquad\quad 2y + y + z = 20,000$

(4) $\quad 0.25y + 0.05z = 1300 \qquad$ • $0.09(2y) + 0.07y = 0.25y$
(5) $\qquad\quad 3y + z = 20,000 \qquad$ • $2y + y = 3y$

Solve the system of equations in two variables by multiplying Equation (5) by -0.05 and adding to Equation (4).

$\qquad 0.25y + 0.05z = 1300$
$\underline{-0.15y - 0.05z = -1000}$
$\qquad\quad 0.10y = 300$
$\qquad\qquad\quad y = 3000$

Substituting the value of y into Equation (1),
$x = 6000$.

Substituting the values of x and y into Equation (3), $z = 11,000$.

The investor placed $6000 in the 9% account, $3000 in the 7% account, and $11,000 in the 5% account.

Your solution

Solution on p. S13

4.4 Exercises

Objective A   *Rate-of-Wind or Rate-of-Current Problems*

1. A motorboat traveling with the current went 36 mi in 2 h. Against the current, it took 3 h to travel the same distance. Find the rate of the boat in calm water and the rate of the current.

2. A cabin cruiser traveling with the current went 45 mi in 3 h. Against the current, it took 5 h to travel the same distance. Find the rate of the cabin cruiser in calm water and the rate of the current.

3. A jet plane flying with the wind went 2200 mi in 4 h. Against the wind, the plane could fly only 1820 mi in the same amount of time. Find the rate of the plane in calm air and the rate of the wind.

4. Flying with the wind, a small plane flew 300 mi in 2 h. Against the wind, the plane could fly only 270 mi in the same amount of time. Find the rate of the plane in calm air and the rate of the wind.

5. A rowing team rowing with the current traveled 20 km in 2 h. Rowing against the current, the team rowed 12 km in the same amount of time. Find the rate of the team in calm water and the rate of the current.

6. A motorboat traveling with the current went 72 km in 3 h. Against the current, the boat could go only 48 km in the same amount of time. Find the rate of the boat in calm water and the rate of the current.

7. A turboprop plane flying with the wind flew 800 mi in 4 h. Flying against the wind, the plane required 5 h to travel the same distance. Find the rate of the wind and the rate of the plane in calm air.

8. Flying with the wind, a pilot flew 600 mi between two cities in 4 h. The return trip against the wind took 5 h. Find the rate of the plane in calm air and the rate of the wind.

9. A plane flying with a tailwind flew 600 mi in 5 h. Against the wind, the plane required 6 h to fly the same distance. Find the rate of the plane in calm air and the rate of the wind.

10. Flying with the wind, a plane flew 720 mi in 3 h. Against the wind, the plane required 4 h to fly the same distance. Find the rate of the plane in calm air and the rate of the wind.

Objective B *Application Problems*

11. A coin bank contains only nickels and dimes. The total value of the coins in the bank is $2.50. If the nickels were dimes and the dimes were nickels, the total value of the coins would be $3.50. Find the number of nickels in the bank.

12. A merchant mixed 10 lb of a cinnamon tea with 5 lb of spice tea. The 15-pound mixture cost $40. A second mixture included 12 lb of the cinnamon tea and 8 lb of the spice tea. The 20-pound mixture cost $54. Find the cost per pound of the cinnamon tea and the spice tea.

13. A carpenter purchased 60 ft of redwood and 80 ft of pine for a total cost of $27. A second purchase, at the same prices, included 100 ft of redwood and 60 ft of pine for a total of $34. Find the cost per foot of redwood and pine.

14. The total value of the quarters and dimes in a coin bank is $5.75. If the quarters were dimes and the dimes were quarters, the total value of the coins would be $6.50. Find the number of quarters in the bank.

15. A contractor buys 16 yd of nylon carpet and 20 yd of wool carpet for $920. A second purchase, at the same prices, includes 18 yd of nylon carpet and 25 yd of wool carpet for $1100. Find the cost per yard of the wool carpet.

16. During one month, a homeowner used 500 units of electricity and 100 units of gas for a total cost of $88. The next month, 400 units of electricity and 150 units of gas were used for a total cost of $76. Find the cost per unit of gas.

17. A company manufactures both 10-speed and standard model bicycles. The cost of materials for a 10-speed bicycle is $35, and the cost of materials for a standard bicycle is $25. The cost of labor to manufacture a 10-speed bicycle is $40, and the cost of labor to manufacture a standard bicycle is $20. During a week in which the company has budgeted $1250 for materials and $1300 for labor, how many 10-speed bicycles does the company plan to manufacture?

18. A company manufactures both color and black-and-white television sets. The cost of materials for a black-and-white TV is $20, and the cost of materials for a color TV is $80. The cost of labor to manufacture a black-and-white TV is $30, and the cost of labor to manufacture a color TV is $50. During a week in which the company has budgeted $4200 for materials and $2800 for labor, how many color TVs does the company plan to manufacture?

19. A chemist has two alloys, one of which is 10% gold and 15% lead, and the other of which is 30% gold and 40% lead. How many grams of each of the two alloys should be used to make an alloy that contains 60 g of gold and 88 g of lead?

20. A pharmacist has two vitamin-supplement powders. The first powder is 20% vitamin B1 and 10% vitamin B2. The second is 15% vitamin B1 and 20% vitamin B2. How many milligrams of each of the two powders should the pharmacist use to make a mixture that contains 130 mg of vitamin B1 and 80 mg of vitamin B2?

21. On Monday, a computer manufacturing company sent out three shipments. The first order, which contained a bill for $114,000, was for 4 Model II, 6 Model VI, and 10 Model IX computers. The second shipment, which contained a bill for $72,000, was for 8 Model II, 3 Model VI, and 5 Model IX computers. The third shipment, which contained a bill for $81,000, was for 2 Model II, 9 Model VI, and 5 Model IX computers. What does the manufacturer charge for each Model VI computer?

22. A relief organization supplies blankets, cots, and lanterns to victims of fires, floods, and other natural disasters. One week the organization purchased 15 blankets, 5 cots, and 10 lanterns for a total cost of $1250. The next week, at the same prices, the organization purchased 20 blankets, 10 cots, and 15 lanterns for a total cost of $2000. The next week, at the same prices, the organization purchased 10 blankets, 15 cots, and 5 lanterns for a total cost of $1625. Find the cost of one blanket, the cost of one cot, and the cost of one lantern.

23. A science museum charges $10 for a regular admission ticket, but members receive a discount of $3 and students are admitted for $5. Last Saturday, 750 tickets were sold for a total of $5400. If 20 more student tickets than regular tickets were sold, how many of each type of ticket were sold?

24. The total value of the nickels, dimes, and quarters in a coin bank is $4. If the nickels were dimes and the dimes were nickels, the total value of the coins would be $3.75. If the quarters were dimes and the dimes were quarters, the total value would be $6.25. Find the number of nickels, dimes, and quarters in the bank.

25. An investor has a total of $25,000 deposited in three different accounts, which earn annual interest rates of 8%, 6%, and 4%. The amount deposited in the 8% account is twice the amount in the 6% account. If the three accounts earn total annual interest of $1520, how much money is deposited in each account?

APPLYING THE CONCEPTS

26. Two angles are complementary. The larger angle is 9° more than eight times the measure of the smaller angle. Find the measures of the two angles. (Complementary angles are two angles whose sum is 90°.)

27. Two angles are supplementary. The larger angle is 40° more than three times the measure of the smaller angle. Find the measures of the two angles. (Supplementary angles are two angles whose sum is 180°.)

28. The sum of the ages of a gold coin and a silver coin is 75 years. The age of the gold coin 10 years from now will be 5 years less than the age of the silver coin 10 years ago. Find the present ages of the two coins.

29. The difference between the ages of an oil painting and a watercolor is 35 years. The age of the oil painting 5 years from now will be twice the age that the watercolor was five years ago. Find the present ages of each.

30. A coin bank contains only dimes and quarters. The total value of all the coins is $1. How many of each type of coin are in the bank? (*Hint:* There is more than one answer to this problem.)

31. An investor has a total of $25,000 deposited in three different accounts, which earn annual interest rates of 8%, 6%, and 4%. The amount deposited in the 8% account is $1000 more than the amount in the 4% account. If the investor wishes to earn $1520 from the three accounts, show that there is more than one way the investor can allocate money to each of the accounts to reach the goal. Explain why this happens here while in Exercise 25 there is only one way to allocate the $25,000. *Suggestion:* Suppose the amount invested at 4% is $8000 and then find the other amounts. Now suppose $10,000 is invested at 4% and then find the other amounts.

4.5 Solving Systems of Linear Inequalities

Objective A *To graph the solution set of a system of linear inequalities* ....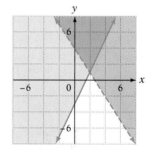

Two or more inequalities considered together are called a **system of inequalities.** The **solution set of a system of inequalities** is the intersection of the solution sets of the individual inequalities. To graph the solution set of a system of inequalities, first graph the solution set of each inequality. The solution set of the system of inequalities is the region of the plane represented by the intersection of the two shaded areas.

➡ Graph the solution set: $2x - y \le 3$
$$3x + 2y > 8$$

Solve each equation for y.

$2x - y \le 3$ $3x + 2y > 8$
$-y \le -2x + 3$ $2y > -3x + 8$
$y \ge 2x - 3$ $y > -\dfrac{3}{2}x + 4$

Graph $y = 2x - 3$ as a solid line. Because the inequality is $\ge$, shade above the line.

Graph $y = -\dfrac{3}{2}x + 4$ as a dotted line. Because the inequality is $>$, shade above the line.

The solution set of the system is the region of the plane represented by the intersection of the solution sets of the individual inequalities.

➡ Graph the solution set: $-x + 2y \ge 4$
$$x - 2y \ge 6$$

Solve each equation for y.

$-x + 2y \ge 4$ $x - 2y \ge 6$
$2y \ge x + 4$ $-2y \ge -x + 6$
$y \ge \dfrac{1}{2}x + 2$ $y \le \dfrac{1}{2}x - 3$

Shade above the solid line $y = \dfrac{1}{2}x + 2$.

Shade below the solid line $y = \dfrac{1}{2}x - 3$.

Because the solution sets of the two inequalities do not intersect, the solution of the system is the empty set.

Example 1

Graph the solution set: $y \geq x - 1$
$\qquad\qquad\qquad\qquad\quad\; y < -2x$

Solution

Shade above the solid line $y = x - 1$.
Shade below the dotted line $y = -2x$.

The solution of the system is the intersection of the solution sets of the individual inequalities.

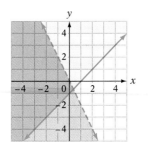

You Try It 1

Graph the solution set: $y \geq 2x - 3$
$\qquad\qquad\qquad\qquad\quad\; y > -3x$

Your solution

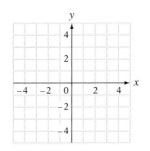

Example 2

Graph the solution set: $2x + 3y > 9$
$\qquad\qquad\qquad\qquad\qquad y < -\dfrac{2}{3}x + 1$

Solution

$2x + 3y > 9$
$\qquad 3y > -2x + 9$
$\qquad\quad y > -\dfrac{2}{3}x + 3$

Graph above the dotted line $y = -\dfrac{2}{3}x + 3$.

Graph below the dotted line $y = -\dfrac{2}{3}x + 1$.

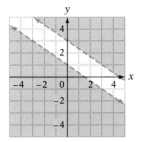

The intersection of the system is the empty set, because the solution sets of the two inequalities do not intersect.

You Try It 2

Graph the solution set: $3x + 4y > 12$
$\qquad\qquad\qquad\qquad\qquad y < \dfrac{3}{4}x - 1$

Your solution

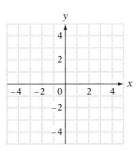

Solutions on p. S13

4.5 Exercises

Objective A

Graph the solution set.

1. $x - y \geq 3$
$x + y \leq 5$

2. $2x - y < 4$
$x + y < 5$

3. $3x - y < 3$
$2x + y \geq 2$

4. $x + 2y \leq 6$
$x - y \leq 3$

5. $2x + y \geq -2$
$6x + 3y \leq 6$

6. $x + y \geq 5$
$3x + 3y \leq 6$

7. $3x - 2y < 6$
$y \leq 3$

8. $x \leq 2$
$3x + 2y > 4$

9. $y > 2x - 6$
$x + y < 0$

10. $x < 3$
$y < -2$

11. $x + 1 \geq 0$
$y - 3 \leq 0$

12. $5x - 2y \geq 10$
$3x + 2y \geq 6$

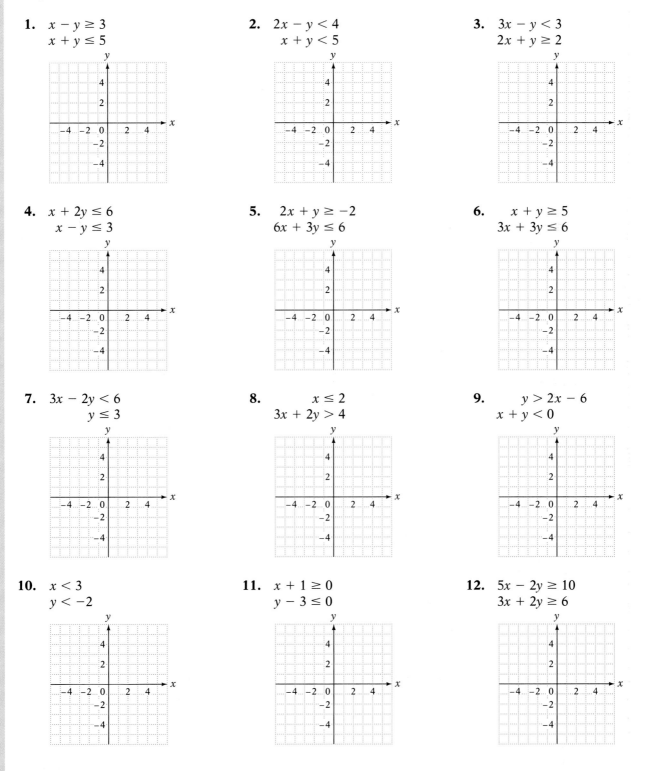

13. $2x + y \geq 4$
$3x - 2y < 6$

14. $3x - 4y < 12$
$x + 2y < 6$

15. $x - 2y \leq 6$
$2x + 3y \leq 6$

16. $x - 3y > 6$
$2x + y > 5$

17. $x - 2y \leq 4$
$3x + 2y \leq 8$
$x > -1$

18. $3x - 2y < 0$
$5x + 3y > 9$
$y < 4$

APPLYING THE CONCEPTS

Graph the solution set.

19. $2x + 3y \leq 15$
$3x - y \leq 6$
$y \geq 0$

20. $x + y \leq 6$
$x - y \leq 2$
$x \geq 0$

21. $x - y \leq 5$
$2x - y \geq 6$
$y \geq 0$

22. $x - 3y \leq 6$
$5x - 2y \geq 4$
$y \geq 0$

23. $2x - y \leq 4$
$3x + y < 1$
$y \leq 0$

24. $x - y \leq 4$
$2x + 3y > 6$
$x \geq 0$

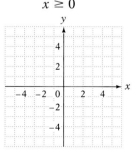

Focus on Problem Solving

Solve an Easier Problem

We begin this problem-solving feature with a restatement of the four steps of Polya's recommended problem-solving model.

1. Understand the problem.
2. Devise a plan.
3. Carry out the plan.
4. Review your solution.

One of the several methods of devising a plan is to try to solve an easier problem. Suppose you are in charge of your softball league, which consists of 15 teams. You must devise a schedule in which each team plays every other team once. How many games must be scheduled?

To solve this problem, we will attempt an easier problem first. Suppose that your league contains only a small number of teams. For instance, if there were only 1 team, you would schedule 0 games. If there were 2 teams, you would schedule 1 game. If there were 3 teams, you would schedule 3 games. The diagram at the left shows that 6 games must be scheduled when there are 4 teams in the league.

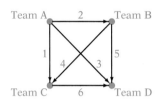

Here is a table of our results so far. (Remember that making a table is another strategy to be used in problem solving.)

Number of Teams	Number of Games	Possible Pattern
1	0	0
2	1	1
3	3	1 + 2
4	6	1 + 2 + 3

1. Draw a diagram with 5 dots to represent the teams. Draw lines from each dot to a second dot, and determine the number of games required.
2. What is the apparent pattern for the number of games required?
3. Assuming that the pattern continues, how many games must be scheduled for the 15 teams of the original problem?

After solving a problem, good problem solvers ask whether it is possible to solve the problem in a different manner. Here is a possible alternative method of solving the scheduling problem.

Begin with one of the 15 teams (say team A) and ask, "How many games must this team play?" Because there are 14 teams left to play, you must schedule 14 games. Now move to team B. It is already scheduled to play team A, and it does not play itself, so there are 13 teams left for it to play. Consequently, you must schedule 14 + 13 games.

4. Continue this reasoning for the remaining teams and determine the number of games that must be scheduled. Does this answer correspond to the answer you obtained with the first method?
5. Making connections to other problems you have solved is an important step toward becoming an excellent problem solver. How does the answer to the scheduling of teams relate to the triangular numbers discussed in the Focus on Problem Solving in the chapter titled Linear Functions and Inequalities in Two Variables?

Projects and Group Activities

Using a Graphing Calculator to Solve a System of Equations

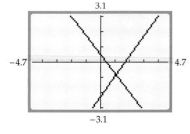

A graphing calculator can be used to solve a system of equations. For this procedure to work on most calculators, it is necessary that the point of intersection be on the screen. This means that you may have to experiment with Xmin, Xmax, Ymin, and Ymax values until the graphs intersect on the screen.

To solve a system of equations graphically, solve each equation for y. Then graph the equations of the system. Their point of intersection is the solution.

For instance, to solve the system of equations

$$4x - 3y = 7$$
$$5x + 4y = 2$$

first solve each equation for y.

$$4x - 3y = 7 \Rightarrow y = \frac{4}{3}x - \frac{7}{3}$$

$$5x + 4y = 2 \Rightarrow y = -\frac{5}{4}x + \frac{1}{2}$$

The keystrokes to solve this system are given below. We are using a viewing window $[-4.7, 4.7]$ by $[-3.1, 3.1]$. The approximate solution is $(1.096774, -0.870968)$.

TI-83	SHARP EL-9600	Casio CFX-9850G
[Y=] [CLEAR] 4 [X,T,θ,n] [÷] 3 [−] 7 [÷] 3 [ENTER] [CLEAR] [(−)] 5 [X,T,θ,n] [÷] 4 [+] 1 [÷] 2 [GRAPH]	[Y=] [CL] 4 [X/θ/T/n] [÷] 3 [−] 7 [÷] 3 [ENTER] [CL] [(−)] 5 [X/θ/T/n] [÷] 4 [+] 1 [÷] 2 [GRAPH]	[MENU] 5 [F2] [F1] 4 [X,θ,T] [÷] 3 [−] 7 [÷] 3 [EXE] [F2] [F1] [CLEAR] [(−)] 5 [X,θ,T] [÷] 4 [+] 1 [÷] 2 [EXE] [GRAPH]

Once the calculator has drawn the graphs, use the TRACE feature and move the cursor to the approximate point of intersection. This will give you an approximate solution of the system of equations. The method by which a more accurate solution can be determined depends on the type of calculator you use. Consult the user's manual under "systems of equations."

Some of the exercises in the first section of this chapter asked you to solve a system of equations by graphing. Try those exercises again, this time using your graphing calculator.

Current models of calculators do not allow you to solve graphically a system of equations in three variables. However, these calculators do have matrix and determinant operations that can be used to solve these systems.

Solving a First-Degree Equation with a Graphing Calculator

A first-degree equation in one variable can be solved graphically[1] by using a graphing calculator. The idea is to rewrite the equation as a system of equations and then solve the system of equations as we illustrated on the previous page. For instance, to solve the equation

$$2x + 1 = 5x - 5$$

write the equation as the following system of equations.

$$y = 2x + 1$$
$$y = 5x - 5$$

Notice that we have used the left and right sides of the original equation to form the system of equations.

Now graph the equations and find the point of intersection. This is shown at the left using a viewing window of $[-9.6, 9.6]$ by $[-9.6, 9.6]$. The solution of the original equation, $2x + 1 = 5x - 5$, is the x-coordinate of the point of intersection. Thus the solution of the equation is 2.

Recall that not all equations have a solution. Consider the equation

$$x - 3(x + 2) = 2x - 2(2x - 2)$$

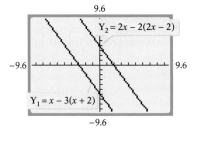

The graphs of the left and right sides of the equation are shown at the left. Note that the lines appear to be parallel and therefore do not intersect. Since the lines do not intersect, there is no solution of the system of equations and thus no solution of the original equation. We algebraically verify this result below.

$$x - 3(x + 2) = 2x - 2(2x - 2)$$
$$x - 3x - 6 = 2x - 4x + 4 \qquad \bullet \text{ Use the Distributive Property.}$$
$$-2x - 6 = -2x + 4 \qquad \bullet \text{ Simplify.}$$
$$-6 = 4 \qquad \bullet \text{ Add } 2x \text{ to each side of the equation.}$$

Because $-6 = 4$ is not a true equation, there is no solution.

One last point about the last equation. Note that in the third line of the solution we obtain the expressions $-2x - 6$ and $-2x + 4$. If we were to graph $y = -2x - 6$ and $y = -2x + 4$, the slopes of the lines are equal (both are -2) and therefore the graphs of the lines are parallel.

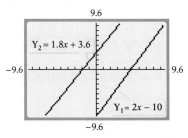

Before we leave graphical solutions, a few words of caution. Graphs can be deceiving and appear not to intersect when they do, and appear to intersect when they do not. For instance, an attempt to graphically solve

$$2x - 10 = 1.8x + 3.6$$

is shown at the left.

If you use the viewing window $[-9.6, 9.6]$ by $[-9.6, 9.6]$, the graphs will appear to be parallel. However, the graphs of $y = 2x - 10$ and $y = 1.8x + 3.6$ do not have the same slope and therefore must intersect. For this equation, you need a larger viewing window to see the point of intersection.

Solve the following equations by using a graphing calculator.

1. $3x - 1 = 5x + 1$
2. $3x + 2 = 4$
3. $3 + 2(2x - 4) = 5(x - 3)$
4. $2x - 4 = 5x - 3(x + 2) + 2$
5. Explain how Problem 4 relates to an *identity* as explained in Section 2.1.
6. Find an appropriate viewing window so that you can determine the solution of the equation $2x - 10 = 1.8x + 3.6$ given above.

[1]Some graphing calculators offer nongraphical techniques for solving an equation.

Chapter Summary

Key Words   Equations considered together are called a *system of equations*.

A *solution of a system of equations* in two variables is an ordered pair that is a solution of each equation of the system.

When the graphs of a system of equations intersect at only one point, the system is called an *independent system of equations*.

When the graphs of a system of equations coincide, the system is called a *dependent system of equations*.

When a system of equations has no solution, it is called an *inconsistent system of equations*.

An equation of the form $Ax + By + Cz = D$, where A, B, C, and D are constants, is called a *linear equation in three variables*.

A *solution of a system of equations in three variables* is an ordered triple that is a solution of each equation of the system.

A *matrix* is a rectangular array of numbers.

A *square matrix* has the same number of rows as columns.

A *determinant* is a number associated with a square matrix.

The *minor of an element* in a 3×3 determinant is the 2×2 determinant obtained by eliminating the row and column that contain that element.

The *cofactor* of an element of a matrix is $(-1)^{i+j}$ times the minor of that element, where i is the row number of the element and j is its column number.

The evaluation of the determinant of a 3×3 or larger matrix is accomplished by *expanding by cofactors*.

Inequalities considered together are called a *system of inequalities*.

The *solution set of a system of inequalities* is the intersection of the solution sets of the individual inequalities.

Essential Rules   A system of equations can be solved by the graphing method, the substitution method, or the addition method.

Cramer's Rule is a method of solving a system of equations by using determinants.

Chapter Review

1. Solve by substitution: $2x - 6y = 15$
   $$x = 4y + 8$$

2. Solve by the addition method: $3x + 2y = 2$
   $$x + y = 3$$

3. Solve by graphing: $x + y = 3$
   $$3x - 2y = -6$$

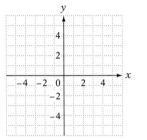

4. Solve by graphing: $2x - y = 4$
   $$y = 2x - 4$$

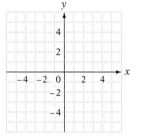

5. Solve by substitution: $3x + 12y = 18$
   $$x + 4y = 6$$

6. Solve by the addition method: $5x - 15y = 30$
   $$x - 3y = 6$$

7. Solve by the addition method.
   $3x - 4y - 2z = 17$
   $4x - 3y + 5z = 5$
   $5x + 5y + 3z = 14$

8. Solve by the addition method.
   $3x + y = 13$
   $2y + 3z = 5$
   $x + 2z = 11$

9. Evaluate the determinant.
   $$\begin{vmatrix} 6 & 1 \\ 2 & 5 \end{vmatrix}$$

10. Evaluate the determinant.
    $$\begin{vmatrix} 1 & 5 & -2 \\ -2 & 1 & 4 \\ 4 & 3 & -8 \end{vmatrix}$$

11. Solve by using Cramer's Rule:
$$2x - y = 7$$
$$3x + 2y = 7$$

12. Solve by using Cramer's Rule:
$$3x - 4y = 10$$
$$2x + 5y = 15$$

13. Solve by using Cramer's Rule:
$$x + y + z = 0$$
$$x + 2y + 3z = 5$$
$$2x + y + 2z = 3$$

14. Solve by using Cramer's Rule:
$$x + 3y + z = 6$$
$$2x + y - z = 12$$
$$x + 2y - z = 13$$

15. Graph the solution set:
$$x + 3y \leq 6$$
$$2x - y \geq 4$$

16. Graph the solution set:
$$2x + 4y \geq 8$$
$$x + y \leq 3$$

17. A cabin cruiser traveling with the current went 60 mi in 3 h. Against the current, it took 5 h to travel the same distance. Find the rate of the cabin cruiser in calm water and the rate of the current.

18. A pilot flying with the wind flew 600 mi in 3 h. Flying against the wind, the pilot required 4 h to travel the same distance. Find the rate of the plane in calm air and the rate of the wind.

19. At a movie theater, admission tickets are $5 for children and $8 for adults. The receipts for one Friday evening were $2500. The next day there were three times as many children as the preceding evening and only half the number of adults as the night before, yet the receipts were still $2500. Find the number of children who attended on Friday evening.

20. A trust administrator divides $20,000 between two accounts. One account earns an annual simple interest rate of 3%, and the second account earns an annual simple interest rate of 7%. The total annual income from the two accounts is $1200. How much is invested in each account?

Chapter Test

1. Solve by graphing: $2x - 3y = -6$
$2x - y = 2$

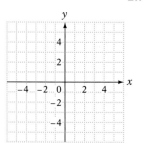

2. Solve by graphing: $x - 2y = -5$
$3x + 4y = -15$

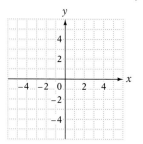

3. Graph the solution set: $2x - y < 3$
$4x + 3y < 11$

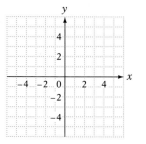

4. Graph the solution set: $x + y > 2$
$2x - y < -1$

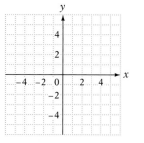

5. Solve by substitution: $3x + 2y = 4$
$x = 2y - 1$

6. Solve by substitution: $5x + 2y = -23$
$2x + y = -10$

7. Solve by substitution: $y = 3x - 7$
$y = -2x + 3$

8. Solve by the addition method:
$3x + 4y = -2$
$2x + 5y = 1$

9. Solve by the addition method:
$4x - 6y = 5$
$6x - 9y = 4$

10. Solve by the addition method:
$3x - y = 2x + y - 1$
$5x + 2y = y + 6$

11. Solve by the addition method:
$2x + 4y - z = 3$
$x + 2y + z = 5$
$4x + 8y - 2z = 7$

12. Solve by the addition method:
$x - y - z = 5$
$2x + z = 2$
$3y - 2z = 1$

13. Evaluate the determinant: $\begin{vmatrix} 3 & -1 \\ -2 & 4 \end{vmatrix}$

14. Evaluate the determinant: $\begin{vmatrix} 1 & -2 & 3 \\ 3 & 1 & 1 \\ 2 & -1 & -2 \end{vmatrix}$

15. Solve by using Cramer's Rule:
$$x - y = 3$$
$$2x + y = -4$$

16. Solve by using Cramer's Rule:
$$5x + 2y = 9$$
$$3x + 5y = -7$$

17. Solve by using Cramer's Rule:
$$x - y + z = 2$$
$$2x - y - z = 1$$
$$x + 2y - 3z = -4$$

18. A plane flying with the wind went 350 mi in 2 h. The return trip, flying against the wind, took 2.8 h. Find the rate of the plane in calm air and the rate of the wind.

19. A clothing manufacturer purchased 60 yd of cotton and 90 yd of wool for a total cost of $900. Another purchase, at the same prices, included 80 yd of cotton and 20 yd of wool for a total cost of $500. Find the cost per yard of the cotton and of the wool.

20. The annual interest earned on two investments is $549. One investment is in a 2.7% tax-free annual simple interest account, and the other investment is in a 5.1% annual simple interest CD. The total amount invested is $15,000. How much is invested in each account?

Cumulative Review

1. Solve: $\frac{3}{2}x - \frac{3}{8} + \frac{1}{4}x = \frac{7}{12}x - \frac{5}{6}$

2. Find the equation of the line that contains the points $(2, -1)$ and $(3, 4)$.

3. Simplify: $3[x - 2(5 - 2x) - 4x] + 6$

4. Evaluate $a + bc \div 2$ when $a = 4$, $b = 8$, and $c = -2$.

5. Solve: $2x - 3 < 9$ or $5x - 1 < 4$

6. Solve: $|x - 2| - 4 < 2$

7. Solve: $|2x - 3| > 5$

8. Given $f(x) = 3x^3 - 2x^2 + 1$, evaluate $f(-3)$.

9. Find the range of $f(x) = 3x^2 - 2x$ if the domain is $\{-2, -1, 0, 1, 2\}$.

10. Given $F(x) = x^2 - 3$, find $F(2)$.

11. Given $f(x) = 3x - 4$, write $f(2 + h) - f(2)$ in simplest form.

12. Graph the solution set of $\{x \mid x \le 2\} \cap \{x \mid x > -3\}$.

–5 –4 –3 –2 –1   0   1   2   3   4   5

13. Find the equation of the line that contains the point $(-2, 3)$ and has slope $-\frac{2}{3}$.

14. Find the equation of the line that contains the point $(-1, 2)$ and is perpendicular to the line $2x - 3y = 7$.

15. Find the distance, to the nearest hundredth, between the points $(-4, 2)$ and $(2, 0)$.

16. Find the midpoint of the line segment connecting the points $(-4, 3)$ and $(3, 5)$.

17. Graph $2x - 5y = 10$ by using the slope and y-intercept.

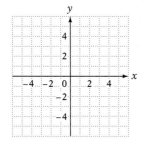

18. Graph the solution set of the inequality $3x - 4y \ge 8$.

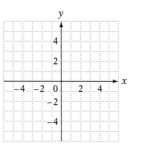

19. Solve by graphing.

$5x - 2y = 10$

$3x + 2y = 6$

20. Solve by graphing.

$3x - 2y \geq 4$

$x + y < 3$

21. Solve by the addition method.

$3x + 2z = 1$

$2y - z = 1$

$x + 2y = 1$

22. Evaluate the determinant.

$$\begin{vmatrix} 2 & -5 & 1 \\ 3 & 1 & 2 \\ 6 & -1 & 4 \end{vmatrix}$$

23. Solve by using Cramer's Rule.

$4x - 3y = 17$

$3x - 2y = 12$

24. Solve by substitution.

$3x - 2y = 7$

$y = 2x - 1$

25. A coin purse contains 40 coins in nickels, dimes, and quarters. There are three times as many dimes as quarters. The total value of the coins is $4.10. How many nickels are in the coin purse?

26. How many milliliters of pure water must be added to 100 ml of a 4% salt solution to make a 2.5% salt solution?

27. Flying with the wind, a small plane required 2 h to fly 150 mi. Against the wind, it took 3 h to fly the same distance. Find the rate of the wind.

28. A restaurant manager buys 100 lb of hamburger and 50 lb of steak for a total cost of $270. A second purchase, at the same prices, includes 150 lb of hamburger and 100 lb of steak. The total cost is $480. Find the price of one pound of steak.

29. Find the lower and upper limits of a 12,000-ohm resistor with a 15% tolerance.

30. The graph shows the relationship between the monthly income and the sales of an account executive. Find the slope of the line between the two points shown on the graph. Write a sentence that states the meaning of the slope.

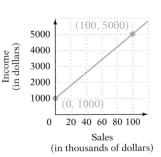

CHAPTER

5

Polynomials

It is the job of urban planners to work toward growth and revitalization of urban areas. They must deal not only with such current problems as deterioration and pollution, but also with projections of long-term needs and plans for the future. Making estimations of changes in population, health care requirements, housing needs, and transportation systems requires working with variables.

Objectives

Section 5.1
To multiply monomials
To divide monomials and simplify expressions with negative exponents
To write a number using scientific notation
To solve application problems

Section 5.2
To evaluate polynomial functions
To add or subtract polynomials

Section 5.3
To multiply a polynomial by a monomial
To multiply two polynomials
To multiply polynomials that have special products
To solve application problems

Section 5.4
To divide polynomials
To divide polynomials by using synthetic division
To evaluate a polynomial using synthetic division

Section 5.5
To factor a monomial from a polynomial
To factor by grouping
To factor a trinomial of the form $x^2 + bx + c$
To factor $ax^2 + bx + c$

Section 5.6
To factor the difference of two perfect squares or a perfect-square trinomial
To factor the sum or the difference of two perfect cubes
To factor a trinomial that is quadratic in form
To factor completely

Section 5.7
To solve an equation by factoring
To solve application problems

Origins of the Word *Algebra*

The word *algebra* has its origins in an Arabic book written around A.D. 825, *Hisab al-jabr w' almuqa-balah* by al-Khowarizmi. The word *al-jabr,* which literally translated means "reunion," was written as the word *algebra* in Latin translations of al-Khowarizmi's work and became synonymous with equations and the solutions of equations. It is interesting to note that an early meaning of the Spanish word *algebrista* was "bonesetter" or "reuniter of broken bones."

This same al-Khowarizmi also made a second contribution to our language of mathematics. One of the translations of his work into Latin shortened his name to *Algoritmi.* A further modification of this word gives us our present word *algorithm.* An algorithm is a procedure or set of instructions used to solve different types of problems. Computer scientists use algorithms when writing computer programs.

A further historical note: Omar Khayyam, a Persian who probably read al-Khowarizmi's work, is especially noted as a poet and the author of the *Rubiat.* However, he was also an excellent mathematician and astronomer and made many contributions to mathematics.

5.1 Exponential Expressions

Objective A   To multiply monomials .... (19) CT

A **monomial** is a number, a variable, or a product of a number and variables.

The examples at the right are monomials. The **degree of a monomial** is the sum of the exponents of the variables.

x	degree 1 $(x = x^1)$
$3x^2$	degree 2
$4x^2y$	degree 3
$6x^3y^4z^2$	degree 9

In this chapter, the variable n is considered a positive integer when used as an exponent.

x^n degree n

The degree of a nonzero constant term is zero.

6   degree 0

The expression $5\sqrt{x}$ is not a monomial because $\sqrt{x}$ cannot be written as a product of variables. The expression $\frac{x}{y}$ is not a monomial because it is a quotient of variables.

The expression x^4 is an exponential expression. The exponent, 4, indicates the number of times the base, x, occurs as a factor.

The product of exponential expressions with the *same* base can be simplified by writing each expression in factored form and writing the result with an exponent.

$$x^3 \cdot x^4 = \overbrace{(x \cdot x \cdot x)}^{\text{3 factors}} \cdot \overbrace{(x \cdot x \cdot x \cdot x)}^{\text{4 factors}}$$
$$\underbrace{}_{\text{7 factors}}$$
$$= x^7$$

Note that adding the exponents results in the same product.

$$x^3 \cdot x^4 = x^{3+4} = x^7$$

> **Rule for Multiplying Exponential Expressions**
>
> If m and n are positive integers, then $x^m \cdot x^n = x^{m+n}$.

➡ Simplify: $(-4x^5y^3)(3xy^2)$

$(-4x^5y^3)(3xy^2) = (-4 \cdot 3)(x^5 \cdot x)(y^3 \cdot y^2)$

- Use the Commutative and Associative Properties of Multiplication to rearrange and group factors.

$= -12(x^{5+1})(y^{3+2})$

- Multiply variables with the same base by adding their exponents.

$= -12x^6y^5$

- Simplify.

As shown below, the power of a monomial can be simplified by writing the power in factored form and then using the Rule for Multiplying Exponential Expressions. It can also be simplified by multiplying each exponent inside the parentheses by the exponent outside the parentheses.

$$(a^2)^3 = a^2 \cdot a^2 \cdot a^2$$
$$= a^{2+2+2}$$
$$= a^6$$

$$(x^3y^4)^2 = (x^3y^4)(x^3y^4)$$
$$= x^{3+3}y^{4+4}$$
$$= x^6y^8$$

- Write in factored form. Then use the Rule for Multiplying Exponential Expressions.

$$(a^2)^3 = a^{2 \cdot 3} = a^6$$

$$(x^3y^4)^2 = x^{3 \cdot 2}y^{4 \cdot 2} = x^6y^8$$

- Multiply each exponent inside the parentheses by the exponent outside the parentheses.

Rule for Simplifying the Power of an Exponential Expression

If m and n are positive integers, then $(x^m)^n = x^{m \cdot n}$.

Rule for Simplifying Powers of Products

If m, n, and p are positive integers, then $(x^m y^n)^p = x^{m \cdot p} y^{n \cdot p}$.

➡ Simplify: $(x^4)^5$

$$(x^4)^5 = x^{4 \cdot 5}$$
$$= x^{20}$$

- Use the Rule for Simplifying Powers of Exponential Expressions to multiply the exponents.

➡ Simplify: $(2a^3b^4)^3$

$$(2a^3b^4)^3 = 2^{1 \cdot 3}a^{3 \cdot 3}b^{4 \cdot 3}$$
$$= 2^3a^9b^{12}$$
$$= 8a^9b^{12}$$

- Use the Rule for Simplifying Powers of Products to multiply each exponent inside the parentheses by the exponent outside the parentheses.

Example 1

Simplify: $(2xy^2)(-3xy^4)^3$

Solution

$$(2xy^2)(-3xy^4)^3 = (2xy^2)[(-3)^3x^3y^{12}]$$
$$= (2xy^2)(-27x^3y^{12})$$
$$= -54x^4y^{14}$$

Example 2

Simplify: $(x^{n+2})^5$

Solution

$$(x^{n+2})^5 = x^{5n+10}$$

Example 3

Simplify: $[(2xy^2)^2]^3$

Solution

$$[(2xy^2)^2]^3 = [2^2x^2y^4]^3 = [4x^2y^4]^3$$
$$= 4^3x^6y^{12} = 64x^6y^{12}$$

You Try It 1

Simplify: $(-3a^2b^4)(-2ab^3)^4$

Your solution

You Try It 2

Simplify: $(y^{n-3})^2$

Your solution

You Try It 3

Simplify: $[(ab^3)^3]^4$

Your solution

Solutions on p. S13

Objective B ***To divide monomials and simplify expressions with negative exponents*** .... (19) CT

The quotient of two exponential expressions with the same base can be simplified by writing each expression in factored form, dividing by the common factors, and then writing the result with an exponent.

$$\frac{x^5}{x^2} = \frac{\overset{1}{\cancel{x}} \cdot \overset{1}{\cancel{x}} \cdot x \cdot x \cdot x}{\underset{1}{\cancel{x}} \cdot \underset{1}{\cancel{x}}} = x^3$$

Note that subtracting the exponents gives the same result.

$$\frac{x^5}{x^2} = x^{5-2} = x^3$$

To divide two monomials with the same base, subtract the exponents of the like bases.

➡ Simplify: $\frac{z^8}{z^2}$

$$\frac{z^8}{z^2} = z^{8-2}$$ • The bases are the same. Subtract the exponents.

$$= z^6$$

➡ Simplify: $\frac{a^5 b^9}{a^4 b}$

$$\frac{a^5 b^9}{a^4 b} = a^{5-4} b^{9-1}$$ • Subtract the exponents of the like bases.

$$= a b^8$$

Consider the expression $\frac{x^4}{x^4}$, $x \neq 0$. This expression can be simplified, as shown below, by subtracting exponents or by dividing by common factors.

$$\frac{x^4}{x^4} = x^{4-4} = x^0 \qquad\qquad \frac{x^4}{x^4} = \frac{\overset{1}{\cancel{x}} \cdot \overset{1}{\cancel{x}} \cdot \overset{1}{\cancel{x}} \cdot \overset{1}{\cancel{x}}}{\underset{1}{\cancel{x}} \cdot \underset{1}{\cancel{x}} \cdot \underset{1}{\cancel{x}} \cdot \underset{1}{\cancel{x}}} = 1$$

The equations $\frac{x^4}{x^4} = x^0$ and $\frac{x^4}{x^4} = 1$ suggest the following definition of x^0.

Definition of Zero as an Exponent

If $x \neq 0$, then $x^0 = 1$. The expression 0^0 is not defined.

➡ Simplify: $(16z^5)^0$, $z \neq 0$

$$(16z^5)^0 = 1$$ • Any nonzero expression to the zero power is 1.

➡ Simplify: $-(7x^4 y^3)^0$

$$-(7x^4 y^3)^0 = -(1) = -1$$ • The negative outside the parentheses is not affected by the exponent.

POINT OF INTEREST

In the 15th century, the expression $12^{\overline{2m}}$ was used to mean $12x^{-2}$. The use of $\overline{m}$ reflects an Italian influence, where m was used for minus and p was used for plus. It was understood that $\overline{2m}$ referred to an unnamed variable. Isaac Newton, in the 17th century, advocated the current use of a negative exponent.

Consider the expression $\dfrac{x^4}{x^6}$, $x \neq 0$. This expression can be simplified, as shown below, by subtracting exponents or by dividing by common factors.

$$\frac{x^4}{x^6} = x^{4-6} = x^{-2} \qquad \frac{x^4}{x^6} = \frac{\overset{1}{\cancel{x}} \cdot \overset{1}{\cancel{x}} \cdot \overset{1}{\cancel{x}} \cdot \overset{1}{\cancel{x}}}{\underset{1}{\cancel{x}} \cdot \underset{1}{\cancel{x}} \cdot \underset{1}{\cancel{x}} \cdot \underset{1}{\cancel{x}} \cdot x \cdot x} = \frac{1}{x^2}$$

The equations $\dfrac{x^4}{x^6} = x^{-2}$ and $\dfrac{x^4}{x^6} = \dfrac{1}{x^2}$ suggest that $x^{-2} = \dfrac{1}{x^2}$.

Definition of a Negative Exponent

If $x \neq 0$ and n is a positive integer, then

$$x^{-n} = \frac{1}{x^n} \quad \text{and} \quad \frac{1}{x^{-n}} = x^n$$

TAKE NOTE

Note from the example at the right that 2^{-4} is a *positive* number. A negative exponent does not change the sign of a number.

➡ Evaluate: 2^{-4}

$2^{-4} = \dfrac{1}{2^4}$ • Use the Definition of a Negative Exponent.

$\quad\;\; = \dfrac{1}{16}$ • Evaluate the expression.

The expression $\left(\dfrac{x^3}{y^4}\right)^2$, $y \neq 0$, can be simplified by squaring $\dfrac{x^3}{y^4}$ or by multiplying each exponent in the quotient by the exponent outside the parentheses.

$$\left(\frac{x^3}{y^4}\right)^2 = \left(\frac{x^3}{y^4}\right)\left(\frac{x^3}{y^4}\right) = \frac{x^3 \cdot x^3}{y^4 \cdot y^4} = \frac{x^{3+3}}{y^{4+4}} = \frac{x^6}{y^8} \qquad \left(\frac{x^3}{y^4}\right)^2 = \frac{x^{3\cdot 2}}{y^{4\cdot 2}} = \frac{x^6}{y^8}$$

Rule for Simplifying Powers of Quotients

If m, n, and q are integers and $y \neq 0$, then $\left(\dfrac{x^m}{y^n}\right)^p = \dfrac{x^{mp}}{y^{np}}$.

➡ Simplify: $\left(\dfrac{a^2}{b^3}\right)^{-2}$

$\left(\dfrac{a^2}{b^3}\right)^{-2} = \dfrac{a^{2(-2)}}{b^{3(-2)}}$ • Use the Rule for Simplifying Powers of Quotients.

$\qquad\qquad = \dfrac{a^{-4}}{b^{-6}} = \dfrac{b^6}{a^4}$ • Use the Definition of Negative Exponents to write the expression with positive exponents.

The preceding example suggests the following rule.

> **Rule for Negative Exponents on Fractional Expressions**
>
> If $a \neq 0$, $b \neq 0$, and n is a positive integer, then $\left(\dfrac{a}{b}\right)^{-n} = \left(\dfrac{b}{a}\right)^{n}$.

An exponential expression is in simplest form when it is written with only positive exponents.

⇒ Simplify: $\dfrac{2}{5a^{-4}}$

$$\frac{2}{5a^{-4}} = \frac{2}{5} \cdot \frac{1}{a^{-4}} = \frac{2}{5} \cdot a^{4} = \frac{2a^{4}}{5}$$

- Use the Definition of Negative Exponents to rewrite the expression with a positive exponent.

Now that zero and negative exponents have been defined, a rule for dividing exponential expressions can be stated.

> **Rule for Dividing Exponential Expressions**
>
> If m and n are integers and $x \neq 0$, then $\dfrac{x^{m}}{x^{n}} = x^{m-n}$.

⇒ Simplify: $\dfrac{x^{4}}{x^{9}}$

$$\frac{x^{4}}{x^{9}} = x^{4-9}$$

- Use the Rule for Dividing Exponential Expressions.

$$= x^{-5}$$

- Subtract the exponents.

$$= \frac{1}{x^{5}}$$

- Use the Definition of Negative Exponents to rewrite the expression with a positive exponent.

The rules for simplifying exponential expressions and powers of exponential expressions are true for all integers. These rules are restated here for convenience.

> **Rules of Exponents**
>
> If m, n, and p are integers, then
>
> $x^{m} \cdot x^{n} = x^{m+n}$ $\qquad$ $(x^{m})^{n} = x^{mn}$ $\qquad$ $(x^{m}y^{n})^{p} = x^{mp}y^{np}$
>
> $\dfrac{x^{m}}{x^{n}} = x^{m-n}, x \neq 0$ $\qquad$ $\left(\dfrac{x^{m}}{y^{n}}\right)^{p} = \dfrac{x^{mp}}{y^{np}}, y \neq 0$ $\qquad$ $x^{-n} = \dfrac{1}{x^{n}}, x \neq 0$
>
> $x^{0} = 1, x \neq 0$

⇒ Simplify: $(3ab^{-4})(-2a^{-3}b^7)$

$$(3ab^{-4})(-2a^{-3}b^7) = [3 \cdot (-2)](a^{1+(-3)}b^{-4+7})$$
$$= -6a^{-2}b^3$$
$$= -\frac{6b^3}{a^2}$$

- When multiplying expressions, add the exponents on like bases.

⇒ Simplify: $\frac{4a^{-2}b^5}{6a^5b^2}$

$$\frac{4a^{-2}b^5}{6a^5b^2} = \frac{2 \cdot 2a^{-2}b^5}{2 \cdot 3a^5b^2} = \frac{2a^{-2}b^5}{3a^5b^2}$$
$$= \frac{2a^{-2-5}b^{5-2}}{3}$$
$$= \frac{2a^{-7}b^3}{3} = \frac{2b^3}{3a^7}$$

- Divide the coefficients by their common factor.
- Use the Rule for Dividing Exponential Expressions.
- Use the Definition of Negative Exponents to rewrite the expression with a positive exponent.

⇒ Simplify: $\left[\frac{6m^2n^3}{8m^7n^2}\right]^{-3}$

$$\left[\frac{6m^2n^3}{8m^7n^2}\right]^{-3} = \left[\frac{3m^{2-7}n^{3-2}}{4}\right]^{-3}$$
$$= \left[\frac{3m^{-5}n}{4}\right]^{-3}$$
$$= \frac{3^{-3}m^{15}n^{-3}}{4^{-3}}$$
$$= \frac{4^3m^{15}}{3^3n^3} = \frac{64m^{15}}{27n^3}$$

- Simplify inside the brackets.
- Subtract the exponents.
- Use the Rule for Simplifying Powers of Quotients.
- Use the Definition of Negative Exponents to rewrite the expression with positive exponents. Then simplify.

Example 4

Simplify: $\frac{-28x^6z^{-3}}{42x^{-1}z^4}$

Solution

$$\frac{-28x^6z^{-3}}{42x^{-1}z^4} = -\frac{14 \cdot 2x^{6-(-1)}z^{-3-4}}{14 \cdot 3}$$
$$= -\frac{2x^7z^{-7}}{3} = -\frac{2x^7}{3z^7}$$

You Try It 4

Simplify: $\frac{20r^{-2}t^{-5}}{-16r^{-3}s^{-2}}$

Your solution

Example 5

Simplify: $\frac{(3a^{-1}b^4)^{-3}}{(6^{-1}a^{-3}b^{-4})^3}$

Solution

$$\frac{(3a^{-1}b^4)^{-3}}{(6^{-1}a^{-3}b^{-4})^3} = \frac{3^{-3}a^3b^{-12}}{6^{-3}a^{-9}b^{-12}} = 3^{-3} \cdot 6^3a^{12}b^0$$
$$= \frac{6^3a^{12}}{3^3} = \frac{216a^{12}}{27} = 8a^{12}$$

You Try It 5

Simplify: $\frac{(9u^{-6}v^4)^{-1}}{(6u^{-3}v^{-2})^{-2}}$

Your solution

Solutions on p. S13

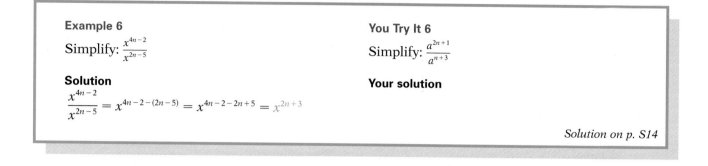

Example 6

Simplify: $\dfrac{x^{4n-2}}{x^{2n-5}}$

Solution

$\dfrac{x^{4n-2}}{x^{2n-5}} = x^{4n-2-(2n-5)} = x^{4n-2-2n+5} = x^{2n+3}$

You Try It 6

Simplify: $\dfrac{a^{2n+1}}{a^{n+3}}$

Your solution

Solution on p. S14

Objective C   *To write a number using scientific notation* ·· **CT**

Integer exponents are used to represent the very large and very small numbers encountered in the fields of science and engineering. For example, the mass of the electron is 0.00000000000000000000000000009 g. Numbers such as this are difficult to read and write, so a more convenient system for writing such numbers has been developed. It is called **scientific notation.**

To express a number in scientific notation, write the number as the product of a number between 1 and 10 and a power of 10. The form for scientific notation is $a \times 10^n$, where $1 \le a < 10$.

For numbers greater than 10, move the decimal point to the right of the first digit. The exponent n is positive and equal to the number of places the decimal point has been moved.

$965,000 \quad = 9.65 \times 10^5$

$3,600,000 \quad = 3.6 \times 10^6$

$92,000,000,000 \quad = 9.2 \times 10^{10}$

For numbers less than 1, move the decimal point to the right of the first nonzero digit. The exponent n is negative. The absolute value of the exponent is equal to the number of places the decimal point has been moved.

$0.0002 \quad = 2 \times 10^{-4}$

$0.0000000974 \quad = 9.74 \times 10^{-8}$

$0.000000000086 = 8.6 \times 10^{-11}$

Converting a number written in scientific notation to decimal notation requires moving the decimal point.

When the exponent is positive, move the decimal point to the right the same number of places as the exponent.

$1.32 \times 10^4 = 13,200$

$1.4 \times 10^8 = 140,000,000$

When the exponent is negative, move the decimal point to the left the same number of places as the absolute value of the exponent.

$1.32 \times 10^{-2} = 0.0132$

$1.4 \times 10^{-4} = 0.00014$

Numerical calculations involving numbers that have more digits than the hand-held calculator is able to handle can be performed using scientific notation.

➡ Simplify: $\dfrac{220,000 \times 0.000000092}{0.0000011}$

$\dfrac{220,000 \times 0.000000092}{0.0000011} = \dfrac{2.2 \times 10^5 \times 9.2 \times 10^{-8}}{1.1 \times 10^{-6}}$

• Write the numbers in scientific notation.

$= \dfrac{(2.2)(9.2) \times 10^{5+(-8)-(-6)}}{1.1}$

• Simplify.

$= 18.4 \times 10^3 = 18,400$

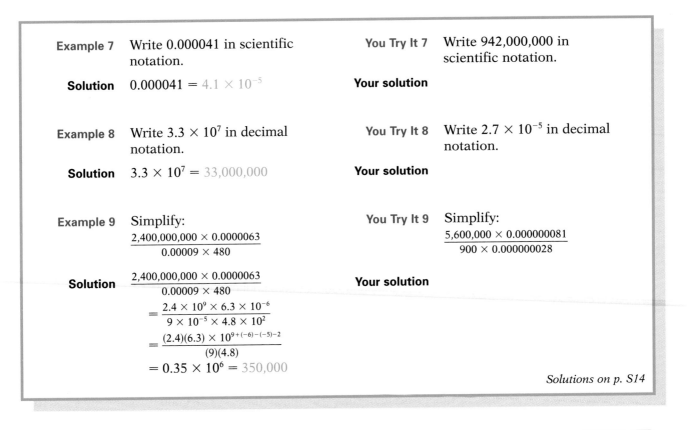

Example 7   Write 0.000041 in scientific notation.

Solution $0.000041 = 4.1 \times 10^{-5}$

You Try It 7   Write 942,000,000 in scientific notation.

Your solution

Example 8   Write 3.3×10^7 in decimal notation.

Solution $3.3 \times 10^7 = 33,000,000$

You Try It 8   Write 2.7×10^{-5} in decimal notation.

Your solution

Example 9   Simplify:

$$\frac{2,400,000,000 \times 0.0000063}{0.00009 \times 480}$$

Solution

$$\frac{2,400,000,000 \times 0.0000063}{0.00009 \times 480}$$

$$= \frac{2.4 \times 10^9 \times 6.3 \times 10^{-6}}{9 \times 10^{-5} \times 4.8 \times 10^2}$$

$$= \frac{(2.4)(6.3) \times 10^{9+(-6)-(-5)-2}}{(9)(4.8)}$$

$$= 0.35 \times 10^6 = 350,000$$

You Try It 9   Simplify:

$$\frac{5,600,000 \times 0.000000081}{900 \times 0.000000028}$$

Your solution

Solutions on p. S14

Objective D   *To solve application problems* ··   (19)   CT

Example 10

How many miles does light travel in one day? The speed of light is 186,000 mi/s. Write the answer in scientific notation.

Strategy

To find the distance traveled:
- Write the speed of light in scientific notation.
- Write the number of seconds in one day in scientific notation.
- Use the equation $d = rt$, where r is the speed of light and t is the number of seconds in one day.

Solution

$r = 186,000 = 1.86 \times 10^5$
$t = 24 \cdot 60 \cdot 60 = 86,400 = 8.64 \times 10^4$
$d = rt$
$d = (1.86 \times 10^5)(8.64 \times 10^4)$
$\quad = 1.86 \times 8.64 \times 10^9$
$\quad = 16.0704 \times 10^9$
$\quad = 1.60704 \times 10^{10}$

Light travels 1.60704×10^{10} mi in one day.

You Try It 10

A computer can do an arithmetic operation in 1×10^{-7} s. In scientific notation, how many arithmetic operations can the computer perform in 1 min?

Your strategy

Your solution

Solution on p. S14

5.1 Exercises

· ·

Objective A

Simplify.

1. $(ab^3)(a^3b)$

2. $(-2ab^4)(-3a^2b^4)$

3. $(9xy^2)(-2x^2y^2)$

4. $(x^2y)^2$

5. $(x^2y^4)^4$

6. $(-2ab^2)^3$

7. $(-3x^2y^3)^4$

8. $(2^2a^2b^3)^3$

9. $(3^3a^5b^3)^2$

10. $(xy)(x^2y)^4$

11. $(x^2y^2)(xy^3)^3$

12. $[(2x)^4]^2$

13. $[(3x)^3]^2$

14. $[(x^2y)^4]^5$

15. $[(ab)^3]^6$

16. $[(2ab)^3]^2$

17. $[(2xy)^3]^4$

18. $[(3x^2y^3)^2]^2$

19. $[(2a^4b^3)^3]^2$

20. $y^n \cdot y^{2n}$

21. $x^n \cdot x^{n+1}$

22. $y^{2n} \cdot y^{4n+1}$

23. $y^{3n} \cdot y^{3n-2}$

24. $(a^n)^{2n}$

25. $(a^{n-3})^{2n}$

26. $(y^{2n-1})^3$

27. $(x^{3n+2})^5$

28. $(b^{2n-1})^n$

29. $(2xy)(-3x^2yz)(x^2y^3z^3)$

30. $(x^2z^4)(2xyz^4)(-3x^3y^2)$

31. $(3b^5)(2ab^2)(-2ab^2c^2)$

32. $(-c^3)(-2a^2bc)(3a^2b)$

33. $(-2x^2y^3z)(3x^2yz^4)$

34. $(2a^2b)^3(-3ab^4)^2$

35. $(-3ab^3)^3(-2^2a^2b)^2$

36. $(4ab)^2(-2ab^2c^3)^3$

37. $(-2ab^2)(-3a^4b^5)^3$

Objective B

Simplify.

38. 2^{-3}

39. $\dfrac{1}{3^{-5}}$

40. $\dfrac{1}{x^{-4}}$

41. $\dfrac{1}{y^{-3}}$

42. $\dfrac{2x^{-2}}{y^4}$

43. $\dfrac{a^3}{4b^{-2}}$

44. $x^{-3}y$

45. xy^{-4}

46. $-5x^0$

47. $\dfrac{1}{2x^0}$

48. $\dfrac{(2x)^0}{-2^3}$

49. $\dfrac{-3^{-2}}{(2y)^0}$

50. $\dfrac{y^{-7}}{y^{-8}}$

51. $\dfrac{y^{-2}}{y^6}$

52. $(x^2y^{-4})^2$

53. $(x^3y^5)^{-2}$

54. $\dfrac{x^{-2}y^{-11}}{xy^{-2}}$

55. $\dfrac{x^4y^3}{x^{-1}y^{-2}}$

56. $\dfrac{a^{-1}b^{-3}}{a^4b^{-5}}$

57. $\dfrac{a^6b^{-4}}{a^{-2}b^5}$

58. $(2a^{-1})^{-2}(2a^{-1})^4$

59. $(3a)^{-3}(9a^{-1})^{-2}$

60. $(x^{-2}y)^2(xy)^{-2}$

61. $(x^{-1}y^2)^{-3}(x^2y^{-4})^{-3}$

62. $\dfrac{50b^{10}}{70b^5}$

63. $\dfrac{x^3y^6}{x^6y^2}$

64. $\dfrac{x^{17}y^5}{-x^7y^{10}}$

65. $\dfrac{-6x^2y}{12x^4y}$

66. $\dfrac{2x^2y^4}{(3xy^2)^3}$

67. $\dfrac{-3ab^2}{(9a^2b^4)^3}$

68. $\left(\dfrac{-12a^2b^3}{9a^5b^9}\right)^3$

69. $\left(\dfrac{12x^3y^2z}{18xy^3z^4}\right)^4$

70. $\dfrac{(4x^2y)^2}{(2xy^3)^3}$

71. $\dfrac{(3a^2b)^3}{(-6ab^3)^2}$

72. $\dfrac{(-4x^2y^3)^2}{(2xy^2)^3}$

73. $\dfrac{(-3a^2b^3)^2}{(-2ab^4)^3}$

74. $\dfrac{(-4xy^3)^3}{(-2x^7y)^4}$

75. $\dfrac{(-8x^2y^2)^4}{(16x^3y^7)^2}$

76. $\dfrac{a^{5n}}{a^{3n}}$

77. $\dfrac{b^{6n}}{b^{10n}}$

78. $\dfrac{-x^{5n}}{x^{2n}}$

79. $\dfrac{y^{2n}}{-y^{8n}}$

80. $\dfrac{x^{2n-1}}{x^{n-3}}$

81. $\dfrac{y^{3n+2}}{y^{2n+4}}$

82. $\dfrac{a^{3n}b^n}{a^nb^{2n}}$

83. $\dfrac{x^ny^{3n}}{x^ny^{5n}}$

84. $\dfrac{a^{3n-2}b^{n+1}}{a^{2n+1}b^{2n+2}}$

85. $\dfrac{x^{2n-1}y^{n-3}}{x^{n+4}y^{n+3}}$

86. $\left(\dfrac{4^{-2}xy^{-3}}{x^{-3}y}\right)^3\left(\dfrac{8^{-1}x^{-2}y}{x^4y^{-1}}\right)^{-2}$

87. $\left(\dfrac{9ab^{-2}}{8a^{-2}b}\right)^{-2}\left(\dfrac{3a^{-2}b}{2a^2b^{-2}}\right)^3$

88. $\left(\dfrac{2ab^{-1}}{ab}\right)^{-1}\left(\dfrac{3a^{-2}b}{a^2b^2}\right)^{-2}$

Objective C

Write in scientific notation.

89. 0.00000467

90. 0.00000005

91. 0.00000000017

92. 4,300,000

93. 200,000,000,000

94. 9,800,000,000

Write in decimal notation.

95. 1.23×10^{-7}

96. 6.2×10^{-12}

97. 8.2×10^{15}

98. 6.34×10^5

99. 3.9×10^{-2}

100. 4.35×10^9

Simplify. Write the answer in decimal notation.

101. $(3 \times 10^{-12})(5 \times 10^{16})$

102. $(8.9 \times 10^{-5})(3.2 \times 10^{-6})$

103. $(0.0000065)(3,200,000,000,000)$

104. $(480,000)(0.0000000096)$

105. $\dfrac{9 \times 10^{-3}}{6 \times 10^5}$

106. $\dfrac{2.7 \times 10^4}{3 \times 10^{-6}}$

107. $\dfrac{0.0089}{500,000,000}$

108. $\dfrac{4,800}{0.00000024}$

109. $\dfrac{0.00056}{0.000000000004}$

110. $\dfrac{0.000000346}{0.0000005}$

111. $\dfrac{(3.2 \times 10^{-11})(2.9 \times 10^{15})}{8.1 \times 10^{-3}}$

112. $\dfrac{(6.9 \times 10^{27})(8.21 \times 10^{-13})}{4.1 \times 10^{15}}$

113. $\dfrac{(0.00000004)(84,000)}{(0.0003)(1,400,000)}$

114. $\dfrac{(720)(0.0000000039)}{(26,000,000,000)(0.018)}$

Objective D *Application Problems*

Solve. Write the answer in scientific notation.

115. How many kilometers does light travel in one day? The speed of light is 300,000 km/s.

116. How many meters does light travel in 8 h? The speed of light is 300,000,000 m/s.

Use a calculator for Exercises 117–125.

117. It took 11 min for the commands from a computer on Earth to travel to the rover Sojourner on Mars, a distance of 119 million miles. How fast did the signals from Earth to Mars travel? Write the answer in scientific notation.

118. In early 1997, the gross federal debt was 5.5×10^{12} dollars. How much would each American citizen have to pay in order to pay off the debt? Use 275,000,000 as the number of citizens.

119. A high-speed centrifuge makes 9×10^{7} revolutions each minute. Find the time in seconds for the centrifuge to make one revolution.

120. How long does it take light to travel to the earth from the sun? The sun is 9.3×10^{7} mi from the earth, and light travels 1.86×10^{5} mi/s.

121. The mass of the earth is 5.9×10^{27} g. The mass of the sun is 2×10^{33} g. How many times heavier is the sun than the earth?

122. One astronomical unit (A.U.) is 9.3×10^{7} mi. The star Pollux in the constellation Gemini is 1.8228×10^{12} mi from Earth. Find the distance from Pollux to Earth in astronomical units.

Gemini

123. The weight of 31 million orchid seeds is one ounce. Find the weight of one orchid seed.

124. One light year, an astronomical unit of distance, is the distance that light will travel in one year. Light travels 1.86×10^{5} mi/s. Find the measure of one light year in miles. Use a 365-day year.

125. The Coma cluster of galaxies is approximately 2.8×10^{8} light years from Earth. Find the distance, in miles, from the Coma cluster to Earth. (See Exercise 124 for the definition of one light year. Use a 365-day year.)

APPLYING THE CONCEPTS

126. Correct the error in the following expressions. Explain which rule or property was used incorrectly.
a. $x^{0} = 0$
b. $(x^{4})^{5} = x^{9}$
c. $x^{2} \cdot x^{3} = x^{6}$

127. Simplify.   **a.** $1 + (1 + (1 + 2^{-1})^{-1})^{-1}$ **b.** $2 - (2 - (2 - 2^{-1})^{-1})^{-1}$

5.2 Introduction to Polynomials

Objective A *To evaluate polynomial functions* .... (19) CT

A **polynomial** is a variable expression in which the terms are monomials.

A polynomial of one term is a monomial. $5x$

A polynomial of two terms is a **binomial.** $5x^2y + 6x$

A polynomial of three terms is a **trinomial.** $3x^2 + 9xy - 5y$

Polynomials with more than three terms do not have special names.

The **degree of a polynomial** is the greatest of the degrees of any of its terms.

$3x + 2$	degree 1
$3x^2 + 2x - 4$	degree 2
$4x^3y^2 + 6x^4$	degree 5
$3x^{2n} - 5x^n - 2$	degree $2n$

The terms of a polynomial in one variable are usually arranged so that the exponents of the variable decrease from left to right. This is called **descending order.**

$2x^2 - x + 8$

$3y^3 - 3y^2 + y - 12$

For a polynomial in more than one variable, descending order may refer to any one of the variables.

The polynomial at the right is shown first in descending order of the x variable and then in descending order of the y variable.

$2x^2 + 3xy + 5y^2$

$5y^2 + 3xy + 2x^2$

Polynomial functions have many applications in mathematics. The linear function given by $f(x) = mx + b$ is an example of a polynomial function. It is a polynomial function of degree one. A second-degree polynomial function, called a **quadratic function,** is given by the equation $f(x) = ax^2 + bx + c, a \neq 0$. A third-degree polynomial function is called a **cubic function.** In general, a polynomial function is an expression whose terms are monomials.

To evaluate a polynomial function, replace the variable by its value and simplify.

⇒ Given $P(x) = x^3 - 3x^2 + 4$, evaluate $P(-3)$.

$P(x) = x^3 - 3x^2 + 4$
$P(-3) = (-3)^3 - 3(-3)^2 + 4$ • Substitute -3 for x and simplify.
$\quad\quad = -27 - 27 + 4$
$\quad\quad = -50$

The **leading coefficient** of a polynomial function is the coefficient of the variable with the largest exponent. The **constant term** is the term without a variable.

⇒ Find the leading coefficient, the constant term, and the degree of the polynomial function $P(x) = 7x^4 - 3x^2 + 2x - 4$.

The leading coefficient is 7, the constant term is -4, and the degree is 4.

The three equations below do not represent polynomial functions.

$f(x) = 3x^2 + 2x^{-1}$ A polynomial function does not have a variable raised to a negative power.

$g(x) = 2\sqrt{x} - 3$ A polynomial function does not have a variable expression within a radical.

$h(x) = \dfrac{x}{x-1}$ A polynomial function does not have a variable in the denominator of a fraction.

The graph of a linear function is a straight line and can be found by plotting just two points. The graph of a polynomial function of degree greater than one is a curve. Consequently, many points may have to be found before an accurate graph can be drawn.

Evaluating the quadratic function given by the equation $f(x) = x^2 - x - 6$ when $x = -3, -2, -1, 0, 1, 2, 3,$ and 4 gives the points shown in Figure 1 below. For instance, $f(-3) = 6$, so $(-3, 6)$ is graphed; $f(2) = -4$, so $(2, -4)$ is graphed; and $f(4) = 6$, so $(4, 6)$ is graphed. Evaluating the function when x is not an integer, such as $x = -\dfrac{3}{2}$ and $x = \dfrac{5}{2}$, produces more points to graph, as shown in Figure 2.

Connecting the points with a smooth curve results in Figure 3, which is the graph of f.

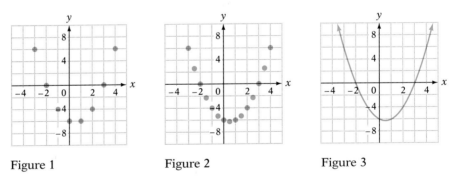

Figure 1   Figure 2   Figure 3

CALCULATOR NOTE

⊞ You can verify the graphs of these polynomial functions by using a graphing calculator. See the Appendix: Guidelines for Using a Graphing Calculator for instructions on graphing functions.

Here is an example of graphing a cubic function, $P(x) = x^3 - 2x^2 - 5x + 6$. Evaluating the function when $x = -2, -1, 0, 1, 2, 3,$ and 4 gives the graph in Figure 4 below. Evaluating at some noninteger values gives the graph in Figure 5. Finally, connecting the dots with a smooth curve gives the graph in Figure 6.

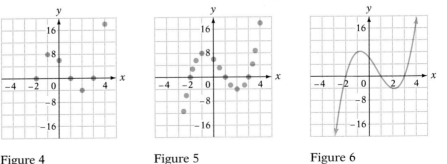

Figure 4   Figure 5   Figure 6

Example 1

Given $P(x) = x^3 + 3x^2 - 2x + 8$, evaluate $P(-2)$.

Solution

$P(x) = x^3 + 3x^2 - 2x + 8$
$P(-2) = (-2)^3 + 3(-2)^2 - 2(-2) + 8$
$\quad\quad = (-8) + 3(4) + 4 + 8$
$\quad\quad = -8 + 12 + 4 + 8$
$\quad\quad = 16$

You Try It 1

Given $R(x) = -2x^4 - 5x^3 + 2x - 8$, evaluate $R(2)$.

Your solution

Example 2

Find the leading coefficient, the constant term, and the degree of the polynomial.
$P(x) = 5x^6 - 4x^5 - 3x^2 + 7$

Solution

The leading coefficient is 5, the constant term is 7, and the degree is 6.

You Try It 2

Find the leading coefficient, the constant term, and the degree of the polynomial.
$r(x) = -3x^4 + 3x^3 + 3x^2 - 2x - 12$

Your solution

Example 3

Which of the following is a polynomial function?
a. $P(x) = 3x^{\frac{1}{2}} + 2x^2 - 3$
b. $T(x) = 3\sqrt{x} - 2x^2 - 3x + 2$
c. $R(x) = 14x^3 - \pi x^2 + 3x + 2$

Solution

a. This is not a polynomial function. A polynomial function does not have a variable raised to a fractional power.
b. This is not a polynomial function. A polynomial function does not have a variable expression within a radical.
c. This is a polynomial function.

You Try It 3

Which of the following is a polynomial function?
a. $R(x) = 5x^{14} - 5$
b. $V(x) = -x^{-1} + 2x - 7$
c. $P(x) = 2x^4 - 3\sqrt{x} - 3$

Your solution

Example 4

Graph $f(x) = x^2 - 2$.

Solution

x	$y = f(x)$
-3	7
-2	2
-1	-1
0	-2
1	-1
2	2
3	7

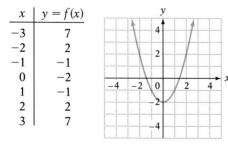

You Try It 4

Graph $f(x) = x^3 + 2$.

Your solution

Solutions on p. S14

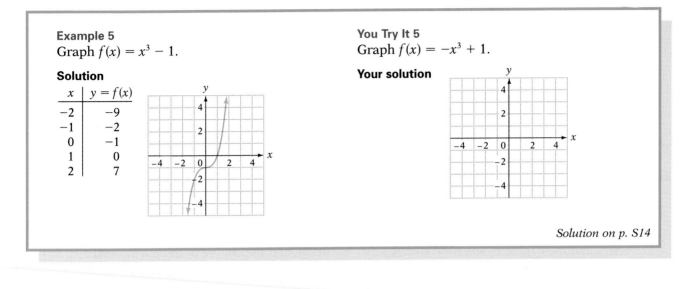

Example 5

Graph $f(x) = x^3 - 1$.

Solution

x	$y = f(x)$
-2	-9
-1	-2
0	-1
1	0
2	7

You Try It 5

Graph $f(x) = -x^3 + 1$.

Your solution

Solution on p. S14

Objective B   **To add or subtract polynomials** .... ⟨19⟩ CT

Polynomials can be added by combining like terms. Either a vertical or a horizontal format can be used.

➡ Simplify $(3x^2 + 2x - 7) + (7x^3 - 3 + 4x^2)$. Use a horizontal format.

Use the Commutative and Associative Properties of Addition to rearrange and group like terms.

$(3x^2 + 2x - 7) + (7x^3 - 3 + 4x^2)$
$= 7x^3 + (3x^2 + 4x^2) + 2x + (-7 - 3)$ • Combine like terms.
$= 7x^3 + 7x^2 + 2x - 10$

➡ Simplify $(4x^2 + 5x - 3) + (7x^3 - 7x + 1) + (2x - 3x^2 + 4x^3 + 1)$. Use a vertical format.

Arrange the terms of each polynomial in descending order with like terms in the same column.

$$
\begin{array}{r}
4x^2 + 5x - 3 \\
7x^3 \qquad - 7x + 1 \\
4x^3 - 3x^2 + 2x + 1 \\
\hline
11x^3 + \; x^2 \qquad - 1
\end{array}
$$

• Add the terms in each column.

The additive inverse of the polynomial $x^2 + 5x - 4$ is $-(x^2 + 5x - 4)$.

To simplify the additive inverse of a polynomial, change the sign of every term inside the parentheses.

$-(x^2 + 5x - 4) = -x^2 - 5x + 4$

To subtract two polynomials, add the additive inverse of the second polynomial to the first.

⇒ Simplify $(3x^2 - 7xy + y^2) - (-4x^2 + 7xy - 3y^2)$. Use a horizontal format.

Rewrite the subtraction as the addition of the additive inverse.

$(3x^2 - 7xy + y^2) - (-4x^4 + 7xy - 3y^2)$
$= (3x^2 - 7xy + y^2) + (4x^2 - 7xy + 3y^2)$
$= 7x^2 - 14xy + 4y^2$ • Combine like terms.

⇒ Simplify $(6x^3 - 3x + 7) - (3x^2 - 5x + 12)$. Use a vertical format.

Rewrite subtraction as the addition of the additive inverse.

$(6x^3 - 3x + 7) - (3x^2 - 5x + 12) = (6x^3 - 3x + 7) + (-3x^2 + 5x - 12)$

Arrange the terms of each polynomial in descending order with like terms in the same column.

$$\begin{array}{r} 6x^3 \qquad\ - 3x +\ \ 7 \\ - 3x^2 + 5x - 12 \\ \hline 6x^3 - 3x^2 + 2x -\ \ 5 \end{array}$$ • Combine the terms in each column.

Function notation can be used when adding or subtracting polynomials.

⇒ Given $P(x) = 3x^2 - 2x + 4$ and $R(x) = -5x^3 + 4x + 7$, find $P(x) + R(x)$.

$P(x) + R(x) = (3x^2 - 2x + 4) + (-5x^3 + 4x + 7)$
$= -5x^3 + 3x^2 + 2x + 11$

⇒ Given $P(x) = -5x^2 + 8x - 4$ and $R(x) = -3x^2 - 5x + 9$, find $P(x) - R(x)$.

$P(x) - R(x) = (-5x^2 + 8x - 4) - (-3x^2 - 5x + 9)$
$= (-5x^2 + 8x - 4) + (3x^2 + 5x - 9)$
$= -2x^2 + 13x - 13$

⇒ Given $P(x) = 3x^2 - 5x + 6$ and $R(x) = 2x^2 - 5x - 7$, find $S(x)$, the sum of the two polynomials.

$S(x) = P(x) + R(x) = (3x^2 - 5x + 6) + (2x^2 - 5x - 7)$
$= 5x^2 - 10x - 1$

Note from the previous example that evaluating $P(x) = 3x^2 - 5x + 6$ and $R(x) = 2x^2 - 5x - 7$ at, for example, $x = 3$, and then adding the values, is the same as evaluating $S(x) = 5x^2 - 10x - 1$ at 3.

$P(3) = 3(3)^2 - 5(3) + 6 = 27 - 15 + 6 = 18$
$R(3) = 2(3)^2 - 5(3) - 7 = 18 - 15 - 7 = -4$

$P(3) + R(3) = 18 + (-4) = 14$

$S(3) = 5(3)^2 - 10(3) - 1 = 5(9) - 30 - 1 = 45 - 30 - 1 = 14$

Example 6
Simplify:
$(4x^2 - 3xy + 7y^2) + (-3x^2 + 7xy + y^2)$
Use a vertical format.

Solution

$$\begin{array}{r} 4x^2 - 3xy + 7y^2 \\ -3x^2 + 7xy + \ y^2 \\ \hline x^2 + 4xy + 8y^2 \end{array}$$

You Try It 6
Simplify:
$(-3x^2 - 4x + 9) + (-5x^2 - 7x + 1)$
Use a vertical format.

Your solution

Example 7
Simplify:
$(3x^2 - 2x + 4) - (7x^2 + 3x - 12)$
Use a vertical format.

Solution
Add the additive inverse of $7x^2 + 3x - 12$ to $3x^2 - 2x + 4$.

$$\begin{array}{r} 3x^2 - 2x + \ 4 \\ -7x^2 - 3x + 12 \\ \hline -4x^2 - 5x + 16 \end{array}$$

You Try It 7
Simplify:
$(-5x^2 + 2x - 3) - (6x^2 + 3x - 7)$
Use a vertical format.

Your solution

Example 8
Given $P(x) = -3x^2 + 2x - 6$ and
$R(x) = 4x^3 - 3x + 4$, find $S(x) = P(x) + R(x)$.
Evaluate $S(-2)$.

Solution
$$\begin{aligned} S(x) &= (-3x^2 + 2x - 6) + (4x^3 - 3x + 4) \\ &= 4x^3 - 3x^2 - x - 2 \end{aligned}$$

$$\begin{aligned} S(-2) &= 4(-2)^3 - 3(-2)^2 - (-2) - 2 \\ &= 4(-8) - 3(4) + 2 - 2 \\ &= -44 \end{aligned}$$

You Try It 8
Given $P(x) = 4x^3 - 3x^2 + 2$ and
$R(x) = -2x^2 + 2x - 3$, find
$S(x) = P(x) + R(x)$. Evaluate $S(-1)$.

Your solution

Example 9
Given $P(x) = (2x^{2n} - 3x^n + 7)$ and
$R(x) = (3x^{2n} + 3x^n + 5)$, find
$D(x) = P(x) - R(x)$.

Solution
$$\begin{aligned} D(x) &= (2x^{2n} - 3x^n + 7) - (3x^{2n} + 3x^n + 5) \\ &= (2x^{2n} - 3x^n + 7) + (-3x^{2n} - 3x^n - 5) \\ &= -x^{2n} - 6x^n + 2 \end{aligned}$$

You Try It 9
Given $P(x) = (5x^{2n} - 3x^n - 7)$ and
$R(x) = (-2x^{2n} - 5x^n + 8)$, find
$D(x) = P(x) - R(x)$.

Your solution

Solutions on p. S14

5.2 Exercises

· ·

Objective A

1. Given $P(x) = 3x^2 - 2x - 8$, evaluate $P(3)$.

2. Given $P(x) = -3x^2 - 5x + 8$, evaluate $P(-5)$.

3. Given $R(x) = 2x^3 - 3x^2 + 4x - 2$, evaluate $R(2)$.

4. Given $R(x) = -x^3 + 2x^2 - 3x + 4$, evaluate $R(-1)$.

5. Given $f(x) = x^4 - 2x^2 - 10$, evaluate $f(-1)$.

6. Given $f(x) = x^5 - 2x^3 + 4x$, evaluate $f(2)$.

Which of the following define a polynomial function? For those that are polynomial functions, identify **a.** the leading coefficient, **b.** the constant term, and **c.** the degree.

7. $P(x) = -x^2 + 3x + 8$

8. $P(x) = 3x^4 - 3x - 7$

9. $R(x) = \dfrac{x}{x + 1}$

10. $R(x) = \dfrac{3x^2 - 2x + 1}{x}$

11. $f(x) = \sqrt{x} - x^2 + 2$

12. $f(x) = x^2 - \sqrt{x + 2} - 8$

13. $g(x) = 3x^5 - 2x^2 + \pi$

14. $g(x) = -4x^5 - 3x^2 + x - \sqrt{7}$

15. $P(x) = 3x^2 - 5x^3 + 2$

16. $P(x) = x^2 - 5x^4 - x^6$

17. $R(x) = 14$

18. $R(x) = \dfrac{1}{x} + 2$

Graph.

19. $P(x) = x^2 - 1$

20. $P(x) = 2x^2 + 3$

21. $R(x) = x^3 + 2$

22. $R(x) = x^4 + 1$

23. $f(x) = x^3 - 2x$

24. $f(x) = x^2 - x - 2$

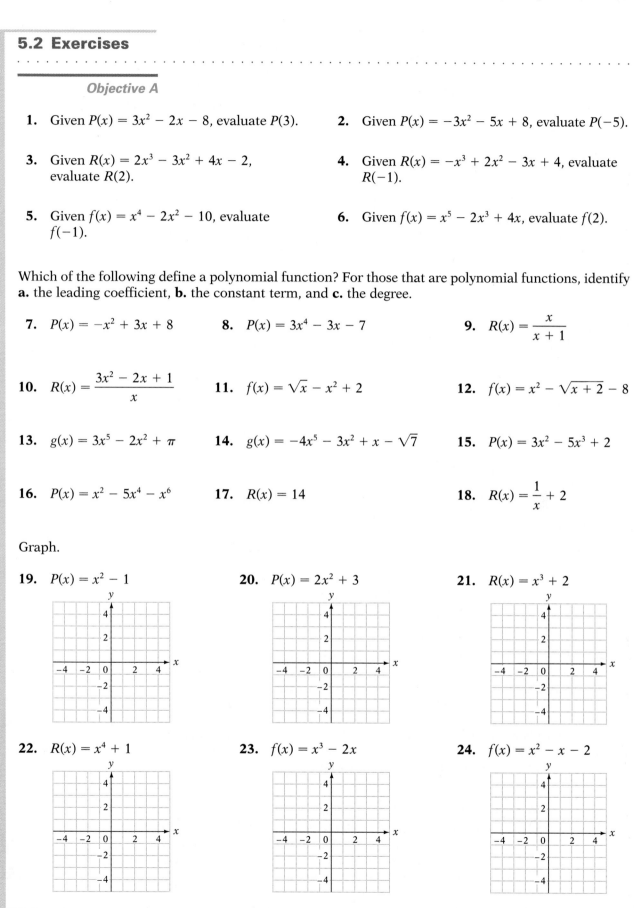

Objective B

Simplify. Use a vertical format.

25. $(5x^2 + 2x - 7) + (x^2 - 8x + 12)$

26. $(3x^2 - 2x + 7) + (-3x^2 + 2x - 12)$

27. $(x^2 - 3x + 8) - (2x^2 - 3x + 7)$

28. $(2x^2 + 3x - 7) - (5x^2 - 8x - 1)$

Simplify. Use a horizontal format for Exercises 29–32.

29. $(3y^2 - 7y) + (2y^2 - 8y + 2)$

30. $(-2y^2 - 4y - 12) + (5y^2 - 5y)$

31. $(2a^2 - 3a - 7) - (-5a^2 - 2a - 9)$

32. $(3a^2 - 9a) - (-5a^2 + 7a - 6)$

33. Given $P(x) = x^2 - 3xy + y^2$ and $R(x) = 2x^2 - 3y^2$, find $P(x) + R(x)$.

34. Given $P(x) = x^{2n} + 7x^n - 3$ and $R(x) = -x^{2n} + 2x^n + 8$, find $P(x) + R(x)$.

35. Given $P(x) = 3x^2 + 2y^2$ and $R(x) = -5x^2 + 2xy - 3y^2$, find $P(x) - R(x)$.

36. Given $P(x) = 2x^{2n} - x^n - 1$ and $R(x) = 5x^{2n} + 7x^n + 1$, find $P(x) - R(x)$.

37. Given $P(x) = 3x^4 - 3x^3 - x^2$ and $R(x) = 3x^3 - 7x^2 + 2x$, find $S(x) = P(x) + R(x)$. Evaluate $S(2)$.

38. Given $P(x) = 3x^4 - 2x + 1$ and $R(x) = 3x^5 - 5x - 8$, find $S(x) = P(x) + R(x)$. Evaluate $S(-1)$.

APPLYING THE CONCEPTS

39. For what value of k is the given equation an identity?
  a. $(2x^3 + 3x^2 + kx + 5) - (x^3 + 2x^2 + 3x + 7) = x^3 + x^2 + 5x - 2$
  b. $(6x^3 + kx^2 - 2x - 1) - (4x^3 - 3x^2 + 1) = 2x^3 - x^2 - 2x - 2$

40. If $P(x)$ is a third-degree polynomial and $Q(x)$ is a fourth-degree polynomial, what can be said about the degree of $P(x) + Q(x)$? Give some examples of polynomials that support your answer.

41. If $P(x)$ is a fifth-degree polynomial and $Q(x)$ is a fourth-degree polynomial, what can be said about the degree of $P(x) - Q(x)$? Give some examples of polynomials that support your answer.

42. The deflection D (in inches) of a beam that is uniformly loaded is given by the polynomial function $D(x) = 0.005x^4 - 0.1x^3 + 0.5x^2$, where x is the distance from one end of the beam. See the figure at the right. The maximum deflection occurs when x is the midpoint of the beam. Determine the maximum deflection for the beam in the diagram.

5.3 Multiplication of Polynomials

Objective A   ***To multiply a polynomial by a monomial*** ....

To multiply a polynomial by a monomial, use the Distributive Property and the Rule for Multiplying Exponential Expressions.

➡ Simplify: $-3x^2(2x^2 - 5x + 3)$

$-3x^2(2x^2 - 5x + 3)$

$= -3x^2(2x^2) - (-3x^2)(5x) + (-3x^2)(3)$ • Use the Distributive Property.

$= -6x^4 + 15x^3 - 9x^2$ • Use the Rule for Multiplying Exponential Expressions.

➡ Simplify: $2x^2 - 3x[2 - x(4x + 1) + 2]$

$2x^2 - 3x[2 - x(4x + 1) + 2]$

$= 2x^2 - 3x[2 - 4x^2 - x + 2]$ • Use the Distributive Property to remove the parentheses.

$= 2x^2 - 3x[-4x^2 - x + 4]$ • Simplify.

$= 2x^2 + 12x^3 + 3x^2 - 12x$ • Use the Distributive Property to remove the brackets.

$= 12x^3 + 5x^2 - 12x$ • Simplify.

➡ Simplify: $x^n(x^n - x^2 + 3)$

$x^n(x^n - x^2 + 3)$

$= x^n(x^n) - x^n(x^2) + x^n(3)$ • Use the Distributive Property.

$= x^{2n} - x^{n+2} + 3x^n$

Example 1
Simplify: $(3a^2 - 2a + 4)(-3a)$

Solution
$(3a^2 - 2a + 4)(-3a)$
$= 3a^2(-3a) - 2a(-3a) + 4(-3a)$
$= -9a^3 + 6a^2 - 12a$

You Try It 1
Simplify: $(2b^2 - 7b - 8)(-5b)$

Your solution

Solution on p. S14

Example 2
Simplify: $y - 3y[y - 2(3y - 6) + 2]$

Solution
$y - 3y[y - 2(3y - 6) + 2]$
$= y - 3y[y - 6y + 12 + 2]$
$= y - 3y[-5y + 14]$
$= y + 15y^2 - 42y$
$= 15y^2 - 41y$

You Try It 2
Simplify: $x^2 - 2x[x - x(4x - 5) + x^2]$

Your solution

Example 3
Simplify: $x^{n+2}(x^{n-1} + 2x - 1)$

Solution
$x^{n+2}(x^{n-1} + 2x - 1)$
$= x^{n+2}(x^{n-1}) + (x^{n+2})(2x) - (x^{n+2})(1)$
$= x^{n+2+(n-1)} + 2x^{n+2+1} - x^{n+2}$
$= x^{2n+1} + 2x^{n+3} - x^{n+2}$

You Try It 3
Simplify: $y^{n+3}(y^{n-2} - 3y^2 + 2)$

Your solution

Solutions on p. S15

Objective B **To multiply two polynomials** ·························· 19 CT

The product of two polynomials is the polynomial obtained by multiplying each term of one polynomial by each term of the other polynomial and then combining like terms.

➡ Multiply: $(2x^2 \quad 2x + 1)(3x + 2)$

Use the Distributive Property to multiply the trinomial by each term of the binomial.

$(2x^2 - 2x + 1)(3x + 2) = (2x^2 - 2x + 1)(3x) + (2x^2 - 2x + 1)(2)$

$= (6x^3 - 6x^2 + 3x) + (4x^2 - 4x + 2)$

$= 6x^3 - 2x^2 - x + 2$

A convenient method of multiplying two polynomials is to use a vertical format similar to that used for multiplication of whole numbers.

➡ Multiply: $(3x^2 - 4x + 8)(2x - 7)$

$$
\begin{array}{r}
3x^2 - 4x + 8 \\
2x - 7 \\
\hline
-21x^2 + 28x - 56 \\
6x^3 - 8x^2 + 16x \\
\hline
6x^3 - 29x^2 + 44x - 56
\end{array}
$$

$-21x^2 + 28x - 56 = -7(3x^2 - 4x + 8)$
$6x^3 - 8x^2 + 16x = 2x(3x^2 - 4x + 8)$

• Like terms are in the same column.

• Combine like terms.

It is frequently necessary to find the product of two binomials. The product can be found by using a method called **FOIL,** which is based on the Distributive Property. The letters of FOIL stand for **F**irst, **O**uter, **I**nner, and **L**ast.

Simplify: $(3x - 2)(2x + 5)$

Multiply the First terms. $(3x - 2)(2x + 5)$ $3x \cdot 2x = 6x^2$

Multiply the Outer terms. $(3x - 2)(2x + 5)$ $3x \cdot 5 = 15x$

Multiply the Inner terms. $(3x - 2)(2x + 5)$ $-2 \cdot 2x = -4x$

Multiply the Last terms. $(3x - 2)(2x + 5)$ $-2 \cdot 5 = -10$

$\qquad\qquad\qquad\qquad\qquad\qquad$ F $\quad$ O $\quad$ I $\quad$ L

Add the products. $(3x - 2)(2x + 5) \quad = \quad 6x^2 + 15x - 4x - 10$

Combine like terms. $\qquad\qquad\qquad = \quad 6x^2 + 11x - 10$

➡ Simplify: $(6x - 5)(3x - 4)$

$(6x - 5)(3x - 4) = 6x(3x) + 6x(-4) + (-5)(3x) + (-5)(-4)$

$= 18x^2 - 24x - 15x + 20$

$= 18x^2 - 39x + 20$

Example 4
Simplify: $(4a^3 - 3a + 7)(a - 5)$

Solution

$$\begin{array}{r} 4a^3 - 3a + 7 \\ a - 5 \\ \hline -20a^3 + 15a - 35 \\ 4a^4 - 3a^2 + 7a \\ \hline 4a^4 - 20a^3 - 3a^2 + 22a - 35 \end{array}$$

Example 5
Simplify: $(5a - 3b)(2a + 7b)$

Solution
$(5a - 3b)(2a + 7b)$
$= 10a^2 + 35ab - 6ab - 21b^2$
$= 10a^2 + 29ab - 21b^2$

Example 6
Simplify: $(a^n - 2b^n)(3a^n - b^n)$

Solution
$(a^n - 2b^n)(3a^n - b^n)$
$= 3a^{2n} - a^nb^n - 6a^nb^n + 2b^{2n}$
$= 3a^{2n} - 7a^nb^n + 2b^{2n}$

You Try It 4
Simplify: $(-2b^2 + 5b - 4)(-3b + 2)$

Your solution

You Try It 5
Simplify: $(3x - 4)(2x - 3)$

Your solution

You Try It 6
Simplify: $(2x^n + y^n)(x^n - 4y^n)$

Your solution

Solutions on p. S15

Objective C *To multiply polynomials that have special products* .... 19 CT

Using FOIL, a pattern can be found for the product of the sum and difference of two terms and for the square of a binomial.

The Sum and Difference of Two Terms

$$(a + b)(a - b) = a^2 - ab + ab - b^2$$
$$= a^2 - b^2$$

Square of the first term ————
Square of the second term ————

The Square of a Binomial

$$(a + b)^2 = (a + b)(a + b) = a^2 + ab + ab + b^2$$
$$= a^2 + 2ab + b^2$$

Square of the first term ————
Twice the product of the two terms ————
Square of the second term ————

⟹ Simplify: $(4x + 3)(4x - 3)$

$(4x + 3)(4x - 3)$ is the sum and difference of the same two terms. The product is the difference of the squares of the terms.

$$(4x + 3)(4x - 3) = (4x)^2 - 3^2$$
$$= 16x^2 - 9$$

⟹ Simplify: $(2x - 3y)^2$

$(2x - 3y)^2$ is the square of a binomial.

$$(2x - 3y)^2 = (2x)^2 + 2(2x)(-3y) + (-3y)^2$$
$$= 4x^2 - 12xy + 9y^2$$

Example 7
Simplify: $(2a - 3)(2a + 3)$

Solution
$(2a - 3)(2a + 3) = 4a^2 - 9$

You Try It 7
Simplify: $(3x - 7)(3x + 7)$

Your solution

Example 8
Simplify: $(x^n + 5)(x^n - 5)$

Solution
$(x^n + 5)(x^n - 5) = x^{2n} - 25$

You Try It 8
Simplify: $(2x^n + 3)(2x^n - 3)$

Your solution

Solutions on p. S15

Example 9

Simplify: $(2x + 7y)^2$

Solution

$(2x + 7y)^2 = 4x^2 + 28xy + 49y^2$

You Try It 9

Simplify: $(3x - 4y)^2$

Your solution

Example 10

Simplify: $(x^{2n} - 2)^2$

Solution

$(x^{2n} - 2)^2 = x^{4n} - 4x^{2n} + 4$

You Try It 10

Simplify: $(2x^n - 8)^2$

Your solution

Solutions on p. S15

Objective D   *To solve application problems* ··

Example 11

The length of a rectangle is $(2x + 3)$ ft. The width is $(x - 5)$ ft. Find the area of the rectangle in terms of the variable x.

Strategy

To find the area, replace the variables L and W in the equation $A = L \cdot W$ by the given values and solve for A.

Solution

$A = L \cdot W$
$A = (2x + 3)(x - 5)$
$\quad = 2x^2 - 10x + 3x - 15$
$\quad = 2x^2 - 7x - 15$

The area is $(2x^2 - 7x - 15)$ ft^2.

You Try It 11

The base of a triangle is $(2x + 6)$ ft. The height is $(x - 4)$ ft. Find the area of the triangle in terms of the variable x.

Your strategy

Your solution

Solution on p. S15

Example 12

The corners are cut from a rectangular piece of cardboard measuring 8 in. by 12 in. The sides are folded up to make a box. Find the volume of the box in terms of the variable x, where x is the length of the side of the square cut from each corner of the rectangle.

You Try It 12

Find the volume of the rectangular solid shown in the diagram below. All dimensions are in feet.

Strategy

Length of the box: $12 - 2x$
Width of the box: $8 - 2x$
Height of the box: x
To find the volume, replace the variables L, W, and H in the equation $V = L \cdot W \cdot H$ and solve for V.

Your strategy

Solution

$V = L \cdot W \cdot H$
$$\begin{aligned}
V &= (12 - 2x)(8 - 2x)x \\
&= (96 - 24x - 16x + 4x^2)x \\
&= (96 - 40x + 4x^2)x \\
&= 96x - 40x^2 + 4x^3 \\
&= 4x^3 - 40x^2 + 96x
\end{aligned}$$

The volume is $(4x^3 - 40x^2 + 96x)$ in^3.

Your solution

Example 13

The radius of a circle is $(3x - 2)$ cm. Find the area of the circle in terms of the variable x. Use 3.14 for π.

Strategy

To find the area, replace the variable r in the equation $A = \pi r^2$ by the given value and solve for A.

Solution

$A = \pi r^2$
$$\begin{aligned}
A &= 3.14(3x - 2)^2 \\
&= 3.14(9x^2 - 12x + 4) \\
&= 28.26x^2 - 37.68x + 12.56
\end{aligned}$$

The area is $(28.26x^2 - 37.68x + 12.56)$ cm^2.

You Try It 13

The radius of a circle is $(2x + 3)$ cm. Find the area of the circle in terms of the variable x. Use 3.14 for π.

Your strategy

Your solution

Solutions on p. S15

5.3 Exercises

· ·

Objective A

Simplify.

1. $2x(x - 3)$

2. $2a(2a + 4)$

3. $3x^2(2x^2 - x)$

4. $-4y^2(4y - 6y^2)$

5. $3xy(2x - 3y)$

6. $-4ab(5a - 3b)$

7. $x^n(x + 1)$

8. $y^n(y^{2n} - 3)$

9. $x^n(x^n + y^n)$

10. $x - 2x(x - 2)$

11. $2b + 4b(2 - b)$

12. $-2y(3 - y) + 2y^2$

13. $-2a^2(3a^2 - 2a + 3)$

14. $4b(3b^3 - 12b^2 - 6)$

15. $3b(3b^4 - 3b^2 + 8)$

16. $(2x^2 - 3x - 7)(-2x^2)$

17. $(-3y^2 - 4y + 2)(y^2)$

18. $(6b^4 - 5b^2 - 3)(-2b^3)$

19. $-5x^2(4 - 3x + 3x^2 + 4x^3)$

20. $-2y^2(3 - 2y - 3y^2 + 2y^3)$

21. $-2x^2y(x^2 - 3xy + 2y^2)$

22. $3ab^2(3a^2 - 2ab + 4b^2)$

23. $x^n(x^{2n} + x^n + x)$

24. $x^{2n}(x^{2n-2} + x^{2n} + x)$

25. $a^{n+1}(a^n - 3a + 2)$

26. $a^{n+4}(a^{n-2} + 5a^2 - 3)$

27. $2y^2 - y[3 - 2(y - 4) - y]$

28. $3x^2 - x[x - 2(3x - 4)]$

29. $2y - 3[y - 2y(y - 3) + 4y]$

30. $4a^2 - 2a[3 - a(2 - a + a^2)]$

Objective B

Simplify.

31. $(x - 2)(x + 7)$

32. $(y + 8)(y + 3)$

33. $(2y - 3)(4y + 7)$

34. $(5x - 7)(3x - 8)$

35. $2(2x - 3y)(2x + 5y)$

36. $-3(7x - 3y)(2x - 9y)$

37. $(xy + 4)(xy - 3)$

38. $(xy - 5)(2xy + 7)$

39. $(2x^2 - 5)(x^2 - 5)$

40. $(x^2 - 4)(x^2 - 6)$

41. $(5x^2 - 5y)(2x^2 - y)$

42. $(x^2 - 2y^2)(x^2 + 4y^2)$

43. $(x^n + 2)(x^n - 3)$

44. $(x^n - 4)(x^n - 5)$

45. $(2a^n - 3)(3a^n + 5)$

46. $(5b^n - 1)(2b^n + 4)$

47. $(2a^n - b^n)(3a^n + 2b^n)$

48. $(3x^n + b^n)(x^n + 2b^n)$

49. $(x + 5)(x^3 - 3x + 4)$

50. $(a + 2)(a^3 - 3a^2 + 7)$

51. $(2a - 3b)(5a^2 - 6ab + 4b^2)$

52. $(3a + b)(2a^2 - 5ab - 3b^2)$

53. $(2y^2 - 1)(y^3 - 5y^2 - 3)$

54. $(2b^2 - 3)(3b^2 - 3b + 6)$

55. $(2x - 5)(2x^4 - 3x^3 - 2x + 9)$

56. $(2a - 5)(3a^4 - 3a^2 + 2a - 5)$

57. $(x^2 + 2x - 3)(x^2 - 5x + 7)$

58. $(x^2 - 3x + 1)(x^2 - 2x + 7)$

59. $(a - 2)(2a - 3)(a + 7)$

60. $(b - 3)(3b - 2)(b - 1)$

61. $(x^n + 1)(x^{2n} + x^n + 1)$

62. $(a^{2n} - 3)(a^{5n} - a^{2n} + a^n)$

63. $(x^n + y^n)(x^n - 2x^ny^n + 3y^n)$

64. $(x^n - y^n)(x^{2n} - 3x^ny^n - y^{2n})$

Objective C

Simplify.

65. $(3x - 2)(3x + 2)$

66. $(4y + 1)(4y - 1)$

67. $(6 - x)(6 + x)$

68. $(10 + b)(10 - b)$

69. $(2a - 3b)(2a + 3b)$

70. $(5x - 7y)(5x + 7y)$

71. $(x^2 + 1)(x^2 - 1)$

72. $(x^2 + y^2)(x^2 - y^2)$

73. $(x^n + 3)(x^n - 3)$

74. $(x^n + y^n)(x^n - y^n)$

75. $(x - 5)^2$

76. $(y + 2)^2$

77. $(3a + 5b)^2$

78. $(5x - 4y)^2$

79. $(x^2 - 3)^2$

80. $(x^2 + y^2)^2$

81. $(2x^2 - 3y^2)^2$

82. $(x^n - 1)^2$

83. $(a^n - b^n)^2$

84. $(2x^n + 5y^n)^2$

85. $y^2 - (x - y)^2$

86. $a^2 + (a + b)^2$

87. $(x - y)^2 - (x + y)^2$

88. $(a + b)^2 + (a - b)^2$

Objective D   *Application Problems*

89. The length of a rectangle is $(3x - 2)$ ft. The width is $(x + 4)$ ft. Find the area of the rectangle in terms of the variable x.

90. The base of a triangle is $(x - 4)$ ft. The height is $(3x + 2)$ ft. Find the area of the triangle in terms of the variable x.

91. Find the area of the figure shown below. All dimensions given are in meters.

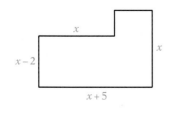

92. Find the area of the figure shown below. All dimensions given are in feet.

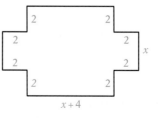

93. The length of the side of a cube is $(x + 3)$ cm. Find the volume of the cube in terms of the variable x.

94. The length of a box is $(3x + 2)$ cm, the width is $(x - 4)$ cm, and the height is x cm. Find the volume of the box in terms of the variable x.

95. Find the volume of the figure shown below. All dimensions given are in inches.

96. Find the volume of the figure shown below. All dimensions given are in centimeters.

97. The radius of a circle is $(5x + 4)$ in. Find the area of the circle in terms of the variable x. Use 3.14 for π.

98. The radius of a circle is $(x - 2)$ in. Find the area of the circle in terms of the variable x. Use 3.14 for π.

APPLYING THE CONCEPTS

99. Find the product.
 a. $(a - b)(a^2 + ab + b^2)$
 b. $(x + y)(x^2 - xy + y^2)$

100. Correct the error in each of the following.
 a. $(x + 3)^2 = x^2 + 9$
 b. $(a - b)^2 = a^2 - b^2$

101. For what value of k is the given equation an identity?
 a. $(3x - k)(2x + k) = 6x^2 + 5x - k^2$
 b. $(4x + k)^2 = 16x^2 + 8x + k^2$

102. Complete.
 a. If $m = n + 1$, then $\dfrac{a^m}{a^n} =$ _____ .
 b. If $m = n + 2$, then $\dfrac{a^m}{a^n} =$ _____ .

103. Subtract the product of $4a + b$ and $2a - b$ from $9a^2 - 2ab$.

104. Subtract the product of $5x - y$ and $x + 3y$ from $6x^2 + 12xy - 2y^2$.

5.4 Division of Polynomials

Objective A *To divide polynomials* .... (19) CT

Some rational expressions cannot be simplified by factoring and dividing by the common factors. In these cases, long division of polynomials is used.

To divide two polynomials, use a method similar to that used for division of whole numbers. To check division of polynomials, use

Dividend = (quotient × divisor) + remainder

➡ Simplify: $(x^2 + 5x - 7) \div (x + 3)$

Step 1

$$
\begin{array}{r}
x \\
x + 3 \overline{) x^2 + 5x - 7} \\
\underline{x^2 + 3x} \downarrow \\
2x - 7
\end{array}
$$

Think: $x\overline{)x^2} = \dfrac{x^2}{x} = x$

Multiply: $x(x + 3) = x^2 + 3x$

Subtract: $(x^2 + 5x) - (x^2 + 3x) = 2x$

Step 2

$$
\begin{array}{r}
x + 2 \\
x + 3 \overline{) x^2 + 5x - 7} \\
\underline{x^2 + 3x} \\
2x - 7 \\
\underline{2x + 6} \\
-13
\end{array}
$$

Think: $x\overline{)2x} = \dfrac{2x}{x} = 2$

Multiply: $2(x + 3) = 2x + 6$

Subtract: $(2x - 7) - (2x + 6) = -13$

The remainder is -13.

$$(x^2 + 5x - 7) \div (x + 3) = x + 2 - \frac{13}{x + 3}$$

Check: $(x + 2)(x + 3) + (-13) = x^2 + 3x + 2x + 6 - 13 = x^2 + 5x - 7$

➡ Simplify: $\dfrac{6 - 6x^2 + 4x^3}{2x + 3}$

Arrange the terms in descending order. Note that there is no term of x in $4x^3 - 6x^2 + 6$. Insert a zero for the missing term so that like terms will be in the same columns.

$$
\begin{array}{r}
2x^2 - 6x + 9 \\
2x + 3 \overline{) 4x^3 - 6x^2 + 0x + 6} \\
\underline{4x^3 + 6x^2} \\
-12x^2 + 0x \\
\underline{-12x^2 - 18x} \\
18x + 6 \\
\underline{18x + 27} \\
-21
\end{array}
$$

$$\frac{4x^3 - 6x^2 + 6}{2x + 3} = 2x^2 - 6x + 9 - \frac{21}{2x + 3}$$

Example 1

Simplify: $\dfrac{12x^2 - 11x + 10}{4x - 5}$

Solution

$$
\begin{array}{r}
3x \;+\; 1 \\
4x - 5 \,\overline{\big)\,12x^2 - 11x + 10} \\
\underline{12x^2 - 15x} \\
4x + 10 \\
\underline{4x - 5} \\
15
\end{array}
$$

$\dfrac{12x^2 - 11x + 10}{4x - 5} = 3x + 1 + \dfrac{15}{4x - 5}$

You Try It 1

Simplify: $\dfrac{15x^2 + 17x - 20}{3x + 4}$

Your solution

Example 2

Simplify: $\dfrac{x^3 + 1}{x + 1}$

Solution

$$
\begin{array}{r}
x^2 \;-\; x \;+\; 1 \\
x + 1 \,\overline{\big)\,x^3 + 0x^2 + 0x + 1} \\
\underline{x^3 + x^2} \\
-\,x^2 + 0x \\
\underline{-\,x^2 - x} \\
x + 1 \\
\underline{x + 1} \\
0
\end{array}
$$

• Insert zeros for the missing terms.

$\dfrac{x^3 + 1}{x + 1} = x^2 - x + 1$

You Try It 2

Simplify: $\dfrac{3x^3 + 8x^2 - 6x + 2}{3x - 1}$

Your solution

Example 3

Simplify:
$(2x^4 - 7x^3 + 3x^2 + 4x - 5) \div (x^2 - 2x - 2)$

Solution

$$
\begin{array}{r}
2x^2 \;-\; 3x \;+\; 1 \\
x^2 - 2x - 2 \,\overline{\big)\,2x^4 - 7x^3 + 3x^2 + 4x - 5} \\
\underline{2x^4 - 4x^3 - 4x^2} \\
-\,3x^3 + 7x^2 + 4x \\
\underline{-\,3x^3 + 6x^2 + 6x} \\
x^2 - 2x - 5 \\
\underline{x^2 - 2x - 2} \\
-\,3
\end{array}
$$

$(2x^4 - 7x^3 + 3x^2 + 4x - 5) \div (x^2 - 2x - 2)$

$= 2x^2 - 3x + 1 - \dfrac{3}{x^2 - 2x - 2}$

You Try It 3

Simplify:
$(3x^4 - 11x^3 + 16x^2 - 16x + 8) \div (x^2 - 3x + 2)$

Your solution

Solutions on pp. S15–S16

Objective B   *To divide polynomials by using synthetic division* .... CT

Synthetic division is a shorter method of dividing a polynomial by a binomial of the form $x - a$.

➡ Simplify $(3x^2 - 4x + 6) \div (x - 2)$ by using long division.

$$
\begin{array}{r}
3x + 2 \\
x - 2 \overline{\smash{)}3x^2 - 4x + 6} \\
\underline{3x^2 - 6x} \\
2x + 6 \\
\underline{2x - 4} \\
10
\end{array}
$$

$$(3x^2 - 4x + 6) \div (x - 2) = 3x + 2 + \frac{10}{x - 2}$$

The variables can be omitted because the position of a term indicates the power of the term.

$$
\begin{array}{r}
3 \quad\; 2 \\
-2 \overline{\smash{)}3 \;-4 \quad 6} \\
\underline{3 \;-6} \\
2 \quad\; 6 \\
\underline{2 \;-4} \\
10
\end{array}
$$

Each number shown in color is exactly the same as the number above it. Removing the colored numbers condenses the vertical spacing.

$$
\begin{array}{r}
3 \quad\; 2 \\
-2 \overline{\smash{)}3 \;-4 \quad 6} \\
\underline{-6 \;-4} \\
2 \quad 10
\end{array}
$$

The number in color in the top row is the same as the one in the bottom row. Writing the 3 from the top row in the bottom row allows the spacing to be condensed even further.

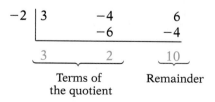

Because the degree of the dividend $(3x^2 - 4x + 6)$ is 2 and the degree of the divisor $(x - 2)$ is 1, the degree of the quotient is $2 - 1 = 1$. This means that, using the terms of the quotient given above, that quotient is $3x + 2$. The remainder is 10.

In general, the degree of the quotient of two polynomials is the difference between the degree of the dividend and the degree of the divisor.

By replacing the constant term in the divisor by its additive inverse, we may add rather than subtract terms. This is illustrated in the following example.

➡ Simplify: $(3x^3 + 6x^2 - x - 2) \div (x + 3)$

The additive inverse of the binomial constant

Coefficients of the polynomial

$$
\begin{array}{c|cccc}
-3 & 3 & 6 & -1 & -2 \\
 & \downarrow & & & \\
\hline
 & 3 & & &
\end{array}
$$

- Bring down the 3.

$$
\begin{array}{c|cccc}
-3 & 3 & 6 & -1 & -2 \\
 & & -9 & & \\
\hline
 & 3 & -3 & &
\end{array}
$$

- Multiply $-3(3)$ and add the product to 6.

$$
\begin{array}{c|cccc}
-3 & 3 & 6 & -1 & -2 \\
 & & -9 & 9 & \\
\hline
 & 3 & -3 & 8 &
\end{array}
$$

- Multiply $-3(-3)$ and add the product to -1.

$$
\begin{array}{c|cccc}
-3 & 3 & 6 & -1 & -2 \\
 & & -9 & 9 & -24 \\
\hline
 & 3 & -3 & 8 & -26
\end{array}
$$

- Multiply $-3(8)$ and add the product to -2.

Terms of the quotient   Remainder

The degree of the dividend is 3 and the degree of the divisor is 1. Therefore, the degree of the quotient is $3 - 1 = 2$.

$$(3x^3 + 6x^2 - x - 2) \div (x + 3) = 3x^2 - 3x + 8 - \frac{26}{x + 3}$$

➡ Simplify: $(2x^3 - x + 2) \div (x - 2)$

The additive inverse of the binomial constant

Coefficients of the polynomial

$$
\begin{array}{c|cccc}
2 & 2 & 0 & -1 & 2 \\
 & \downarrow & & & \\
\hline
 & 2 & & &
\end{array}
$$

- Insert a 0 for the missing term and bring down the 2.

$$
\begin{array}{c|cccc}
2 & 2 & 0 & -1 & 2 \\
 & & 4 & & \\
\hline
 & 2 & 4 & &
\end{array}
$$

- Multiply $2(2)$ and add the product to 0.

$$
\begin{array}{c|cccc}
2 & 2 & 0 & -1 & 2 \\
 & & 4 & 8 & \\
\hline
 & 2 & 4 & 7 &
\end{array}
$$

- Multiply $2(4)$ and add the product to -1.

$$
\begin{array}{c|cccc}
2 & 2 & 0 & -1 & 2 \\
 & & 4 & 8 & 14 \\
\hline
 & 2 & 4 & 7 & 16
\end{array}
$$

- Multiply $2(7)$ and add the product to 2.

Terms of the quotient   Remainder

$$(2x^3 - x + 2) \div (x - 2) = 2x^2 + 4x + 7 + \frac{16}{x - 2}$$

Example 4
Simplify: $(7 - 3x + 5x^2) \div (x - 1)$

Solution
Arrange the coefficients in decreasing powers of x.

$$\begin{array}{r|rrr} 1 & 5 & -3 & 7 \\ & & 5 & 2 \\ \hline & 5 & 2 & 9 \end{array}$$

$(5x^2 - 3x + 7) \div (x - 1) = 5x + 2 + \dfrac{9}{x - 1}$

You Try It 4
Simplify: $(6x^2 + 8x - 5) \div (x + 2)$

Your solution

Example 5
Simplify: $(2x^3 + 4x^2 - 3x + 12) \div (x + 4)$

Solution

$$\begin{array}{r|rrrr} -4 & 2 & 4 & -3 & 12 \\ & & -8 & 16 & -52 \\ \hline & 2 & -4 & 13 & -40 \end{array}$$

$(2x^3 + 4x^2 - 3x + 12) \div (x + 4)$
$= 2x^2 - 4x + 13 - \dfrac{40}{x + 4}$

You Try It 5
Simplify: $(5x^3 - 12x^2 - 8x + 16) \div (x - 2)$

Your solution

Example 6
Simplify: $(3x^4 - 8x^2 + 2x + 1) \div (x + 2)$

Solution
Insert a zero for the missing term.

$$\begin{array}{r|rrrrr} -2 & 3 & 0 & -8 & 2 & 1 \\ & & -6 & 12 & -8 & 12 \\ \hline & 3 & -6 & 4 & -6 & 13 \end{array}$$

$(3x^4 - 8x^2 + 2x + 1) \div (x + 2)$
$= 3x^3 - 6x^2 + 4x - 6 + \dfrac{13}{x + 2}$

You Try It 6
Simplify: $(2x^4 - 3x^3 - 8x^2 - 2) \div (x - 3)$

Your solution

Solutions on p. S16

Objective C To evaluate a polynomial using synthetic division ················· CT

A polynomial can be evaluated by using synthetic division. Consider the polynomial $P(x) = 2x^4 - 3x^3 + 4x^2 - 5x + 1$. One way to evaluate the polynomial when $x = 2$ is to replace x by 2 and then simplify the numerical expression.

$P(x) = 2x^4 - 3x^3 + 4x^2 - 5x + 1$

$P(2) = 2(2)^4 - 3(2)^3 + 4(2)^2 - 5(2) + 1$
$= 2(16) - 3(8) + 4(4) - 5(2) + 1$
$= 32 - 24 + 16 - 10 + 1$
$= 15$

Now use synthetic division to divide $(2x^4 - 3x^3 + 4x^2 - 5x + 1) \div (x - 2)$.

$$\begin{array}{r|rrrrr} 2 & 2 & -3 & 4 & -5 & 1 \\ & & 4 & 2 & 12 & 14 \\ \hline & 2 & 1 & 6 & 7 & 15 \end{array}$$

$\underbrace{\qquad\qquad\qquad}_{\text{Terms of the quotient}}$ $\underbrace{\quad}_{\text{Remainder}}$

Note that the remainder is 15, which is the same value as $P(2)$. This is not a coincidence. The following theorem states that this situation is always true.

Remainder Theorem

If the polynomial $P(x)$ is divided by $x - a$, the remainder is $P(a)$.

➡ Evaluate $P(x) = x^4 - 3x^2 + 4x - 5$ when $x = -2$ by using the Remainder Theorem.

$\overbrace{\qquad\qquad}$ The value at which the polynomial is evaluated

$$\begin{array}{r|rrrrr} -2 & 1 & 0 & -3 & 4 & -5 \\ & & -2 & 4 & -2 & -4 \\ \hline & 1 & -2 & 1 & 2 & -9 \end{array}$$

• A 0 is inserted for the x^3 term.

⟵ The remainder

$P(-2) = -9$

Example 7
Use synthetic division to evaluate
$P(x) = x^2 - 6x + 4$ when $x = 3$.

Solution

$$\begin{array}{r|rrr} 3 & 1 & -6 & 4 \\ & & 3 & -9 \\ \hline & 1 & -3 & -5 \end{array}$$

$P(3) = -5$

You Try It 7
Use synthetic division to evaluate
$P(x) = 2x^2 - 3x - 5$ when $x = 2$.

Your solution

Example 8
Use synthetic division to evaluate
$P(x) = -x^4 + 3x^3 + 2x^2 - x - 5$ when
$x = -2$.

Solution

$$\begin{array}{r|rrrrr} -2 & -1 & 3 & 2 & -1 & -5 \\ & & 2 & -10 & 16 & -30 \\ \hline & -1 & 5 & -8 & 15 & -35 \end{array}$$

$P(-2) = -35$

You Try It 8
Use synthetic division to evaluate
$P(x) = 2x^3 - 5x^2 + 7$ when $x = -3$.

Your solution

Solutions on p. S16

5.4 Exercises

Objective A

Divide by using long division.

1. $(x^2 + 3x - 40) \div (x - 5)$

2. $(x^2 - 14x + 24) \div (x - 2)$

3. $(x^3 - 3x + 2) \div (x - 3)$

4. $(x^3 + 4x^2 - 8) \div (x + 4)$

5. $(6x^2 + 13x + 8) \div (2x + 1)$

6. $(12x^2 + 13x - 14) \div (3x - 2)$

7. $(10x^2 + 9x - 5) \div (2x - 1)$

8. $(18x^2 - 3x + 2) \div (3x + 2)$

9. $(8x^3 - 9) \div (2x - 3)$

10. $(64x^3 + 4) \div (4x + 2)$

11. $(6x^4 - 13x^2 - 4) \div (2x^2 - 5)$

12. $(12x^4 - 11x^2 + 10) \div (3x^2 + 1)$

13. $\dfrac{-10 - 33x + 3x^3 - 8x^2}{3x + 1}$

14. $\dfrac{10 - 49x + 38x^2 - 8x^3}{1 - 4x}$

15. $\dfrac{x^3 - 5x^2 + 7x - 4}{x - 3}$

16. $\dfrac{2x^3 - 3x^2 + 6x + 4}{2x + 1}$

17. $\dfrac{16x^2 - 13x^3 + 2x^4 + 20 - 9x}{x - 5}$

18. $\dfrac{x - x^2 + 5x^3 + 3x^4 - 2}{x + 2}$

19. $\dfrac{2x^3 + 4x^2 - x + 2}{x^2 + 2x - 1}$

20. $\dfrac{3x^3 - 2x^2 + 5x - 4}{x^2 - x + 3}$

21. $\dfrac{x^4 + 2x^3 - 3x^2 - 6x + 2}{x^2 - 2x - 1}$

22. $\dfrac{x^4 - 3x^3 + 4x^2 - x + 1}{x^2 + x - 3}$

23. $\dfrac{x^4 + 3x^2 - 4x + 5}{x^2 + 2x + 3}$

24. $\dfrac{x^4 + 2x^3 - x + 2}{x^2 - x - 1}$

Objective B

Divide by using synthetic division.

25. $(2x^2 - 6x - 8) \div (x + 1)$

26. $(3x^2 + 19x + 20) \div (x + 5)$

27. $(3x^2 - 14x + 16) \div (x - 2)$

28. $(4x^2 - 23x + 28) \div (x - 4)$

29. $(3x^2 - 4) \div (x - 1)$

30. $(4x^2 - 8) \div (x - 2)$

31. $(2x^3 - x^2 + 6x + 9) \div (x + 1)$

32. $(3x^3 + 10x^2 + 6x - 4) \div (x + 2)$

33. $(18 + x - 4x^3) \div (2 - x)$

34. $(12 - 3x^2 + x^3) \div (x + 3)$

35. $(2x^3 + 5x^2 - 5x + 20) \div (x + 4)$

36. $(5x^3 + 3x^2 - 17x + 6) \div (x + 2)$

37. $\dfrac{5 + 5x - 8x^2 + 4x^3 - 3x^4}{2 - x}$

38. $\dfrac{3 - 13x - 5x^2 + 9x^3 - 2x^4}{3 - x}$

39. $\dfrac{3x^4 + 3x^3 - x^2 + 3x + 2}{x + 1}$

40. $\dfrac{4x^4 + 12x^3 - x^2 - x + 2}{x + 3}$

41. $\dfrac{2x^4 - x^2 + 2}{x - 3}$

42. $\dfrac{x^4 - 3x^3 - 30}{x + 2}$

Objective C

Use the Remainder Theorem to evaluate each of the polynomials.

43. $P(x) = 2x^2 - 3x - 1;\ P(3)$

44. $Q(x) = 3x^2 - 5x - 1;\ Q(2)$

45. $R(x) = x^3 - 2x^2 + 3x - 1;\ R(4)$

46. $F(x) = x^3 + 4x^2 - 3x + 2;\ F(3)$

47. $P(z) = 2z^3 - 4z^2 + 3z - 1;\ P(-2)$

48. $R(t) = 3t^3 + t^2 - 4t + 2;\ R(-3)$

49. $Z(p) = 2p^3 - p^2 + 3; Z(-3)$

50. $P(y) = 3y^3 + 2y^2 - 5; P(-2)$

51. $Q(x) = x^4 + 3x^3 - 2x^2 + 4x - 9; Q(2)$

52. $Y(z) = z^4 - 2z^3 - 3z^2 - z + 7; Z(3)$

53. $F(x) = 2x^4 - x^3 + 2x - 5; F(-3)$

54. $Q(x) = x^4 - 2x^3 + 4x - 2; Q(-2)$

55. $P(x) = x^3 - 3; P(5)$

56. $S(t) = 4t^3 + 5; S(-4)$

57. $R(t) = 4t^4 - 3t^2 + 5; R(-3)$

58. $P(z) = 2z^4 + z^2 - 3; Z(-4)$

59. $Q(x) = x^5 - 4x^3 - 2x^2 + 5x - 2; Q(2)$

60. $T(x) = 2x^5 + 4x^4 - x^2 + 4; T(3)$

61. $R(x) = 2x^5 - x^3 + 4x - 1; R(-2)$

62. $P(x) = x^5 - x^3 + 4x + 1; P(-3)$

APPLYING THE CONCEPTS

63. Divide by using long division.

   a. $\dfrac{a^3 + b^3}{a + b}$
   b. $\dfrac{x^5 + y^5}{x + y}$
   c. $\dfrac{x^6 - y^6}{x + y}$

64. For what value of k will the remainder be zero?

   a. $(x^3 - x^2 - 3x + k) \div (x + 3)$
   b. $(2x^3 - x + k) \div (x - 1)$

65. Divide.

   a. $(2x^3 + 7x^2 + 2x - 8) \div (4x + 8)$
   b. $(4x^3 + 13x^2 - 22x + 24) \div (6x - 12)$

   c. $(2x^4 - 3x^3 + 4x^2 + x - 10) \div (x^2 - x + 1)$
   d. $(x^4 + 4x^3 + 2x^2 - x + 5) \div (x^2 - 2x - 3)$

66. Show how synthetic division can be modified so that the divisor can be of the form $ax + b$.

5.5 **Factoring Polynomials**

Objective A   *To factor a monomial from a polynomial* ....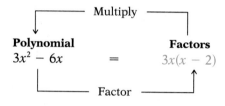

The greatest common factor (GCF) of two or more monomials is the product of each common factor with the smallest exponent.

$$16a^4b = 2^4a^4b$$
$$40a^2b^5 = 2^3 \cdot 5a^2b^5$$
$$\text{GCF} = 2^3a^2b = 8a^2b$$

Note that the exponent of each variable in the GCF is the same as the smallest exponent of the variable in either of the monomials.

To **factor a polynomial** means to write the polynomial as a product of other polynomials.

In the example at the right, $3x$ is the GCF of the terms $3x^2$ and $6x$. $3x$ is a **common monomial factor** of the terms of the binomial. $x - 2$ is a **binomial factor** of $3x^2 - 6x$.

```
            ┌──────── Multiply ────────┐
            ↓                          │
      Polynomial                   Factors
      3x² − 6x        =           3x(x − 2)
            │                          ↑
            └──────── Factor ──────────┘
```

➡ Factor: $4x^3y^2 + 12x^3y + 20xy^3$

   The GCF of $4x^3y^2$, $12x^3y$, and $20xy^3$ is $4xy$.

   $4x^3y^2 + 12x^3y + 20xy^3$

   $= 4xy\left(\dfrac{4x^3y^2}{4xy} + \dfrac{12x^3y}{4xy} + \dfrac{20xy^3}{4xy}\right)$

   $= 4xy(x^2y + 3x^2 + 5y^2)$

- Find the GCF of the terms of the polynomial.

- Factor the GCF from each term of the polynomial. Think of this as dividing each term of the polynomial by the GCF.

Example 1
Factor: $4x^2y^2 - 6xy^2 + 12xy^3$

Solution
The GCF of $4x^2y^2$, $6xy^2$, and $12xy^3$ is $2xy^2$.

$4x^2y^2 - 6xy^2 + 12xy^3 = 2xy^2(2x - 3 + 6y)$

You Try It 1
Factor: $3x^3y - 6x^2y^2 - 3xy^3$

Your solution

Solution on p. S16

Example 2
Factor: $x^{2n} + x^{n+1} + x^n$

Solution
The GCF of x^{2n}, x^{n+1}, and x^n is x^n.

$x^{2n} + x^{n+1} + x^n = x^n(x^n + x + 1)$

You Try It 2
Factor: $6t^{2n} - 9t^n$

Your solution

Solution on p. S16

Objective B **To factor by grouping** .... 20 CT

In the examples at the right, the binomials in parentheses are called binomial factors.

$4x^4(2x - 3)$
$-2r^2s(5r + 2s)$

The Distributive Property is used to factor a common binomial factor from an expression.

➡ Factor: $4a(2b + 3) - 5(2b + 3)$

The common binomial factor is $(2b + 3)$. Use the Distributive Property to write the expression as a product of factors.

$4a(2b + 3) - 5(2b + 3) = (2b + 3)(4a - 5)$

Consider the binomial $y - x$. Factoring -1 from this binomial gives

$$y - x = -(x - y)$$

This equation is used to factor a common binomial from an expression.

TAKE NOTE

For the simplification at the right,

$6r(r - s) - 7(s - r)$
$= 6r(r - s) - 7[(-1)(r - s)]$
$= 6r(r - s) + 7(r - s)$

➡ Factor: $6r(r - s) - 7(s - r)$

$6r(r - s) - 7(s - r) = 6r(r - s) + 7(r - s)$
$= (r - s)(6r + 7)$

• $s - r = -(r - s)$

Some polynomials can be factored by grouping terms so that a common binomial factor is found.

➡ Factor: $3xz - 4yz - 3xa + 4ya$

$3xz - 4yz - 3xa + 4ya$
$= (3xz - 4yz) - (3xa - 4ya)$

$= z(3x - 4y) - a(3x - 4y)$
$= (3x - 4y)(z - a)$

• Group the first two terms and the last two terms. Note that $-3xa + 4ya = -(3xa - 4ya)$.
• Factor the GCF from each group.
• Write the expression as the product of factors.

➡ Factor: $8y^2 + 4y - 6ay - 3a$

$8y^2 + 4y - 6ay - 3a$
$= (8y^2 + 4y) - (6ay + 3a)$

$= 4y(2y + 1) - 3a(2y + 1)$
$= (2y + 1)(4y - 3a)$

- Group the first two terms and the last two terms. Note that $-6ay - 3a = -(6ay + 3a)$.
- Factor the GCF from each group.
- Write the expression as the product of factors.

Example 3
Factor: $x^2(5y - 2) - 7(5y - 2)$

Solution
$x^2(5y - 2) - 7(5y - 2)$
$= (5y - 2)(x^2 - 7)$

You Try It 3
Factor: $3(6x - 7y) - 2x^2(6x - 7y)$

Your solution

Example 4
Factor: $15x^2 + 6x - 5xz - 2z$

Solution
$15x^2 + 6x - 5xz - 2z$
$= (15x^2 + 6x) - (5xz + 2z)$
$= 3x(5x + 2) - z(5x + 2)$
$= (5x + 2)(3x - z)$

You Try It 4
Factor: $4a^2 - 6a - 6ax + 9x$

Your solution

Solutions on p. S16

Objective C   **To factor a trinomial of the form $x^2 + bx + c$** .... (20) CT

A **quadratic trinomial** is a trinomial of the form $ax^2 + bx + c$, where a, b, and c are nonzero constants. The degree of a quadratic trinomial is 2. Here are examples of quadratic trinomials:

$$4x^2 - 3x - 7 \qquad\qquad z^2 + z + 10 \qquad\qquad 2y^2 + 4y - 9$$
$$(a = 4, b = -3, c = -7) \qquad (a = 1, b = 1, c = 10) \qquad (a = 2, b = 4, c = -9)$$

To **factor a quadratic trinomial** means to express the trinomial as the product of two binomials. For example,

Trinomial		**Factored Form**
$2x^2 - x - 1$	$=$	$(2x + 1)(x - 1)$
$y^2 - 3y + 2$	$=$	$(y - 1)(y - 2)$

In this objective, trinomials of the form $x^2 + bx + c$ ($a = 1$) will be factored. The next objective deals with trinomials where $a \neq 1$.

The method by which factors of a trinomial are found is based on FOIL. Consider the following binomial products, noting the relationship between the constant terms of the binomials and the terms of the trinomial.

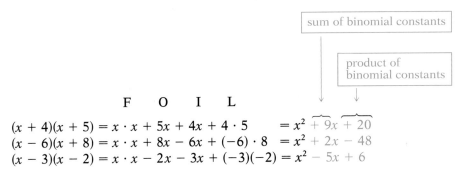

Observe two important points from these examples.

1. The constant term of the trinomial is the *product* of the constant terms of the binomials. The coefficient of x in the trinomial is the *sum* of the constant terms of the binomials.

2. When the constant term of the trinomial is positive, the constant terms of the binomials have the *same* sign. When the constant term of the trinomial is negative, the constant terms of the binomials have *opposite* signs.

⇒ Factor: $x^2 - 7x + 12$

The constant term is positive. The signs of the binomial constants will be the same.

Find two negative factors of 12 whose sum is -7.

Negative Factors of 12	Sum
$-1, -12$	-13
$-2, -6$	-8
$-3, -4$	-7

TAKE NOTE

You can always check a proposed factorization by multiplying all the factors.

Write the trinomial in factored form. $x^2 - 7x + 12 = (x - 3)(x - 4)$

Check: $(x - 3)(x - 4) = x^2 - 4x - 3x + 12 = x^2 - 7x + 12$

⇒ Factor: $y^2 + 10y - 24$

The constant term is negative. The signs of the binomial constants will be opposite.

Find two factors of -24 that have opposite signs and whose sum is 10. All of the possible factors are shown at the right. In practice, once the correct pair is found, the remaining choices need not be checked.

Factors of -24	Sum
$-1,\ 24$	23
$1, -24$	-23
$-2,\ 12$	10
$2, -12$	-10
$-3,\ 8$	5
$3, -8$	-5
$-4,\ 6$	2
$4, -6$	-2

Write the trinomial in factored form. $y^2 + 10y - 24 = (y - 2)(y + 12)$

Check: $(y - 2)(y + 12) = y^2 + 12y - 2y - 24 = y^2 + 10y - 24$

When only integers are used, some trinomials do not factor. For example, to factor $x^2 + 11x + 5$, it would be necessary to find two positive integers whose product is 5 and whose sum is 11. This is not possible, because the only positive factors of 5 are 1 and 5, and the sum of 1 and 5 is 6. The polynomial $x^2 + 11x + 5$ is a prime polynomial. Such a polynomial is said to be **nonfactorable over the integers.** Binomials of the form $x + a$ or $x - a$ are also prime polynomials.

Example 5
Factor: $x^2 + 2x - 4$

Solution
There are no factors of -4 whose signs are opposite and whose sum is 2.

The trinomial is nonfactorable over the integers.

You Try It 5
Factor: $x^2 - x - 20$

Your solution

Example 6
Factor: $10 - 3x - x^2$

Solution
When the coefficient of x^2 is -1, factoring -1 from the trinomial may make factoring the trinomial easier.

$$10 - 3x - x^2 = -x^2 - 3x + 10$$
$$= -(x^2 + 3x - 10)$$
$$= -(x - 2)(x + 5)$$

You Try It 6
Factor: $x^2 + 5xy + 6y^2$

Your solution

Solutions on p. S16

Objective D   To factor $ax^2 + bx + c$ .... 21 CT

There are various methods of factoring trinomials of the form $ax^2 + bx + c$, where $a \neq 1$. Factoring by using trial factors and factoring by grouping will be discussed in this objective. Factoring by using trial factors is illustrated first.

To use the trial factor method, use the factors of a and the factors of c to write all of the possible binomial factors of the trinomial. Then use FOIL to determine the correct factorization. To reduce the number of trial factors that must be considered, remember the following.

1. Use the signs of the constant term and the coefficient of x in the trinomial to determine the signs of the binomial factors. If the constant term is positive, the signs of the binomial factors will be the same as the sign of the coefficient of x in the trinomial. If the sign of the constant term is negative, the constant terms in the binomials will have opposite signs.

2. If the terms of the trinomial do not have a common factor, then the terms in either one of the binomial factors will not have a common factor.

➡️ Factor: $3x^2 - 8x + 4$

The terms have no common factor.
The constant term is positive.
The coefficient of x is negative.
The binomial constants will be negative.

Positive Factors of 3 (coefficient of x^2)	Negative Factors of 4 (constant term)
1, 3	−1, −4
	−2, −2

Write trial factors. Use the *Outer* and *Inner* products of FOIL to determine the middle term of the trinomial.

Trial Factors	Middle Term
$(x - 1)(3x - 4)$	$-4x - 3x = -7x$
$(x - 4)(3x - 1)$	$-x - 12x = -13x$
$(x - 2)(3x - 2)$	$-2x - 6x = -8x$

Write the trinomial in factored form.

$$3x^2 - 8x + 4 = (x - 2)(3x - 2)$$

➡️ Factor: $10 - x - 2x^2$

The terms have no common factor.
The coefficient of x^2 is −2.
Thus the signs of the binomials will be opposites.

Positive Factors of 10 (constant term)	Factors of −2 (coefficient of x^2)
1, 10	1, −2
2, 5	−1, 2

Write trial factors. Use the *Outer* and *Inner* products of FOIL to determine the middle term of the trinomial.

Trial Factors	Middle Term
$(1 + x)(10 - 2x)$	common factor
$(1 - x)(10 + 2x)$	common factor
$(2 + x)(5 - 2x)$	$-4x + 5x = x$
$(2 - x)(5 + 2x)$	$4x - 5x = -x$

Write the trinomial in factored form.

$$10 - x - 2x^2 = (2 - x)(5 + 2x)$$

➡️ Factor: $10y^3 + 44y^2 - 30y$

The GCF is $2y$. Factor the GCF from the terms.

$$10y^3 + 44y^2 - 30y = 2y(5y^2 + 22y - 15)$$

Factor the trinomial.
The constant term is negative.
The binomial constants will have opposite signs.

Positive Factors of 5 (coefficient of y^2)	Factors of −15 (constant term)
1, 5	−1, 15
	1, −15
	−3, 5
	3, −5

Write trial factors. Use the *Outer* and *Inner* products of FOIL to determine the middle term of the trinomial.

It is not necessary to test trial factors that have a common factor.

Trial Factors	Middle Term
$(y - 1)(5y + 15)$	common factor
$(y + 15)(5y - 1)$	$-y + 75y = 74y$
$(y + 1)(5y - 15)$	common factor
$(y - 15)(5y + 1)$	$y - 75y = -74y$
$(y - 3)(5y + 5)$	common factor
$(y + 5)(5y - 3)$	$-3y + 25y = 22y$
$(y + 3)(5y - 5)$	common factor
$(y - 5)(5y + 3)$	$3y - 25y = -22y$

Write the trinomial in factored form.

$$10y^3 + 44y^2 - 30y = 2y(y + 5)(5y - 3)$$

For previous examples, all the trial factors were listed. Once the correct factors have been found, however, the remaining trial factors can be omitted.

Trinomials of the form $ax^2 + bx + c$ can also be factored by grouping. This method is an extension of the method discussed in the previous objective.

To factor $ax^2 + bx + c$, first find two factors of $a \cdot c$ whose sum is b. Then use factoring by grouping to write the factorization of the trinomial.

For the trinomial $3x^2 - 8x + 4$, $a = 3$, $b = -8$, and $c = 4$. To find two factors of $a \cdot c$ whose sum is b, first find the product $a \cdot c$ ($a \cdot c = 3 \cdot 4 = 12$). Then find two factors of 12 whose sum is -8. (-2 and -6 are two factors of 12 whose sum is -8.)

⇒ Factor: $3x^2 + 11x + 8$

Find two positive factors of 24 ($ac = 3 \cdot 8$) whose sum is 11, the coefficient of x.

Positive Factors of 24	Sum
1, 24	25
2, 12	14
3, 8	11

The required sum has been found. The remaining factors need not be checked.

Use the factors of 24 whose sum is 11 to write $11x$ as $3x + 8x$.
Factor by grouping.

$3x^2 + 11x + 8 = 3x^2 + 3x + 8x + 8$

$$= (3x^2 + 3x) + (8x + 8)$$
$$= 3x(x + 1) + 8(x + 1)$$
$$= (x + 1)(3x + 8)$$

Check: $(x + 1)(3x + 8) = 3x^2 + 8x + 3x + 8 = 3x^2 + 11x + 8$

⇒ Factor: $4z^2 - 17z - 21$

Find two factors of -84 [$ac = 4 \cdot (-21)$] whose sum is -17, the coefficient of z.

Once the required sum is found, the remaining factors need not be checked.

Factors of −84	Sum
1, −84	−83
−1, 84	83
2, −42	−40
−2, 42	40
3, −28	−25
−3, 28	25
4, −21	−17

Use the factors of -84 whose sum is -17 to write $-17z$ as $4z - 21z$.

$4z^2 - 17z - 21 = 4z^2 + 4z - 21z - 21$

Factor by grouping. Recall that $-21z - 21 = -(21z + 21)$.

$$= (4z^2 + 4z) - (21z + 21)$$
$$= 4z(z + 1) - 21(z + 1)$$
$$= (z + 1)(4z - 21)$$

Check: $(z + 1)(4z - 21) = 4z^2 - 21z + 4z - 21 = 4z^2 - 17z - 21$

➡ Factor: $3x^2 - 11x + 4$

Find two negative factors of 12 $(3 \cdot 4)$ whose sum is -11.

Negative Factors of 12	Sum
$-1, -12$	-13
$-2, -6$	-8
$-3, -4$	-7

Because no integer factors of 12 have a sum of -11, $3x^2 - 11x + 4$ is nonfactorable over the integers. $3x^2 - 11x + 4$ is a prime polynomial over the integers.

Either method of factoring discussed in this objective will always lead to a correct factorization of trinomials of the form $ax^2 + bx + c$ that are not prime polynomials.

Example 7
Factor: $6x^2 + 11x - 10$

Solution
$6x^2 + 11x - 10 = (2x + 5)(3x - 2)$

You Try It 7
Factor: $4x^2 + 15x - 4$

Your solution

Example 8
Factor: $12x^2 - 32x + 5$

Solution
$12x^2 - 32x + 5 = (6x - 1)(2x - 5)$

You Try It 8
Factor: $10x^2 + 39x + 14$

Your solution

Example 9
Factor: $30y + 2xy - 4x^2y$

Solution
The GCF of $30y$, $2xy$, and $4x^2y$ is $2y$.

$$30y + 2xy - 4x^2y = 2y(15 + x - 2x^2)$$
$$= 2y(5 + 2x)(3 - x)$$

You Try It 9
Factor: $3a^3b^3 + 3a^2b^2 - 60ab$

Your solution

Solutions on p. S16

5.5 Exercises

. . . .

Objective A

Factor.

1. $6a^2 - 15a$

2. $32b^2 + 12b$

3. $4x^3 - 3x^2$

4. $12a^5b^2 + 16a^4b$

5. $3a^2 - 10b^3$

6. $9x^2 + 14y^4$

7. $x^5 - x^3 - x$

8. $y^4 - 3y^2 - 2y$

9. $16x^2 - 12x + 24$

10. $2x^5 + 3x^4 - 4x^2$

11. $5b^2 - 10b^3 + 25b^4$

12. $x^2y^4 - x^2y - 4x^2$

13. $x^{2n} - x^n$

14. $2a^{5n} + a^{2n}$

15. $x^{3n} - x^{2n}$

16. $y^{4n} + y^{2n}$

17. $a^{2n+2} + a^2$

18. $b^{n+5} - b^5$

19. $12x^2y^2 - 18x^3y + 24x^2y$

20. $14a^4b^4 - 42a^3b^3 + 28a^3b^2$

21. $24a^3b^2 - 4a^2b^2 - 16a^2b^4$

22. $10x^2y + 20x^2y^2 + 30x^2y^3$

23. $y^{2n+2} + y^{n+2} - y^2$

24. $a^{2n+2} + a^{2n+1} + a^n$

Objective B

Factor.

25. $x(a + 2) - 2(a + 2)$

26. $3(x + y) + a(x + y)$

27. $a(x - 2) - b(2 - x)$

28. $3(a - 7) - b(7 - a)$

29. $x(a - 2b) + y(2b - a)$

30. $b(3 - 2c) - 5(2c - 3)$

31. $xy + 4y - 2x - 8$

32. $ab + 7b - 3a - 21$

33. $ax + bx - ay - by$

34. $2ax - 3ay - 2bx + 3by$

35. $x^2y - 3x^2 - 2y + 6$

36. $a^2b + 3a^2 + 2b + 6$

37. $6 + 2y + 3x^2 + x^2y$

38. $15 + 3b - 5a^2 - a^2b$

39. $2ax^2 + bx^2 - 4ay - 2by$

40. $4a^2x + 2a^2y - 6bx - 3by$

41. $6xb + 3ax - 4by - 2ay$

42. $a^2x - 3a^2y + 2x - 6y$

43. $x^ny - 5x^n + y - 5$

44. $a^nx^n + 2a^n + x^n + 2$

45. $2x^3 - x^2 + 4x - 2$

$(2x - 1)(x^2 - 2)$

Objective C

Factor.

46. $x^2 - 8x + 15$

47. $x^2 + 12x + 20$

48. $a^2 + 12a + 11$

49. $a^2 + a - 72$

50. $b^2 + 2b - 35$

51. $a^2 + 7a + 6$

52. $y^2 - 16y + 39$

53. $y^2 - 18y + 72$

54. $b^2 + 4b - 32$

55. $x^2 + x - 132$

56. $a^2 - 15a + 56$

57. $x^2 + 15x + 50$

58. $y^2 + 13y + 12$

59. $b^2 - 6b - 16$

60. $x^2 + 4x - 5$

61. $a^2 - 3ab + 2b^2$

62. $a^2 + 11ab + 30b^2$

63. $a^2 + 8ab - 33b^2$

64. $x^2 - 14xy + 24y^2$ **65.** $x^2 + 5xy + 6y^2$ **66.** $y^2 + 2xy - 63x^2$

67. $2 + x - x^2$ **68.** $21 - 4x - x^2$ **69.** $5 + 4x - x^2$

70. $50 + 5a - a^2$ **71.** $x^2 - 5x + 6$ **72.** $x^2 - 7x - 12$

Objective D

Factor.

73. $2x^2 + 7x + 3$ **74.** $2x^2 - 11x - 40$ **75.** $6y^2 + 5y - 6$

76. $4y^2 - 15y + 9$ **77.** $6b^2 - b - 35$ **78.** $2a^2 + 13a + 6$

79. $3y^2 - 22y + 39$ **80.** $12y^2 - 13y - 72$ **81.** $6a^2 - 26a + 15$

82. $5x^2 + 26x + 5$ **83.** $4a^2 - a - 5$ **84.** $11x^2 - 122x + 11$

85. $10x^2 - 29x + 10$ **86.** $2x^2 + 5x + 12$ **87.** $4x^2 - 6x + 1$

88. $6x^2 + 5xy - 21y^2$ **89.** $6x^2 + 41xy - 7y^2$ **90.** $4a^2 + 43ab + 63b^2$

91. $7a^2 + 46ab - 21b^2$ **92.** $10x^2 - 23xy + 12y^2$ **93.** $18x^2 + 27xy + 10y^2$

94. $24 + 13x - 2x^2$ **95.** $6 - 7x - 5x^2$ **96.** $8 - 13x + 6x^2$

97. $30 + 17a - 20a^2$ **98.** $15 - 14a - 8a^2$ **99.** $35 - 6b - 8b^2$

100. $12y^3 + 22y^2 - 70y$ **101.** $5y^4 - 29y^3 + 20y^2$ **102.** $30a^2 + 85ab + 60b^2$

103. $20x^2 - 38x^3 - 30x^4$ **104.** $4x^2y^2 - 32xy + 60$ **105.** $a^4b^4 - 3a^3b^3 - 10a^2b^2$

106. $2a^2b^4 + 9ab^3 - 18b^2$ **107.** $90a^2b^2 + 45ab + 10$ **108.** $3x^3y^2 + 12x^2y - 96x$

109. $4x^4 - 45x^2 + 80$ **110.** $x^4 + 2x^2 + 15$ **111.** $2a^5 + 14a^3 + 20a$

112. $3b^6 - 9b^4 - 30b^2$ **113.** $3x^4y^2 - 39x^2y^2 + 120y^2$ **114.** $2a^3b^3 - 10a^2b^2 + 12ab$

115. $3x^3y^3 + 6x^2y^2 - 24xy$ **116.** $2x^4 + 14x^2 + 24$ **117.** $y^5 - 8y^3 + 15y$

118. $12x + x^2 - 6x^3$ **119.** $3y - 16y^2 + 16y^3$ **120.** $12x^{2n} - 30x^n + 12$

121. $12y^{2n} - 51y^n + 45$ **122.** $2x^{3n} + 4x^{2n} - 30x^n$ **123.** $x^{3n} + 10x^{2n} + 16x^n$

APPLYING THE CONCEPTS

124. Is $x^2 + 9$ a prime polynomial? Explain your answer.

125. Find all integers k such that the trinomial can be factored.
   a. $x^2 + kx + 8$ **b.** $x^2 + kx - 6$ **c.** $2x^2 + kx + 3$

   d. $2x^2 + kx - 5$ **e.** $3x^2 + kx + 5$ **f.** $2x^2 + kx - 3$

126. Write the regions of the shaded areas in factored form.

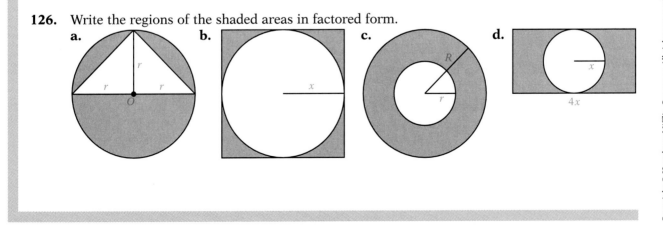

   a.   **b.**   **c.**   **d.**

5.6 Special Factoring

Objective A   *To factor the difference of two perfect squares or a perfect-square trinomial* ....

The product of a term and itself is called a **perfect square.** The exponents on variables of perfect squares are always even numbers.

Term		Perfect Square
5	$5 \cdot 5 =$	25
x	$x \cdot x =$	x^2
$3y^4$	$3y^4 \cdot 3y^4 =$	$9y^8$
x^n	$x^n \cdot x^n =$	x^{2n}

The **square root** of a perfect square is one of the two equal factors of the perfect square. "$\sqrt{}$" is the symbol for square root. To find the exponent of the square root of a variable term, multiply the exponent by $\frac{1}{2}$.

$$\sqrt{25} = 5$$
$$\sqrt{x^2} = x$$
$$\sqrt{9y^8} = 3y^4$$
$$\sqrt{x^{2n}} = x^n$$

The difference of two perfect squares is the product of the sum and difference of two terms. The factors of the difference of two perfect squares are the sum and difference of the square roots of the perfect squares.

> **Factors of the Difference of Two Perfect Squares**
>
> $a^2 - b^2 = (a + b)(a - b)$

The sum of two perfect squares, $a^2 + b^2$, is nonfactorable over the integers.

➡ Factor: $4x^2 - 81y^2$

Write the binomial as the difference of two perfect squares.

$$4x^2 - 81y^2 = (2x)^2 - (9y)^2$$

The factors are the sum and difference of the square roots of the perfect squares.

$$= (2x + 9y)(2x - 9y)$$

A perfect-square trinomial is the square of a binomial.

> **Factors of a Perfect-Square Trinomial**
>
> $a^2 + 2ab + b^2 = (a + b)^2$
> $a^2 - 2ab + b^2 = (a - b)^2$

In factoring a perfect-square trinomial, remember that the terms of the binomial are the square roots of the perfect squares of the trinomial. The sign in the binomial is the sign of the middle term of the trinomial.

➡ Factor: $4x^2 + 12x + 9$

Because $4x^2$ is a perfect square $[4x^2 = (2x)^2]$ and 9 is a perfect square $(9 = 3^2)$, try factoring $4x^2 + 12x + 9$ as the square of a binomial.

$4x^2 + 12x + 9 \overset{?}{=} (2x + 3)^2$

Check: $(2x + 3)^2 = (2x + 3)(2x + 3) = 4x^2 + 6x + 6x + 9 = 4x^2 + 12x + 9$

The check verifies that $4x^2 + 12x + 9 = (2x + 3)^2$.

It is important to check a proposed factorization as we did above. The next example illustrates the importance of this check.

➡ Factor: $x^2 + 13x + 36$

Because x^2 is a perfect square and 36 is a perfect square, try factoring $x^2 + 13x + 36$ as the square of a binomial.

$x^2 + 13x + 36 \overset{?}{=} (x + 6)^2$

Check: $(x + 6)^2 = (x + 6)(x + 6) = x^2 + 6x + 6x + 36 = x^2 + 12x + 36$

In this case, the proposed factorization of $x^2 + 13x + 36$ does *not* check. Try another factorization. The numbers 4 and 9 are factors of 36 whose sum is 13.

$x^2 + 13x + 36 = (x + 4)(x + 9)$

Example 1
Factor: $25x^2 - 1$

Solution
$25x^2 - 1 = (5x)^2 - (1)^2$
$ = (5x + 1)(5x - 1)$

You Try It 1
Factor: $x^2 - 36y^4$

Your solution

Example 2
Factor: $4x^2 - 20x + 25$

Solution
$4x^2 - 20x + 25 = (2x - 5)^2$

You Try It 2
Factor: $9x^2 + 12x + 4$

Your solution

Example 3
Factor: $(x + y)^2 - 4$

Solution
$(x + y)^2 - 4 = (x + y)^2 - (2)^2$
$ = (x + y + 2)(x + y - 2)$

You Try It 3
Factor: $(a + b)^2 - (a - b)^2$

Your solution

Solutions on p. S16

Objective B   *To factor the sum or the difference of two perfect cubes* ....

The product of the same three factors is called a **perfect cube.** The exponents on variables of perfect cubes are always divisible by 3.

Term		Perfect Cube
2	$2 \cdot 2 \cdot 2 = 2^3 =$	8
$3y$	$3y \cdot 3y \cdot 3y = (3y)^3 =$	$27y^3$
y^2	$y^2 \cdot y^2 \cdot y^2 = (y^2)^3 =$	y^6

The **cube root** of a perfect cube is one of the three equal factors of the perfect cube. "$\sqrt[3]{}$" is the symbol for cube root. To find the exponent of the cube root of a variable term, multiply the exponent by $\frac{1}{3}$.

$$\sqrt[3]{8} = 2$$
$$\sqrt[3]{27y^3} = 3y$$
$$\sqrt[3]{y^6} = y^2$$

The following rules are used to factor the sum or difference of two perfect cubes.

Factoring the Sum or Difference of Two Perfect Cubes

$a^3 + b^3 = (a + b)(a^2 - ab + b^2)$
$a^3 - b^3 = (a - b)(a^2 + ab + b^2)$

To factor $8x^3 - 27$:

Write the binomial as the difference of two perfect cubes.

$$8x^3 - 27 = (2x)^3 - 3^3$$

The terms of the binomial factor are the cube roots of the perfect cubes. The sign of the binomial factor is the same sign as in the given binomial. The trinomial factor is obtained from the binomial factor.

$$= (2x - 3)(4x^2 + 6x + 9)$$

Square of the first term ⌐

Opposite of the product of the two terms ⌐

Square of the last term ⌐

➡ Factor: $a^3 + 64y^3$

$a^3 + 64y^3 = a^3 + (4y)^3$
   • Write the binomial as the sum of two perfect cubes.

$= (a + 4y)(a^2 - 4ay + 16y^2)$
   • Factor.

➡ Factor: $64y^4 - 125y$

$64y^4 - 125y = y(64y^3 - 125)$
   • Factor out y, the GCF.

$= y[(4y)^3 - 5^3]$
   • Write the binomial as the difference of two perfect cubes.

$= y(4y - 5)(16y^2 + 20y + 25)$
   • Factor.

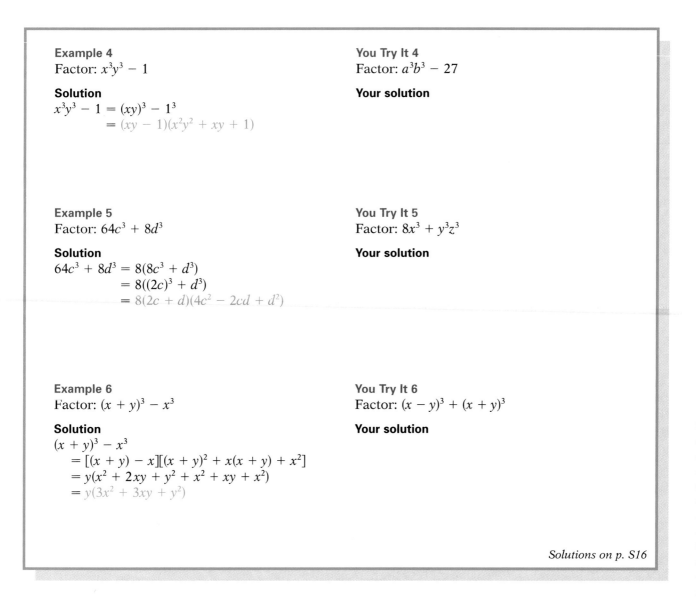

Example 4
Factor: $x^3y^3 - 1$

Solution
$x^3y^3 - 1 = (xy)^3 - 1^3$
$= (xy - 1)(x^2y^2 + xy + 1)$

You Try It 4
Factor: $a^3b^3 - 27$

Your solution

Example 5
Factor: $64c^3 + 8d^3$

Solution
$64c^3 + 8d^3 = 8(8c^3 + d^3)$
$= 8((2c)^3 + d^3)$
$= 8(2c + d)(4c^2 - 2cd + d^2)$

You Try It 5
Factor: $8x^3 + y^3z^3$

Your solution

Example 6
Factor: $(x + y)^3 - x^3$

Solution
$(x + y)^3 - x^3$
$= [(x + y) - x][(x + y)^2 + x(x + y) + x^2]$
$= y(x^2 + 2xy + y^2 + x^2 + xy + x^2)$
$= y(3x^2 + 3xy + y^2)$

You Try It 6
Factor: $(x - y)^3 + (x + y)^3$

Your solution

Solutions on p. S16

Objective C To factor a trinomial that is quadratic in form .... 〔21〕 CT

Certain trinomials that are not quadratic can be expressed as quadratic trinomials by making suitable variable substitutions. A trinomial is *quadratic in form* if it can be written as $au^2 + bu + c$.

Each of the trinomials shown below is quadratic in form.

$$x^4 + 5x^2 + 6 \qquad\qquad 2x^2y^2 + 3xy - 9$$

$$(x^2)^2 + 5(x^2) + 6 \qquad\qquad 2(xy)^2 + 3(xy) - 9$$

Let $u = x^2$. $u^2 + 5u + 6$ Let $u = xy$. $2u^2 + 3u - 9$

When we use this method to factor a trinomial that is quadratic in form, the variable part of the first term in each binomial will be u.

For example, $x^4 + 5x^2 + 6$ is quadratic in form by letting $u = x^2$. Thus, $x^4 + 5x^2 + 6 = (x^2)^2 + 5(x^2) + 6 = u^2 + 5u + 6$.

➡ Factor: $x^4 + 5x^2 + 6$

$$x^4 + 5x^2 + 6 = u^2 + 5u + 6 \qquad \bullet \text{ Let } u = x^2.$$
$$= (u + 3)(u + 2) \qquad \bullet \text{ Factor.}$$
$$= (x^2 + 3)(x^2 + 2) \qquad \bullet \text{ Replace } u \text{ by } x^2.$$

Here is another example, in which $u = \sqrt{x}$.

➡ Factor: $x - 2\sqrt{x} - 15$

$$x - 2\sqrt{x} - 15 = u^2 - 2u - 15 \qquad \bullet \text{ Let } u = \sqrt{x}. \text{ Then } u^2 = x.$$
$$= (u - 5)(u + 3) \qquad \bullet \text{ Factor.}$$
$$= (\sqrt{x} - 5)(\sqrt{x} + 3) \qquad \bullet \text{ Replace } u \text{ by } \sqrt{x}.$$

Example 7
Factor: $6x^2y^2 - xy - 12$

Solution
Let $u = xy$.

$$6x^2y^2 - xy - 12 = 6u^2 - u - 12$$
$$= (3u + 4)(2u - 3)$$
$$= (3xy + 4)(2xy - 3)$$

You Try It 7
Factor: $3x^4 + 4x^2 - 4$

Your solution

Solution on p. S17

Objective D   *To factor completely* ·· (21) CT

When factoring a polynomial completely, ask the following questions about the polynomial.

1. Is there a common factor? If so, factor out the GCF.

2. If the polynomial is a binomial, is it the difference of two perfect squares, the sum of two perfect cubes, or the difference of two perfect cubes? If so, factor.

3. If the polynomial is a trinomial, is it a perfect-square trinomial or the product of two binomials? If so, factor.

4. Can the polynomial be factored by grouping? If so, factor.

5. Is each factor nonfactorable over the integers? If not, factor.

Example 8

Factor: $6a^3 + 15a^2 - 36a$

Solution

$6a^3 + 15a^2 - 36a = 3a(2a^2 + 5a - 12)$
$= 3a(2a - 3)(a + 4)$

You Try It 8

Factor: $18x^3 - 6x^2 - 60x$

Your solution

Example 9

Factor: $x^2y + 2x^2 - y - 2$

Solution

$x^2y + 2x^2 - y - 2 = (x^2y + 2x^2) - (y + 2)$
$= x^2(y + 2) - (y + 2)$
$= (y + 2)(x^2 - 1)$
$= (y + 2)(x + 1)(x - 1)$

You Try It 9

Factor: $4x - 4y - x^3 + x^2y$

Your solution

Example 10

Factor: $x^{4n} - y^{4n}$

Solution

$x^{4n} - y^{4n} = (x^{2n})^2 - (y^{2n})^2$
$= (x^{2n} + y^{2n})(x^{2n} - y^{2n})$
$= (x^{2n} + y^{2n})[(x^n)^2 - (y^n)^2]$
$= (x^{2n} + y^{2n})(x^n + y^n)(x^n - y^n)$

You Try It 10

Factor: $x^{4n} - x^{2n}y^{2n}$

Your solution

Example 11

Factor: $x^{n+3} + x^ny^3$

Solution

$x^{n+3} + x^ny^3 = x^n(x^3 + y^3)$
$= x^n(x + y)(x^2 - xy + y^2)$

You Try It 11

Factor: $ax^5 - ax^2y^6$

Your solution

Solutions on p. S17

5.6 Exercises

. . . .

Objective A

Factor.

1. $x^2 - 16$

2. $y^2 - 49$

3. $4x^2 - 1$

4. $81x^2 - 4$

5. $16x^2 - 121$

6. $49y^2 - 36$

7. $1 - 9a^2$

8. $16 - 81y^2$

9. $x^2y^2 - 100$

10. $a^2b^2 - 25$

11. $x^2 + 4$

12. $a^2 + 16$

13. $25 - a^2b^2$

14. $64 - x^2y^2$

15. $a^{2n} - 1$

16. $b^{2n} - 16$

17. $x^2 - 12x + 36$

18. $y^2 - 6y + 9$

19. $b^2 - 2b + 1$

20. $a^2 + 14a + 49$

21. $16x^2 - 40x + 25$

22. $49x^2 + 28x + 4$

23. $4a^2 + 4a - 1$

24. $9x^2 + 12x - 4$

25. $b^2 + 7b + 14$

26. $y^2 - 5y + 25$

27. $x^2 + 6xy + 9y^2$

28. $4x^2y^2 + 12xy + 9$

29. $25a^2 - 40ab + 16b^2$

30. $4a^2 - 36ab + 81b^2$

31. $x^{2n} + 6x^n + 9$

32. $y^{2n} - 16y^n + 64$

33. $(x - 4)^2 - 9$

34. $16 - (a - 3)^2$

35. $(x - y)^2 - (a + b)^2$

36. $(x - 2y)^2 - (x + y)^2$

Objective B

Factor.

37. $x^3 - 27$

38. $y^3 + 125$

39. $8x^3 - 1$

40. $64a^3 + 27$

41. $x^3 - y^3$

42. $x^3 - 8y^3$

43. $m^3 + n^3$

44. $27a^3 + b^3$

45. $64x^3 + 1$

46. $1 - 125b^3$

47. $27x^3 - 8y^3$

48. $64x^3 + 27y^3$

49. $x^3y^3 + 64$

50. $8x^3y^3 + 27$

51. $16x^3 - y^3$

52. $27x^3 - 8y^2$

53. $8x^3 - 9y^3$

54. $27a^3 - 16$

55. $(a - b)^3 - b^3$

56. $a^3 + (a + b)^3$

57. $x^{6n} + y^{3n}$

58. $x^{3n} + y^{3n}$

59. $x^{3n} + 8$

60. $a^{3n} + 64$

Objective C

Factor.

61. $x^2y^2 - 8xy + 15$

62. $x^2y^2 - 8xy - 33$

63. $x^2y^2 - 17xy + 60$

64. $a^2b^2 + 10ab + 24$

65. $x^4 - 9x^2 + 18$

66. $y^4 - 6y^2 - 16$

67. $b^4 - 13b^2 - 90$

68. $a^4 + 14a^2 + 45$

69. $x^4y^4 - 8x^2y^2 + 12$

70. $a^4b^4 + 11a^2b^2 - 26$

71. $x^{2n} + 3x^n + 2$

72. $a^{2n} - a^n - 12$

73. $3x^2y^2 - 14xy + 15$

74. $5x^2y^2 - 59xy + 44$

75. $6a^2b^2 - 23ab + 21$

76. $10a^2b^2 + 3ab - 7$

77. $2x^4 - 13x^2 - 15$

78. $3x^4 + 20x^2 + 32$

79. $2x^{2n} - 7x^n + 3$

80. $4x^{2n} + 8x^n - 5$

81. $6a^{2n} + 19a^n + 10$

Objective D

Factor.

82. $5x^2 + 10x + 5$

83. $12x^2 - 36x + 27$

84. $3x^4 - 81x$

85. $27a^4 - a$

86. $7x^2 - 28$

87. $20x^2 - 5$

88. $y^4 - 10y^3 + 21y^2$

89. $y^5 + 6y^4 - 55y^3$

90. $x^4 - 16$

91. $16x^4 - 81$

92. $8x^5 - 98x^3$

93. $16a - 2a^4$

94. $x^3y^3 - x^3$

95. $a^3b^6 - b^3$

96. $x^6y^6 - x^3y^3$

97. $8x^4 - 40x^3 + 50x^2$

98. $6x^5 + 74x^4 + 24x^3$

99. $x^4 - y^4$

100. $16a^4 - b^4$

101. $x^6 + y^6$

102. $x^4 - 5x^2 - 4$

103. $a^4 - 25a^2 - 144$

104. $3b^5 - 24b^2$

105. $16a^4 - 2a$

106. $x^4y^2 - 5x^3y^3 + 6x^2y^4$

107. $a^4b^2 - 8a^3b^3 - 48a^2b^4$

108. $16x^3y + 4x^2y^2 - 42xy^3$

109. $24a^2b^2 - 14ab^3 - 90b^4$

110. $x^3 - 2x^2 - x + 2$

111. $x^3 - 2x^2 - 4x + 8$

112. $4x^2y^2 - 4x^2 - 9y^2 + 9$

113. $4x^4 - x^2 - 4x^2y^2 + y^2$

114. $x^5 - 4x^3 - 8x^2 + 32$

115. $x^6y^3 + x^3 - x^3y^3 - 1$

116. $a^{2n+2} - 6a^{n+2} + 9a^2$

117. $x^{2n+1} + 2x^{n+1} + x$

118. $2x^{n+2} - 7x^{n+1} + 3x^n$

119. $3b^{n+2} + 4b^{n+1} - 4b^n$

APPLYING THE CONCEPTS

120. Find all integers k such that the trinomial is a perfect square.
   a. $x^2 + kx + 36$ **b.** $4x^2 - kx + 25$ **c.** $49x^2 + kxy + 64y^2$

   d. $x^2 + 8x + k$ **e.** $x^2 - 12x + k$ **f.** $x^2 + 4xy + ky^2$

121. Factor: $x^2(x - 3) - 3x(x - 3) + 2(x - 3)$

122. Factor $x^4 + 64$. *Suggestion:* Add and subtract $16x^2$ so that the expression becomes $(x^4 + 16x^2 + 64) - 16x^2$. Now factor by grouping.

123. Using the strategy of Exercise 122, factor $x^4 + x^2y^2 + y^4$. *Suggestion:* Add and subtract x^2y^2.

124. Can a third-degree polynomial have factors $(x - 1)$, $(x + 1)$, $(x - 3)$, and $(x + 4)$? Why or why not?

125. Given that $(x - 3)$ and $(x + 4)$ are factors of $x^3 + 6x^2 - 7x - 60$, explain how you can find a third *first-degree* factor of $x^3 + 6x^2 - 7x - 60$. Then find the factor.

5.7 Solving Equations by Factoring

Objective A   *To solve an equation by factoring* .... (22) CT

Consider the equation $ab = 0$. If a is not zero, then b must be zero. Conversely, if b is not zero, then a must be zero. This is summarized in the Principle of Zero Products.

> **Principle of Zero Products**
>
> If the product of two factors is zero, then at least one of the factors must be zero.
>
> If $ab = 0$, then $a = 0$ or $b = 0$.

The Principle of Zero Products is used to solve equations.

➡ Solve: $(x - 4)(x + 2) = 0$

By the Principle of Zero Products, if $(x - 4)(x + 2) = 0$, then $x - 4 = 0$ or $x + 2 = 0$.

$$x - 4 = 0 \qquad\qquad x + 2 = 0$$
$$x = 4 \qquad\qquad x = -2$$

Check:

$$
\begin{array}{c|c}
(x - 4)(x + 2) = 0 & (x - 4)(x + 2) = 0 \\
\hline
(4 - 4)(4 + 2) \mid 0 & (-2 - 4)(-2 + 2) \mid 0 \\
0 \cdot 6 \mid 0 & -6 \cdot 0 \mid 0 \\
0 = 0 & 0 = 0
\end{array}
$$

−2 and 4 check as solutions. The solutions are −2 and 4.

An equation of the form $ax^2 + bx + c = 0$, $a \neq 0$, is a **quadratic equation.** A quadratic equation is in standard form when the polynomial is written in descending order and equal to zero.

Some quadratic equations can be solved by factoring and then using the Principle of Zero Products.

➡ Solve: $2x^2 - x = 1$

$$
\begin{aligned}
2x^2 - x &= 1 \\
2x^2 - x - 1 &= 0 \qquad &\bullet\ \text{Write the equation in standard form.} \\
(2x + 1)(x - 1) &= 0 \qquad &\bullet\ \text{Factor.} \\
2x + 1 = 0 \qquad x - 1 &= 0 \qquad &\bullet\ \text{Use the Principle of Zero Products.} \\
2x = -1 \qquad x &= 1 \qquad &\bullet\ \text{Solve each equation.} \\
x = -\frac{1}{2} & &
\end{aligned}
$$

The solutions are $-\dfrac{1}{2}$ and 1. **You should check these solutions.**

⇒ Solve: $t^4 - 2t^2 + 1 = 0$

$$t^4 - 2t^2 + 1 = 0$$
$$(t^2 - 1)(t^2 - 1) = 0$$
$$(t - 1)(t + 1)(t - 1)(t + 1) = 0$$

$t - 1 = 0, \quad t + 1 = 0, \quad t - 1 = 0, \quad t + 1 = 0$
$\quad\quad t = 1 \quad\quad\quad t = -1 \quad\quad\quad t = 1 \quad\quad\quad t = -1$

• Factor the trinomial.
• Factor completely.

• Use the Principle of Zero Products.

The solutions are -1 and 1. These solutions are called **repeated** solutions.

Example 1
Solve: $x^2 + (x + 2)^2 = 100$

Solution
$$x^2 + (x + 2)^2 = 100$$
$$x^2 + x^2 + 4x + 4 = 100$$
$$2x^2 + 4x - 96 = 0$$
$$2(x - 6)(x + 8) = 0$$
$x - 6 = 0 \quad\quad\quad x + 8 = 0$
$\quad x = 6 \quad\quad\quad\quad x = -8$

The solutions are -8 and 6.

You Try It 1
Solve: $(x + 4)(x - 1) = 14$

Your solution

Solution on p.S17

Objective B   To solve application problems ....

Example 2
The length of a rectangle is 8 in. more than the width. The area of the rectangle is 240 in². Find the width of the rectangle.

Strategy
Draw a diagram. Then use the formula for the area of a rectangle.

Solution
$$A = LW$$
$$240 = (x + 8)x$$
$$240 = x^2 + 8x$$
$$0 = x^2 + 8x - 240$$
$$0 = (x + 20)(x - 12)$$
$x + 20 = 0 \quad\quad\quad x - 12 = 0$
$\quad\quad x = -20 \quad\quad\quad x = 12$

The width cannot be negative.
The width is 12 in.

You Try It 2
The height of a triangle is 3 cm more than the base of the triangle. The area of the triangle is 54 cm². Find the height of the triangle and the length of the base.

Your strategy

Your solution

Solution on p. S17

Section 5.7 / Solving Equations by Factoring

5.7 Exercises

· ·

Objective A

Solve.

1. $(x - 5)(x + 3) = 0$

2. $(x - 2)(x + 6) = 0$

3. $(x + 7)(x - 8) = 0$

4. $x(2x + 5)(x - 6) = 0$

5. $2x(3x - 2)(x + 4) = 0$

6. $6x(3x - 7)(x + 7) = 0$

7. $x^2 + 2x - 15 = 0$

8. $t^2 + 3t - 10 = 0$

9. $z^2 - 4z + 3 = 0$

10. $6x^2 - 9x = 0$

11. $r^2 - 10 = 3r$

12. $t^2 - 12 = 4t$

13. $4t^2 = 4t + 3$

14. $5y^2 + 11y = 12$

15. $4v^2 - 4v + 1 = 0$

16. $9s^2 - 6s + 1 = 0$

17. $x^2 - 9 = 0$

18. $t^2 - 16 = 0$

19. $4y^2 - 1 = 0$

20. $9z^2 - 4 = 0$

21. $x + 15 = x(x - 1)$

22. $x^2 - x - 2 = (2x - 1)(x - 3)$

23. $v^2 + v + 5 = (3v + 2)(v - 4)$

24. $z^2 + 5z - 4 = (2z + 1)(z - 4)$

25. $4x^2 + x - 10 = (x - 2)(x + 1)$

26. $x^3 + 2x^2 - 15x = 0$

27. $c^3 + 3c^2 - 10c = 0$

28. $z^4 - 18z^2 + 81 = 0$

29. $y^4 - 8y^2 + 16 = 0$

30. $x^3 + x^2 - 4x - 4 = 0$

31. $a^3 + a^2 - 9a - 9 = 0$

32. $2x^3 - x^2 - 2x + 1 = 0$

33. $3x^3 + 2x^2 - 12x - 8 = 0$

34. $2x^3 + 3x^2 - 18x - 27 = 0$

35. $5x^3 + 2x^2 - 20x - 8 = 0$

Objective B   *Application Problems*

36. The sum of a number and its square is 72. Find the number.

37. The sum of a number and its square is 210. Find the number.

38. The length of a rectangle is 2 ft more than twice the width. The area of the rectangle is 84 ft². Find the length and width of the rectangle.

39. The length of a rectangle is 8 cm more than three times the width. The area of the rectangle is 380 cm². Find the length and width of the rectangle.

40. The height of a triangle is 8 cm more than the length of the base. The area of the triangle is 64 cm². Find the base and height of the triangle.

41. One leg of a right triangle is 2 ft more than twice the other leg. The hypotenuse is 1 ft more than the longer leg. Find the length of the hypotenuse of the right triangle.

42. An object is thrown downward, with an initial speed of 16 ft/s, from the top of a building 480 ft high. How many seconds later will the object hit the ground? Use the equation $d = vt + 16t^2$, where d is the distance in feet, v is the initial speed, and t is the time in seconds.

43. A stone is thrown into a well with an initial speed of 8 ft/s. The well is 80 ft deep. How many seconds later will the stone hit the bottom of the well? Use the equation $d = vt + 16t^2$, where d is the distance in feet, v is the initial speed, and t is the time in seconds.

APPLYING THE CONCEPTS

44. Write an equation whose solutions are 3, 2, and -1.

45. A rectangular piece of cardboard is 10 in. longer than it is wide. Squares 2 in. on a side are to be cut from each corner, and then the sides are to be folded up to make an open box with a volume of 112 in³. Find the length and width of the piece of cardboard.

46. The following seems to show that $1 = 2$. Explain the error.

$$a = b$$
$$a^2 = ab$$ • Multiply each side of the equation by a.
$$a^2 - b^2 = ab - b^2$$ • Subtract b^2 from each side of the equation.
$$(a - b)(a + b) = b(a - b)$$ • Factor.
$$a + b = b$$ • Divide each side by $a - b$.
$$b + b = b$$ • Because $a = b$, substitute b for a.
$$2b = b$$
$$2 = 1$$ • Divide both sides by b.

Focus on Problem Solving

Find a Counterexample

When you are faced with an assertion, it may be that the assertion is false. For instance, consider the statement "Every prime number is an odd number." This assertion is false because the prime number 2 is an even number.

Finding an example that illustrates that an assertion is false is called finding a *counterexample.* The number 2 is a counterexample to the assertion that every prime number is an odd number.

If you are given an unfamiliar problem, one strategy to consider as a means of solving the problem is to try to find a counterexample. For each of the following problems, answer *true* if the assertion is always true. If the assertion is not true, answer *false* and give a counterexample. If there are terms used that you do not understand, consult a reference to find the meaning of the term.

1. If x is a real number, then x^2 is always positive.

2. The product of an odd integer and an even integer is an even integer.

3. If m is a positive integer, then $2m + 1$ is always a positive odd integer.

4. If $x < y$, then $x^2 < y^2$.

5. Given any three positive numbers a, b, and c, it is possible to construct a triangle whose sides have lengths a, b, and c.

6. The product of two irrational numbers is an irrational number.

7. If n is a positive integer greater than 2, then $1 \cdot 2 \cdot 3 \cdot 4 \cdot \cdots \cdot n + 1$ is a prime number.

8. Draw a polygon with more than three sides. Select two different points inside the polygon and join the points with a line segment. The line segment always lies completely inside the polygon.

9. Let A, B, and C be three points in the plane that are not collinear. Let d_1 be the distance from A to B, and let d_2 be the distance from A to C. Then the distance between B and C is less than $d_1 + d_2$.

10. Consider the line segment AB shown at the left. Two points, C and D, are randomly selected on the line segment and three new segments are formed: AC, CD, and DB. The three new line segments can always be connected to form a triangle.

It may not be easy to establish that an assertion is true or to find a counterexample to the assertion. For instance, consider the assertion that every positive integer greater than 3 can be written as the sum of two primes. For example, $6 = 3 + 3$, $8 = 3 + 5$, $9 = 2 + 7$. Is this assertion always true? (*Note:* This assertion, called Goldbach's conjecture, has never been proved, nor has a counterexample been found!)

A   C   D   B

Projects and Group Activities

Reverse Polish Notation   Following the Order of Operations Agreement is sometimes referred to as algebraic logic. It is a system used by many calculators. Algebraic logic is not the only system used by calculators. Another system is called RPN logic. RPN stands for Reverse Polish Notation.

During the 1950s, Jan Lukasiewicz, a Polish logician, developed a parenthesis-free notational system for writing mathematical expressions. In this system, the operator (such as addition, multiplication, or division) follows the operands (the numbers to be added, multiplied, or divided). For RPN calculators, an [ENTER] key is used to store a number temporarily until another number and the operation are entered. Here are some examples, along with the algebraic logic equivalent.

To Calculate	*RPN Logic*	*Algebraic Logic*
1. $3 + 4$	3 [ENTER] 4 [+]	3 [+] 4 [=]
2. $5 \times 6 \times 7$	5 [ENTER] 6 [×] 7 [×]	5 [×] 6 [×] 7 [=]
3. $4 \times (7 + 3)$	4 [ENTER] 7 [ENTER] 3 [+] [×]	4 [×] [(] 7 [+] 3 [)] [=]
4. $(3 + 4) \times (5 + 2)$	3 [ENTER] 4 [+] 5 [ENTER] 2 [+] [×]	[(] 3 [+] 4 [)] [×] [(] 5 [+] 2 [)] [=]

Examples 3 and 4 above illustrate the concept of being "parenthesis-free." Note that the examples under RPN logic do not require parentheses, whereas those under algebraic logic do. If the parentheses keys are not used for Examples 3 and 4, a calculator, following algebraic logic, would use the Order of Operations Agreement. The result in Example 3 would be

$$4 \times 7 + 3 = 28 + 3 = 31 \qquad \text{instead of} \qquad 4 \times (7 + 3) = 4 \times 10 = 40$$

RPN logic may seem strange, but it is actually very efficient. A glimpse of its efficiency can be seen from Example 4. For the RPN operation, nine keys were pushed, whereas 12 keys were pushed for the algebraic operation. Note also that RPN logic does not use the "equals" key. The result of an operation is displayed after the operation key is pressed.

Try the following exercises, which ask you to change from algebraic logic to RPN logic or to evaluate an RPN logic expression.

Change to RPN logic.

1. $12 \div 6$ **2.** $7 \times 5 + 6$ **3.** $(9 + 3) \div 4$

4. $(5 + 7) \div (2 + 4)$ **5.** $6 \times 7 \times 10$ **6.** $(1 + 4 \times 5) \div 7$

Evaluate each of the following expressions by using RPN logic.

7. 18 ENTER 2 ÷   **8.** 6 ENTER 5 ENTER 3 × +

9. 3 ENTER 5 × 4 +   **10.** 7 ENTER 4 ENTER 5 × + 3 ÷

11. 228 ENTER 6 ENTER 9 ENTER 12 × + ÷

12. 1 ENTER 1 ENTER 1 ENTER 3 + ÷ +

Pythagorean Triples   Recall that the Pythagorean Theorem states that if a and b are the legs of a right triangle and c is the length of the hypotenuse, then $a^2 + b^2 = c^2$.

$$c^2 = a^2 + b^2$$

For instance, the triangle with legs 3 and 4 and hypotenuse 5 is a right triangle because $3^2 + 4^2 = 5^2$. The numbers 3, 4, and 5 are called a **Pythagorean triple** because they are natural numbers that satisfy the equation of the Pythagorean Theorem.

1.   Determine if the numbers are a Pythagorean triple.
   a. 5, 7, and 9   **b.** 8, 15, and 17
   c. 11, 60, and 61   **d.** 28, 45, and 53

Mathematicians have investigated Pythagorean triples and have found formulas that will generate these triples. One such set of formulas is

$$a = m^2 - n^2 \qquad b = 2mn \qquad c = m^2 + n^2, \text{ where } m > n$$

For instance, let $m = 2$ and $n = 1$. Then $a = 2^2 - 1^2 = 3$, $b = 2(2)(1) = 4$, and $c = 2^2 + 1^2 = 5$. This is the Pythagorean triple given above.

2.   Find the Pythagorean triple produced by each of the following.
   a. $m = 3$ and $n = 1$ **b.** $m = 5$ and $n = 2$
   c. $m = 4$ and $n = 2$ **d.** $m = 6$ and $n = 1$

3.   Find values of m and n that yield the Pythagorean triple 11, 60, 61.

4.   Verify that $a^2 + b^2 = c^2$ when $a = m^2 - n^2$, $b = 2mn$, and $c = m^2 + n^2$.

5.   The early Greek builders used a rope with 12 equally spaced knots to make right-angle corners for buildings. Explain how they used the rope.

6.   Find three odd integers a, b, and c such that $a^2 + b^2 = c^2$.

Chapter Summary

Key Words   A *monomial* is a number, a variable, or a product of a number and variables.

A *polynomial* is a variable expression in which the terms are monomials. A *binomial* is a polynomial of two terms. A *trinomial* is a polynomial of three terms.

The *degree of a polynomial* in one variable is the greatest of the degrees of any of its terms.

A number written in *scientific notation* is a number written in the form $a \times 10^n$, where $1 \le a < 10$.

Synthetic division is a shorter method of dividing a polynomial by a binomial of the form $x - a$. This method uses only the coefficients of the variable terms.

To *factor a polynomial* means to write the polynomial as the product of other polynomials. A polynomial is *nonfactorable over the integers* if it does not factor using only integers. Such a polynomial is called a *prime polynomial*.

A *quadratic trinomial* is a polynomial of the form $ax^2 + bx + c$, where a, b, and c are nonzero constants. To *factor a quadratic trinomial* means to express the trinomial as the product of two binomials.

The product of a term and itself is a *perfect square*. The *square root* of a perfect square is one of the two equal factors of the perfect square.

The product of the same three factors is called a *perfect cube*. The *cube root* of a perfect cube is one of the three equal factors of the perfect cube.

An equation of the form $ax^2 + bx + c = 0$, $a \ne 0$, is a *quadratic equation*.

Essential Rules

Definition of a Negative Exponent

For $x \ne 0$, $x^{-n} = \dfrac{1}{x^n}$ and $\dfrac{1}{x^{-n}} = x^n$.

Rule for Negative Exponents on Fractional Expressions

For $a \ne 0$, $b \ne 0$, $\left(\dfrac{a}{b}\right)^{-n} = \left(\dfrac{b}{a}\right)^n$.

Rule for Multiplying Exponential Expressions

$x^m \cdot x^n = x^{m+n}$

Rule for Simplifying the Power of an Exponential Expression

$(x^m)^n = x^{mn}$

Rule for Simplifying Powers of Products

$(x^m y^n)^p = x^{mp} y^{np}$

Rule for Dividing Exponential Expressions

For $x \ne 0$, $\dfrac{x^m}{x^n} = x^{m-n}$.

Zero as an Exponent

For $x \ne 0$, $x^0 = 1$.

Rule for Simplifying Powers of Quotients

For $y \ne 0$, $\left(\dfrac{x^m}{y^n}\right)^p = \dfrac{x^{mp}}{y^{np}}$.

Remainder Theorem

If the polynomial $P(x)$ is divided by $x - a$, the remainder is $P(a)$.

The Product of the Sum and Difference of Two Terms, and the Difference of Two Squares

$(a + b)(a - b) = a^2 - b^2$

The Square of a Binomial, and a Perfect Square Trinomial

$(a + b)^2 = a^2 + 2ab + b^2$
$(a - b)^2 = a^2 - 2ab + b^2$

The Sum or Difference of Two Cubes

$a^3 + b^3 = (a + b)(a^2 - ab + b^2)$
$a^3 - b^3 = (a - b)(a^2 + ab + b^2)$

Principle of Zero Products

If $ab = 0$, then $a = 0$ or $b = 0$.

Chapter Review

1. Factor: $18a^5b^2 - 12a^3b^3 + 30a^2b$

2. Simplify: $\dfrac{15x^2 + 2x - 2}{3x - 2}$

3. Simplify: $(2x^{-1}y^2z^5)^4(-3x^3yz^{-3})^2$

4. Factor: $2ax + 4bx - 3ay - 6by$

5. Factor: $12 + x - x^2$

6. Use the Remainder Theorem to evaluate $P(x) = x^3 - 2x^2 + 3x - 5$ when $x = 2$.

7. Simplify: $(5x^2 - 8xy + 2y^2) - (x^2 - 3y^2)$

8. Factor: $24x^2 + 38x + 15$

9. Factor: $4x^2 + 12xy + 9y^2$

10. Simplify: $(-2a^2b^4)(3ab^2)$

11. Factor: $64a^3 - 27b^3$

12. Simplify: $\dfrac{4x^3 + 27x^2 + 10x + 2}{x + 6}$

13. Given $P(x) = 2x^3 - x + 7$, evaluate $P(-2)$.

14. Factor: $x^2 - 3x - 40$

15. Factor: $x^2y^2 - 9$

16. Simplify: $4x^2y(3x^3y^2 + 2xy - 7y^3)$

17. Factor: $x^{2n} - 12x^n + 36$

18. Solve: $6x^2 + 60 = 39x$

19. Simplify: $5x^2 - 4x[x - 3(3x + 2) + x]$

20. Factor: $3a^6 - 15a^4 - 18a^2$

21. Simplify: $(4x - 3y)^2$

22. Simplify: $\dfrac{x^4 - 4}{x - 4}$

23. Factor: $15x^4 + x^2 - 6$

24. Simplify: $\dfrac{(2a^4b^{-3}c^2)^3}{(2a^3b^2c^{-1})^4}$

25. Simplify: $(x - 4)(3x + 2)(2x - 3)$

26. Factor: $21x^4y^4 + 23x^2y^2 + 6$

27. Solve: $x^3 + 16 = x(x + 16)$

28. Simplify: $(5a + 2b)(5a - 2b)$

29. Write 2.54×10^{-3} in decimal notation.

30. Factor: $6x^2 - 31x + 18$

31. Graph $y = x^2 + 1$.

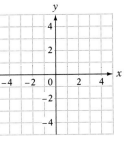

32. Identify **a.** the leading coefficient, **b.** the constant term, and **c.** the degree of the polynomial $P(x) = 3x^5 - 6x^2 + 7x + 8$.

33. The mass of the moon is 3.7×10^{-8} times the mass of the sun. The mass of the sun is 2.19×10^{27} tons. Find the mass of the moon. Write the answer in scientific notation.

34. The sum of a number and its square is 56. Find the number.

35. The most distant object visible from Earth without the aid of a telescope is the Great Galaxy of Andromeda. It takes light from the Great Galaxy of Andromeda 2.2×10^6 years to travel to Earth. Light travels about 6.7×10^8 mph. How far from Earth is the Great Galaxy of Andromeda? Use a 365-day year.

36. The length of a rectangle is $(5x + 3)$ cm. The width is $(2x - 7)$ cm. Find the area of the rectangle in terms of the variable x.

Chapter Test

1. Factor: $16t^2 + 24t + 9$

2. Simplify: $-6rs^2(3r - 2s - 3)$

3. Given $P(x) = 3x^2 - 8x + 1$, evaluate $P(2)$.

4. Factor: $27x^3 - 8$

5. Factor: $16x^2 - 25$

6. Simplify: $(3t^3 - 4t^2 + 1)(2t^2 - 5)$

7. Simplify: $-5x[3 - 2(2x - 4) - 3x]$

8. Factor: $12x^3 + 12x^2 - 45x$

9. Solve: $6x^3 + x^2 - 6x - 1 = 0$

10. Simplify:
$(6x^3 - 7x^2 + 6x - 7) - (4x^3 - 3x^2 + 7)$

11. Write the number 0.000000501 in scientific notation.

12. Simplify: $\dfrac{14x^2 + x + 1}{7x - 3}$

13. Simplify: $(7 - 5x)(7 + 5x)$

14. Factor: $6a^4 - 13a^2 - 5$

15. Simplify: $(3a + 4b)(2a - 7b)$

16. Factor: $3x^4 - 23x^2 - 36$

17. Simplify: $(-4a^2b)^3(-ab^4)$

18. Solve: $6x^2 = x + 1$

19. Use the Remainder Theorem to evaluate $P(x) = -x^3 + 4x - 8$ when $x = -2$.

20. Simplify: $\dfrac{(2a^{-4}b^2)^3}{4a^{-2}b^{-1}}$

21. Simplify: $\dfrac{x^3 - 2x^2 - 5x + 7}{x + 3}$

22. Factor: $12 - 17x + 6x^2$

23. Factor: $6x^2 - 4x - 3xa + 2a$

24. Write the number of seconds in one week in scientific notation.

25. An arrow is shot into the air with an upward velocity of 48 ft/s from a hill 32 ft high. How many seconds later will the arrow be 64 ft above the ground? Use the equation $h = 32 + 48t - 16t^2$, where h is the height in feet and t is the time in seconds.

26. The length of a rectangle is $(5x + 1)$ ft. The width is $(2x - 1)$ ft. Find the area of the rectangle in terms of the variable x.

Cumulative Review

1. Simplify: $8 - 2[-3 - (-1)]^2 + 4$

2. Evaluate $\dfrac{2a - b}{b - c}$ when $a = 4$, $b = -2$, and $c = 6$.

3. Identify the property that justifies the statement $2x + (-2x) = 0$.

4. Simplify: $2x - 4[x - 2(3 - 2x) + 4]$

5. Solve: $\dfrac{2}{3} - y = \dfrac{5}{6}$

6. Solve: $8x - 3 - x = -6 + 3x - 8$

7. Divide: $\dfrac{x^3 - 3}{x - 3}$

8. Solve: $3 - |2 - 3x| = -2$

9. Given $P(x) = 3x^2 - 2x + 2$, evaluate $P(-2)$.

10. What values of x are excluded from the domain of the function $f(x) = \dfrac{x + 1}{x + 2}$?

11. Find the range of the function given by $F(x) = 3x^2 - 4$ if the domain is $\{-2, -1, 0, 1, 2\}$.

12. Find the slope of the line containing the points $(-2, 3)$ and $(4, 2)$.

13. Find the equation of the line that contains the point $(-1, 2)$ and has slope $-\dfrac{3}{2}$.

14. Find the equation of the line that contains the point $(-2, 4)$ and is perpendicular to the line $3x + 2y = 4$.

15. Solve by using Cramer's Rule:
$$2x - 3y = 2$$
$$x + y = -3$$

16. Solve by the addition method:
$$x - y + z = 0$$
$$2x + y - 3z = -7$$
$$-x + 2y + 2z = 5$$

17. Graph $3x - 4y = 12$ by using the x- and y-intercepts.

18. Graph the solution set: $-3x + 2y < 6$

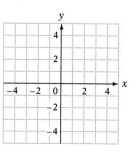

19. Solve by graphing:
$$x - 2y = 3$$
$$-2x + y = -3$$

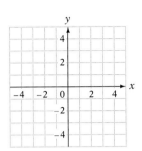

20. Graph the solution set:
$$2x + y < 3$$
$$-6x + 3y \geq 4$$

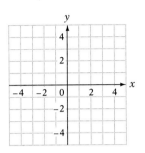

21. Simplify: $(4a^{-2}b^3)(2a^3b^{-1})^{-2}$

22. Simplify: $\dfrac{(5x^3y^{-3}z)^{-2}}{y^4z^{-2}}$

23. Simplify: $3 - (3 - 3^{-1})^{-1}$

24. Simplify: $(2x + 3)(2x^2 - 3x + 1)$

25. Factor: $-4x^3 + 14x^2 - 12x$

26. Factor: $a(x - y) - b(y - x)$

27. Factor: $x^4 - 16$

28. Factor: $2x^3 - 16$

29. The sum of two integers is twenty-four. The difference between four times the smaller integer and nine is three less than twice the larger integer. Find the integers.

30. How many ounces of pure gold that costs $360 per ounce must be mixed with 80 oz of an alloy that costs $120 per ounce to make a mixture that costs $200 per ounce?

31. Two bicycles are 25 mi apart and are traveling toward each other. One cyclist is traveling at $\frac{2}{3}$ the rate of the other cyclist. They pass in 2 h. Find the rate of each cyclist.

32. A space vehicle travels 2.4×10^5 mi from Earth to the moon at an average velocity of 2×10^4 mph. How long does it take the vehicle to reach the moon?

33. The graph shows the relationship between the distance traveled and the time of travel. Find the slope of the line between the two points on the graph. Write a sentence that states the meaning of the slope.

6

Rational Expressions

Objectives

Section 6.1
To simplify a rational expression
To multiply rational expressions
To divide rational expressions

Section 6.2
To rewrite rational expressions in terms of a common denominator
To add or subtract rational expressions

Section 6.3
To simplify a complex fraction

Section 6.4
To solve a proportion
To solve application problems

Section 6.5
To solve a fractional equation
To solve work problems
To solve uniform motion problems

Section 6.6
To solve variation problems

Geophysicists study the composition and physical characteristics of Earth and its magnetic, electric, and gravitational fields. A main responsibility of an *exploration geophysicist* is to use techniques to locate oil and other minerals. *Hydrologists* study the waters underground and on the surface of our planet. *Geomagneticians* study Earth's magnetic field. Although these are only a few of the careers within geophysics, all physicists use equations containing rational expressions. The exercises for Section 5 provide a few examples.

The Abacus

Numerations of the ancient civilizations were unsuited for the purpose of calculation. The abacus is an ancient device used to add, subtract, multiply, and divide and to calculate square and cube roots. There are many variations of the abacus, but the one shown here has been used in China for many hundreds of years.

The abacus shown here consists of 13 rows of beads. A crossbar separates the beads. Each upper bead represents five units, and each lower bead represents one unit. The place holder of each row is shown above the abacus. The first row of beads represents numbers from one to nine, the second row represents numbers from ten to ninety, and so on.

Trillions	Hundred-billions	Ten-billions	Billions	Hundred-millions	Ten-millions	Millions	Hundred-thousands	Ten-thousands	Thousands	Hundreds	Tens	Ones

The number shown at the right is 7036.

From the thousands' row:
one upper bead—5000
two lower beads—2000

From the hundreds' row: no beads
From the tens' row: three lower beads—30
From the ones' row:
one upper bead—5
one lower bead—1

Add: 1247 + 2516

1247 is shown at the right.

Add 6 to the ones' column.

Move the 10 (the upper two beads in the ones' row) to the tens' row (one lower bead). This makes five beads in the lower tens' row. Remove five beads from the lower row and place one bead in the upper row.

Continue adding in each row until the problem is completed. Carry if necessary.

1247 + 2516 = 3763

6.1 Multiplication and Division of Rational Expressions

Objective A   ***To simplify a rational expression*** .... ⟨23⟩ CT

An expression in which the numerator or denominator is a polynomial is called a **rational expression.** Examples of rational expressions are shown at the right.

$$\frac{9}{z} \qquad \frac{3x + 4}{2x^2 + 1} \qquad \frac{x^3 - x + 1}{x^2 - 3x - 5}$$

The expression $\dfrac{\sqrt{x} + 3}{x}$ is not a rational expression because $\sqrt{x} + 3$ is not a polynomial.

A function that is written in terms of a rational expression is a **rational function.** Each of the following equations represents a rational function.

$$f(x) = \frac{x^2 + 3}{2x - 1} \qquad g(t) = \frac{3}{t^2 - 4} \qquad R(z) = \frac{z^2 + 3z - 1}{z^2 + z - 12}$$

To evaluate a rational function, replace the variable by its value. Then simplify.

➡ Evaluate $f(-2)$ given $f(x) = \dfrac{x^2}{3x^2 - x - 9}$.

$$f(x) = \frac{x^2}{3x^2 - x - 9}$$
$$f(-2) = \frac{(-2)^2}{3(-2)^2 - (-2) - 9} = \frac{4}{12 + 2 - 9} = \frac{4}{5}$$

Because division by zero is not defined, the domain of a rational function must exclude those numbers for which the value of the polynomial in the denominator is zero.

The graph of $f(x) = \dfrac{1}{x - 2}$ is shown at the right. Note that the graph never intersects the line $x = 2$ (shown as a dotted line). This value of x is excluded from the domain of $f(x) = \dfrac{1}{x - 2}$.

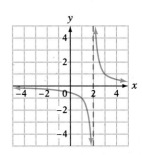

➡ Determine the domain of $g(x) = \dfrac{x^2 + 4}{3x - 6}$.

The domain of g must exclude values of x for which the denominator is zero. To find these values, set the denominator equal to zero and solve for x.

$3x - 6 = 0$	• Set the denominator equal to zero.
$3x = 6$	• Solve for x.
$x = 2$	• This value must be *excluded* from the domain.

The domain of g is $\{x \mid x \neq 2\}$.

A rational expression is in simplest form when the numerator and denominator have no common factors. The Multiplication Property of One is used to write a rational expression in simplest form.

➡ Simplify: $\dfrac{x^2 - 25}{x^2 + 13x + 40}$

$$\frac{x^2 - 25}{x^2 + 13x + 40} = \frac{(x - 5)}{(x + 8)} \cdot \frac{(x + 5)}{(x + 5)} = \frac{x - 5}{x + 8} \cdot 1 = \frac{x - 5}{x + 8} \qquad x \neq -8, -5$$

The requirement $x \neq -8, -5$ is necessary because division by 0 is not allowed.

The simplification above is usually shown with slashes to indicate that a common factor has been removed:

$$\frac{x^2 - 25}{x^2 + 13x + 40} = \frac{(x - 5)\overset{1}{\cancel{(x + 5)}}}{(x + 8)\underset{1}{\cancel{(x + 5)}}} = \frac{x - 5}{x + 8} \qquad x \neq -8, -5$$

We will show a simplification with slashes. We will also omit the restrictions that prevent division by zero. Nonetheless, those restrictions *always* are implied.

TAKE NOTE

Recall that $b - a = -(a - b)$.

Therefore, $4 - x = -(x - 4)$.

In general,

$\dfrac{b - a}{a - b} = \dfrac{-\overset{1}{\cancel{(a - b)}}}{\underset{1}{\cancel{a - b}}} = \dfrac{-1}{1}$

$= -1.$

➡ Simplify: $\dfrac{12 + 5x - 2x^2}{2x^2 - 3x - 20}$

$$\frac{12 + 5x - 2x^2}{2x^2 - 3x - 20} = \frac{(4 - x)(3 + 2x)}{(x - 4)(2x + 5)}$$

• Factor the numerator and denominator.

$$= \frac{\overset{-1}{\cancel{(4 - x)}}(3 + 2x)}{\underset{1}{\cancel{(x - 4)}}(2x + 5)}$$

• $\dfrac{4 - x}{x - 4} = \dfrac{-\overset{1}{\cancel{(x - 4)}}}{\underset{1}{\cancel{x - 4}}} = \dfrac{-1}{1} = -1$

$$= -\frac{2x + 3}{2x + 5}$$

• Write the answer in simplest form.

Example 1

Given $f(x) = \dfrac{3x - 4}{x^2 - 2x + 1}$, find $f(-2)$.

Solution

$f(x) = \dfrac{3x - 4}{x^2 - 2x + 1}$

$f(-2) = \dfrac{3(-2) - 4}{(-2)^2 - 2(-2) + 1} = \dfrac{-6 - 4}{4 + 4 + 1}$

$\qquad = \dfrac{-10}{9} = -\dfrac{10}{9}$

You Try It 1

Given $f(x) = \dfrac{3 - 5x}{x^2 + 5x + 6}$, find $f(2)$.

Your solution

Solution on p. S17

Example 2

Find the domain of $f(x) = \dfrac{x^2 - 1}{x^2 - 2x - 15}$.

Solution

Set the denominator equal to zero. Then solve for x.

$x^2 - 2x - 15 = 0$
$(x - 5)(x + 3) = 0$
$x - 5 = 0 \quad x + 3 = 0$
$\quad x = 5 \qquad x = -3$

The domain is $\{x \mid x \neq -3, 5\}$.

You Try It 2

Find the domain of $f(x) = \dfrac{2x + 1}{2x^2 - 7x + 3}$.

Your solution

Example 3

Simplify: $\dfrac{6x^3 - 9x^2}{12x^2 - 18x}$

Solution

$$\dfrac{6x^3 - 9x^2}{12x^2 - 18x} = \dfrac{3x^2(2x - 3)}{6x(2x - 3)}$$

$$= \dfrac{3x^2\cancel{(2x - 3)}}{6x\cancel{(2x - 3)}} = \dfrac{x}{2}$$

You Try It 3

Simplify: $\dfrac{6x^4 - 24x^3}{12x^3 - 48x^2}$

Your solution

Example 4

Simplify: $\dfrac{12x^3y^2 + 6x^3y^3}{6x^2y^2}$

Solution

$$\dfrac{12x^3y^2 + 6x^3y^3}{6x^2y^2} = \dfrac{6x^3y^2(2 + y)}{6x^2y^2}$$

$$= x(2 + y)$$

You Try It 4

Simplify: $\dfrac{21a^3b - 14a^3b^2}{7a^2b}$

Your solution

Example 5

Simplify: $\dfrac{2x - 8x^2}{16x^3 - 28x^2 + 6x}$

Solution

$$\dfrac{2x - 8x^2}{16x^3 - 28x^2 + 6x} = \dfrac{2x(1 - 4x)}{2x(8x^2 - 14x + 3)}$$

$$= \dfrac{2x(1 - 4x)}{2x(4x - 1)(2x - 3)}$$

$$= \dfrac{\overset{-1}{2x\cancel{(1 - 4x)}}}{\underset{1}{2x\cancel{(4x - 1)}(2x - 3)}}$$

$$= -\dfrac{1}{2x - 3}$$

You Try It 5

Simplify: $\dfrac{20x - 15x^2}{15x^3 - 5x^2 - 20x}$

Your solution

Solutions on pp. S17–S18

Example 6

Simplify: $\dfrac{x^{2n} + x^n - 2}{x^{2n} - 1}$

Solution

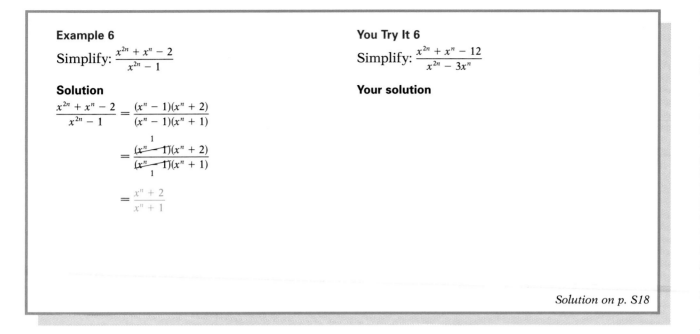

$\dfrac{x^{2n} + x^n - 2}{x^{2n} - 1} = \dfrac{(x^n - 1)(x^n + 2)}{(x^n - 1)(x^n + 1)}$

$= \dfrac{\overset{1}{\cancel{(x^n - 1)}}(x^n + 2)}{\underset{1}{\cancel{(x^n - 1)}}(x^n + 1)}$

$= \dfrac{x^n + 2}{x^n + 1}$

You Try It 6

Simplify: $\dfrac{x^{2n} + x^n - 12}{x^{2n} - 3x^n}$

Your solution

Solution on p. S18

Objective B *To multiply rational expressions* ....

The product of two fractions is a fraction whose numerator is the product of the numerators of the two fractions and whose denominator is the product of the denominators of the two fractions.

$$\frac{a}{b} \cdot \frac{c}{d} = \frac{ac}{bd} \qquad\qquad \frac{5}{a + 2} \cdot \frac{b - 3}{3} = \frac{5(b - 3)}{(a + 2)3} = \frac{5b - 15}{3a + 6}$$

The product of two rational expressions can often be simplified by factoring the numerator and the denominator.

➡ Simplify: $\dfrac{x^2 - 2x}{2x^2 + x - 15} \cdot \dfrac{2x^2 - x - 10}{x^2 - 4}$

$\dfrac{x^2 - 2x}{2x^2 + x - 15} \cdot \dfrac{2x^2 - x - 10}{x^2 - 4}$

$= \dfrac{x(x - 2)}{(x + 3)(2x - 5)} \cdot \dfrac{(x + 2)(2x - 5)}{(x + 2)(x - 2)}$ • Factor the numerator and the denominator of each fraction.

$= \dfrac{x(x - 2)(x + 2)(2x - 5)}{(x + 3)(2x - 5)(x + 2)(x - 2)}$ • Multiply.

$= \dfrac{x\overset{1}{\cancel{(x - 2)}}\overset{1}{\cancel{(x + 2)}}\overset{1}{\cancel{(2x - 5)}}}{(x + 3)\underset{1}{\cancel{(2x - 5)}}\underset{1}{\cancel{(x + 2)}}\underset{1}{\cancel{(x - 2)}}}$ • Simplify.

$= \dfrac{x}{x + 3}$ • Write the answer in simplest form.

Example 7

Simplify: $\dfrac{2x^2 - 6x}{3x - 6} \cdot \dfrac{6x - 12}{8x^3 - 12x^2}$

Solution

$\dfrac{2x^2 - 6x}{3x - 6} \cdot \dfrac{6x - 12}{8x^3 - 12x^2} = \dfrac{2x(x - 3)}{3(x - 2)} \cdot \dfrac{6(x - 2)}{4x^2(2x - 3)}$

$= \dfrac{2x(x - 3) \cdot 6(x - 2)}{3(x - 2) \cdot 4x^2(2x - 3)}$

$= \dfrac{2x(x - 3) \cdot \overset{1}{6(x - 2)}}{3(x - 2) \cdot 4x^2(2x - 3)}$

$= \dfrac{x - 3}{x(2x - 3)}$

You Try It 7

Simplify: $\dfrac{12 + 5x - 3x^2}{x^2 + 2x - 15} \cdot \dfrac{2x^2 + x - 45}{3x^2 + 4x}$

Your solution

Example 8

Simplify: $\dfrac{6x^2 + x - 2}{6x^2 + 7x + 2} \cdot \dfrac{2x^2 + 9x + 4}{4 - 7x - 2x^2}$

Solution

$\dfrac{6x^2 + x - 2}{6x^2 + 7x + 2} \cdot \dfrac{2x^2 + 9x + 4}{4 - 7x - 2x^2}$

$= \dfrac{(2x - 1)(3x + 2)}{(3x + 2)(2x + 1)} \cdot \dfrac{(2x + 1)(x + 4)}{(1 - 2x)(4 + x)}$

$= \dfrac{(2x - 1)(3x + 2) \cdot (2x + 1)(x + 4)}{(3x + 2)(2x + 1) \cdot (1 - 2x)(4 + x)}$

$= \dfrac{\overset{-1}{(2x - 1)}\overset{1}{(3x + 2)}\overset{1}{(2x + 1)}\overset{1}{(x + 4)}}{\underset{1}{(3x + 2)}\underset{1}{(2x + 1)}\underset{1}{(1 - 2x)}\underset{1}{(x + 4)}}$

$= -1$

You Try It 8

Simplify: $\dfrac{2x^2 - 13x + 20}{x^2 - 16} \cdot \dfrac{2x^2 + 9x + 4}{6x^2 - 7x - 5}$

Your solution

Solutions on p. S18

Objective C   *To divide rational expressions* .... (23) CT

The **reciprocal** of a rational expression is the rational expression with the numerator and denominator interchanged.

Rational Expression $\left\{ \begin{array}{cc} \dfrac{a}{b} & \dfrac{b}{a} \\[2mm] \dfrac{a^2 - 2y}{4} & \dfrac{4}{a^2 - 2y} \end{array} \right\}$ Reciprocal

To divide two rational expressions, multiply by the reciprocal of the divisor.

$$\dfrac{a}{b} \div \dfrac{c}{d} = \dfrac{a}{b} \cdot \dfrac{d}{c} = \dfrac{ad}{bc}$$

$$\dfrac{2}{a} \div \dfrac{5}{b} = \dfrac{2}{a} \cdot \dfrac{b}{5} = \dfrac{2b}{5a}$$

$$\dfrac{x + y}{2} \div \dfrac{x - y}{5} = \dfrac{x + y}{2} \cdot \dfrac{5}{x - y} = \dfrac{(x + y)5}{2(x - y)} = \dfrac{5x + 5y}{2x - 2y}$$

Example 9

Simplify: $\dfrac{12x^2y}{25a^2b^5} \div \dfrac{9x^3y^4}{10a^3b^4}$

Solution

$\dfrac{12x^2y}{25a^2b^5} \div \dfrac{9x^3y^4}{10a^3b^4} = \dfrac{12x^2y}{25a^2b^5} \cdot \dfrac{10a^3b^4}{9x^3y^4}$

$= \dfrac{12x^2y \cdot 10a^3b^4}{25a^2b^5 \cdot 9x^3y^4}$

$= \dfrac{8a}{15xy^3b}$

You Try It 9

Simplify: $\dfrac{7a^3b^7}{15x^2y^3} \div \dfrac{21a^5b^2}{20x^4y}$

Your solution

Example 10

Simplify: $\dfrac{12x^2y^2 - 24xy^2}{5z^2} \div \dfrac{4x^3y - 8x^2y}{3z^4}$

Solution

$\dfrac{12x^2y^2 - 24xy^2}{5z^2} \div \dfrac{4x^3y - 8x^2y}{3z^4}$

$= \dfrac{12x^2y^2 - 24xy^2}{5z^2} \cdot \dfrac{3z^4}{4x^3y - 8x^2y}$

$= \dfrac{12xy^2(x-2)}{5z^2} \cdot \dfrac{3z^4}{4x^2y(x-2)}$

$= \dfrac{12xy^2(x-2)3z^4}{5z^2 \cdot 4x^2y(x-2)}$

$= \dfrac{12xy^2(x-2)3z^4}{5z^2 \cdot 4x^2y(x-2)}$

$= \dfrac{9yz^2}{5x}$

You Try It 10

Simplify: $\dfrac{6x^2 - 3xy}{10ab^4} \div \dfrac{16x^2y^2 - 8xy^3}{15a^2b^2}$

Your solution

Example 11

Simplify: $\dfrac{3y^2 - 10y + 8}{3y^2 + 8y - 16} \div \dfrac{2y^2 - 7y + 6}{2y^2 + 5y - 12}$

Solution

$\dfrac{3y^2 - 10y + 8}{3y^2 + 8y - 16} \div \dfrac{2y^2 - 7y + 6}{2y^2 + 5y - 12}$

$= \dfrac{3y^2 - 10y + 8}{3y^2 + 8y - 16} \cdot \dfrac{2y^2 + 5y - 12}{2y^2 - 7y + 6}$

$= \dfrac{(y-2)(3y-4)}{(3y-4)(y+4)} \cdot \dfrac{(y+4)(2y-3)}{(y-2)(2y-3)}$

$= \dfrac{(y-2)(3y-4)(y+4)(2y-3)}{(3y-4)(y+4)(y-2)(2y-3)}$

$= \dfrac{(y-2)(3y-4)(y+4)(2y-3)}{(3y-4)(y+4)(y-2)(2y-3)}$

$= 1$

You Try It 11

Simplify: $\dfrac{6x^2 - 7x + 2}{3x^2 + x - 2} \div \dfrac{4x^2 - 8x + 3}{5x^2 + x - 4}$

Your solution

Solutions on p. S18

6.1 Exercises

Objective A

1. Given $f(x) = \dfrac{2}{x - 3}$, find $f(4)$.

2. Given $f(x) = \dfrac{-7}{5 - x}$, find $f(-2)$.

3. Given $f(x) = \dfrac{x - 2}{x + 4}$, find $f(-2)$.

4. Given $f(x) = \dfrac{x - 3}{2x - 1}$, find $f(3)$.

5. Given $f(x) = \dfrac{1}{x^2 - 2x + 1}$, find $f(-2)$.

6. Given $f(x) = \dfrac{-3}{x^2 - 4x + 2}$, find $f(-1)$.

7. Given $f(x) = \dfrac{x - 2}{2x^2 + 3x + 8}$, find $f(3)$.

8. Given $f(x) = \dfrac{x^2}{3x^2 - 3x + 5}$, find $f(4)$.

9. Given $f(x) = \dfrac{x^2 - 2x}{x^3 - x + 4}$, find $f(-1)$.

10. Given $f(x) = \dfrac{8 - x^2}{x^3 - x^2 + 4}$, find $f(-3)$.

Find the domain of the function.

11. $f(x) = \dfrac{4}{x - 3}$

12. $G(x) = \dfrac{-2}{x + 2}$

13. $H(x) = \dfrac{x}{x + 4}$

14. $F(x) = \dfrac{3x}{x - 5}$

15. $h(x) = \dfrac{5x}{3x + 9}$

16. $f(x) = \dfrac{-2x}{6 - 2x}$

17. $q(x) = \dfrac{4 - x}{(x - 4)(3x - 2)}$

18. $p(x) = \dfrac{2x + 1}{(2x + 5)(3x - 6)}$

19. $f(x) = \dfrac{2x - 1}{x^2 + x - 6}$

20. $G(x) = \dfrac{3 - 4x}{x^2 + 4x - 5}$

21. $f(x) = \dfrac{x + 1}{x^2 + 1}$

22. $g(x) = \dfrac{x^2 + 1}{x^2}$

Simplify.

23. $\dfrac{4 - 8x}{4}$

24. $\dfrac{8y + 2}{2}$

25. $\dfrac{6x^2 - 2x}{2x}$

26. $\dfrac{3y - 12y^2}{3y}$

27. $\dfrac{8x^2(x - 3)}{4x(x - 3)}$

28. $\dfrac{16y^4(y + 8)}{12y^3(y + 8)}$

29. $\dfrac{-36a^2 - 48a}{18a^3 + 24a^2}$

30. $\dfrac{a^2 + 4a}{4a - 16}$

31. $\dfrac{3x - 6}{x^2 + 2x}$

32. $\dfrac{16x^3 - 8x^2 + 12x}{4x}$

33. $\dfrac{3x^3y^3 - 12x^2y^2 + 15xy}{3xy}$

34. $\dfrac{-10a^4 - 20a^3 + 30a^2}{-10a^2}$

35. $\dfrac{x^{2n} + x^n y^n}{x^{2n} - y^{2n}}$

36. $\dfrac{a^{2n} - b^{2n}}{5a^{3n} + 5a^{2n}b^n}$

37. $\dfrac{x^2 - 7x + 12}{x^2 - 9x + 20}$

38. $\dfrac{6 - x - x^2}{3x^2 - 10x + 8}$

39. $\dfrac{3x^2 + 10x - 8}{8 - 14x + 3x^2}$

40. $\dfrac{14 - 19x - 3x^2}{3x^2 - 23x + 14}$

41. $\dfrac{a^2 - b^2}{a^3 + b^3}$

42. $\dfrac{x^4 - y^4}{x^2 + y^2}$

43. $\dfrac{8x^3 - y^3}{4x^2 - y^2}$

44. $\dfrac{x^2 - 4}{a(x + 2) - b(x + 2)}$

45. $\dfrac{x^2(a - 2) - a + 2}{ax^2 - ax}$

46. $\dfrac{x^4 + 3x^2 + 2}{x^4 - 1}$

47. $\dfrac{x^4 - 2x^2 - 3}{x^4 + 2x^2 + 1}$

48. $\dfrac{x^2y^2 + 4xy - 21}{x^2y^2 - 10xy + 21}$

49. $\dfrac{6x^2y^2 + 11xy + 4}{9x^2y^2 + 9xy - 4}$

50. $\dfrac{a^{2n} - a^n - 2}{a^{2n} + 3a^n + 2}$

51. $\dfrac{a^{2n} + a^n - 12}{a^{2n} - 2a^n - 3}$

52. $\dfrac{a^{2n} - 1}{a^{2n} - 2a^n + 1}$

53. $\dfrac{a^{2n} + 2a^n b^n + b^{2n}}{a^{2n} - b^{2n}}$

54. $\dfrac{(x - 3) - b(x - 3)}{b(x + 3) - x - 3}$

55. $\dfrac{x^2(a + b) + a + b}{x^4 - 1}$

Objective B

Simplify.

56. $\dfrac{27a^2b^5}{16xy^2} \cdot \dfrac{20x^2y^3}{9a^2b}$

57. $\dfrac{15x^2y^4}{24ab^3} \cdot \dfrac{28a^2b^4}{35xy^4}$

58. $\dfrac{3x - 15}{4x^2 - 2x} \cdot \dfrac{20x^2 - 10x}{15x - 75}$

59. $\dfrac{2x^2 + 4x}{8x^2 - 40x} \cdot \dfrac{6x^3 - 30x^2}{3x^2 + 6x}$

60. $\dfrac{x^2y^3}{x^2 - 4x - 5} \cdot \dfrac{2x^2 - 13x + 15}{x^4y^3}$

61. $\dfrac{2x^2 - 5x + 3}{x^6y^3} \cdot \dfrac{x^4y^4}{2x^2 - x - 3}$

62. $\dfrac{x^2 - 3x + 2}{x^2 - 8x + 15} \cdot \dfrac{x^2 + x - 12}{8 - 2x - x^2}$

63. $\dfrac{x^2 + x - 6}{12 + x - x^2} \cdot \dfrac{x^2 + x - 20}{x^2 - 4x + 4}$

64. $\dfrac{x^{n+1} + 2x^n}{4x^2 - 6x} \cdot \dfrac{8x^2 - 12x}{x^{n+1} - x^n}$

65. $\dfrac{x^{2n} + 2x^n}{x^{n+1} + 2x} \cdot \dfrac{x^2 - 3x}{x^{n+1} - 3x^n}$

66. $\dfrac{x^{2n} - x^n - 6}{x^{2n} + x^n - 2} \cdot \dfrac{x^{2n} - 5x^n - 6}{x^{2n} - 2x^n - 3}$

67. $\dfrac{x^{2n} + 3x^n + 2}{x^{2n} - x^n - 6} \cdot \dfrac{x^{2n} + x^n - 12}{x^{2n} - 1}$

68. $\dfrac{x^3 - y^3}{2x^2 + xy - 3y^2} \cdot \dfrac{2x^2 + 5xy + 3y^2}{x^2 + xy + y^2}$

69. $\dfrac{x^4 - 5x^2 + 4}{3x^2 - 4x - 4} \cdot \dfrac{3x^2 - 10x - 8}{x^2 - 4}$

70. $\dfrac{x^2 + x - 6}{3x^2 + 5x - 12} \cdot \dfrac{2x^2 - 14x}{16x^2 - 4x} \cdot \dfrac{12x^2 - 19x + 4}{x^2 + 5x - 14}$

71. $\dfrac{x^2 - y^2}{x^2 + xy + y^2} \cdot \dfrac{x^2 - xy}{3x^2 - 3xy} \cdot \dfrac{x^3 - y^3}{x^2 - 2xy + y^2}$

Objective C

Simplify.

72. $\dfrac{6x^2y^4}{35a^2b^5} \div \dfrac{12x^3y^3}{7a^4b^5}$

73. $\dfrac{12a^4b^7}{13x^2y^2} \div \dfrac{18a^5b^6}{26xy^3}$

74. $\dfrac{2x - 6}{6x^2 - 15x} \div \dfrac{4x^2 - 12x}{18x^3 - 45x^2}$

75. $\dfrac{4x^2 - 4y^2}{6x^2y^2} \div \dfrac{3x^2 + 3xy}{2x^2y - 2xy^2}$

76. $\dfrac{2x^2 - 2y^2}{14x^2y^4} \div \dfrac{x^2 + 2xy + y^2}{35xy^3}$

77. $\dfrac{8x^3 + 12x^2y}{4x^2 - 9y^2} \div \dfrac{16x^2y^2}{4x^2 - 12xy + 9y^2}$

78. $\dfrac{x^2 - 8x + 15}{x^2 + 2x - 35} \div \dfrac{15 - 2x - x^2}{x^2 + 9x + 14}$

79. $\dfrac{2x^2 + 13x + 20}{8 - 10x - 3x^2} \div \dfrac{6x^2 - 13x - 5}{9x^2 - 3x - 2}$

80. $\dfrac{x^{2n} + x^n}{2x - 2} \div \dfrac{4x^n + 4}{x^{n+1} - x^n}$

81. $\dfrac{x^{2n} - 4}{4x^n + 8} \div \dfrac{x^{n+1} - 2x}{4x^3 - 12x^2}$

82. $\dfrac{14 + 17x - 6x^2}{3x^2 + 14x + 8} \div \dfrac{4x^2 - 49}{2x^2 + 15x + 28}$

83. $\dfrac{16x^2 - 9}{6 - 5x - 4x^2} \div \dfrac{16x^2 + 24x + 9}{4x^2 + 11x + 6}$

84. $\dfrac{2x^{2n} - x^n - 6}{x^{2n} - x^n - 2} \div \dfrac{2x^{2n} + x^n - 3}{x^{2n} - 1}$

85. $\dfrac{x^{4n} - 1}{x^{2n} + x^n - 2} \div \dfrac{x^{2n} + 1}{x^{2n} + 3x^n + 2}$

86. $\dfrac{6x^2 + 6x}{3x + 6x^2 + 3x^3} \div \dfrac{x^2 - 1}{1 - x^3}$

87. $\dfrac{x^3 + y^3}{2x^3 + 2x^2 y} \div \dfrac{3x^3 - 3x^2 y + 3xy^2}{6x^2 - 6y^2}$

88. $\dfrac{x^2 - 9}{x^2 - x - 6} \div \dfrac{2x^2 + x - 15}{x^2 + 7x + 10} \cdot \dfrac{2x^2 - x - 10}{x^2 - 25}$

89. $\dfrac{3x^2 + 10x - 8}{x^2 + 4x + 3} \cdot \dfrac{x^2 + 6x + 9}{3x^2 - 5x + 2} \div \dfrac{x^2 + x - 12}{x^2 - 1}$

APPLYING THE CONCEPTS

90. State in your own words the procedure for
a. simplifying rational expressions.
b. multiplying rational expressions.
c. dividing rational expressions.

91. Simplify:
a. $\dfrac{3x^2 + 6x}{4x^2 - 16} \cdot \dfrac{2x + 8}{x^2 + 2x} \div \dfrac{3x - 9}{5x - 20}$
b. $\dfrac{5y^2 - 20}{3y^2 - 12y} \cdot \dfrac{9y^3 + 6y}{2y^2 - 4y} \div \dfrac{y^3 + 2y^2}{2y^2 - 8y}$

For each of the following, if the simplification is correct, write OK. If it is incorrect, rewrite the exercise correctly.

92. $\dfrac{12x^2 + 6x}{3x} = \dfrac{\cancel{3x}(4x + 2)}{\cancel{3x}} = 4x + 2$

93. $\dfrac{14y^2 + 7y}{y} = \dfrac{7\cancel{y}(2y + 1)}{\cancel{y}} = 7(2y + 1)$

94. $\dfrac{3x + 2}{x} = \dfrac{3\cancel{x} + 2}{\cancel{x}} = 5$

95. $\dfrac{5b^2 + 3b}{b^2} = \dfrac{5\cancel{b}^2 + 3b}{\cancel{b}^2} = 3b + 5$

96. $\dfrac{4x^3 + 2x}{2x} = \dfrac{\cancel{2x}(2x^2 + 0)}{\cancel{2x}} = 2x^2$

97. $\dfrac{\overset{1}{\cancel{x^2}} + \overset{1}{\cancel{3x}} - \overset{1}{\cancel{4}}}{\underset{1}{\cancel{x^2}} + \underset{1}{\cancel{3x}} + \underset{1}{\cancel{4}}} = \dfrac{1 + 1 - 1}{1 + 1 + 1} = \dfrac{1}{3}$

6.2 Addition and Subtraction of Rational Expressions

Objective A   *To rewrite rational expressions in terms of a common denominator* .... (24) CT

When adding or subtracting rational expressions, it is frequently necessary to express the rational expressions in terms of a common denominator. This common denominator is the least common multiple (LCM) of the denominators.

The LCM of two or more polynomials is the simplest polynomial that contains the factors of each polynomial. To find the LCM, first factor each polynomial completely. The LCM is the product of each factor the greatest number of times it occurs in any one factorization.

⇒ Find the LCM of $3x^2 + 15x$ and $6x^4 + 24x^3 - 30x^2$.

Factor each polynomial.

$3x^2 + 15x = 3x(x + 5)$
$6x^4 + 24x^3 - 30x^2 = 6x^2(x^2 + 4x - 5)$
$\qquad\qquad\qquad\qquad = 6x^2(x - 1)(x + 5)$

The LCM is the product of the LCM of the numerical coefficients and each variable factor the greatest number of times it occurs in any one factorization.

$\text{LCM} = 6x^2(x - 1)(x + 5)$

TAKE NOTE

This is the only section in this text in which the numerator in the final answer is in unfactored form. In building fractions, the fraction is not in simplest form, and leaving the fractions in unfactored form removes the temptation to cancel.

⇒ Write the fractions $\dfrac{5}{6x^2y}$ and $\dfrac{a}{9xy^3}$ in terms of the LCM of the denominators.

The LCM is $18x^2y^3$.

- Find the LCM of the denominators.

$$\frac{5}{6x^2y} = \frac{5}{6x^2y} \cdot \frac{3y^2}{3y^2} = \frac{15y^2}{18x^2y^3}$$

$$\frac{a}{9xy^3} = \frac{a}{9xy^3} \cdot \frac{2x}{2x} = \frac{2ax}{18x^2y^3}$$

- For each fraction, multiply the numerator and denominator by the factor whose product with the denominator is the LCM.

⇒ Write the fractions $\dfrac{x + 2}{x^2 - 2x}$ and $\dfrac{5x}{3x - 6}$ in terms of the LCM of the denominators.

The LCM is $3x(x - 2)$.

- Find the LCM of the denominators.

$$\frac{x + 2}{x^2 - 2x} = \frac{x + 2}{x(x - 2)} \cdot \frac{3}{3} = \frac{3x + 6}{3x(x - 2)}$$

$$\frac{5x}{3x - 6} = \frac{5x}{3(x - 2)} \cdot \frac{x}{x} = \frac{5x^2}{3x(x - 2)}$$

- For each fraction, multiply the numerator and denominator by the factor whose product with the denominator is the LCM.

Example 1

Write the fractions $\dfrac{3x}{x - 1}$ and $\dfrac{4}{2x + 5}$ in terms of the LCM of the denominators.

Solution

The LCM is $(x - 1)(2x + 5)$.

$$\frac{3x}{x - 1} = \frac{3x}{x - 1} \cdot \frac{2x + 5}{2x + 5} = \frac{6x^2 + 15x}{(x - 1)(2x + 5)}$$

$$\frac{4}{2x + 5} = \frac{4}{2x + 5} \cdot \frac{x - 1}{x - 1} = \frac{4x - 4}{(x - 1)(2x + 5)}$$

You Try It 1

Write the fractions $\dfrac{2x}{2x - 5}$ and $\dfrac{3}{x + 4}$ in terms of the LCM of the denominators.

Your solution

Example 2

Write the fractions $\dfrac{2a - 3}{a^2 - 2a}$ and $\dfrac{a + 1}{2a^2 - a - 6}$ in terms of the LCM of the denominators.

Solution

$a^2 - 2a = a(a - 2)$;
$2a^2 - a - 6 = (2a + 3)(a - 2)$

The LCM is $a(a - 2)(2a + 3)$.

$$\frac{2a - 3}{a^2 - 2a} = \frac{2a - 3}{a(a - 2)} \cdot \frac{2a + 3}{2a + 3}$$

$$= \frac{4a^2 - 9}{a(a - 2)(2a + 3)}$$

$$\frac{a + 1}{2a^2 - a - 6} = \frac{a + 1}{(a - 2)(2a + 3)} \cdot \frac{a}{a}$$

$$= \frac{a^2 + a}{a(a - 2)(2a + 3)}$$

You Try It 2

Write the fractions $\dfrac{3x}{2x^2 - 11x + 15}$ and $\dfrac{x - 2}{x^2 - 3x}$ in terms of the LCM of the denominators.

Your solution

Example 3

Write the fractions $\dfrac{2x - 3}{3x - x^2}$ and $\dfrac{3x}{x^2 - 4x + 3}$ in terms of the LCM of the denominators.

Solution

$3x - x^2 = x(3 - x) = -x(x - 3)$;
$x^2 - 4x + 3 = (x - 3)(x - 1)$

The LCM is $x(x - 3)(x - 1)$.

$$\frac{2x - 3}{3x - x^2} = -\frac{2x - 3}{x(x - 3)} \cdot \frac{x - 1}{x - 1}$$

$$= -\frac{2x^2 - 5x + 3}{x(x - 3)(x - 1)}$$

$$\frac{3x}{x^2 - 4x + 3} = \frac{3x}{(x - 3)(x - 1)} \cdot \frac{x}{x}$$

$$= \frac{3x^2}{x(x - 3)(x - 1)}$$

You Try It 3

Write the fractions $\dfrac{2x - 7}{2x - x^2}$ and $\dfrac{3x - 2}{3x^2 - 5x - 2}$ in terms of the LCM of the denominators.

Your solution

Solutions on p. S18

Objective B **To add or subtract rational expressions** .... (24) CT

When adding rational expressions in which the denominators are the same, add the numerators. The denominator of the sum is the common denominator.

$$\frac{a}{c} + \frac{b}{c} = \frac{a+b}{c}$$

$$\frac{4x}{15} + \frac{8x}{15} = \frac{4x+8x}{15} = \frac{12x}{15} = \frac{4x}{5}$$

• Note that the sum is written in simplest form.

$$\frac{a}{a^2-b^2} + \frac{b}{a^2-b^2} = \frac{a+b}{a^2-b^2} = \frac{a+b}{(a-b)(a+b)} = \frac{\overset{1}{\cancel{(a+b)}}}{(a-b)\cancel{(a+b)}_{1}} = \frac{1}{a-b}$$

When subtracting rational expressions with *like* denominators, subtract the numerators. The denominator of the difference is the common denominator. Write the answer in simplest form.

$$\frac{7x-12}{2x^2+5x-12} - \frac{3x-6}{2x^2+5x-12} = \frac{(7x-12)-(3x-6)}{2x^2+5x-12} = \frac{4x-6}{2x^2+5x-12}$$

$$= \frac{2\overset{1}{\cancel{(2x-3)}}}{\cancel{(2x-3)}_{1}(x+4)} = \frac{2}{x+4}$$

Before two rational expressions with *different* denominators can be added or subtracted, each rational expression must be expressed in terms of a common denominator. This common denominator is the LCM of the denominators of the rational expressions.

➡ Simplify: $\dfrac{x}{x-3} - \dfrac{x+1}{x-2}$

The LCM is $(x-3)(x-2)$.

• Find the LCM of the denominators.

$$\frac{x}{x-3} - \frac{x+1}{x-2} = \frac{x}{x-3} \cdot \frac{x-2}{x-2} - \frac{x+1}{x-2} \cdot \frac{x-3}{x-3}$$

• Express each fraction in terms of the LCM.

$$= \frac{x(x-2)-(x+1)(x-3)}{(x-3)(x-2)}$$

• Subtract the fractions.

$$= \frac{(x^2-2x)-(x^2-2x-3)}{(x-3)(x-2)}$$

$$= \frac{3}{(x-3)(x-2)}$$

• Simplify.

➡ Simplify: $\dfrac{3x}{2x-3} + \dfrac{3x+6}{2x^2+x-6}$

The LCM is $(2x-3)(x+2)$.

• Find the LCM of the denominators.

$$\frac{3x}{2x-3} + \frac{3x+6}{2x^2+x-6} = \frac{3x}{2x-3} \cdot \frac{x+2}{x+2} + \frac{3x+6}{(2x-3)(x+2)}$$

• Express each fraction in terms of the LCM.

$$= \frac{3x(x+2)+(3x+6)}{(2x-3)(x+2)}$$

• Add the fractions.

$$= \frac{(3x^2+6x)+(3x+6)}{(2x-3)(x+2)}$$

$$= \frac{3x^2+9x+6}{(2x-3)(x+2)} = \frac{3\cancel{(x+2)}(x+1)}{(2x-3)\cancel{(x+2)}}$$

• Simplify.

$$= \frac{3(x+1)}{2x-3}$$

Example 4

Simplify: $\dfrac{2}{x} - \dfrac{3}{x^2} + \dfrac{1}{xy}$

Solution

The LCM is x^2y.

$\dfrac{2}{x} - \dfrac{3}{x^2} + \dfrac{1}{xy} = \dfrac{2}{x} \cdot \dfrac{xy}{xy} - \dfrac{3}{x^2} \cdot \dfrac{y}{y} + \dfrac{1}{xy} \cdot \dfrac{x}{x}$

$= \dfrac{2xy}{x^2y} - \dfrac{3y}{x^2y} + \dfrac{x}{x^2y} = \dfrac{2xy - 3y + x}{x^2y}$

You Try It 4

Simplify: $\dfrac{2}{b} - \dfrac{1}{a} + \dfrac{4}{ab}$

Your solution

Example 5

Simplify: $\dfrac{x}{2x - 4} - \dfrac{4 - x}{x^2 - 2x}$

Solution

$2x - 4 = 2(x - 2); \; x^2 - 2x = x(x - 2)$

The LCM is $2x(x - 2)$.

$\dfrac{x}{2x - 4} - \dfrac{4 - x}{x^2 - 2x} = \dfrac{x}{2(x - 2)} \cdot \dfrac{x}{x} - \dfrac{4 - x}{x(x - 2)} \cdot \dfrac{2}{2}$

$= \dfrac{x^2 - (4 - x)2}{2x(x - 2)}$

$= \dfrac{x^2 - (8 - 2x)}{2x(x - 2)} = \dfrac{x^2 + 2x - 8}{2x(x - 2)}$

$= \dfrac{(x + 4)(x - 2)}{2x(x - 2)} = \dfrac{(x + 4)\cancel{(x - 2)}^{\,1}}{2x\cancel{(x - 2)}_{\,1}}$

$= \dfrac{x + 4}{2x}$

You Try It 5

Simplify: $\dfrac{a - 3}{a^2 - 5a} + \dfrac{a - 9}{a^2 - 25}$

Your solution

Example 6

Simplify: $\dfrac{x}{x + 1} - \dfrac{2}{x - 2} - \dfrac{3}{x^2 - x - 2}$

Solution

The LCM is $(x + 1)(x - 2)$.

$\dfrac{x}{x + 1} - \dfrac{2}{x - 2} - \dfrac{3}{x^2 - x - 2}$

$= \dfrac{x}{x + 1} \cdot \dfrac{x - 2}{x - 2} - \dfrac{2}{x - 2} \cdot \dfrac{x + 1}{x + 1} - \dfrac{3}{(x + 1)(x - 2)}$

$= \dfrac{x(x - 2) - 2(x + 1) - 3}{(x + 1)(x - 2)}$

$= \dfrac{x^2 - 2x - 2x - 2 - 3}{(x + 1)(x - 2)}$

$= \dfrac{x^2 - 4x - 5}{(x + 1)(x - 2)} = \dfrac{\cancel{(x + 1)}^{\,1}(x - 5)}{\cancel{(x + 1)}_{\,1}(x - 2)} = \dfrac{x - 5}{x - 2}$

You Try It 6

Simplify: $\dfrac{2x}{x - 4} - \dfrac{x - 1}{x + 1} + \dfrac{2}{x^2 - 3x - 4}$

Your solution

Solutions on p. S19

6.2 Exercises

· ·

Objective A

Write each fraction in terms of the LCM of the denominators.

1. $\dfrac{3}{4x^2y}, \dfrac{17}{12xy^4}$

2. $\dfrac{5}{16a^3b^3}, \dfrac{7}{30a^5b}$

3. $\dfrac{x-2}{3x(x-2)}, \dfrac{3}{6x^2}$

4. $\dfrac{5x-1}{4x(2x+1)}, \dfrac{2}{5x^3}$

5. $\dfrac{3x-1}{2x^2-10x}, -3x$

6. $\dfrac{4x-3}{3x(x-2)}, 2x$

7. $\dfrac{3x}{2x-3}, \dfrac{5x}{2x+3}$

8. $\dfrac{2}{7y-3}, \dfrac{-3}{7y+3}$

9. $\dfrac{2x}{x^2-9}, \dfrac{x+1}{x-3}$

10. $\dfrac{3x}{16-x^2}, \dfrac{2x}{16-4x}$

11. $\dfrac{3}{3x^2-12y^2}, \dfrac{5}{6x-12y}$

12. $\dfrac{2x}{x^2-36}, \dfrac{x-1}{6x-36}$

13. $\dfrac{3x}{x^2-1}, \dfrac{5x}{x^2-2x+1}$

14. $\dfrac{x^2+2}{x^3-1}, \dfrac{3}{x^2+x+1}$

15. $\dfrac{x-3}{8-x^3}, \dfrac{2}{4+2x+x^2}$

16. $\dfrac{2x}{x^2+x-6}, \dfrac{-4x}{x^2+5x+6}$

17. $\dfrac{2x}{x^2+2x-3}, \dfrac{-x}{x^2+6x+9}$

18. $\dfrac{3x}{2x^2-x-3}, \dfrac{-2x}{2x^2-11x+12}$

19. $\dfrac{-4x}{4x^2-16x+15}, \dfrac{3x}{6x^2-19x+10}$

20. $\dfrac{3}{2x^2+5x-12}, \dfrac{2x}{3-2x}, \dfrac{3x-1}{x+4}$

21. $\dfrac{5}{6x^2-17x+12}, \dfrac{2x}{4-3x}, \dfrac{x+1}{2x-3}$

22. $\dfrac{3x}{x-4}, \dfrac{4}{x+5}, \dfrac{x+2}{20-x-x^2}$

23. $\dfrac{2x}{x-3}, \dfrac{-2}{x+5}, \dfrac{x-1}{15-2x-x^2}$

24. $\dfrac{2}{x^{2n}-1}, \dfrac{5}{x^{2n}+2x^n+1}$

25. $\dfrac{x-5}{x^{2n}+3x^n+2}, \dfrac{2x}{x^n+2}$

Objective B

Simplify.

26. $\dfrac{3}{2xy} - \dfrac{7}{2xy} - \dfrac{9}{2xy}$

27. $-\dfrac{3}{4x^2} + \dfrac{8}{4x^2} - \dfrac{3}{4x^2}$

28. $\dfrac{x}{x^2-3x+2} - \dfrac{2}{x^2-3x+2}$

29. $\dfrac{3x}{3x^2+x-10} - \dfrac{5}{3x^2+x-10}$

30. $\dfrac{3}{2x^2y} - \dfrac{8}{5x} - \dfrac{9}{10xy}$

31. $\dfrac{2}{5ab} - \dfrac{3}{10a^2b} + \dfrac{4}{15ab^2}$

32. $\dfrac{2}{3x} - \dfrac{3}{2xy} + \dfrac{4}{5xy} - \dfrac{5}{6x}$

33. $\dfrac{3}{4ab} - \dfrac{2}{5a} + \dfrac{3}{10b} - \dfrac{5}{8ab}$

34. $\dfrac{2x-1}{12x} - \dfrac{3x+4}{9x}$

35. $\dfrac{3x-4}{6x} - \dfrac{2x-5}{4x}$

36. $\dfrac{3x+2}{4x^2y} - \dfrac{y-5}{6xy^2}$

37. $\dfrac{2y-4}{5xy^2} + \dfrac{3-2x}{10x^2y}$

38. $\dfrac{2x}{x-3} - \dfrac{3x}{x-5}$

39. $\dfrac{3a}{a-2} - \dfrac{5a}{a+1}$

40. $\dfrac{3}{2a-3} + \dfrac{2a}{3-2a}$

41. $\dfrac{x}{2x-5} - \dfrac{2}{5x-2}$

42. $\dfrac{1}{x+h} - \dfrac{1}{h}$

43. $\dfrac{1}{a-b} + \dfrac{1}{b}$

44. $\dfrac{2}{x} - 3 - \dfrac{10}{x-4}$

45. $\dfrac{6a}{a-3} - 5 + \dfrac{3}{a}$

46. $\dfrac{1}{2x-3} - \dfrac{5}{2x} + 1$

47. $\dfrac{5}{x} - \dfrac{5x}{5 - 6x} + 2$

48. $\dfrac{3}{x^2 - 1} + \dfrac{2x}{x^2 + 2x + 1}$

49. $\dfrac{1}{x^2 - 6x + 9} - \dfrac{1}{x^2 - 9}$

50. $\dfrac{x}{x + 3} - \dfrac{3 - x}{x^2 - 9}$

51. $\dfrac{1}{x + 2} - \dfrac{3x}{x^2 + 4x + 4}$

52. $\dfrac{2x - 3}{x + 5} - \dfrac{x^2 - 4x - 19}{x^2 + 8x + 15}$

53. $\dfrac{-3x^2 + 8x + 2}{x^2 + 2x - 8} - \dfrac{2x - 5}{x + 4}$

54. $\dfrac{x^n}{x^{2n} - 1} - \dfrac{2}{x^n + 1}$

55. $\dfrac{2}{x^n - 1} + \dfrac{x^n}{x^{2n} - 1}$

56. $\dfrac{2}{x^n - 1} - \dfrac{6}{x^{2n} + x^n - 2}$

57. $\dfrac{2x^n - 6}{x^{2n} - x^n - 6} + \dfrac{x^n}{x^n + 2}$

58. $\dfrac{2x - 2}{4x^2 - 9} - \dfrac{5}{3 - 2x}$

59. $\dfrac{x^2 + 4}{4x^2 - 36} - \dfrac{13}{x + 3}$

60. $\dfrac{x - 2}{x + 1} - \dfrac{3 - 12x}{2x^2 - x - 3}$

61. $\dfrac{3x - 4}{4x + 1} + \dfrac{3x + 6}{4x^2 + 9x + 2}$

62. $\dfrac{x + 1}{x^2 + x - 6} - \dfrac{x + 2}{x^2 + 4x + 3}$

63. $\dfrac{x + 1}{x^2 + x - 12} - \dfrac{x - 3}{x^2 + 7x + 12}$

64. $\dfrac{x^2 + 6x}{x^2 + 3x - 18} - \dfrac{2x - 1}{x + 6} + \dfrac{x - 2}{3 - x}$

65. $\dfrac{2x^2 - 2x}{x^2 - 2x - 15} - \dfrac{2}{x + 3} + \dfrac{x}{5 - x}$

66. $\dfrac{7 - 4x}{2x^2 - 9x + 10} + \dfrac{x - 3}{x - 2} - \dfrac{x + 1}{2x - 5}$

67. $\dfrac{x}{3x + 4} + \dfrac{3x + 2}{x - 5} - \dfrac{7x^2 + 24x + 28}{3x^2 - 11x - 20}$

68. $\dfrac{32x - 9}{2x^2 + 7x - 15} + \dfrac{x - 2}{3 - 2x} + \dfrac{3x + 2}{x + 5}$

69. $\dfrac{x + 1}{1 - 2x} - \dfrac{x + 3}{4x - 3} + \dfrac{10x^2 + 7x - 9}{8x^2 - 10x + 3}$

70. $\dfrac{x^2}{x^3 - 8} - \dfrac{x + 2}{x^2 + 2x + 4}$

71. $\dfrac{2x}{4x^2 + 2x + 1} + \dfrac{4x + 1}{8x^3 - 1}$

72. $\dfrac{2x^2}{x^4 - 1} - \dfrac{1}{x^2 - 1} + \dfrac{1}{x^2 + 1}$

73. $\dfrac{x^2 - 12}{x^4 - 16} + \dfrac{1}{x^2 - 4} - \dfrac{1}{x^2 + 4}$

74. $\left[\dfrac{x + 8}{4} + \dfrac{4}{x}\right] \div \dfrac{x + 4}{16x^2}$

75. $\left[\dfrac{a - 3}{a^2} - \dfrac{a - 3}{9}\right] \div \dfrac{a^2 - 9}{3a}$

76. $\dfrac{3}{x - 2} - \dfrac{x^2 + x}{2x^3 + 3x^2} \cdot \dfrac{2x^2 + x - 3}{x^2 + 3x + 2}$

77. $\dfrac{x^2 - 4x + 4}{2x + 1} \cdot \dfrac{2x^2 + x}{x^3 - 4x} - \dfrac{3x - 2}{x + 1}$

78. $\left[\dfrac{x - y}{x^2} - \dfrac{x - y}{y^2}\right] \div \dfrac{x^2 - y^2}{xy}$

79. $\left[\dfrac{a - 2b}{b} + \dfrac{b}{a}\right] \div \left[\dfrac{b + a}{a} - \dfrac{2a}{b}\right]$

80. $\dfrac{2}{x - 3} - \dfrac{x}{x^2 - x - 6} \cdot \dfrac{x^2 - 2x - 3}{x^2 - x}$

81. $\dfrac{2x}{x^2 - x - 6} - \dfrac{6x - 6}{2x^2 - 9x + 9} \div \dfrac{x^2 + x - 2}{2x - 3}$

APPLYING THE CONCEPTS

82. Explain the procedure for subtracting rational expressions with different denominators.

83. Correct the following expressions.

a. $\dfrac{3}{4} + \dfrac{x}{5} = \dfrac{3 + x}{4 + 5}$ **b.** $\dfrac{4x + 5}{4} = x + 5$ **c.** $\dfrac{1}{x} + \dfrac{1}{y} = \dfrac{1}{x + y}$

84. Simplify.

a. $\left(\dfrac{b}{6} - \dfrac{6}{b}\right) \div \left(\dfrac{6}{b} - 4 + \dfrac{b}{2}\right)$ **b.** $\left(\dfrac{x + 1}{2x - 1} - \dfrac{x - 1}{2x + 1}\right) \cdot \left(\dfrac{2x - 1}{x} - \dfrac{2x - 1}{x^2}\right)$

85. Rewrite as the sum of two fractions in simplest form.

a. $\dfrac{3x + 6y}{xy}$ **b.** $\dfrac{4a^2 + 3ab}{a^2b^2}$ **c.** $\dfrac{3m^2n + 2mn^2}{12m^3n^2}$

86. Let $f(x) = \dfrac{x}{x + 2}$, $g(x) = \dfrac{4}{x - 3}$, and $S(x) = \dfrac{x^2 + x + 8}{x^2 - x - 6}$. Evaluate $f(4)$, $g(4)$, and $S(4)$. Does $f(4) + g(4) = S(4)$? Let a be a real number ($a \neq -2$, $a \neq 3$). Express $S(a)$ in terms of $f(a)$ and $g(a)$.

6.3 Complex Fractions

Objective A *To simplify a complex fraction* .... (25) CT

A **complex fraction** is a fraction whose numerator or denominator contains one or more fractions. Examples of complex fractions are shown below.

$$\frac{5}{2+\dfrac{1}{2}}, \qquad \frac{5+\dfrac{1}{y}}{5-\dfrac{1}{y}}, \qquad \frac{x+4+\dfrac{1}{x+2}}{x-2+\dfrac{1}{x+2}}$$

➡ Simplify: $\dfrac{\dfrac{1}{x}+\dfrac{1}{y}}{\dfrac{1}{x}-\dfrac{1}{y}}$

The LCM of x and y is xy.

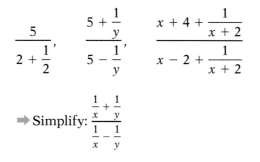

- Find the LCM of the denominators of the fractions in the numerator and denominator.
- Multiply the numerator and denominator of the complex fraction by the LCM.

$$= \frac{\dfrac{1}{x}\cdot xy + \dfrac{1}{y}\cdot xy}{\dfrac{1}{x}\cdot xy - \dfrac{1}{y}\cdot xy} = \frac{y+x}{y-x}$$

Example 1 Simplify: $\dfrac{1+\dfrac{1}{y-2}}{1-\dfrac{2}{y+1}}$

Solution
The LCM of $y-2$ and $y+1$ is $(y-2)(y+1)$.

$$\frac{1+\dfrac{1}{y-2}}{1-\dfrac{2}{y+1}} = \frac{1+\dfrac{1}{y-2}}{1-\dfrac{2}{y+1}}\cdot\frac{(y-2)(y+1)}{(y-2)(y+1)}$$

$$= \frac{(y-2)(y+1) + \dfrac{1}{y-2}(y-2)(y+1)}{(y-2)(y+1) - \dfrac{2}{y+1}(y-2)(y+1)}$$

$$= \frac{y^2-y-2+y+1}{y^2-y-2-2y+4} = \frac{y^2-1}{y^2-3y+2} = \frac{\overset{1}{\cancel{(y-1)}}(y+1)}{\underset{1}{\cancel{(y-1)}}(y-2)}$$

$$= \frac{y+1}{y-2}$$

You Try It 1 Simplify: $\dfrac{1-\dfrac{2}{x+3}}{1-\dfrac{1}{x+2}}$

Your solution

Solution on p. S19

Example 2

Simplify: $\dfrac{2x - 1 + \dfrac{7}{x + 4}}{3x - 8 + \dfrac{17}{x + 4}}$

You Try It 2

Simplify: $\dfrac{2x + 5 + \dfrac{14}{x - 3}}{4x + 16 + \dfrac{49}{x - 3}}$

Solution

The LCM is $x + 4$.

$$\dfrac{2x - 1 + \dfrac{7}{x + 4}}{3x - 8 + \dfrac{17}{x + 4}} = \dfrac{2x - 1 + \dfrac{7}{x + 4}}{3x - 8 + \dfrac{17}{x + 4}} \cdot \dfrac{x + 4}{x + 4}$$

$$= \dfrac{(2x - 1)(x + 4) + \dfrac{7}{x + 4}(x + 4)}{(3x - 8)(x + 4) + \dfrac{17}{x + 4}(x + 4)}$$

$$= \dfrac{2x^2 + 7x - 4 + 7}{3x^2 + 4x - 32 + 17} = \dfrac{2x^2 + 7x + 3}{3x^2 + 4x - 15}$$

$$= \dfrac{(2x + 1)(x + 3)}{(3x - 5)(x + 3)} = \dfrac{(2x + 1)\overset{1}{\cancel{(x + 3)}}}{(3x - 5)\underset{1}{\cancel{(x + 3)}}}$$

$$= \dfrac{2x + 1}{3x - 5}$$

Your solution

Example 3

Simplify: $1 + \dfrac{a}{2 + \dfrac{1}{a}}$

You Try It 3

Simplify: $2 - \dfrac{1}{2 - \dfrac{1}{x}}$

Solution

The LCM is a.

$$1 + \dfrac{a}{2 + \dfrac{1}{a}} = 1 + \dfrac{a}{2 + \dfrac{1}{a}} \cdot \dfrac{a}{a}$$

$$= 1 + \dfrac{a \cdot a}{2 \cdot a + \dfrac{1}{a} \cdot a} = 1 + \dfrac{a^2}{2a + 1}$$

The LCM of 1 and $2a + 1$ is $2a + 1$.

$$1 + \dfrac{a^2}{2a + 1} = 1 \cdot \dfrac{2a + 1}{2a + 1} + \dfrac{a^2}{2a + 1} = \dfrac{2a + 1}{2a + 1} + \dfrac{a^2}{2a + 1}$$

$$= \dfrac{2a + 1 + a^2}{2a + 1} = \dfrac{a^2 + 2a + 1}{2a + 1}$$

$$= \dfrac{(a + 1)^2}{2a + 1}$$

Your solution

Solutions on p. S19

6.3 Exercises

Objective A

Simplify.

1. $\dfrac{2 - \dfrac{1}{3}}{4 + \dfrac{11}{3}}$

2. $\dfrac{3 + \dfrac{5}{2}}{8 - \dfrac{3}{2}}$

3. $\dfrac{3 - \dfrac{2}{3}}{5 + \dfrac{5}{6}}$

4. $\dfrac{5 - \dfrac{3}{4}}{2 + \dfrac{1}{2}}$

5. $\dfrac{1 + \dfrac{1}{x}}{1 - \dfrac{1}{x^2}}$

6. $\dfrac{\dfrac{1}{y^2} - 1}{1 + \dfrac{1}{y}}$

7. $\dfrac{a - 2}{\dfrac{4}{a} - a}$

8. $\dfrac{\dfrac{25}{a} - a}{5 + a}$

9. $\dfrac{\dfrac{1}{a^2} - \dfrac{1}{a}}{\dfrac{1}{a^2} + \dfrac{1}{a}}$

10. $\dfrac{\dfrac{1}{b} + \dfrac{1}{2}}{\dfrac{4}{b^2} - 1}$

11. $\dfrac{2 - \dfrac{4}{x + 2}}{5 - \dfrac{10}{x + 2}}$

12. $\dfrac{4 + \dfrac{12}{2x - 3}}{5 + \dfrac{15}{2x - 3}}$

13. $\dfrac{\dfrac{3}{2a - 3} + 2}{\dfrac{-6}{2a - 3} - 4}$

14. $\dfrac{\dfrac{-5}{b - 5} - 3}{\dfrac{10}{b - 5} + 6}$

15. $\dfrac{\dfrac{x}{x + 1} - \dfrac{1}{x}}{\dfrac{x}{x + 1} + \dfrac{1}{x}}$

16. $\dfrac{\dfrac{2a}{a - 1} - \dfrac{3}{a}}{\dfrac{1}{a - 1} + \dfrac{2}{a}}$

17. $\dfrac{1 - \dfrac{1}{x} - \dfrac{6}{x^2}}{1 - \dfrac{4}{x} + \dfrac{3}{x^2}}$

18. $\dfrac{1 - \dfrac{3}{x} - \dfrac{10}{x^2}}{1 + \dfrac{11}{x} + \dfrac{18}{x^2}}$

19. $\dfrac{1 + \dfrac{1}{x} - \dfrac{12}{x^2}}{\dfrac{9}{x^2} + \dfrac{3}{x} - 2}$

20. $\dfrac{\dfrac{15}{x^2} - \dfrac{2}{x} - 1}{\dfrac{4}{x^2} - \dfrac{5}{x} + 4}$

21. $a + \dfrac{a}{a + \dfrac{1}{a}}$

22. $4 - \dfrac{2}{2 - \dfrac{3}{x}}$

23. $\dfrac{1 - \dfrac{1}{x - 4}}{1 - \dfrac{6}{x + 1}}$

24. $\dfrac{1 + \dfrac{3}{x + 2}}{1 + \dfrac{6}{x - 1}}$

25. $\dfrac{x - \dfrac{1}{x}}{x + \dfrac{1}{x}}$

26. $\dfrac{a - \dfrac{1}{a}}{\dfrac{1}{a} + a}$

27. $\dfrac{\dfrac{1}{x + h} - \dfrac{1}{x}}{h}$

28. $\dfrac{\dfrac{1}{(x + h)^2} - \dfrac{1}{x^2}}{h}$

29. $\dfrac{1 - \dfrac{2}{x - 3}}{1 + \dfrac{3}{2 - x}}$

30. $\dfrac{1 + \dfrac{x}{x + 1}}{1 + \dfrac{x - 1}{x + 2}}$

31. $\dfrac{x - 4 + \dfrac{9}{2x + 3}}{x + 3 - \dfrac{5}{2x + 3}}$

32. $\dfrac{2x - 3 - \dfrac{10}{4x - 5}}{3x + 2 + \dfrac{11}{4x - 5}}$

33. $\dfrac{3x - 2 - \dfrac{5}{2x - 1}}{x - 6 + \dfrac{9}{2x - 1}}$

34. $\dfrac{x + 4 - \dfrac{7}{2x - 5}}{2x + 7 - \dfrac{28}{2x - 5}}$

35. $\dfrac{\dfrac{1}{a} - \dfrac{3}{a - 2}}{\dfrac{2}{a} + \dfrac{5}{a - 2}}$

36. $\dfrac{\dfrac{2}{b} - \dfrac{5}{b + 3}}{\dfrac{3}{b} + \dfrac{3}{b + 3}}$

37. $\dfrac{\dfrac{1}{y^2} - \dfrac{1}{xy} - \dfrac{2}{x^2}}{\dfrac{1}{y^2} - \dfrac{3}{xy} + \dfrac{2}{x^2}}$

38. $\dfrac{\dfrac{2}{b^2} - \dfrac{5}{ab} - \dfrac{3}{a^2}}{\dfrac{2}{b^2} + \dfrac{7}{ab} + \dfrac{3}{a^2}}$

39. $\dfrac{\dfrac{x - 1}{x + 1} - \dfrac{x + 1}{x - 1}}{\dfrac{x - 1}{x + 1} + \dfrac{x + 1}{x - 1}}$

40. $\dfrac{\dfrac{y}{y + 2} - \dfrac{y}{y - 2}}{\dfrac{y}{y + 2} + \dfrac{y}{y - 2}}$

41. $a - \dfrac{a}{1 - \dfrac{a}{1 - a}}$

42. $3 - \dfrac{3}{3 - \dfrac{3}{3 - x}}$

43. $3 - \dfrac{2}{1 - \dfrac{2}{3 - \dfrac{2}{x}}}$

44. $a + \dfrac{a}{2 + \dfrac{1}{1 - \dfrac{2}{a}}}$

APPLYING THE CONCEPTS

45. Find the sum of the reciprocals of three consecutive even integers.

46. If $a = \dfrac{b^2 + 4b + 4}{b^2 - 4}$ and $b = \dfrac{1}{c}$, express a in terms of c.

47. Simplify.

a. $\dfrac{x^{-1}}{x^{-1} + 2^{-1}}$

b. $\dfrac{-x^{-1} + x}{x^{-1} - x}$

c. $\dfrac{x^{-1} - x^{-2} - 6x^{-3}}{x^{-1} - 4x^{-3}}$

48. According to Einstein's theory of relativity, the kinetic energy of a body is given by $E = \dfrac{mv}{\sqrt{1 - \dfrac{v^2}{c^2}}}$, where c is the velocity of light, v is the velocity of the object, and m is its mass. Using this formula, explain how the kinetic energy of the object changes as its velocity approaches the speed of light.

6.4 Ratio and Proportion

Objective A   *To solve a proportion* .... (25) CT

Quantities such as 3 feet, 5 liters, and 2 miles are number quantities written with units. In these examples the units are feet, liters, and miles.

A **ratio** is the quotient of two quantities that have the same unit.

The weekly wages of a painter are $725. The painter spends $75 a week for food. The ratio of the wages spent for food to the total weekly wages is written

$$\frac{\$75}{\$725} = \frac{75}{725} = \frac{3}{29}$$

A ratio is in simplest form when the two numbers do not have a common factor. Note that the units are not written.

A **rate** is the quotient of two quantities that have different units.

A car travels 180 mi on 3 gal of gas. The miles-to-gallons rate is

$$\frac{180 \text{ mi}}{3 \text{ gal}} = \frac{60 \text{ mi}}{1 \text{ gal}}$$

A rate is in simplest form when the two numbers do not have a common factor. The units are written as part of the rate.

A **proportion** is an equation that states the equality of two ratios or rates. For example, $\frac{90 \text{ km}}{4 \text{ L}} = \frac{45 \text{ km}}{2 \text{ L}}$ and $\frac{3}{4} = \frac{x + 2}{16}$ are proportions.

➡ Solve the proportion: $\frac{2}{7} = \frac{x}{5}$

$$\frac{2}{7} = \frac{x}{5}$$

$$35 \cdot \frac{2}{7} = 35 \cdot \frac{x}{5}$$

$$10 = 7x$$

$$\frac{10}{7} = x$$

- Multiply each side of the proportion by the LCM of the denominators.
- Solve the equation.

The solution is $\frac{10}{7}$.

Example 1

Solve the proportion: $\frac{3}{12} = \frac{5}{x + 5}$

Solution $\frac{3}{12} = \frac{5}{x + 5}$

$$\frac{3}{12} \cdot 12(x + 5) = \frac{5}{x + 5} \cdot 12(x + 5)$$

$$3(x + 5) = 5 \cdot 12$$

$$3x + 15 = 60$$

$$3x = 45$$

$$x = 15$$

The solution is 15.

You Try It 1

Solve the proportion: $\frac{5}{x - 2} = \frac{3}{4}$

Your solution

Solution on p. S19

Example 2

Solve the proportion: $\dfrac{3}{x-2} = \dfrac{4}{2x+1}$

You Try It 2

Solve the proportion: $\dfrac{5}{2x-3} = \dfrac{-2}{x+1}$

Solution

$$\frac{3}{x-2} = \frac{4}{2x+1}$$

$$\frac{3}{x-2}(2x+1)(x-2) = \frac{4}{2x+1}(2x+1)(x-2)$$

$$3(2x+1) = 4(x-2)$$

$$6x+3 = 4x-8$$

$$2x+3 = -8$$

$$2x = -11$$

$$x = -\frac{11}{2}$$

The solution is $-\dfrac{11}{2}$.

Your solution

Solution on p. S20

Objective B   To solve application problems · (25) CT

Example 3

A stock investment of 50 shares pays a dividend of $106. At this rate, how many additional shares are required to earn a dividend of $424?

You Try It 3

Two pounds of cashews cost $3.10. At this rate, how much would 15 lb of cashews cost?

Strategy

To find the additional number of shares that are required, write and solve a proportion using x to represent the additional number of shares. Then $50 + x$ is the total number of shares of stock.

Your strategy

Solution

$$\frac{106}{50} = \frac{424}{50+x}$$

$$\frac{53}{25} = \frac{424}{50+x}$$

$$\frac{53}{25}(25)(50+x) = \frac{424}{50+x}(25)(50+x)$$

$$53(50+x) = 424(25)$$

$$2650 + 53x = 10{,}600$$

$$53x = 7950$$

$$x = 150$$

An additional 150 shares of stock are required.

Your solution

Solution on p. S20

6.4 Exercises

· ·

Objective A

Solve the proportion.

1. $\dfrac{x}{30} = \dfrac{3}{10}$

2. $\dfrac{5}{15} = \dfrac{x}{75}$

3. $\dfrac{2}{x} = \dfrac{8}{30}$

4. $\dfrac{80}{16} = \dfrac{15}{x}$

5. $\dfrac{x+1}{10} = \dfrac{2}{5}$

6. $\dfrac{5-x}{10} = \dfrac{3}{2}$

7. $\dfrac{4}{x+2} = \dfrac{3}{4}$

8. $\dfrac{8}{3} = \dfrac{24}{x+3}$

9. $\dfrac{x}{4} = \dfrac{x-2}{8}$

10. $\dfrac{8}{x-5} = \dfrac{3}{x}$

11. $\dfrac{16}{2-x} = \dfrac{4}{x}$

12. $\dfrac{6}{x-5} = \dfrac{1}{x}$

13. $\dfrac{8}{x-2} = \dfrac{4}{x+1}$

14. $\dfrac{4}{x-4} = \dfrac{2}{x-2}$

15. $\dfrac{x}{3} = \dfrac{x+1}{7}$

16. $\dfrac{x-3}{2} = \dfrac{3+x}{5}$

17. $\dfrac{8}{3x-2} = \dfrac{2}{2x+1}$

18. $\dfrac{3}{2x-4} = \dfrac{-5}{x+2}$

19. $\dfrac{3x+1}{3x-4} = \dfrac{x}{x-2}$

20. $\dfrac{x-2}{x-5} = \dfrac{2x}{2x+5}$

Objective B   *Application Problems*

21. A television commercial claims that "four out of five dentists surveyed recommended Trident gum for their patients who chew gum." At this rate, how many dentists among 8250 attending a convention would be expected to recommend Trident?

22. A movie theatre that can seat 1500 people has a parking lot with 600 spaces. At the same rate, how many parking spaces should a new theatre with 2200 seats create?

23. A team of biologists captured and tagged approximately 2400 northern squawfish at the Bonneville Dam on the Colorado River. Later, 225 squawfish were recaptured and nine of them had tags. How many squawfish would you estimate are in the area?

24. According to the Voter News Service survey conducted during the 1996 elections, of 140 voters surveyed, 21 were 18–29 years old. At this rate, how many of the 96,000,000 people who voted in the election were 18–29 years old?

25. Of 250 people who purchased home computers from a national company, 45 received machines with defective CD-ROM drives. At this rate, how many of the 2800 computers the company sold nationwide would you expect to have bad CD-ROM drives?

26. During a recent year, 3293 cars were stolen in Montgomery County, Maryland. Police were able to recover 2305 of these. At this rate, if 19,000 cars were stolen throughout the state of Maryland, how many of these would you expect to be recovered?

27. On an architectural drawing, $\frac{1}{4}$ in. represents one foot. Using this scale, find the dimensions of a room that measures $4\frac{1}{2}$ in. by 6 in. on the drawing.

28. One hundred forty-four ceramic tiles are required to tile a 25-square-foot area. At this rate, how many tiles are required to tile 275 ft²?

29. One and one-half ounces of a medication are required for a 140-pound adult. At the same rate, how many additional ounces of medication are required for 210-pound adult?

30. After working for a company for 9 months, an employee accrued 6 vacation days. At this rate, how much longer will it be before she can take a 3-week vacation (15 work days)?

31. The U.S. Postal Service handles about 3.5 billion pieces of mail during a typical week (which is normally 6 business days). At this rate, how many pieces of mail would the Postal Service handle in a year? Assume there are 300 business days during the year.

32. To raise money, a school is sponsoring a magazine subscription drive. By visiting 90 homes in the neighborhood, one student was able to sell $375 worth of subscriptions. At this rate, how many additional homes will the student have to visit in order to meet a $1000 goal?

APPLYING THE CONCEPTS

33. If $\frac{a}{b} = \frac{c}{d}$, show that $\frac{a+b}{b} = \frac{c+d}{d}$.

34. Explain in your own words how to solve a proportion.

35. Three people put their money together to buy lottery tickets. The first person put in $20, the second person put in $25, and the third person put in $30. One of the tickets was a winning ticket. If they won $4.5 million, what was the first person's share of the winnings?

36. Four people put their money together to buy lottery tickets. The first person put in $25, the second person put in $40, the third person put in $60, and the last person put in $100. One of the tickets was a winning ticket. If they won $11.25 million, what was each person's share of the winnings?

6.5 Rational Equations

Objective A   *To solve a fractional equation* ································· (25) CT

To solve an equation containing fractions, **clear denominators** by multiplying each side of the equation by the LCM of the denominators. Then solve for the variable.

After each side of a fractional equation has been multiplied by the LCM of the denominators, the resulting equation is sometimes a quadratic equation.

The solutions to the resulting equation must be checked, because multiplying each side of an equation by a variable expression may produce an equation that has a solution that is not a solution of the original equation.

➡ Solve: $\dfrac{3x}{x-5} = x + \dfrac{12}{x-5}$

$$\dfrac{3x}{x-5} = x + \dfrac{12}{x-5}$$

$$(x-5)\left(\dfrac{3x}{x-5}\right) = (x-5)\left(x + \dfrac{12}{x-5}\right)$$

- Multiply each side of the equation by the LCM of the denominators.

$$3x = (x-5)x + (x-5)\left(\dfrac{12}{x-5}\right)$$

$$3x = x^2 - 5x + 12$$

$$0 = x^2 - 8x + 12$$

- Solve the quadratic equation by factoring.

$$0 = (x-2)(x-6)$$

$$x = 2 \qquad x = 6$$

2 and 6 check as solutions.

The solutions are 2 and 6.

TAKE NOTE

If each side of an equation is multiplied by a variable expression, it is essential that the solutions be checked. As Example 1 on p. 346 shows, a proposed solution to an equation may not check when it is substituted into the original equation.

➡ Solve the literal equation $\dfrac{1}{R_1} + \dfrac{1}{R_2} = \dfrac{1}{R}$ for R.

$$\dfrac{1}{R_1} + \dfrac{1}{R_2} = \dfrac{1}{R}$$

$$RR_1R_2\left(\dfrac{1}{R_1} + \dfrac{1}{R_2}\right) = RR_1R_2\left(\dfrac{1}{R}\right)$$

- Multiply each side of the equation by the LCM of the denominators.

$$\dfrac{RR_1R_2}{R_1} + \dfrac{RR_1R_2}{R_2} = \dfrac{RR_1R_2}{R}$$

$$RR_2 + RR_1 = R_1R_2$$

$$R(R_2 + R_1) = R_1R_2$$

- Factor.

$$\dfrac{R(R_1 + R_2)}{R_1 + R_2} = \dfrac{R_1R_2}{R_1 + R_2}$$

$$R = \dfrac{R_1R_2}{R_1 + R_2}$$

This literal equation is true for all real numbers, $R_1 + R_2 \neq 0$.

Example 1 Solve: $\dfrac{3x}{x-3} = 2 + \dfrac{9}{x-3}$

Solution $\dfrac{3x}{x-3} = 2 + \dfrac{9}{x-3}$

$$(x-3)\left(\dfrac{3x}{x-3}\right) = (x-3)\left(2 + \dfrac{9}{x-3}\right)$$

$$3x = (x-3)2 + (x-3)\left(\dfrac{9}{x-3}\right)$$

$$3x = 2x - 6 + 9$$
$$3x = 2x + 3$$
$$x = 3$$

3 does not check as a solution.
The equation has no solution.

You Try It 1 Solve: $\dfrac{x}{x-2} + x = \dfrac{6}{x-2}$

Your solution

Example 2 Solve: $\dfrac{1}{a} + \dfrac{1}{a+1} = \dfrac{3}{2}$

Solution $\dfrac{1}{a} + \dfrac{1}{a+1} = \dfrac{3}{2}$

$$2a(a+1)\left(\dfrac{1}{a} + \dfrac{1}{a+1}\right) = 2a(a+1)\dfrac{3}{2}$$

$$2(a+1) + 2a = a(a+1) \cdot 3$$
$$2a + 2 + 2a = 3a^2 + 3a$$
$$0 = 3a^2 - a - 2$$
$$0 = (3a+2)(a-1)$$

$$3a + 2 = 0 \qquad a - 1 = 0$$
$$3a = -2 \qquad\quad a = 1$$
$$a = -\dfrac{2}{3}$$

$-\dfrac{2}{3}$ and 1 check as solutions.

The solutions are $-\dfrac{2}{3}$ and 1.

You Try It 2 Solve: $\dfrac{5}{x-2} = 2x + \dfrac{3x-1}{x-2}$

Your solution

Example 3 Solve for f: $\dfrac{1}{f} = \dfrac{1}{a} + \dfrac{1}{b}$

Solution $\dfrac{1}{f} = \dfrac{1}{a} + \dfrac{1}{b}$

$$fab\left(\dfrac{1}{f}\right) = fab\left(\dfrac{1}{a} + \dfrac{1}{b}\right)$$

$$\dfrac{fab}{f} = \dfrac{fab}{a} + \dfrac{fab}{b}$$
$$ab = fb + fa$$
$$ab = f(b+a)$$
$$\dfrac{ab}{b+a} = \dfrac{f(b+a)}{b+a}$$

$$\dfrac{ab}{b+a} = f$$

You Try It 3 Solve for T_1: $\dfrac{P_1 V_1}{T_1} = \dfrac{P_2 V_2}{T_2}$

Your solution

Solutions on p. S20

Objective B **To solve work problems** .... (26) CT

If a mason can build a retaining wall in 12 h, then in 1 h the mason can build $\frac{1}{12}$ of the wall. The mason's rate of work is $\frac{1}{12}$ of the wall each hour. The **rate of work** is that part of a task that is completed in one unit of time. If an apprentice can build the wall in x hours, the rate of work for the apprentice is $\frac{1}{x}$ of the wall each hour.

In solving a work problem, the goal is to determine the time it takes to complete a task. The basic equation that is used to solve work problems is

Rate of work × time worked = part of task completed

For example, if a pipe can fill a tank in 5 h, then in 2 h the pipe will fill $\frac{1}{5} \times 2 = \frac{2}{5}$ of the tank. In t hours, the pipe will fill $\frac{1}{5} \times t = \frac{t}{5}$ of the tank.

⇒ A mason can build a wall in 10 h. An apprentice can build a wall in 15 h. How long will it take to build the wall when they work together?

> **Strategy for Solving a Work Problem**
>
> 1. For each person or machine, write a numerical or variable expression for the rate of work, the time worked, and the part of the task completed. The results can be recorded in a table.

Unknown time to build the wall working together: t

	Rate of Work	·	Time Worked	=	Part of Task Completed
Mason	$\frac{1}{10}$	·	t	=	$\frac{t}{10}$
Apprentice	$\frac{1}{15}$	·	t	=	$\frac{t}{15}$

> 2. Determine how the parts of the task completed are related. Use the fact that the sum of the parts of the task completed must equal 1, the complete task.

The sum of the part of the task completed by the mason and the part of the task completed by the apprentice is 1.

$$\frac{t}{10} + \frac{t}{15} = 1$$
$$30\left(\frac{t}{10} + \frac{t}{15}\right) = 30(1)$$
$$3t + 2t = 30$$
$$5t = 30$$
$$t = 6$$

Working together, they will build the wall in 6 h.

Example 4

An electrician requires 12 h to wire a house. The electrician's apprentice can wire a house in 16 h. After working alone on one job for 4 h, the electrician quits, and the apprentice completes the task. How long does it take the apprentice to finish wiring the house?

You Try It 4

Two water pipes can fill a tank with water in 6 h. The larger pipe working alone can fill the tank in 9 h. How long will it take the smaller pipe working alone to fill the tank?

Strategy

○ Time required for the apprentice to finish wiring the house: t

	Rate	Time	Part
Electrician	$\dfrac{1}{12}$	4	$\dfrac{4}{12}$
Apprentice	$\dfrac{1}{16}$	t	$\dfrac{t}{16}$

○ The sum of the part of the task completed by the electrician and the part of the task completed by the apprentice is 1.

Your strategy

Solution

$$\frac{4}{12} + \frac{t}{16} = 1$$

$$\frac{1}{3} + \frac{t}{16} = 1$$

$$48\left(\frac{1}{3} + \frac{t}{16}\right) = 48(1)$$

$$16 + 3t = 48$$

$$3t = 32$$

$$t = \frac{32}{3}$$

It will take the apprentice $10\frac{2}{3}$ h to finish wiring the house.

Your solution

Solution on p. S20

Objective C   To solve uniform motion problems .... 《26》 CT

A car that travels constantly in a straight line at 55 mph is in uniform motion. **Uniform motion** means that the speed of an object does not change.

The basic equation used to solve uniform motion problems is

Distance = rate × time

An alternative form of this equation can be written by solving the equation for time.

$$\frac{\textbf{Distance}}{\textbf{Rate}} = \textbf{time}$$

This form of the equation is useful when the total time of travel for two objects or the time of travel between two points is known.

➡ A motorist drove 150 mi on country roads before driving 50 mi of mountain roads. The rate of speed on the country roads was three times the rate on the mountain roads. The time spent traveling the 200 mi was 5 h. Find the rate of the motorist on the country roads.

> **Strategy for Solving a Uniform Motion Problem**
>
> 1. For each object, write a numerical or variable expression for the distance, rate, and time. The results can be recorded in a table.

The unknown rate of speed on the mountain roads: r
Rate of speed on the country roads: $3r$

	Distance	÷	Rate	=	Time
Country roads	150	÷	$3r$	=	$\frac{150}{3r}$
Mountain roads	50	÷	r	=	$\frac{50}{r}$

> 2. Determine how the times traveled by each object are related. For example, it may be known that the times are equal or the total time may be known.

The total time of the trip is 5 h.

$$\frac{150}{3r} + \frac{50}{r} = 5$$
$$3r\left(\frac{150}{3r} + \frac{50}{r}\right) = 3r(5)$$
$$150 + 150 = 15r$$
$$300 = 15r$$
$$20 = r$$

The rate of speed on the country roads was $3r$.
Replace r with 20 and evaluate.

$$3r = 3(20) = 60$$

The rate of speed on the country roads was 60 mph.

Example 5

A marketing executive traveled 810 mi on a corporate jet in the same amount of time as it took to travel an additional 162 mi by helicopter. The rate of the jet was 360 mph faster than the rate of the helicopter. Find the rate of the jet.

You Try It 5

A plane can fly at a rate of 150 mph in calm air. Traveling with the wind, the plane flew 700 mi in the same amount of time as it flew 500 mi against the wind. Find the rate of the wind.

Strategy

- Rate of the helicopter: r
  Rate of the jet: $r + 360$

Your strategy

	Distance	Rate	Time
Jet	810	$r + 360$	$\dfrac{810}{r + 360}$
Helicopter	162	r	$\dfrac{162}{r}$

- The time traveled by jet is equal to the time traveled by helicopter.

Solution

$$\frac{810}{r + 360} = \frac{162}{r}$$

$$r(r + 360)\left(\frac{810}{r + 360}\right) = r(r + 360)\left(\frac{162}{r}\right)$$

$$810r = (r + 360)162$$

$$810r = 162r + 58{,}320$$

$$648r = 58{,}320$$

$$r = 90$$

$$r + 360 = 90 + 360 = 450$$

The rate of the jet was 450 mph.

Your solution

Solution on p. S21

6.5 Exercises

Objective A

Solve.

1. $\dfrac{x}{2} + \dfrac{5}{6} = \dfrac{x}{3}$

2. $\dfrac{x}{5} - \dfrac{2}{9} = \dfrac{x}{15}$

3. $\dfrac{8}{2x - 1} = 2$

4. $3 = \dfrac{18}{3x - 4}$

5. $1 - \dfrac{3}{y} = 4$

6. $7 + \dfrac{6}{y} = 5$

7. $\dfrac{3}{x - 2} = \dfrac{4}{x}$

8. $\dfrac{5}{x} = \dfrac{2}{x + 3}$

9. $\dfrac{6}{2y + 3} = \dfrac{6}{y}$

10. $\dfrac{3}{x - 4} + 2 = \dfrac{5}{x - 4}$

11. $\dfrac{5}{y + 3} - 2 = \dfrac{7}{y + 3}$

12. $5 + \dfrac{8}{a - 2} = \dfrac{4a}{a - 2}$

13. $\dfrac{-4}{a - 4} = 3 - \dfrac{a}{a - 4}$

14. $\dfrac{x}{x + 1} - x = \dfrac{-4}{x + 1}$

15. $\dfrac{2x}{x + 2} + 3x = \dfrac{-5}{x + 2}$

16. $\dfrac{x}{x - 3} + x = \dfrac{3x - 4}{x - 3}$

17. $\dfrac{x}{2x - 9} - 3x = \dfrac{10}{9 - 2x}$

18. $\dfrac{2}{4y^2 - 9} + \dfrac{1}{2y - 3} = \dfrac{3}{2y + 3}$

19. $\dfrac{5}{x - 2} - \dfrac{2}{x + 2} = \dfrac{3}{x^2 - 4}$

20. $\dfrac{5}{x^2 - 7x + 12} = \dfrac{2}{x - 3} + \dfrac{5}{x - 4}$

21. $\dfrac{9}{x^2 + 7x + 10} = \dfrac{5}{x + 2} - \dfrac{3}{x + 5}$

Solve the formula for the given variable.

22. $F = \dfrac{Gm_1m_2}{r^2}; \ m_2$ (Physics)

23. $\dfrac{P_1V_1}{T_1} = \dfrac{P_2V_2}{T_2}; \ P_2$ (Chemistry)

24. $\dfrac{1}{R} = \dfrac{1}{R_1} + \dfrac{1}{R_2}; \ R_2$ (Physics)

25. $\dfrac{1}{f} = \dfrac{1}{a} + \dfrac{1}{b}; \ b$ (Physics)

Objective B   *Application Problems*

Solve.

26. A ski resort can manufacture enough man-made snow to open its steepest run in 12 h, whereas naturally falling snow would take 36 h to provide enough snow. If the resort makes snow at the same time that it is snowing naturally, how long will it take to be able to open the run?

27. An experienced bricklayer can work twice as fast as an apprentice bricklayer. After they work together on a job for 6 h, the experienced bricklayer quits. The apprentice requires 10 more hours to finish the job. How long would it take the experienced bricklayer working alone to do the job?

28. A roofer requires 8 h to shingle a roof. After the roofer and an apprentice work on a roof for 2 h, the roofer moves on to another job. The apprentice requires 10 more hours to finish the job. How long would it take the apprentice working alone to do the job?

29. An employee is faxing a long document that will take 40 min to send on her fastest machine. After 15 min, she realizes the fax won't make her deadline and she starts sending some of the pages with a second slower fax machine. Twenty minutes later the document finishes faxing. How long would it have taken the slower machine alone to send the fax?

30. The larger of the two printers being used to print the payroll for a major corporation requires 30 min to print the payroll. After both printers have been operating for 10 min, the larger printer malfunctions. The smaller printer requires 40 more minutes to complete the payroll. How long would it take the smaller printer working alone to print the payroll?

31. Three machines are filling soda bottles. The machines can fill the daily quota of soda bottles in 10 h, 12 h, and 15 h, respectively. How long would it take to fill the daily quota of soda bottles with all three machines working?

32. A goat can eat all the grass in a farmer's field in 12 days, whereas a cow can finish it in 15 days and a horse in 20 days. How long before all the grass is eaten if all three animals are allowed to graze in the field?

33. The inlet pipe can fill a water tank in 45 min. The outlet pipe can empty the tank in 30 min. How long would it take to empty a full tank with both pipes open?

34. Three computers can print out a task in 20 min, 30 min, and 60 min, respectively. How long would it take to complete the task with all three computers working?

35. Two circus clowns are blowing up balloons, but some of the balloons are popping before they can be sold. The first clown can blow up a balloon every 2 min, the second clown requires 3 min for each balloon, and every 5 min one balloon pops. How long will it take the clowns, working together, to have 76 balloons?

36. An oil tank has two inlet pipes and one outlet pipe. One inlet pipe can fill the tank in 12 h, and the other inlet pipe can fill the tank in 20 h. The outlet pipe can empty the tank in 10 h. How long would it take to fill the tank with all three pipes open?

37. Two clerks are addressing advertising envelopes for a company. One clerk can address one envelope every 30 s, whereas it takes 40 s for the second clerk to address one envelope. How long will it take them, working together, to address 140 envelopes?

38. A single-engine airplane carries enough fuel for an 8-hour flight. After the airplane has been flying for 1 h, the fuel tank begins to leak at a rate that would empty the tank in 12 h. How long does the plane have until it will run out of fuel?

Objective C   *Application Problems*

Solve.

39. The rate of a bicyclist is 7 mph faster than the rate of a long-distance runner. The bicyclist travels 30 mi in the same amount of time as it takes the runner to travel 16 mi. Find the rate of the runner.

40. A passenger train travels 240 mi in the same amount of time as it takes a freight train to travel 168 mi. The rate of the passenger train is 18 mph faster than the rate of the freight train. Find the rate of each train.

41. A tortoise and a hare have joined a 360-foot race. Since the hare can run 180 times faster than the tortoise, it reaches the finish line 14 min and 55 s before the tortoise. How fast was each animal running?

42. A cabin cruiser travels 20 mi in the same amount of time as it takes a power boat to travel 45 mi. The rate of the cabin cruiser is 10 mph less than the rate of the power boat. Find the rate of the cabin cruiser.

43. A cyclist and a jogger start from a town at the same time and head for a destination 30 mi away. The rate of the cyclist is twice the rate of the jogger. The cyclist arrives 3 h ahead of the jogger. Find the rate of the cyclist.

44. A Porsche 911 Turbo has a top speed 20 mph faster than a Dodge Viper top speed. At top speed, the Porsche can travel 630 mi in the same amount of time that the Viper can travel 560 mi. What is the speed of each car?

45. A canoe can travel 8 mph in still water. Rowing with the current of a river, the canoe can travel 15 mi in the same amount of time as it takes to travel 9 mi against the current. Find the rate of the current.

46. A tour boat used for river excursions can travel 7 mph in calm water. The amount of time it takes to travel 20 mi with the current is the same amount of time as it takes to travel 8 mi against the current. Find the rate of the current.

47. Some military fighter planes are capable of flying at a rate of 950 mph. One of these planes flew 6150 mi with the wind in the same amount of time it took to fly 5250 mi against the wind. Find the rate of the wind.

48. A plane can fly at a rate of 175 mph in calm air. Traveling with the wind, the plane flew 615 mi in the same amount of time as it took to fly 435 mi against the wind. Find the rate of the wind.

49. A jet can travel 550 mph in calm air. Flying with the wind, the jet can travel 3059 mi in the same amount of time as it takes to fly 2450 mi against the wind. Find the rate of the wind. Round to the nearest hundredth.

50. A jet-ski can comfortably travel across calm water at 35 mph. If a rider traveled 8 mi down a river in the same amount of time it took to travel 6 mi back up the river, find the rate of the river's current.

51. A river excursion motorboat can travel 6 mph in calm water. A recent trip of going 16 mi down a river and then returning took 6 h. Find the rate of the river's current.

52. A pilot can fly a plane at 125 mph in calm air. A recent trip of 300 mi flying with the wind and 300 mi returning against the wind took 5 h. Find the rate of the wind.

APPLYING THE CONCEPTS

53. Solve for x.

   a. $\dfrac{x-2}{y} = \dfrac{x+2}{5y}$ **b.** $\dfrac{x}{x+y} = \dfrac{2x}{4y}$ **c.** $\dfrac{x-y}{x} = \dfrac{2x}{9y}$

54. The denominator of a fraction is 4 more than the numerator. If the numerator and denominator of the fraction are increased by 3, the new fraction is $\dfrac{5}{6}$. Find the original fraction.

55. Because of bad weather conditions, a bus driver reduced the usual speed along a 165-mile bus route by 5 mph. The bus arrived only 15 min later than its usual arrival time. How fast does the bus usually travel?

56. Explain the difference between dealing with the denominator in simplifying a rational expression and dealing with the denominator in solving a rational equation.

6.6 Variation

Objective A *To solve variation problems* ··· (27) CT

Direct variation is a special function that can be expressed as the equation $y = kx$, where k is a constant. The equation $y = kx$ is read "y varies directly as x" or "y is proportional to x." The constant k is called the **constant of variation** or the **constant of proportionality.**

The circumference (C) of a circle varies directly as the diameter (d). The direct variation equation is written $C = \pi d$. The constant of variation is π.

A nurse makes \$20 per hour. The total wage (w) of the nurse is directly proportional to the number of hours (h) worked. The equation of variation is $w = 20h$. The constant of proportionality is 20.

A direct variation equation can be written in the form $y = kx^n$, where n is a positive number. For example, the equation $y = kx^2$ is read "y varies directly as the square of x."

The area (A) of a circle varies directly as the square of the radius (r) of the circle. The direct variation equation is $A = \pi r^2$. The constant of variation is π.

⇒ Given that V varies directly as r and that $V = 20$ when $r = 4$, find the constant of variation and the equation of variation.

$V = kr$ • Write the basic direct variation equation.
$20 = k \cdot 4$ • Replace V and r by the given values. Then solve for k.
$5 = k$ • This is the constant of variation.
$V = 5r$ • Write the direct variation equation by substituting the value of k into the basic direct variation equation.

⇒ The tension (T) in a spring varies directly as the distance (x) it is stretched. If $T = 8$ lb when $x = 2$ in., find T when $x = 4$ in.

$T = kx$ • Write the basic direct variation equation.
$8 = k \cdot 2$ • Replace T and x by the given values.
$4 = k$ • Solve for the constant of variation.
$T = 4x$ • Write the direct variation equation.

To find T when $x = 4$ in., substitute 4 for x in the equation and solve for T.

$T = 4x$
$T = 4 \cdot 4 = 16$

The tension is 16 lb.

Inverse variation is a function that can be expressed as the equation $y = \dfrac{k}{x}$, where k is a constant. The equation $y = \dfrac{k}{x}$ is read "y varies inversely as x" or "y is inversely proportional to x."

In general, an inverse variation equation can be written $y = \dfrac{k}{x^n}$, where n is a positive number. For example, the equation $y = \dfrac{k}{x^2}$ is read "y varies inversely as the square of x."

➡ Given that P varies inversely as the square of x and that $P = 5$ when $x = 2$, find the variation constant and the equation of variation.

$P = \dfrac{k}{x^2}$ • Write the basic inverse variation equation.

$5 = \dfrac{k}{2^2}$ • Replace P and x by the given values. Then solve for k.

$5 = \dfrac{k}{4}$

$20 = k$ • This is the constant of variation.

$P = \dfrac{20}{x^2}$ • Write the inverse variation equation by substituting the value of k into the basic inverse variation equation.

➡ The length (L) of a rectangle with fixed area is inversely proportional to the width (w). If $L = 6$ ft when $w = 2$ ft, find L when $w = 3$ ft.

$L = \dfrac{k}{w}$ • Write the basic inverse variation equation.

$6 = \dfrac{k}{2}$ • Replace L and w by the given values.

$12 = k$ • Solve for the constant of variation.

$L = \dfrac{12}{w}$ • Write the inverse variation equation.

To find L when $w = 3$ ft, substitute 3 for w in the equation and solve for L.

$L = \dfrac{12}{w}$

$L = \dfrac{12}{3} = 4$

The length is 4 ft.

Joint variation is a variation in which a variable varies directly as the product of two or more other variables. A joint variation can be expressed as the equation $z = kxy$, where k is a constant. The equation $z = kxy$ is read "z varies jointly as x and y."

The area (A) of a triangle varies jointly as the base (b) and the height (h). The joint variation equation is written $A = \dfrac{1}{2}bh$. The constant of variation is $\dfrac{1}{2}$.

A **combined variation** is a variation in which two or more types of variation occur at the same time. For example, in physics, the volume (V) of a gas varies directly as the temperature (T) and inversely as the pressure (P). This combined variation is written $V = \dfrac{kT}{P}$.

➡ A ball is being twirled on the end of a string. The tension (T) in the string is directly proportional to the square of the speed (v) of the ball and inversely proportional to the length (r) of the string. If the tension is 96 lb when the length of the string is 0.5 ft and the speed is 4 ft/s, find the tension when the length of the string is 1 ft and the speed is 5 ft/s.

$$T = \frac{kv^2}{r}$$ • Write the basic combined variation equation.

$$96 = \frac{k \cdot 4^2}{0.5}$$ • Replace *T*, *v*, and *r* by the given values.

$$96 = \frac{k \cdot 16}{0.5}$$

$$96 = k \cdot 32$$ • Solve for the constant of variation.
$$3 = k$$

$$T = \frac{3v^2}{r}$$ • Write the combined variation equation.

To find T when $r = 1$ ft and $v = 5$ ft/s, substitute 1 for r and 5 for v and solve for T.

$$T = \frac{3v^2}{r} = \frac{3 \cdot 5^2}{1} = 3 \cdot 25 = 75$$

The tension is 75 lb.

Example 1

The amount (A) of medication prescribed for a person is directly related to the person's weight (W). For a 50-kilogram person, 2 ml of medication are prescribed. How many milliliters of medication are required for a person who weighs 75 kg?

Strategy

To find the required amount of medication:
• Write the basic direct variation equation, replace the variables by the given values, and solve for k.
• Write the direct variation equation, replacing k by its value. Substitute 75 for W and solve for A.

Solution

$$A = kW$$
$$2 = k \cdot 50$$
$$\frac{1}{25} = k$$

$$A = \frac{1}{25}W = \frac{1}{25} \cdot 75 = 3$$

The required amount of medication is 3 ml.

You Try It 1

The distance (s) a body falls from rest varies directly as the square of the time (t) of the fall. An object falls 64 ft in 2 s. How far will it fall in 5 s?

Your strategy

Your solution

Solution on p. S21

Example 2

A company that produces personal computers has determined that the number of computers it can sell (s) is inversely proportional to the price (P) of the computer. Two thousand computers can be sold when the price is $2500. How many computers can be sold if the price of a computer is $2000?

Strategy

To find the number of computers:

• Write the basic inverse variation equation, replace the variables by the given values, and solve for k.

• Write the inverse variation equation, replacing k by its value. Substitute 2000 for P and solve for s.

Solution
$$s = \frac{k}{P}$$

$$2000 = \frac{k}{2500}$$

$$5{,}000{,}000 = k$$

$$s = \frac{5{,}000{,}000}{P} = \frac{5{,}000{,}000}{2000} = 2500$$

At $2000 each, 2500 computers can be sold.

You Try It 2

The resistance (R) to the flow of electric current in a wire of fixed length is inversely proportional to the square of the diameter (d) of the wire. If a wire of diameter 0.01 cm has a resistance of 0.5 ohm, what is the resistance in a wire that is 0.02 cm in diameter?

Your strategy

Your solution

Example 3

The pressure (P) of a gas varies directly as the temperature (T) and inversely as the volume (V). When $T = 50°$ and $V = 275$ in³, $P = 20$ lb/in². Find the pressure of a gas when $T = 60°$ and $V = 250$ in³.

Strategy

To find the pressure:

• Write the basic combined variation equation, replace the variables by the given values, and solve for k.

• Write the combined variation equation, replacing k by its value. Substitute 60 for T and 250 for V, and solve for P.

Solution
$$P = \frac{kT}{V}$$

$$20 = \frac{k \cdot 50}{275}$$

$$110 = k$$

$$P = \frac{110T}{V} = \frac{110 \cdot 60}{250} = 26.4$$

The pressure is 26.4 lb/in².

You Try It 3

The strength (s) of a rectangular beam varies jointly as its width (W) and as the square of its depth (d) and inversely as its length (L). If the strength of a beam 2 in. wide, 12 in. deep, and 12 ft long is 1200 lb, find the strength of a beam 4 in. wide, 8 in. deep, and 16 ft long.

Your strategy

Your solution

Solutions on p. S21

6.6 Exercises

Objective A   *Application Problems*

1. The profit (P) realized by a company varies directly as the number of products it sells (s). If a company makes a profit of $4000 on the sale of 250 products, what is the profit when the company sells 5000 products?

2. The income (I) of a computer analyst varies directly as the number of hours (h) worked. If the analyst earns $256 for working 8 h, how much will the analyst earn by working 36 h?

3. The pressure (p) on a diver in the water varies directly as the depth (d). If the pressure is 4.5 lb/in² when the depth is 10 ft, what is the pressure when the depth is 15 ft?

4. The distance (d) a spring will stretch varies directly as the force (f) applied to the spring. If a force of 6 lb is required to stretch a spring 3 in., what force is required to stretch the spring 4 in.?

5. The distance (d) an object will fall is directly proportional to the square of the time (t) of the fall. If an object falls 144 ft in 3 s, how far will the object fall in 10 s?

6. The period (p) of a pendulum, or the time it takes the pendulum to make one complete swing, varies directly as the square root of the length (L) of the pendulum. If the period of a pendulum is 1.5 s when the length is 2 ft, find the period when the length is 5 ft. Round to the nearest hundredth.

7. The distance (s) a ball will roll down an inclined plane is directly proportional to the square of the time (t). If the ball rolls 6 ft in 1 s, how far will it roll in 3 s?

8. The stopping distance (s) of a car varies directly as the square of its speed (v). If a car traveling 30 mph requires 63 ft to stop, find the stopping distance for a car traveling 55 mph.

9. The length (L) of a rectangle of fixed area varies inversely as the width (w). If the length of a rectangle is 8 ft when the width is 5 ft, find the length of the rectangle when the width is 4 ft.

10. The time (t) for a car to travel between two cities is inversely proportional to the rate (r) of travel. If it takes 5 h to travel between the cities at a rate of 55 mph, find the time to travel between the two cities at a rate of 65 mph. Round to the nearest tenth.

11. The speed (v) of a gear varies inversely as the number of teeth (t). If a gear that has 45 teeth makes 24 revolutions per minute, how many revolutions per minute will a gear that has 36 teeth make?

12. The pressure (p) in a liquid varies directly as the product of the depth (d) and the density (D) of the liquid. If the pressure is 150 lb/in^2 when the depth is 100 in. and the density is 1.2, find the pressure when the density remains the same and the depth is 75 in.

13. The current (l) in a wire varies directly as the voltage (v) and inversely as the resistance (r). If the current is 10 amps when the voltage is 110 volts and the resistance is 11 ohms, find the current when the voltage is 180 volts and the resistance is 24 ohms.

14. The repulsive force (f) between the north poles of two magnets is inversely proportional to the square of the distance (d) between them. If the repulsive force is 20 lb when the distance is 4 in., find the repulsive force when the distance is 2 in.

15. The intensity (l) of a light source is inversely proportional to the square of the distance (d) from the source. If the intensity is 12 foot-candles at a distance of 10 ft, what is the intensity when the distance is 5 ft?

APPLYING THE CONCEPTS

16. In the inverse variation equation $y = \dfrac{k}{x}$, what is the effect on x if y doubles?

17. In the direct variation equation $y = kx$, what is the effect on y when x doubles?

Complete using the word *directly* or *inversely*.

18. If a varies directly as b and inversely as c, then c varies _____ as b and _____ as a.

19. If a varies _____ as b and c, then abc is constant.

20. If the length of a rectangle is held constant, the area of the rectangle varies _____ as the width.

21. If the area of a rectangle is held constant, the length of the rectangle varies _____ as the width.

Focus on Problem Solving

Implication Sentences that are constructed using "If..., then..." occur frequently in problem-solving situations. These sentences are called **implications.** The sentence "If it rains, then I will stay home" is an implication. The phrase *it rains* is called the **antecedent** of the implication. The phrase *I will stay home* is the **consequent** of the implication.

The sentence "If $x = 4$, then $x^2 = 16$" is a true sentence. The **contrapositive** of an implication is formed by switching the antecedent and the consequent and then negating each one. The contrapositive of "If $x = 4$, then $x^2 = 16$" is "If $x^2 \neq 16$, then $x \neq 4$." This sentence is also true. It is a principle of logic that an implication and its contrapositive are either both true or both false.

The **converse** of an implication is formed by switching the antecedent and the consequent. The converse of "If $x = 4$, then $x^2 = 16$" is "If $x^2 = 16$, then $x = 4$." Note that the converse is not a true statement, because if $x^2 = 16$, then x could equal -4. The converse of an implication may or may not be true.

Those statements for which the implication and the converse are both true are very important. They can be stated in the form "x if and only if y." For instance, a number is divisible by 5 if and only if the last digit of the number is 0 or 5. The implication "If a number is divisible by 5, then it ends in 0 or 5" and the converse "If a number ends in 0 or 5, then it is divisible by 5" are both true.

For each of the following, state the contrapositive and the converse of the implication. If the converse and the implication are both true statements, write a sentence using the phrase "if and only if."

1. If a number is divisible by 8, then it is divisible by 4.

2. If $4z = 20$, then $z = 5$.

3. If p is a prime number greater than 2, then p is an odd number.

4. If x is a rational number, then $x = \frac{a}{b}$, where a and b are integers and $b \neq 0$.

5. If $\sqrt{x} = a$, then $a^2 = x$.

6. If the equation of a graph is $y = mx + b$, then the graph of the equation is a straight line.

7. If $a = 0$ or $b = 0$, then $ab = 0$.

8. If the coordinates of a point are $(5, 0)$, then the point is on the x-axis.

9. If a quadrilateral is a square, then the quadrilateral has four sides of equal length.

Projects and Group Activities

Continued Fractions

The following complex fraction is called a **continued fraction.**

$$1 + \cfrac{1}{1 + \cfrac{1}{1 + \cfrac{1}{1 + \cfrac{1}{1 + \cdots}}}}$$

The dots indicate that the pattern continues to repeat forever.

A **convergent** for a continued fraction is an approximation of the repeated pattern. For instance,

$$c_2 = 1 + \cfrac{1}{1 + \cfrac{1}{1 + 1}} \qquad c_3 = 1 + \cfrac{1}{1 + \cfrac{1}{1 + \cfrac{1}{1 + 1}}} \qquad c_4 = 1 + \cfrac{1}{1 + \cfrac{1}{1 + \cfrac{1}{1 + \cfrac{1}{1 + 1}}}}$$

1. Calculate c_5 for the continued fraction above.

This particular continued fraction is related to the golden rectangle, which has been used in architectural designs as diverse as the Parthenon in Athens, built around 440 B.C., and the United Nations building. A golden rectangle is one for which

$$\frac{\text{length}}{\text{width}} = \frac{\text{length} + \text{width}}{\text{length}}$$

An example of a golden rectangle is shown at the right.

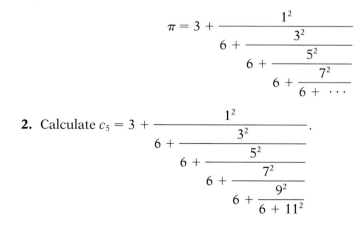

Here is another continued fraction that was discovered by Leonhard Euler (1707–1793). Calculating the convergents of this continued fraction yields approximations that are closer and closer to π.

$$\pi = 3 + \cfrac{1^2}{6 + \cfrac{3^2}{6 + \cfrac{5^2}{6 + \cfrac{7^2}{6 + \cdots}}}}$$

2. Calculate $c_5 = 3 + \cfrac{1^2}{6 + \cfrac{3^2}{6 + \cfrac{5^2}{6 + \cfrac{7^2}{6 + \cfrac{9^2}{6 + 11^2}}}}}$.

Graphing Rational Expressions

The domain of a function is the set of the first coordinates of all the ordered pairs of the function. When a function is given by an equation, the domain of the function is all real numbers for which the function evaluates to a real number. For rational functions, we must exclude from the domain all those values of the variable for which the denominator of the rational function is zero. The graphing calculator is a useful tool to show the graphs of functions with excluded values in the domain of the function.

$f(x) = \dfrac{2x - 6}{x^2 - 3x - 4}$

The domain is
$\{x \mid x \neq -1, x \neq 4\}$.

The graph of the function $f(x) = \dfrac{2x - 6}{x^2 - 3x - 4}$ is shown at the left. Note that the graph never intersects the lines $x = -1$ and $x = 4$ (shown as dashed lines). These are the two values excluded from the domain of f. The graph of the function f gets closer to the dashed line $x = 4$ as x gets closer to 4. The graph of the function f also gets closer to $x = -1$ as x gets closer to -1. The lines that are "approached" by the function are called **asymptotes.**

$f(x) = \dfrac{3x + 2}{x^2 + 1}$

The domain is
$\{x \mid x \in \text{real numbers}\}$.

The graph of the function $f(x) = \dfrac{3x + 2}{x^2 + 1}$ is shown at the left. The domain must exclude values of x for which $x^2 + 1 = 0$. It is not possible that $x^2 + 1 = 0$, because $x^2 \geq 0$, and a positive number added to a number equal to or greater than zero cannot equal zero. Therefore, there are no real numbers that must be excluded from the domain of f.

Exercises 11–22 in Section 6.1 ask you to find the domains of rational functions by algebraic means. Try these exercises again, this time using a graphing calculator.

Graphing Variation Expressions

1. Graph $y = kx$ when $k = 2$.
   What kind of function does the graph represent?

2. Graph $y = kx$ when $k = \dfrac{1}{2}$.
   What kind of function does the graph represent?

3. Graph $y = \dfrac{k}{x}$ when $k = 2$ and $x > 0$.
   Is this the graph of a function?

Chapter Summary

Key Words A fraction in which the numerator and denominator are polynomials is called a *rational expression*.

A rational expression is in *simplest form* when the numerator and denominator have no common factors.

The *least common multiple* (LCM) of two or more polynomials is the simplest polynomial that contains the factors of each polynomial.

The *reciprocal* of a rational expression is the rational expression with the numerator and denominator interchanged.

A *complex fraction* is a fraction whose numerator or denominator contains one or more fractions.

A *ratio* is the quotient of two quantities that have the same unit.

A *rate* is the quotient of two quantities that have different units.

A *proportion* is an equation that states the equality of two ratios or rates.

Direct variation is a special function that can be expressed as the equation $y = kx$, where k is a constant called the *constant of variation* or the *constant of proportionality*.

Inverse variation is a function that can be expressed as the equation $y = \dfrac{k}{x}$, where k is a constant.

Joint variation is a variation in which a variable varies directly as the product of two or more variables. A joint variation can be expressed as the equation $z = kxy$, where k is a constant.

Combined variation is a variation in which two or more types of variation occur at the same time.

Essential Rules

To Multiply Fractions: $\dfrac{a}{b} \cdot \dfrac{c}{d} = \dfrac{ac}{bd}$

To Divide Fractions: $\dfrac{a}{b} \div \dfrac{c}{d} = \dfrac{a}{b} \cdot \dfrac{d}{c}$

To Add Fractions: $\dfrac{a}{c} + \dfrac{b}{c} = \dfrac{a + b}{c}$

To Subtract Fractions: $\dfrac{a}{c} - \dfrac{b}{c} = \dfrac{a - b}{c}$

Equation for Work Problems: $\begin{array}{c}\text{Rate of} \\ \text{work}\end{array} \times \text{time worked} = \begin{array}{c}\text{part of task} \\ \text{completed}\end{array}$

Uniform Motion Equation: Distance = rate × time

Chapter Review

1. Simplify: $\dfrac{a^6b^4 + a^4b^6}{a^5b^4 - a^4b^4} \cdot \dfrac{a^2 - b^2}{a^4 - b^4}$

2. Simplify: $\dfrac{x}{x - 3} - 4 - \dfrac{2x - 5}{x + 2}$

3. Given $P(x) = \dfrac{x}{x - 3}$, find $P(4)$.

4. Solve: $\dfrac{3x - 2}{x + 6} = \dfrac{3x + 1}{x + 9}$

5. Simplify: $\dfrac{\dfrac{3x + 4}{3x - 4} + \dfrac{3x - 4}{3x + 4}}{\dfrac{3x - 4}{3x + 4} - \dfrac{3x + 4}{3x - 4}}$

6. Write each fraction in terms of the LCM of the denominators.

$$\frac{4x}{4x - 1}, \frac{3x - 1}{4x + 1}$$

7. Solve $S = \dfrac{a}{1 - r}$ for r.

8. Given $P(x) = \dfrac{x^2 - 2}{3x^2 - 2x + 5}$, find $P(-2)$.

9. Solve: $\dfrac{10}{5x + 3} = \dfrac{2}{10x - 3}$

10. Determine the domain of $f(x) = \dfrac{2x - 7}{3x^2 + 3x - 18}$.

11. Simplify: $\dfrac{3x^4 + 11x^2 - 4}{3x^4 + 13x^2 + 4}$

12. Determine the domain of $g(x) = \dfrac{2x}{x - 3}$.

13. Simplify: $\dfrac{x^3 - 8}{x^3 + 2x^2 + 4x} \cdot \dfrac{x^3 + 2x^2}{x^2 - 4}$

14. Simplify: $\dfrac{3x^2 + 2}{x^2 - 4} - \dfrac{9x - x^2}{x^2 - 4}$

15. Solve $Q = \dfrac{N - S}{N}$ for N.

16. Solve: $\dfrac{30}{x^2 + 5x + 4} + \dfrac{10}{x + 4} = \dfrac{4}{x + 1}$

17. Simplify: $x + \dfrac{\dfrac{4}{x} - 1}{\dfrac{1}{x} - \dfrac{3}{x^2}}$

18. Write each fraction in terms of the LCM of the denominators.

$$\dfrac{x - 3}{x - 5}, \dfrac{x}{x^2 - 9x + 20}, \dfrac{1}{4 - x}$$

19. Solve: $\dfrac{6}{2x - 3} = \dfrac{5}{x + 5} + \dfrac{5}{2x^2 + 7x - 15}$

20. Simplify: $\dfrac{x^{n+1} + x}{x^{2n} - 1} \div \dfrac{x^{n+2} - x^2}{x^{2n} - 2x^n + 1}$

21. Simplify: $\dfrac{27x^3 - 8}{9x^3 + 6x^2 + 4x} \div \dfrac{9x^2 - 12x + 4}{9x^2 - 4}$

22. Simplify: $\dfrac{6x}{3x^2 - 7x + 2} - \dfrac{2}{3x - 1} + \dfrac{3x}{x - 2}$

23. Simplify: $\dfrac{x^3 - 27}{x^2 - 9}$

24. Simplify: $\dfrac{5}{3a^2b^3} + \dfrac{7}{8ab^4}$

25. A helicopter travels 9 mi in the same amount of time that it takes an airplane to travel 10 mi. The rate of the airplane is 20 mph faster than the rate of the helicopter. Find the rate of the helicopter.

26. A student reads 2 pages of text in 5 min. At the same rate, how long will it take to read 150 pages?

27. The current (I) in an electric circuit varies inversely as the resistance (R). If the current in the circuit is 4 amps when the resistance is 50 ohms, find the current in the circuit when the resistance is 100 ohms.

28. On a certain map, 2.5 in. represents 10 mi. How many miles would be represented by 12 in.?

29. The stopping distance (s) of a car varies directly as the square of the speed (v) of the car. For a car traveling at 50 mph, the stopping distance is 170 ft. Find the stopping distance of a car that is traveling at 30 mph.

30. An electrician requires 65 min to install a ceiling fan. The electrician and an apprentice working together take 40 min to install the fan. How long would it take the apprentice working alone to install the ceiling fan?

Chapter Test

1. Solve the proportion: $\dfrac{3}{x+1} = \dfrac{2}{x}$

2. Simplify: $\dfrac{x^2 + x - 6}{x^2 + 7x + 12} \div \dfrac{x^2 - 3x + 2}{x^2 + 6x + 8}$

3. Simplify: $\dfrac{2x - 1}{x + 2} - \dfrac{x}{x - 3}$

4. Write each fraction in terms of the LCM of the denominators.

$\dfrac{x + 1}{x^2 + x - 6}, \dfrac{2x}{x^2 - 9}$

5. Solve: $\dfrac{4x}{2x - 1} = 2 - \dfrac{1}{2x - 1}$

6. Simplify: $\dfrac{v^3 - 4v}{2v^2 - 5v + 2}$

7. Simplify: $\dfrac{3x^2 - 12}{5x - 15} \cdot \dfrac{2x^2 - 18}{x^2 + 5x + 6}$

8. Determine the domain of $f(x) = \dfrac{3x^2 - x + 1}{x^2 - 9}$.

9. Simplify: $\dfrac{1 - \dfrac{1}{x} - \dfrac{12}{x^2}}{1 + \dfrac{6}{x} + \dfrac{9}{x^2}}$

10. Simplify: $\dfrac{1 - \dfrac{1}{x + 2}}{1 - \dfrac{3}{x + 4}}$

11. Simplify: $\dfrac{2x^2 - x - 3}{2x^2 - 5x + 3} \div \dfrac{3x^2 - x - 4}{x^2 - 1}$

12. Solve: $\dfrac{4x}{x + 1} - x = \dfrac{2}{x + 1}$

13. Simplify: $\dfrac{2a^2 - 8a + 8}{4 + 4a - 3a^2}$

14. Solve $\dfrac{1}{r} = \dfrac{1}{2} - \dfrac{2}{t}$ for t.

15. Given $f(x) = \dfrac{3 - x^2}{x^3 - 2x^2 + 4}$, find $f(-1)$.

16. Simplify: $\dfrac{x + 2}{x^2 + 3x - 4} - \dfrac{2x}{x^2 - 1}$

17. A cyclist travels 20 mi in the same amount of time as it takes a hiker to walk 6 mi. The rate of the cyclist is 7 mph faster than the rate of the hiker. Find the rate of the cyclist.

18. The electrical resistance (r) of a cable varies directly as its length (l) and inversely as the square of its diameter (d). If a cable 16,000 ft long and $\frac{1}{4}$ in. in diameter has a resistance of 3.2 ohms, what is the resistance of a cable that is 8000 ft long and $\frac{1}{2}$ in. in diameter?

19. An interior designer uses 2 rolls of wallpaper for every 45 ft² of wall space in an office. At this rate, how many rolls of wallpaper are needed for an office that has 315 ft² of wall space?

20. One landscaper can till the soil for a lawn in 30 min, whereas it takes a second landscaper 15 min to do the same job. How long would it take to till the soil for the lawn with both landscapers working together?

Cumulative Review

1. Simplify: $8 - 4[-3 - (-2)]^2 \div 5$

2. Solve: $\dfrac{2x - 3}{6} - \dfrac{x}{9} = \dfrac{x - 4}{3}$

3. Solve: $5 - |x - 4| = 2$

4. Find the domain of $\dfrac{x}{x - 3}$.

5. Given $P(x) = \dfrac{x - 1}{2x - 3}$, find $P(-2)$.

6. Write 0.000000035 in scientific notation.

7. Simplify: $\dfrac{(2a^{-2}b^3)^{-2}}{(4a)^{-1}}$

8. Solve: $x - 3(1 - 2x) \ge 1 - 4(2 - 2x)$

9. Simplify: $(2a^2 - 3a + 1)(-2a^2)$

10. Factor: $2x^{2n} + 3x^n - 2$

11. Factor: $x^3y^3 - 27$

12. Simplify: $\dfrac{x^4 + x^3y - 6x^2y^2}{x^3 - 2x^2y}$

13. Find the equation of the line that contains the point $(-2, -1)$ and is parallel to the line $3x - 2y = 6$.

14. Solve: $8x^2 - 6x - 9 = 0$

15. Simplify: $\dfrac{4x^3 + 2x^2 - 10x + 1}{x - 2}$

16. Simplify: $\dfrac{16x^2 - 9y^2}{16x^2y - 12xy^2} \div \dfrac{4x^2 - xy - 3y^2}{12x^2y^2}$

17. Write each fraction in terms of the LCM of the denominators. $\dfrac{xy}{2x^2 + 2x}, \dfrac{2}{2x^4 - 2x^3 - 4x^2}$

18. Simplify: $\dfrac{5x}{3x^2 - x - 2} - \dfrac{2x}{x^2 - 1}$

19. Graph $-3x + 5y = -15$ by using the x- and y-intercepts.

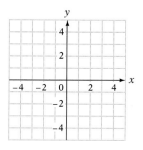

20. Graph the solution set: $\quad x + y \le 3$
    $-2x + y > 4$

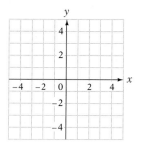

21. Evaluate the determinant:

$$\begin{vmatrix} 6 & 5 \\ 2 & -3 \end{vmatrix}$$

22. Simplify: $\dfrac{x - 4 + \dfrac{5}{x + 2}}{x + 2 - \dfrac{1}{x + 2}}$

23. Solve:
$$\begin{aligned} x + y + z &= 3 \\ -2x + y + 3z &= 2 \\ 2x - 4y + z &= -1 \end{aligned}$$

24. Solve: $|3x - 2| > 4$

25. Solve the proportion: $\dfrac{2}{x - 3} = \dfrac{5}{2x - 3}$

26. Solve: $\dfrac{3}{x^2 - 36} = \dfrac{2}{x - 6} - \dfrac{5}{x + 6}$

27. Solve $I = \dfrac{E}{R + r}$ for r.

28. Simplify: $(1 - x^{-1})^{-1}$

29. The sum of two integers is fifteen. Five times the smaller integer is five more than twice the larger integer. Find the integers.

30. How many pounds of almonds that cost $5.40 per pound must be mixed with 50 lb of peanuts that cost $2.60 per pound to make a mixture that costs $4.00 per pound?

31. A pre-election survey showed that three out of five voters would vote in an election. At this rate, how many people would be expected to vote in a city of 125,000?

32. A new computer can work six times faster than an older computer. Working together, the computers can complete a job in 12 min. How long would it take the new computer working alone to do the job?

33. A plane can fly at a rate of 300 mph in calm air. Traveling with the wind, the plane flew 900 mi in the same amount of time as it took to fly 600 mi against the wind. Find the rate of the wind.

34. Two people start from the same point on a circular exercise track that is 0.25 mi in circumference. The first person walks at 3 mph, and the second person jogs at 5 mph. After 1 h, how far apart (along the track) are the two people?

CHAPTER

Exponents and Radicals

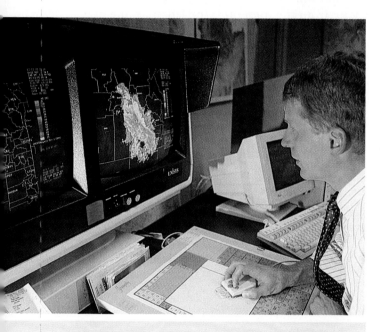

Meteorologists use data such as air pressure, temperature, humidity, and wind velocity to predict the weather. Today meteorologists are aided by computers and weather satellites. For example, weather satellites can measure the diameter of a storm. Then a meteorologist can use the formula $t = \left(\dfrac{d}{2}\right)^{3/2}$, where d is the diameter of a storm in miles, to approximate t, the duration of the storm in hours. The expression $t = \left(\dfrac{d}{2}\right)^{3/2}$ is an exponential expression with a rational exponent.

Objectives

Section 7.1
To simplify expressions with rational exponents
To write exponential expressions as radical expressions and to write radical expressions as exponential expressions
To simplify expressions of the form $\sqrt[n]{a^n}$

Section 7.2
To simplify radical expressions
To add or subtract radical expressions
To multiply radical expressions
To divide radical expressions

Section 7.3
To simplify a complex number
To add or subtract complex numbers
To multiply complex numbers
To divide complex numbers

Section 7.4
To solve a radical equation
To solve application problems

Golden Rectangle

The golden rectangle fascinated the early Greeks and appeared in much of their architecture. They considered this particular rectangle the most pleasing to the eye and believed that when it was used in the design of a building, it would make the structure pleasant to see.

The golden rectangle is constructed from a square by drawing a line from the midpoint of the base of the square to the opposite vertex. Now extend the base of the square, starting from the midpoint, the length of the line. The resulting rectangle is called the golden rectangle.

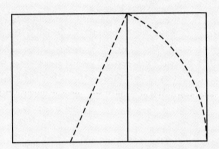

The Parthenon in Athens, Greece, is the classic example of the use of the golden rectangle in Greek architecture. A rendering of the Parthenon is shown here.

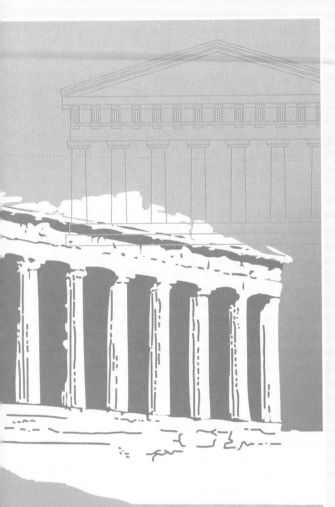

7.1 Rational Exponents and Radical Expressions

Objective A   *To simplify expressions with rational exponents* .... (28) (29) CT

In this section, the definition of an exponent is extended beyond integers so that any rational number can be used as an exponent. The definition is expressed in such a way that the Rules of Exponents hold true for rational exponents.

Consider the expression $(a^{1/n})^n$ for $a > 0$ and n a positive integer. Now simplify, assuming that the Power Rule of Exponents is true.

$$(a^{1/n})^n = a^{\frac{1}{n} \cdot n} = a^1 = a$$

Because $(a^{1/n})^n = a$, the number $a^{1/n}$ is the number whose nth power is a.

If $a > 0$ and n is a positive number, then $a^{1/n}$ is called the nth root of a.

$25^{1/2} = 5$ because $(5)^2 = 25$. $8^{1/3} = 2$ because $(2)^3 = 8$.

In the expression $a^{1/n}$, if a is a negative number and n is a positive even integer, then $a^{1/n}$ is not a real number.

$(-4)^{1/2}$ is not a real number, because there is no real number whose second power is -4.

When n is a positive odd integer, a can be a positive or a negative number.

$(-27)^{1/3} = -3$ because $(-3)^3 = -27$.

Using the definition of $a^{1/n}$ and the Rules of Exponents, it is possible to define any exponential expression that contains a rational exponent.

> **Rule for Rational Exponents**
> If m and n are positive integers and $a^{1/n}$ is a real number, then
> $$a^{m/n} = (a^{1/n})^m$$

The expression $a^{m/n}$ can also be written $a^{m/n} = a^{m \cdot \frac{1}{n}} = (a^m)^{1/n}$.

As shown above, expressions that contain rational exponents do not always represent real numbers when the base of the exponential expression is a negative number. For this reason, all variables in this chapter represent positive numbers unless otherwise stated.

➡ Simplify: $27^{2/3}$

$27^{2/3} = (3^3)^{2/3}$ • Rewrite 27 as 3^3.

        $= 3^{3(2/3)}$ • Multiply the exponents.

        $= 3^2$ • Simplify.

        $= 9$

TAKE NOTE

Note that $32^{-2/5} = \frac{1}{4}$, a positive number. The negative exponent does not affect the sign of a number.

➡ Simplify: $32^{-2/5}$

$32^{-2/5} = (2^5)^{-2/5}$ • Rewrite 32 as 2^5.

        $= 2^{-2}$ • Multiply the exponents.

        $= \dfrac{1}{2^2}$ • Use the Rule of Negative Exponents.

        $= \dfrac{1}{4}$ • Simplify.

➡ Simplify: $a^{1/2} \cdot a^{2/3} \cdot a^{-1/4}$

$a^{1/2} \cdot a^{2/3} \cdot a^{-1/4} = a^{1/2 + 2/3 - 1/4}$ • Use the Rule for Multiplying Exponential Expressions.

              $= a^{6/12 + 8/12 - 3/12}$

              $= a^{11/12}$ • Simplify.

➡ Simplify: $(x^6 y^4)^{3/2}$

$(x^6 y^4)^{3/2} = x^{6(3/2)} y^{4(3/2)}$ • Use the Rule for Simplifying Powers of Products.

          $= x^9 y^6$ • Simplify.

➡ Simplify: $\left(\dfrac{8a^3 b^{-4}}{64a^{-9} b^2}\right)^{2/3}$

$\left(\dfrac{8a^3 b^{-4}}{64a^{-9} b^2}\right)^{2/3} = \left(\dfrac{2^3 a^3 b^{-4}}{2^6 a^{-9} b^2}\right)^{2/3}$ • Rewrite 8 as 2^3 and 64 as 2^6.

             $= (2^{-3} a^{12} b^{-6})^{2/3}$ • Use the Rule for Dividing Exponential Expressions.

             $= 2^{-2} a^8 b^{-4}$ • Use the Rule for Simplifying Powers of Products.

             $= \dfrac{a^8}{2^2 b^4} = \dfrac{a^8}{4b^4}$ • Use the Rule of Negative Exponents and simplify.

Example 1 Simplify: $64^{-2/3}$

Solution $64^{-2/3} = (2^6)^{-2/3} = 2^{-4}$
$$= \frac{1}{2^4} = \frac{1}{16}$$

You Try It 1 Simplify: $16^{-3/4}$

Your solution

Example 2 Simplify: $(-49)^{3/2}$

Solution The base of the exponential expression is a negative number, while the denominator of the exponent is a positive even number.

Therefore, $(-49)^{3/2}$ is not a real number.

You Try It 2 Simplify: $(-81)^{3/4}$

Your solution

Example 3 Simplify: $(x^{1/2}y^{-3/2}z^{1/4})^{-3/2}$

Solution $(x^{1/2}y^{-3/2}z^{1/4})^{-3/2}$
$$= x^{-3/4}y^{9/4}z^{-3/8}$$
$$= \frac{y^{9/4}}{x^{3/4}z^{3/8}}$$

You Try It 3 Simplify: $(x^{3/4}y^{1/2}z^{-2/3})^{-4/3}$

Your solution

Example 4 Simplify: $\dfrac{x^{1/2}y^{-5/4}}{x^{-4/3}y^{1/3}}$

Solution $\dfrac{x^{1/2}y^{-5/4}}{x^{-4/3}y^{1/3}}$
$$= x^{3/6-(-8/6)}y^{-15/12-4/12}$$
$$= x^{11/6}y^{-19/12} = \frac{x^{11/6}}{y^{19/12}}$$

You Try It 4 Simplify: $\left(\dfrac{16a^{-2}b^{4/3}}{9a^4b^{-2/3}}\right)^{-1/2}$

Your solution

Solutions on p. S22

Objective B *To write exponential expressions as radical expressions and to write radical expressions as exponential expressions* .... 《28》 《29》 CT

Recall that $a^{1/n}$ is the nth root of a. The expression $\sqrt[n]{a}$ is another symbol for the nth root of a.

If a is a real number, then $a^{1/n} = \sqrt[n]{a}$.

In the expression $\sqrt[n]{a}$, the symbol $\sqrt{}$ is called a **radical**, n is the **index** of the radical, and a is the **radicand**. When $n = 2$, the radical expression represents a square root and the index 2 is usually not written.

An exponential expression with a rational exponent can be written as a radical expression.

> **Rule for Writing Exponential Expressions as Radical Expressions**
>
> If $a^{1/n}$ is a real number, then $a^{m/n} = a^{m \cdot 1/n} = (a^m)^{1/n} = \sqrt[n]{a^m}$.

The expression $a^{m/n}$ can also be written $a^{m/n} = (a^{1/n})^m = (\sqrt[n]{a})^m$.

The exponential expression at the right has been written as a radical expression.

$$y^{2/3} = (y^2)^{1/3}$$
$$= \sqrt[3]{y^2}$$

The radical expressions at the right have been written as exponential expressions.

$$\sqrt[5]{x^6} = (x^6)^{1/5} = x^{6/5}$$
$$\sqrt{17} = (17)^{1/2} = 17^{1/2}$$

➡ Write $(5x)^{2/5}$ as a radical expression.

$(5x)^{2/5} = \sqrt[5]{(5x)^2}$
   • The denominator of the rational exponent is the index of the radical. The numerator is the power of the radicand.

$= \sqrt[5]{25x^2}$
   • Simplify.

➡ Write $\sqrt[3]{x^4}$ as an exponential expression with a rational exponent.

$\sqrt[3]{x^4} = (x^4)^{1/3}$
   • The index of the radical is the denominator of the rational exponent. The power of the radicand is the numerator of the rational exponent.

$= x^{4/3}$
   • Simplify.

➡ Write $\sqrt[3]{a^3 + b^3}$ as an exponential expression with a rational exponent.

$\sqrt[3]{a^3 + b^3} = (a^3 + b^3)^{1/3}$

Note that $(a^3 + b^3)^{1/3} \neq a + b$.

Example 5 Write $(3x)^{5/4}$ as a radical expression.

Solution $(3x)^{5/4} = \sqrt[4]{(3x)^5} = \sqrt[4]{243x^5}$

You Try It 5 Write $(2x^3)^{3/4}$ as a radical expression.

Your solution

Example 6 Write $-2x^{2/3}$ as a radical expression.

Solution $-2x^{2/3} = -2(x^2)^{1/3} = -2\sqrt[3]{x^2}$

You Try It 6 Write $-5a^{5/6}$ as a radical expression.

Your solution

Example 7 Write $\sqrt[4]{3a}$ as an exponential expression.

Solution $\sqrt[4]{3a} = (3a)^{1/4}$

You Try It 7 Write $\sqrt[3]{3ab}$ as an exponential expression.

Your solution

Example 8 Write $\sqrt{a^2 - b^2}$ as an exponential expression.

Solution $\sqrt{a^2 - b^2} = (a^2 - b^2)^{1/2}$

You Try It 8 Write $\sqrt[4]{x^4 + y^4}$ as an exponential expression.

Your solution

Solutions on p. S22

Objective C **To simplify expressions of the form** $\sqrt[n]{a^n}$ .... 〔28〕 〔29〕 ⬚CT

Every positive number has two square roots, one a positive and one a negative number. For example, because $(5)^2 = 25$ and $(-5)^2 = 25$, there are two square roots of 25: 5 and -5.

The symbol $\sqrt{}$ is used to indicate the positive or **principal square root.** To indicate the negative square root of a number, a negative sign is placed in front of the radical.

$$\sqrt{25} = 5$$

$$-\sqrt{25} = -5$$

The square root of zero is zero.

$$\sqrt{0} = 0$$

The square root of a negative number is not a real number, because the square of a real number must be positive.

$\sqrt{-25}$ is not a real number.

Note that

$$\sqrt{(-5)^2} = \sqrt{25} = 5 \quad \text{and} \quad \sqrt{5^2} = \sqrt{25} = 5$$

This is true for all real numbers and stated as the following result.

For any real number a, $\sqrt{a^2} = |a|$ and $-\sqrt{a^2} = -|a|$. If a is a positive real number, then $\sqrt{a^2} = a$ and $(\sqrt{a})^2 = a$.

Besides square roots, we can also determine cube roots, fourth roots, and so on.

$\sqrt[3]{8} = 2$, because $2^3 = 8$.

• The cube root of a positive number is positive.

$\sqrt[3]{-8} = -2$, because $(-2)^3 = -8$.

• The cube root of a negative number is negative.

$\sqrt[4]{625} = 5$, because $5^4 = 625$.

$\sqrt[5]{243} = 3$, because $3^5 = 243$.

The following properties hold true for finding the nth root of a real number.

If n is an even integer, then $\sqrt[n]{a^n} = |a|$ and $-\sqrt[n]{a^n} = -|a|$. If n is an odd integer, then $\sqrt[n]{a^n} = a$.

For example,

$$\sqrt[6]{y^6} = |y| \qquad -\sqrt[12]{x^{12}} = -|x| \qquad \sqrt[5]{b^5} = b$$

We have agreed that all variables in this chapter represent positive numbers unless otherwise stated, so it is not necessary to use the absolute value signs.

TAKE NOTE

Note that when the index is an even natural number, the nth root requires absolute value symbols.

$\sqrt[6]{y^6} = |y|$ but $\sqrt[5]{y^5} = y$

Because we stated that variables within radicals represent *positive* numbers, we will omit the absolute value symbols when writing an answer.

➡ Simplify: $\sqrt[3]{64}$

$\sqrt[3]{64} = \sqrt[3]{2^6}$
$= (2^6)^{1/3}$
$= 2^2 = 4$

- Write the prime factorization of the radicand in simplest form.
- Write the radical expression as an exponential expression.
- Use the Rule for Simplifying the Power of an Exponential Expression.

➡ Simplify: $\sqrt[4]{x^4 y^8}$

The radicand is a perfect fourth power because the exponents on the variables are divisible by 4.

$\sqrt[4]{x^4 y^8} = (x^4 y^8)^{1/4}$

$= xy^2$

- Write the radical expression as an exponential expression.
- Use the Rule for Simplifying Powers of Products.

➡ Simplify: $\sqrt[5]{32x^{15}}$

$\sqrt[5]{32x^{15}} = (2^5 x^{15})^{1/5}$

$= 2x^3$

- Write the prime factorization of 32. Write the radical expression as an exponential expression.
- Use the Rule for Simplifying Powers of Products.

Example 9
Simplify: $\sqrt{49x^2 y^{12}}$

Solution
$\sqrt{49x^2 y^{12}} = \sqrt{7^2 x^2 y^{12}}$
$= (7^2 x^2 y^{12})^{1/2}$
$= 7xy^6$

You Try It 9
Simplify: $\sqrt{121x^{10} y^4}$

Your solution

Example 10
Simplify: $\sqrt[3]{-125a^6 b^9}$

Solution
$\sqrt[3]{-125a^6 b^9} = \sqrt[3]{(-5)^3 a^6 b^9}$
$= [(-5)^3 a^6 b^9]^{1/3}$
$= -5a^2 b^3$

You Try It 10
Simplify: $\sqrt[3]{-8x^{12} y^3}$

Your solution

Example 11
Simplify: $-\sqrt[4]{16a^4 b^8}$

Solution
$-\sqrt[4]{16a^4 b^8} = -\sqrt[4]{2^4 a^4 b^8}$
$= -(2^4 a^4 b^8)^{1/4}$
$= -2ab^2$

You Try It 11
Simplify: $-\sqrt[4]{81x^{12} y^8}$

Your solution

Solutions on p. S22

7.1 Exercises

Objective A

Simplify.

1. $8^{1/3}$

2. $16^{1/2}$

3. $9^{3/2}$

4. $25^{3/2}$

5. $27^{-2/3}$

6. $64^{-1/3}$

7. $32^{2/5}$

8. $16^{3/4}$

9. $(-25)^{5/2}$

10. $(-36)^{1/4}$

11. $\left(\dfrac{25}{49}\right)^{-3/2}$

12. $\left(\dfrac{8}{27}\right)^{-2/3}$

13. $x^{1/2}x^{1/2}$

14. $a^{1/3}a^{5/3}$

15. $y^{-1/4}y^{3/4}$

16. $x^{2/5} \cdot x^{-4/5}$

17. $x^{-2/3} \cdot x^{3/4}$

18. $x \cdot x^{-1/2}$

19. $a^{1/3} \cdot a^{3/4} \cdot a^{-1/2}$

20. $y^{-1/6} \cdot y^{2/3} \cdot y^{1/2}$

21. $\dfrac{a^{1/2}}{a^{3/2}}$

22. $\dfrac{b^{1/3}}{b^{4/3}}$

23. $\dfrac{y^{-3/4}}{y^{1/4}}$

24. $\dfrac{x^{-3/5}}{x^{1/5}}$

25. $\dfrac{y^{2/3}}{y^{-5/6}}$

26. $\dfrac{b^{3/4}}{b^{-3/2}}$

27. $(x^2)^{-1/2}$

28. $(a^8)^{-3/4}$

29. $(x^{-2/3})^6$

30. $(y^{-5/6})^{12}$

31. $(a^{-1/2})^{-2}$

32. $(b^{-2/3})^{-6}$

33. $(x^{-3/8})^{-4/5}$

34. $(y^{-3/2})^{-2/9}$

35. $(a^{1/2} \cdot a)^2$

36. $(b^{2/3} \cdot b^{1/6})^6$

37. $(x^{-1/2} \cdot x^{3/4})^{-2}$

38. $(a^{1/2} \cdot a^{-2})^3$

39. $(y^{-1/2} \cdot y^{2/3})^{2/3}$

40. $(b^{-2/3} \cdot b^{1/4})^{-4/3}$

41. $(x^8 y^2)^{1/2}$

42. $(a^3 b^9)^{2/3}$

43. $(x^4y^2z^6)^{3/2}$

44. $(a^8b^4c^4)^{3/4}$

45. $(x^{-3}y^6)^{-1/3}$

46. $(a^2b^{-6})^{-1/2}$

47. $(x^{-2}y^{1/3})^{-3/4}$

48. $(a^{-2/3}b^{2/3})^{3/2}$

49. $\left(\dfrac{x^{1/2}}{y^2}\right)^4$

50. $\left(\dfrac{b^{-3/4}}{a^{-1/2}}\right)^8$

51. $\dfrac{x^{1/4} \cdot x^{-1/2}}{x^{2/3}}$

52. $\dfrac{b^{1/2} \cdot b^{-3/4}}{b^{1/4}}$

53. $\left(\dfrac{y^{2/3} \cdot y^{-5/6}}{y^{1/9}}\right)^9$

54. $\left(\dfrac{a^{1/3} \cdot a^{-2/3}}{a^{1/2}}\right)^4$

55. $\left(\dfrac{b^2 \cdot b^{-3/4}}{b^{-1/2}}\right)^{-1/2}$

56. $\dfrac{(x^{-5/6} \cdot x^3)^{-2/3}}{x^{4/3}}$

57. $(a^{2/3}b^2)^6(a^3b^3)^{1/3}$

58. $(x^3y^{-1/2})^{-2}(x^{-3}y^2)^{1/6}$

59. $(16m^{-2}n^4)^{-1/2}(mn^{1/2})$

60. $(27m^3n^{-6})^{1/3}(m^{-1/3}n^{5/6})^6$

61. $\left(\dfrac{x^{1/2}y^{-3/4}}{y^{2/3}}\right)^{-6}$

62. $\left(\dfrac{x^{1/2}y^{-5/4}}{y^{-3/4}}\right)^{-4}$

63. $\left(\dfrac{2^{-6}b^{-3}}{a^{-1/2}}\right)^{-2/3}$

64. $\left(\dfrac{49c^{5/3}}{a^{-1/4}b^{5/6}}\right)^{-3/2}$

65. $y^{3/2}(y^{1/2} - y^{-1/2})$

66. $y^{3/5}(y^{2/5} + y^{-3/5})$

67. $a^{-1/4}(a^{5/4} - a^{9/4})$

68. $x^{4/3}(x^{2/3} + x^{-1/3})$

69. $x^n \cdot x^{3n}$

70. $a^{2n} \cdot a^{-5n}$

71. $x^n \cdot x^{n/2}$

72. $a^{n/2} \cdot a^{-n/3}$

73. $\dfrac{y^{n/2}}{y^{-n}}$

74. $\dfrac{b^{m/3}}{b^m}$

75. $(x^{2n})^n$

76. $(x^{5n})^{2n}$

77. $(x^{n/4}y^{n/8})^8$

78. $(x^{n/2}y^{n/3})^6$

79. $(x^{n/5}y^{n/10})^{20}$

80. $(x^{n/2}y^{n/5})^{10}$

_____

Objective B

Rewrite the exponential expression as a radical expression.

81. $3^{1/4}$

82. $5^{1/2}$

83. $a^{3/2}$

84. $b^{4/3}$

85. $(2t)^{5/2}$

86. $(3x)^{2/3}$

87. $-2x^{2/3}$

88. $-3a^{2/5}$

89. $(a^2b)^{2/3}$

90. $(x^2y^3)^{3/4}$

91. $(a^2b^4)^{3/5}$

92. $(a^3b^7)^{3/2}$

93. $(4x-3)^{3/4}$

94. $(3x-2)^{1/3}$

95. $x^{-2/3}$

96. $b^{-3/4}$

Rewrite the radical expression as an exponential expression.

97. $\sqrt{14}$

98. $\sqrt{7}$

99. $\sqrt[3]{x}$

100. $\sqrt[4]{y}$

101. $\sqrt[3]{x^4}$

102. $\sqrt[4]{a^3}$

103. $\sqrt[5]{b^3}$

104. $\sqrt[4]{b^5}$

105. $\sqrt[3]{2x^2}$

106. $\sqrt[5]{4y^7}$

107. $-\sqrt{3x^5}$

108. $-\sqrt[4]{4x^5}$

109. $3x\sqrt[3]{y^2}$

110. $2y\sqrt{x^3}$

111. $\sqrt{a^2-2}$

112. $\sqrt{3-y^2}$

Objective C

Simplify.

113. $\sqrt{x^{16}}$ **114.** $\sqrt{y^{14}}$ **115.** $-\sqrt{x^8}$ **116.** $-\sqrt{a^6}$

117. $\sqrt[3]{x^3 y^9}$ **118.** $\sqrt[3]{a^6 b^{12}}$ **119.** $-\sqrt[3]{x^{15} y^3}$ **120.** $-\sqrt[3]{a^9 b^9}$

121. $\sqrt{16 a^4 b^{12}}$ **122.** $\sqrt{25 x^8 y^2}$ **123.** $\sqrt{-16 x^4 y^2}$ **124.** $\sqrt{-9 a^4 b^8}$

125. $\sqrt[3]{27 x^9}$ **126.** $\sqrt[3]{8 a^{21} b^6}$ **127.** $\sqrt[3]{-64 x^9 y^{12}}$ **128.** $\sqrt[3]{-27 a^3 b^{15}}$

129. $-\sqrt[4]{x^8 y^{12}}$ **130.** $-\sqrt[4]{a^{16} b^4}$ **131.** $\sqrt[5]{x^{20} y^{10}}$ **132.** $\sqrt[5]{a^5 b^{25}}$

133. $\sqrt[4]{81 x^4 y^{20}}$ **134.** $\sqrt[4]{16 a^8 b^{20}}$ **135.** $\sqrt[5]{32 a^5 b^{10}}$ **136.** $\sqrt[5]{-32 x^{15} y^{20}}$

APPLYING THE CONCEPTS

137. Determine whether the following statements are true or false. If the statement is false, correct the right-hand side of the equation.
     a. $\sqrt{(-2)^2} = -2$ **b.** $\sqrt[3]{(-3)^3} = -3$ **c.** $\sqrt[n]{a} = a^{1/n}$

     d. $\sqrt[n]{a^n + b^n} = a + b$ **e.** $(a^{1/2} + b^{1/2})^2 = a + b$ **f.** $\sqrt[m]{a^n} = a^{mn}$

138. Simplify.
     a. $\sqrt[3]{\sqrt{x^6}}$ **b.** $\sqrt[4]{\sqrt{a^8}}$ **c.** $\sqrt{\sqrt{81 y^8}}$

     d. $\sqrt{\sqrt[n]{a^{4n}}}$ **e.** $\sqrt[n]{\sqrt{b^{6n}}}$ **f.** $\sqrt{\sqrt[3]{x^{12} y^{24}}}$

139. Show how to locate $\sqrt{2}$ on the number line.

140. If x is any real number, is $\sqrt{x^2} = x$ always true? Show why or why not.

7.2 Operations on Radical Expressions

Objective A   *To simplify radical expressions* .... (30) CT

If a number is not a perfect power, its root can only be approximated; examples include $\sqrt{5}$ and $\sqrt[3]{3}$. These numbers are **irrational numbers.** Their decimal representations never terminate or repeat.

$$\sqrt{5} = 2.2360679\ldots \qquad \sqrt[3]{3} = 1.4422495\ldots$$

A radical expression is in simplest form when the radicand contains no factor that is a perfect power. The Product Property of Radicals is used to simplify radical expressions whose radicands are not perfect powers.

The Product Property of Radicals

If $\sqrt[n]{a}$ and $\sqrt[n]{b}$ are positive real numbers, then
$\sqrt[n]{ab} = \sqrt[n]{a} \cdot \sqrt[n]{b}$ and $\sqrt[n]{a} \cdot \sqrt[n]{b} = \sqrt[n]{ab}$.

➡ Simplify: $\sqrt{48}$

$\sqrt{48} = \sqrt{2^4 \cdot 3}$

- Write the prime factorization of the radicand in exponential form.

$= \sqrt{2^4}\sqrt{3}$

- Use the Product Property of Radicals to write the expression as a product.

$= 2^2\sqrt{3} = 4\sqrt{3}$

- Simplify.

➡ Simplify: $\sqrt{18x^2y^3}$

$\sqrt{18x^2y^3} = \sqrt{2 \cdot 3^2x^2y^3}$

- Write the prime factorization of the radicand in exponential form.

$= \sqrt{3^2x^2y^2 \cdot 2y}$

- Write the radical as the product of a perfect square and factors that do not contain a perfect square.

$= \sqrt{3^2x^2y^2}\sqrt{2y}$

- Use the Product Property of Radicals to write the expression as a product.

$= 3xy\sqrt{2y}$

- Simplify.

➡ Simplify: $\sqrt[3]{x^7}$

$\sqrt[3]{x^7} = \sqrt[3]{x^6 \cdot x}$

- Write the radicand as the product of a perfect cube and a factor that does not contain a perfect cube.

$= \sqrt[3]{x^6}\sqrt[3]{x}$

- Use the Product Property of Radicals to write the expression as a product.

$= x^2\sqrt[3]{x}$

- Simplify.

⇒ Simplify: $\sqrt[4]{32x^7}$

$\sqrt[4]{32x^7} = \sqrt[4]{2^5x^7}$ • Write the prime factorization of the coefficient of the radicand in exponential form.

$= \sqrt[4]{2^4x^4(2x^3)}$ • Write the radicand as the product of a perfect fourth power and factors that do not contain a perfect fourth power.

$= \sqrt[4]{2^4x^4}\,\sqrt[4]{2x^3}$ • Use the Product Property of Radicals to write the expression as a product.

$= 2x\,\sqrt[4]{2x^3}$ • Simplify.

Example 1   Simplify: $\sqrt[4]{x^9}$

Solution $\sqrt[4]{x^9} = \sqrt[4]{x^8 \cdot x} = \sqrt[4]{x^8}\,\sqrt[4]{x}$
$= x^2\,\sqrt[4]{x}$

You Try It 1   Simplify: $\sqrt[5]{x^7}$

Your solution

Example 2   Simplify: $\sqrt[3]{-27a^5b^{12}}$

Solution $\sqrt[3]{-27a^5b^{12}}$
$= \sqrt[3]{(-3)^3a^5b^{12}}$
$= \sqrt[3]{(-3)^3a^3b^{12}(a^2)}$
$= \sqrt[3]{(-3)^3a^3b^{12}}\,\sqrt[3]{a^2}$
$= -3ab^4\,\sqrt[3]{a^2}$

You Try It 2   Simplify: $\sqrt[3]{-64x^8y^{18}}$

Your solution

Solutions on p. S22

Objective B   To add or subtract radical expressions .... (31) CT

The Distributive Property is used to simplify the sum or difference of radical expressions that have the same radicand and the same index. For example,

$$3\sqrt{5} + 8\sqrt{5} = (3 + 8)\sqrt{5} = 11\sqrt{5}$$
$$2\sqrt[3]{3x} - 9\sqrt[3]{3x} = (2 - 9)\sqrt[3]{3x} = -7\sqrt[3]{3x}$$

Radical expressions that are in simplest form and have unlike radicands or different indices cannot be simplified by the Distributive Property. The expressions below cannot be simplified by the Distributive Property.

$$3\sqrt[4]{2} - 6\sqrt[4]{3} \qquad\qquad 2\sqrt[4]{4x} + 3\sqrt[3]{4x}$$

⇒ Simplify: $3\sqrt{32x^2} - 2x\sqrt{2} + \sqrt{128x^2}$

First simplify each term. Then combine like terms by using the Distributive Property.

$$3\sqrt{32x^2} - 2x\sqrt{2} + \sqrt{128x^2} = 3\sqrt{2^5x^2} - 2x\sqrt{2} + \sqrt{2^7x^2}$$
$$= 3\sqrt{2^4x^2}\,\sqrt{2} - 2x\sqrt{2} + \sqrt{2^6x^2}\,\sqrt{2}$$
$$= 3 \cdot 2^2x\sqrt{2} - 2x\sqrt{2} + 2^3x\sqrt{2}$$
$$= 12x\sqrt{2} - 2x\sqrt{2} + 8x\sqrt{2}$$
$$= 18x\sqrt{2}$$

Example 3

Simplify: $5b\sqrt[4]{32a^7b^5} - 2a\sqrt[4]{162a^3b^9}$

Solution

$5b\sqrt[4]{32a^7b^5} - 2a\sqrt[4]{162a^3b^9}$

$= 5b\sqrt[4]{2^5a^7b^5} - 2a\sqrt[4]{3^4 \cdot 2a^3b^9}$

$= 5b\sqrt[4]{2^4a^4b^4}\sqrt[4]{2a^3b} - 2a\sqrt[4]{3^4b^8}\sqrt[4]{2a^3b}$

$= 5b \cdot 2ab\sqrt[4]{2a^3b} - 2a \cdot 3b^2\sqrt[4]{2a^3b}$

$= 10ab^2\sqrt[4]{2a^3b} - 6ab^2\sqrt[4]{2a^3b}$

$= 4ab^2\sqrt[4]{2a^3b}$

You Try It 3

Simplify: $3xy\sqrt[3]{81x^5y} - \sqrt[3]{192x^8y^4}$

Your solution

Solution on p. S22

Objective C   To multiply radical expressions .... (30) (31) CT

The Product Property of Radicals is used to multiply radical expressions with the same index.

$$\sqrt{3x} \cdot \sqrt{5y} = \sqrt{3x \cdot 5y} = \sqrt{15xy}$$

➡ Simplify: $\sqrt[3]{2a^5b}\sqrt[3]{16a^2b^2}$

$\sqrt[3]{2a^5b}\sqrt[3]{16a^2b^2} = \sqrt[3]{32a^7b^3}$

$= \sqrt[3]{2^5a^7b^3}$

$= \sqrt[3]{2^3a^6b^3}\sqrt[3]{2^2a}$

$= 2a^2b\sqrt[3]{4a}$

- Use the Product Property of Radicals to multiply the radicands.
- Simplify.

➡ Simplify: $\sqrt{2x}(\sqrt{8x} - \sqrt{3})$

$\sqrt{2x}(\sqrt{8x} - \sqrt{3}) = \sqrt{2x}(\sqrt{8x}) - \sqrt{2x}(\sqrt{3})$

$= \sqrt{16x^2} - \sqrt{6x}$

$= \sqrt{2^4x^2} - \sqrt{6x}$

$= 2^2x - \sqrt{6x}$

$= 4x - \sqrt{6x}$

- Use the Distributive Property.
- Simplify.

➡ Simplify: $(2\sqrt{5} - 3)(3\sqrt{5} + 4)$

$(2\sqrt{5} - 3)(3\sqrt{5} + 4) = 6(\sqrt{5})^2 + 8\sqrt{5} - 9\sqrt{5} - 12$

$= 30 + 8\sqrt{5} - 9\sqrt{5} - 12$

$= 18 - \sqrt{5}$

- Use the FOIL method to multiply the numbers.
- Combine like terms.

➡ Simplify: $(4\sqrt{a} - \sqrt{b})(2\sqrt{a} + 5\sqrt{b})$

$(4\sqrt{a} - \sqrt{b})(2\sqrt{a} + 5\sqrt{b})$
$$= 8(\sqrt{a})^2 + 20\sqrt{ab} - 2\sqrt{ab} - 5(\sqrt{b})^2$$ • Use the FOIL method.
$$= 8a + 18\sqrt{ab} - 5b$$

The expressions $a + b$ and $a - b$ are **conjugates** of each other. Recall that $(a + b)(a - b) = a^2 - b^2$. This identity is used to simplify conjugate radical expressions.

➡ Simplify: $(\sqrt{11} - 3)(\sqrt{11} + 3)$

$(\sqrt{11} - 3)(\sqrt{11} + 3) = (\sqrt{11})^2 - 3^2 = 11 - 9$ • The radical expressions are conjugates.
$$= 2$$

Example 4
Simplify: $\sqrt{3x}(\sqrt{27x^2} - \sqrt{3x})$

Solution
$\sqrt{3x}(\sqrt{27x^2} - \sqrt{3x}) = \sqrt{81x^3} - \sqrt{9x^2}$
$$= \sqrt{3^4 x^3} - \sqrt{3^2 x^2}$$
$$= \sqrt{3^4 x^2}\sqrt{x} - \sqrt{3^2 x^2}$$
$$= 3^2 x\sqrt{x} - 3x$$
$$= 9x\sqrt{x} - 3x$$

You Try It 4
Simplify: $\sqrt{5b}(\sqrt{3b} - \sqrt{10})$

Your solution

Example 5
Simplify: $(2\sqrt[3]{x} - 3)(3\sqrt[3]{x} - 4)$

Solution
$(2\sqrt[3]{x} - 3)(3\sqrt[3]{x} - 4)$
$$= 6\sqrt[3]{x^2} - 8\sqrt[3]{x} - 9\sqrt[3]{x} + 12$$
$$= 6\sqrt[3]{x^2} - 17\sqrt[3]{x} + 12$$

You Try It 5
Simplify: $(2\sqrt[3]{2x} - 3)(\sqrt[3]{2x} - 5)$

Your solution

Example 6
Simplify: $(2\sqrt{x} - \sqrt{2y})(2\sqrt{x} + \sqrt{2y})$

Solution
$(2\sqrt{x} - \sqrt{2y})(2\sqrt{x} + \sqrt{2y})$
$$= (2\sqrt{x})^2 - (\sqrt{2y})^2$$
$$= 4x - 2y$$

You Try It 6
Simplify: $(\sqrt{a} - 3\sqrt{y})(\sqrt{a} + 3\sqrt{y})$

Your solution

Solutions on p. S22

Objective D   *To divide radical expressions* .... ⟨30⟩ ⟨31⟩ CT

The Quotient Property of Radicals is used to divide radical expressions with the same index.

The Quotient Property of Radicals

If $\sqrt[n]{a}$ and $\sqrt[n]{b}$ are real numbers, and $b \neq 0$, then

$$\sqrt[n]{\frac{a}{b}} = \frac{\sqrt[n]{a}}{\sqrt[n]{b}} \quad \text{and} \quad \frac{\sqrt[n]{a}}{\sqrt[n]{b}} = \sqrt[n]{\frac{a}{b}}$$

➡ Simplify: $\sqrt[3]{\dfrac{81x^5}{y^6}}$

$$\sqrt[3]{\frac{81x^5}{y^6}} = \frac{\sqrt[3]{81x^5}}{\sqrt[3]{y^6}}$$ • Use the Quotient Property of Radicals.

$$= \frac{\sqrt[3]{3^4 x^5}}{\sqrt[3]{y^6}}$$ • Simplify each radical expression.

$$= \frac{\sqrt[3]{3^3 x^3}\,\sqrt[3]{3x^2}}{\sqrt[3]{y^6}}$$

$$= \frac{3x\sqrt[3]{3x^2}}{y^2}$$

➡ Simplify: $\dfrac{\sqrt{5a^4 b^7 c^2}}{\sqrt{ab^3 c}}$

$$\frac{\sqrt{5a^4 b^7 c^2}}{\sqrt{ab^3 c}} = \sqrt{\frac{5a^4 b^7 c^2}{ab^3 c}}$$ • Use the Quotient Property of Radicals.

$$= \sqrt{5a^3 b^4 c}$$ • Simplify the radicand.

$$= \sqrt{a^2 b^4}\,\sqrt{5ac}$$

$$= ab^2 \sqrt{5ac}$$

A radical expression is in simplest form when no radical remains in the denominator of the radical expression. The procedure used to remove a radical from the denominator is called **rationalizing the denominator.**

➡ Simplify: $\dfrac{5}{\sqrt{2}}$

$$\frac{5}{\sqrt{2}} = \frac{5}{\sqrt{2}} \cdot 1 = \frac{5}{\sqrt{2}} \cdot \frac{\sqrt{2}}{\sqrt{2}}$$ • Multiply by $\dfrac{\sqrt{2}}{\sqrt{2}}$, which equals 1.

$$= \frac{5\sqrt{2}}{2}$$ • $\sqrt{2} \cdot \sqrt{2} = (\sqrt{2})^2 = 2$

➡ Simplify: $\dfrac{3x}{\sqrt[3]{4x}}$

$$\frac{3x}{\sqrt[3]{4x}} = \frac{3x}{\sqrt[3]{2^2x}} \cdot \frac{\sqrt[3]{2x^2}}{\sqrt[3]{2x^2}}$$

- Because $\sqrt[3]{2^2x} \cdot \sqrt[3]{2x^2} = \sqrt[3]{2^3x^3}$, a perfect cube, multiply the expression by $\dfrac{\sqrt[3]{2x^2}}{\sqrt[3]{2x^2}}$, which equals 1.

$$= \frac{3x\sqrt[3]{2x^2}}{\sqrt[3]{2^3x^3}} = \frac{3x\sqrt[3]{2x^2}}{2x}$$

- Simplify.

$$= \frac{3\sqrt[3]{2x^2}}{2}$$

➡ Simplify: $\dfrac{\sqrt{x} - \sqrt{y}}{\sqrt{x} + \sqrt{y}}$

To simplify a fraction that has a binomial radical expression in the denominator, multiply the numerator and denominator by the conjugate of the denominator. Then simplify.

$$\frac{\sqrt{x} - \sqrt{y}}{\sqrt{x} + \sqrt{y}} = \frac{\sqrt{x} - \sqrt{y}}{\sqrt{x} + \sqrt{y}} \cdot \frac{\sqrt{x} - \sqrt{y}}{\sqrt{x} - \sqrt{y}}$$

$$= \frac{(\sqrt{x})^2 - \sqrt{xy} - \sqrt{xy} + (\sqrt{y})^2}{(\sqrt{x})^2 - (\sqrt{y})^2} = \frac{x - 2\sqrt{xy} + y}{x - y}$$

Example 7

Simplify: $\dfrac{5}{\sqrt{5x}}$

Solution

$$\frac{5}{\sqrt{5x}} = \frac{5}{\sqrt{5x}} \cdot \frac{\sqrt{5x}}{\sqrt{5x}} = \frac{5\sqrt{5x}}{(\sqrt{5x})^2}$$

$$= \frac{5\sqrt{5x}}{5x} = \frac{\sqrt{5x}}{x}$$

You Try It 7

Simplify: $\dfrac{y}{\sqrt{3y}}$

Your solution

Example 8

Simplify: $\dfrac{3}{\sqrt[4]{2x}}$

Solution

$$\frac{3}{\sqrt[4]{2x}} = \frac{3}{\sqrt[4]{2x}} \cdot \frac{\sqrt[4]{2^3x^3}}{\sqrt[4]{2^3x^3}}$$

$$= \frac{3\sqrt[4]{8x^3}}{\sqrt[4]{2^4x^4}} = \frac{3\sqrt[4]{8x^3}}{2x}$$

You Try It 8

Simplify: $\dfrac{3}{\sqrt[3]{3x^2}}$

Your solution

Example 9

Simplify: $\dfrac{3}{5 - 2\sqrt{3}}$

Solution

$$\frac{3}{5 - 2\sqrt{3}} = \frac{3}{5 - 2\sqrt{3}} \cdot \frac{5 + 2\sqrt{3}}{5 + 2\sqrt{3}} = \frac{15 + 6\sqrt{3}}{5^2 - (2\sqrt{3})^2}$$

$$= \frac{15 + 6\sqrt{3}}{25 - 12} = \frac{15 + 6\sqrt{3}}{13}$$

You Try It 9

Simplify: $\dfrac{3 + \sqrt{6}}{2 - \sqrt{6}}$

Your solution

Solutions on p. S22

7.2 Exercises

Objective A

Simplify.

1. $\sqrt{x^4y^3z^5}$

2. $\sqrt{x^3y^6z^9}$

3. $\sqrt{8a^3b^8}$

4. $\sqrt{24a^9b^6}$

5. $\sqrt{45x^2y^3z^5}$

6. $\sqrt{60xy^7z^{12}}$

7. $\sqrt{-9x^3}$

8. $\sqrt{-x^2y^5}$

9. $\sqrt[3]{a^{16}b^8}$

10. $\sqrt[3]{a^5b^8}$

11. $\sqrt[3]{-125x^2y^4}$

12. $\sqrt[3]{-216x^5y^9}$

13. $\sqrt[3]{a^4b^5c^6}$

14. $\sqrt[3]{a^8b^{11}c^{15}}$

15. $\sqrt[4]{16x^9y^5}$

16. $\sqrt[4]{64x^8y^{10}}$

Objective B

Simplify.

17. $2\sqrt{x} - 8\sqrt{x}$

18. $3\sqrt{y} + 12\sqrt{y}$

19. $\sqrt{8} - \sqrt{32}$

20. $\sqrt{27a} - \sqrt{8a}$

21. $\sqrt{18b} + \sqrt{75b}$

22. $2\sqrt{2x^3} + 4x\sqrt{8x}$

23. $3\sqrt{8x^2y^3} - 2x\sqrt{32y^3}$

24. $2\sqrt{32x^2y^3} - xy\sqrt{98y}$

25. $2a\sqrt{27ab^5} + 3b\sqrt{3a^3b}$

26. $\sqrt[3]{128} + \sqrt[3]{250}$

27. $\sqrt[3]{16} - \sqrt[3]{54}$

28. $2\sqrt[3]{3a^4} - 3a\sqrt[3]{81a}$

29. $2b\sqrt[3]{16b^2} + \sqrt[3]{128b^5}$

30. $3\sqrt[3]{x^5y^7} - 8xy\sqrt[3]{x^2y^4}$

31. $3\sqrt[4]{32a^5} - a\sqrt[4]{162a}$

32. $2a\sqrt[4]{16ab^5} + 3b\sqrt[4]{256a^5b}$

33. $2\sqrt{50} - 3\sqrt{125} + \sqrt{98}$

34. $3\sqrt{108} - 2\sqrt{18} - 3\sqrt{48}$

35. $\sqrt{9b^3} - \sqrt{25b^3} + \sqrt{49b^3}$

36. $\sqrt{4x^7y^5} + 9x^2\sqrt{x^3y^5} - 5xy\sqrt{x^5y^3}$

37. $2x\sqrt{8xy^2} - 3y\sqrt{32x^3} + \sqrt{4x^3y^3}$

38. $5a\sqrt{3a^3b} + 2a^2\sqrt{27ab} - 4\sqrt{75a^5b}$

39. $\sqrt[3]{54xy^3} - 5\sqrt[3]{2xy^3} + y\sqrt[3]{128x}$

40. $2\sqrt[3]{24x^3y^4} + 4x\sqrt[3]{81y^4} - 3y\sqrt[3]{24x^3y}$

41. $2a\sqrt[4]{32b^5} - 3b\sqrt[4]{162a^4b} + \sqrt[4]{2a^4b^5}$

42. $6y\sqrt[4]{48x^5} - 2x\sqrt[4]{243xy^4} - 4\sqrt[4]{3x^5y^4}$

Objective C

Simplify.

43. $\sqrt{8}\,\sqrt{32}$

44. $\sqrt{14}\,\sqrt{35}$

45. $\sqrt[3]{4}\,\sqrt[3]{8}$

46. $\sqrt[3]{6}\,\sqrt[3]{36}$

47. $\sqrt{x^2y^5}\,\sqrt{xy}$

48. $\sqrt{a^3b}\,\sqrt{ab^4}$

49. $\sqrt{2x^2y}\,\sqrt{32xy}$

50. $\sqrt{5x^3y}\,\sqrt{10x^3y^4}$

51. $\sqrt[3]{x^2y}\,\sqrt[3]{16x^4y^2}$

52. $\sqrt[3]{4a^2b^3}\,\sqrt[3]{8ab^5}$

53. $\sqrt[4]{12ab^3}\,\sqrt[4]{4a^5b^2}$

54. $\sqrt[4]{36a^2b^4}\,\sqrt[4]{12a^5b^3}$

55. $\sqrt{3}\,(\sqrt{27} - \sqrt{3})$

56. $\sqrt{10}\,(\sqrt{10} - \sqrt{5})$

57. $\sqrt{x}\,(\sqrt{x} - \sqrt{2})$

58. $\sqrt{y}\,(\sqrt{y} - \sqrt{5})$

59. $\sqrt{2x}\,(\sqrt{8x} - \sqrt{32})$

60. $\sqrt{3a}\,(\sqrt{27a^2} - \sqrt{a})$

61. $(\sqrt{x} - 3)^2$

62. $(\sqrt{2x} + 4)^2$

63. $(4\sqrt{5} + 2)^2$

64. $2\sqrt{3x^2} \cdot 3\sqrt{12xy^3} \cdot \sqrt{6x^3y}$

65. $2\sqrt{14xy} \cdot 4\sqrt{7x^2y} \cdot 3\sqrt{8xy^2}$

66. $\sqrt[3]{8ab}\ \sqrt[3]{4a^2b^3}\ \sqrt[3]{9ab^4}$

67. $\sqrt[3]{2a^2b}\ \sqrt[3]{4a^3b^2}\ \sqrt[3]{8a^5b^6}$

68. $(\sqrt{2} - 3)(\sqrt{2} + 4)$

69. $(\sqrt{5} - 5)(2\sqrt{5} + 2)$

70. $(\sqrt{y} - 2)(\sqrt{y} + 2)$

71. $(\sqrt{x} - y)(\sqrt{x} + y)$

72. $(\sqrt{2x} - 3\sqrt{y})(\sqrt{2x} + 3\sqrt{y})$

73. $(2\sqrt{3x} - \sqrt{y})(2\sqrt{3x} + \sqrt{y})$

Objective D

Simplify.

74. $\dfrac{\sqrt{32x^2}}{\sqrt{2x}}$

75. $\dfrac{\sqrt{60y^4}}{\sqrt{12y}}$

76. $\dfrac{\sqrt{42a^3b^5}}{\sqrt{14a^2b}}$

77. $\dfrac{\sqrt{65ab^4}}{\sqrt{5ab}}$

78. $\dfrac{1}{\sqrt{5}}$

79. $\dfrac{1}{\sqrt{2}}$

80. $\dfrac{1}{\sqrt{2x}}$

81. $\dfrac{2}{\sqrt{3y}}$

82. $\dfrac{5}{\sqrt{5x}}$

83. $\dfrac{9}{\sqrt{3a}}$

84. $\sqrt{\dfrac{x}{5}}$

85. $\sqrt{\dfrac{y}{2}}$

86. $\dfrac{3}{\sqrt[3]{2}}$

87. $\dfrac{5}{\sqrt[3]{9}}$

88. $\dfrac{3}{\sqrt[3]{4x^2}}$

89. $\dfrac{5}{\sqrt[3]{3y}}$

90. $\dfrac{\sqrt{40x^3y^2}}{\sqrt{80x^2y^3}}$

91. $\dfrac{\sqrt{15a^2b^5}}{\sqrt{30a^5b^3}}$

92. $\dfrac{\sqrt{24a^2b}}{\sqrt{18ab^4}}$

93. $\dfrac{\sqrt{12x^3y}}{\sqrt{20x^4y}}$

94. $\dfrac{5}{\sqrt{3} - 2}$ **95.** $\dfrac{-2}{1 - \sqrt{2}}$ **96.** $\dfrac{-3}{2 - \sqrt{3}}$ **97.** $\dfrac{-4}{3 - \sqrt{2}}$

98. $\dfrac{2}{\sqrt{5} + 2}$ **99.** $\dfrac{5}{2 - \sqrt{7}}$ **100.** $\dfrac{3}{\sqrt{y} - 2}$ **101.** $\dfrac{-7}{\sqrt{x} - 3}$

102. $\dfrac{\sqrt{2} - \sqrt{3}}{\sqrt{2} + \sqrt{3}}$ **103.** $\dfrac{\sqrt{3} + \sqrt{4}}{\sqrt{2} + \sqrt{3}}$ **104.** $\dfrac{2 + 3\sqrt{7}}{5 - 2\sqrt{7}}$

105. $\dfrac{2 + 3\sqrt{5}}{1 - \sqrt{5}}$ **106.** $\dfrac{2\sqrt{3} - 1}{3\sqrt{3} + 2}$ **107.** $\dfrac{2\sqrt{a} - \sqrt{b}}{4\sqrt{a} + 3\sqrt{b}}$

108. $\dfrac{2\sqrt{x} - 4}{\sqrt{x} + 2}$ **109.** $\dfrac{3\sqrt{y} - y}{\sqrt{y} + 2y}$ **110.** $\dfrac{3\sqrt{x} - 4\sqrt{y}}{3\sqrt{x} - 2\sqrt{y}}$

APPLYING THE CONCEPTS

111. Determine whether the following statements are true or false. If the statement is false, correct the right-hand side of the equation.

a. $\sqrt[2]{3} \cdot \sqrt[3]{4} = \sqrt[5]{12}$ **b.** $\sqrt{3} \cdot \sqrt{3} = 3$ **c.** $\sqrt[3]{x} \cdot \sqrt[3]{x} = x$

d. $\sqrt{x} + \sqrt{y} = \sqrt{x + y}$ **e.** $\sqrt[2]{2} + \sqrt[3]{3} = \sqrt[5]{2 + 3}$ **f.** $8\sqrt[5]{a} - 2\sqrt[5]{a} = 6\sqrt[5]{a}$

112. Multiply: $(\sqrt[3]{a} + \sqrt[3]{b})(\sqrt[3]{a^2} - \sqrt[3]{ab} + \sqrt[3]{b^2})$

113. Simplify.

a. $(\sqrt{2} - 2)^3$ **b.** $\dfrac{2}{\sqrt{x + 4} + 2}$ **c.** $\dfrac{\sqrt{b + 9} - 3}{\sqrt{b + 9} + 3}$

114. Rewrite $\dfrac{\sqrt[4]{(a + b)^3}}{\sqrt{a + b}}$ as an expression with a single radical.

115. Explain in your own words what it means to rationalize the denominator of a radical expression and how to do so.

7.3 Complex Numbers

Objective A   To simplify a complex number ....

The radical expression $\sqrt{-4}$ is not a real number, because there is no real number whose square is -4. However, the solution of an algebraic equation is sometimes the square root of a negative number.

For example, the equation $x^2 + 1 = 0$ does not have a real number solution, because there is no real number whose square is a negative number.

$$x^2 + 1 = 0$$
$$x^2 = -1$$

Around the 17th century, a new number, called an **imaginary number,** was defined so that a negative number would have a square root. The letter i was chosen to represent the number whose square is -1.

$$i^2 = -1$$

An imaginary number is defined in terms of i.

> If a is a positive real number, then the principal square root of negative a is the imaginary number $i\sqrt{a}$.
>
> $$\sqrt{-a} = i\sqrt{a}$$

Here are some examples.

$$\sqrt{-16} = i\sqrt{16} = 4i$$
$$\sqrt{-12} = i\sqrt{12} = 2i\sqrt{3}$$
$$\sqrt{-21} = i\sqrt{21}$$
$$\sqrt{-1} = i\sqrt{1} = i$$

It is customary to write i in front of a radical to avoid confusing $\sqrt{a}\,i$ with $\sqrt{ai}$.

The real numbers and imaginary numbers make up the complex numbers.

> **Complex Number**
>
> A **complex number** is a number of the form $a + bi$, where a and b are real numbers and $i = \sqrt{-1}$. The number a is the **real part** of $a + bi$, and b is the **imaginary part.**

Examples of complex numbers are shown at the right.

Real Part	Imaginary Part
a +	bi
3 +	$2i$
8 −	$10i$

```
                        ┌─── Real Numbers      A *real number* is a complex
                        │       a + 0i         number in which $b = 0$.
     Complex numbers────┤
         a + bi         │
                        │
                        └─── Imaginary Numbers  An *imaginary number* is a
                                0 + bi         complex number in which
                                               $a = 0$.
```

➡ Simplify: $\sqrt{20} - \sqrt{-50}$

$$\sqrt{20} - \sqrt{-50} = \sqrt{20} - i\sqrt{50}$$

• Write the complex number in the form $a + bi$.

$$= \sqrt{2^2 \cdot 5} - i\sqrt{5^2 \cdot 2}$$

• Use the Product Property of Radicals to simplify each radical.

$$= 2\sqrt{5} - 5i\sqrt{2}$$

Example 1
Simplify: $\sqrt{-80}$

Solution
$\sqrt{-80} = i\sqrt{80} = i\sqrt{2^4 \cdot 5} = 4i\sqrt{5}$

Example 2
Simplify: $\sqrt{25} + \sqrt{-40}$

Solution
$\sqrt{25} + \sqrt{-40} = \sqrt{25} + i\sqrt{40}$
$$= \sqrt{5^2} + i\sqrt{2^2 \cdot 2 \cdot 5}$$
$$= 5 + 2i\sqrt{10}$$

You Try It 1
Simplify: $\sqrt{-45}$

Your solution

You Try It 2
Simplify: $\sqrt{98} - \sqrt{-60}$

Your solution

Solutions on p. S23

Objective B   To add or subtract complex numbers ··· CT

The Addition and Subtraction of Complex Numbers

To add two complex numbers, add the real parts and add the imaginary parts. To subtract two complex numbers, subtract the real parts and subtract the imaginary parts.

$$(a + bi) + (c + di) = (a + c) + (b + d)i$$
$$(a + bi) - (c + di) = (a - c) + (b - d)i$$

➡ Simplify: $(3 - 7i) - (4 - 2i)$

$$(3 - 7i) - (4 - 2i) = (3 - 4) + [-7 - (-2)]i$$

• Subtract the real parts and subtract the imaginary parts of the complex numbers.

$$= -1 - 5i$$

➡ Simplify: $(3 + \sqrt{-12}) + (7 - \sqrt{-27})$

$(3 + \sqrt{-12}) + (7 - \sqrt{-27})$

$\quad = (3 + i\sqrt{12}) + (7 - i\sqrt{27})$

$\quad = (3 + i\sqrt{2^2 \cdot 3}) + (7 - i\sqrt{3^2 \cdot 3})$

$\quad = (3 + 2i\sqrt{3}) + (7 - 3i\sqrt{3})$

$\quad = 10 - i\sqrt{3}$

- Write each complex number in the form $a + bi$.
- Use the Product Property of Radicals to simplify each radical.

- Add the complex numbers.

Example 3

Simplify: $(3 + 2i) + (6 - 5i)$

Solution

$(3 + 2i) + (6 - 5i) = 9 - 3i$

You Try It 3

Simplify: $(-4 + 2i) - (6 - 8i)$

Your solution

Example 4

Simplify: $(9 - \sqrt{-8}) - (5 + \sqrt{-32})$

Solution

$(9 - \sqrt{-8}) - (5 + \sqrt{-32})$

$\quad = (9 - i\sqrt{8}) - (5 + i\sqrt{32})$

$\quad = (9 - i\sqrt{2^2 \cdot 2}) - (5 + i\sqrt{2^4 \cdot 2})$

$\quad = (9 - 2i\sqrt{2}) - (5 + 4i\sqrt{2})$

$\quad = 4 - 6i\sqrt{2}$

You Try It 4

Simplify: $(16 - \sqrt{-45}) - (3 + \sqrt{-20})$

Your solution

Example 5

Simplify: $(6 + 4i) + (-6 - 4i)$

Solution

$(6 + 4i) + (-6 - 4i) = 0 + 0i = 0$

This illustrates that the additive inverse of $a + bi$ is $-a - bi$.

You Try It 5

Simplify: $(3 - 2i) + (-3 + 2i)$

Your solution

Solutions on p. S23

Objective C   **To multiply complex numbers** .... CT

When multiplying complex numbers, we often find that the term i^2 is a part of the product. Recall that $i^2 = -1$.

➡ Simplify: $2i \cdot 3i$

$2i \cdot 3i = 6i^2$ • Multiply the imaginary numbers.

$\quad = 6(-1)$ • Replace i^2 by -1.

$\quad = -6$ • Simplify.

TAKE NOTE

This example illustrates an important point. When working with a number that has a square root of a negative number, always rewrite the number with *i* before continuing.

➡ Simplify: $\sqrt{-6} \cdot \sqrt{-24}$

$\sqrt{-6} \cdot \sqrt{-24} = i\sqrt{6} \cdot i\sqrt{24}$ • Write each radical as the product of a real number and *i*.

$= i^2\sqrt{144}$ • Multiply the imaginary numbers.

$= -\sqrt{144}$ • Replace i^2 by -1.

$= -12$ • Simplify the radical expression.

Note from the last example that it would have been incorrect to multiply the radicands of the two radical expressions. To illustrate,

$$\sqrt{-6} \cdot \sqrt{-24} = \sqrt{(-6)(-24)} = \sqrt{144} = 12, \, not \, -12$$

The Product Property of Radicals does not hold true when both radicands are negative and the index is an even number.

➡ Simplify: $4i(3 - 2i)$

$4i(3 - 2i) = 12i - 8i^2$ • Use the Distributive Property to remove parentheses.

$= 12i - 8(-1)$ • Replace i^2 by -1.

$= 8 + 12i$ • Write the answer in the form $a + bi$.

The product of two complex numbers is defined as follows.

The Product of Complex Numbers

$(a + bi)(c + di) = (ac - bd) + (ad + bc)i$

One way to remember this rule is to use the FOIL method.

➡ Simplify: $(2 + 4i)(3 - 5i)$

$(2 + 4i)(3 - 5i) = 6 - 10i + 12i - 20i^2$ • Use the FOIL method to find the product.

$= 6 + 2i - 20i^2$

$= 6 + 2i - 20(-1)$ • Replace i^2 by -1.

$= 26 + 2i$ • Write the answer in the form $a + bi$.

The conjugate of $a + bi$ is $a - bi$. The product of conjugates, $(a + bi)(a - bi)$, is the real number $a^2 + b^2$.

$$(a + bi)(a - bi) = a^2 - b^2i^2$$
$$= a^2 - b^2(-1)$$
$$= a^2 + b^2$$

➡ Simplify: $(2 + 3i)(2 - 3i)$

$(2 + 3i)(2 - 3i) = 2^2 + 3^2$ • The product of the conjugates is $2^2 + 3^2$.

$= 4 + 9$

$= 13$

Note that the product of a complex number and its conjugate is a real number.

Example 6

Simplify: $(2i)(-5i)$

Solution

$(2i)(-5i) = -10i^2 = (-10)(-1) = 10$

You Try It 6

Simplify: $(-3i)(-10i)$

Your solution

Example 7

Simplify: $\sqrt{-10} \cdot \sqrt{-5}$

Solution

$\sqrt{-10} \cdot \sqrt{-5} = i\sqrt{10} \cdot i\sqrt{5}$
$\qquad = i^2\sqrt{50} = -\sqrt{5^2 \cdot 2} = -5\sqrt{2}$

You Try It 7

Simplify: $-\sqrt{-8} \cdot \sqrt{-5}$

Your solution

Example 8

Simplify: $3i(2 - 4i)$

Solution

$3i(2 - 4i) = 6i - 12i^2$
$\qquad = 6i - 12(-1)$
$\qquad = 12 + 6i$

You Try It 8

Simplify: $-6i(3 + 4i)$

Your solution

Example 9

Simplify: $\sqrt{-8}\,(\sqrt{6} - \sqrt{-2})$

Solution

$\sqrt{-8}\,(\sqrt{6} - \sqrt{-2}) = i\sqrt{8}\,(\sqrt{6} - i\sqrt{2})$
$\qquad\qquad = i\sqrt{48} - i^2\sqrt{16}$
$\qquad\qquad = i\sqrt{2^4 \cdot 3} - (-1)\sqrt{2^4}$
$\qquad\qquad = 4i\sqrt{3} + 4 = 4 + 4i\sqrt{3}$

You Try It 9

Simplify: $\sqrt{-3}\,(\sqrt{27} - \sqrt{-6})$

Your solution

Example 10

Simplify: $(3 - 4i)(2 + 5i)$

Solution

$(3 - 4i)(2 + 5i) = 6 + 15i - 8i - 20i^2$
$\qquad\qquad = 6 + 7i - 20i^2$
$\qquad\qquad = 6 + 7i - 20(-1) = 26 + 7i$

You Try It 10

Simplify: $(4 - 3i)(2 - i)$

Your solution

Example 11

Simplify: $(4 + 5i)(4 - 5i)$

Solution

$(4 + 5i)(4 - 5i) = 4^2 + 5^2 = 16 + 25 = 41$

You Try It 11

Simplify: $(3 + 6i)(3 - 6i)$

Your solution

Solutions on p. S23

Objective D ***To divide complex numbers*** ··· CT

A rational expression containing one or more complex numbers is in simplest form when no imaginary number remains in the denominator.

➡ Simplify: $\dfrac{2-3i}{2i}$

$$\dfrac{2-3i}{2i} = \dfrac{2-3i}{2i} \cdot \dfrac{i}{i}$$

• Multiply the numerator and denominator by $\dfrac{i}{i}$.

$$= \dfrac{2i - 3i^2}{2i^2}$$

$$= \dfrac{2i - 3(-1)}{2(-1)}$$

• Replace i^2 by -1.

$$= \dfrac{3 + 2i}{-2}$$

• Simplify.

$$= -\dfrac{3}{2} - i$$

• Write the answer in the form $a + bi$.

➡ Simplify: $\dfrac{3+2i}{1+i}$

$$\dfrac{3+2i}{1+i} = \dfrac{3+2i}{1+i} \cdot \dfrac{1-i}{1-i}$$

• Multiply the numerator and denominator by the conjugate of $1 + i$.

$$= \dfrac{3 - 3i + 2i - 2i^2}{1^2 + 1^2}$$

$$= \dfrac{3 - i - 2(-1)}{1 + 1}$$

• Replace i^2 by -1 and simplify.

$$= \dfrac{5 - i}{2} = \dfrac{5}{2} - \dfrac{1}{2}i$$

• Write the answer in the form $a + bi$.

Example 12

Simplify: $\dfrac{5+4i}{3i}$

Solution

$$\dfrac{5+4i}{3i} = \dfrac{5+4i}{3i} \cdot \dfrac{i}{i} = \dfrac{5i + 4i^2}{3i^2}$$

$$= \dfrac{5i + 4(-1)}{3(-1)} = \dfrac{-4 + 5i}{-3} = \dfrac{4}{3} - \dfrac{5}{3}i$$

Example 13

Simplify: $\dfrac{5-3i}{4+2i}$

Solution

$$\dfrac{5-3i}{4+2i} = \dfrac{5-3i}{4+2i} \cdot \dfrac{4-2i}{4-2i}$$

$$= \dfrac{20 - 10i - 12i + 6i^2}{4^2 + 2^2}$$

$$= \dfrac{20 - 22i + 6(-1)}{20}$$

$$= \dfrac{14 - 22i}{20} = \dfrac{7 - 11i}{10} = \dfrac{7}{10} - \dfrac{11}{10}i$$

You Try It 12

Simplify: $\dfrac{2-3i}{4i}$

Your solution

You Try It 13

Simplify: $\dfrac{2+5i}{3-2i}$

Your solution

Solutions on p. S23

7.3 Exercises

Objective A

Simplify.

1. $\sqrt{-4}$

2. $\sqrt{-64}$

3. $\sqrt{-98}$

4. $\sqrt{-72}$

5. $\sqrt{-27}$

6. $\sqrt{-75}$

7. $\sqrt{16} + \sqrt{-4}$

8. $\sqrt{25} + \sqrt{-9}$

9. $\sqrt{12} - \sqrt{-18}$

10. $\sqrt{60} - \sqrt{-48}$

11. $\sqrt{160} - \sqrt{-147}$

12. $\sqrt{96} - \sqrt{-125}$

Objective B

Simplify.

13. $(2 + 4i) + (6 - 5i)$

14. $(6 - 9i) + (4 + 2i)$

15. $(-2 - 4i) - (6 - 8i)$

16. $(3 - 5i) + (8 - 2i)$

17. $(8 - \sqrt{-4}) - (2 + \sqrt{-16})$

18. $(5 - \sqrt{-25}) - (11 - \sqrt{-36})$

19. $(12 - \sqrt{-50}) + (7 - \sqrt{-8})$

20. $(5 - \sqrt{-12}) - (9 + \sqrt{-108})$

21. $(\sqrt{8} + \sqrt{-18}) + (\sqrt{32} - \sqrt{-72})$

22. $(\sqrt{40} - \sqrt{-98}) - (\sqrt{90} + \sqrt{-32})$

Objective C

Simplify.

23. $(7i)(-9i)$

24. $(-6i)(-4i)$

25. $\sqrt{-2}\,\sqrt{-8}$

26. $\sqrt{-5}\,\sqrt{-45}$

27. $\sqrt{-3}\,\sqrt{-6}$

28. $\sqrt{-5}\,\sqrt{-10}$

29. $2i(6 + 2i)$

30. $-3i(4 - 5i)$

31. $\sqrt{-2}(\sqrt{8} + \sqrt{-2})$

32. $\sqrt{-3}(\sqrt{12} - \sqrt{-6})$

33. $(5 - 2i)(3 + i)$

34. $(2 - 4i)(2 - i)$

35. $(6 + 5i)(3 + 2i)$

36. $(4 - 7i)(2 + 3i)$

37. $(1 - i)\left(\dfrac{1}{2} + \dfrac{1}{2}i\right)$

38. $\left(\dfrac{4}{5} - \dfrac{2}{5}i\right)\left(1 + \dfrac{1}{2}i\right)$

39. $\left(\dfrac{6}{5} + \dfrac{3}{5}i\right)\left(\dfrac{2}{3} - \dfrac{1}{3}i\right)$

40. $(2 - i)\left(\dfrac{2}{5} + \dfrac{1}{5}i\right)$

Objective D

Simplify.

41. $\dfrac{3}{i}$

42. $\dfrac{4}{5i}$

43. $\dfrac{2 - 3i}{-4i}$

44. $\dfrac{16 + 5i}{-3i}$

45. $\dfrac{4}{5 + i}$

46. $\dfrac{6}{5 + 2i}$

47. $\dfrac{2}{2 - i}$

48. $\dfrac{5}{4 - i}$

49. $\dfrac{1 - 3i}{3 + i}$

50. $\dfrac{2 + 12i}{5 + i}$

51. $\dfrac{\sqrt{-10}}{\sqrt{8} - \sqrt{-2}}$

52. $\dfrac{\sqrt{-2}}{\sqrt{12} - \sqrt{-8}}$

53. $\dfrac{2 - 3i}{3 + i}$

54. $\dfrac{3 + 5i}{1 - i}$

55. $\dfrac{5 + 3i}{3 - i}$

56. $\dfrac{3 - 2i}{2i + 3}$

APPLYING THE CONCEPTS

57. The property that the product of conjugates of the form $(a + bi)(a - bi) = a^2 + b^2$ can be used to factor the sum of two perfect squares over the set of complex numbers. For instance, $x^2 + 4 = (x + 2i)(x - 2i)$. Factor the following expressions over the set of complex numbers.
a. $y^2 + 1$
b. $49x^2 + 16$
c. $9a^2 + 64$

58. **a.** Is $3i$ a solution of $2x^2 + 18 = 0$?
b. Is $3 + i$ a solution of $x^2 - 6x + 10 = 0$?

59. Given $\sqrt{i} = \dfrac{\sqrt{2}}{2} + \dfrac{\sqrt{2}}{2}i$, find $\sqrt{-i}$.

60. Evaluate i^n for $n = 0, 1, 2, 3, 4, 5, 6$, and 7. Make a conjecture for the value of i^n for any natural number. Using your conjecture, evaluate i^{76}.

7.4 Solving Equations Containing Radical Expressions

Objective A *To solve a radical equation* .... (32) CT

An equation that contains a variable expression in a radicand is a **radical equation.**

$$\left. \begin{array}{l} \sqrt[3]{2x - 5} + x = 7 \\ \sqrt{x + 1} - \sqrt{x} = 4 \end{array} \right\} \begin{array}{l} \text{Radical} \\ \text{Equations} \end{array}$$

The following property is used to solve a radical equation.

The Property of Raising Each Side of an Equation to a Power

If two numbers are equal, then the same powers of the numbers are equal.

If $a = b$, then $a^n = b^n$.

➡ Solve: $\sqrt{x - 2} - 6 = 0$

$$\sqrt{x - 2} - 6 = 0$$
$$\sqrt{x - 2} = 6 \qquad \bullet \text{ Isolate the radical by adding 6 to each side of the equation.}$$
$$(\sqrt{x - 2})^2 = 6^2 \qquad \bullet \text{ Square each side of the equation.}$$
$$x - 2 = 36 \qquad \bullet \text{ Simplify and solve for } x.$$
$$x = 38$$

Check:
$$\begin{array}{r|r} \sqrt{x - 2} - 6 = 0 & \\ \hline \sqrt{38 - 2} - 6 & 0 \\ \sqrt{36} - 6 & 0 \\ 6 - 6 & 0 \\ 0 = 0 & \end{array}$$

38 checks as a solution. The solution is 38.

➡ Solve: $\sqrt[3]{x + 2} = -3$

$$\sqrt[3]{x + 2} = -3$$
$$(\sqrt[3]{x + 2})^3 = (-3)^3 \qquad \bullet \text{ Cube each side of the equation.}$$
$$x + 2 = -27 \qquad \bullet \text{ Solve the resulting equation.}$$
$$x = -29$$

Check:
$$\begin{array}{r|r} \sqrt[3]{x + 2} = -3 & \\ \hline \sqrt[3]{-29 + 2} & -3 \\ \sqrt[3]{-27} & -3 \\ -3 = -3 & \end{array}$$

-29 checks as a solution. The solution is -29.

Raising each side of an equation to an even power may result in an equation that has a solution that is not a solution of the original equation. This is called an **extraneous solution.** Here is an example:

➡ Solve: $\sqrt{2x - 1} + \sqrt{x} = 2$

$$\sqrt{2x - 1} + \sqrt{x} = 2$$

$$\sqrt{2x - 1} = 2 - \sqrt{x}$$ • Solve for one of the radical expressions.

$$(\sqrt{2x - 1})^2 = (2 - \sqrt{x})^2$$ • Square each side. Recall that $(a - b)^2 = a^2 - 2ab + b^2$.

$$2x - 1 = 4 - 4\sqrt{x} + x$$

$$x - 5 = -4\sqrt{x}$$

$$(x - 5)^2 = (-4\sqrt{x})^2$$

$$x^2 - 10x + 25 = 16x$$

$$x^2 - 26x + 25 = 0$$ • Solve the quadratic equation by factoring.

$$(x - 25)(x - 1) = 0$$

$$x = 25 \text{ or } x = 1$$

Check:

$\sqrt{2x - 1} + \sqrt{x} = 2$		$\sqrt{2x - 1} + \sqrt{x} = 2$	
$\sqrt{2(25) - 1} + \sqrt{25}$	2	$\sqrt{2(1) - 1} + \sqrt{1}$	2
$7 + 5$	2	$1 + 1$	2
$12 \neq 2$		$2 = 2$	

25 does not check as a solution. 1 checks as a solution. The solution is 1. Here 25 is an extraneous solution.

Example 1
Solve: $\sqrt{x - 1} + \sqrt{x + 4} = 5$

Solution

$$\sqrt{x - 1} + \sqrt{x + 4} = 5$$

$$\sqrt{x + 4} = 5 - \sqrt{x - 1}$$

$$(\sqrt{x + 4})^2 = (5 - \sqrt{x - 1})^2$$

$$x + 4 = 25 - 10\sqrt{x - 1} + x - 1$$

$$2 = \sqrt{x - 1}$$

$$2^2 = (\sqrt{x - 1})^2$$

$$4 = x - 1$$

$$5 = x$$

The solution checks. The solution is 5.

You Try It 1
Solve: $\sqrt{x} - \sqrt{x + 5} = 1$

Your solution

Example 2
Solve: $\sqrt[3]{3x - 1} = -4$

Solution

$$\sqrt[3]{3x - 1} = -4$$

$$(\sqrt[3]{3x - 1})^3 = (-4)^3$$

$$3x - 1 = -64$$

$$3x = -63$$

$$x = -21$$

The solution checks. The solution is -21.

You Try It 2
Solve: $\sqrt[4]{x - 8} = 3$

Your solution

Solutions on p. S23

Objective B   **To solve application problems** ....

A right triangle contains one 90° angle. The side opposite the 90° angle is called the **hypotenuse.** The other two sides are called **legs.**

Pythagoras, a Greek mathematician, discovered that the square of the hypotenuse of a right triangle is equal to the sum of the squares of the two legs. This is called the **Pythagorean Theorem.**

$$c^2 = a^2 + b^2$$

Example 3

A ladder 20 ft long is leaning against a building. How high on the building will the ladder reach when the bottom of the ladder is 8 ft from the building? Round to the nearest tenth.

Strategy

To find the distance, use the Pythagorean Theorem. The hypotenuse is the length of the ladder. One leg is the distance from the bottom of the ladder to the base of the building. The distance along the building from the ground to the top of the ladder is the unknown leg.

Solution

$$c^2 = a^2 + b^2$$
$$20^2 = 8^2 + b^2$$
$$400 = 64 + b^2$$
$$336 = b^2$$
$$(336)^{1/2} = (b^2)^{1/2}$$
$$\sqrt{336} = b$$
$$18.3 \approx b$$

The distance is 18.3 ft.

You Try It 3

Find the diagonal of a rectangle that is 6 cm long and 3 cm wide. Round to the nearest tenth.

Your strategy

Your solution

Solution on p. S23

Example 4

An object is dropped from a high building. Find the distance the object has fallen when the speed reaches 96 ft/s. Use the equation $v = \sqrt{64d}$, where v is the speed of the object and d is the distance.

Strategy

To find the distance the object has fallen, replace v in the equation with the given value and solve for d.

Solution

$$v = \sqrt{64d}$$
$$96 = \sqrt{64d}$$
$$(96)^2 = (\sqrt{64d})^2$$
$$9216 = 64d$$
$$144 = d$$

The object has fallen 144 ft.

Example 5

Find the length of a pendulum that makes one swing in 1.5 s. The equation for the time of one swing is given by $T = 2\pi\sqrt{\dfrac{L}{32}}$, where T is the time in seconds and L is the length in feet. Use 3.14 for π. Round to the nearest hundredth.

Strategy

To find the length of the pendulum, replace T in the equation with the given value and solve for L.

Solution

$$T = 2\pi\sqrt{\frac{L}{32}}$$
$$1.5 = 2(3.14)\sqrt{\frac{L}{32}}$$
$$\frac{1.5}{2(3.14)} = \sqrt{\frac{L}{32}}$$
$$\left[\frac{1.5}{2(3.14)}\right]^2 = \left(\sqrt{\frac{L}{32}}\right)^2$$
$$\left(\frac{1.5}{6.28}\right)^2 = \frac{L}{32}$$
$$1.83 \approx L$$

The length of the pendulum is 1.83 ft.

You Try It 4

How far would a submarine periscope have to be above the water to locate a ship 5.5 mi away? The equation for the distance in miles that the lookout can see is $d = \sqrt{1.5h}$, where h is the height in feet above the surface of the water. Round to the nearest hundredth.

Your strategy

Your solution

You Try It 5

Find the distance required for a car to reach a velocity of 88 ft/s when the acceleration is 22 ft/s². Use the equation $v = \sqrt{2as}$, where v is the velocity, a is the acceleration, and s is the distance.

Your strategy

Your solution

Solutions on pp. S23–S24

7.4 Exercises

Objective A

Solve.

1. $\sqrt[3]{4x} = -2$

2. $\sqrt[3]{6x} = -3$

3. $\sqrt{3x - 2} = 5$

4. $\sqrt{3x + 9} - 12 = 0$

5. $\sqrt{4x - 3} - 5 = 0$

6. $\sqrt{4x - 2} = \sqrt{3x + 9}$

7. $\sqrt{2x + 4} = \sqrt{5x - 9}$

8. $\sqrt[3]{x - 2} = 3$

9. $\sqrt[3]{2x - 6} = 4$

10. $\sqrt[3]{3x - 9} = \sqrt[3]{2x + 12}$

11. $\sqrt[3]{x - 12} = \sqrt[3]{5x + 16}$

12. $\sqrt[4]{4x + 1} = 2$

13. $\sqrt[3]{2x - 3} + 5 = 2$

14. $\sqrt[3]{x - 4} + 7 = 5$

15. $\sqrt{x} + \sqrt{x - 5} = 5$

16. $\sqrt{x + 3} + \sqrt{x - 1} = 2$

17. $\sqrt{2x + 5} - \sqrt{2x} = 1$

18. $\sqrt{3x} - \sqrt{3x - 5} = 1$

19. $\sqrt{2x} - \sqrt{x - 1} = 1$

20. $\sqrt{2x - 5} + \sqrt{x + 1} = 3$

21. $\sqrt{2x + 2} + \sqrt{x} = 3$

Objective B   *Application Problems*

22. An object is dropped from a bridge. Find the distance the object has fallen when the speed reaches 100 ft/s. Use the equation $v = \sqrt{64d}$, where v is the speed in feet per second and d is the distance in feet.

$v = 100$ ft/s

23. The time it takes for an object to fall a certain distance is given by the equation $t = \sqrt{\dfrac{2d}{g}}$, where t is the time in seconds, d is the distance in feet, and g is the acceleration due to gravity. The acceleration due to gravity on Earth is 32 feet per second per second. If an object is dropped from atop a tall building, how far will it fall in 6 s?

24. The time it takes for an object to fall a certain distance is given by the equation $t = \sqrt{\dfrac{2d}{g}}$, where t is the time in seconds, d is the distance in feet, and g is the acceleration due to gravity. If an astronaut above the moon's surface drops an object, how far will it have fallen in 3 s? The acceleration on the moon's surface is 5.5 feet per second per second.

25. High definition television (HDTV) gives consumers a wider viewing area, more like a film seen in a theater. A regular television with a 27-inch diagonal measurement has a screen 16.2 in. tall. An HDTV screen with the same 16.2-inch height would have a diagonal measuring 33 in. How many inches wider is the HDTV screen? Round to the nearest hundredth.

26. At what height above Earth's surface would a satellite be in orbit if it is traveling at a speed of 7500 m/s? Use the equation $v = \sqrt{\dfrac{4 \times 10^{14}}{h + 6.4 \times 10^6}}$, where v is the speed of the satellite in meters and h is the height above Earth's surface in meters. Round to the nearest thousand.

27. Find the length of a pendulum that makes one swing in 3 s. The equation for the time of one swing of a pendulum is given by $T = 2\pi\sqrt{\dfrac{L}{32}}$, where T is the time in seconds and L is the length in feet. Round to the nearest hundredth.

APPLYING THE CONCEPTS

28. Solve the following equations. Describe the solution by using the following terms: integer, rational number, irrational number, real number, and imaginary number. Note that more than one term may be used to describe the answer.
   a. $x^2 + 3 = 7$ **b.** $x^2 + 1 = 0$ **c.** $x^{3/4} = 8$

29. Solve: $\sqrt{3x - 2} = \sqrt{2x - 3} + \sqrt{x - 1}$

30. Solve $a^2 + b^2 = c^2$ for a.

31. Beginning with a square with each side of length s, draw a line segment from the midpoint of the base of the square to a vertex as shown. Call this distance a. Make a rectangle whose width is that of the square and whose length is $\frac{s}{2} + a$. Find:

   a. The area of the rectangle in terms of s.
   b. The ratio of the length to the width.

   The rectangle formed in this way is called a golden rectangle. It was described at the beginning of this chapter.

32. Solve $V = \frac{4}{3}\pi r^3$ for r.

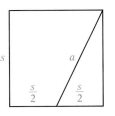

33. Find the length of the side labeled x.

Focus on Problem Solving

Another Look at Polya's Four-Step Process

Polya's four general steps to follow when attempting to solve a problem are to understand the problem, devise a plan, carry out the plan, and review the solution. (See the Focus on Problem Solving in the chapter entitled "Review of Real Numbers.") In the process of devising a plan (Step 2), it may be appropriate to write a mathematical expression or an equation. We will illustrate this with the following problem.

Number the letters of the alphabet in sequence from 1 to 26. (See the list at the left.) Find a word for which the product of the numerical values of the letters of the word equals 1,000,000. We will agree that a "word" is any sequence of letters that contains at least one vowel but is not necessarily in the dictionary.

A = 1
B = 2
C = 3
D = 4
E = 5
F = 6
G = 7
H = 8
I = 9
J = 10
K = 11
L = 12
M = 13
N = 14
O = 15
P = 16
Q = 17
R = 18
S = 19
T = 20
U = 21
V = 22
W = 23
X = 24
Y = 25
Z = 26

Understand the Problem

Consider REZB. The product of the letters is $18 \cdot 5 \cdot 26 \cdot 2 = 4680$. This "word" is a sequence of letters with at least one vowel. However, the product of the numerical values of the letters is not 1,000,000. Thus this word does not solve our problem.

Devise a Plan

Actually, we should have known that the product of the letters in REZB could not equal 1,000,000. The letter R has a factor of 9, and the letter Z has a factor of 13. Neither of these two numbers is a factor of 1,000,000. Consequently, R and Z cannot be letters in the word we are trying to find. This observation leads to an important observation: each of the letters that make up our word must be a factor of 1,000,000. To find these letters, consider the prime factorization of 1,000,000.

$$1,000,000 = 2^6 \cdot 5^6$$

Looking at the prime factorization, we note that only letters that contain 2 or 5 as factors are possible candidates. These letters are B, D, E, H, J, P, T, and Y. One additional point: Because 1 times any number is the number, the letter A can be part of any word we construct.

Our task is now to construct a word from these letters such that the product is 1,000,000. From the prime factorization above, we must have 2 as a factor six times and 5 as a factor six times.

Carry Out the Plan

We must construct a word with the characteristics described in our plan. Here is a possibility:

THEBEYE

Review the Solution

You should multiply the values of all the letters and verify that the product is 1,000,000. To ensure that you have an understanding of the problem, try to find other "words" that satisfy the conditions of the problem.

Projects and Group Activities

Complex Numbers   That a negative number might be the solution of an equation was not readily accepted by mathematicians until the middle of the 16th century. Hieronimo Cardano was the first to take notice of these numbers in his book *Ars Magna* (*The Great Art*), which was published in 1545. However, he called these solutions fictitious. In that same book, in one case, he also considered a solution of an equation of the form $5 + \sqrt{-15}$, a number we now call a complex number.

Complex numbers were thought to have no real or geometric interpretation and therefore to be "imaginary." One mathematician called them "ghosts of real numbers." Then, in 1806, Jean-Robert Argand published a book that included a geometric description of complex numbers. (Actually, Caspar Wessel first proposed this idea in 1797. However, his work went unnoticed.)

An Argand diagram consists of a horizontal and a vertical axis. The horizontal axis is the *real axis;* the vertical axis is the *imaginary axis.* A complex number of the form $a + bi$ is shown as the point in the plane whose coordinates are (a, b). The graphs of $2 + 4i$, $-4 - 3i$, $4(4 + 0i)$, and $2i(0 + 2i)$ are shown at the right.

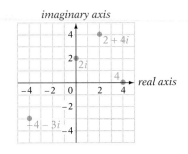

By using the Argand diagram, it is possible to give various interpretations of complex numbers and the operations on them. We will focus on only one small aspect: a geometric explanation of multiplying by i, the imaginary unit.

Before doing this, recall that real number multiplication is repeated addition. For instance, $2 \cdot 3 = 2 + 2 + 2$. Geometrically, this can be shown on a number line.

Thus, multiplying by 3 triples the size of the arrow that represents 2. In general, multiplying a real number by a number greater than 1 increases the magnitude of the number.

Consider the complex number $3 + 4i$. Multiply this number by i.

$$i(3 + 4i) = -4 + 3i$$

The two complex numbers are shown in the graph at the right.

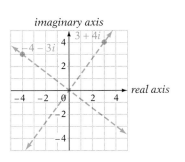

1. Find the slope of the line that passes through the origin and the point $(3, 4)$.

2. Find the slope of the line that passes through the origin and the point $(-4, 3)$.

3. Find the product of the slopes of the two lines. What does this product tell you?

4. Find the distance of the points $(3, 4)$ and $(-4, 3)$ from the origin.

A conclusion that can be drawn from the answers to the foregoing questions is that multiplying a number by i rotates that number $90°$. This is shown in the figure at the right.

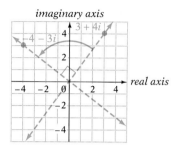

This property of complex numbers is important in the study of electricity and magnetism. Complex numbers are used extensively by electrical engineers to study electrical circuits.

Solving Radical Equations with a Graphing Calculator

The radical equation $\sqrt{x-2} - 6 = 0$ is solved algebraically on page 401. To solve $\sqrt{x-2} - 6 = 0$ with a graphing calculator, use the left side of the equation and write an equation in two variables.

$$y = \sqrt{x-2} - 6$$

The graph of $y = \sqrt{x-2} - 6$ is shown at the left. The solution set of the equation $y = \sqrt{x-2} - 6$ is the set of ordered pairs (x, y) whose coordinates make the equation a true statement. The x-coordinate where $y = 0$ is the solution of the equation $\sqrt{x-2} - 6 = 0$. The solution is the x-intercept of the curve given by the equation $y = \sqrt{x-2} - 6$. The solution is 38.

The solution of the radical equation $\sqrt[3]{x-2} = -0.8$ is 1.488. A graphing calculator with the trace feature can find any rational or irrational solution to a predetermined degree of accuracy. The graph of $y = \sqrt[3]{x-2} + 0.8$ is shown at the left.

You were to solve Exercises 1–21 on page 405 by algebraic means. Try some of those exercises again, this time using a graphing calculator. Guidelines for using graphing calculators are found in the appendix, page 647.

Use a graphing calculator to find the solution of each equation correct to the nearest thousandth.

1. $\sqrt{x + 0.3} = 1.3$ **2.** $\sqrt[3]{x + 1.2} = -1.1$ **3.** $\sqrt[4]{3x - 1.5} = 1.4$

Chapter Summary

Key Words   The *nth root of a* is $a^{1/n}$. The expression $\sqrt[n]{a}$ is another symbol for the *n*th root of *a*.

In the expression $\sqrt[n]{a}$, the symbol $\sqrt{}$ is called a *radical*, *n* is the *index* of the radical, and *a* is the *radicand*.

The symbol $\sqrt{}$ is used to indicate the positive or *principal square root* of a number.

Conjugates are binomial expressions that differ only in the sign of a term. The expressions $a - b$ and $a + b$ are conjugates.

The procedure used to remove a radical from the denominator is called *rationalizing the denominator.*

A *complex number* is a number of the form $a + bi$, where *a* and *b* are real numbers and $i = \sqrt{-1}$.

For the complex number $a + bi$, *a* is called the *real part* of the complex number and *b* is called the *imaginary part* of the complex number.

Essential Rules   *Rational Exponents*

If *m* and *n* are positive integers and $a^{1/n}$ is a real number, then $a^{m/n} = (a^{1/n})^m$.

The Product Property of Radicals

If $\sqrt[n]{a}$ and $\sqrt[n]{b}$ are positive real numbers, then $\sqrt[n]{a} \, \sqrt[n]{b} = \sqrt[n]{ab}$ and $\sqrt[n]{ab} = \sqrt[n]{a} \, \sqrt[n]{b}$.

The Quotient Property of Radicals

If $\sqrt[n]{a}$ and $\sqrt[n]{b}$ are positive real numbers and $b \neq 0$, $\dfrac{\sqrt[n]{a}}{\sqrt[n]{b}} = \sqrt[n]{\dfrac{a}{b}}$ and $\sqrt[n]{\dfrac{a}{b}} = \dfrac{\sqrt[n]{a}}{\sqrt[n]{b}}$.

Addition and Subtraction of Complex Numbers

$(a + bi) + (c + di) = (a + c) + (b + d)i$
$(a + bi) - (c + di) = (a - c) + (b - d)i$

Multiplication of Complex Numbers

$(a + bi)(c + di) = (ac - bd) + (ad + bc)i$

Property of Raising Both Sides of an Equation to a Power

If *a* and *b* are real numbers and $a = b$, then $a^n = b^n$.

Pythagorean Theorem

$c^2 = a^2 + b^2$

Chapter Review

1. Simplify: $(16x^{-4}y^{12})^{1/4}(100x^6y^{-2})^{1/2}$

2. Solve: $\sqrt[4]{3x-5}=2$

3. Simplify: $(6-5i)(4+3i)$

4. Rewrite $7y\sqrt[3]{x^2}$ as an exponential expression.

5. Simplify: $(\sqrt{3}+8)(\sqrt{3}-2)$

6. Solve: $\sqrt{4x+9}+10=11$

7. Simplify: $\dfrac{x^{-3/2}}{x^{7/2}}$

8. Simplify: $\dfrac{8}{\sqrt{3y}}$

9. Simplify: $\sqrt[3]{-8a^6b^{12}}$

10. Simplify: $\sqrt{50a^4b^3}-ab\sqrt{18a^2b}$

11. Simplify: $\dfrac{x+2}{\sqrt{x}+\sqrt{2}}$

12. Simplify: $\dfrac{5+2i}{3i}$

13. Simplify: $\sqrt{18a^3b^6}$

14. Simplify:
$(\sqrt{50}+\sqrt{-72})-(\sqrt{162}-\sqrt{-8})$

15. Simplify: $3x\sqrt[3]{54x^8y^{10}}-2x^2y\sqrt[3]{16x^5y^7}$

16. Simplify: $\sqrt[3]{16x^4y}\,\sqrt[3]{4xy^5}$

17. Simplify: $i(3-7i)$

18. Rewrite $3x^{3/4}$ as a radical expression.

19. Simplify: $\sqrt[5]{-64a^8b^{12}}$

20. Simplify: $\dfrac{5 + 9i}{1 - i}$

21. Simplify: $\sqrt{-12}\,\sqrt{-6}$

22. Solve: $\sqrt{x - 5} + \sqrt{x + 6} = 11$

23. Simplify: $\sqrt[4]{81a^8b^{12}}$

24. Simplify: $\sqrt{-50}$

25. Simplify: $(-8 + 3i) - (4 - 7i)$

26. Simplify: $(5 - \sqrt{6})^2$

27. Simplify: $4x\sqrt{12x^2y} + \sqrt{3x^4y} - x^2\sqrt{27y}$

28. The velocity of the wind determines the amount of power generated by a windmill. A typical equation for this relationship is $v = 4.05\,\sqrt[3]{P}$, where v is the velocity in miles per hour and P is the power in watts. Find the amount of power generated by a 20-mph wind. Round to the nearest whole number.

29. Find the distance required for a car to reach a velocity of 88 ft/s when the acceleration is 16 ft/s². Use the equation $v = \sqrt{2as}$, where v is the velocity, a is the acceleration, and s is the distance.

30. A 12-foot ladder is leaning against a building. How far from the building is the bottom of the ladder when the top of the ladder touches the building 10 ft above the ground? Round to the nearest hundredth.

Chapter Test

1. Write $\frac{1}{2}\sqrt[4]{x^3}$ as an exponential expression.

2. Simplify:
$$\sqrt[3]{54x^7y^3} - x\sqrt[3]{128x^4y^3} - x^2\sqrt[3]{2xy^3}$$

3. Write $3y^{2/5}$ as a radical expression.

4. Simplify: $(2 + 5i)(4 - 2i)$

5. Simplify: $(2\sqrt{x} + \sqrt{y})^2$

6. Simplify: $\dfrac{r^{2/3}\,r^{-1}}{r^{-1/2}}$

7. Solve: $\sqrt{x + 12} - \sqrt{x} = 2$

8. Simplify: $\sqrt[3]{8x^3y^6}$

9. Simplify: $\sqrt{3x}\,(\sqrt{x} - \sqrt{25x}\,)$

10. Simplify: $(5 - 2i) - (8 - 4i)$

11. Simplify: $\sqrt{32x^4y^7}$

12. Simplify: $(2\sqrt{3} + 4)(3\sqrt{3} - 1)$

13. Simplify: $(2 + i) + (2 - i)(3 + 2i)$

14. Simplify: $\dfrac{4 - 2\sqrt{5}}{2 - \sqrt{5}}$

15. Simplify: $\sqrt{18a^3} + a\sqrt{50a}$

16. Simplify: $(\sqrt{a} - 3\sqrt{b})(2\sqrt{a} + 5\sqrt{b})$

17. Simplify: $\dfrac{(2x^{1/3}y^{-2/3})^6}{(x^{-4}y^8)^{1/4}}$

18. Simplify: $\dfrac{\sqrt{x}}{\sqrt{x} - \sqrt{y}}$

19. Simplify: $\dfrac{2 + 3i}{1 - 2i}$

20. Solve: $\sqrt[3]{2x - 2} + 4 = 2$

21. Simplify: $\left(\dfrac{4a^4}{b^2}\right)^{-3/2}$

22. Simplify: $\sqrt[3]{27a^4b^3c^7}$

23. Simplify: $\dfrac{\sqrt{32x^5y}}{\sqrt{2xy^3}}$

24. Simplify: $(\sqrt{-8})(\sqrt{-2})$

25. An object is dropped from a high building. Find the distance the object has fallen when the speed reaches 192 ft/s. Use the equation $v = \sqrt{64d}$, where v is the speed of the object and d is the distance.

Cumulative Review

1. Identify the property that justifies the statement $(a + 2)b = ab + 2b$.

2. Given $f(x) = 3x^2 - 2x + 1$, evaluate $f(-3)$.

3. Solve: $5 - \dfrac{2}{3}x = 4$

4. Solve: $2[4 - 2(3 - 2x)] = 4(1 - x)$

5. Solve: $2 + |4 - 3x| = 5$

6. Solve: $6x - 3(2x + 2) > 3 - 3(x + 2)$

7. Solve: $|2x + 3| \le 9$

8. Factor: $81x^2 - y^2$

9. Factor: $x^5 + 2x^3 - 3x$

10. Find the equation of the line that passes through the points $(2, 3)$ and $(-1, 2)$.

11. Find the value of the determinant:
$$\begin{vmatrix} 1 & 2 & -3 \\ 0 & -1 & 2 \\ 3 & 1 & -2 \end{vmatrix}$$

12. Solve $P = \dfrac{R - C}{n}$ for C.

13. Simplify: $(2^{-1}x^2y^{-6})(2^{-1}y^{-4})^{-2}$

14. Simplify: $\dfrac{x^2y^3}{x^2 + 2x - 8} \cdot \dfrac{2x^2 - 7x + 6}{xy^4}$

15. Simplify: $\sqrt{40x^3} - x\sqrt{90x}$

16. Solve: $\dfrac{x}{x - 2} - 2x = \dfrac{-3}{x - 2}$

17. Find the slope and y-intercept of and graph $3x - 2y = -6$.

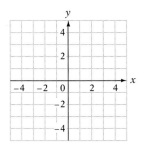

18. Graph the solution set of $3x + 2y \le 4$.

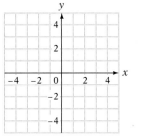

19. Simplify: $\dfrac{2i}{3-i}$

20. Solve: $\sqrt[3]{3x-4}+5=1$

21. Simplify: $\dfrac{x}{2x-3}+\dfrac{4}{x+4}$

22. Solve by using Cramer's Rule:
$$2x-y=4$$
$$-2x+3y=5$$

23. A collection of 30 stamps consists of 13¢ stamps and 18¢ stamps. The total value of the stamps is $4.85. Find the number of 18¢ stamps.

24. A sales executive traveled 25 mi by car and then an additional 625 mi by plane. The rate of the plane was five times faster than the rate of the car. The total time of the trip was 3 h. Find the rate of the plane.

25. How long does it take light to travel to Earth from the moon when the moon is 232,500 mi from Earth? Light travels 1.86×10^5 mi/s.

26. How far would a submarine periscope have to be above the water to locate a ship 7 mi away? The equation for the distance in miles that the lookout can see is $d=\sqrt{1.5h}$, where h is the height in feet above the surface of the water. Round to the nearest tenth of a foot.

27. The graph shows the amount invested and the annual income from an investment. Find the slope of the line between the two points shown on the graph. Then write a sentence that states the meaning of the slope.

8

Quadratic Equations

Objectives

Section 8.1
To solve a quadratic equation by factoring
To write a quadratic equation given its solutions
To solve a quadratic equation by taking square roots

Section 8.2
To solve a quadratic equation by completing
the square

Section 8.3
To solve a quadratic equation by using the
quadratic formula

Section 8.4
To solve an equation that is quadratic in form
To solve a radical equation that is reducible to a
quadratic equation
To solve a fractional equation that is reducible to a
quadratic equation

Section 8.5
To solve a nonlinear inequality

Section 8.6
To solve application problems

Building inspectors inspect the structural integrity of buildings. Inspectors may specialize in structural steel or reinforced concrete structures. Before construction begins, plan examiners determine whether the plans for the building or other structure comply with building code regulations and are suited to the engineering and environmental demands of the building site. Some of the equations that determine the loads various beams can safely carry are quadratic equations, the subject of this chapter.

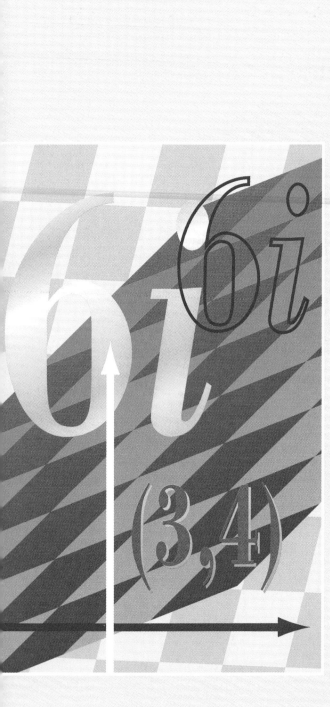

Complex Numbers

Negative numbers were not universally accepted in the mathematical community until well into the 14th century. It is no wonder, then, that *imaginary numbers* took an even longer time to gain acceptance.

Beginning in the mid-16th century, mathematicians were beginning to integrate imaginary numbers into their writings. One notation for $3i$ was R (0 m 3). Literally, this was interpreted as $\sqrt{0-3}$.

By the mid-18th century, the symbol i was introduced. Still later it was shown that complex numbers could be thought of as points in the plane. The complex number $3 + 4i$ was associated with the point (3, 4).

By the end of the 19th century, complex numbers were fully integrated into mathematics. This was due in large part to some eminent mathematicians who used complex numbers to prove theorems that had previously eluded proof.

8.1 Solving Quadratic Equations by Factoring or by Taking Square Roots

Objective A *To solve a quadratic equation by factoring* .... 〔33〕 CT

Recall that a **quadratic equation** is an equation of the form $ax^2 + bx + c = 0$, where a, b, and c are constants and $a \neq 0$.

Quadratic Equations $\begin{cases} 3x^2 - x + 2 = 0, & a = 3, \quad b = -1, \quad c = 2 \\ -x^2 + 4 = 0, & a = -1, \quad b = 0, \quad c = 4 \\ 6x^2 - 5x = 0, & a = 6, \quad b = -5, \quad c = 0 \end{cases}$

A quadratic equation is in **standard form** when the polynomial is in descending order and equal to zero. Because the degree of the polynomial $ax^2 + bx + c$ is 2, a quadratic equation is also called a **second-degree equation.**

As we discussed earlier, quadratic equations sometimes can be solved by using the Principle of Zero Products. This method is reviewed here.

The Principle of Zero Products

If a and b are real numbers and $ab = 0$, then $a = 0$ or $b = 0$.

The Principle of Zero Products states that if the product of two factors is zero, then at least one of the factors must be zero.

➡ Solve by factoring: $3x^2 = 2 - 5x$

$$3x^2 = 2 - 5x$$
$$3x^2 + 5x - 2 = 0 \qquad \bullet \text{ Write the equation in standard form.}$$
$$(3x - 1)(x + 2) = 0 \qquad \bullet \text{ Factor.}$$
$$3x - 1 = 0 \qquad x + 2 = 0 \qquad \bullet \text{ Use the Principle of Zero Products to write two equations.}$$
$$3x = 1 \qquad x = -2 \qquad \bullet \text{ Solve each equation.}$$
$$x = \frac{1}{3}$$

$\frac{1}{3}$ and -2 check as solutions. The solutions are $\frac{1}{3}$ and -2.

➡ Solve by factoring: $x^2 - 6x = -9$

$$x^2 - 6x = -9$$
$$x^2 - 6x + 9 = 0 \qquad \bullet \text{ Write the equation in standard form.}$$
$$(x - 3)(x - 3) = 0 \qquad \bullet \text{ Factor.}$$
$$x - 3 = 0 \qquad x - 3 = 0 \qquad \bullet \text{ Use the Principle of Zero Products.}$$
$$x = 3 \qquad x = 3 \qquad \bullet \text{ Solve each equation.}$$

3 checks as a solution. The solution is 3.

TAKE NOTE

When a quadratic equation has two solutions that are the same number, the solution is called a **double root** of the equation. 3 is a double root of $x^2 - 6x = -9$.

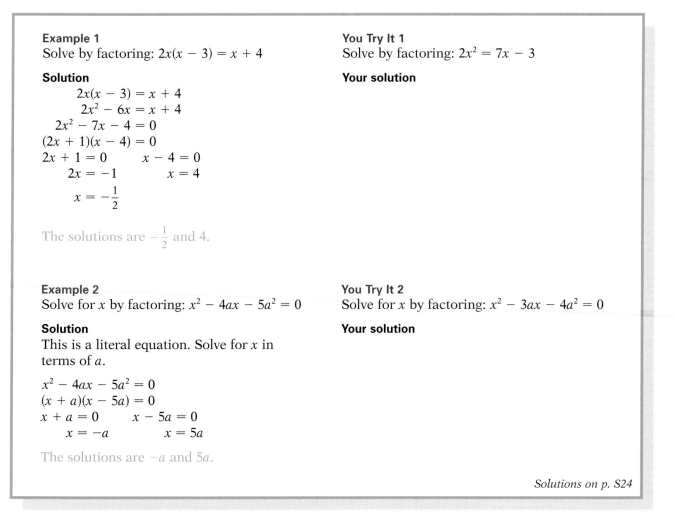

Example 1
Solve by factoring: $2x(x - 3) = x + 4$

Solution
$$2x(x - 3) = x + 4$$
$$2x^2 - 6x = x + 4$$
$$2x^2 - 7x - 4 = 0$$
$$(2x + 1)(x - 4) = 0$$
$$2x + 1 = 0 \qquad x - 4 = 0$$
$$2x = -1 \qquad x = 4$$
$$x = -\frac{1}{2}$$

The solutions are $-\frac{1}{2}$ and 4.

You Try It 1
Solve by factoring: $2x^2 = 7x - 3$

Your solution

Example 2
Solve for x by factoring: $x^2 - 4ax - 5a^2 = 0$

Solution
This is a literal equation. Solve for x in terms of a.

$$x^2 - 4ax - 5a^2 = 0$$
$$(x + a)(x - 5a) = 0$$
$$x + a = 0 \qquad x - 5a = 0$$
$$x = -a \qquad x = 5a$$

The solutions are $-a$ and $5a$.

You Try It 2
Solve for x by factoring: $x^2 - 3ax - 4a^2 = 0$

Your solution

Solutions on p. S24

Objective B   *To write a quadratic equation given its solutions* .... 33 CT

As shown below, the solutions of the equation $(x - r_1)(x - r_2) = 0$ are r_1 and r_2.

$$(x - r_1)(x - r_2) = 0$$
$$x - r_1 = 0 \qquad\qquad x - r_2 = 0$$
$$x = r_1 \qquad\qquad x = r_2$$

Check:

$$\frac{(x - r_1)(x - r_2) = 0}{(r_1 - r_1)(r_1 - r_2)}$$
$$0 \cdot (r_1 - r_2)$$
$$0 = 0$$

$$\frac{(x - r_1)(x - r_2) = 0}{(r_2 - r_1)(r_2 - r_2)}$$
$$(r_2 - r_1) \cdot 0$$
$$0 = 0$$

Using the equation $(x - r_1)(x - r_2) = 0$ and the fact that r_1 and r_2 are solutions of this equation, it is possible to write a quadratic equation given its solutions.

➡ Write a quadratic equation that has solutions 4 and -5.

$$(x - r_1)(x - r_2) = 0$$
$$(x - 4)[x - (-5)] = 0$$
$$(x - 4)(x + 5) = 0$$
$$x^2 + x - 20 = 0$$

• Replace r_1 by 4 and r_2 by -5.
• Simplify.
• Multiply.

⇒ Write a quadratic equation with integer coefficients and solutions $\frac{2}{3}$ and $\frac{1}{2}$.

$$(x - r_1)(x - r_2) = 0$$

$$\left(x - \frac{2}{3}\right)\left(x - \frac{1}{2}\right) = 0$$ • Replace r_1 by $\frac{2}{3}$ and r_2 by $\frac{1}{2}$.

$$x^2 - \frac{7}{6}x + \frac{1}{3} = 0$$ • Multiply.

$$6\left(x^2 - \frac{7}{6}x + \frac{1}{3}\right) = 6 \cdot 0$$ • Multiply each side of the equation by the LCM of the denominators.

$$6x^2 - 7x + 2 = 0$$

Example 3

Write a quadratic equation with integer coefficients and solutions $\frac{1}{2}$ and -4.

Solution

$$(x - r_1)(x - r_2) = 0$$

$$\left(x - \frac{1}{2}\right)[x - (-4)] = 0$$

$$\left(x - \frac{1}{2}\right)(x + 4) = 0$$

$$x^2 + \frac{7}{2}x - 2 = 0$$

$$2\left(x^2 + \frac{7}{2}x - 2\right) = 2 \cdot 0$$

$$2x^2 + 7x - 4 = 0$$

You Try It 3

Write a quadratic equation with integer coefficients and solutions 3 and $-\frac{1}{2}$.

Your solution

Solution on p. S24

Objective C   To solve a quadratic equation by taking square roots .... 〔33〕 CT

The solution of the quadratic equation $x^2 = 16$ is shown at the right.

$$x^2 = 16$$
$$x^2 - 16 = 0$$
$$(x - 4)(x + 4) = 0$$
$$x - 4 = 0 \qquad x + 4 = 0$$
$$x = 4 \qquad\quad x = -4$$

As shown below, the solutions can also be found by taking the square root of each side of the equation and writing the positive and negative square roots of the number. The notation $x = \pm 4$ means $x = 4$ or $x = -4$.

$$x^2 = 16$$
$$\sqrt{x^2} = \sqrt{16}$$
$$x = \pm 4$$

The solutions are 4 and -4.

⇒ Solve by taking square roots: $3x^2 = 54$

$$3x^2 = 54$$

$$x^2 = 18$$ • Solve for x^2.

$$\sqrt{x^2} = \sqrt{18}$$ • Take the square root of each side of the equation.

$$x = \pm\sqrt{18} = \pm 3\sqrt{2}$$ • Simplify.

$3\sqrt{2}$ and $-3\sqrt{2}$ check as solutions. The solutions are $3\sqrt{2}$ and $-3\sqrt{2}$.

Solving a quadratic equation by taking the square root of each side of the equation can lead to solutions that are complex numbers.

⇒ Solve by taking square roots: $2x^2 + 18 = 0$

$$2x^2 + 18 = 0$$
$$2x^2 = -18 \qquad \text{• Solve for } x^2.$$
$$x^2 = -9$$
$$\sqrt{x^2} = \sqrt{-9} \qquad \text{• Take the square root of each side of the equation.}$$
$$x = \pm\sqrt{-9} = \pm 3i \qquad \text{• Simplify.}$$

Check:

$2x^2 + 18 = 0$		$2x^2 + 18 = 0$	
$2(3i)^2 + 18$	0	$2(-3i)^2 + 18$	0
$2(-9) + 18$	0	$2(-9) + 18$	0
$-18 + 18$	0	$-18 + 18$	0
	$0 = 0$		$0 = 0$

The solutions are $3i$ and $-3i$.

An equation containing the square of a binomial can be solved by taking square roots.

⇒ Solve by taking square roots: $(x + 2)^2 - 24 = 0$

$$(x + 2)^2 - 24 = 0$$
$$(x + 2)^2 = 24 \qquad \text{• Solve for } (x + 2)^2.$$
$$\sqrt{(x + 2)^2} = \sqrt{24} \qquad \text{• Take the square root of each side of the equation.}$$
$$x + 2 = \pm\sqrt{24} = \pm 2\sqrt{6} \qquad \text{• Simplify.}$$
$$x + 2 = 2\sqrt{6} \qquad x + 2 = -2\sqrt{6} \qquad \text{• Solve for } x.$$
$$x = -2 + 2\sqrt{6} \qquad x = -2 - 2\sqrt{6}$$

The solutions are $-2 + 2\sqrt{6}$ and $-2 - 2\sqrt{6}$.

Example 4
Solve by taking square roots:
$3(x - 2)^2 + 12 = 0$

Solution
$$3(x - 2)^2 + 12 = 0$$
$$3(x - 2)^2 = -12$$
$$(x - 2)^2 = -4$$
$$\sqrt{(x - 2)^2} = \sqrt{-4}$$
$$x - 2 = \pm\sqrt{-4} = \pm 2i$$
$$x - 2 = 2i \qquad x - 2 = -2i$$
$$x = 2 + 2i \qquad x = 2 - 2i$$

The solutions are $2 + 2i$ and $2 - 2i$.

You Try It 4
Solve by taking square roots:
$2(x + 1)^2 - 24 = 0$

Your solution

Solution on p. S24

8.1 Exercises

Objective A

Solve by factoring.

1. $x^2 - 4x = 0$

2. $y^2 + 6y = 0$

3. $t^2 - 25 = 0$

4. $p^2 - 81 = 0$

5. $s^2 - s - 6 = 0$

6. $v^2 + 4v - 5 = 0$

7. $y^2 - 6y + 9 = 0$

8. $x^2 + 10x + 25 = 0$

9. $9z^2 - 18z = 0$

10. $4y^2 + 20y = 0$

11. $r^2 - 3r = 10$

12. $p^2 + 5p = 6$

13. $v^2 + 10 = 7v$

14. $t^2 - 16 = 15t$

15. $2x^2 - 9x - 18 = 0$

16. $3y^2 - 4y - 4 = 0$

17. $4z^2 - 9z + 2 = 0$

18. $2s^2 - 9s + 9 = 0$

19. $3w^2 + 11w = 4$

20. $2r^2 + r = 6$

21. $6x^2 = 23x + 18$

22. $6x^2 = 7x - 2$

23. $4 - 15u - 4u^2 = 0$

24. $3 - 2y - 8y^2 = 0$

25. $x + 18 = x(x - 6)$

26. $t + 24 = t(t + 6)$

27. $4s(s + 3) = s - 6$

28. $3v(v - 2) = 11v + 6$

29. $u^2 - 2u + 4 = (2u - 3)(u + 2)$

30. $(3v - 2)(2v + 1) = 3v^2 - 11v - 10$

31. $(3x - 4)(x + 4) = x^2 - 3x - 28$

Solve for x by factoring.

32. $x^2 + 14ax + 48a^2 = 0$

33. $x^2 - 9bx + 14b^2 = 0$

34. $x^2 + 9xy - 36y^2 = 0$

35. $x^2 - 6cx - 7c^2 = 0$

36. $x^2 - ax - 20a^2 = 0$

37. $2x^2 + 3bx + b^2 = 0$

38. $3x^2 - 4cx + c^2 = 0$

39. $3x^2 - 14ax + 8a^2 = 0$

40. $3x^2 - 11xy + 6y^2 = 0$

41. $3x^2 - 8ax - 3a^2 = 0$

42. $3x^2 - 4bx - 4b^2 = 0$

43. $4x^2 + 8xy + 3y^2 = 0$

44. $6x^2 - 11cx + 3c^2 = 0$

45. $6x^2 + 11ax + 4a^2 = 0$

46. $12x^2 - 5xy - 2y^2 = 0$

Objective B

Write a quadratic equation that has integer coefficients and has as solutions the given pair of numbers.

47. 2 and 5

48. 3 and 1

49. -2 and -4

50. -1 and -3

51. 6 and -1

52. -2 and 5

53. 3 and -3

54. 5 and -5

55. 4 and 4

56. 2 and 2

57. 0 and 5

58. 0 and -2

59. 0 and 3

60. 0 and -1

61. 3 and $\frac{1}{2}$

62. 2 and $\frac{2}{3}$

63. $-\frac{3}{4}$ and 2

64. $-\frac{1}{2}$ and 5

65. $-\frac{5}{3}$ and -2

66. $-\frac{3}{2}$ and -1

67. $-\frac{2}{3}$ and $\frac{2}{3}$

68. $-\frac{1}{2}$ and $\frac{1}{2}$

69. $\frac{1}{2}$ and $\frac{1}{3}$

70. $\frac{3}{4}$ and $\frac{2}{3}$

71. $\frac{6}{5}$ and $-\frac{1}{2}$

72. $\frac{3}{4}$ and $-\frac{3}{2}$

73. $-\frac{1}{4}$ and $-\frac{1}{2}$

74. $-\frac{5}{6}$ and $-\frac{2}{3}$

75. $\frac{3}{5}$ and $-\frac{1}{10}$

76. $\frac{7}{2}$ and $-\frac{1}{4}$

Objective C

Solve by taking square roots.

77. $y^2 = 49$

78. $x^2 = 64$

79. $z^2 = -4$

80. $v^2 = -16$

81. $s^2 - 4 = 0$

82. $r^2 - 36 = 0$

83. $4x^2 - 81 = 0$

84. $9x^2 - 16 = 0$

85. $y^2 + 49 = 0$

86. $z^2 + 16 = 0$

87. $v^2 - 48 = 0$

88. $s^2 - 32 = 0$

89. $r^2 - 75 = 0$

90. $u^2 - 54 = 0$

91. $z^2 + 18 = 0$

92. $t^2 + 27 = 0$ **93.** $(x - 1)^2 = 36$ **94.** $(x + 2)^2 = 25$

95. $3(y + 3)^2 = 27$ **96.** $4(s - 2)^2 = 36$ **97.** $5(z + 2)^2 = 125$

98. $2(y - 3)^2 = 18$ **99.** $\left(v - \dfrac{1}{2}\right)^2 = \dfrac{1}{4}$ **100.** $\left(r + \dfrac{2}{3}\right)^2 = \dfrac{1}{9}$

101. $(x + 5)^2 - 6 = 0$ **102.** $(t - 1)^2 - 15 = 0$

103. $(v - 3)^2 + 45 = 0$ **104.** $(x + 5)^2 + 32 = 0$

105. $\left(u + \dfrac{2}{3}\right)^2 - 18 = 0$ **106.** $\left(z - \dfrac{1}{2}\right)^2 - 20 = 0$

APPLYING THE CONCEPTS

Write a quadratic equation that has as solutions the given pair of numbers.

107. $\sqrt{2}$ and $-\sqrt{2}$ **108.** $\sqrt{5}$ and $-\sqrt{5}$ **109.** i and $-i$ **110.** $2i$ and $-2i$

111. $2\sqrt{2}$ and $-2\sqrt{2}$ **112.** $3\sqrt{2}$ and $-3\sqrt{2}$ **113.** $i\sqrt{2}$ and $-i\sqrt{2}$ **114.** $2i\sqrt{3}$ and $-2i\sqrt{3}$

Solve for x.

115. $4a^2x^2 = 36b^2, a > 0, b > 0$ **116.** $3y^2x^2 = 27z^2, y > 0, z > 0$ **117.** $(x + a)^2 - 4 = 0$

118. $(x - b)^2 - 1 = 0$ **119.** $(2x - 1)^2 = (2x + 3)^2$ **120.** $(x - 4)^2 = (x + 2)^2$

121. Show that the solutions of the equation $ax^2 + bx = 0$ are 0 and $-\dfrac{b}{a}$, $a > 0, b > 0$.

122. Show that the solutions of the equation $ax^2 + c = 0, a > 0, c > 0$, are $\dfrac{\sqrt{ca}}{a}i$ and $-\dfrac{\sqrt{ca}}{a}i$.

123. Explain why the restriction that $a \neq 0$ is given in the definition of a quadratic equation.

124. If $x^2 = 16$, then $\sqrt{x^2} = \sqrt{16}$ and therefore $x = \pm 4$. Explain why the $\pm$ sign is necessary.

8.2 Solving Quadratic Equations by Completing the Square

Objective A   *To solve a quadratic equation by completing the square* .... 34 CT

Recall that a perfect-square trinomial is the square of a binomial.

Perfect-Square Trinomial		Square of a Binomial
$x^2 + 18x + 16$	$=$	$(x + 4)^2$
$x^2 - 10x + 25$	$=$	$(x - 5)^2$
$x^2 + 2ax + a^2$	$=$	$(x + a)^2$

For each perfect-square trinomial, the square of $\frac{1}{2}$ of the coefficient of x equals the constant term.

$$\left(\frac{1}{2} \text{ coefficient of } x\right)^2 = \text{constant term}$$

$$x^2 + 8x + 16, \quad \left(\frac{1}{2} \cdot 8\right)^2 = 16$$

$$x^2 - 10x + 25, \quad \left[\frac{1}{2}(-10)\right]^2 = 25$$

$$x^2 + 2ax + a^2, \quad \left(\frac{1}{2} \cdot 2a\right)^2 = a^2$$

POINT OF INTEREST

Early attempts to solve quadratic equations were primarily geometric. The Persian mathematician al-Khowarizmi (c. A.D. 800) essentially completed a square of $x^2 + 12x$ as follows.

This relationship can be used to write the constant term for a perfect-square trinomial. Adding to a binomial the constant term that makes it a perfect-square trinomial is called **completing the square.**

➡ Complete the square on $x^2 + 12x$. Write the resulting perfect-square trinomial as the square of a binomial.

$$\left[\frac{1}{2}(12)\right]^2 = (6)^2 = 36$$

• Find the constant term.

$$x^2 + 12x + 36$$

• Complete the square on $x^2 + 12x$ by adding the constant term.

$$x^2 + 12x + 36 = (x + 6)^2$$

• Write the resulting perfect-square trinomial as the square of a binomial.

➡ Complete the square on $z^2 - 3z$. Write the resulting perfect-square trinomial as the square of a binomial.

$$\left[\frac{1}{2} \cdot (-3)\right]^2 = \left(-\frac{3}{2}\right)^2 = \frac{9}{4}$$

• Find the constant term.

$$z^2 - 3z + \frac{9}{4}$$

• Complete the square on $z^2 - 3z$ by adding the constant term.

$$z^2 - 3z + \frac{9}{4} = \left(z - \frac{3}{2}\right)^2$$

• Write the resulting perfect-square trinomial as the square of a binomial.

Any quadratic equation can be solved by completing the square. Add to each side of the equation the term that completes the square. Rewrite the equation in the form $(x + a)^2 = b$. Take the square root of each side of the equation.

➡ Solve by completing the square: $x^2 - 6x - 15 = 0$

$$x^2 - 6x - 15 = 0$$

$$x^2 - 6x = 15$$
       • Add 15 to each side of the equation.

$$x^2 - 6x + 9 = 15 + 9$$
       • Complete the square. Add $\left[\dfrac{1}{2}(-6)\right]^2 = (-3)^2 = 9$ to each side of the equation.

$$(x - 3)^2 = 24$$
       • Factor the trinomial.

$$\sqrt{(x - 3)^2} = \sqrt{24}$$
       • Take the square root of each side of the equation.

$$x - 3 = \pm\sqrt{24} = \pm 2\sqrt{6}$$
       • Solve for x.

$$x - 3 = 2\sqrt{6} \qquad\qquad x - 3 = -2\sqrt{6}$$
$$x = 3 + 2\sqrt{6} \qquad\qquad x = 3 - 2\sqrt{6}$$

Check:

$$\begin{array}{c|c} x^2 - 6x - 15 = 0 & \\ \hline (3 + 2\sqrt{6})^2 - 6(3 + 2\sqrt{6}) - 15 & 0 \\ 9 + 12\sqrt{6} + 24 - 18 - 12\sqrt{6} - 15 & 0 \\ 0 = 0 & \end{array}$$

$$\begin{array}{c|c} x^2 - 6x - 15 = 0 & \\ \hline (3 - 2\sqrt{6})^2 - 6(3 - 2\sqrt{6}) - 15 & 0 \\ 9 - 12\sqrt{6} + 24 - 18 + 12\sqrt{6} - 15 & 0 \\ 0 = 0 & \end{array}$$

The solutions are $3 + 2\sqrt{6}$ and $3 - 2\sqrt{6}$.

➡ Solve by completing the square: $2x^2 - x - 2 = 0$

In order for us to complete the square on an expression, the coefficient of the squared term must be 1. After adding the constant term to each side of the equation, multiply each side of the equation by $\dfrac{1}{2}$.

$$2x^2 - x - 2 = 0$$

$$2x^2 - x = 2$$
       • Add 2 to each side of the equation.

$$\frac{1}{2}(2x^2 - x) = \frac{1}{2} \cdot 2$$
       • Multiply each side of the equation by $\dfrac{1}{2}$.

$$x^2 - \frac{1}{2}x = 1$$
       • The coefficient of x^2 is now 1.

$$x^2 - \frac{1}{2}x + \frac{1}{16} = 1 + \frac{1}{16}$$

- **Complete the square. Add**
$$\left[\frac{1}{2}\left(-\frac{1}{2}\right)\right]^2 = \left(-\frac{1}{4}\right)^2 = \frac{1}{16} \text{ to each side of the equation.}$$

$$\left(x - \frac{1}{4}\right)^2 = \frac{17}{16}$$

- **Factor the perfect-square trinomial.**

$$\sqrt{\left(x - \frac{1}{4}\right)^2} = \sqrt{\frac{17}{16}}$$

- **Take the square root of each side of the equation.**

$$x - \frac{1}{4} = \pm\frac{\sqrt{17}}{4}$$

- **Solve for x.**

$$x - \frac{1}{4} = \frac{\sqrt{17}}{4} \qquad x - \frac{1}{4} = -\frac{\sqrt{17}}{4}$$

$$x = \frac{1}{4} + \frac{\sqrt{17}}{4} \qquad x = \frac{1}{4} - \frac{\sqrt{17}}{4}$$

The solutions are $\dfrac{1 + \sqrt{17}}{4}$ and $\dfrac{1 - \sqrt{17}}{4}$.

POINT OF INTEREST

Mathematicians have studied quadratic equations for centuries. Many of the initial equations were a result of trying to solve a geometry problem. One of the most famous, which dates from around 500 B.C., is "squaring the circle." The question was "Is it possible to construct a square whose area is that of a given circle?" For these early mathematicians, to *construct* meant to draw with only a straightedge and a compass. It was approximately 2300 years later that mathematicians were able to prove that such a construction is impossible.

➡ Solve by completing the square: $x^2 - 3x + 5 = 0$

$$x^2 - 3x + 5 = 0$$

$$x^2 - 3x = -5$$

- **Add the opposite of the constant term to each side of the equation.**

$$x^2 - 3x + \frac{9}{4} = -5 + \frac{9}{4}$$

- **Add to each side of the equation the term that completes the square on $x^2 - 3x$.**

$$\left(x - \frac{3}{2}\right)^2 = -\frac{11}{4}$$

- **Factor the perfect-square trinomial.**

$$\sqrt{\left(x - \frac{3}{2}\right)^2} = \sqrt{-\frac{11}{4}}$$

- **Take the square root of each side of the equation.**

$$x - \frac{3}{2} = \pm\frac{i\sqrt{11}}{2}$$

- **Simplify.**

$$x - \frac{3}{2} = \frac{i\sqrt{11}}{2} \qquad x - \frac{3}{2} = -\frac{i\sqrt{11}}{2}$$

- **Solve for x.**

$$x = \frac{3}{2} + \frac{i\sqrt{11}}{2} \qquad x = \frac{3}{2} - \frac{i\sqrt{11}}{2}$$

$\dfrac{3}{2} + \dfrac{\sqrt{11}}{2}i$ and $\dfrac{3}{2} - \dfrac{\sqrt{11}}{2}i$ check as solutions.

The solutions are $\dfrac{3}{2} + \dfrac{\sqrt{11}}{2}i$ and $\dfrac{3}{2} - \dfrac{\sqrt{11}}{2}i$.

Example 1

Solve by completing the square:
$4x^2 - 8x + 1 = 0$

Solution

$4x^2 - 8x + 1 = 0$

$4x^2 - 8x = -1$

$\dfrac{1}{4}(4x^2 - 8x) = \dfrac{1}{4}(-1)$

$x^2 - 2x = -\dfrac{1}{4}$

$x^2 - 2x + 1 = -\dfrac{1}{4} + 1$ • Complete the square.

$(x - 1)^2 = \dfrac{3}{4}$

$\sqrt{(x - 1)^2} = \sqrt{\dfrac{3}{4}}$

$x - 1 = \pm\dfrac{\sqrt{3}}{2}$

$x - 1 = \dfrac{\sqrt{3}}{2} \qquad x - 1 = -\dfrac{\sqrt{3}}{2}$

$x = 1 + \dfrac{\sqrt{3}}{2} \qquad x = 1 - \dfrac{\sqrt{3}}{2}$

$= \dfrac{2 + \sqrt{3}}{2} \qquad\quad = \dfrac{2 - \sqrt{3}}{2}$

The solutions are $\dfrac{2 + \sqrt{3}}{2}$ and $\dfrac{2 - \sqrt{3}}{2}$.

You Try It 1

Solve by completing the square:
$4x^2 - 4x - 1 = 0$

Your solution

Example 2

Solve by completing the square:
$x^2 + 4x + 5 = 0$

Solution

$x^2 + 4x + 5 = 0$

$x^2 + 4x = -5$

$x^2 + 4x + 4 = -5 + 4$ • Complete the square.

$(x + 2)^2 = -1$

$\sqrt{(x + 2)^2} = \sqrt{-1}$

$x + 2 = \pm i$

$x + 2 = i \qquad\quad x + 2 = -i$

$x = -2 + i \qquad x = -2 - i$

The solutions are $-2 + i$ and $-2 - i$.

You Try It 2

Solve by completing the square:
$2x^2 + x - 5 = 0$

Your solution

Solutions on pp. S24–S25

8.2 Exercises

· ·

Objective A

Solve by completing the square.

1. $x^2 - 4x - 5 = 0$

2. $y^2 + 6y + 5 = 0$

3. $v^2 + 8v - 9 = 0$

4. $w^2 - 2w - 24 = 0$

5. $z^2 - 6z + 9 = 0$

6. $u^2 + 10u + 25 = 0$

7. $r^2 + 4r - 7 = 0$

8. $s^2 + 6s - 1 = 0$

9. $x^2 - 6x + 7 = 0$

10. $y^2 + 8y + 13 = 0$

11. $z^2 - 2z + 2 = 0$

12. $t^2 - 4t + 8 = 0$

13. $s^2 - 5s - 24 = 0$

14. $v^2 + 7v - 44 = 0$

15. $x^2 + 5x - 36 = 0$

16. $y^2 - 9y + 20 = 0$

17. $p^2 - 3p + 1 = 0$

18. $r^2 - 5r - 2 = 0$

19. $t^2 - t - 1 = 0$

20. $u^2 - u - 7 = 0$

21. $y^2 - 6y = 4$

22. $w^2 + 4w = 2$

23. $x^2 = 8x - 15$

24. $z^2 = 4z - 3$

25. $v^2 = 4v - 13$

26. $x^2 = 2x - 17$

27. $p^2 + 6p = -13$

28. $x^2 + 4x = -20$

29. $y^2 - 2y = 17$

30. $x^2 + 10x = 7$

31. $z^2 = z + 4$

32. $r^2 = 3r - 1$

33. $x^2 + 13 = 2x$

34. $6v^2 - 7v = 3$

35. $4x^2 - 4x + 5 = 0$

36. $4t^2 - 4t + 17 = 0$

37. $9x^2 - 6x + 2 = 0$

38. $9y^2 - 12y + 13 = 0$

39. $2s^2 = 4s + 5$

40. $3u^2 = 6u + 1$

41. $2r^2 = 3 - r$

42. $2x^2 = 12 - 5x$

43. $y - 2 = (y - 3)(y + 2)$

44. $8s - 11 = (s - 4)(s - 2)$

45. $6t - 2 = (2t - 3)(t - 1)$

46. $2z + 9 = (2z + 3)(z + 2)$

47. $(x - 4)(x + 1) = x - 3$

48. $(y - 3)^2 = 2y + 10$

APPLYING THE CONCEPTS

49. What is the meaning of the phrase "complete the square"?

50. Explain how to complete the square of $x^2 + bx$.

51. Write out the steps for solving a quadratic equation by completing the square.

Solve by completing the square. Approximate the solutions to the nearest thousandth.

52. $z^2 + 2z = 4$

53. $t^2 - 4t = 7$

54. $2x^2 = 4x - 1$

Solve for x by completing the square.

55. $x^2 - ax - 2a^2 = 0$

56. $x^2 + 3ax - 4a^2 = 0$

57. $x^2 + 3ax - 10a^2 = 0$

58. After a baseball is hit, the height h (in feet) of the ball above the ground t seconds after it is hit can be approximated by the equation $h = -16t^2 + 70t + 4$. Using this equation, determine when the ball will hit the ground. (*Hint:* The ball hits the ground when $h = 0$.)

59. After a baseball is hit, there are two equations that can be considered. One gives the height h (in feet) the ball is above the ground t seconds after it is hit. The second is the distance s (in feet) the ball is from home plate t seconds after it is hit. A model of this situation is given by $h = -16t^2 + 70t + 4$ and $s = 44.5t$. Using this model, determine whether the ball will clear a fence 325 ft from home plate.

8.3 Solving Quadratic Equations by Using the Quadratic Formula

Objective A   *To solve a quadratic equation by using the quadratic formula* .... (34) CT

A general formula known as the **quadratic formula** can be derived by applying the method of completing the square to the standard form of a quadratic equation. This formula can be used to solve any quadratic equation.

Solve $ax^2 + bx + c = 0$ by completing the square.

Add the opposite of the constant term to each side of the equation.

$$ax^2 + bx + c = 0$$
$$ax^2 + bx + c + (-c) = 0 + (-c)$$

Multiply each side of the equation by the reciprocal of a, the coefficient of x^2.

$$ax^2 + bx = -c$$
$$\frac{1}{a}(ax^2 + bx) = \frac{1}{a}(-c)$$
$$x^2 + \frac{b}{a}x = -\frac{c}{a}$$

Complete the square by adding $\left(\frac{1}{2} \cdot \frac{b}{a}\right)^2 = \frac{b^2}{4a^2}$ to each side of the equation.

$$x^2 + \frac{b}{a}x + \frac{b^2}{4a^2} = \frac{b^2}{4a^2} - \frac{c}{a}$$

Simplify the right side of the equation.

$$x^2 + \frac{b}{a}x + \frac{b^2}{4a^2} = \frac{b^2}{4a^2} - \left(\frac{c}{a} \cdot \frac{4a}{4a}\right)$$
$$x^2 + \frac{b}{a}x + \frac{b^2}{4a^2} = \frac{b^2}{4a^2} - \frac{4ac}{4a^2}$$
$$x^2 + \frac{b}{a}x + \frac{b^2}{4a^2} = \frac{b^2 - 4ac}{4a^2}$$

Factor the perfect-square trinomial on the left side of the equation.

$$\left(x + \frac{b}{2a}\right)^2 = \frac{b^2 - 4ac}{4a^2}$$

Take the square root of each side of the equation.

$$\sqrt{\left(x + \frac{b}{2a}\right)^2} = \sqrt{\frac{b^2 - 4ac}{4a^2}}$$
$$x + \frac{b}{2a} = \pm\frac{\sqrt{b^2 - 4ac}}{2a}$$

Solve for x.

$$x + \frac{b}{2a} = \frac{\sqrt{b^2 - 4ac}}{2a}$$
$$x = -\frac{b}{2a} + \frac{\sqrt{b^2 - 4ac}}{2a}$$
$$= \frac{-b + \sqrt{b^2 - 4ac}}{2a}$$

$$x + \frac{b}{2a} = -\frac{\sqrt{b^2 - 4ac}}{2a}$$
$$x = -\frac{b}{2a} - \frac{\sqrt{b^2 - 4ac}}{2a}$$
$$= \frac{-b - \sqrt{b^2 - 4ac}}{2a}$$

POINT OF INTEREST

Although mathematicians have studied quadratic equations since around 500 B.C., it was not until the 18th century that the formula was written as it is today. Of further note, the word *quadratic* has the same Latin root as does the word *square*.

The Quadratic Formula

The solutions of $ax^2 + bx + c = 0$, $a \neq 0$, are

$$\frac{-b + \sqrt{b^2 - 4ac}}{2a} \quad \text{and} \quad \frac{-b - \sqrt{b^2 - 4ac}}{2a}$$

The quadratic formula is frequently written as $x = \dfrac{-b \pm \sqrt{b^2 - 4ac}}{2a}$.

➡ Solve by using the quadratic formula: $2x^2 + 5x + 3 = 0$

From the standard form of the equation, $a = 2$, $b = 5$, and $c = 3$. Replace a, b, and c in the quadratic formula with these values.

TAKE NOTE

The solutions of this quadratic equation are rational numbers. When this happens, the equation could have been solved by factoring and using the Principle of Zero Products. This may be easier than applying the quadratic formula.

$$x = \frac{-b \pm \sqrt{b^2 - 4ac}}{2a}$$

$$= \frac{-(5) \pm \sqrt{(5)^2 - 4(2)(3)}}{2(2)} \qquad \bullet \; a = 2, b = 5, c = 3$$

$$= \frac{-5 \pm \sqrt{25 - 24}}{4}$$

$$= \frac{-5 \pm \sqrt{1}}{4} = \frac{-5 \pm 1}{4}$$

$$x = \frac{-5 + 1}{4} = -1 \qquad x = \frac{-5 - 1}{4} = \frac{-6}{4} = -\frac{3}{2}$$

The solutions are -1 and $-\dfrac{3}{2}$.

➡ Solve by using the quadratic formula: $3x^2 = 4x + 6$

Write the equation in standard form.

$$3x^2 = 4x + 6$$
$$3x^2 - 4x - 6 = 0 \qquad \bullet \; \text{Subtract } 4x \text{ and } 6 \text{ from each side of the equation.}$$

From the standard form of the equation, $a = 3$, $b = -4$, and $c = -6$. Replace a, b, and c in the quadratic formula with these values.

$$x = \frac{-b \pm \sqrt{b^2 - 4ac}}{2a}$$

$$= \frac{-(-4) \pm \sqrt{(-4)^2 - 4(3)(-6)}}{2(3)} \qquad \bullet \; a = 3, b = -4, c = -6$$

$$= \frac{4 \pm \sqrt{16 - (-72)}}{6}$$

$$= \frac{4 \pm \sqrt{88}}{6} = \frac{4 \pm 2\sqrt{22}}{6}$$

$$= \frac{\cancel{2}(2 \pm \sqrt{22})}{\cancel{2} \cdot 3} = \frac{2 \pm \sqrt{22}}{3}$$

Check:

$$
\begin{array}{c|c}
\multicolumn{2}{c}{3x^2 = 4x + 6} \\
\hline
3\left(\dfrac{2 + \sqrt{22}}{3}\right)^2 & 4\left(\dfrac{2 + \sqrt{22}}{3}\right) + 6 \\
3\left(\dfrac{4 + 4\sqrt{22} + 22}{9}\right) & \dfrac{8}{3} + \dfrac{4\sqrt{22}}{3} + \dfrac{18}{3} \\
3\left(\dfrac{26 + 4\sqrt{22}}{9}\right) & \dfrac{26}{3} + \dfrac{4\sqrt{22}}{3} \\
\dfrac{26 + 4\sqrt{22}}{3} = & \dfrac{26 + 4\sqrt{22}}{3}
\end{array}
\qquad
\begin{array}{c|c}
\multicolumn{2}{c}{3x^2 = 4x + 6} \\
\hline
3\left(\dfrac{2 - \sqrt{22}}{3}\right)^2 & 4\left(\dfrac{2 - \sqrt{22}}{3}\right) + 6 \\
3\left(\dfrac{4 - 4\sqrt{22} + 22}{9}\right) & \dfrac{8}{3} - \dfrac{4\sqrt{22}}{3} + \dfrac{18}{3} \\
3\left(\dfrac{26 - 4\sqrt{22}}{9}\right) & \dfrac{26}{3} - \dfrac{4\sqrt{22}}{3} \\
\dfrac{26 - 4\sqrt{22}}{3} = & \dfrac{26 - 4\sqrt{22}}{3}
\end{array}
$$

The solutions are $\dfrac{2 + \sqrt{22}}{3}$ and $\dfrac{2 - \sqrt{22}}{3}$.

⇒ Solve by using the quadratic formula: $4x^2 = 8x - 13$

$$4x^2 = 8x - 13$$
$$4x^2 - 8x + 13 = 0$$ • Write the equation in standard form.

$$x = \frac{-b \pm \sqrt{b^2 - 4ac}}{2a}$$ • Use the quadratic formula.

$$= \frac{-(-8) \pm \sqrt{(-8)^2 - 4 \cdot 4 \cdot 13}}{2 \cdot 4}$$ • $a = 4, b = -8, c = 13$

$$= \frac{8 \pm \sqrt{64 - 208}}{8} = \frac{8 \pm \sqrt{-144}}{8}$$

$$= \frac{8 \pm 12i}{8} = \frac{2 \pm 3i}{2}$$

The solutions are $1 + \frac{3}{2}i$ and $1 - \frac{3}{2}i$.

Of the three preceding examples, the first two had real number solutions; the last one had complex number solutions.

In the quadratic formula, the quantity $b^2 - 4ac$ is called the **discriminant**. When a, b, and c are real numbers, the discriminant determines whether a quadratic equation will have a double root, two real number solutions that are not equal, or two complex number solutions.

THE EFFECT OF THE DISCRIMINANT ON THE SOLUTIONS OF A QUADRATIC EQUATION

1. If $b^2 - 4ac = 0$, the equation has one real number solution, a double root.
2. If $b^2 - 4ac > 0$, the equation has two unequal real number solutions.
3. If $b^2 - 4ac < 0$, the equation has two complex number solutions.

⇒ Use the discriminant to determine whether $x^2 - 4x - 5 = 0$ has one real number solution, two real number solutions, or two complex number solutions.

$$b^2 - 4ac$$ • Evaluate the discriminant. $a = 1, b = -4, c = -5$
$$(-4)^2 - 4(1)(-5) = 16 + 20 = 36$$
$$36 > 0$$

Because $b^2 - 4ac > 0$, the equation has two real number solutions.

Example 1 Solve by using the quadratic formula: $2x^2 - x + 5 = 0$

Solution
$$2x^2 - x + 5 = 0$$
$$a = 2, b = -1, c = 5$$
$$x = \frac{-b \pm \sqrt{b^2 - 4ac}}{2a}$$
$$= \frac{-(-1) \pm \sqrt{(-1)^2 - 4(2)(5)}}{2 \cdot 2}$$
$$= \frac{1 \pm \sqrt{1 - 40}}{4} = \frac{1 \pm \sqrt{-39}}{4}$$
$$= \frac{1 \pm i\sqrt{39}}{4}$$

The solutions are $\frac{1}{4} + \frac{\sqrt{39}}{4}i$ and $\frac{1}{4} - \frac{\sqrt{39}}{4}i$.

You Try It 1 Solve by using the quadratic formula: $x^2 - 2x + 10 = 0$

Your solution

Solution on p. S25

Example 2

Solve by using the quadratic formula:
$2x^2 = (x - 2)(x - 3)$

Solution

$2x^2 = (x - 2)(x - 3)$

$2x^2 = x^2 - 5x + 6$

$x^2 + 5x - 6 = 0$

$a = 1, b = 5, c = -6$

$x = \dfrac{-b \pm \sqrt{b^2 - 4ac}}{2a}$

$= \dfrac{-5 \pm \sqrt{5^2 - 4(1)(-6)}}{2 \cdot 1}$

$= \dfrac{-5 \pm \sqrt{25 + 24}}{2} = \dfrac{-5 \pm \sqrt{49}}{2}$

$= \dfrac{-5 \pm 7}{2}$

$x = \dfrac{-5 + 7}{2} \qquad x = \dfrac{-5 - 7}{2}$

$\quad = \dfrac{2}{2} = 1 \qquad\quad = \dfrac{-12}{2} = -6$

The solutions are 1 and -6.

You Try It 2

Solve by using the quadratic formula:
$4x^2 = 4x - 1$

Your solution

Example 3

Use the discriminant to determine whether
$4x^2 - 2x + 5 = 0$ has one real number
solution, two real number solutions, or two
complex number solutions.

Solution

$a = 4, b = -2, c = 5$

$b^2 - 4ac = (-2)^2 - 4(4)(5)$

$\qquad\quad = 4 - 80$

$\qquad\quad = -76$

$-76 < 0$

Because the discriminant is less than zero,
the equation has two complex number
solutions.

You Try It 3

Use the discriminant to determine whether
$3x^2 - x - 1 = 0$ has one real number
solution, two real number solutions, or two
complex number solutions.

Your solution

Solutions on p. S25

8.3 Exercises

. . . .

Objective A

Solve by using the quadratic formula.

1. $x^2 - 3x - 10 = 0$

2. $z^2 - 4z - 8 = 0$

3. $y^2 + 5y - 36 = 0$

4. $z^2 - 3z - 40 = 0$

5. $w^2 = 8w + 72$

6. $t^2 = 2t + 35$

7. $v^2 = 24 - 5v$

8. $x^2 = 18 - 7x$

9. $2y^2 + 5y - 3 = 0$

10. $4p^2 - 7p + 3 = 0$

11. $8s^2 = 10s + 3$

12. $12t^2 = 5t + 2$

13. $x^2 = 14x - 24$

14. $v^2 = 12v - 24$

15. $2z^2 - 2z - 1 = 0$

16. $6w^2 = 19w - 10$

17. $z^2 + 2z + 2 = 0$

18. $p^2 - 4p + 5 = 0$

19. $y^2 - 2y + 5 = 0$

20. $x^2 + 6x + 13 = 0$

21. $s^2 - 4s + 13 = 0$

22. $t^2 - 6t + 10 = 0$

23. $2w^2 - 2w + 5 = 0$

24. $4v^2 + 8v + 3 = 0$

25. $2x^2 + 6x + 5 = 0$

26. $2y^2 + 2y + 13 = 0$

27. $4t^2 - 6t + 9 = 0$

Use the discriminant to determine whether the quadratic equation has one real number solution, two real number solutions, or two complex number solutions.

28. $2z^2 - z + 5 = 0$

29. $3y^2 + y + 1 = 0$

30. $9x^2 - 12x + 4 = 0$

31. $4x^2 + 20x + 25 = 0$

32. $2v^2 - 3v - 1 = 0$

33. $3w^2 + 3w - 2 = 0$

APPLYING THE CONCEPTS

34. Name the three methods of solving a quadratic equation that have been discussed. What are the advantages and disadvantages of each?

For what values of p does the quadratic equation have two real number solutions that are not equal? Write the answer in set-builder notation.

35. $x^2 - 6x + p = 0$ **36.** $x^2 + 10x + p = 0$

For what values of p does the quadratic equation have two complex number solutions? Write the answer in set-builder notation.

37. $x^2 - 2x + p = 0$ **38.** $x^2 + 4x + p = 0$

39. Show that the equation $x^2 + bx - 1 = 0$ always has real number solutions regardless of the value of b.

40. Show that the equation $2x^2 + bx - 2 = 0$ always has real number solutions regardless of the value of b.

41. Can the quadratic formula be used to solve *any* quadratic equation? If so, explain why. If not, give an example of a quadratic equation that cannot be solved by using the quadratic formula.

42. One of the steps in the derivation of the quadratic formula is $x + \frac{b}{2a} = \pm\sqrt{\frac{b^2 - 4ac}{2a}}$. Carefully explain the occurrence of the $\pm$ sign. (*Hint:* Recall that $\sqrt{x^2} = |x|$.)

43. *Survival of the Spotted Owl* The National Forest Management Act of 1976 specifies that harvesting timber on national forests must be accomplished in conjunction with environmental considerations. One such consideration is providing a habitat for the spotted owl. One model of the survival of the spotted owl requires the solution of the equation $x^2 - s_a x - s_j s_s f = 0$ for x. Different values of s_a, s_j, s_s, and f are given in the table at the right. The values are particularly important because they are related to the survival of the owl. If $x > 1$, then the model predicts a growth in the population; if $x = 1$, the population remains steady; for $x < 1$, the population decreases. The important solution of the equation is the larger of the two roots of the equation.

	U.S. Forest Service	Lande
s_j	0.34	0.11
s_s	0.97	0.71
s_a	0.97	0.94
f	0.24	0.24

Source: Biles, Charles and Barry Noon. "The Spotted Owl." *The Journal of Undergraduate Mathematics and Its Application* vol. 11, no. 2, 1990.

a. Determine the larger root of this equation for values provided by the U.S. Forest Service. Round to the nearest hundredth. Does it predict that the population will increase, remain steady, or decrease?

b. Determine the larger root of this equation for the values provided by R. Lande in *Oecologia* (vol. 75, 1988). Round to the nearest hundredth. Does it predict that the population will increase, remain steady, or decrease?

8.4 Solving Equations That Are Reducible to Quadratic Equations

Objective A *To solve an equation that is quadratic in form* .... (35) CT

Certain equations that are not quadratic can be expressed in quadratic form by making suitable substitutions. An equation is quadratic in form if it can be written as $au^2 + bu + c = 0$.

The equation $x^4 - 4x^2 - 5 = 0$ is quadratic in form.

$$x^4 - 4x^2 - 5 = 0$$
$$(x^2)^2 - 4(x^2) - 5 = 0$$
$$u^2 - 4u - 5 = 0 \qquad \bullet \text{ Let } x^2 = u.$$

The equation $y - y^{1/2} - 6 = 0$ is quadratic in form.

$$y - y^{1/2} - 6 = 0$$
$$(y^{1/2})^2 - (y^{1/2}) - 6 = 0$$
$$u^2 - u - 6 = 0 \qquad \bullet \text{ Let } y^{1/2} = u.$$

The key to recognizing equations that are quadratic in form: When the equation is written in standard form, the exponent on one variable term is $\frac{1}{2}$ the exponent on the other variable term.

➡ Solve: $z + 7z^{1/2} - 18 = 0$

The equation is quadratic in form.

$$z + 7z^{1/2} - 18 = 0$$
$$(z^{1/2})^2 + 7(z^{1/2}) - 18 = 0$$
$$u^2 + 7u - 18 = 0 \qquad \bullet \text{ Let } z^{1/2} = u.$$
$$(u - 2)(u + 9) = 0 \qquad \bullet \text{ Solve by factoring.}$$

$$u - 2 = 0 \qquad u + 9 = 0$$
$$u = 2 \qquad u = -9$$

$$z^{1/2} = 2 \qquad z^{1/2} = -9 \qquad \bullet \text{ Replace } u \text{ by } z^{1/2}.$$
$$\sqrt{z} = 2 \qquad \sqrt{z} = -9$$
$$(\sqrt{z})^2 = 2^2 \qquad (\sqrt{z})^2 = (-9)^2 \qquad \bullet \text{ Solve for } z.$$
$$z = 4 \qquad z = 81$$

TAKE NOTE

When each side of an equation is squared, the resulting equation may have a solution that is not a solution of the original equation.

Check each solution.

$$\text{Check:} \quad \frac{z + 7z^{1/2} - 18 = 0}{\begin{array}{l} 4 + 7(4)^{1/2} - 18 \\ 4 + 7 \cdot 2 - 18 \\ 4 + 14 - 18 \\ \quad 0 = 0 \end{array}} \Big| 0 \qquad \frac{z + 7z^{1/2} - 18 = 0}{\begin{array}{l} 81 + 7(81)^{1/2} - 18 \\ 81 + 7 \cdot 9 - 18 \\ 81 + 63 - 18 \\ \quad 126 \neq 0 \end{array}} \Big| 0$$

4 checks as a solution, but 81 does not check as a solution. The solution is 4.

Example 1   Solve: $x^4 + x^2 - 12 = 0$

Solution

$$x^4 + x^2 - 12 = 0$$
$$(x^2)^2 + (x^2) - 12 = 0$$
$$u^2 + u - 12 = 0$$
$$(u - 3)(u + 4) = 0$$

$$u - 3 = 0 \qquad u + 4 = 0$$
$$u = 3 \qquad\quad u = -4$$

Replace u by x^2.

$$x^2 = 3 \qquad\qquad x^2 = -4$$
$$\sqrt{x^2} = \sqrt{3} \qquad\quad \sqrt{x^2} = \sqrt{-4}$$
$$x = \pm\sqrt{3} \qquad\quad x = \pm 2i$$

The solutions are $\sqrt{3}, -\sqrt{3}, 2i,$ and $-2i$.

You Try It 1   Solve: $x - 5x^{1/2} + 6 = 0$

Your solution

Solution on p. S25

Objective B   **To solve a radical equation that is reducible to a quadratic equation** .... 35 CT

Certain equations containing radicals can be expressed as quadratic equations.

➡ Solve: $\sqrt{x + 2} + 4 = x$

$$\sqrt{x + 2} + 4 = x$$

$$\sqrt{x + 2} = x - 4 \qquad\qquad \text{• Solve for the radical expression.}$$

$$(\sqrt{x + 2})^2 = (x - 4)^2 \qquad\qquad \text{• Square each side of the equation.}$$

$$x + 2 = x^2 - 8x + 16 \qquad\qquad \text{• Simplify.}$$

$$0 = x^2 - 9x + 14 \qquad\qquad \text{• Write the equation in standard form.}$$

$$0 = (x - 7)(x - 2) \qquad\qquad \text{• Solve for } x.$$

$$x - 7 = 0 \qquad x - 2 = 0$$
$$x = 7 \qquad\quad x = 2$$

Check each solution.

Check:
$$\begin{array}{c|c} \sqrt{x + 2} + 4 = x & \\ \hline \sqrt{7 + 2} + 4 & 7 \\ \sqrt{9} + 4 & \\ 3 + 4 & \\ 7 = 7 & \end{array}$$
$$\begin{array}{c|c} \sqrt{x + 2} + 4 = x & \\ \hline \sqrt{2 + 2} + 4 & 2 \\ \sqrt{4} + 4 & \\ 2 + 4 & \\ 6 \neq 2 & \end{array}$$

7 checks as a solution, but 2 does not check as a solution. The solution is 7.

Example 2

Solve: $\sqrt{7y - 3} + 3 = 2y$

Solution

$$\sqrt{7y - 3} + 3 = 2y$$
$$\sqrt{7y - 3} = 2y - 3$$
$$(\sqrt{7y - 3})^2 = (2y - 3)^2$$
$$7y - 3 = 4y^2 - 12y + 9$$
$$0 = 4y^2 - 19y + 12$$
$$0 = (4y - 3)(y - 4)$$

$$4y - 3 = 0 \qquad y - 4 = 0$$
$$4y = 3 \qquad\qquad y = 4$$
$$y = \frac{3}{4}$$

4 checks as a solution.

$\frac{3}{4}$ does not check as a solution.

The solution is 4.

You Try It 2

Solve: $\sqrt{2x + 1} + x = 7$

Your solution

Example 3

Solve: $\sqrt{2y + 1} - \sqrt{y} = 1$

Solution

$$\sqrt{2y + 1} - \sqrt{y} = 1$$

Solve for one of the radical expressions.

$$\sqrt{2y + 1} = \sqrt{y} + 1$$
$$(\sqrt{2y + 1})^2 = (\sqrt{y} + 1)^2$$
$$2y + 1 = y + 2\sqrt{y} + 1$$
$$y = 2\sqrt{y}$$

Square each side of the equation.

$$y^2 = (2\sqrt{y})^2$$
$$y^2 = 4y$$
$$y^2 - 4y = 0$$
$$y(y - 4) = 0$$
$$y = 0 \qquad y - 4 = 0$$
$$y = 4$$

0 and 4 check as solutions.

The solutions are 0 and 4.

You Try It 3

Solve: $\sqrt{2x - 1} + \sqrt{x} = 2$

Your solution

Solutions on pp. S25–S26

Objective C **To solve a fractional equation that is reducible to a quadratic equation** .... ◁ 35 ▷ CT

After each side of a fractional equation has been multiplied by the LCM of the denominators, the resulting equation may be a quadratic equation.

➡ Solve: $\dfrac{1}{r} + \dfrac{1}{r+1} = \dfrac{3}{2}$

$$\dfrac{1}{r} + \dfrac{1}{r+1} = \dfrac{3}{2}$$

$$2r(r+1)\left(\dfrac{1}{r} + \dfrac{1}{r+1}\right) = 2r(r+1) \cdot \dfrac{3}{2}$$

• Multiply each side of the equation by the LCM of the denominators.

$$2(r+1) + 2r = r(r+1) \cdot 3$$
$$2r + 2 + 2r = 3r(r+1)$$
$$4r + 2 = 3r^2 + 3r$$
$$0 = 3r^2 - r - 2$$

• Write the equation in standard form.

$$0 = (3r+2)(r-1)$$

• Solve for r by factoring.

$$3r + 2 = 0 \qquad\qquad r - 1 = 0$$
$$3r = -2 \qquad\qquad r = 1$$
$$r = -\dfrac{2}{3}$$

$-\dfrac{2}{3}$ and 1 check as solutions. The solutions are $-\dfrac{2}{3}$ and 1.

Example 4

Solve: $\dfrac{9}{x-3} = 2x + 1$

Solution

$$\dfrac{9}{x-3} = 2x + 1$$

$$(x-3)\dfrac{9}{x-3} = (x-3)(2x+1)$$

$$9 = 2x^2 - 5x - 3$$
$$0 = 2x^2 - 5x - 12$$
$$0 = (2x+3)(x-4)$$

$$2x + 3 = 0 \qquad x - 4 = 0$$
$$2x = -3 \qquad\quad x = 4$$
$$x = -\dfrac{3}{2}$$

The solutions are $-\dfrac{3}{2}$ and 4.

You Try It 4

Solve: $3y + \dfrac{25}{3y-2} = -8$

Your solution

Solution on p. S26

8.4 Exercises

· ·

Objective A

Solve.

1. $x^4 - 13x^2 + 36 = 0$

2. $y^4 - 5y^2 + 4 = 0$

3. $z^4 - 6z^2 + 8 = 0$

4. $t^4 - 12t^2 + 27 = 0$

5. $p - 3p^{1/2} + 2 = 0$

6. $v - 7v^{1/2} + 12 = 0$

7. $x - x^{1/2} - 12 = 0$

8. $w - 2w^{1/2} - 15 = 0$

9. $z^4 + 3z^2 - 4 = 0$

10. $y^4 + 5y^2 - 36 = 0$

11. $x^4 + 12x^2 - 64 = 0$

12. $x^4 - 81 = 0$

13. $p + 2p^{1/2} - 24 = 0$

14. $v + 3v^{1/2} - 4 = 0$

15. $y^{2/3} - 9y^{1/3} + 8 = 0$

16. $z^{2/3} - z^{1/3} - 6 = 0$

17. $9w^4 - 13w^2 + 4 = 0$

18. $4y^4 - 7y^2 - 36 = 0$

Objective B

Solve.

19. $\sqrt{x + 1} + x = 5$

20. $\sqrt{x - 4} + x = 6$

21. $x = \sqrt{x} + 6$

22. $\sqrt{2y - 1} = y - 2$

23. $\sqrt{3w + 3} = w + 1$

24. $\sqrt{2s + 1} = s - 1$

25. $\sqrt{4y + 1} - y = 1$

26. $\sqrt{3s + 4} + 2s = 12$

27. $\sqrt{10x + 5} - 2x = 1$

28. $\sqrt{t + 8} = 2t + 1$

29. $\sqrt{p + 11} = 1 - p$

30. $x - 7 = \sqrt{x - 5}$

31. $\sqrt{x - 1} - \sqrt{x} = -1$

32. $\sqrt{y} + 1 = \sqrt{y + 5}$

33. $\sqrt{2x - 1} = 1 - \sqrt{x - 1}$

34. $\sqrt{x + 6} + \sqrt{x + 2} = 2$

35. $\sqrt{t + 3} + \sqrt{2t + 7} = 1$

36. $\sqrt{5 - 2x} = \sqrt{2 - x} + 1$

Objective C

Solve.

37. $x = \dfrac{10}{x - 9}$

38. $z = \dfrac{5}{z - 4}$

39. $\dfrac{t}{t + 1} = \dfrac{-2}{t - 1}$

40. $\dfrac{2v}{v - 1} = \dfrac{5}{v + 2}$

41. $\dfrac{y - 1}{y + 2} + y = 1$

42. $\dfrac{2p - 1}{p - 2} + p = 8$

43. $\dfrac{3r + 2}{r + 2} - 2r = 1$

44. $\dfrac{2v + 3}{v + 4} + 3v = 4$

45. $\dfrac{2}{2x + 1} + \dfrac{1}{x} = 3$

46. $\dfrac{3}{s} - \dfrac{2}{2s - 1} = 1$

47. $\dfrac{16}{z - 2} + \dfrac{16}{z + 2} = 6$

48. $\dfrac{2}{y + 1} + \dfrac{1}{y - 1} = 1$

49. $\dfrac{t}{t - 2} + \dfrac{2}{t - 1} = 4$

50. $\dfrac{4t + 1}{t + 4} + \dfrac{3t - 1}{t + 1} = 2$

51. $\dfrac{5}{2p - 1} + \dfrac{4}{p + 1} = 2$

APPLYING THE CONCEPTS

Solve.

52. $(\sqrt{x} - 2)^2 - 5\sqrt{x} + 14 = 0$ (*Hint:* Let $u = \sqrt{x} - 2$.)

53. $(\sqrt{x} - 1)^2 - 4\sqrt{x} - 1 = 0$ (*Hint:* Let $u = \sqrt{x} - 1$.)

54. $(\sqrt{x} + 3)^2 - 4\sqrt{x} - 17 = 0$ (*Hint:* Let $u = \sqrt{x} + 3$.)

8.5 Quadratic Inequalities and Rational Inequalities

Objective A   *To solve a nonlinear inequality* .... CT

A **quadratic inequality** is one that can be written in the form $ax^2 + bx + c < 0$ or $ax^2 + bx + c > 0$, where $a \neq 0$. The symbols $\leq$ and $\geq$ can also be used. The solution set of a quadratic inequality can be found by solving a compound inequality.

To solve $x^2 - 3x - 10 > 0$, first factor the trinomial.

$$x^2 - 3x - 10 > 0$$
$$(x + 2)(x - 5) > 0$$

There are two cases for which the product of the factors will be positive: (1) both factors are positive, or (2) both factors are negative.

$$(1) \ x + 2 > 0 \ \text{ and } \ x - 5 > 0$$
$$(2) \ x + 2 < 0 \ \text{ and } \ x - 5 < 0$$

Solve each pair of compound inequalities.

$$(1) \ x + 2 > 0 \quad \text{and} \quad x - 5 > 0$$
$$x > -2 \qquad\qquad x > 5$$
$$\{x \,|\, x > -2\} \cap \{x \,|\, x > 5\} = \{x \,|\, x > 5\}$$

$$(2) \ x + 2 < 0 \quad \text{and} \quad x - 5 < 0$$
$$x < -2 \qquad\qquad x < 5$$
$$\{x \,|\, x < -2\} \cap \{x \,|\, x < 5\} = \{x \,|\, x < -2\}$$

Because the two cases for which the product will be positive are connected by *or*, the solution set is the union of the solution sets of the individual inequalities.

$$\{x \,|\, x > 5\} \cup \{x \,|\, x < -2\} = \{x \,|\, x > 5 \ \text{ or } \ x < -2\}$$

Although the solution set of any quadratic inequality can be found by using the method outlined above, frequently a graphical method is easier to use.

⟹ Solve and graph the solution set of $x^2 - x - 6 < 0$.

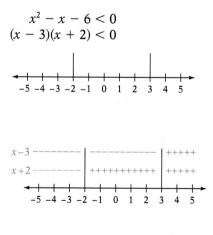

Factor the trinomial.

$$x^2 - x - 6 < 0$$
$$(x - 3)(x + 2) < 0$$

On a number line, draw lines indicating the numbers that make each factor equal to zero.

$$x - 3 = 0 \qquad x + 2 = 0$$
$$x = 3 \qquad\qquad x = -2$$

For each factor, place plus signs above the number line for those regions where the factor is positive and negative signs where the factor is negative.

Because $x^2 - x - 6 < 0$, the solution set will be the regions where one factor is positive and the other factor is negative.

Write the solution set.

$$\{x \,|\, -2 < x < 3\}$$

The graph of the solution set of $x^2 - x - 6 < 0$

➡ Solve and graph the solution set of $(x - 2)(x + 1)(x - 4) > 0$.

On a number line, identify for each factor the regions where the factor is positive and those where the factor is negative.

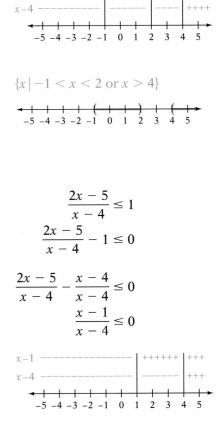

There are two regions where the product of the three factors is positive.

Write the solution set. $\{x \mid -1 < x < 2 \text{ or } x > 4\}$

The graph of the solution set of $(x - 2)(x + 1)(x - 4) > 0$

➡ Solve: $\dfrac{2x - 5}{x - 4} \le 1$

$$\frac{2x - 5}{x - 4} \le 1$$

Rewrite the inequality so that 0 appears on the right side of the inequality.

$$\frac{2x - 5}{x - 4} - 1 \le 0$$

Simplify.

$$\frac{2x - 5}{x - 4} - \frac{x - 4}{x - 4} \le 0$$

$$\frac{x - 1}{x - 4} \le 0$$

On a number line, identify for each factor of the numerator and each factor of the denominator the regions where the factor is positive and those where the factor is negative.

The region where the quotient of the two factors is negative is between 1 and 4.

Write the solution set. $\{x \mid 1 \le x < 4\}$

Note that 1 is part of the solution set but that 4 is not because the denominator of the rational expression is zero when $x = 4$.

Example 1
Solve and graph the solution set of $2x^2 - x - 3 \ge 0$.

Solution

$$2x^2 - x - 3 \ge 0$$
$$(2x - 3)(x + 1) \ge 0$$

$$\left\{x \mid x \le -1 \text{ or } x \ge \frac{3}{2}\right\}$$

You Try It 1
Solve and graph the solution set of $2x^2 - x - 10 \le 0$.

Your solution

Solution on p. S26

8.5 Exercises

* *

Objective A

Solve and graph the solution set.

1. $(x - 4)(x + 2) > 0$

2. $(x + 1)(x - 3) > 0$

3. $x^2 - 3x + 2 \geq 0$

4. $x^2 + 5x + 6 > 0$

5. $x^2 - x - 12 < 0$

6. $x^2 + x - 20 < 0$

7. $(x - 1)(x + 2)(x - 3) < 0$

8. $(x + 4)(x - 2)(x + 1) > 0$

9. $(x + 4)(x - 2)(x - 1) \geq 0$

10. $(x - 1)(x + 5)(x - 2) \leq 0$

11. $\dfrac{x - 4}{x + 2} > 0$

12. $\dfrac{x + 2}{x - 3} > 0$

13. $\dfrac{x - 3}{x + 1} \leq 0$

14. $\dfrac{x - 1}{x} > 0$

15. $\dfrac{(x - 1)(x + 2)}{x - 3} \leq 0$

16. $\dfrac{(x + 3)(x - 1)}{x - 2} \geq 0$

Solve.

17. $x^2 - 16 > 0$

18. $x^2 - 4 \geq 0$

19. $x^2 - 9x \leq 36$

20. $x^2 + 4x > 21$

21. $4x^2 - 8x + 3 < 0$

22. $2x^2 + 11x + 12 \geq 0$

23. $\dfrac{3}{x - 1} < 2$

24. $\dfrac{x}{(x - 1)(x + 2)} \geq 0$

25. $\dfrac{x - 2}{(x + 1)(x - 1)} \leq 0$

26. $\dfrac{1}{x} < 2$

27. $\dfrac{x}{2x - 1} \geq 1$

28. $\dfrac{x}{2x - 3} \leq 1$

29. $\dfrac{x}{2 - x} \leq -3$

30. $\dfrac{3}{x - 2} > \dfrac{2}{x + 2}$

31. $\dfrac{3}{x - 5} > \dfrac{1}{x + 1}$

APPLYING THE CONCEPTS

Graph the solution set.

32. $(x + 2)(x - 3)(x + 1)(x + 4) > 0$

33. $(x - 1)(x + 3)(x - 2)(x - 4) \geq 0$

34. $(x^2 + 2x - 8)(x^2 - 2x - 3) < 0$

35. $(x^2 + 2x - 3)(x^2 + 3x + 2) \geq 0$

36. $(x^2 + 1)(x^2 - 3x + 2) > 0$

37. $\dfrac{x^2(3 - x)(2x + 1)}{(x + 4)(x + 2)} \geq 0$

38. $x < x^2$

39. $x^3 > x$

40. $(x - 4)^2 > -2$

8.6 Applications of Quadratic Equations

Objective A   *To solve application problems* ································· (36) CT

The application problems in this section are similar to problems solved earlier in the text. Each of the strategies for the problems in this section will result in a quadratic equation.

➡ A small pipe takes 16 min longer to empty a tank than does a larger pipe. Working together, the pipes can empty the tank in 6 min. How long would it take each pipe working alone to empty the tank?

> **Strategy for Solving an Application Problem**
>
> 1. Determine the type of problem. Is it a uniform motion problem, a geometry problem, an integer problem, or a work problem?

The problem is a work problem.

> 2. Choose a variable to represent the unknown quantity. Write numerical or variable expressions for all the remaining quantities. These results can be recorded in a table.

The unknown time of the larger pipe: t
The unknown time of the smaller pipe: $t + 16$

	Rate of Work	·	Time Worked	=	Part of Task Completed
Larger pipe	$\dfrac{1}{t}$	·	6	=	$\dfrac{6}{t}$
Smaller pipe	$\dfrac{1}{t + 16}$	·	6	=	$\dfrac{6}{t + 16}$

> 3. Determine how the quantities are related.

$$\frac{6}{t} + \frac{6}{t + 16} = 1$$

• The sum of the parts of the task completed must equal 1.

$$t(t + 16)\left(\frac{6}{t} + \frac{6}{t + 16}\right) = t(t + 16) \cdot 1$$
$$(t + 16)6 + 6t = t^2 + 16t$$
$$6t + 96 + 6t = t^2 + 16t$$
$$0 = t^2 + 4t - 96$$
$$0 = (t + 12)(t - 8)$$

$$t + 12 = 0 \qquad t - 8 = 0$$
$$t = -12 \qquad t = 8$$

Because time cannot be negative, the solution $t = -12$ is not possible.

The time for the smaller pipe is $t + 16$.

$t + 16 = 8 + 16 = 24$ • Replace *t* by 8 and evaluate.

The larger pipe requires 8 min to empty the tank.
The smaller pipe requires 24 min to empty the tank.

Example 1

In 8 h, two campers rowed 15 mi down a river and then rowed back to their campsite. The rate of the river's current was 1 mph. Find the rate at which the campers rowed.

Strategy

• This is a uniform motion problem.

• Unknown rowing rate of the campers: r

	Distance	Rate	Time
Down river	15	$r + 1$	$\dfrac{15}{r + 1}$
Up river	15	$r - 1$	$\dfrac{15}{r - 1}$

• The total time of the trip was 8 h.

Solution

$$\frac{15}{r + 1} + \frac{15}{r - 1} = 8$$

$$(r + 1)(r - 1)\left(\frac{15}{r + 1} + \frac{15}{r - 1}\right) = (r + 1)(r - 1)8$$

$$(r - 1)15 + (r + 1)15 = (r^2 - 1)8$$

$$15r - 15 + 15r + 15 = 8r^2 - 8$$

$$30r = 8r^2 - 8$$

$$0 = 8r^2 - 30r - 8$$

$$0 = 2(4r^2 - 15r - 4)$$

$$0 = 2(4r + 1)(r - 4)$$

$$4r + 1 = 0 \qquad r - 4 = 0$$
$$4r = -1 \qquad \quad r = 4$$
$$r = -\frac{1}{4}$$

The solution $r = -\dfrac{1}{4}$ is not possible, because the rate cannot be a negative number.

The rowing rate was 4 mph.

You Try It 1

The length of a rectangle is 3 m more than the width. The area is 54 m². Find the length of the rectangle.

Your strategy

Your solution

Solution on p. S26

8.6 Exercises

. . . .

Objective A   *Application Problems*

1. The base of a triangle is one less than five times the height of the triangle. The area of the triangle is 21 cm². Find the height and the length of the base of the triangle.

2. The height of a triangle is 3 in. less than the base of the triangle. The area of the triangle is 90 in². Find the height and the length of the base of the triangle.

3. The length of a rectangle is 2 ft less than three times the width of the rectangle. The area of the rectangle is 65 ft². Find the length and width of the rectangle.

4. The length of a rectangle is 2 cm less than twice the width. The area of the rectangle is 180 cm². Find the length and width of the rectangle.

5. The state of Colorado is almost perfectly rectangular, with its north border 111 mi longer than its west border. If the state encompasses 104,000 mi², estimate the dimensions of Colorado. Round to the nearest mile.

6. A car with good tire tread can stop in less distance than a car with poor tread. The formula for the stopping distance, d, of a car with good tread on dry cement is approximated by $d = 0.04v^2 + 0.5v$, where v is the speed of the car. If the driver must be able to stop within 60 ft, what is the maximum safe speed, to the nearest mile per hour, of the car?

7. A square piece of cardboard is formed into a box by cutting 10-centimeter squares from each of the four corners and then folding up the sides, as shown in the figure. If the volume, V, of the box is to be 49,000 cm³, what size square piece of cardboard is needed? Recall that $V = LWH$.

8. The height of a projectile fired upward is given by the formula $s = v_0 t - 16t^2$, where s is the height, v_0 is the initial velocity, and t is the time. Find the time for a projectile to return to Earth if it has an initial velocity of 200 ft/s.

9. The height of a projectile fired upward is given by the formula $s = v_0 t - 16t^2$, where s is the height, v_0 is the initial velocity, and t is the time. Find the time for a projectile to reach a height of 64 ft if it has an initial velocity of 128 ft/s. Round to the nearest hundredth of a second.

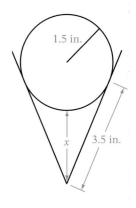

10. A perfectly spherical scoop of mint chocolate chip ice cream is placed in a cone, as shown in the figure. How far is the bottom of the scoop of ice cream from the bottom of the cone? (*Hint:* A line segment from the center of the ice cream to the point at which the ice cream touches the cone is perpendicular to the edge of the cone.)

11. A small pipe can fill a tank in 6 min more time than it takes a larger pipe to fill the same tank. Working together, both pipes can fill the tank in 4 min. How long would it take each pipe working alone to fill the tank?

12. A cruise ship made a trip of 100 mi in 8 h. The ship traveled the first 40 mi at a constant rate before increasing its speed by 5 mph. Then it traveled another 60 mi at the increased speed. Find the rate of the cruise ship for the first 40 mi.

13. The Concorde's speed in calm air is 1320 mph. Flying with the wind, the Concorde can fly from New York to London, a distance of approximately 4000 mi, in 0.5 h less than the time required to make the return trip. Find the rate of the wind to the nearest mile per hour.

14. A car travels 120 mi. A second car, traveling 10 mph faster than the first car, makes the same trip in 1 h less time. Find the speed of each car.

15. For a portion of the Green River in Utah, the rate of the river's current is 4 mph. A tour guide can row 5 mi down this river and back in 3 h. Find the rowing rate of the guide in calm water.

16. The height of an arch is given by the equation

    $h(x) = -\dfrac{3}{64}x^2 + 27$, where $|x|$ is the distance in feet

    from the center of the arch.

    a. What is the maximum height of the arch?
    b. What is the height of the arch 8 ft to the right of the center?
    c. How far from the center is the arch 8 ft tall?

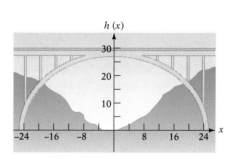

APPLYING THE CONCEPTS

17. Some forecasters are predicting that revenue generated by business on the Internet from 1997–2002 will expand to values that can be approximated by the model $R(t) = 15.8t^2 - 17.2t + 10.2$, where R is the annual revenue in billions of dollars and t is the time in years, with $t = 0$ corresponding to 1997. According to this model, in what year will the revenue reach $200 billion? Round to the nearest year. Explain why there is just one answer to this problem. (Source: Forrester Research)

18. Using Torricelli's Principle, it can be shown that the depth, d, of a liquid in a bottle with a hole of area 0.5 cm² in its side can be approximated by $d = 0.0034t^2 - 0.52518t + 20$, where t is the time since a stopper was removed from the hole. When will the depth be 10 cm? Round to the nearest tenth of a second.

Focus on Problem Solving

Inductive and Deductive Reasoning

Consider the following sums of odd positive integers.

$1 + 3 = 4 = 2^2$	Sum of the first two odd numbers is 2^2.
$1 + 3 + 5 = 9 = 3^2$	Sum of the first three odd numbers is 3^2.
$1 + 3 + 5 + 7 = 16 = 4^2$	Sum of the first four odd numbers is 4^2.
$1 + 3 + 5 + 7 + 9 = 25 = 5^2$	Sum of the first five odd numbers is 5^2.

1. Make a conjecture about the value of the sum

$$1 + 3 + 5 + 7 + 9 + 11 + 13 + 15$$

without adding the numbers.

If the pattern continues, a possible conjecture is that the sum of the first eight odd positive integers is $8^2 = 64$. By adding the numbers, you can verify that this is correct. Inferring that the pattern established by a few cases is valid for all cases is an example of **inductive reasoning.**

2. Use inductive reasoning to find the next figure in the sequence below.

The fact that a pattern appears to be true does not *prove* that it is true for all cases. For example, consider the polynomial $n^2 - n + 41$. If we begin substituting positive integer values for n and evaluating the expression, we produce the following table.

n	$n^2 - n + 41$	
1	$1^2 - 1 + 41 = 41$	41 is a prime number.
2	$2^2 - 2 + 41 = 43$	43 is a prime number.
3	$3^2 - 3 + 41 = 47$	47 is a prime number.
4	$4^2 - 4 + 41 = 53$	53 is a prime number.

Even if we try a number like 30, we have $30^2 - 30 + 41 = 911$ and 911 is a prime number. Thus it appears that the value of this polynomial is a prime number for any value of n. However, the conjecture is not true. For instance, if $n = 41$, we have $41^2 - 41 + 41 = 41^2 = 1681$, which is not a prime number because it is divisible by 41. This illustrates that inductive reasoning may lead to incorrect conclusions and that an inductive proof must be available to prove conjectures. There is such a proof, called *mathematical induction*, that you may study in a future math course.

Now consider the true statement that the sum of the measures of the interior angles of a triangle is 180°. The figure on the left is a triangle; therefore the sum of the measures of the interior angles must be 180°. This is an example of *deductive reasoning.* **Deductive reasoning** uses a rule or statement of fact to reach a conclusion.

$\angle A + \angle B + \angle C = 180°$

3. Use deductive reasoning to complete the following sentence. All even numbers are divisible by 2. Because 14,386 is an even number, . . .

For Exercises 4 and 5 on the next page, determine whether inductive or deductive reasoning is being used.

4. The tenth number in the list 1, 4, 9, 16, 25, . . . is 100.

5. All quadrilaterals have four sides. A square is a quadrilateral. Therefore a square has four sides.

6. Explain the difference between inductive and deductive reasoning.

Projects and Group Activities

Completing the Square

Essentially all of the investigations into mathematics before the Renaissance were geometric. The solutions of quadratic equations were calculated from a construction of a certain area. Proofs of theorems, even theorems about numbers, were based entirely on geometry. In this project, we will examine the solution of a quadratic equation.

➡ Solve: $x^2 + 6x = 7$

Begin with a line of unknown length, x, and one of length 6, the coefficient of x. Using these lines, construct a rectangle as shown in Figure 1.

Area $= x^2 + 6x$

Figure 1

Now draw another area that has exactly the same area as Figure 1 by cutting one-half of the rectangle off and placing it on the bottom of the square. See Figure 2.

The unshaded area in Figure 2 has exactly the same area as Figure 1. However, when the shaded area is added to Figure 2 to make a square, the area of the square is 9 square units larger than that of Figure 1. In equation form,

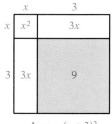

Area $= (x + 3)^2$

Figure 2

(Area of Figure 1) + 9 = area of Figure 2

or

$$x^2 + 6x + 9 = (x + 3)^2$$

From the original equation, $x^2 + 6x = 7$. Thus,

$$
\begin{aligned}
x^2 + 6x + 9 &= (x + 3)^2 \\
7 + 9 &= (x + 3)^2 \qquad \bullet\ x^2 + 6x = 7 \\
16 &= (x + 3)^2 \\
4 &= x + 3 \qquad\quad \bullet\ \text{See note below.} \\
1 &= x
\end{aligned}
$$

Note: Although early mathematicians knew that a quadratic equation may have two solutions, both solutions were allowed only if they were positive. After all, a geometric construction could not have a negative length. Therefore, the solution of this equation was 1; the solution -7 would have been dismissed as *fictitious*, the actual word that was frequently used through the 15th century for negative-number solutions of an equation.

Try to solve the quadratic equation $x^2 + 4x = 12$ by geometrically completing the square.

Using a Graphing Calculator to Solve a Quadratic Equation

Figure 3

Figure 4

Recall that an x-intercept of the graph of an equation is a point at which the graph crosses the x-axis. For the graph in Figure 3, the x-intercepts are $(-2, 0)$ and $(3, 0)$.

Recall also that to find the x-intercept of a graph, set $y = 0$ and then solve for x. For the equation in Figure 3, if we set $y = 0$, the resulting equation is $0 = x^2 - x - 6$, which is a quadratic equation. Solving this equation by factoring, we have

$$0 = x^2 - x - 6$$
$$0 = (x + 2)(x - 3)$$

$$x + 2 = 0 \qquad\qquad x - 3 = 0$$
$$x = -2 \qquad\qquad\quad x = 3$$

Thus the solutions of the equation are the x-coordinates of the x-intercepts of the graph.

This connection between the solutions of an equation and the x-intercepts of a graph allows us to graphically find the real number solutions of an equation. Using a graphing calculator, graph the equation and estimate the x-intercepts. For instance, to graphically approximate the solutions of $2x^2 + 5x - 1 = 0$, graph $y = 2x^2 + 5x - 1$ and approximate the x-coordinates of the x-intercepts. You can use the following keystrokes to graph the equation and approximate the solutions of the equation. The result is the graph in Figure 4.

TI-83 [Y=] [CLEAR] 2 [X,T,θ,n] [∧] 2 [+]
5 [X,T,θ,n] [−] 1 [2nd] QUIT [ZOOM] 5 [ENTER] [2nd] CALC 2

Use the arrow keys to move to the left of the leftmost x-intercept. Then press ENTER. Now use the arrow keys to move to a point just to the right of the leftmost x-intercept. Then press ENTER. Press ENTER again. The x-coordinate at the bottom of the screen is one approximate solution of the equation. To find the other solution, proceed in the same manner for the next x-intercept.

SHARP EL-9360 [Y=] [CL] 2 [X/θ/T/n] [a^b] 2 [▶] [+] 5 [X/θ/T/n] [−] 1 [ZOOM] 5.
This will produce the graph. Now press [2nd] CALC 5 [ENTER]. After pressing 5, the x-intercept will show on the bottom of the screen. Now press [2nd] CALC 5 [ENTER] to find the other x-intercept.

CASIO CFX-9850 [MENU] 5 [F2] [F1] 2 [X/θ/T] [x^2] [+] 5 [X/θ/T] [−] 1 [EXE]
[F6] [SHIFT] G-Solv [F1]. Now press [▶] to find the other x-intercept.

Attempting to find the solutions of an equation graphically will not necessarily find all the solutions. Because the x-coordinates of the x-intercepts of a graph are *real* numbers, only real number solutions can be found. For instance, consider the equation $x^2 + 4x + 5 = 0$. The graph of $y = x^2 + 4x + 5$ is shown in Figure 5. Note that the graph has no x-intercepts and, consequently, no real number solutions. However, $x^2 + 4x + 5 = 0$ does have complex number solutions that can be obtained by using the quadratic formula. They are $-2 + i$ and $-2 - i$.

Figure 5

Solving Nonlinear Inequalities Using a Graphing Calculator

Figure 6

Inequalities such as those in Section 8.5 can also be solved by using a graphing calculator. For example, to solve $\frac{x-1}{x+1} < 2$, graph $y = \frac{x-1}{x+1}$ (the left side of the inequality) and $y = 2$ (the right side of the inequality). Since $\frac{x-1}{x+1}$ is required to be less than 2, the solution set is those values of x for which the graph of $y = \frac{x-1}{x+1}$ is below the graph of $y = 2$. (See Figure 6.) By moving the cursor to the point of intersection, the approximate endpoints of the intervals for the solution set can be determined. (See Projects and Group Activities in the chapter entitled "Systems of Linear Equations and Inequalities" for information on graphing two equations on the same screen.) From the graph, the solution set is $\{x \mid x < -3 \text{ or } x > -1\}$.

The solution set of a quadratic inequality such as $x^2 - x - 2 < 0$ can be found in a similar manner. Graph $y = x^2 - x - 2$ and determine those values of x for which the graph is below the x-axis ($y = 0$) by finding the x-intercepts. From Figure 7, the solution set is $\{x \mid -1 < x < 2\}$.

Figure 7

Chapter Summary

Key Words

A *quadratic equation* is an equation of the form $ax^2 + bx + c = 0$, where a, b, and c are real numbers and $a \neq 0$. A quadratic equation is also called a *second-degree equation*.

A quadratic equation is in *standard form* when the polynomial is in descending order and equal to zero.

When a quadratic equation has two solutions that are the same number, the solution is called a *double root* of the equation.

For an equation of the form $ax^2 + bx + c = 0$, the quantity $b^2 - 4ac$ is called the *discriminant*.

A quadratic inequality is one that can be written in the form $ax^2 + bx + c > 0$ or $ax^2 + bx + c < 0$, where $a \neq 0$. The symbols $\leq$ or $\geq$ can also be used.

Essential Rules

The Principle of Zero Products
If $ab = 0$, then $a = 0$ or $b = 0$.

The Quadratic Formula
$$x = \frac{-b \pm \sqrt{b^2 - 4ac}}{2a}$$

The Effect of the Discriminant on the Solutions of a Quadratic Equation

1. If $b^2 - 4ac = 0$, the equation has one real number solution, a double root.
2. If $b^2 - 4ac > 0$, the equation has two unequal real number solutions.
3. If $b^2 - 4ac < 0$, the equation has two complex number solutions.

Chapter Review

1. Solve by factoring: $2x^2 - 3x = 0$

2. Solve by factoring: $6x^2 + 9cx = 6c^2$

3. Solve by taking square roots:
   $x^2 = 48$

4. Solve by taking square roots:
   $\left(x + \dfrac{1}{2}\right)^2 + 4 = 0$

5. Solve by completing the square:
   $x^2 + 4x + 3 = 0$

6. Solve by completing the square:
   $7x^2 - 14x + 3 = 0$

7. Solve by using the quadratic formula:
   $12x^2 - 25x + 12 = 0$

8. Solve by using the quadratic formula:
   $x^2 - x + 8 = 0$

9. Write a quadratic equation that has integer coefficients and has solutions 0 and -3.

10. Write a quadratic equation that has integer coefficients and has solutions $\dfrac{3}{4}$ and $-\dfrac{2}{3}$.

11. Solve by completing the square:
    $x^2 - 2x + 8 = 0$

12. Solve by completing the square:
    $(x - 2)(x + 3) = x - 10$

13. Solve by using the quadratic formula:
    $3x(x - 3) = 2x - 4$

14. Using the discriminant, determine the number and type of solutions for $3x^2 - 5x + 1 = 0$.

15. Solve: $(x + 3)(2x - 5) < 0$

16. Solve: $(x - 2)(x + 4)(2x + 3) \leq 0$

17. Solve: $x^{2/3} + x^{1/3} - 12 = 0$

18. Solve: $2(x - 1) + 3\sqrt{x - 1} - 2 = 0$

19. Solve: $3x = \dfrac{9}{x - 2}$

20. Solve: $\dfrac{3x + 7}{x + 2} + x = 3$

21. Solve and graph the solution set:
$\dfrac{x - 2}{2x - 3} \geq 0$

22. Solve and graph the solution set:
$\dfrac{(2x - 1)(x + 3)}{x - 4} \leq 0$

23. Solve: $x = \sqrt{x} + 2$

24. Solve: $2x = \sqrt{5x + 24} + 3$

25. Solve: $\dfrac{x - 2}{2x + 3} - \dfrac{x - 4}{x} = 2$

26. Solve: $1 - \dfrac{x + 4}{2 - x} = \dfrac{x - 3}{x + 2}$

27. The length of a rectangle is two more than twice the width. The area of the rectangle is 60 cm². Find the length and width of the rectangle.

28. The sum of the squares of three consecutive even integers is fifty-six. Find the three integers.

29. An older computer requires 12 min longer to print the payroll than does a newer computer. Together the computers can print the payroll in 8 min. Find the time for the new computer working alone to print the payroll.

30. A car travels 200 mi. A second car, making the same trip, travels 10 mph faster than the first car and makes the trip in 1 h less. Find the speed of each car.

Chapter Test

1. Solve by factoring: $3x^2 + 10x = 8$

2. Solve by factoring: $6x^2 - 5x - 6 = 0$

3. Write a quadratic equation that has integer coefficients and has solutions 3 and -3.

4. Write a quadratic equation that has integer coefficients and has solutions $\frac{1}{2}$ and -4.

5. Solve by taking square roots:
$3(x - 2)^2 - 24 = 0$

6. Solve by completing the square:
$x^2 - 6x - 2 = 0$

7. Solve by completing the square:
$3x^2 - 6x = 2$

8. Solve by using the quadratic formula:
$2x^2 - 2x = 1$

9. Solve by using the quadratic formula:
$x^2 + 4x + 12 = 0$

10. Use the discriminant to determine whether $3x^2 - 4x = 1$ has one real number solution, two real number solutions, or two complex number solutions.

11. Use the discriminant to determine whether $x^2 - 6x = -15$ has one real number solution, two real number solutions, or two complex number solutions.

12. Solve: $2x + 7x^{1/2} - 4 = 0$

13. Solve: $x^4 - 4x^2 + 3 = 0$

14. Solve: $\sqrt{2x + 1} + 5 = 2x$

15. Solve: $\sqrt{x - 2} = \sqrt{x} - 2$

16. Solve: $\dfrac{2x}{x - 3} + \dfrac{5}{x - 1} = 1$

17. Solve and graph the solution set of $(x - 2)(x + 4)(x - 4) < 0$.

18. Solve and graph the solution set of $\dfrac{2x - 3}{x + 4} \leq 0$.

19. The base of a triangle is 3 ft more than three times the height. The area of the triangle is 30 ft². Find the base and height of the triangle.

20. The rate of a river's current is 2 mph. A canoe was rowed 6 mi down the river and back in 4 h. Find the rowing rate in calm water.

Cumulative Review

1. Evaluate $2a^2 - b^2 \div c^2$ when $a = 3$, $b = -4$, and $c = -2$.

2. Solve: $\dfrac{2x - 3}{4} - \dfrac{x + 4}{6} = \dfrac{3x - 2}{8}$

3. Find the slope of the line containing the points $(3, -4)$ and $(-1, 2)$.

4. Find the equation of the line that contains the point $(1, 2)$ and is parallel to the line $x - y = 1$.

5. Factor: $-3x^3y + 6x^2y^2 - 9xy^3$

6. Factor: $6x^2 - 7x - 20$

7. Factor: $a^nx + a^ny - 2x - 2y$

8. Simplify: $(3x^3 - 13x^2 + 10) \div (3x - 4)$

9. Simplify: $\dfrac{x^2 + 2x + 1}{8x^2 + 8x} \cdot \dfrac{4x^3 - 4x^2}{x^2 - 1}$

10. Find the distance between the points $(-2, 3)$ and $(2, 5)$.

11. Solve $S = \dfrac{n}{2}(a + b)$ for b.

12. Simplify: $-2i(7 - 4i)$

13. Simplify: $a^{-1/2}(a^{1/2} - a^{3/2})$

14. Simplify: $\dfrac{\sqrt[3]{8x^4y^5}}{\sqrt[3]{16xy^6}}$

15. Solve: $\dfrac{x}{x + 2} - \dfrac{4x}{x + 3} = 1$

16. Solve: $\dfrac{x}{2x + 3} - \dfrac{3}{4x^2 - 9} = \dfrac{x}{2x - 3}$

17. Solve: $x^4 - 6x^2 + 8 = 0$

18. Solve: $\sqrt{3x + 1} - 1 = x$

19. Solve: $|3x - 2| < 8$

20. Find the x- and y-intercepts of the graph of $6x - 5y = 15$.

21. Graph the solution set:
$$x + y \leq 3$$
$$2x - y < 4$$

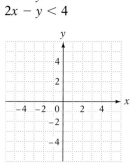

22. Solve the system of equations.
$$x + y + z = 2$$
$$-x + 2y - 3z = -9$$
$$x - 2y - 2z = -1$$

23. Given $f(x) = \dfrac{2x - 3}{x^2 - 1}$, find $f(-2)$.

24. Find the domain of the function
$$f(x) = \frac{x - 2}{x^2 - 2x - 15}.$$

25. Solve and graph the solution set of $x^3 + x^2 - 6x < 0$.

26. Solve and graph the solution set of
$$\frac{(x - 1)(x - 5)}{x + 3} \geq 0.$$

27. A piston rod for an automobile is $9\dfrac{3}{8}$ in. with a tolerance of $\dfrac{1}{64}$ in. Find the lower and upper limits of the length of the piston rod.

28. The base of a triangle is $(x + 8)$ ft. The height is $(2x - 4)$ ft. Find the area of the triangle in terms of the variable x.

29. Use the discriminant to determine whether $2x^2 + 4x + 3 = 0$ has one real number solution, two real number solutions, or two complex number solutions.

30. The graph shows the relationship between the cost of a building and the depreciation allowed for income tax purposes. Find the slope of the line between the two points shown on the graph. Write a sentence that states the meaning of the slope.

9

Functions and Relations

Forestry technicians compile data on the characteristics of forest land tracts, such as species and population of trees, disease and insect damage, tree seedling mortality, and conditions that may cause fire danger. They also train and lead conservation workers in seasonal activities such as planting tree seedlings, putting out forest fires, and maintaining recreational facilities. These technicians may use functions to model, for instance, the progress of a tree disease as it spreads through a tract of forest.

Objectives

Section 9.1
To graph a quadratic function
To find the *x*-intercepts of a parabola
To find the minimum or maximum of a quadratic function
To solve application problems

Section 9.2
To graph functions

Section 9.3
To perform operations on functions
To find the composition of two functions

Section 9.4
To determine whether a function is one-to-one
To find the inverse of a function

History of the Equals Sign

A portion of a page of the first book that used an equals sign, $\geq$, is shown here. This book was written in 1557 by Robert Recorde and was titled *The Whetstone of Witte*.

Note in the illustration the words "bicause noe 2 thynges can be moare equalle." Recorde decided that two things could not be more equal than two parallel lines of the same length. Therefore, it made sense to use this symbol to show equality.

This page also illustrates the use of the plus sign, $\leq$, and the minus sign, $-$. These symbols had been widely used for only about 100 years when this book was written.

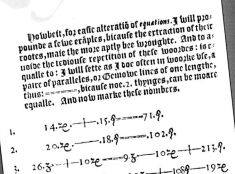

9.1 Properties of Quadratic Functions

Objective A   To graph a quadratic function ································· (37) [CT]

Recall that a linear function is one that can be expressed by the equation $f(x) = mx + b$. The graph of a linear function has certain characteristics. It is a straight line with slope m and y-intercept $(0, b)$. A **quadratic function** is one that can be expressed by the equation $f(x) = ax^2 + bx + c$, $a \neq 0$. The graph of this function, called a **parabola,** also has certain characteristics. The graph of a quadratic function can be drawn by finding ordered pairs that belong to the function.

⟹ Graph $f(x) = x^2 - 2x - 3$.

By evaluating the function for various values of x, find enough ordered pairs to determine the shape of the graph.

x	$f(x) = x^2 - 2x - 3$	$f(x)$	(x, y)
-2	$f(-2) = (-2)^2 - 2(-2) - 3$	5	$(-2, 5)$
-1	$f(-1) = (-1)^2 - 2(-1) - 3$	0	$(-1, 0)$
0	$f(0) = (0)^2 - 2(0) - 3$	-3	$(0, -3)$
1	$f(1) = (1)^2 - 2(1) - 3$	-4	$(1, -4)$
2	$f(2) = (2)^2 - 2(2) - 3$	-3	$(2, -3)$
3	$f(3) = (3)^2 - 2(3) - 3$	0	$(3, 0)$
4	$f(4) = (4)^2 - 2(4) - 3$	5	$(4, 5)$

$f(x) = x^2 - 2x - 3$

Because the value of $f(x) = x^2 - 2x - 3$ is a real number for all values of x, the domain of f is all real numbers. From the graph, it appears that no value of y is less than -4. Thus the range is $\{y \mid y \geq -4\}$. The range can also be determined algebraically, as shown below, by completing the square.

TAKE NOTE

In completing the square, 1 is both added and subtracted. Because $1 - 1 = 0$, the expression $x^2 - 2x - 3$ is not changed. Note that

$(x - 1)^2 - 4$
$= (x^2 - 2x + 1) - 4$
$= x^2 - 2x - 3$

which is the original expression.

$f(x) = x^2 - 2x - 3$
$\quad = (x^2 - 2x) - 3$ • Group the variable terms.
$\quad = (x^2 - 2x + 1) - 1 - 3$ • Complete the square on $x^2 - 2x$. Add and subtract $\left[\dfrac{1}{2}(-2)\right]^2 = 1$ to and from $x^2 - 2x$.
$\quad = (x - 1)^2 - 4$ • Factor and combine like terms.

Because the square of a positive number is always positive, we have

$(x - 1)^2 \geq 0$
$(x - 1)^2 - 4 \geq -4$ • Subtract 4 from each side of the inequality.
$f(x) \geq -4$ • $f(x) = (x - 1)^2 - 4$
$y \geq -4$

From the last inequality, the range is $\{y \mid y \geq -4\}$.

In general, the graph of $f(x) = ax^2 + bx + c$, $a \neq 0$, resembles a "cup" shape as shown at the right. The parabola opens up when $a > 0$ and opens down when $a < 0$. The **vertex** of the parabola is the point with the smallest (parabola opens up) y-coordinate or the largest (parabola opens down) y-coordinate.

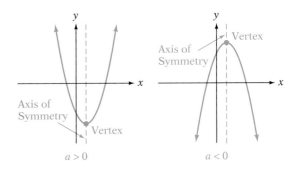

The **axis of symmetry** is the line that passes through the vertex of the parabola and is parallel to the y-axis. To understand the axis of symmetry, think of folding the graph along that line. The two portions of the graph will match up.

The vertex and axis of symmetry of a parabola can be found by completing the square.

⇒ Find the vertex of the graph of $F(x) = x^2 + 4x + 3$.

To find the coordinates of the vertex, complete the square.

$$
\begin{aligned}
F(x) &= x^2 + 4x + 3 \\
&= (x^2 + 4x) + 3 \qquad \text{• Group the variable terms.} \\
&= (x^2 + 4x + 4) - 4 + 3 \qquad \text{• Complete the square on } x^2 + 4x. \text{ Add and subtract} \\
& \qquad\qquad\qquad\qquad\qquad \left[\frac{1}{2}(4)\right]^2 = 4 \text{ to and from } x^2 + 4x. \\
&= (x + 2)^2 - 1 \qquad \text{• Factor and combine like terms.}
\end{aligned}
$$

Because a, the coefficient of x^2, is positive ($a = 1$), the parabola opens up and the vertex is the point with the least y-coordinate. Because $(x + 2)^2 \geq 0$ for all values of x, the least y-coordinate occurs when $(x + 2)^2 = 0$. This quantity is zero when $x = -2$. Therefore, the x-coordinate of the vertex is -2.

$F(x) = x^2 + 4x + 3$

To find the y-coordinate of the vertex, evaluate the function at $x = -2$.

$$
\begin{aligned}
F(x) &= (x + 2)^2 - 1 \\
F(-2) &= (-2 + 2)^2 - 1 = -1
\end{aligned}
$$

The y-coordinate of the vertex is -1.

From the results above, the coordinates of the vertex are $(-2, -1)$. The axis of symmetry is the line whose equation is $x = -2$.

By following the process illustrated in the last example and completing the square on $f(x) = ax^2 + bx + c$, we can find a formula for the coordinates of the vertex of a parabola.

Vertex of a Parabola

Let $f(x) = ax^2 + bx + c$ be the equation of a parabola. The coordinates of the vertex are $\left(-\dfrac{b}{2a}, f\left(-\dfrac{b}{2a}\right)\right)$. The equation of the axis of symmetry is $x = -\dfrac{b}{2a}$.

⟹ Find the vertex of and graph the parabola whose equation is
$g(x) = -2x^2 + 3x + 1$.

From the equation $g(x) = -2x^2 + 3x + 1$, $a = -2$, $b = 3$, and $c = 1$. Use the formula for the vertex of a parabola.

x-coordinate: $-\dfrac{b}{2a} = -\dfrac{3}{2(-2)} = \dfrac{3}{4}$ • $a = -2,\ b = 3$

y-coordinate: $g\left(-\dfrac{b}{2a}\right)$ • $-\dfrac{b}{2a} = \dfrac{3}{4}$

$g\left(\dfrac{3}{4}\right) = -2\left(\dfrac{3}{4}\right)^2 + 3\left(\dfrac{3}{4}\right) + 1$

$= \dfrac{17}{8}$ The vertex is $\left(\dfrac{3}{4}, \dfrac{17}{8}\right)$.

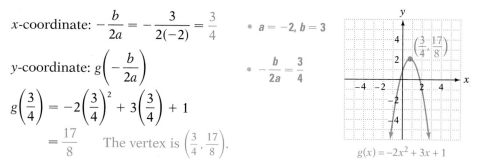

$g(x) = -2x^2 + 3x + 1$

Because a is negative, the graph opens down. Find a few ordered pairs that belong to the function and then sketch the graph.

Once the y-coordinate of the vertex is known, the range of the function can be determined. Here, the graph of g opens down, so the y-coordinate of the vertex is the largest value of y. Therefore the range of g is $\left\{y \,\middle|\, y \le \dfrac{17}{8}\right\}$. The domain is all real numbers.

TAKE NOTE

Once the coordinates of the vertex are found, the range of the quadratic function can be determined.

Example 1   Find the vertex and axis of symmetry of the parabola whose equation is $y = -x^2 + 4x + 1$. Then graph the equation.

You Try It 1   Find the vertex and axis of symmetry of the parabola whose equation is $y = 4x^2 + 4x + 1$. Then graph the equation.

Solution x-coordinate of the vertex:

$-\dfrac{b}{2a} = -\dfrac{4}{2(-1)} = 2$

y-coordinate of vertex:
$y = -x^2 + 4x + 1$
$= -(2)^2 + 4(2) + 1$
$= 5$

Vertex: $(2, 5)$
Axis of symmetry: $x = 2$

Your solution

Example 2   Find the domain and range of $f(x) = 0.5x^2 - 3$. Then graph the equation.

You Try It 2   Find the domain and range of $f(x) = -x^2 - 2x - 1$. Then graph the equation.

Solution x-coordinate of the vertex:

$-\dfrac{b}{2a} = -\dfrac{0}{2(0.5)} = 0$

y-coordinate of vertex:
$f(x) = 0.5x^2 - 3$
$f(0) = 0.5(0)^2 - 3$
$= -3$

Vertex: $(0, -3)$
The domain is all real numbers.
The range is $\{y \,|\, y \ge -3\}$.

Your solution

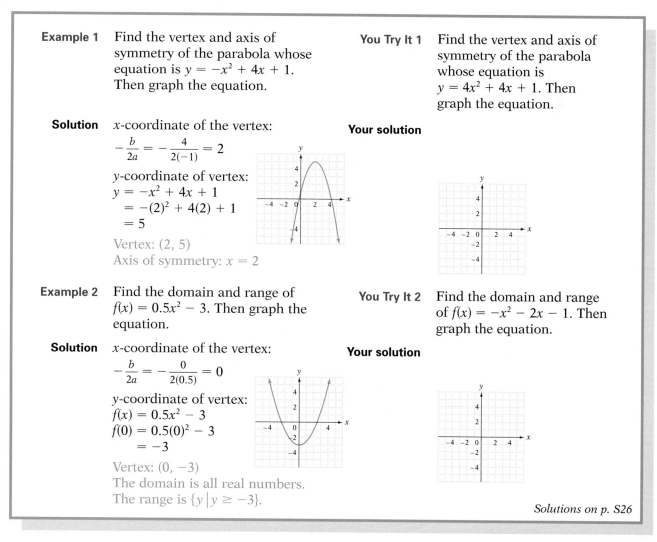

Solutions on p. S26

Objective B   *To find the x-intercepts of a parabola* ....

Recall that a point at which a graph crosses the *x*- or *y*-axis is called an *intercept* of the graph. The *x*-intercepts of the graph of an equation occur when $y = 0$; the *y*-intercepts occur when $x = 0$.

The graph of $y = x^2 + 3x - 4$ is shown at the right. The points whose coordinates are $(-4, 0)$ and $(1, 0)$ are the *x*-intercepts of the graph. The point whose coordinates are $(0, -4)$ is the *y*-intercept of the graph.

➡ Find the *x*-intercepts for the parabola whose equation is $y = 4x^2 - 4x + 1$.

To find the *x*-intercepts, let $y = 0$ and then solve for *x*.

$y = 4x^2 - 4x + 1$
$0 = 4x^2 - 4x + 1$ • Let *y* = 0.

$0 = (2x - 1)(2x - 1)$ • Solve for *x* by factoring.

$2x - 1 = 0$	$2x - 1 = 0$
$2x = 1$	$2x = 1$
$x = \dfrac{1}{2}$	$x = \dfrac{1}{2}$

The *x*-intercept is $\left(\dfrac{1}{2}, 0\right)$.

In the preceding example, the parabola has only one *x*-intercept. In this case, the parabola is said to be **tangent** to the *x*-axis at $x = \dfrac{1}{2}$.

➡ Find the *x*-intercepts of $y = 2x^2 - x - 6$.

To find the *x*-intercepts, let $y = 0$ and solve for *x*.

$y = 2x^2 - x - 6$
$0 = 2x^2 - x - 6$ • Let *y* = 0.
$0 = (2x + 3)(x - 2)$ • Solve for *x* by factoring and using the Principle of Zero Products.

| $2x + 3 = 0$ | $x - 2 = 0$ |
| $x = -\dfrac{3}{2}$ | $x = 2$ |

The *x*-intercepts are $\left(-\dfrac{3}{2}, 0\right)$ and $(2, 0)$.

TAKE NOTE

A zero of a function is the *x*-coordinate of the *x*-intercept of the graph of the function. Because the *x*-intercepts of the graph of $f(x) = 2x^2 - x - 6$ are $\left(-\dfrac{3}{2}, 0\right)$ and (2, 0), the zeros are $-\dfrac{3}{2}$ and 2.

If the equation above, $y = 2x^2 - x - 6$, is written in functional notation as $f(x) = 2x^2 - x - 6$, then to find the *x*-intercepts you would let $f(x) = 0$ and solve for *x*. Recall that a value of *x* for which $f(x) = 0$ is a *zero* of the function. Thus, $-\dfrac{3}{2}$ and 2 are *zeros* of $f(x) = 2x^2 - x - 6$.

⇒ Find the zeros of $f(x) = x^2 - 2x - 1$.

To find the zeros, let $f(x) = 0$ and solve for x.

$f(x) = x^2 - 2x - 1$

$0 = x^2 - 2x - 1$

$x = \dfrac{-b \pm \sqrt{b^2 - 4ac}}{2a}$

$= \dfrac{-(-2) \pm \sqrt{(-2)^2 - 4(1)(-1)}}{2(1)}$

$= \dfrac{2 \pm \sqrt{4 + 4}}{2} = \dfrac{2 \pm \sqrt{8}}{2}$

$= \dfrac{2 \pm 2\sqrt{2}}{2}$

$= 1 \pm \sqrt{2}$

• Because $x^2 - 2x - 1$ does not easily factor, use the quadratic formula to solve for x.

• $a = 1, b = -2, c = -1$

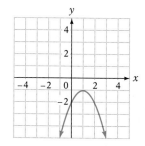

The zeros of the function are $1 - \sqrt{2}$ and $1 + \sqrt{2}$.

The graph of $f(x) = x^2 - 2x - 1$ is shown above. Note that the zeros are the x-intercepts of the graph of f.

The preceding examples suggest that there is a relationship among the x-intercepts of the graph of a function, the zeros of a function, and the solutions of an equation. In fact, those three concepts are different ways of discussing the same number. The choice depends on the focus of the discussion. If we are discussing graphing, then the intercept is our focus; if we are discussing functions, then the zero of the function is our focus; and if we are discussing equations, the solution of the equation is our focus.

The graph of a parabola may not have x-intercepts. The graph of $y = -x^2 + 2x - 2$ is shown at the right. Note that the graph does not pass through the x-axis and thus there are no x-intercepts. This means there are no real number zeros of $f(x) = -x^2 + 2x - 2$ and that there are no real number solutions of $-x^2 + 2x - 2 = 0$.

Using the quadratic formula, the solutions of the equation $-x^2 + 2x - 2 = 0$ are $1 - i$ and $1 + i$. Thus the zeros of $f(x) = -x^2 + 2x - 2$ are the complex numbers $1 - i$ and $1 + i$.

Recall that the discriminant of $ax^2 + bx + c$ is the expression $b^2 - 4ac$ and that this expression can be used to determine whether $ax^2 + bx + c = 0$ has zero, one, or two real number solutions. Because there is a connection between the solutions of $ax^2 + bx + c = 0$ and the x-intercepts of the graph of $y = ax^2 + bx + c$, the discriminant can be used to determine the number of x-intercepts of a parabola.

> **The Effect of the Discriminant on the Number of x-Intercepts of a Parabola**
>
> **1.** If $b^2 - 4ac = 0$, the parabola has one x-intercept.
> **2.** If $b^2 - 4ac > 0$, the parabola has two x-intercepts.
> **3.** If $b^2 - 4ac < 0$, the parabola has no x-intercepts.

⇨ Use the discriminant to determine the number of x-intercepts of the parabola whose equation is $y = 2x^2 - x + 2$.

$$b^2 - 4ac$$
$$(-1)^2 - 4(2)(2) = 1 - 16 = -15$$
$$-15 < 0$$

• Evaluate the discriminant.
• $a = 2$, $b = -1$, $c = 2$

The discriminant is less than zero. Therefore, the parabola has no x-intercepts.

Example 3 Find the x-intercepts of $y = 2x^2 - 5x + 2$.

Solution
$$y = 2x^2 - 5x + 2$$
$$0 = 2x^2 - 5x + 2$$
$$0 = (2x - 1)(x - 2)$$

$$2x - 1 = 0 \qquad x - 2 = 0$$
$$2x = 1 \qquad\qquad x = 2$$
$$x = \frac{1}{2}$$

The x-intercepts are $\left(\frac{1}{2}, 0\right)$ and $(2, 0)$.

You Try It 3 Find the x-intercepts of $y = x^2 + 3x + 4$.

Your solution

Example 4 Find the zeros of $f(x) = x^2 + 4x + 5$.

Solution
$$f(x) = x^2 + 4x + 5$$
$$0 = x^2 + 4x + 5$$

• Let $f(x) = 0$.

$$x = \frac{-b \pm \sqrt{b^2 - 4ac}}{2a}$$

• Use the quadratic formula.

$$= \frac{-4 \pm \sqrt{4^2 - 4(1)(5)}}{2(1)}$$

• $a = 1$, $b = 4$, $c = 5$

$$= \frac{-4 \pm \sqrt{16 - 20}}{2} = \frac{-4 \pm \sqrt{-4}}{2}$$

$$= \frac{-4 \pm 2i}{2} = -2 \pm i$$

The zeros of the function are $-2 + i$ and $-2 - i$.

You Try It 4 Find the zeros of $g(x) = x^2 - x + 6$.

Your solution

Example 5 Use the discriminant to determine the number of x-intercepts of $y = x^2 - 6x + 9$.

Solution
$$a = 1, b = -6, c = 9$$
$$b^2 - 4ac$$
$$(-6)^2 - 4(1)(9) = 36 - 36 = 0$$

Because the discriminant is equal to zero, the parabola has one x-intercept.

You Try It 5 Use the discriminant to determine the number of x-intercepts of $y = x^2 - x - 6$.

Your solution

Solutions on pp. S26–S27

Objective C   *To find the minimum or maximum of a quadratic function* ....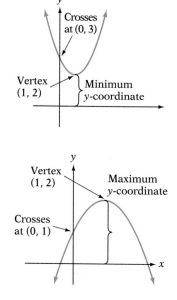

The graph of $f(x) = x^2 - 2x + 3$ is shown at the right. Because a is positive, the parabola opens up. The vertex of the parabola is the lowest point on the parabola. It is the point that has the minimum y-coordinate. Therefore, the value of the function at this point is a **minimum.**

The graph of $f(x) = -x^2 + 2x + 1$ is shown at the right. Because a is negative, the parabola opens down. The vertex of the parabola is the highest point on the parabola. It is the point that has the maximum y-coordinate. Therefore, the value of the function at this point is a **maximum.**

POINT OF INTEREST

Calculus is a branch of mathematics that demonstrates, among other things, how to find the maximum or minimum of functions other than quadratic functions. These are very important problems in applied mathematics. For instance, an automotive engineer wants to design a car whose shape will *minimize* the effects of air flow. The same engineer tries to *maximize* the efficiency of a car's engine. Similarly, an economist may try to determine what business practices will *minimize* cost and *maximize* profit.

To find the minimum or maximum value of a quadratic function, first find the x-coordinate of the vertex. Then evaluate the function at that value.

⇒ Find the maximum value of the function $f(x) = -2x^2 + 4x + 3$.

Find the x-coordinate of the vertex.

$$x = -\frac{b}{2a} = -\frac{4}{2(-2)} = 1$$ • $a = -2$, $b = 4$

Evaluate the function at $x = 1$.
$$f(x) = -2x^2 + 4x + 3$$
$$f(1) = -2(1)^2 + 4(1) + 3$$ • Replace x by 1.
$$= -2 + 4 + 3$$
$$= 5$$

Because $a < 0$, the graph of $f(x) = -2x^2 + 4x + 3$ opens down. Therefore, the function has a maximum value. The maximum value of the function is 5.

Example 6
Find the minimum value of
$f(x) = 2x^2 - 3x + 1$.

Solution
$$x = -\frac{b}{2a} = -\frac{-3}{2(2)} = \frac{3}{4}$$
$$f(x) = 2x^2 - 3x + 1$$
$$f\left(\frac{3}{4}\right) = 2\left(\frac{3}{4}\right)^2 - 3\left(\frac{3}{4}\right) + 1 = \frac{9}{8} - \frac{9}{4} + 1$$
$$= -\frac{1}{8}$$

Because a is positive, the graph opens up. The function has a minimum value.

The minimum value of the function is $-\frac{1}{8}$.

You Try It 6
Find the maximum value of
$f(x) = -3x^2 + 4x - 1$.

Your solution

Solution on p. S27

Objective D *To solve application problems* .... CT

Example 7

A mining company has determined that the cost, C, in dollars per ton of mining a mineral is given by the equation $C(x) = 0.2x^2 - 2x + 12$, where x is the number of tons mined of the mineral. Find the number of tons of the mineral that should be mined to minimize the cost. What is the minimum cost?

Strategy

• To find the number of tons that will minimize the cost, find the x-coordinate of the vertex.

• To find the minimum cost, evaluate $C(x)$ at the x-coordinate of the vertex.

Solution

$$x = -\frac{b}{2a} = -\frac{(-2)}{2(0.2)} = 5$$

To minimize cost, 5 tons should be mined.

$C(x) = 0.2x^2 - 2x + 12$

$C(5) = 0.2(5)^2 - 2(5) + 12 = 5 - 10 + 12 = 7$

The minimum cost per ton is $7.

You Try It 7

The height, s, in feet of a ball thrown straight up is given by the equation $s(t) = -16t^2 + 64t$, where t is the time in seconds. Find the time it takes the ball to reach its maximum height. What is the maximum height?

Your strategy

Your solution

Example 8

A mason is forming a rectangular floor for a storage shed. The perimeter of the rectangle is 44 ft. What dimensions would give the floor a maximum area?

Strategy

$P = 2L + 2W$

$44 = 2L + 2W$ • $P = 44$

$22 = L + W$ • Divide each side by 2.

$22 - L = W$ • Solve for W.

Express the area of the rectangle in terms of L.

$A = LW$

$A = L(22 - L)$ • $W = 22 - L$

$A = -L^2 + 22L$

• To find the length, find the L-coordinate of the vertex of $A = -L^2 + 22L$.

• To find the width, replace L in $22 - L = W$ by the L-coordinate of the vertex.

Solution $L = -\frac{b}{2a} = -\frac{22}{2(-1)} = 11$

The length is 11 ft.

$22 - L = 22 - 11 = 11$

The width is 11 ft.

You Try It 8

A rectangular fence is being constructed along a stream for a children's play area. If there are 100 ft of fence available, what dimensions of the rectangle will produce a maximum play area?

Your strategy

Your solution

Solutions on p. S27

9.1 Exercises

Objective A

Find the vertex and axis of symmetry of the parabola given by each equation. Then graph the equation.

1. $y = x^2 - 2x - 4$

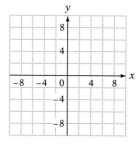

2. $y = x^2 + 4x - 4$

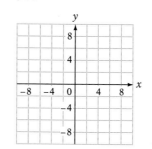

3. $y = -x^2 + 2x - 3$

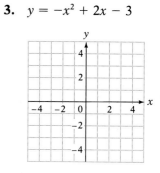

4. $y = -x^2 + 4x - 5$

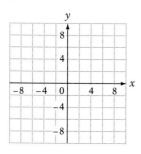

5. $f(x) = x^2 + 6x + 5$

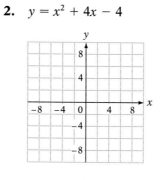

6. $f(x) = x^2 - x - 6$

7. $G(x) = x^2 - x - 2$

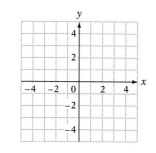

8. $F(x) = x^2 - 3x + 2$

9. $y = 2x^2 - 4x + 1$

10. $y = -2x^2 + 6x$

11. $y = x^2 + 4x + 5$

12. $y = -x^2 + 2x - 1$

13. $y = \dfrac{1}{2}x^2 + 4$

14. $y = -\dfrac{1}{4}x^2 - 1$

15. $h(x) = \dfrac{1}{2}x^2 - x + 1$

16. $P(x) = -\dfrac{1}{2}x^2 + 2x - 3$

17. $y = \dfrac{1}{2}x^2 + 2x - 6$

18. $y = -\dfrac{1}{2}x^2 + x - 3$

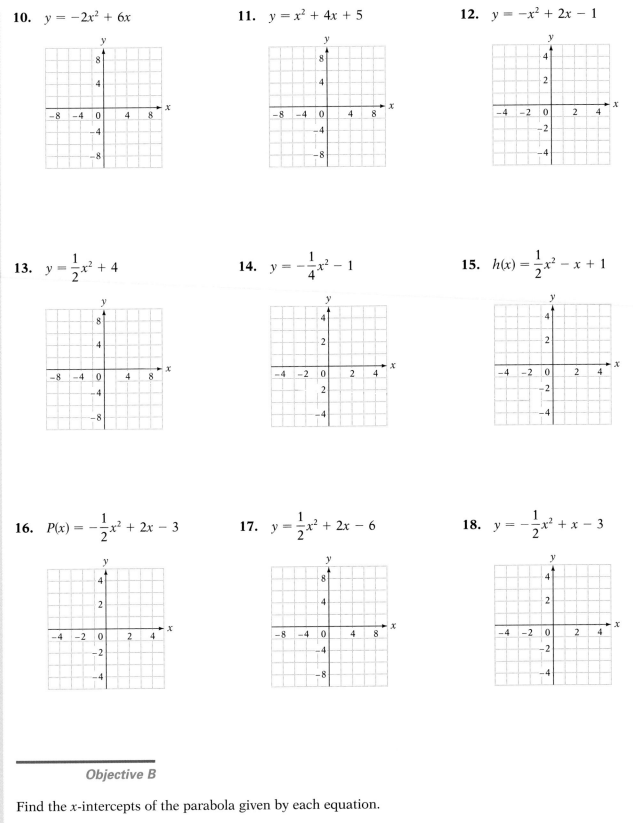

Objective B

Find the *x*-intercepts of the parabola given by each equation.

19. $y = x^2 - 4$

20. $y = x^2 - 9$

21. $y = 2x^2 - 4x$

22. $y = 3x^2 + 6x$

23. $y = x^2 - x - 2$

24. $y = x^2 - 2x - 8$

25. $y = 2x^2 - x - 1$

26. $y = 2x^2 - 5x - 3$

27. $y = x^2 + 2x - 1$

28. $y = x^2 + 4x - 3$

29. $y = x^2 + 6x + 10$

30. $y = -x^2 - 4x - 5$

31. $y = x^2 - 2x - 2$

32. $y = -x^2 - 2x + 1$

33. $y = -x^2 + 4x + 1$

Find the zeros of each quadratic function.

34. $f(x) = x^2 + 3x + 2$

35. $f(x) = x^2 - 6x + 9$

36. $f(x) = -x^2 + 4x - 5$

37. $f(x) = -x^2 + 3x + 8$

38. $f(x) = 2x^2 - 3x$

39. $f(x) = -3x^2 + 4x$

40. $f(x) = 2x^2 - 4$

41. $f(x) = 3x^2 + 6$

42. $f(x) = 2x^2 + 3x + 2$

43. $f(x) = 3x^2 - x + 4$

44. $f(x) = -3x^2 - 4x + 1$

45. $f(x) = -2x + x + 5$

Use the discriminant to determine the number of x-intercepts of the graph.

46. $y = 2x^2 + x + 1$

47. $y = 2x^2 + 2x - 1$

48. $y = -x^2 - x + 3$

49. $y = -2x^2 + x + 1$

50. $y = x^2 - 8x + 16$

51. $y = x^2 - 10x + 25$

52. $y = -3x^2 - x - 2$

53. $y = -2x^2 + x - 1$

54. $y = 4x^2 - x - 2$

55. $y = 2x^2 + x + 4$

56. $y = -2x^2 - x - 5$

57. $y = -3x^2 + 4x - 5$

58. $y = 4x^2 - 2x - 3$

59. $y = -3x^2 + 2x - 8$

60. $y = 4x^2 + 2x - 5$

Objective C

Find the minimum or maximum value of each quadratic function.

61. $f(x) = x^2 - 2x + 3$

62. $f(x) = x^2 + 3x - 4$

63. $f(x) = -2x^2 + 4x - 3$

64. $f(x) = -2x^2 - 3x + 4$

65. $f(x) = 2x^2 + 4x$

66. $f(x) = -2x^2 - 3x$

67. $f(x) = -2x^2 + 4x - 5$

68. $f(x) = -3x^2 + x - 6$

69. $f(x) = 2x^2 + 3x - 8$

70. $f(x) = -x^2 - x + 2$

71. $f(x) = 3x^2 + 3x - 2$

72. $f(x) = x^2 - 5x + 3$

73. $f(x) = -3x^2 + 4x - 2$

74. $f(x) = -2x^2 - 5x + 1$

75. $f(x) = 3x^2 + 5x + 2$

Objective D   Application Problems

76. The height in feet, *s*, of a rock thrown upward at an initial speed of 64 ft/s from a cliff 50 ft above an ocean beach is given by $s(t) = -16t^2 + 64t + 50$, where *t* is the time in seconds. Find the maximum height the rock will attain above the beach.

77. An event in the Summer Olympics is 10-meter springboard diving. The height, *s*, of a diver in this event above the water *t* seconds after jumping is given by $s(t) = -4.9t^2 + 7.8t + 10$. What is the maximum height, to the nearest tenth of a meter, that the diver will be above the water?

78. A tour operator believes that the profit, *P*, from selling *x* tickets is given by $P(x) = 40x - 0.25x^2$. Using this model, what is the maximum profit the tour operator can expect?

79. The suspension cable that supports a small footbridge hangs in the shape of a parabola. The height in feet of the cable above the bridge is given by the function $h(x) = 0.25x^2 - 0.8x + 25$, where *x* is the distance from one end of the bridge. What is the minimum height of the cable above the bridge?

80. A manufacturer of microwave ovens believes that the revenue the company receives is related to the price, *P*, of an oven by $R(P) = 125P - \frac{1}{4}P^2$. What price will give the maximum revenue?

81. An equation of the thickness (in inches), *h*, of the mirror at the Palomar Mountain Observatory is given by $h(x) = 0.000379x^2 - 0.0758x + 24$, where *x* is measured from the edge of the mirror. Find the minimum thickness of the mirror.

82. The height, *s*, of water squirting from a fire hose nozzle is given by the equation $s(x) = -\frac{1}{30}x^2 + 2x + 5$, where *x* is the horizontal distance from the nozzle. How high on a building 40 ft from the fire hose will the water land?

83. The height, *h*, of a baseball hit by Tony Gwinn that is a distance of *d* feet from him can be given by $h(d) = -0.0015d^2 + 0.52d + 5$. Will this ball clear a 5-foot wall 340 ft from where it was hit?

84. A designer of stained glass windows has 26 ft of wire that is to be bent so that the bottom portion is a rectangle and the top is an equilateral triangle. The enclosed area of this figure depends on the length of the base and is given by $A(x) = \frac{1}{4}(\sqrt{3} - 6)x^2 + 13x$. What is the maximum area, to the nearest tenth, that can be enclosed by this shape?

85. A framer is designing a frame to enclose two photographs. If the framer has 14 ft of board and wishes to make a design like the one at the right, what dimensions will enclose the largest area?

$P = 4x + 3y$
$A = 2xy$

86. The perimeter of a rectangular window is 24 ft. Find the dimensions of the window that will enclose the largest area. What is the maximum area?

APPLYING THE CONCEPTS

87. Show that the minimum value of
$$S(x) = (2 - x)^2 + (5 - x)^2 + (4 - x)^2 + (7 - x)^2$$
occurs when x is the average of the numbers 2, 5, 4, and 7.

88. In your own words, explain how the x-intercepts of a graph and the real zeros of a function are related.

89. Complete the graph at the right in such a way that the entire graph is symmetric about the y-axis.

90. Determine whether the following statements are always true, sometimes true, or never true.
   a. An axis of symmetry of a parabola passes through the vertex.
   b. A parabola has two x-intercepts.
   c. A quadratic function has a minimum value.

91. Graph $y = \sqrt{x + 2}$ and $y^2 = x + 2$. Discuss the similarities and differences between the two graphs.

92. When $f(x) = 0$, values of x for $f(x) = x^2 + 2x + 3$ are complex numbers. What does this say about the x-intercepts of the graph of f?

93. An equation of the form $y = x^2 + bx + c$ can be written in the form $y = (x - h)^2 + k$, where (h, k) are the coordinates of the vertex of the parabola. Use the process of completing the square to rewrite the equation in the form $y = a(x - h)^2 + k$. Find the vertex.
   a. $y = x^2 - 4x + 7$ **b.** $y = x^2 - 2x - 2$ **c.** $y = x^2 - 6x + 3$

   d. $y = x^2 + 4x - 1$ **e.** $y = x^2 + x + 2$ **f.** $y = x^2 - x - 3$

94. A wire 1 m long is cut and then a square and circle are formed from the two pieces of wire. Determine the area of each figure so that the sum of the areas is a maximum.

9.2 Graphs of Functions

Objective A   ***To graph functions*** ....

The graphs of the polynomial functions $L(x) = mx + b$ (a straight line) and $Q(x) = ax^2 + bx + c, a \neq 0$ (a parabola) have been discussed earlier. The graphs of other functions can also be drawn by finding ordered pairs that belong to the function, plotting the points that correspond to the ordered pairs, and then drawing a curve through the points.

➡ Graph: $F(x) = x^3$

Select several values of x and evaluate the function.

x	$F(x) = x^3$	$F(x)$	(x, y)
-2	$(-2)^3$	-8	$(-2, -8)$
-1	$(-1)^3$	-1	$(-1, -1)$
0	0^3	0	$(0, 0)$
1	1^3	1	$(1, 1)$
2	2^3	8	$(2, 8)$

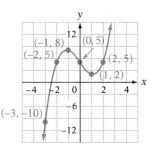

Plot the ordered pairs and draw a graph through the points.

➡ Graph: $g(x) = x^3 - 4x + 5$

Select several values of x and evaluate the function.

x	$g(x) = x^3 - 4x + 5$	$g(x)$	(x, y)
-3	$(-3)^3 - 4(-3) + 5$	-10	$(-3, -10)$
-2	$(-2)^3 - 4(-2) + 5$	5	$(-2, 5)$
-1	$(-1)^3 - 4(-1) + 5$	8	$(-1, 8)$
0	$(0)^3 - 4(0) + 5$	5	$(0, 5)$
1	$(1)^3 - 4(1) + 5$	2	$(1, 2)$
2	$(2)^3 - 4(2) + 5$	5	$(2, 5)$

Plot the ordered pairs and draw a graph through the points.

Note from the graphs of the two different cubic functions that the shapes of the graphs can be quite different. The following graphs of typical cubic polynomial functions show the general shape of a cubic polynomial.

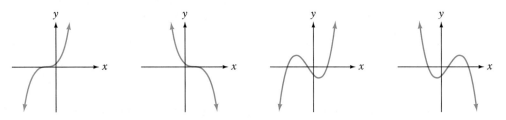

As the degree of a polynomial increases, the graph of the polynomial function can change significantly. In these cases, it may be necessary to plot many points before an accurate graph can be drawn. Only polynomials of degree 3 are considered here.

➡ Graph: $f(x) = |x + 2|$

This is an absolute-value function.

x	$f(x) = \lvert x + 2 \rvert$	$f(x)$	(x, y)
-3	$\lvert -3 + 2 \rvert$	1	$(-3, 1)$
-2	$\lvert -2 + 2 \rvert$	0	$(-2, 0)$
-1	$\lvert -1 + 2 \rvert$	1	$(-1, 1)$
0	$\lvert 0 + 2 \rvert$	2	$(0, 2)$
1	$\lvert 1 + 2 \rvert$	3	$(1, 3)$
2	$\lvert 2 + 2 \rvert$	4	$(2, 4)$

In general, the graph of the absolute value of a linear polynomial is V-shaped.

➡ Graph: $R(x) = \sqrt{2x - 4}$

This is a radical function. Because the square root of a negative number is not a real number, the domain of this function requires that $2x - 4 \geq 0$. Solve this inequality for x.

$2x - 4 \geq 0$

$\quad 2x \geq 4$

$\quad\quad x \geq 2$

The domain is $\{x \mid x \geq 2\}$. This means that only values of x that are greater than or equal to 2 can be chosen as values at which to evaluate the function. In this case, some of the y-coordinates must be approximated.

x	$f(x) = \sqrt{2x - 4}$	$f(x)$	(x, y)
2	$\sqrt{2(2) - 4}$	0	$(2, 0)$
3	$\sqrt{2(3) - 4}$	1.41	$(3, 1.41)$
4	$\sqrt{2(4) - 4}$	2	$(4, 2)$
5	$\sqrt{2(5) - 4}$	2.45	$(5, 2.45)$
6	$\sqrt{2(6) - 4}$	2.83	$(6, 2.83)$

Recall that a function is a special type of relation, one for which no two ordered pairs have the same first coordinate. Graphically, this means that the graph of a function cannot pass through two points that have the same x-coordinate and different y-coordinates. For instance, the graph at the right is not the graph of a function because there are ordered pairs with the same x-coordinate and different y-coordinates.

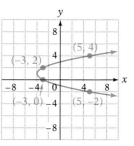

The last graph illustrates a general statement that can be made about whether a graph defines a function. It is called the *vertical-line test*.

Vertical-Line Test

A graph defines a function if any vertical line intersects the graph at no more than one point.

For example, the graph of a nonvertical straight line is the graph of a function. Any vertical line intersects the graph no more than once. The graph of a circle, however, is not the graph of a function. There are vertical lines that intersect the graph at more than one point.

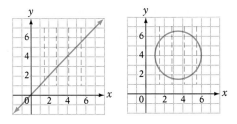

There may be practical situations in which a graph is not the graph of a function. The problem below is an example.

One of the causes of smog is an inversion layer where temperatures at higher altitudes are warmer than those at lower altitudes. The graph at the right shows the altitudes at which various temperatures were recorded. As shown by the dashed lines in the graph, there are two altitudes at which the temperature was 25°C. This means that there are two ordered pairs (shown in the graph) with the same first coordinate but different second coordinates. The graph does not define a function.

When a graph does define a function, the domain and range can be estimated from the graph.

➡ Determine the domain and range of the function given by the graph at the right.

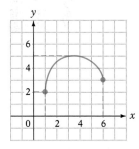

TAKE NOTE

In this first example, the domain and range are given in set-builder notation. For the second example, the domain and range are given in interval notation. Either method may be used.

The solid dots on the graph indicate its beginning and ending points.

The domain is the set of x-coordinates.
Domain: $\{x \mid 1 \leq x \leq 6\}$

The range is the set of y-coordinates.
Range: $\{y \mid 2 \leq y \leq 5\}$

➡ Determine the domain and range of the function given by the graph at the right. Write the answer in interval notation.

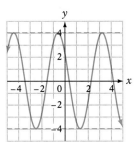

The arrows on the graph indicate that the graph continues in the same manner.

The domain is the set of x-coordinates.
Domain: $(-\infty, \infty)$

The range is the set of y-coordinates.
Range: $[-4, 4]$

Example 1
Use the vertical-line test to determine whether the graph shown is the graph of a function.

Solution
A vertical line intersects the graph more than once. The graph is not the graph of a function.

You Try It 1
Use the vertical-line test to determine whether the graph shown is the graph of a function.

Your solution

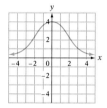

Example 2
Graph and write in set-builder notation the domain and range of the function defined by $f(x) = x^3 - 3x$.

Solution
Domain: $\{x \mid x$ is a real number$\}$
Range: $\{y \mid y$ is a real number$\}$

You Try It 2
Graph and write in interval notation the domain and range of the function defined by $f(x) = -\frac{1}{2}x^3 + 2x$.

Your solution

Example 3
Graph and write in interval notation the domain and range of the function defined by $f(x) = |x| + 2$.

Solution
Domain: $(-\infty, \infty)$
Range: $[2, \infty)$

You Try It 3
Graph and write in set-builder notation the domain and range of the function defined by $f(x) = |x + 2|$.

Your solution

Example 4
Graph and write in set-builder notation the domain and range of the function defined by $f(x) = \sqrt{2 - x}$.

Solution
Domain: $\{x \mid x \le 2\}$
Range: $\{y \mid y \ge 0\}$

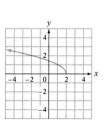

You Try It 4
Graph and write in interval notation the domain and range of the function defined by $f(x) = -\sqrt{x - 1}$.

Your solution

Solutions on pp. S27–S28

9.2 Exercises

Objective A

Use the vertical-line test to determine whether the graph is the graph of a function.

1.

2.

3.

4.

5.

6.
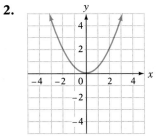

Graph the function and state its domain and range.

7. $f(x) = 3|2 - x|$
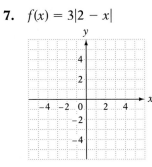

8. $f(x) = x^3 - 1$
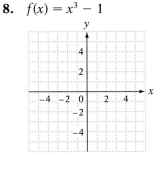

9. $f(x) = 1 - x^3$
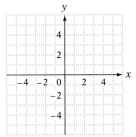

10. $f(x) = \sqrt{1 + x}$
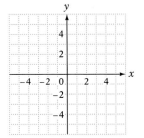

11. $f(x) = \sqrt{4 - x}$

12. $f(x) = |2x - 1|$
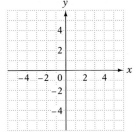

13. $f(x) = x^3 + 4x^2 + 4x$ **14.** $f(x) = x^3 - x^2 - x + 1$ **15.** $f(x) = -\sqrt{x + 2}$

16. $f(x) = -\sqrt{x - 3}$ **17.** $f(x) = |2x + 2|$ **18.** $f(x) = 2|x + 1|$

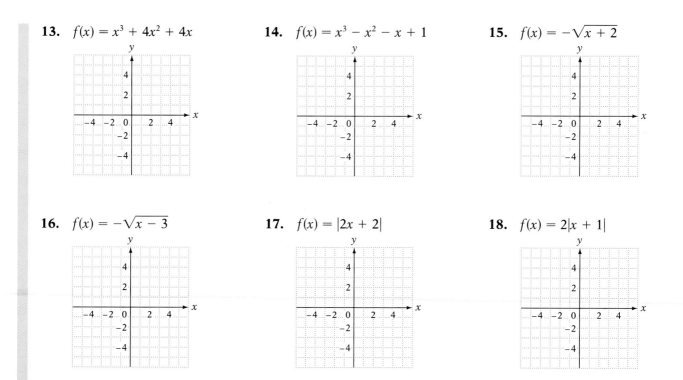

APPLYING THE CONCEPTS

19. If $f(x) = \sqrt{x - 2}$ and $f(a) = 4$, find a.

20. If $f(x) = \sqrt{x + 5}$ and $f(a) = 3$, find a.

21. $f(a, b) =$ the sum of a and b
$g(a, b) =$ the product of a and b
Find $f(2, 5) + g(2, 5)$.

22. $f(a, b) =$ the greatest common divisor of a and b
$g(a, b) =$ the least common multiple of a and b
Find $f(14, 35) + g(14, 35)$.

23. Let $f(x)$ be the digit in the xth decimal place of the repeating decimal $0.\overline{387}$. For example, $f(3) = 7$ because 7 is the digit in the third decimal place. Find $f(14)$.

24. Given $f(x) = (x + 1)(x - 1)$, for what values of x is $f(x)$ negative? Write your answer in set-builder notation.

25. Given $f(x) = (x + 2)(x - 2)$, for what values of x is $f(x)$ negative? Write your answer in set-builder notation.

26. Given $f(x) = -|x + 3|$, for what value of x is $f(x)$ greatest?

27. Given $f(x) = |2x - 2|$, for what value of x is $f(x)$ smallest?

9.3 Algebra of Functions

Objective A   *To perform operations on functions* .... (38) CT

The operations of addition, subtraction, multiplication, and division of functions are defined as follows.

Operations on Functions

If f and g are functions and x is an element of the domain of each function, then

$$(f + g)(x) = f(x) + g(x) \qquad (f \cdot g)(x) = f(x) \cdot g(x)$$

$$(f - g)(x) = f(x) - g(x) \qquad \left(\frac{f}{g}\right)(x) = \frac{f(x)}{g(x)}, \, g(x) \neq 0$$

⇒ Given $f(x) = x^2 + 1$ and $g(x) = 3x - 2$, find $(f + g)(3)$ and $(f \cdot g)(-1)$.

$$(f + g)(3) = f(3) + g(3)$$
$$= [(3)^2 + 1] + [3(3) - 2]$$
$$= 10 + 7 = 17$$

$$(f \cdot g)(-1) = f(-1) \cdot g(-1)$$
$$= [(-1)^2 + 1] \cdot [3(-1) - 2]$$
$$= 2 \cdot (-5) = -10$$

Consider the functions f and g from the last example. Let $S(x)$ be the sum of the two functions. Then

$$S(x) = (f + g)(x) = f(x) + g(x)$$ • The definition of addition
$$= [x^2 + 1] + [3x - 2]$$ • $f(x) = x^2 + 1, g(x) = 3x - 2$
$$S(x) = x^2 + 3x - 1$$

Now evaluate $S(3)$.

$$S(x) = x^2 + 3x - 1$$
$$S(3) = (3)^2 + 3(3) - 1$$
$$= 9 + 9 - 1$$
$$= 17 = (f + g)(3)$$

Note that $S(3) = 17$ and $(f + g)(3) = 17$. This shows that adding $f(x) + g(x)$ and then evaluating is the same as evaluating $f(x)$ and $g(x)$ and then adding. The same is true for the other operations on functions. For instance, let $P(x)$ be the product of the functions f and g. Then

$$P(x) = (f \cdot g)(x) = f(x) \cdot g(x)$$
$$= (x^2 + 1)(3x - 2)$$
$$= 3x^3 - 2x^2 + 3x - 2$$
$$P(-1) = 3(-1)^3 - 2(-1)^2 + 3(-1) - 2$$
$$= -3 - 2 - 3 - 2$$
$$= -10 = (f \cdot g)(-1)$$

⟹ Given $f(x) = 2x^2 - 5x + 3$ and $g(x) = x^2 - 1$, find $\left(\dfrac{f}{g}\right)(1)$.

$$\left(\frac{f}{g}\right)(1) = \frac{f(1)}{g(1)}$$

$$= \frac{2(1)^2 - 5(1) + 3}{(1)^2 - 1}$$

$$= \frac{0}{0} \qquad \bullet \text{ Not a real number}$$

Because $\dfrac{0}{0}$ is not defined, the expression $\left(\dfrac{f}{g}\right)(1)$ cannot be evaluated.

Example 1

Given $f(x) = x^2 - x + 1$ and $g(x) = x^3 - 4$, find $(f - g)(3)$.

Solution

$$\begin{aligned}
(f - g)(3) &= f(3) - g(3) \\
&= (3^2 - 3 + 1) - (3^3 - 4) \\
&= 7 - 23 \\
&= -16
\end{aligned}$$

$(f - g)(3) = -16$

You Try It 1

Given $f(x) = x^2 + 2x$ and $g(x) = 5x - 2$, find $(f + g)(-2)$.

Your solution

Example 2

Given $f(x) = x^2 + 2$ and $g(x) = 2x + 3$, find $(f \cdot g)(-2)$.

Solution

$$\begin{aligned}
(f \cdot g)(-2) &= f(-2) \cdot g(-2) \\
&= [(-2)^2 + 2] \cdot [2(-2) + 3] \\
&= 6(-1) \\
&= -6
\end{aligned}$$

$(f \cdot g)(-2) = -6$

You Try It 2

Given $f(x) = 4 - x^2$ and $g(x) = 3x - 4$, find $(f \cdot g)(3)$.

Your solution

Example 3

Given $f(x) = x^2 + 4x + 4$ and $g(x) = x^3 - 2$, find $\left(\dfrac{f}{g}\right)(3)$.

Solution

$$\left(\frac{f}{g}\right)(3) = \frac{f(3)}{g(3)}$$

$$= \frac{3^2 + 4(3) + 4}{3^3 - 2}$$

$$= \frac{25}{25}$$

$$= 1$$

$\left(\dfrac{f}{g}\right)(3) = 1$

You Try It 3

Given $f(x) = x^2 - 4$ and $g(x) = x^2 + 2x + 1$, find $\left(\dfrac{f}{g}\right)(4)$.

Your solution

Solutions on p. S28

Objective B   ***To find the composition of two functions*** .... ⟨38⟩ CT

A function can be evaluated at the value of another function. Consider

$$f(x) = 2x + 7 \qquad \text{and} \qquad g(x) = x^2 + 1$$

The expression $f[g(-2)]$ means to evaluate the function f at $g(-2)$.

$$g(-2) = (-2)^2 + 1 = 4 + 1 = 5$$
$$f[g(-2)] = f(5) = 2(5) + 7 = 10 + 7 = 17$$

> **Definition of the Composition of Two Functions**
>
> Let f and g be two functions such that $g(x)$ is in the domain of f for all x in the domain of g. Then the **composition** of the two functions, denoted by $f \circ g$, is the function whose value at x is given by $(f \circ g)(x) = f[g(x)]$.

The function defined by $f[g(x)]$ is called the **composite** of f and g.

The requirement in the definition of the composition of two functions that $g(x)$ be in the domain of f for all x in the domain of g is important. For instance, let

$$f(x) = \frac{1}{x - 1} \qquad \text{and} \qquad g(x) = 3x - 5$$

When $x = 2$,

$$g(2) = 3(2) - 5 = 1$$

$$f[g(2)] = f(1) = \frac{1}{1 - 1} = \frac{1}{0} \qquad \bullet \text{ This is not a real number.}$$

In this case, $g(2)$ is not in the domain of f. Thus the composition is not defined at 2.

➡ Given $f(x) = x^3 - x + 1$ and $g(x) = 2x^2 - 10$, evaluate $(g \circ f)(2)$.

$$f(2) = (2)^3 - (2) + 1$$
$$= 7$$
$$(g \circ f)(2) = g[f(2)]$$
$$= g(7)$$
$$= 2(7)^2 - 10 = 88$$
$$(g \circ f)(2) = 88$$

➡ Given $f(x) = 3x - 2$ and $g(x) = x^2 - 2x$, find $(f \circ g)(x)$.

$$(f \circ g)(x) = f[g(x)] = 3(x^2 - 2x) - 2$$
$$= 3x^2 - 6x - 2$$

In general, the composition of functions is not a commutative operation. That is, $(f \circ g)(x) \neq (g \circ f)(x)$. To show this, let $f(x) = x + 3$ and $g(x) = x^2 + 1$. Then

$$(f \circ g)(x) = f[g(x)] \qquad\qquad (g \circ f)(x) = g[f(x)]$$
$$= (x^2 + 1) + 3 \qquad\qquad\quad = (x + 3)^2 + 1$$
$$= x^2 + 4 \qquad\qquad\qquad\quad = x^2 + 6x + 10$$

Thus $(f \circ g)(x) \neq (g \circ f)(x)$.

Example 4

Given $f(x) = x^2 - x$ and $g(x) = 3x - 2$, find $f[g(3)]$.

Solution

$$g(x) = 3x - 2$$
$$g(3) = 3(3) - 2 = 9 - 2 = 7$$
$$f(x) = x^2 - x$$
$$f[g(3)] = f(7) = 7^2 - 7 = 42$$

You Try It 4

Given $f(x) = 1 - 2x$ and $g(x) = x^2$, find $f[g(-1)]$.

Your solution

Example 5

Given $f(x) = 2x^2 - x + 1$ and $g(x) = 1 - x^2$, find $g[f(-1)]$.

Solution

$$f(x) = 2x^2 - x + 1$$
$$f(-1) = 2(-1)^2 - (-1) + 1 = 4$$
$$g(x) = 1 - x^2$$
$$g[f(-1)] = g(4) = 1 - 4^2 = -15$$

You Try It 5

Given $f(x) = 3x - 1$ and $g(x) = \dfrac{x}{x^2 - 2}$, find $g[f(1)]$.

Your solution

Example 6

Given $s(t) = t^2 + 3t - 1$ and $v(t) = 2t + 1$, determine $s[v(t)]$.

Solution

$$s(t) = t^2 + 3t - 1$$
$$s[v(t)] = (2t + 1)^2 + 3(2t + 1) - 1$$
$$= (4t^2 + 4t + 1) + 6t + 3 - 1$$
$$= 4t^2 + 10t + 3$$

You Try It 6

Given $L(s) = s + 1$ and $M(s) = s^3 + 1$, determine $M[L(s)]$.

Your solution

Example 7

Given $P(x) = x^2$ and $S(x) = \sqrt{x}$, determine $P[S(x)]$.

Solution

$$P(x) = x^2$$
$$P[S(x)] = (\sqrt{x})^2 = x$$

You Try It 7

Given $V(x) = x^2 + 1$ and $W(x) = -\sqrt{x - 1}$, find $V[W(x)]$.

Your solution

Solutions on p. S28

9.3 Exercises

. . . .

Objective A

For $f(x) = 2x^2 - 3$ and $g(x) = -2x + 4$, find:

1. $f(2) - g(2)$

2. $f(3) - g(3)$

3. $f(0) + g(0)$

4. $f(1) + g(1)$

5. $(f \cdot g)(2)$

6. $(f \cdot g)(-1)$

7. $\left(\dfrac{f}{g}\right)(4)$

8. $\left(\dfrac{f}{g}\right)(-1)$

9. $\left(\dfrac{g}{f}\right)(-3)$

For $f(x) = 2x^2 + 3x - 1$ and $g(x) = 2x - 4$, find:

10. $f(-3) + g(-3)$

11. $f(1) + g(1)$

12. $f(-2) - g(-2)$

13. $f(4) - g(4)$

14. $(f \cdot g)(-2)$

15. $(f \cdot g)(1)$

16. $\left(\dfrac{f}{g}\right)(2)$

17. $\left(\dfrac{f}{g}\right)(-3)$

18. $(f \cdot g)\left(\dfrac{1}{2}\right)$

For $f(x) = x^2 + 3x - 5$ and $g(x) = x^3 - 2x + 3$, find:

19. $f(2) - g(2)$

20. $(f \cdot g)(-3)$

21. $\left(\dfrac{f}{g}\right)(-2)$

Objective B

Given $f(x) = 2x - 3$ and $g(x) = 4x - 1$, evaluate the composite function.

22. $f[g(0)]$

23. $g[f(0)]$

24. $f[g(2)]$

25. $g[f(-2)]$

26. $f[g(x)]$

27. $g[f(x)]$

Given $h(x) = 2x + 4$ and $f(x) = \frac{1}{2}x + 2$, evaluate the composite function.

28. $h[f(0)]$

29. $f[h(0)]$

30. $h[f(2)]$

31. $f[h(-1)]$

32. $h[f(x)]$

33. $f[h(x)]$

Given $g(x) = x^2 + 3$ and $h(x) = x - 2$, evaluate the composite function.

34. $g[h(0)]$

35. $h[g(0)]$

36. $g[h(4)]$

37. $h[g(-2)]$

38. $g[h(x)]$

39. $h[g(x)]$

Given $f(x) = x^2 + x + 1$ and $h(x) = 3x + 2$, evaluate the composite function.

40. $f[h(0)]$

41. $h[f(0)]$

42. $f[h(-1)]$

43. $h[f(-2)]$

44. $f[h(x)]$

45. $h[f(x)]$

Given $f(x) = x - 2$ and $g(x) = x^3$, evaluate the composite function.

46. $f[g(2)]$

47. $f[g(-1)]$

48. $g[f(2)]$

49. $g[f(-1)]$

50. $f[g(x)]$

51. $g[f(x)]$

APPLYING THE CONCEPTS

For the function $g(x) = x^2 - 1$, find:

52. $g(2 + h)$

53. $g(3 + h) - g(3)$

54. $g(-1 + h) - g(-1)$

55. $\dfrac{g(1 + h) - g(1)}{h}$

56. $\dfrac{g(-2 + h) - g(-2)}{h}$

57. $\dfrac{g(a + h) - g(a)}{h}$

Given $f(x) = 2x$, $g(x) = 3x - 1$, and $h(x) = x - 2$, find:

58. $f(g[h(2)])$

59. $g(h[f(1)])$

60. $h(g[f(-1)])$

61. $f(h[g(0)])$

62. $f(g[h(x)])$

63. $g(f[h(x)])$

9.4 One-to-One and Inverse Functions

Objective A   *To determine whether a function is one-to-one* .... 38 CT

Recall that a function is a set of ordered pairs in which no two ordered pairs that have the same first coordinate have different second coordinates. This means that given any x, there is only one y that can be paired with that x. A *one-to-one* function satisfies the additional condition that given any y, there is only one x that can be paired with the given y. One-to-one functions are commonly written as 1–1.

One-to-One Function

A function f is a 1–1 function if for any a and b in the domain of f, $f(a) = f(b)$ implies that $a = b$.

This definition states that if the y-coordinates of an ordered pair are equal, $f(a) = f(b)$, then the x-coordinates must be equal, $a = b$.

The function defined by $f(x) = 2x + 1$ is a 1–1 function. To show this, determine $f(a)$ and $f(b)$. Then form the equation $f(a) = f(b)$.

$$f(a) = 2a + 1 \qquad f(b) = 2b + 1$$

$$f(a) = f(b)$$
$$2a + 1 = 2b + 1$$
$$2a = 2b \qquad \bullet \text{ Subtract 1 from each side of the equation.}$$
$$a = b \qquad \bullet \text{ Divide each side of the equation by 2.}$$

Because $f(a) = f(b)$ implies that $a = b$, the function is a 1–1 function.

Consider the function defined by $g(x) = x^2 - x$. Evaluate the function at -2 and 3.

$$g(-2) = (-2)^2 - (-2) = 6 \qquad g(3) = 3^2 - 3 = 6$$

From this evaluation, $g(-2) = 6$ and $g(3) = 6$, but $-2 \neq 3$. Thus f is not a 1–1 function.

The graphs of $f(x) = 2x + 1$ and $g(x) = x^2 - x$ are shown below. Note that a horizontal line intersects the graph of f at no more than one point. However, a horizontal line intersects the graph of g at more than one point.

$f(x) = 2x + 1$ $\qquad\qquad$ $g(x) = x^2 - x$

Looking at the graph of f on the previous page, note that for each y-coordinate there is only one x-coordinate. Thus f is a 1–1 function. From the graph of g, however, there are *two* x-coordinates for a given y-coordinate. For instance, $(-2, 6)$ and $(3, 6)$ are the coordinates of two points on the graph for which the y-coordinates are the same and the x-coordinates are different. Therefore, g is not a 1–1 function.

> **Horizontal-Line Test**
>
> The graph of a function represents the graph of a 1–1 function if any horizontal line intersects the graph at no more than one point.

Example 1

Determine whether the graph is the graph of a 1–1 function.

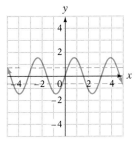

Solution

Because a horizontal line intersects the graph more than once, the graph is not the graph of a 1–1 function.

You Try It 1

Determine whether the graph is the graph of a 1–1 function.

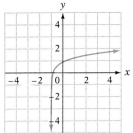

Your solution

Solution on p. S28

Objective B   *To find the inverse of a function* ···

The **inverse of a function** is the set of ordered pairs formed by reversing the coordinates of each ordered pair of the function.

For example, the set of ordered pairs of the function defined by $f(x) = 2x$ with domain $\{-2, -1, 0, 1, 2\}$ is $\{(-2, -4), (-1, -2), (0, 0), (1, 2), (2, 4)\}$. The set of ordered pairs of the inverse function is $\{(-4, -2), (-2, -1), (0, 0), (2, 1), (4, 2)\}$.

From the ordered pairs of f, we have

$$\text{Domain} = \{-2, -1, 0, 1, 2\} \quad \text{and} \quad \text{Range} = \{-4, -2, 0, 2, 4\}$$

From the ordered pairs of the inverse function, we have

$$\text{Domain} = \{-4, -2, 0, 2, 4\} \quad \text{and} \quad \text{Range} = \{-2, -1, 0, 1, 2\}$$

Note that the domain of the inverse function is the range of the function, and the range of the inverse function is the domain of the function.

Now consider the function defined by $g(x) = x^2$ with domain $\{-2, -1, 0, 1, 2\}$. The set of ordered pairs of this function is $\{(-2, 4), (-1, 1), (0, 0), (1, 1), (2, 4)\}$. Reversing the ordered pairs gives $\{(4, -2), (1, -1), (0, 0), (1, 1), (4, 2)\}$. These ordered pairs do not satisfy the condition of a function, because there are ordered pairs with the same first coordinate and different second coordinates. This example illustrates that not all functions have an inverse function.

The graphs of $f(x) = 2x$ and $g(x) = x^2$ with the set of real numbers as the domain are shown below.

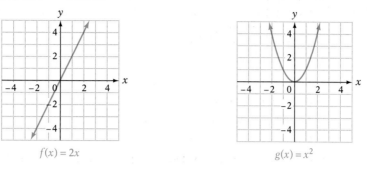

$f(x) = 2x$ $\qquad\qquad\qquad\qquad$ $g(x) = x^2$

By the horizontal-line test, f is a 1–1 function but g is not.

> **Condition for an Inverse Function**
>
> A function f has an inverse function if and only if f is a 1–1 function.

TAKE NOTE

It is important to note that f^{-1} is the symbol for the *inverse* function and does not mean reciprocal.

$$f^{-1}(x) \neq \frac{1}{f(x)}$$

The symbol f^{-1} is used to denote the inverse of the function f. The symbol $f^{-1}(x)$ is read "f inverse of x."

$f^{-1}(x)$ is *not* the reciprocal of $f(x)$ but is the notation for the inverse of a 1–1 function.

To find the inverse of a function, interchange x and y. Then solve for y.

➡ Find the inverse of the function defined by $f(x) = 3x + 6$.

$$f(x) = 3x + 6$$
$$y = 3x + 6 \qquad \bullet \text{ Replace } f(x) \text{ by } y.$$
$$x = 3y + 6 \qquad \bullet \text{ Interchange } x \text{ and } y.$$
$$x - 6 = 3y \qquad \bullet \text{ Solve for } y.$$
$$\frac{x}{3} - 2 = y$$
$$f^{-1}(x) = \frac{1}{3}x - 2 \qquad \bullet \text{ Replace } y \text{ by } f^{-1}(x).$$

The inverse of the function is given by $f^{-1}(x) = \frac{1}{3}x - 2$.

The fact that the set of ordered pairs of the inverse of a function are the reverse of those of the function has a graphic interpretation. In the graph in the middle, the points from the figure on the left are plotted with the coordinates reversed. The inverse function is graphed by drawing a smooth curve through those points, as shown in the figure on the right below.

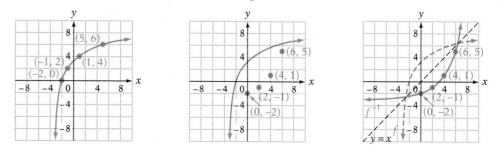

Note the dashed graph of $y = x$ is shown in the figure on the right on the previous page. If two functions are inverses of each other, their graphs are mirror images with respect to the graph of the line $y = x$.

The composition of a function and its inverse has a special property.

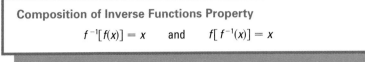

Composition of Inverse Functions Property

$$f^{-1}[f(x)] = x \quad \text{and} \quad f[f^{-1}(x)] = x$$

This property can be used to determine whether two functions are inverses of each other.

➡ Are $f(x) = 2x - 4$ and $g(x) = \frac{1}{2}x + 2$ inverses of each other?

To determine whether the functions are inverses, use the Composition of Inverse Functions Property.

$$f[g(x)] = 2\left(\frac{1}{2}x + 2\right) - 4 \qquad\qquad g[f(x)] = \frac{1}{2}(2x - 4) + 2$$
$$= x + 4 - 4 \qquad\qquad\qquad\qquad = x - 2 + 2$$
$$= x \qquad\qquad\qquad\qquad\qquad\quad = x$$

Because $f[g(x)] = x$ and $g[f(x)] = x$, the functions are inverses of each other.

Example 2
Find the inverse of the function defined by $f(x) = 2x - 3$.

Solution

    $f(x) = 2x - 3$

      $y = 2x - 3$ • Replace $f(x)$ by y.

      $x = 2y - 3$ • Interchange x and y.

  $x + 3 = 2y$ • Solve for y.

$$\frac{x}{2} + \frac{3}{2} = y$$

$$f^{-1}(x) = \frac{x}{2} + \frac{3}{2} \quad \text{• Replace } y \text{ by } f^{-1}(x).$$

The inverse of the function is given by

$$f^{-1}(x) = \frac{x}{2} + \frac{3}{2}.$$

You Try It 2
Find the inverse of the function defined by
$$f(x) = \frac{1}{2}x + 4.$$

Your solution

Example 3
Are $f(x) = 3x - 6$ and $g(x) = \frac{1}{3}x + 2$ inverses of each other?

Solution

$$f[g(x)] = 3\left(\frac{1}{3}x + 2\right) - 6 = x + 6 - 6 = x$$

$$g[f(x)] = \frac{1}{3}(3x - 6) + 2 = x - 2 + 2 = x$$

Yes, the functions are inverses of each other.

You Try It 3
Are $f(x) = 2x - 6$ and $g(x) = \frac{1}{2}x - 3$ inverses of each other?

Your solution

Solutions on p. S28

9.4 Exercises

Objective A

Determine whether the graph represents the graph of a 1–1 function.

1.

2.

3.

4.

5.

6.

7.

8.

9.

10.

11.

12.
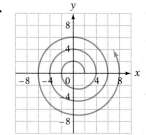

Objective B

Find the inverse of the function. If the function does not have an inverse function, write "no inverse."

13. $\{(1, 0), (2, 3), (3, 8), (4, 15)\}$

14. $\{(1, 0), (2, 1), (-1, 0), (-2, 0)\}$

15. $\{(3, 5), (-3, -5), (2, 5), (-2, -5)\}$

16. $\{(-5, -5), (-3, -1), (-1, 3), (1, 7)\}$

17. $\{(0, -2), (-1, 5), (3, 3), (-4, 6)\}$

18. $\{(-2, -2), (0, 0), (2, 2), (4, 4)\}$

19. $\{(-2, -3), (-1, 3), (0, 3), (1, 3)\}$

20. $\{(2, 0), (1, 0), (3, 0), (4, 0)\}$

Find $f^{-1}(x)$.

21. $f(x) = 4x - 8$

22. $f(x) = 3x + 6$

23. $f(x) = 2x + 4$

24. $f(x) = x - 5$

25. $f(x) = \dfrac{1}{2}x - 1$

26. $f(x) = \dfrac{1}{3}x + 2$

27. $f(x) = -2x + 2$

28. $f(x) = -3x - 9$

29. $f(x) = \dfrac{2}{3}x + 4$

30. $f(x) = \dfrac{3}{4}x - 4$

31. $f(x) = -\dfrac{1}{3}x + 1$

32. $f(x) = -\dfrac{1}{2}x + 2$

33. $f(x) = 2x - 5$

34. $f(x) = 3x + 4$

35. $f(x) = 5x - 2$

36. $f(x) = 4x - 2$

37. $f(x) = 6x - 3$

38. $f(x) = -8x + 4$

39. $f(x) = -6x + 2$

40. $f(x) = 8x + 6$

41. $f(x) = 3x - 4$

42. $f(x) = \dfrac{5}{8}x + 5$

43. $f(x) = -\dfrac{2}{3}x + 4$

44. $f(x) = 5x + 5$

45. $f(x) = 3x - 2$

46. $f(x) = \dfrac{1}{4}x + 4$

47. $f(x) = -\dfrac{3}{4}x - 2$

Use the Composition of Inverse Functions Property to determine whether the functions are inverses of each other.

48. $f(x) = 4x;\ g(x) = \dfrac{x}{4}$

49. $g(x) = x + 5;\ h(x) = x - 5$

50. $f(x) = 3x;\ h(x) = \dfrac{1}{3x}$

51. $h(x) = x + 2;\ g(x) = 2 - x$

52. $g(x) = 3x + 2;\ f(x) = \dfrac{1}{3}x - \dfrac{2}{3}$

53. $h(x) = 4x - 1;\ f(x) = \dfrac{1}{4}x + \dfrac{1}{4}$

54. $f(x) = \dfrac{1}{2}x - \dfrac{3}{2};\ g(x) = 2x + 3$

55. $g(x) = -\dfrac{1}{2}x - \dfrac{1}{2};\ h(x) = -2x + 1$

56. $f(x) = \dfrac{3}{2}x + 2;\ g(x) = \dfrac{2}{3}x - \dfrac{4}{3}$

57. $f(x) = 3x - 2;\ g(x) = 2 - 3x$

58. $h(x) = \dfrac{3}{2}x + \dfrac{4}{3};\ g(x) = \dfrac{2}{3}x + \dfrac{3}{4}$

59. $g(x) = -\dfrac{1}{2}x - 2;\ f(x) = -2x - 4$

60. $g(x) = -\dfrac{2}{3}x + 3;\ h(x) = \dfrac{3}{2}x - \dfrac{9}{2}$

61. $f(x) = -\dfrac{1}{2}x + \dfrac{3}{2};\ h(x) = -2x + 3$

APPLYING THE CONCEPTS

Given the graph of the 1–1 function, draw the graph of the inverse of the function by using the technique shown on page 493.

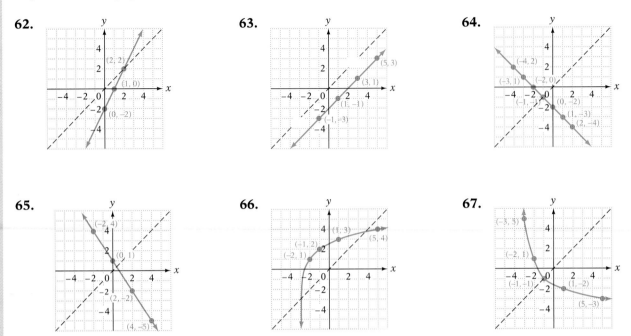

62.

63.

64.

65.

66.

67.

Each of the tables below defines a function. Is the inverse of the function a function? Explain your answer.

68. Grading Scale Table

Score	Grade
90–100	A
80–89	B
70–79	C
60–69	D
0–59	F

69. First-Class Postage

Weight	Cost
$0 < w < 1$	$ .32
$1 < w \le 2$	$ .55
$2 < w \le 3$	$ .78
$3 < w \le 4$	$1.01

If f is a 1–1 function and $f(0) = 1$, $f(3) = -1$, and $f(5) = -3$, find:

70. $f^{-1}(-3)$

71. $f^{-1}(-1)$

72. $f^{-1}(1)$

If f is a 1–1 function and $f(-3) = 3$, $f(-4) = 7$, and $f(0) = 8$, find:

73. $f^{-1}(3)$

74. $f^{-1}(7)$

75. $f^{-1}(8)$

76. Is the inverse of a constant function a function? Explain your answer.

77. The graphs of all functions given by $f(x) = mx + b$, $m \ne 0$, are straight lines. Are all of these functions 1–1 functions? If so, explain why. If not, give an example of a linear function that is not 1–1.

Focus On Problem Solving

Proof in Mathematics

Mathematics is based on the concept of proof, which in turn is based on principles of logic. It was Aristotle (384 B.C. to 322 B.C.) who took the logical principles that had developed over time and set them in a structured form. From this structured form, several methods of proof were developed.

$$\text{A true} \overset{\text{implies}}{\longrightarrow} \text{B true} \overset{\text{implies}}{\longrightarrow} \text{C true}$$

$$\text{A true} \overset{\text{implies}}{\longrightarrow} \text{C true}$$

A **deductive proof** is one that proceeds in a carefully ordered sequence of steps. It is the type of proof you may have seen in a geometry class. Deductive proofs have a model as shown at the left.

Here is an example of a deductive proof. It proves that the product of a negative and a positive number is a negative number. The proof is based on the fact that every real number has exactly one additive inverse. For instance, the additive inverse of 4 is -4 and the additive inverse of $-\frac{2}{3}$ is $\frac{2}{3}$.

Theorem: If a and b are positive real numbers, then $(-a)b = -(ab)$.

Proof:
$$(-a)b + ab = (-a + a)b \qquad \bullet \text{ Distributive Property}$$
$$= 0 \cdot b \qquad \bullet \text{ Inverse Property of Addition}$$
$$= 0 \qquad \bullet \text{ Multiplication Property of Zero}$$

Since $(-a)b + ab = 0$, $(-a)b$ is the additive inverse of ab. But $-(ab)$ is also the additive inverse of ab and because every number has exactly one additive inverse, $(-a)b = -(ab)$.

Here is another example of a deductive proof. It is a proof of part of the Pythagorean Theorem.

Theorem: If a and b are the lengths of the legs of a right triangle and c is the length of the hypotenuse, then $a^2 + b^2 = c^2$.

Proof: Let $\triangle DBA$ be a right triangle and let BC be the altitude to the hypotenuse of $\triangle DBA$, as shown at the left. Then $\triangle BCD$ and $\triangle BCA$ are right triangles.

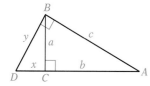

1. $\triangle DBA$ is a right triangle with height BC.

   Given.

2. $\triangle DBC$ is similar to $\triangle BCA$ and $\triangle DBA$ is similar to $\triangle BCA$.

   Theorem from geometry: the altitude to the hypotenuse of a right triangle forms triangles that are similar to each other.

3. $\dfrac{a}{b} = \dfrac{x}{a}$

   The ratios of corresponding sides of similar triangles are equal.

4. $a^2 = bx$

   Multiply each side by ab.

5. $\dfrac{x + b}{c} = \dfrac{c}{b}$

   The ratios of corresponding sides of similar triangles are equal.

6. $bx + b^2 = c^2$

   Multiply each side by cb.

7. $a^2 + b^2 = c^2$

   Substitution Property from (**4**).

Because the first statement of the proof is true and each subsequent statement of the proof is true, the first statement means the last statement is true. Therefore we have proved: If a and b are the lengths of the legs of a right triangle and c is the length of the hypotenuse, then $a^2 + b^2 = c^2$.

Projects and Group Activities

Properties of Polynomials

The graph of a fifth-degree polynomial with four *turning points* is shown at the right. In this project you will graph various polynomials and try to make a conjecture as to the relationship between the degree of a polynomial and the number of turning points in its graph. For each of the following, graph the equation. Record the degree of the equation and the number of turning points.

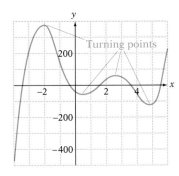

TAKE NOTE

Suggestions for graphing equations can be found in the Appendix: Guidelines for Using Graphing Calculators. For this particular activity, it may be necessary to adjust the viewing window so that you can get a reasonably accurate graph of the equation. Try Ymax = 100, Ymin = −100, and Yscl = 10.

1. Graph: $y = x^3 + 1$
2. Graph: $y = x^3 + 2x^2 - 5x - 6$
3. Graph: $y = x^4 - x^3 - 11x^2 - x - 12$
4. Graph: $y = x^4 - 2x^3 - 13x^2 + 14x + 24$
5. Graph: $y = x^5 - 2$
6. Graph: $y = x^5 - 3x^4 - 11x^3 + 27x^2 + 10x - 24$
7. Graph: $y = x^5 - 2x^4 - 10x^3 + 10x^2 - 11x + 12$

Make a conjecture as to the relationship between the degree of a polynomial and the number of turning points in its graph. Graph a few more polynomials of your choosing and see if your conjecture is valid for those graphs. If not, refine your conjecture and test it again.

The Greatest-Integer Function

The greatest-integer function is defined by the equation $f(x) = \lfloor x \rfloor$, where the symbol $\lfloor x \rfloor$ means the greatest integer less than or equal to x. Here are some examples.

$$\lfloor 4.2 \rfloor = 4 \qquad \lfloor 5.9999 \rfloor = 5 \qquad \lfloor \pi \rfloor = 3 \qquad \lfloor -2.3 \rfloor = -3 \qquad \lfloor 2 \rfloor = 2$$

In each of these examples, the value of the function is an integer that is less than or equal to the number in the symbol $\lfloor \ \rfloor$.

The graph of the greatest-integer function is shown at the right. A closed dot indicates that the point is part of the graph; an open dot means that the point is not part of the graph.

The greatest-integer function is sometimes called a step function because its graph resembles steps.

Graphing calculators have the greatest-integer function programmed into the calculator. It is usually symbolized by Int and must be accessed through one of the menus. For the TI-83, press $\boxed{\text{MATH}}$ $\boxed{\blacktriangleright}$ 5; for the Sharp 9600, press $\boxed{\text{MATH}}$ $\boxed{\text{B}}$ 5; and for the Casio CFX-9850, $\boxed{\text{MENU}}$ 1 $\boxed{\text{OPTN}}$ $\boxed{\text{F6}}$ $\boxed{\text{F4}}$ $\boxed{\text{F2}}$.

1. Using a viewing window of $[-4.7, 4.7]$ (use $[-6.3, 6.3]$ for the Casio CFX-9850 and Sharp 9600) by $[-5, 5]$, graph the greatest integer function. You may notice that the graph is drawn with jagged lines connecting the steps. These lines are *not* part of the graph. They are a result of the method by which calculators draw a graph. You can get a better idea of the graph by graphing it in *dot* mode. Use the keystrokes on the next page.

To change to dot mode, use these keystrokes.

TI-83	Sharp EL-9600	Casio CFX-9850
Press MODE , use the arrow keys to select Dot, then press ENTER	2nd F FORMAT E 2 2nd F QUIT	MENU 5 SHIFT SET UP F2

To change back to connected mode, use these keystrokes.

TI-83	Sharp EL-9600	Casio CFX-9850
Press MODE , use the arrow keys to select Connected, then press ENTER	2nd F FORMAT E 1 2nd F QUIT	MENU 5 SHIFT SET UP F1

The greatest-integer function can be combined with other functions to produce interesting graphs. The function defined by $f(x) = |x| - \lfloor x \rfloor$ is sometimes called a *ramp* function because its graph appears as a series of ramps. The ramp function plays an important role in the study of electronics.

2. Change your calculator to *dot* mode. Using a viewing window of $[-0.1, 4.6]$ (use $[-0.1, 6.2]$ for the Casio CFX-9850 and the Sharp 9600) by $[-0.1, 1.5]$, graph the ramp function. Here are some suggested keystrokes.

TI-83	Sharp EL-9600	Casio CFX-9850
Y= CLEAR MATH ▶ 1 X,T,θ,n) – MATH ▶ 5 X,T,θ,n) GRAPH	Y= CL MATH B 1 X/θ/T/n ▶ – MATH B 5 X/θ/T/n ENTER	5 F2 F1 OPTN F5 F1 X/θ/T – OPTN F5 F2 X/θ/T EXE F6

Finding the Maximum or Minimum of a Function Using a Graphing Calculator

Recall that for a quadratic function, the maximum or minimum value of the function is the y-coordinate of the vertex of the graph of the function. We determined the coordinates of the vertex algebraically by using $\left(-\frac{b}{2a}, f\left(-\frac{b}{2a}\right)\right)$. It also is possible to use a graphing calculator to approximate this value. The method that is used to find this value depends on the calculator model. However, it is generally true for most calculators that the point at which the function has a maximum or minimum must be shown on the screen. If it is not, you must select a different viewing window.

3. Find the maximum value of $f(x) = -x^2 - 3x + 2$ by using a graphing calculator.

4. Find the minimum value of $f(x) = x^2 - 4x - 2$ by using a graphing calculator.

5. Find the maximum value of $f(x) = -\sqrt{2}x^2 - \pi x + 2$ by using a graphing calculator.

6. Find the minimum value of $f(x) = \frac{x^2}{\sqrt{5}} - \sqrt{7}x - \sqrt{11}$ by using a graphing calculator.

The first project on the previous page focused on turning points of a graph. These points are also called *local maximums* or *local minimums*. For the graph at the left, there is a local maximum at A and a local minimum at B. These are called *local* because they are not really the maximum or minimum value of the function. For instance, the value of the function at C is greater than the value at A and the value of the function at D is smaller than the value of the function at B.

TAKE NOTE

See the Appendix: Guidelines for Using Graphing Calculators for suggestions for finding the maximum and minimum of a function by using a graphing calculator.

P1

In future math courses you may study methods that will allow you to exactly determine the local maximums or local minimums. However, by using a graphing calculator, it is possible to approximate these values.

For the following exercises, use a viewing window of $[-10, 10]$ by $[-100, 100]$ and set Yscl at 10.

7. Find the local maximum and minimum for $f(x) = 2x^3 - 3x^2 - 36x + 10$.

8. Find the local maximum and minimum for $f(x) = -x^3 + 4x^2 + 4x - 16$.

9. Find the local maximum and minimums for $f(x) = x^4 - 3x^3 - 7x^2 + x + 6$.

Chapter Summary

Key Words   A *quadratic function* is one that can be expressed by $f(x) = ax^2 + bx + c$, where $a \neq 0$. The graph of a quadratic function is a *parabola*.

The *vertex* of a parabola is the point with the smallest y-coordinate or the largest y-coordinate. The *axis of symmetry* is the line that passes through the vertex of the parabola and is parallel to the y-axis.

The *inverse* of a function is the set of ordered pairs formed by reversing the coordinates of each ordered pair of the function.

Essential Rules   *Vertical-Line Test*   A graph defines a function if any vertical line intersects the graph at no more than one point.

Operations on Functions   If f and g are functions and x is an element of the domain of each function, then

$(f + g)(x) = f(x) + g(x)$ $\qquad\qquad$ $(f - g)(x) = f(x) - g(x)$

$(f \cdot g)(x) = f(x) \cdot g(x)$ $\qquad\qquad$ $\left(\dfrac{f}{g}\right)(x) = \dfrac{f(x)}{g(x)}, g(x) \neq 0$

Composition of Functions   The composition of two functions f and g, symbolized by $f \circ g$, is the function whose value at x is given by

$(f \circ g)(x) = f[g(x)]$.

One-to-One Functions   A function is a 1–1 function if, for any a and b in the domain of f, $f(a) = f(b)$ implies $a = b$.

Horizontal-Line Test   The graph of a function represents the graph of a 1–1 function if any horizontal line intersects the graph at no more than one point.

Condition for an Inverse Function   A function f has an inverse function if and only if f is a 1–1 function.

Composition of Inverse Functions Property $f^{-1}[f(x)] = x$ and $f[f^{-1}(x)] = x$.

Chapter Review

1. Is the graph below the graph of a function?

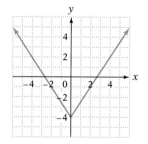

2. Is the graph below the graph of a 1–1 function?

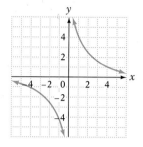

3. Graph $f(x) = 3x^3 - 2$. State the domain and range.

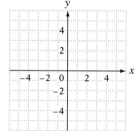

4. Graph $f(x) = \sqrt{x + 4}$. State the domain and range.

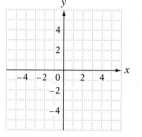

5. Use the discriminant to determine the number of x-intercepts of $y = -3x^2 + 4x + 6$.

6. Find the x-intercepts of $y = 3x^2 + 9x$.

7. Find the zeros of $f(x) = 3x^2 + 2x + 2$.

8. Find the maximum value of $f(x) = -2x^2 + 4x + 1$.

9. Find the minimum value of $f(x) = x^2 - 7x + 8$.

10. Given $f(x) = x^2 + 4$ and $g(x) = 4x - 1$, find $f[g(0)]$.

11. Given $f(x) = 6x + 8$ and $g(x) = 4x + 2$, find $g[f(-1)]$.

12. Given $f(x) = 3x^2 - 4$ and $g(x) = 2x + 1$, find $f[g(x)]$.

13. Are the functions given by $f(x) = -\frac{1}{4}x + \frac{5}{4}$ and $g(x) = -4x + 5$ inverses of each other?

14. Graph $f(x) = x^2 + 2x - 4$. State the domain and range.

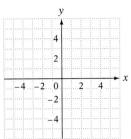

15. Find the vertex and axis of symmetry of the parabola whose equation is $y = x^2 - 2x + 3$.

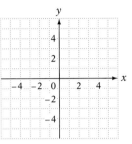

16. Graph $f(x) = |x| - 3$. State the domain and range.

17. Is the graph below the graph of a 1–1 function?

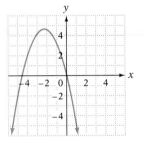

For problems 18 to 21, use $f(x) = x^2 + 2x - 3$ and $g(x) = x^2 - 2$.

18. Evaluate: $(f + g)(2)$

19. Evaluate: $(f - g)(-4)$

20. Evaluate: $(f \cdot g)(-4)$

21. Evaluate: $\left(\dfrac{f}{g}\right)(3)$

22. Given $f(x) = 2x^2 + x - 5$ and $g(x) = 3x - 1$, find $g[f(x)]$.

23. Find the inverse of $f(x) = -6x + 4$.

24. Find the inverse of $f(x) = \dfrac{2}{3}x - 12$.

25. Find the inverse of $f(x) = \dfrac{1}{2}x + 8$.

26. The perimeter of a rectangle is 28 ft. What dimensions would give the rectangle a maximum area?

Chapter Test

1. Find the x-intercepts of $y = 2x^2 - 3x + 4$.

2. Find the zeros of $g(x) = x^2 + 3x - 8$.

3. Use the discriminant to determine the number of zeros of the parabola $y = 3x^2 + 2x - 4$.

4. Given $f(x) = x^2 + 2x - 3$ and $g(x) = x^3 - 1$, find $(f - g)(2)$.

5. Given $f(x) = x^3 + 1$ and $g(x) = 2x - 3$, find $(f \cdot g)(-3)$.

6. Given $f(x) = 4x - 5$ and $g(x) = x^2 + 3x + 4$, find $\left(\dfrac{f}{g}\right)(-2)$.

7. Given $f(x) = x^2 + 4$ and $g(x) = 2x^2 + 2x + 1$, find $(f - g)(-4)$.

8. Given $f(x) = 4x + 2$ and $g(x) = \dfrac{x}{x + 1}$, find $f[g(3)]$.

9. Given $f(x) = 2x^2 - 7$ and $g(x) = x - 1$, find $f[g(x)]$.

10. Find the maximum value of the function $f(x) = -x^2 + 8x - 7$.

11. Find the inverse of the function $f(x) = 4x - 2$.

12. Find the inverse of the function
$f(x) = \frac{1}{4}x - 4$.

13. Find the inverse of the function
$\{(2, 6), (3, 5), (4, 4), (5, 3)\}$.

14. Are the functions $f(x) = \frac{1}{2}x + 2$ and
$g(x) = 2x - 4$ inverses of each other?

15. Find the maximum product of two numbers
whose sum is 20.

16. Graph $f(x) = -\sqrt{3 - x}$. State the domain
and range.

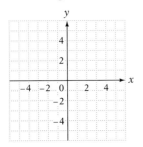

17. Graph $f(x) = \left|\frac{1}{2}x\right| - 2$. State the domain
and range.

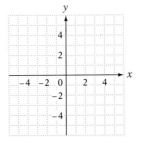

18. Graph $f(x) = x^3 - 3x + 2$. State the domain
and range.

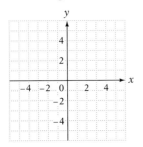

19. Determine whether the graph is the graph of
a 1–1 function.

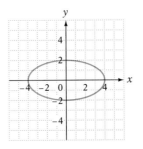

20. The perimeter of a rectangle is 200 cm. What
dimensions would give the rectangle a maximum area? What is the maximum area?

Cumulative Review

1. Evaluate $-3a + \left| \dfrac{3b - ab}{3b - c} \right|$ when $a = 2$, $b = 2$, and $c = -2$.

2. Graph $\{x \mid x < -3\} \cap \{x \mid x > -4\}$.

$$\xleftarrow{\;+\;+\;+\;+\;+\;+\;+\;+\;+\;+\;+\;}\rightarrow$$
$$-5\ -4\ -3\ -2\ -1\ \ 0\ \ 1\ \ 2\ \ 3\ \ 4\ \ 5$$

3. Solve: $\dfrac{3x - 1}{6} - \dfrac{5 - x}{4} = \dfrac{5}{6}$

4. Solve: $4x - 2 < -10$ or $3x - 1 > 8$

5. Solve: $|8 - 2x| \geq 0$

6. Simplify: $\left(\dfrac{3a^3b}{2a} \right)^2 \left(\dfrac{a^2}{-3b^2} \right)^3$

7. Simplify: $(x - 4)(2x^2 + 4x - 1)$

8. Factor: $a^4 - 2a^2 - 8$

9. Factor: $x^3y + x^2y^2 - 6xy^3$

10. Solve: $(b + 2)(b - 5) = 2b + 14$

11. Solve: $x^2 - 2x > 15$

12. Simplify: $\dfrac{x^2 + 4x - 5}{2x^2 - 3x + 1} - \dfrac{x}{2x - 1}$

13. Solve: $\dfrac{5}{x^2 + 7x + 12} = \dfrac{9}{x + 4} - \dfrac{2}{x + 3}$

14. Simplify: $\dfrac{4 - 6i}{2i}$

15. Graph $f(x) = \dfrac{1}{4}x^2$. Find the vertex and axis of symmetry.

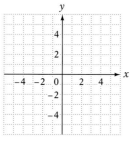

16. Graph the solution set of $3x - 4y \geq 8$.

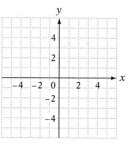

17. Find the equation of the line containing the points $(-3, 4)$ and $(2, -6)$.

18. Find the equation of the line that contains the point $(-3, 1)$ and is perpendicular to the line $2x - 3y = 6$.

19. Solve: $3x^2 = 3x - 1$

20. Solve: $\sqrt{8x + 1} = 2x - 1$

21. Find the minimum value of the function $f(x) = 2x^2 - 3$.

22. Find the range of $f(x) = |3x - 4|$ if the domain is $\{0, 1, 2, 3\}$.

23. Is this set of ordered pairs a function? $\{(-3, 0), (-2, 0), (-1, 1), (0, 1)\}$

24. Solve: $\sqrt[3]{5x - 2} = 2$

25. Given $g(x) = 3x - 5$ and $h(x) = \frac{1}{2}x + 4$, find $g[h(2)]$.

26. Find the inverse of the function given by $f(x) = -3x + 9$.

27. Find the cost per pound of a tea mixture made from 30 lb of tea costing $4.50 per pound and 45 lb of tea costing $3.60 per pound.

28. How many pounds of an 80% copper alloy must be mixed with 50 lb of a 20% copper alloy to make an alloy that is 40% copper?

29. Six ounces of an insecticide are mixed with 16 gal of water to make a spray for spraying an orange grove. How much additional insecticide is required if it is to be mixed with 28 gal of water?

30. A large pipe can fill a tank in 8 min less time than it takes a smaller pipe to fill the same tank. Working together, both pipes can fill the tank in 3 min. How long would it take the larger pipe working alone to fill the tank?

31. The distance, d, a spring stretches varies directly as the force, f, used to stretch the spring. If a force of 50 lb can stretch the spring 30 in., how far can a force of 40 lb stretch the spring?

32. The frequency of vibration, f, in an open pipe organ varies inversely as the length, L, of the pipe. If the air in a pipe 2 m long vibrates 60 times per minute, find the frequency in a pipe that is 1.5 m long.

10

Exponential and Logarithmic Functions

Nuclear medicine technologists operate cameras that detect and map the presence of a radioactive drug in a patient's body. They prepare a dosage of the radiopharmaceutical and administer it to the patient. When preparing radiopharmaceuticals, exponential equations are used to model the amount of radiation in the radiopharmaceutical.

Objectives

Section 10.1
To evaluate an exponential function
To graph an exponential function

Section 10.2
To write equivalent exponential and logarithmic equations
To use the Properties of Logarithms to simplify expressions containing logarithms
To use the change-of-base formula

Section 10.3
To graph a logarithmic function

Section 10.4
To solve an exponential equation
To solve a logarithmic equation

Section 10.5
To solve application problems

Napier Rods

The labor involved in calculating the products of large numbers has led many people to devise ways to shorten the procedure. One such shortcut was first described in the early 1600s by John Napier and is based on Napier Rods.

Making a Napier Rod consists of placing a number and the first nine multiples of that number on a rectangular piece of paper (Napier's Rod). This is done for the first nine positive integers. It is necessary to have more than one rod for each number. The rod for 7 is shown at the left.

To illustrate how these rods were used to multiply, let's look at an example.

Multiply: 2893
          × 246

Place the rods for 2, 8, 9, and 3 next to one another. The products for 2, 4, and 6 are found by using the numbers along the second, fourth, and sixth rows.

Each number is found by adding the digits diagonally downward on the diagonal and carrying to the next diagonal when necessary. The products for 2, 4, and 6 are shown at the left.

Note that the sum of the third diagonal in the product for 6 is 13, so carrying to the next diagonal is necessary.

The final product is then found by addition.

Before the invention of the electronic calculator, logarithms were used to ease the drudgery of lengthy calculations. John Napier is also credited with the invention of logarithms.

10.1 Exponential Functions

Objective A **To evaluate an exponential function** ....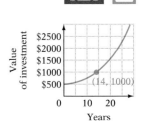

The growth of a $500 savings account that earns 5% annual interest compounded daily is shown at the right. In approximately 14 years, the savings account contains approximately $1000, twice the initial amount. The growth of this savings account is an example of an exponential function.

The pressure of the atmosphere at a certain height is shown in the graph at the right. This is another example of an exponential function. From the graph, we read that the air pressure is approximately 6.5 lb/in² at an altitude of 20,000 ft.

Definition of an Exponential Function

The **exponential function** with base *b* is defined by

$$f(x) = b^x$$

where $b > 0$, $b \neq 1$, and *x* is any real number.

In the definition of an exponential function, *b*, the base, is required to be positive. If the base were a negative number, the value of the function would be a complex number for some values of *x*. For instance, the value of $f(x) = (-4)^x$ when $x = \frac{1}{2}$ is $f\left(\frac{1}{2}\right) = (-4)^{1/2} = \sqrt{-4} = 2i$. To avoid complex number values of a function, the base of the exponential function is a positive number.

➡ Evaluate $f(x) = 2^x$ at $x = 3$ and $x = -2$.

$f(3) = 2^3 = 8$ • Substitute 3 for *x* and simplify.

$f(-2) = 2^{-2} = \dfrac{1}{2^2} = \dfrac{1}{4}$ • Substitute −2 for *x* and simplify.

To evaluate an exponential expression for an irrational number such as $\sqrt{2}$, we obtain an approximation to the value of the function by approximating the irrational number. For instance, the value of $f(x) = 4^x$ when $x = \sqrt{2}$ can be approximated by using an approximation of $\sqrt{2}$.

$$f(\sqrt{2}) = 4^{\sqrt{2}} \approx 4^{1.4142} \approx 7.1029$$

TAKE NOTE

The natural exponential function is an extremely important function. It is used extensively in applied problems in virtually all disciplines from archeology to zoology. Leonhard Euler (1707–1783) was the first to use the letter e as the base of the natural exponential function.

Because $f(x) = b^x$ $(b > 0, b \neq 1)$ can be evaluated at both rational and irrational numbers, the domain of f is all real numbers. And because $b^x > 0$ for all values of x, the range of f is the positive real numbers.

A frequently used base in applications of exponential functions is an irrational number designated by e. The number e is approximately 2.71828183. It is an irrational number, so it has a nonterminating, nonrepeating decimal representation.

Natural Exponential Function

The function defined by $f(x) = e^x$ is called the **natural exponential function.**

The e^x key on a calculator can be used to evaluate the natural exponential function.

Example 1

Evaluate $f(x) = \left(\dfrac{1}{2}\right)^x$ at $x = 2$ and $x = -3$.

Solution

$$f(x) = \left(\frac{1}{2}\right)^x$$

$$f(2) = \left(\frac{1}{2}\right)^2 = \frac{1}{4}$$

$$f(-3) = \left(\frac{1}{2}\right)^{-3} = 2^3 = 8$$

You Try It 1

Evaluate $f(x) = \left(\dfrac{2}{3}\right)^x$ at $x = 3$ and $x = -2$.

Your solution

Example 2

Evaluate $f(x) = 2^{3x-1}$ at $x = 1$ and $x = -1$.

Solution

$$f(x) = 2^{3x-1}$$
$$f(1) = 2^{3(1)-1} = 2^2 = 4$$

$$f(-1) = 2^{3(-1)-1} = 2^{-4} = \frac{1}{2^4} = \frac{1}{16}$$

You Try It 2

Evaluate $f(x) = 2^{2x+1}$ at $x = 0$ and $x = -2$.

Your solution

Example 3

Evaluate $f(x) = e^{2x}$ at $x = 1$ and $x = -1$. Round to the nearest ten-thousandth.

Solution

$$f(x) = e^{2x}$$
$$f(1) = e^{2 \cdot 1} = e^2 \approx 7.3891$$
$$f(-1) = e^{-2 \cdot 1} = e^{-2} \approx 0.1353$$

You Try It 3

Evaluate $f(x) = e^{2x-1}$ at $x = 2$ and $x = -2$. Round to the nearest ten-thousandth.

Your solution

Solutions on p. S29

Objective B **To graph an exponential function** ....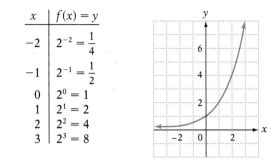

Some properties of an exponential function can be seen in its graph.

⇒ Graph $f(x) = 2^x$.

Think of this as the equation $y = 2^x$.

Choose values of x and find the corresponding values of y. The results can be recorded in a table.

Graph the ordered pairs on a rectangular coordinate system.

x	$f(x) = y$
-2	$2^{-2} = \dfrac{1}{4}$
-1	$2^{-1} = \dfrac{1}{2}$
0	$2^0 = 1$
1	$2^1 = 2$
2	$2^2 = 4$
3	$2^3 = 8$

Connect the points with a smooth curve.

Note that a vertical line would intersect the graph at only one point. Therefore, by the vertical-line test, the graph of $f(x) = 2^x$ is the graph of a function. Also note that a horizontal line would intersect the graph at only one point. Therefore, the graph of $f(x) = 2^x$ is the graph of a one-to-one function.

⇒ Graph $f(x) = \left(\dfrac{1}{2}\right)^x$.

Think of this as the equation $y = \left(\dfrac{1}{2}\right)^x$.

Choose values of x and find the corresponding values of y.

Graph the ordered pairs on a rectangular coordinate system.

Connect the points with a smooth curve.

x	$f(x) = y$
-3	$\left(\dfrac{1}{2}\right)^{-3} = 8$
-2	$\left(\dfrac{1}{2}\right)^{-2} = 4$
-1	$\left(\dfrac{1}{2}\right)^{-1} = 2$
0	$\left(\dfrac{1}{2}\right)^{0} = 1$
1	$\left(\dfrac{1}{2}\right)^{1} = \dfrac{1}{2}$
2	$\left(\dfrac{1}{2}\right)^{2} = \dfrac{1}{4}$

Applying the vertical-line and horizontal-line tests reveals that the graph of $f(x) = \left(\dfrac{1}{2}\right)^x$ is also the graph of a one-to-one function.

⇒ Graph $f(x) = 2^{-x}$.

Think of this as the equation $y = 2^{-x}$.

Choose values of x and find the corresponding values of y.

Graph the ordered pairs on a rectangular coordinate system.

Connect the points with a smooth curve.

x	y
-3	8
-2	4
-1	2
0	1
1	$\dfrac{1}{2}$
2	$\dfrac{1}{4}$

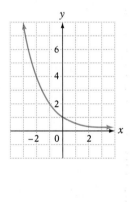

Note that because $2^{-x} = (2^{-1})^x = \left(\dfrac{1}{2}\right)^x$, the graphs of $f(x) = 2^{-x}$ and $f(x) = \left(\dfrac{1}{2}\right)^x$ are the same.

Example 4

Graph: $f(x) = 3^{\frac{1}{2}x - 1}$

Solution

x	y
-2	$\frac{1}{9}$
0	$\frac{1}{3}$
2	1
4	3

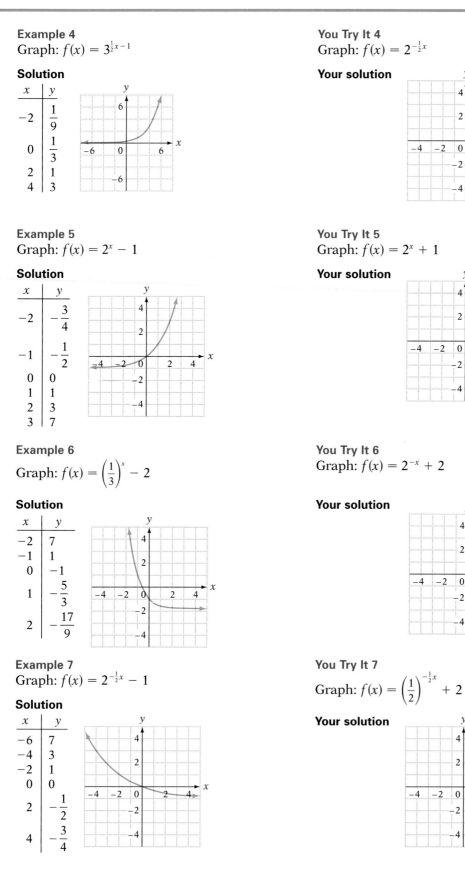

You Try It 4

Graph: $f(x) = 2^{-\frac{1}{2}x}$

Your solution

Example 5

Graph: $f(x) = 2^x - 1$

Solution

x	y
-2	$-\frac{3}{4}$
-1	$-\frac{1}{2}$
0	0
1	1
2	3
3	7

You Try It 5

Graph: $f(x) = 2^x + 1$

Your solution

Example 6

Graph: $f(x) = \left(\dfrac{1}{3}\right)^x - 2$

Solution

x	y
-2	7
-1	1
0	-1
1	$-\frac{5}{3}$
2	$-\frac{17}{9}$

You Try It 6

Graph: $f(x) = 2^{-x} + 2$

Your solution

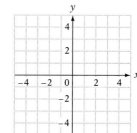

Example 7

Graph: $f(x) = 2^{-\frac{1}{2}x} - 1$

Solution

x	y
-6	7
-4	3
-2	1
0	0
2	$-\frac{1}{2}$
4	$-\frac{3}{4}$

You Try It 7

Graph: $f(x) = \left(\dfrac{1}{2}\right)^{-\frac{1}{2}x} + 2$

Your solution

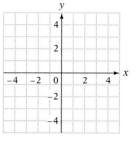

Solutions on p. S29

10.1 Exercises

Objective A

1. Given $f(x) = 3^x$, evaluate:
  a. $f(2)$ **b.** $f(0)$ **c.** $f(-2)$

2. Given $H(x) = 2^x$, evaluate:
  a. $H(-3)$ **b.** $H(0)$ **c.** $H(2)$

3. Given $g(x) = 2^{x+1}$, evaluate:
  a. $g(3)$ **b.** $g(1)$ **c.** $g(-3)$

4. Given $F(x) = 3^{x-2}$, evaluate:
  a. $F(-4)$ **b.** $F(-1)$ **c.** $F(0)$

5. Given $P(x) = \left(\dfrac{1}{2}\right)^{2x}$, evaluate:
  a. $P(0)$ **b.** $P\left(\dfrac{3}{2}\right)$ **c.** $P(-2)$

6. Given $R(t) = \left(\dfrac{1}{3}\right)^{3t}$, evaluate:
  a. $R\left(-\dfrac{1}{3}\right)$ **b.** $R(1)$ **c.** $R(-2)$

7. Given $G(x) = e^{x/2}$, evaluate the following. Round to the nearest ten-thousandth.
  a. $G(4)$ **b.** $G(-2)$ **c.** $G\left(\dfrac{1}{2}\right)$

8. Given $f(x) = e^{2x}$, evaluate the following. Round to the nearest ten-thousandth.
  a. $f(-2)$ **b.** $f\left(-\dfrac{2}{3}\right)$ **c.** $f(2)$

9. Given $H(r) = e^{-r+3}$, evaluate the following. Round to the nearest ten-thousandth.
  a. $H(-1)$ **b.** $H(3)$ **c.** $H(5)$

10. Given $P(t) = e^{-\frac{1}{2}t}$, evaluate the following. Round to the nearest ten-thousandth.
  a. $P(-3)$ **b.** $P(4)$ **c.** $P\left(\dfrac{1}{2}\right)$

11. Given $F(x) = 2^{x^2}$, evaluate:
  a. $F(2)$ **b.** $F(-2)$ **c.** $F\left(\dfrac{3}{4}\right)$

12. Given $Q(x) = 2^{-x^2}$, evaluate:
  a. $Q(3)$ **b.** $Q(-1)$ **c.** $Q(-2)$

13. Given $f(x) = e^{-x^2/2}$, evaluate the following. Round to the nearest ten-thousandth.
  a. $f(-2)$ **b.** $f(2)$ **c.** $f(-3)$

14. Given $f(x) = e^{-2x} + 1$, evaluate the following. Round to the nearest ten-thousandth.
  a. $f(-1)$ **b.** $f(3)$ **c.** $f(-2)$

Graph.

15. $f(x) = 3^x$

16. $f(x) = 3^{-x}$

17. $f(x) = 2^{x+1}$

18. $f(x) = 2^{x-1}$

19. $f(x) = \left(\dfrac{1}{3}\right)^x$

20. $f(x) = \left(\dfrac{2}{3}\right)^x$

21. $f(x) = 2^{-x} + 1$

22. $f(x) = 2^x - 3$

23. $f(x) = \left(\dfrac{1}{3}\right)^{-x}$

24. $f(x) = \left(\dfrac{3}{2}\right)^{-x}$

25. $f(x) = \left(\dfrac{1}{2}\right)^{-x} + 2$

26. $f(x) = \left(\dfrac{1}{2}\right)^x - 1$

APPLYING THE CONCEPTS

Use a graphing calculator to graph each of the following.

27. $P(x) = (\sqrt{3})^x$

28. $F(x) = (\sqrt{5})^x$

29. $Q(x) = (\sqrt{3})^{-x}$

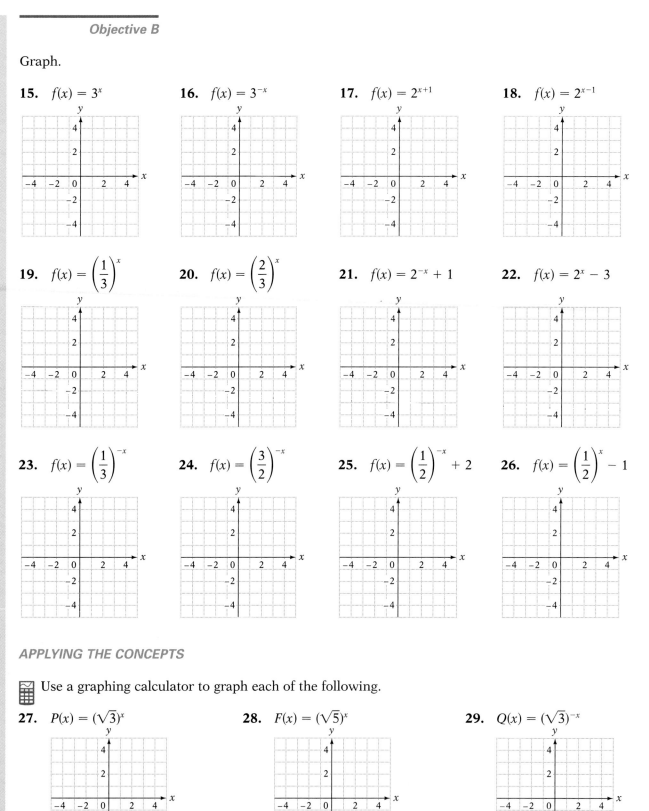

30. $A(x) = (\sqrt{2})^{-x}$

31. $\sinh(x) = \dfrac{e^x - e^{-x}}{2}$

32. $\cosh(x) = \dfrac{e^x + e^{-x}}{2}$

33. $N(x) = e^{-x^2/2}$

34. $M(x) = xe^{-x^2/2}$

35. $f(x) = 2^x - x^2$

36. $h(x) = 3^x - x^3$

37. $f(x) = \pi^x$

38. $g(x) = \pi^{-x}$

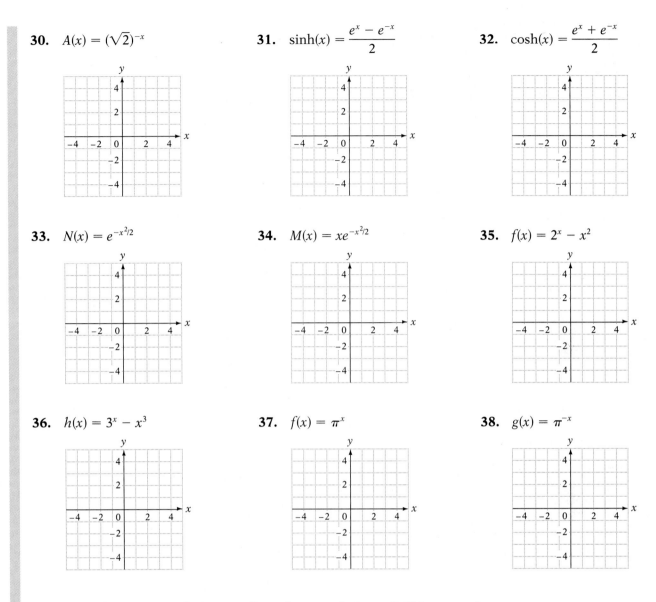

39. According to population studies, the population of China can be approximated by the equation $P(t) = 1.17(1.012)^t$, where $t = 0$ corresponds to 1993 and $P(t)$ is the population, in billions, of China in t years.

   a. Graph this equation. *Suggestion:* Use Xmin = 0, Xmax = 19, Ymin = −0.5, Ymax = 1.75, and Yscl = 0.25.

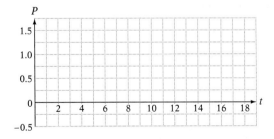

   b. The point whose approximate coordinates are (5, 1.242) is on this graph. Write a sentence that explains the meaning of these coordinates.

40. The growth of the population of India can be approximated by the equation $P(t) = 0.883(1.017)^t$, where $t = 0$ corresponds to 1993 and $P(t)$ is the population, in billions, of India in t years.

   a. Graph this equation. *Suggestion:* Use Xmin = 0, Xmax = 20, Ymin = −0.5, Ymax = 1.75, and Yscl = 0.25.

   b. The point whose approximate coordinates are (8, 1.01) is on this graph. Write a sentence that explains the meaning of these coordinates.

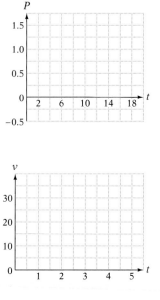

41. If air resistance is ignored, the speed v, in feet per second, of an object t seconds after it has been dropped is given by $v = 32t$. However, if air resistance is considered, then the speed depends on the mass (and on other things). For a certain mass, the speed t seconds after it has been dropped is given by $v = 32(1 - e^{-t})$.

   a. Graph this equation. *Suggestion:* Use Xmin = 0, Xmax = 5.5, Ymin = 0, Ymax = 40, and Yscl = 5.

   b. The point whose approximate coordinates are (2, 27.7) is on this graph. Write a sentence that explains the meaning of these coordinates.

42. If air resistance is ignored, the speed v, in feet per second, of an object t seconds after it has been dropped is given by $v = 32t$. However, if air resistance is considered, then the speed depends on the mass (and on other things). For a certain mass, the speed t seconds after it has been dropped is given by $v = 64(1 - e^{-t/2})$.

   a. Graph this equation. *Suggestion:* Use Xmin = 0, Xmax = 11, Ymin = 0, Ymax = 80, and Yscl = 10.

   b. The point whose approximate coordinates are (4, 55.3) is on this graph. Write a sentence that explains the meaning of these coordinates.

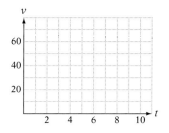

43. If $f(x) = b^x$, determine whether the following statements are always true, sometimes true, or never true.

   a. If $b > 0$ and $b \neq 1$, then $f(x) = b^x$ is a one-to-one function.

   b. If $b > 0$ and $b \neq 1$, then $f(x) = b^x$ is greater than zero.

44. Evaluate $\left(1 + \dfrac{1}{n}\right)^n$ for $n = 100, 1000, 10{,}000$, and $100{,}000$ and compare the results with the value of e, the base of the natural exponential function. On the basis of your evaluation, complete the following sentence:

   As n increases, $\left(1 + \dfrac{1}{n}\right)^n$ becomes closer to _____.

45. Evaluate $(1 + x)^{1/x}$ for $x = 0.1, 0.01, 0.001, 0.00001$, and 0.0000001 and compare the results with the value of e, the base of the natural exponential function. On the basis of your evaluation, complete the following sentence: As x gets closer to 0, $(1 + x)^{1/x}$ becomes closer to _____.

10.2 Introduction to Logarithms

Objective A **To write equivalent exponential and logarithmic equations** .....

Because the exponential function is a 1–1 function, it has an inverse function, which is called a *logarithm*. A logarithm is used to answer a question similar to the following one: "If $16 = 2^y$, what is the value of y?" Because $16 = 2^4$, the logarithm, base 2, of 16 is 4. This is written $\log_2 16 = 4$. Note that a logarithm is an exponent that solves a certain equation.

> **Definition of Logarithm**
>
> For $b > 0$, $b \neq 1$, $y = \log_b x$ is equivalent to $x = b^y$.

Read $\log_b x$ as "the logarithm of x, base b" or "log base b of x."

The table at the right shows equivalent statements written in both exponential and logarithmic form.

Exponential Form	Logarithmic Form
$2^4 = 16$	$\log_2 16 = 4$
$\left(\frac{2}{3}\right)^2 = \frac{4}{9}$	$\log_{2/3}\left(\frac{4}{9}\right) = 2$
$10^{-1} = 0.1$	$\log_{10}(0.1) = -1$

➡ Write $\log_3 81 = 4$ in exponential form.

$\log_3 81 = 4$ is equivalent to $3^4 = 81$.

➡ Write $10^{-2} = 0.01$ in logarithmic form.

$10^{-2} = 0.01$ is equivalent to $\log_{10}(0.01) = -2$.

The 1–1 property of exponential functions can be used to evaluate some logarithms.

> **1–1 Property of Exponential Functions**
>
> For $b > 0$, $b \neq 1$, if $b^u = b^v$, then $u = v$.

➡ Evaluate $\log_2 8$.

$\log_2 8 = x$ • Write an equation.

$8 = 2^x$ • Write the equation in its equivalent exponential form.

$2^3 = 2^x$ • Write 8 as 2^3.

$3 = x$ • Use the 1–1 Property of Exponential Functions.

$\log_2 8 = 3$

➡ Solve $\log_4 x = -2$ for x.

$$\log_4 x = -2$$
$$4^{-2} = x \qquad \text{• Write the equation in its equivalent exponential form.}$$
$$\frac{1}{16} = x \qquad \text{• Simplify the negative exponent.}$$

The solution is $\frac{1}{16}$. In this example, $\frac{1}{16}$ is called the *antilogarithm,* base 4, of -2.

Definition of Antilogarithm

If $\log_b M = N$, the **antilogarithm**, base b, of N is M. In exponential form,

$$M = b^N$$

The antilogarithm of a number can be determined by rewriting $\log_b M = N$ in exponential form, $b^N = M$. Thus M, the antilogarithm of N, is b^N. For instance, if $\log_5 x = 3$, then x (the antilogarithm, base 5, of 3) is $5^3 = x = 125$.

Logarithms, base 10, are called **common logarithms.** Usually the base, 10, is omitted when writing the common logarithm of a number. Therefore, $\log_{10} x$ is written $\log x$. To find the common logarithm of most numbers, a calculator is necessary. Because the logarithms of most numbers are irrational numbers, the value in the display of a calculator is an approximation of the number. Using a calculator reveals that

$$\log 384 \approx 2.\overbrace{5843312}^{\text{Mantissa}}$$

Characteristic

The decimal part of a *common logarithm* is called the **mantissa;** the integer part is called the **characteristic.**

When e (the base of the natural exponential function) is used as a base of a logarithm, the logarithm is referred to as the **natural logarithm** and is abbreviated $\ln x$. This is read "el en x." Using a calculator, we learn that

$$\ln 23 \approx 3.135494216$$

The integer and decimal parts of a natural logarithm do not have special names.

Example 1   Evaluate: $\log_3\left(\frac{1}{9}\right)$

Solution $\log_3\left(\frac{1}{9}\right) = x$

$$\frac{1}{9} = 3^x$$
$$3^{-2} = 3^x$$
$$-2 = x$$
$$\log_3\left(\frac{1}{9}\right) = -2$$

You Try It 1   Evaluate: $\log_4 64$

Your solution

Solution on p. S29

Example 2   Solve for x: $\log_5 x = 2$

Solution $\log_5 x = 2$
$5^2 = x$
$25 = x$

The solution is 25.

You Try It 2   Solve for x: $\log_2 x = -4$

Your solution

Example 3   Solve $\log x = -1.5$ for x.
Round to the nearest ten-thousandth.

Solution $\log x = -1.5$
$10^{-1.5} = x$

$0.0316 \approx x$ • **Use a calculator.**

You Try It 3   Solve $\ln x = 3$ for x.
Round to the nearest ten-thousandth.

Your solution

Solutions on p. S29

Objective B   *To use the Properties of Logarithms to simplify expressions containing logarithms* ....

Because a logarithm is a special kind of exponent, the Properties of Logarithms are similar to the Properties of Exponents.

The property of logarithms that states that the logarithm of the product of two numbers equals the sum of the logarithms of the two numbers is similar to the property of exponents that states that to multiply two exponential expressions with the same base, we add the exponents.

TAKE NOTE

Pay close attention to this theorem. Note, for instance, that this theorem states that $\log_3(4 \cdot p) = \log_3 4 + \log_3 p$. It also states that $\log_5 9 + \log_5 z = \log_5 (9z)$. It does *not* state any relationship that involves $\log_b(x + y)$. **This expression cannot be simplified.**

> **The Logarithm Property of the Product of Two Numbers**
>
> For any positive real numbers x, y, and b, $b \neq 1$,
> $\log_b(xy) = \log_b x + \log_b y$.

A proof of this property can be found in the Appendix.

➡ Write $\log_b(6z)$ in expanded form.

$\log_b(6z) = \log_b 6 + \log_b z$ • **Use the Logarithm Property of Products.**

➡ Write $\log_b 12 + \log_b r$ as a single logarithm.

$\log_b 12 + \log_b r = \log_b(12r)$ • **Use the Logarithm Property of Products.**

The Logarithm Property of Products can be extended to include the logarithm of the product of more than two factors. For instance,

$$\log_b(xyz) = \log_b x + \log_b y + \log_b z$$

$$\log_b(7rt) = \log_b 7 + \log_b r + \log_b t$$

A second property of logarithms involves the logarithm of the quotient of two numbers. This property of logarithms is also based on the fact that a logarithm is an exponent and that to divide two exponential expressions with the same base, we subtract the exponents.

TAKE NOTE

This theorem is used to rewrite expressions such as

$$\log_5\left(\frac{m}{8}\right) = \log_5 m - \log_5 8.$$

It does *not* state any

relationship that involves $\dfrac{\log_b x}{\log_b y}$. **This expression cannot be simplified.**

> **The Logarithm Property of the Quotient of Two Numbers**
>
> For any positive real numbers x, y, and b, $b \neq 1$,
>
> $$\log_b \frac{x}{y} = \log_b x - \log_b y.$$

A proof of this property can be found in the Appendix.

➡ Write $\log_b \dfrac{p}{8}$ in expanded form.

$$\log_b \frac{p}{8} = \log_b p - \log_b 8 \qquad \bullet \text{ Use the Logarithm Property of Quotients.}$$

➡ Write $\log_b y - \log_b v$ as a single logarithm.

$$\log_b y - \log_b v = \log_b \frac{y}{v} \qquad \bullet \text{ Use the Logarithm Property of Quotients.}$$

A third property of logarithms is used to simplify powers of a number.

POINT OF INTEREST

Logarithms were developed independently by Jobst Burgi (1552–1632) and John Napier (1550–1617) as a means of simplifying the calculations of astronomers. The idea was to devise a method by which two numbers could be multiplied by performing additions. Napier is usually given credit for logarithms because he published his result first.

In Napier's original work, the logarithm of 10,000,000 was 0. After this work was published, Napier, in discussions with Henry Briggs (1561–1631), decided that tables of logarithms would be easier to use if the logarithm of 1 was 0. Napier died before new tables could be determined, and Briggs took on the task. His table consisted of logarithms accurate to 30 decimal places, all accomplished without a calculator!

The logarithms Briggs calculated are the common logarithms mentioned earlier.

> **The Logarithm Property of the Power of a Number**
>
> For any positive real numbers x and b, $b \neq 1$, and for any real number r, $\log_b x^r = r\log_b x$.

A proof of this property can be found in the Appendix.

➡ Rewrite $\log_b x^3$ in terms of $\log_b x$.

$$\log_b x^3 = 3 \log_b x \qquad \bullet \text{ Use the Logarithm Property of Powers.}$$

➡ Rewrite $\dfrac{2}{3} \log_b x$ with a coefficient of 1.

$$\frac{2}{3} \log_b x = \log_b x^{2/3} \qquad \bullet \text{ Use the Logarithm Property of Powers.}$$

The following table summarizes the properties of logarithms that we have discussed, along with three other properties.

> **Summary of the Properties of Logarithms**
>
> Let x, y, and b be positive real numbers with $b \neq 1$. Then
>
> | | |
> |---|---|
> | Product Property | $\log_b(x \cdot y) = \log_b x + \log_b y$ |
> | Quotient Property | $\log_b\left(\dfrac{x}{y}\right) = \log_b x - \log_b y$ |
> | Power Property | $\log_b x^r = r \log_b x$, r a real number |
> | Logarithm of One | $\log_b 1 = 0$ |
> | Inverse Property | $b^{\log_b x} = x$ and $\log_b b^x = x$ |
> | 1–1 Property | If $\log_b x = \log_b y$, then $x = y$. |

➡ Write $\log_b \frac{xy}{z}$ in expanded form.

$$\log_b \frac{xy}{z} = \log_b (xy) - \log_b z \qquad \text{• Use the Logarithm Property of Quotients.}$$

$$= \log_b x + \log_b y - \log_b z \qquad \text{• Use the Logarithm Property of Products.}$$

➡ Write $\log_b \frac{x^2}{y^3}$ in expanded form.

$$\log_b \frac{x^2}{y^3} = \log_b x^2 - \log_b y^3 \qquad \text{• Use the Logarithm Property of Quotients.}$$

$$= 2 \log_b x - 3 \log_b y \qquad \text{• Use the Logarithm Property of Powers.}$$

➡ Write $2 \log_b x + 4 \log_b y$ as a single logarithm with a coefficient of 1.

$$2 \log_b x + 4 \log_b y = \log_b x^2 + \log_b y^4 \qquad \text{• Use the Logarithm Property of Powers.}$$

$$= \log_b x^2 y^4 \qquad \text{• Use the Logarithm Property of Products.}$$

Example 4

Write $\log \sqrt{x^3 y}$ in expanded form.

Solution

$$\log \sqrt{x^3 y} = \log (x^3 y)^{1/2} = \frac{1}{2} \log (x^3 y)$$

$$= \frac{1}{2} (\log x^3 + \log y)$$

$$= \frac{1}{2} (3 \log x + \log y)$$

$$= \frac{3}{2} \log x + \frac{1}{2} \log y$$

You Try It 4

Write $\log_8 \sqrt[3]{xy^2}$ in expanded form.

Your solution

Example 5

Write $\frac{1}{2} (\log_3 x - 3 \log_3 y + \log_3 z)$ as a single logarithm with a coefficient of 1.

Solution

$$\frac{1}{2} (\log_3 x - 3 \log_3 y + \log_3 z)$$

$$= \frac{1}{2} (\log_3 x - \log_3 y^3 + \log_3 z)$$

$$= \frac{1}{2} \left(\log_3 \frac{x}{y^3} + \log_3 z \right)$$

$$= \frac{1}{2} \left(\log_3 \frac{xz}{y^3} \right) = \log_3 \left(\frac{xz}{y^3} \right)^{1/2} = \log_3 \sqrt{\frac{xz}{y^3}}$$

You Try It 5

Write $\frac{1}{3} (\log_4 x - 2 \log_4 y + \log_4 z)$ as a single logarithm with a coefficient of 1.

Your solution

Example 6

Find $\log_4 4^7$.

Solution

$$\log_4 4^7 = 7 \qquad \text{• Inverse Property}$$

You Try It 6

Find $\log_9 1$.

Your solution

Solutions on pp. S29–S30

Objective C *To use the change-of-base formula* ·· 🎞 40 CT

Although only common logarithms and natural logarithms are programmed into a calculator, the logarithms for other positive bases can be found.

➡ Evaluate $\log_5 22$.

$$\log_5 22 = x$$ • Write an equation.

$$5^x = 22$$ • Write the equation in its equivalent exponential form.

$$\log 5^x = \log 22$$ • Apply the common logarithm to each side of the equation.

$$x \log 5 = \log 22$$ • Use the Power Property of Logarithms.

$$x = \frac{\log 22}{\log 5}$$ • Exact answer

$$x \approx 1.92057$$ • Approximate answer

$$\log_5 22 \approx 1.92057$$

In the third step above, the natural logarithm, instead of the common logarithm, could have been applied to each side of the equation. The same result would have been obtained.

Using a procedure similar to the one for $\log_5 22$, a formula for changing bases can be derived.

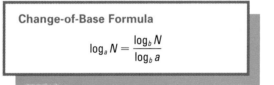

Change-of-Base Formula

$$\log_a N = \frac{\log_b N}{\log_b a}$$

➡ Evaluate $\log_2 14$.

$$\log_2 14 = \frac{\log 14}{\log 2}$$ • Use the Change-of-Base Formula with $N = 14$, $a = 2$, $b = 10$.

$$\approx 3.80735$$

For the last example, common logarithms were used. Here is the same example using natural logarithms. Note that the answers are the same.

$$\log_2 14 = \frac{\ln 14}{\ln 2} \approx 3.80735$$

Example 7

Evaluate $\log_8 0.137$ by using natural logarithms.

Solution

$$\log_8 0.137 = \frac{\ln 0.137}{\ln 8} \approx -0.95592$$

Example 8

Evaluate $\log_2 90.813$ by using common logarithms.

Solution

$$\log_2 90.813 = \frac{\log 90.813}{\log 2} \approx 6.50483$$

You Try It 7

Evaluate $\log_7 6.45$ by using common logarithms.

Your solution

You Try It 8

Evaluate $\log_3 0.834$ by using natural logarithms.

Your solution

Solutions on p. S30

10.2 Exercises

Objective A

Write the exponential expression in logarithmic form.

1. $5^2 = 25$

2. $10^3 = 1000$

3. $4^{-2} = \dfrac{1}{16}$

4. $3^{-3} = \dfrac{1}{27}$

5. $10^y = x$

6. $e^y = x$

7. $a^x = w$

8. $b^y = c$

Write the logarithmic expression in exponential form.

9. $\log_3 9 = 2$

10. $\log_2 32 = 5$

11. $\log 0.01 = -2$

12. $\log_5 \dfrac{1}{5} = -1$

13. $\ln x = y$

14. $\log x = y$

15. $\log_b u = v$

16. $\log_c x = y$

Evaluate.

17. $\log_3 81$

18. $\log_7 49$

19. $\log_2 128$

20. $\log_5 125$

21. $\log 100$

22. $\log 0.001$

23. $\ln e^3$

24. $\ln e^2$

25. $\log_8 1$

26. $\log_3 243$

27. $\log_5 625$

28. $\log_2 64$

Solve for x.

29. $\log_3 x = 2$

30. $\log_5 x = 1$

31. $\log_4 x = 3$

32. $\log_2 x = 6$

33. $\log_7 x = -1$

34. $\log_8 x = -2$

35. $\log_6 x = 0$

36. $\log_4 x = 0$

Solve for x. Round to the nearest hundredth.

37. $\log x = 2.5$

38. $\log x = 3.2$

39. $\log x = -1.75$

40. $\log x = -2.1$

41. $\ln x = 2$

42. $\ln x = 1.4$

43. $\ln x = -\dfrac{1}{2}$

44. $\ln x = -1.7$

Objective B

Express as a single logarithm with a coefficient of 1.

45. $\log_3 x^3 + \log_3 y^2$ **46.** $\log_7 x + \log_7 z^2$ **47.** $\ln x^4 - \ln y^2$

48. $\ln x^2 - \ln y$ **49.** $3 \log_7 x$ **50.** $4 \log_8 y$

51. $3 \ln x + 4 \ln y$ **52.** $2 \ln x - 5 \ln y$ **53.** $2(\log_4 x + \log_4 y)$

54. $3(\log_5 r + \log_5 t)$ **55.** $2 \log_3 x - \log_3 y + 2 \log_3 z$ **56.** $4 \log_5 r - 3 \log_5 s + \log_5 t$

57. $\ln x - (2 \ln y + \ln z)$ **58.** $2 \log_b x - 3(\log_b y + \log_b z)$

59. $\frac{1}{2}(\log_6 x - \log_6 y)$ **60.** $\frac{1}{3}(\log_8 x - \log_8 y)$

61. $2(\log_4 s - 2 \log_4 t + \log_4 r)$ **62.** $3(\log_9 x + 2 \log_9 y - 2 \log_9 z)$

63. $\ln x - 2(\ln y + \ln z)$ **64.** $\ln t - 3(\ln u + \ln v)$

65. $3 \log_2 t - 2(\log_2 r - \log_2 v)$ **66.** $2 \log_{10} x - 3(\log_{10} y - \log_{10} z)$

67. $\frac{1}{2}(3 \log_4 x - 2 \log_4 y + \log_4 z)$ **68.** $\frac{1}{3}(4 \log_5 t - 5 \log_5 u - 7 \log_5 v)$

69. $\frac{1}{2}(\ln x - 3 \ln y)$ **70.** $\frac{1}{3}\ln a + \frac{2}{3}\ln b$

71. $\frac{1}{2}\log_2 x - \frac{2}{3}\log_2 y + \frac{1}{2}\log_2 z$ **72.** $\frac{2}{3}\log_3 x + \frac{1}{3}\log_3 y - \frac{1}{2}\log_3 z$

Write the logarithm in expanded form.

73. $\log_8(xz)$

74. $\log_7(rt)$

75. $\log_3 x^5$

76. $\log_2 y^7$

77. $\log_b\left(\dfrac{r}{s}\right)$

78. $\log_c\left(\dfrac{z}{4}\right)$

79. $\log_3(x^2 y^6)$

80. $\log_4(t^4 u^2)$

81. $\log_7\left(\dfrac{u^3}{v^4}\right)$

82. $\log_{10}\left(\dfrac{s^5}{t^2}\right)$

83. $\log_2(rs)^2$

84. $\log_3(x^2 y)^3$

85. $\ln(x^2 yz)$

86. $\ln(xy^2 z^3)$

87. $\log_5\left(\dfrac{xy^2}{z^4}\right)$

88. $\log_b\left(\dfrac{r^2 s}{t^3}\right)$

89. $\log_8\left(\dfrac{x^2}{yz^2}\right)$

90. $\log_9\left(\dfrac{x}{y^2 z^3}\right)$

91. $\log_4\sqrt{x^3 y}$

92. $\log_3\sqrt{x^5 y^3}$

93. $\log_7\sqrt{\dfrac{x^3}{y}}$

94. $\log_b\sqrt[3]{\dfrac{r^2}{t}}$

95. $\ln\left(x\sqrt{\dfrac{y}{z}}\right)$

96. $\ln\left(y\sqrt[3]{\dfrac{r}{s}}\right)$

97. $\log_3\dfrac{t}{\sqrt{x}}$

98. $\log_4\dfrac{x}{\sqrt{y^2 z}}$

99. $\log_7\left(\dfrac{\sqrt{uv}}{x}\right)$

100. $\log_2\left(\dfrac{\sqrt{xy}}{z^2}\right)$

Objective C

Evaluate. Round to the nearest ten-thousandth.

101. $\log_{10} 7$ **102.** $\log_{10} 9$ **103.** $\log_{10}\left(\dfrac{3}{5}\right)$ **104.** $\log_{10}\left(\dfrac{13}{3}\right)$

105. $\ln 4$ **106.** $\ln 6$ **107.** $\ln\left(\dfrac{17}{6}\right)$ **108.** $\ln\left(\dfrac{13}{17}\right)$

109. $\log_8 6$ **110.** $\log_4 8$ **111.** $\log_5 30$ **112.** $\log_6 28$

113. $\log_3(0.5)$ **114.** $\log_5(0.6)$ **115.** $\log_7(1.7)$ **116.** $\log_6(3.2)$

117. $\log_5 15$ **118.** $\log_3 25$ **119.** $\log_{12} 120$ **120.** $\log_9 90$

121. $\log_4 2.55$ **122.** $\log_8 6.42$ **123.** $\log_5 67$ **124.** $\log_8 35$

APPLYING THE CONCEPTS

125. For each of the following, answer True or False. Assume all variables represent positive numbers.

    a. $\log_3(-9) = -2$ **b.** $x^y = z$ and $\log_x z = y$ are equivalent equations.

    c. $\log(x^{-1}) = \dfrac{1}{\log x}$ **d.** $\log(x + y) = \log x + \log y$

    e. $\log(x \cdot y) = \log x \cdot \log y$ **f.** $\log\left(\dfrac{x}{y}\right) = \log x - \log y$

    g. $\dfrac{\log x}{\log y} = \dfrac{x}{y}$ **h.** If $\log x = \log y$, then $x = y$.

126. Complete each statement using the equation $\log_a b = c$.

    a. $a^c = $ _____   **b.** $\text{antilog}_a(\log_a b) = $ _____

10.3 Graphs of Logarithmic Functions

Objective A   *To graph a logarithmic function* ....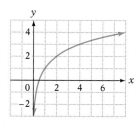

The graph of a logarithmic function can be drawn by using the relationship between the exponential and logarithmic functions.

➡ Graph: $f(x) = \log_2 x$

Think of this as the equation $y = \log_2 x$.

$$f(x) = \log_2 x$$
$$y = \log_2 x$$

Write the equivalent exponential equation.

$$x = 2^y$$

Because the equation is solved for x in terms of y, it is easier to choose values of y and find the corresponding values of x. The results can be recorded in a table.

x	y
$\frac{1}{4}$	-2
$\frac{1}{2}$	-1
1	0
2	1
4	2

Graph the ordered pairs on a rectangular coordinate system.

Connect the points with a smooth curve.

Applying the vertical-line and horizontal-line tests reveals that $f(x) = \log_2 x$ is a one-to-one function.

➡ Graph: $f(x) = \log_2(x) + 1$

Think of $f(x) = \log_2(x) + 1$ as the equation $y = \log_2(x) + 1$.

$$y = \log_2(x) + 1$$

$$y - 1 = \log_2(x)$$ • Solve for $\log_2(x)$.

$$2^{y-1} = x$$ • Write the equivalent exponential equation.

Choose values of y and find the corresponding values of x.

Graph the ordered pairs on a rectangular coordinate system.

Connect the points with a smooth curve.

x	y
$\frac{1}{4}$	-1
$\frac{1}{2}$	0
1	1
2	2
4	3

Example 1

Graph: $f(x) = \log_3 x$

Solution

$f(x) = \log_3 x$

$y = \log_3 x$

$3^y = x$ • Write the equivalent exponential equation.

x	y
$\dfrac{1}{9}$	-2
$\dfrac{1}{3}$	-1
1	0
3	1

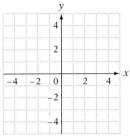

You Try It 1

Graph: $f(x) = \log_2 (x - 1)$

Your solution

Example 2

Graph: $f(x) = 2 \log_3 x$

Solution

$f(x) = 2 \log_3 x$

$y = 2 \log_3 x$

$\dfrac{y}{2} = \log_3 x$

$3^{y/2} = x$ • Write the equivalent exponential equation.

x	y
$\dfrac{1}{9}$	-4
$\dfrac{1}{3}$	-2
1	0
3	2

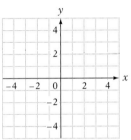

You Try It 2

Graph: $f(x) = \log_3 (2x)$

Your solution

Example 3

Graph: $f(x) = -\log_2 (x - 2)$

Solution

$f(x) = -\log_2 (x - 2)$

$y = -\log_2 (x - 2)$

$-y = \log_2 (x - 2)$

$2^{-y} = x - 2$ • Write the equivalent exponential equation.

$2^{-y} + 2 = x$

x	y
6	-2
4	-1
3	0
$\dfrac{5}{2}$	1
$\dfrac{9}{4}$	2
$\dfrac{17}{8}$	3

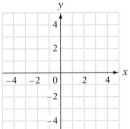

You Try It 3

Graph: $f(x) = -\log_3 (x + 1)$

Your solution

Solutions on p. S30

10.3 Exercises

Graph.

1. $f(x) = \log_4 x$

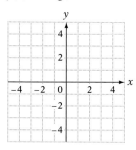

2. $f(x) = \log_2(x + 1)$

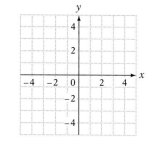

3. $f(x) = \log_3(2x - 1)$

4. $f(x) = \log_2\left(\dfrac{1}{2}x\right)$

5. $f(x) = 3 \log_2 x$

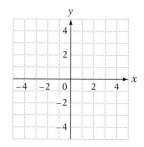

6. $f(x) = \dfrac{1}{2}\log_2 x$

7. $f(x) = -\log_2 x$

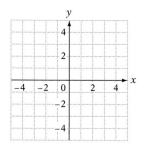

8. $f(x) = -\log_3 x$

9. $f(x) = \log_2(x - 1)$

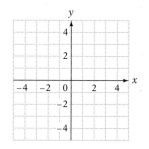

10. $f(x) = \log_3(2 - x)$

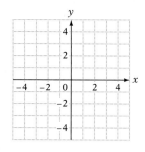

11. $f(x) = -\log_2(x - 1)$

12. $f(x) = -\log_2(1 - x)$

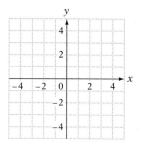

APPLYING THE CONCEPTS

Use a graphing calculator to graph the following.

13. $f(x) = \log_2 x - 3$

14. $f(x) = \log_3 x + 2$

15. $f(x) = -\log_2 x + 2$

16. $f(x) = -\dfrac{1}{2}\log_2 x - 1$

17. $f(x) = x - \log_2(1 - x)$

18. $f(x) = x + \log_3(2 - x)$

19. $f(x) = \dfrac{x}{2} - 2\log_2(x + 1)$

20. $f(x) = \dfrac{x}{3} - 3\log_2(x + 3)$

21. $f(x) = x^2 - 10\ln(x - 1)$

22. The Power Property of Logarithms tells us that $\ln x^2 = 2\ln x$. Graph $f(x) = \ln x^2$ and $g(x) = 2\ln x$. Are the graphs the same? Explain.

23. Astronomers use the *distance modulus* of a star as a method of determining the star's distance from Earth. The formula is $M = 5\log s - 5$, where M is the distance modulus and s is the star's distance from the Earth in parsecs. (One parsec $\approx 1.9 \times 10^{13}$ miles.)
  a. Graph the equation.
  b. The point with coordinates (25.1, 2) is on the graph. Write a sentence that describes the meaning of this ordered pair.

24. Without practice, the proficiency of a typist decreases. The equation $S = 60 - 7\ln(t + 1)$, where S is the typing speed in words per minute and t is the number of months without typing, approximates this decrease.
  a. Graph the equation.
  b. The point with coordinates (4, 49) is on the graph. Write a sentence that describes the meaning of this ordered pair.

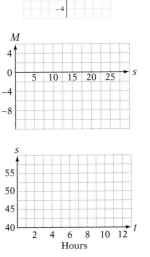

Hours

10.4 Solving Exponential and Logarithmic Equations

Objective A *To solve an exponential equation*

An **exponential equation** is one in which the variable occurs in the exponent. The examples at the right are exponential equations.

$$6^{2x+1} = 6^{3x-2}$$
$$4^x = 3$$
$$2^{x+1} = 7$$

An exponential equation in which each side of the equation can be expressed in terms of the same base can be solved by using the 1–1 Property of Exponential Functions.

Recall the one-to-one property of an exponential function.

$$\text{If } b^x = b^y, \text{ then } x = y.$$

➡ Solve: $10^{3x+5} = 10^{x-3}$

$$10^{3x+5} = 10^{x-3}$$
$$3x + 5 = x - 3$$
$$2x + 5 = -3$$
$$2x = -8$$
$$x = -4$$

• Use the 1–1 Property of Exponential Functions to equate the exponents.
• Solve the resulting equation.

Check:

$10^{3x+5} = 10^{x-3}$	
$10^{3(-4)+5}$	10^{-4-3}
10^{-12+5}	10^{-7}
$10^{-7} = 10^{-7}$	

The solution is -4.

➡ Solve: $9^{x+1} = 27^{x-1}$

$$9^{x+1} = 27^{x-1}$$
$$(3^2)^{x+1} = (3^3)^{x-1}$$
$$3^{2x+2} = 3^{3x-3}$$
$$2x + 2 = 3x - 3$$
$$2 = x - 3$$
$$5 = x$$

• $3^2 = 9; 3^3 = 27$

• Use the 1–1 Property of Exponential Functions to equate the exponents.
• Solve for x.

Check:

$9^{x+1} = 27^{x-1}$	
9^{5+1}	27^{5-1}
9^6	27^4
$531,441 = 531,441$	

The solution is 5.

When each side of an exponential equation cannot easily be expressed in terms of the same base, logarithms are used to solve the exponential equation.

TAKE NOTE

When evaluating $\dfrac{\log 7}{\log 4}$, first find the logarithm of each number.
log 7 ≈ 0.84510;
log 4 ≈ 0.60206. Now divide the logarithms.
$\dfrac{\log 7}{\log 4} \approx \dfrac{0.84510}{0.60206} \approx 1.4037$

➡ Solve: $4^x = 7$

$$4^x = 7$$
$$\log 4^x = \log 7$$

- Take the common logarithm of each side of the equation.

$$x \log 4 = \log 7$$

- Rewrite the equation using the Properties of Logarithms.

$$x = \frac{\log 7}{\log 4} \approx 1.4037$$

- Solve for x.

The solution is 1.4037.

- Note that $\dfrac{\log 7}{\log 4} \neq \log 7 - \log 4$.

➡ Solve: $3^{x+1} = 5$

$$3^{x+1} = 5$$
$$\log 3^{x+1} = \log 5$$

- Take the common logarithm of each side of the equation.

$$(x + 1)\log 3 = \log 5$$

- Rewrite the equation using the Properties of Logarithms.

$$x + 1 = \frac{\log 5}{\log 3}$$
$$x + 1 \approx 1.4650$$
$$x \approx 0.4650$$

- Solve for x.

The solution is 0.4650.

Example 1
Solve for x: $3^{2x} = 4$

Solution
$$3^{2x} = 4$$
$$\log 3^{2x} = \log 4$$
$$2x \log 3 = \log 4$$
$$2x = \frac{\log 4}{\log 3}$$
$$x = \frac{\log 4}{2 \log 3}$$
$$x \approx 0.6309$$

The solution is 0.6309.

You Try It 1
Solve for x: $4^{3x} = 25$

Your solution

Example 2
Solve for n: $(1.1)^n = 2$

Solution
$$(1.1)^n = 2$$
$$\log (1.1)^n = \log 2$$
$$n \log 1.1 = \log 2$$
$$n = \frac{\log 2}{\log 1.1}$$
$$n \approx 7.2725$$

The solution is 7.2725.

You Try It 2
Solve for n: $(1.06)^n = 1.5$

Your solution

Solutions on p. S30

Objective B   *To solve a logarithmic equation* ···································· 🔲 40 🔲 CT

A logarithmic equation can be solved by using the Properties of Logarithms.

➡ Solve: $\log_9 x + \log_9(x - 8) = 1$

$$\log_9 x + \log_9(x - 8) = 1$$
$$\log_9[x(x - 8)] = 1$$

- Use the Logarithm Property of Products to rewrite the left side of the equation.

$$9^1 = x(x - 8)$$
$$9 = x^2 - 8x$$
$$0 = x^2 - 8x - 9$$
$$0 = (x - 9)(x + 1)$$

- Write the equation in exponential form.
- Simplify.
- Solve for x.
- Factor and use the Principle of Zero Products.

$$x - 9 = 0 \qquad x + 1 = 0$$
$$x = 9 \qquad\quad x = -1$$

Replacing x by 9 in the original equation reveals that 9 checks as a solution. Replacing x by -1 in the original equation results in the expression $\log_9(-1)$. Because the logarithm of a negative number is not a real number, -1 does not check as a solution. Therefore the solution of the equation is 9.

➡ Solve: $\log_3 6 - \log_3(2x + 3) = \log_3(x + 1)$

$$\log_3 6 - \log_3(2x + 3) = \log_3(x + 1)$$
$$\log_3 \frac{6}{2x + 3} = \log_3(x + 1)$$

- Use the Quotient Property of Logarithms to rewrite the left side of the equation.

$$\frac{6}{2x + 3} = x + 1$$

- Use the 1–1 Property of Logarithms.

$$6 = (2x + 3)(x + 1)$$
$$6 = 2x^2 + 5x + 3$$
$$0 = 2x^2 + 5x - 3$$
$$0 = (2x - 1)(x + 3)$$

- Simplify.
- Solve for x.

$$2x - 1 = 0 \qquad x + 3 = 0$$
$$x = \frac{1}{2} \qquad\quad x = -3$$

Replacing x by $\frac{1}{2}$ in the original equation reveals that $\frac{1}{2}$ checks as a solution. Replacing x by -3 in the original equation results in the expression $\log_3(-2)$. Because the logarithm of a negative number is not a real number, -3 does not check as a solution. Therefore the solution of the equation is $\frac{1}{2}$.

Example 3

Solve for x: $\log_3 (2x - 1) = 2$

Solution

$\log_3 (2x - 1) = 2$

$3^2 = 2x - 1$ • Write in exponential form.
$9 = 2x - 1$
$10 = 2x$
$5 = x$

The solution is 5.

You Try It 3

Solve for x: $\log_4 (x^2 - 3x) = 1$

Your solution

Example 4

Solve for x: $\log_2 x - \log_2 (x - 1) = \log_2 2$

Solution

$\log_2 x - \log_2 (x - 1) = \log_2 2$

$\log_2 \left(\dfrac{x}{x - 1} \right) = \log_2 2$ • Use the Quotient Property of Logarithms.

$\dfrac{x}{x - 1} = 2$ • Use the 1–1 Property of Logarithms.

$(x - 1)\left(\dfrac{x}{x - 1} \right) = (x - 1)2$

$x = 2x - 2$
$-x = -2$
$x = 2$

The solution is 2.

You Try It 4

Solve for x: $\log_3 x + \log_3 (x + 3) = \log_3 4$

Your solution

Example 5

Solve for x:
$\log_2 (3x + 8) = \log_2 (2x + 2) + \log_2 (x - 2)$

Solution

$\log_2 (3x + 8) = \log_2 (2x + 2) + \log_2 (x - 2)$
$\log_2 (3x + 8) = \log_2[(2x + 2)(x - 2)]$
$\log_2 (3x + 8) = \log_2 (2x^2 - 2x - 4)$
$3x + 8 = 2x^2 - 2x - 4$ • By the 1–1 Property of Logarithms

$0 = 2x^2 - 5x - 12$
$0 = (2x + 3)(x - 4)$
$2x + 3 = 0 x - 4 = 0$
$x = -\dfrac{3}{2} x = 4$

$-\dfrac{3}{2}$ does not check as a solution;

4 checks as a solution. The solution is 4.

You Try It 5

Solve for x: $\log_3 x + \log_3 (x + 6) = 3$

Your solution

Solutions on p. S30

10.4 Exercises

. . . .

Objective A

Solve for x. Round to the nearest ten-thousandth.

1. $5^{4x-1} = 5^{x-2}$

2. $7^{4x-3} = 7^{2x+1}$

3. $8^{x-4} = 8^{5x+8}$

4. $10^{4x-5} = 10^{x+4}$

5. $9^x = 3^{x+1}$

6. $2^{x-1} = 4^x$

7. $8^{x+2} = 16^x$

8. $9^{3x} = 81^{x-4}$

9. $16^{2-x} = 32^{2x}$

10. $27^{2x-3} = 81^{4-x}$

11. $25^{3-x} = 125^{2x-1}$

12. $8^{4x-7} = 64^{x-3}$

13. $5^x = 6$

14. $7^x = 10$

15. $e^x = 3$

16. $e^x = 2$

17. $10^x = 21$

18. $10^x = 37$

19. $2^{-x} = 7$

20. $3^{-x} = 14$

21. $2^{x-1} = 6$

22. $4^{x+1} = 9$

23. $3^{2x-1} = 4$

24. $4^{-x+2} = 12$

Objective B

Solve for x.

25. $\log_2(2x - 3) = 3$

26. $\log_4(3x + 1) = 2$

27. $\log_2(x^2 + 2x) = 3$

28. $\log_3(x^2 + 6x) = 3$

29. $\log_5\left(\dfrac{2x}{x - 1}\right) = 1$

30. $\log_6\left(\dfrac{3x}{x + 1}\right) = 1$

31. $\log x = \log(1 - x)$

32. $\ln(3x - 2) = \ln(x + 1)$

33. $\ln 5 = \ln(4x - 13)$

34. $\log_3(x - 2) = \log_3(2x)$

35. $\ln(3x + 2) = 4$

36. $\ln(2x + 3) = -1$

37. $\log_2(8x) - \log_2(x^2 - 1) = \log_2 3$

38. $\log_5(3x) - \log_5(x^2 - 1) = \log_5 2$

39. $\log_9 x + \log_9(2x - 3) = \log_9 2$

40. $\log_6 x + \log_6(3x - 5) = \log_6 2$

41. $\log_8(6x) = \log_8 2 + \log_8(x - 4)$

42. $\log_7(5x) = \log_7 3 + \log_7(2x + 1)$

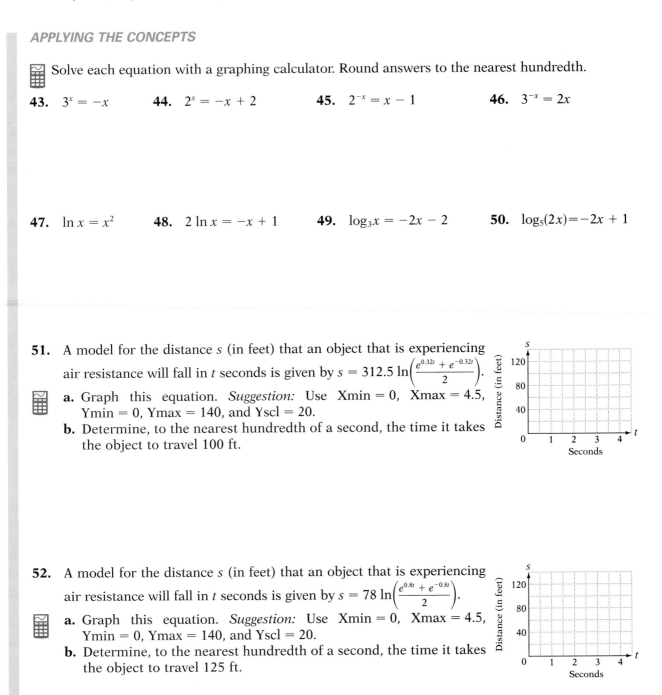

Solve each equation with a graphing calculator. Round answers to the nearest hundredth.

43. $3^x = -x$ **44.** $2^x = -x + 2$ **45.** $2^{-x} = x - 1$ **46.** $3^{-x} = 2x$

47. $\ln x = x^2$ **48.** $2 \ln x = -x + 1$ **49.** $\log_3 x = -2x - 2$ **50.** $\log_5(2x) = -2x + 1$

51. A model for the distance s (in feet) that an object that is experiencing air resistance will fall in t seconds is given by $s = 312.5 \ln\left(\dfrac{e^{0.32t} + e^{-0.32t}}{2}\right)$.
   a. Graph this equation. *Suggestion:* Use Xmin = 0, Xmax = 4.5, Ymin = 0, Ymax = 140, and Yscl = 20.
   b. Determine, to the nearest hundredth of a second, the time it takes the object to travel 100 ft.

52. A model for the distance s (in feet) that an object that is experiencing air resistance will fall in t seconds is given by $s = 78 \ln\left(\dfrac{e^{0.8t} + e^{-0.8t}}{2}\right)$.
   a. Graph this equation. *Suggestion:* Use Xmin = 0, Xmax = 4.5, Ymin = 0, Ymax = 140, and Yscl = 20.
   b. Determine, to the nearest hundredth of a second, the time it takes the object to travel 125 ft.

53. The following "proof" shows that $0.5 < 0.25$. Explain the error.

$$1 < 2$$
$$1 \cdot \log 0.5 < 2 \cdot \log 0.5$$
$$\log 0.5 < \log (0.5)^2$$
$$0.5 < (0.5)^2$$
$$0.5 < 0.25$$

10.5 Applications of Exponential and Logarithmic Functions

Objective A   *To solve application problems* .... (39) (40) CT

A biologist places one single-celled bacterium in a culture, and each hour that particular species of bacteria divides into two bacteria. After one hour there will be two bacteria. After two hours, each of the two bacteria will divide and there will be four bacteria. After three hours, each of the four bacteria will divide and there will be eight bacteria.

POINT OF INTEREST

Parkinson's Law (C. Northcote Parkinson) is sometimes stated as "A job will expand to fill the time alloted for the job." However, Parkinson actually said that in any new government administration, administrative employees will be added at the rate of about 5% to 6% per year. This is an example of exponential growth and means that a staff of 500 will grow to approximately 630 by the end of a 4-year term.

The table at the right shows the number of bacteria in the culture after various intervals of time, t, in hours. Values in this table could also be found by using the exponential equation $N = 2^t$.

Time, t	Number of Bacteria, N
0	1
1	2
2	4
3	8
4	16

The equation $N = 2^t$ is an example of an **exponential growth equation.** In general, any equation that can be written in the form $A = A_0 b^{kt}$, where A is the size at time t, A_0 is the initial size, $b > 1$, and k is a positive real number, is an exponential growth equation. These equations are important not only in population growth studies but also in physics, chemistry, psychology, and economics.

Recall that interest is the amount of money paid (or received) when borrowing (or investing) money. **Compound interest** is interest that is computed not only on the original principal, but also on the interest already earned. The compound interest formula is an exponential equation.

The **compound interest formula** is $P = A(1 + i)^n$, where A is the original value of an investment, i is the interest rate per compounding period, n is the total number of compounding periods, and P is the value of the investment after n periods.

➡ An investment broker deposits $1000 into an account that earns 12% annual interest compounded quarterly. What is the value of the investment after two years?

$i = \dfrac{12\%}{4} = \dfrac{0.12}{4} = 0.03$
* Find i, the interest rate per quarter. The quarterly rate is the annual rate divided by 4, the number of quarters in one year.

$n = 4 \cdot 2 = 8$
* Find n, the number of compounding periods. The investment is compounded quarterly, 4 times a year, for 2 years.

$P = A(1 + i)^n$
* Use the compound interest formula.

$P = 1000(1 + 0.03)^8$
* Replace A, i, and n by their values.

$P \approx 1267$
* Solve for P.

The value of the investment after two years is approximately $1267.

Exponential decay offers another example of an exponential equation. One of the most common illustrations is the decay of a radioactive substance. For instance, tritium, a radioactive nucleus of hydrogen that has been used in luminous watch dials, has a half-life of approximately 12 years. This means that one-half of any given amount of tritium will disintegrate in 12 years.

The table at the right indicates the amount of an initial 10-microgram sample of tritium that remains after various intervals of time, t, in years. Values in this table could also be found by using the exponential equation $A = 10(0.5)^{t/12}$.

Time, t	Amount, A
0	10
12	5
24	2.5
36	1.25
48	0.625

The equation $A = 10(0.5)^{t/12}$ is an example of an **exponential decay equation.** Comparing this equation to the exponential growth equation, note that for exponential growth, the base of the exponential equation is greater than 1, whereas for exponential decay, the base is between 0 and 1.

A method by which an archaeologist can measure the age of a bone is called carbon dating. Carbon dating is based on a radioactive isotope of carbon called carbon-14, which has a half-life of approximately 5570 years. The exponential decay equation is given by $A = A_0(0.5)^{t/5570}$, where A_0 is the original amount of carbon-14 present in the bone, t is the age of the bone, and A is the amount of carbon-14 present after t years.

➡ A bone that originally contained 100 mg of carbon-14 now has 70 mg of carbon-14. What is the approximate age of the bone?

$$A = A_0(0.5)^{t/5570}$$ • Use the exponential decay equation.

$$70 = 100(0.5)^{t/5570}$$ • Replace A by 70 and A_0 by 100 and solve for t.

$$0.7 = (0.5)^{t/5570}$$ • Divide each side by 100.

$$\log 0.7 = \log(0.5)^{t/5570}$$ • Take the common logarithm of each side of the equation. Then simplify.

$$\log 0.7 = \frac{t}{5570} \log(0.5)$$

$$\frac{5570 \log 0.7}{\log 0.5} = t$$

$$2866 \approx t$$

The bone is approximately 2866 years old.

A chemist measures the acidity or alkalinity of a solution by the concentration of hydrogen ions, H^+, in the solution using the formula $pH = -\log(H^+)$. A neutral solution such as distilled water has a pH of 7, acids have a pH of less than 7, and alkaline solutions (also called basic solutions) have a pH of greater than 7.

➡ Find the pH of a certain orange juice that has a hydrogen ion concentration, H^+, of 2.9×10^{-4}. Round to the nearest tenth.

$$pH = -\log(H^+)$$

$$= -\log(2.9 \times 10^{-4})$$ • $H^+ = 2.9 \times 10^{-4}$

$$\approx 3.5376$$

The pH of the orange juice is approximately 3.5.

The **Richter scale** measures the magnitude, M, of an earthquake in terms of the intensity, I, of its shock waves. The relationship between the magnitude and the intensity is given by $M = \log \dfrac{I_1}{I_0}$, where I_0 is a constant.

⇒ How many times as intense is an earthquake that has a magnitude of 6 on the Richter scale than one that has a magnitude of 2?

$6 = \log \dfrac{I_1}{I_0}$ • Use the Richter equation to write a system of equations, one for magnitude 6 and one for magnitude 2.

$2 = \log \dfrac{I_2}{I_0}$

(1) $6 = \log I_1 - \log I_0$ • Rewrite the equations using the Quotient Property of Logarithms.
(2) $2 = \log I_2 - \log I_0$

$4 = \log I_1 - \log I_2$ • Solve the system of equations by subtracting Equation (2) from Equation (1).

$4 = \log \dfrac{I_1}{I_2}$ • Rewrite the equations using the Quotient Property of Logarithms.

$\dfrac{I_1}{I_2} = 10^4 = 10{,}000$ • Solve for $\dfrac{I_1}{I_2}$ using the equivalence of $y = \log x$ and $x = 10^y$.

An earthquake that has magnitude 6 on the Richter scale has an intensity that is 10,000 times greater than an earthquake of magnitude 2.

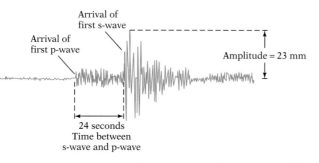

Arrival of first s-wave

Arrival of first p-wave

Amplitude = 23 mm

24 seconds
Time between
s-wave and p-wave

The graph at the left is a *seismogram,* which is used to measure the magnitude of an earthquake. The magnitude, M, is determined by the amplitude, A, of the wave and the difference in time, t, between the occurrence of two types of waves, called *s-waves* and *p-waves.* The equation is given by $M = \log A + 3 \log 8t - 2.92$.

⇒ Determine the magnitude of the earthquake for the seismogram given in the figure. Round to the nearest tenth.

$M = \log A + 3 \log 8t - 2.92$
$ = \log 23 + 3 \log[8(24)] - 2.92$ • Replace A by 23 and t by 24.
$ \approx 1.36173 + 6.84990 - 2.92$ • Simplify.
$ \approx 5.3$

The earthquake has a magnitude of 5.3 on the Richter scale.

The percent of light that will pass through a substance is given by $\log P = -kd$, where P is the percent of light passing through the substance, k is a constant depending on the substance, and d is the thickness of the substance in meters.

⇒ For certain parts of the ocean, $k = 0.03$. Using this value, at what depth will the percent of light be 50% of the light at the surface of the ocean? Round to the nearest meter.

$\log P = -kd$
$\log(0.5) = -0.03d$ • Replace P by 0.5 (50%) and k by 0.03.
$\dfrac{\log(0.5)}{-0.03} = d$ • Solve for d.
$10.0343 \approx d$

At a depth of about 10 m, the light will be 50% of the light at the surface.

Example 1
An investment of $3000 is placed into an account that earns 12% annual interest compounded monthly. In approximately how many years will the investment be worth twice the original amount?

Strategy
To find the time, solve the compound interest formula for n. Use $P = 6000$, $A = 3000$, and $i = \frac{12\%}{12} = \frac{0.12}{12} = 0.01$.

Solution
$$P = A(1 + i)^n$$
$$6000 = 3000(1 + 0.01)^n$$
$$6000 = 3000(1.01)^n$$
$$2 = (1.01)^n$$
$$\log 2 = \log(1.01)^n$$
$$\log 2 = n \log 1.01$$
$$\frac{\log 2}{\log 1.01} = n$$
$$70 \approx n$$

70 months ÷ 12 ≈ 5.8 years

In approximately 6 years, the investment will be worth $6000.

Example 2
The number of words per minute that a student can type will increase with practice and can be approximated by the equation $N = 100[1 - (0.9)^t]$, where N is the number of words typed per minute after t days of instruction. Find the number of words a student will type per minute after 8 days of instruction.

Strategy
To find the number of words per minute, replace t by its given value in the equation and solve for N.

Solution
$N = 100[1 - (0.9)^t]$
$= 100[1 - (0.9)^8]$
≈ 56.95

After 8 days of instruction, a student will type approximately 57 words per minute.

You Try It 1
Find the hydrogen ion concentration, H^+, of vinegar that has a pH of 2.9.

Your strategy

Your solution

You Try It 2
An earthquake that measures 5 on the Richter scale can cause serious damage to buildings. The San Francisco earthquake of 1906 would have measured about 7.8 on this scale. How many times stronger was the San Francisco earthquake than the least forceful earthquake that can cause serious damage to buildings? Round to the nearest whole number.

Your strategy

Your solution

Solutions on p. S31

10.5 Exercises

Objective A

For Exercises 1–4, use the compound interest formula $P = A(1 + i)^n$ given in this section. Round answers to the nearest dollar.

1. The Prime Investment Club deposits $5000 into an account that earns 9% annual interest compounded monthly. What is the value of the investment after 2 years?

2. An insurance broker deposits $4000 into an account that earns 7% annual interest compounded monthly. In approximately how many years will the investment be worth $8000?

3. A manager estimates that in 4 years the company will need to purchase a new bottling machine at a cost of $25,000. How much money must be deposited in an account that earns 10% annual interest compounded monthly so that the value of the account in 4 years will be $25,000?

4. The comptroller of a company has determined that it will be necessary to purchase a new computer in 3 years. The estimated cost of the computer is $10,000. How much money must be deposited in an account that earns 9% annual interest compounded quarterly so that the value of the account in 3 years will be $10,000?

For Exercises 5–8, use the exponential decay equation $A = A_0(0.5)^{t/k}$ given in this section. Round answers to the nearest tenth.

5. An isotope of technetium is used to prepare images of internal body organs. This isotope has a half-life of approximately 6 h. If a patient is injected with 30 mg of this isotope, how long (in hours) will it take for the technetium level to reach 20 mg?

6. Iodine-131 has a half-life of approximately 8 days and is used to study the functioning of the thyroid gland. If a patient is given an injection that contains 8 micrograms of iodine-131, how long (in days) will it take for the iodine level to reach 5 micrograms?

7. A sample of promethium-147 (used in some luminous paints) contains 25 mg. One year later, the sample contains 18.95 mg. What is the half-life of promethium-147, in years?

8. Francium-223 is a very rare radioactive isotope discovered in 1939 by Marguerite Percy. In a laboratory, a 3-microgram sample of francium-223 will decay to 2.54 micrograms in 5 min. What is the half-life of francium-223, in minutes?

9. The percent, P, of correct welds a student can make increases with practice according to the equation $P = 100(1 - 0.75^t)$, where t is the time in weeks. To the nearest week, how many weeks of practice are necessary before a student will make 80% of the welds correctly?

10. The training division of a large corporation has determined that the percent, P, of correct responses for new employees on a product knowledge test can be modeled by the equation $P = 100(1 - 0.8^t)$, where t is the time in days. To the nearest percent, what percent of the questions will the employee answer correctly after 10 days of training?

For Exercises 11 and 12, use the equation $pH = -\log(H^+)$ studied in this section.

11. Find the pH of the digestive solution of the stomach, for which the hydrogen ion concentration is 0.045.

12. Find the hydrogen ion concentration of cow's milk, which has an approximate pH of 6.6.

For Exercises 13 and 14, use the equation $\log P = -kd$, which gives the relationship between the percent, P (as a decimal), of light passing through a substance and its thickness, d.

13. The value of k for a swimming pool is approximately 0.05. At what depth (in meters) will the percent of light be 75% of the light at the surface of the pool?

14. The constant k for a piece of blue stained glass is 20. What percent of light will pass through a piece of this glass that is 0.005 m thick?

For Exercises 15 and 16, use the equation $M = \log \dfrac{I_1}{I_0}$ given in this section.

15. An earthquake that occurred in China in 1978 measured 8.2 on the Richter scale. In 1988, an earthquake in Armenia measured 6.9 on the Richter scale. How many times stronger was China's earthquake?

16. In October 1989, an earthquake of magnitude 7.1 on the Richter scale struck San Francisco, California. In January 1994, an earthquake measuring 6.6 on the Richter scale occurred in the San Fernando Valley in California. How many times stronger was the San Francisco earthquake than the San Fernando Valley earthquake?

For Exercises 17 and 18, use the equation $M = \log A + 3 \log(8t) - 2.92$ given in this section.

17. Find the magnitude of an earthquake that has a seismogram with an amplitude of 30 mm and for which $t = 21$ s.

18. Find the magnitude of an earthquake that has a seismogram with an amplitude of 28 mm and for which $t = 28$ s.

For Exercises 19 and 20, use the equation $D = 10(\log I + 16)$, where D is the number of decibels of a sound and I is the power of the sound in watts.

19. Find the number of decibels of normal conversation. The power of the sound of normal conversation is approximately 3.2×10^{-10} watts.

20. The loudest sound made by any animal is made by the blue whale and can be heard over 500 mi away. The power of the sound made by the blue whale is 630 watts. Find the number of decibels of the sound emitted by the blue whale.

Astronomers use the distance modulus formula $M = 5 \log r - 5$, where M is the distance modulus of a star and r is the distance from Earth to the star in parsecs (1 parsec $= 1.918 \times 10^{13}$ mi). Use this formula for Exercises 21 to 24.

21. The distance modulus of the star Betelgeuse is 5.89. How many parsecs from Earth is this star?

22. The distance modulus of Alpha Centauri is -1.11. How many parsecs from Earth is this star?

23. The distance modulus of the star Antares is 5.4, which is twice that of the star Pollux. Is Antares twice as far from Earth as Pollux? If not, how many times farther from Earth is Antares than Pollux?

24. If one star has a distance modulus of 2 and a second star has a distance modulus of 6, is the second star three times as far from Earth as the first star?

The formula $T = 14.29 \ln(0.00411r + 1)$ is one model for the time, T (in years), before our natural oil resources, r (in billions of barrels of oil), will be depleted. Use this formula for Exercises 25 and 26.

25. According to this model, how many barrels of oil are necessary for our natural oil resources to last 20 more years?

26. According to this model, how many barrels of oil are necessary for our natural oil resources to last 50 more years?

APPLYING THE CONCEPTS

27. Some banks now use continuous compounding of an amount invested. In this case, the equation that relates the value of an initial investment of A dollars after t years at an annual interest rate of $r\%$ is given by $P = Ae^{rt}$. Using this equation, find the value after 5 years of an investment of $2500 into an account that earns 5% annual interest.

28. Using the continuous compounding interest formula in Exercise 27, find how many years it will take an investment to double if the annual interest rate is 6%. Does the time it takes the investment to double in value depend on the amount of the initial investment?

29. Solve for r: $T = 14.29 \ln(0.00411r + 1)$

30. Solve for r: $M = 5 \log r - 5$

31. If $M = 5 \log r_1 - 5$ and $2M = 5 \log r_2 - 5$, express r_1 in terms of r_2.

Focus on Problem Solving

Proof by Contradiction

The four-step plan for solving problems that we have used before is restated here.

1. Understand the problem.
2. Devise a plan.
3. Carry out the plan.
4. Review the solution.

One of the techniques that can be used in the second step is a method called *proof by contradiction*. In this method you assume that the conditions of the problem you are trying to solve can be met and then show that your assumption leads to a condition you already know is not true.

To illustrate this method, suppose we try to prove that $\sqrt{2}$ is a rational number. We begin by recalling that a rational number is one that can be written as the quotient of integers. Therefore, let a and b be two integers with no common factors. If $\sqrt{2}$ is a rational number, then

$$\sqrt{2} = \frac{a}{b}$$

$$(\sqrt{2})^2 = \left(\frac{a}{b}\right)^2 \qquad \bullet \text{ Square each side.}$$

$$2 = \frac{a^2}{b^2}$$

$$2b^2 = a^2 \qquad \bullet \text{ Multiply each side by } b^2.$$

From the last equation, a^2 is an even number. Because a^2 is an even number, a is an even number. Now divide each side of the last equation by 2.

$$2b^2 = a^2 = a \cdot a$$

$$b^2 = a \cdot x \qquad \bullet \ x = \frac{a}{2}$$

Because a is an even number, $a \cdot x$ is an even number. Because $a \cdot x$ is an even number, b^2 is an even number, and this in turn means that b is an even number. This result, however, contradicts the assumption that a and b are two integers with no common factors. Because this assumption is now known not to be true, we conclude that our original assumption, that $\sqrt{2}$ is a rational number, is false. This proves that $\sqrt{2}$ is an irrational number.

Try a proof by contradiction for the following problem: "Is it possible to write numbers using each of the digits 0, 1, 2, 3, 4, 5, 6, 7, 8, and 9 exactly once so that the sum of the numbers is exactly 100?"* Here are some suggestions. First note that the sum of the 10 digits is 45. This means that some of the digits used must be tens digits. Let x be the sum of those digits.

1. What is the sum of the remaining units digits?
2. Express "the sum of the units digits and the tens digits equals 100" as an equation. (*Note:* Writing an equation is one of the possible problem-solving strategies.)
3. Solve the equation for x.
4. Explain why this result means that it is impossible to satisfy both conditions of the problem.

*G. Polya, *How to Solve It: A New Aspect of Mathematical Method,* copyright © 1957 by G. Polya. Reprinted by permission of Princeton University Press.

Projects and Group Activities

Fractals* Fractals have a wide variety of applications. They have been used to create special effects for movies such as *Star Trek II: The Wrath of Khan* and to explain the behavior of some biological and economic systems. One aspect of fractals that has fascinated mathematicians is that they apparently have *fractional dimension*.

To understand the idea of fractional dimension, one must first understand the terms "scale factor" and "size." Consider a unit square (a square of length 1). By joining four of these squares, we can create another square, the length of which is 2, and the size of which is 4. (Here, size = number of square units.) Four of these larger squares can in turn be put together to make a third square of length 4 and size 16. This process of grouping together four squares can in theory be done an infinite number of times; yet at each step, the following quantities will be the same:

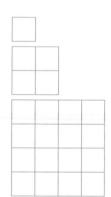

$$\text{scale factor} = \frac{\text{new length}}{\text{old length}} \qquad \text{size ratio} = \frac{\text{new size}}{\text{old size}}$$

Consider the unit square as Step 1, the four unit squares as Step 2, etc.

1. Calculate the scale factor going from **a.** Step 1 to Step 2, **b.** Step 2 to Step 3, and **c.** Step 3 to Step 4.

2. Calculate the size ratio going from **a.** Step 1 to Step 2, **b.** Step 2 to Step 3, and **c.** Step 3 to Step 4.

3. What is **a.** the scale factor and **b.** the size ratio going from Step n to Step $n + 1$?

Mathematicians have defined dimension using the formula $d = \dfrac{\log(\text{size ratio})}{\log(\text{scale factor})}$.

For the squares discussed above, $d = \dfrac{\log(\text{size ratio})}{\log(\text{scale factor})} = \dfrac{\log 4}{\log 2} = 2$.

So by this definition of dimension, squares are two-dimensional figures.

Now consider a unit cube (Step 1). Group eight unit cubes to form a cube that is 2 units on each side (Step 2). Group eight of the cubes from Step 2 to form a cube that is 4 units on each side (Step 3).

4. Calculate **a.** the scale factor and **b.** the size ratio for this process.

5. Show that the cubes are three-dimensional figures.

In each of the above examples, if the process is continued indefinitely, we still have a square or a cube. Consider a process that is more difficult to envision. Let Step 1 be an equilateral triangle whose base has length 1 unit, and let Step 2 be a grouping of three of these equilateral triangles, such that the space between them is another equilateral triangle with a base of length 1 unit. Three shapes from Step 2 are arranged with an equilateral triangle in their center, and so on. It is hard to imagine the result if this is done an infinite number of times, but mathematicians have shown that the result is a single figure of fractional dimension. (Similar processes have been used to create fascinating artistic patterns and to explain scientific phenomena.)

6. Show that for this process **a.** the scale factor is 2 and **b.** the size ratio is 3.

7. Calculate the dimension of the fractal. (Note that it is a *fractional* dimension!)

*Adapted with permission from "Student Math Notes," by Tami Martin, *News Bulletin*, November 1991.

Graphing Logarithmic Functions Using a Graphing Calculator

A graphing calculator can be used to draw the graphs of logarithmic functions. For the graphs below, a suggested viewing window will be given as [XMIN, XMAX] by [YMIN, YMAX] but the keystrokes for that window will not be shown.

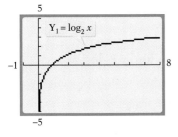

To graph a logarithmic function, first note that there are two logarithm keys, LOG and LN. The first key gives logarithms to the base 10 and the second gives the values of natural logarithms. The graph of $y = \ln x$ is shown at the left.

To graph a logarithmic function other than base 10 or base e, the change of base formula is used. Here is the change of base formula discussed earlier.

$$\log_a N = \frac{\log_b N}{\log_b a}$$

To graph $y = \log_2 x$, we can change from base 2 logarithms to the equivalent base 10 logarithms* as follows.

$$y = \log_2 x = \frac{\log_{10} x}{\log_{10} 2} \qquad \bullet \; a = 2, b = 10, N = x$$

We now graph the equivalent equation $y = \dfrac{\log x}{\log 2}$ using a viewing window of $[-1, 8]$ by $[-5, 5]$.

The graphs of more complicated functions involving logarithms are produced in much the same way as was shown above. To graph $y = -2\log_3(2x + 5) + 1$, enter into the calculator $y = \dfrac{-2\log(2x + 5)}{\log 3} + 1$.

*We are using base 10 here. You can also produce the graphs by using natural logarithms.

Chapter Summary

Key Words   A function of the form $f(x) = b^x$ is an *exponential function,* where b is a positive real number not equal to one. The number b is the *base* of the exponential function.

For $b > 0, b \neq 1, y = \log_b x$ *is equivalent to* $x = b^y$.

$\log_b x$ is the logarithm of x to the base b.

Common logarithms are logarithms to the base 10. (We usually omit the base 10 when writing the common logarithm of a number.)

The *mantissa* is the decimal part of a common logarithm.

The *characteristic* is the integer part of a common logarithm.

If $\log_b M = N$, the *common antilogarithm,* base b, of N is M. In exponential form, $M = b^N$.

An *exponential equation* is an equation in which the variable occurs in the exponent.

Essential Rules   *The Logarithm Property of the Product of Two Numbers*
For any positive real numbers x, y, and b, $b \neq 1$, $\log_b (xy) = \log_b x + \log_b y$.

The Logarithm Property of the Quotient of Two Numbers
For any positive real numbers x, y, and b, $b \neq 1$, $\log_b \dfrac{x}{y} = \log_b x - \log_b y$.

The Logarithm Property of the Power of a Number
For any positive real numbers x and b, $b \neq 1$, and for any real number r, $\log_b x^r = r \log_b x$.

Additional Properties of Logarithms
For any positive real number b, $b \neq 1$, and for any real number n, $\log_b b^n = n$.
For any positive real number b, $b \neq 1$, $\log_b 1 = 0$.

Change-of-Base Formula
$$\log_a N = \frac{\log_b N}{\log_b a}$$

One-to-One Property of the Exponential Function
If $b^x = b^y$, then $x = y$.

To Solve Numerical Problems Using Logarithms
If $\log_b x = \log_b y$, then $x = y$.

Chapter Review

1. Evaluate $f(x) = e^{x-2}$ at $x = 2$.

2. Write $\log_5 25 = 2$ in exponential form.

3. Graph: $f(x) = 3^{-x} + 2$

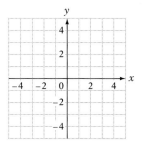

4. Graph: $f(x) = \log_3(x - 1)$

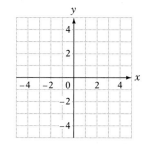

5. Write $\log_3 \sqrt[5]{x^2 y^4}$ in expanded form.

6. Write $2\log_3 x - 5\log_3 y$ as a single logarithm with a coefficient of 1.

7. Solve: $27^{2x+4} = 81^{x-3}$

8. Solve: $\log_5 \dfrac{7x + 2}{3x} = 1$

9. Find $\log_6 22$. Round to the nearest ten-thousandth.

10. Solve: $\log_2 x = 5$

11. Solve: $\log_3(x + 2) = 4$

12. Solve: $\log_{10} x = 3$

13. Write $\dfrac{1}{3}(\log_7 x + 4\log_7 y)$ as a single logarithm with a coefficient of 1.

14. Write $\log_8 \sqrt{\dfrac{x^5}{y^3}}$ in expanded form.

15. Write $2^5 = 32$ in logarithmic form.

16. Find $\log_3 1.6$. Round to the nearest ten-thousandth.

17. Solve $3^{x+2} = 5$. Round to the nearest thousandth.

18. Evaluate $f(x) = \left(\dfrac{2}{3}\right)^{x+2}$ at $x = -3$.

19. Solve: $\log_8(x + 2) - \log_8 x = \log_8 4$

20. Solve: $\log_6(2x) = \log_6 2 + \log_6(3x - 4)$

21. Graph: $f(x) = \left(\dfrac{2}{3}\right)^{x+1}$

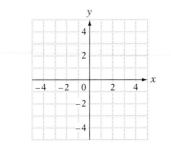

22. Graph: $f(x) = \log_2(2x - 1)$

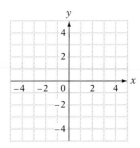

23. Use the compound interest formula $P = A(1 + i)^n$, where A is the original value of an investment, i is the interest rate per compounding period, and n is the number of compounding periods, to find the value of an investment after 2 years. The amount of the investment is \$4000, and it is invested at 8% compounded monthly.

24. Using the Richter equation $M = \log \dfrac{I}{I_0}$, where M is the magnitude of an earthquake, I is the intensity of its shock waves, and I_0 is a constant, how many times stronger is an earthquake with magnitude 6 on the Richter scale than one with magnitude 3 on the scale?

25. Use the exponential decay equation $A = A_0\left(\dfrac{1}{2}\right)^{t/k}$, where A is the amount of a radioactive material present after time t, k is the half-life, and A_0 is the original amount of radioactive material, to find the half-life of a material that decays from 25 mg to 15 mg in 20 days. Round to the nearest whole number.

26. The number of decibels, D, of a sound can be given by the equation $D = 10(\log I + 16)$, where I is the power of the sound measured in watts. Find the number of decibels of sound emitted from a busy street corner for which the power of the sound is 5×10^{-6} watts.

Chapter Test

1. Evaluate $f(x) = \left(\frac{2}{3}\right)^x$ at $x = 0$.

2. Evaluate $f(x) = 3^{x+1}$ at $x = -2$.

3. Graph: $f(x) = 2^x - 3$

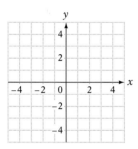

4. Graph: $f(x) = 2^x + 2$

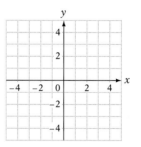

5. Evaluate: $\log_4 16$

6. Solve for x: $\log_3 x = -2$

7. Graph: $f(x) = \log_2(2x)$

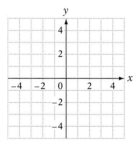

8. Graph: $f(x) = \log_3(x + 1)$

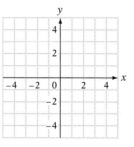

9. Write $\log_6 \sqrt{xy^3}$ in expanded form.

10. Write $\frac{1}{2}(\log_3 x - \log_3 y)$ as a single logarithm with a coefficient of 1.

11. Write $\ln\left(\dfrac{x}{\sqrt{z}}\right)$ in expanded form.

12. Write $3\ln x - \ln y - \dfrac{1}{2}\ln z$ as a single logarithm with a coefficient of 1.

13. Solve for x: $3^{7x+1} = 3^{4x-5}$

14. Solve for x: $8^x = 2^{x-6}$

15. Solve for x: $3^x = 17$

16. Solve for x: $\log x + \log(x-4) = \log 12$

17. Solve for x: $\log_6 x + \log_6(x-1) = 1$

18. Find $\log_5 9$.

19. Find $\log_3 19$.

20. Use the exponential decay equation $A = A_0\left(\dfrac{1}{2}\right)^{t/k}$, where A is the amount of a radioactive material present after time t, k is the half-life, and A_0 is the original amount of radioactive material, to find the half-life of a material that decays from 10 mg to 9 mg in 5 h. Round to the nearest whole number.

Cumulative Review

1. Solve: $4 - 2[x - 3(2 - 3x) - 4x] = 2x$

2. Find the equation of the line that contains the point $(2, -2)$ and is parallel to the line $2x - y = 5$.

3. Factor: $4x^{2n} + 7x^n + 3$

4. Simplify: $\dfrac{1 - \dfrac{5}{x} + \dfrac{6}{x^2}}{1 + \dfrac{1}{x} - \dfrac{6}{x^2}}$

5. Simplify: $\dfrac{\sqrt{xy}}{\sqrt{x} - \sqrt{y}}$

6. Solve by completing the square: $x^2 - 4x - 6 = 0$

7. Write a quadratic equation that has integer coefficients and has solutions $\frac{1}{3}$ and -3.

8. Graph the solution set: $2x - y < 3$
$\qquad\qquad\qquad\qquad\quad x + y < 1$

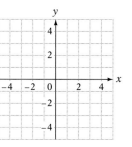

9. Solve by the addition method.
$$3x - y + z = 3$$
$$x + y + 4z = 7$$
$$3x - 2y + 3z = 8$$

10. Simplify: $\dfrac{x - 4}{2 - x} - \dfrac{1 - 6x}{2x^2 - 7x + 6}$

11. Solve: $x^2 + 4x - 5 \le 0$

12. Solve: $|2x - 5| \le 3$

13. Graph: $f(x) = \left(\dfrac{1}{2}\right)^x + 1$

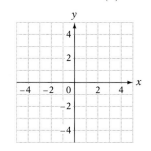

14. Graph: $f(x) = \log_2 x - 1$

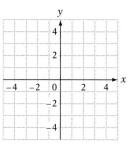

15. Evaluate the function $f(x) = 2^{-x-1}$ at $x = -3$.

16. Solve for x: $\log_5 x = 3$

17. Write $3 \log_b x - 5 \log_b y$ as a single logarithm with a coefficient of 1.

18. Find $\log_3 7$.

19. Solve for x: $4^{5x-2} = 4^{3x+2}$

20. Solve for x: $\log x + \log(2x + 3) = \log 2$

21. A bank offers two types of checking accounts. One account has a charge of $5 per month plus 2 cents per check. The second account has a charge of $2 per month plus 8 cents per check. How many checks can a customer who has the second type of account write if it is to cost the customer less than the first type of checking account?

22. Find the cost per pound of a mixture made from 16 lb of chocolate that costs $4.00 per pound and 24 lb of chocolate that costs $2.50 per pound.

23. A plane can fly at a rate of 225 mph in calm air. Traveling with the wind, the plane flew 1000 mi in the same amount of time that it took to fly 800 mi against the wind. Find the rate of the wind.

24. The distance, d, that a spring stretches varies directly as the force, f, used to stretch the spring. If a force of 20 lb stretches a spring 6 in., how far will a force of 34 lb stretch the spring?

25. A carpenter purchased 80 ft of redwood and 140 ft of fir for a total cost of $67. A second purchase, at the same prices, included 140 ft of redwood and 100 ft of fir for a total cost of $81. Find the cost of redwood and of fir.

26. The compound interest formula is $P = A(1 + i)^n$, where A is the original value of an investment, i is the interest rate per compounding period, n is the total number of compounding periods, and P is the value of the investment after n periods. Use the compound interest formula to find the number of years in which an investment of $5000 will double in value. The investment earns 9% annual interest and is compounded semiannually.

CHAPTER

11

Conic Sections

The principal responsibility of a pharmacist is to prepare and dispense medication ordered by physicians. A pharmacist must be knowledgeable of the effects of drugs on people and have a thorough understanding of procedures for testing drug purity and strength. One of the Projects at the end of this chapter deals with drug dosage.

Objectives

Section 11.1
To graph a parabola

Section 11.2
To find the equation of a circle and then graph the circle

To write the equation of a circle in standard form

Section 11.3
To graph an ellipse with center at the origin

To graph a hyperbola with center at the origin

Section 11.4
To solve a nonlinear system of equations

Section 11.5
To graph the solution set of a quadratic inequality in two variables

To graph the solution set of a nonlinear system of inequalities

Conic Sections

The graphs of three curves—the ellipse, the parabola, and the hyperbola—are discussed in this chapter. These curves were studied by the Greeks and were known prior to 400 B.C. The names of these curves were first used by Apollonius around 250 B.C. in *Conic Sections,* the most authoritative Greek discussion of these curves. Apollonius borrowed the names from a school founded by Pythagoras.

The diagram at the right shows the path of a planet around the sun. The curve traced out by the planet is an ellipse. The **aphelion** is the position of the planet when it is farthest from the sun. The **perihelion** is the planet's position when it is nearest to the sun.

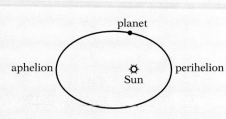

A telescope, like the one at the Palomar Observatory, has a cross section that is in the shape of a parabola. A parabolic mirror has the unusual property that all light rays parallel to the axis of symmetry that hit the mirror are reflected to the same point. This point is called the **focus of the parabola.**

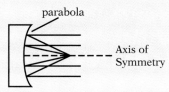

Some comets, unlike Halley's Comet, travel with such speed that they are not captured by the sun's gravitational field. The path of the comet as it comes around the sun is in the shape of a hyperbola.

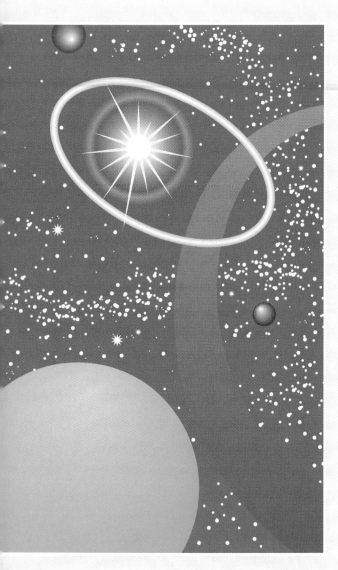

11.1 The Parabola

Objective A   *To graph a parabola* ································· (41) [CT]

The **conic sections** are curves that can be constructed from the intersection of a plane and a right circular cone. The parabola, which was introduced earlier, is one of these curves. Here we will review some of that previous discussion and look at equations of parabolas that were not discussed before.

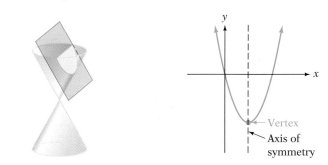

Every parabola has an axis of symmetry and a vertex that is on the axis of symmetry. To understand the axis of symmetry, think of folding the paper along that axis. The two halves of the curve will match up.

The graph of the equation $y = ax^2 + bx + c$, $a \neq 0$, is a parabola with the axis of symmetry parallel to the y-axis. The parabola opens up when $a > 0$ and opens down when $a < 0$. When the parabola opens up, the vertex is the lowest point on the parabola. When the parabola opens down, the vertex is the highest point on the parabola.

The coordinates of the vertex can be found by completing the square.

⟹ Find the vertex of the parabola whose equation is $y = x^2 - 4x + 5$.

$y = x^2 - 4x + 5$
$y = (x^2 - 4x) + 5$ • Group the terms involving x.
$y = (x^2 - 4x + 4) - 4 + 5$ • Complete the square of $x^2 - 4x$. Note that 4 is added and subtracted. Because $4 - 4 = 0$, the equation is not changed.

$y = (x - 2)^2 + 1$ • Factor the trinomial and combine like terms.

The coefficient of x^2 is positive, so the parabola opens up. The vertex is the lowest point on the parabola, or the point that has the least y-coordinate.

Because $(x - 2)^2 \geq 0$ for all x, the least y-coordinate occurs when $(x - 2)^2 = 0$, which occurs when $x = 2$. This means the x-coordinate of the vertex is 2.

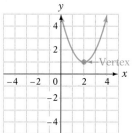

To find the y-coordinate of the vertex, replace x in $y = (x - 2)^2 + 1$ by 2 and solve for y.

$y = (x - 2)^2 + 1$
$\ = (2 - 2)^2 + 1 = 1$

The vertex is (2, 1).

By following the procedure of the last example and completing the square on the equation $y = ax^2 + bx + c$, we find that the **x-coordinate of the vertex** is $-\dfrac{b}{2a}$. The y-coordinate of the vertex can then be determined by substituting this value of x into $y = ax^2 + bx + c$ and solving for y.

Because the axis of symmetry is parallel to the y-axis and passes through the vertex, the equation of the **axis of symmetry** is $x = -\dfrac{b}{2a}$.

⟹ Find the vertex and axis of symmetry of the parabola whose equation is $y = -3x^2 + 6x + 1$. Then sketch its graph.

x-coordinate: $-\dfrac{b}{2a} = -\dfrac{6}{2(-3)} = 1$
         • Find the x-coordinate of the vertex and the axis of symmetry. $a = -3$, $b = 6$

The x-coordinate of the vertex is 1.
The axis of symmetry is the line $x = 1$.

To find the y-coordinate of the vertex, replace x by 1 and solve for y.

$y = -3x^2 + 6x + 1$
  $= -3(1)^2 + 6(1) + 1 = 4$

The vertex is $(1, 4)$.

Because a is negative, the parabola opens down.

Find a few ordered pairs and use symmetry to sketch the graph.

⟹ Find the vertex and axis of symmetry of the parabola whose equation is $y = x^2 - 2$. Then sketch its graph.

x-coordinate: $-\dfrac{b}{2a} = -\dfrac{0}{2(1)} = 0$
         • Find the x-coordinate of the vertex and the axis of symmetry. $a = 1$, $b = 0$

The x-coordinate of the vertex is 0.
The axis of symmetry is the line $x = 0$.

To find the y-coordinate of the vertex, replace x by 0 and solve for y.

$y = x^2 - 2$
  $= 0^2 - 2 = -2$

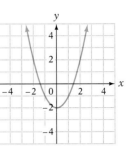

The vertex is $(0, -2)$.

Because a is positive, the parabola opens up.

Find a few ordered pairs and use symmetry to sketch the graph.

The graph of an equation of the form $x = ay^2 + by + c$, $a \neq 0$, is also a parabola. In this case, the parabola opens to the right when a is positive and opens to the left when a is negative.

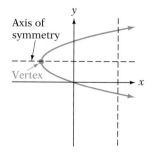

For a parabola of this form, the **y-coordinate of the vertex** is $-\dfrac{b}{2a}$. The **axis of symmetry** is the line $y = -\dfrac{b}{2a}$.

Using the vertical line test, the graph of a parabola of this form is not the graph of a function. The graph of $x = ay^2 + by + c$ is a relation.

⇨ Find the vertex and axis of symmetry of the parabola whose equation is $x = 2y^2 - 8y + 5$. Then sketch its graph.

y-coordinate: $-\dfrac{b}{2a} = -\dfrac{-8}{2(2)} = 2$

     • Find the y-coordinate of the vertex and the axis of symmetry. $a = 2$, $b = -8$

The y-coordinate of the vertex is 2.
The axis of symmetry is the line $y = 2$.

To find the x-coordinate of the vertex, replace y by 2 and solve for x.

$x = 2y^2 - 8y + 5$
$ = 2(2)^2 - 8(2) + 5 = -3$

The vertex is $(-3, 2)$.

Since a is positive, the parabola opens to the right.

Find a few ordered pairs and use symmetry to sketch the graph.

⇨ Find the vertex and axis of symmetry of the parabola whose equation is $x = -2y^2 - 4y - 3$. Then sketch its graph.

y-coordinate: $-\dfrac{b}{2a} = -\dfrac{-4}{2(-2)} = -1$

     • Find the y-coordinate of the vertex and the axis of symmetry. $a = -2$, $b = -4$

The y-coordinate of the vertex is -1.
The axis of symmetry is the line $y = -1$.

To find the x-coordinate of the vertex, replace y by -1 and solve for x.

$x = -2y^2 - 4y - 3$
$ = -2(-1)^2 - 4(-1) - 3 = -1$

The vertex is $(-1, -1)$.

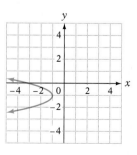

Because a is negative, the parabola opens to the left.

Find a few ordered pairs and use symmetry to sketch the graph.

Example 1

Find the vertex and axis of symmetry of the parabola whose equation is $y = x^2 - 4x + 3$. Then sketch its graph.

Solution

$$-\frac{b}{2a} = -\frac{-4}{2(1)} = 2$$

Axis of symmetry:
$$x = 2$$

$$y = 2^2 - 4(2) + 3$$
$$= -1$$

Vertex: $(2, -1)$

You Try It 1

Find the vertex and axis of symmetry of the parabola whose equation is $y = x^2 + 2x + 1$. Then sketch its graph.

Your solution

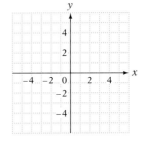

Example 2

Find the vertex and axis of symmetry of the parabola whose equation is $x = 2y^2 - 4y + 1$. Then sketch its graph.

Solution

$$-\frac{b}{2a} = -\frac{-4}{2(2)} = 1$$

Axis of symmetry:
$$y = 1$$

$$x = 2(1)^2 - 4(1) + 1$$
$$= -1$$

Vertex: $(-1, 1)$

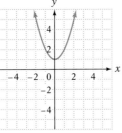

You Try It 2

Find the vertex and axis of symmetry of the parabola whose equation is $x = -y^2 - 2y + 2$. Then sketch its graph.

Your solution

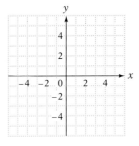

Example 3

Find the vertex and axis of symmetry of the parabola whose equation is $y = x^2 + 1$. Then sketch its graph.

Solution

$$-\frac{b}{2a} = -\frac{0}{2(1)} = 0$$

Axis of symmetry:
$$x = 0$$

$$y = 0^2 + 1$$
$$= 1$$

Vertex: $(0, 1)$

You Try It 3

Find the vertex and axis of symmetry of the parabola whose equation is $y = x^2 - 2x - 1$. Then sketch its graph.

Your solution

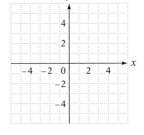

Solutions on p. S31

11.1 Exercises

· ·

Objective A

Find the vertex and axis of symmetry of the parabola given by each equation. Then sketch its graph.

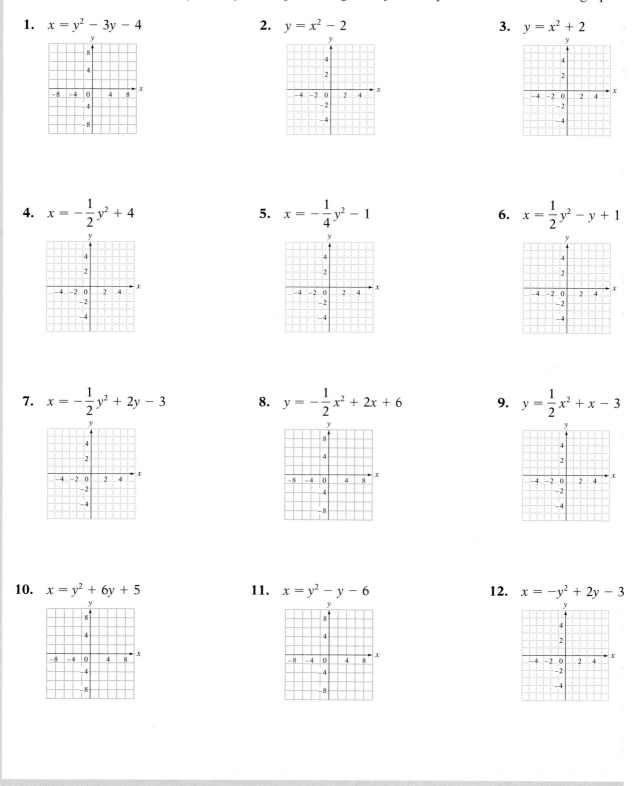

1. $x = y^2 - 3y - 4$

2. $y = x^2 - 2$

3. $y = x^2 + 2$

4. $x = -\dfrac{1}{2}y^2 + 4$

5. $x = -\dfrac{1}{4}y^2 - 1$

6. $x = \dfrac{1}{2}y^2 - y + 1$

7. $x = -\dfrac{1}{2}y^2 + 2y - 3$

8. $y = -\dfrac{1}{2}x^2 + 2x + 6$

9. $y = \dfrac{1}{2}x^2 + x - 3$

10. $x = y^2 + 6y + 5$

11. $x = y^2 - y - 6$

12. $x = -y^2 + 2y - 3$

13. $y = 2x^2 + 4x - 5$

14. $y = 2x^2 - x - 5$

15. $y = 2x^2 - x - 3$

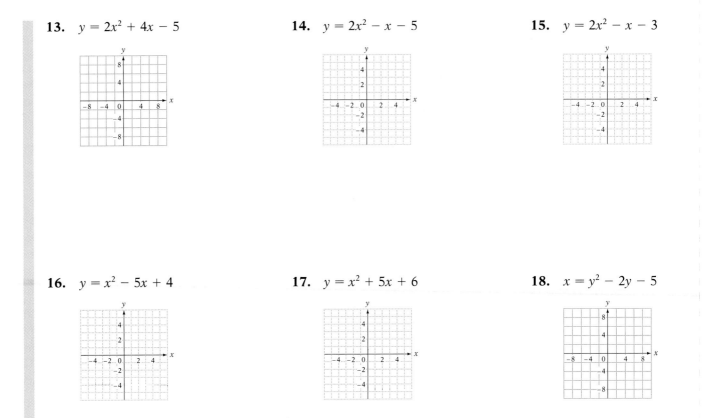

16. $y = x^2 - 5x + 4$

17. $y = x^2 + 5x + 6$

18. $x = y^2 - 2y - 5$

APPLYING THE CONCEPTS

19. Determine whether the following statements are always true, sometimes true, or never true.
   a. The graph of a parabola is the graph of a function.
   b. The axis of symmetry of a parabola passes through the vertex.
   c. The graph of a parabola has two x-intercepts.

20. Explain why $x = y^2 + 4$ is not an equation that defines y as a function of x.

21. When $y = 0$, the x values of the equation $y = x^2 + 2x + 3$ are imaginary numbers. What does this mean for the graph of the equation?

11.2   The Circle

Objective A   **To find the equation of a circle and then graph the circle** ....

A **circle** is a conic section formed by the intersection of a cone and a plane parallel to the base of the cone.

A **circle** can be defined as all the points (x, y) in the plane that are a fixed distance from a given point (h, k) called the **center.** The fixed distance is the **radius** of the circle.

Using the distance formula, the equation of a circle can be determined.

Let (h, k) be the coordinates of the center of the circle, let r be the radius, and let (x, y) be any point on the circle. Then, by the distance formula,

$$r = \sqrt{(x - h)^2 + (y - k)^2}$$

Squaring each side of the equation gives the equation of a circle.

$$r^2 = [\sqrt{(x - h)^2 + (y - k)^2}]^2$$
$$r^2 = (x - h)^2 + (y - k)^2$$

The Standard Form of the Equation of a Circle

Let r be the radius of a circle and let (h, k) be the coordinates of the center of the circle. Then the equation of the circle is given by

$$(x - h)^2 + (y - k)^2 = r^2$$

➡ Sketch a graph of $(x - 1)^2 + (y + 2)^2 = 9$.

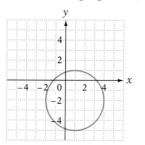

- The standard form of the equation is
  $(x - 1)^2 + [y - (-2)]^2 = 3^2$.
  Center: $(1, -2)$ Radius: 3

➡️ Find the equation of the circle with radius 4 and center $(-1, 2)$. Then sketch its graph.

$$(x - h)^2 + (y - k)^2 = r^2$$

$$[x - (-1)]^2 + (y - 2)^2 = 4^2$$
$$(x + 1)^2 + (y - 2)^2 = 16$$

- Use the standard form of the equation of a circle.
- Replace *r* by 4, *h* by −1, and *k* by 2.

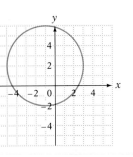

- Sketch the graph by drawing a circle with center $(-1, 2)$ and radius 4.

TAKE NOTE

Applying the vertical-line test reveals that the graph of a circle is not the graph of a function. The graph of a circle is the graph of a relation.

➡️ Find the equation of the circle that passes through the point whose coordinates are $(3, -4)$ and whose center is $(2, 1)$.

Because a point on the circle is known and the center is known, use the distance formula to find the radius of the circle.

$$r = \sqrt{(x_1 - x_2)^2 + (y_1 - y_2)^2}$$
$$= \sqrt{(3 - 2)^2 + (-4 - 1)^2}$$
$$= \sqrt{1^2 + (-5)^2}$$
$$= \sqrt{1 + 25}$$
$$= \sqrt{26}$$

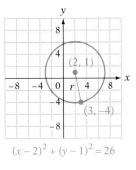

$$(x - 2)^2 + (y - 1)^2 = 26$$

Using $r = \sqrt{26}$ and $(h, k) = (2, 1)$, write the equation of the circle.
Note that $r^2 = (\sqrt{26})^2 = 26$.

$$(x - h)^2 + (y - k)^2 = r^2$$
$$(x - 2)^2 + (y - 1)^2 = 26$$

Example 1
Sketch a graph of $(x + 2)^2 + (y - 1)^2 = 4$.

Solution

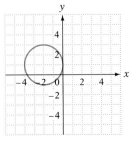

You Try It 1
Sketch a graph of $(x - 2)^2 + (y + 3)^2 = 9$.

Your solution

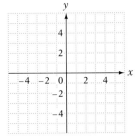

Solution on p. S31

Example 2

Find the equation of the circle with radius 5 and center $(-1, 3)$. Then sketch its graph.

Solution

$$(x - h)^2 + (y - k)^2 = r^2$$
$$[x - (-1)]^2 + (y - 3)^2 = 5^2$$
$$(x + 1)^2 + (y - 3)^2 = 25$$

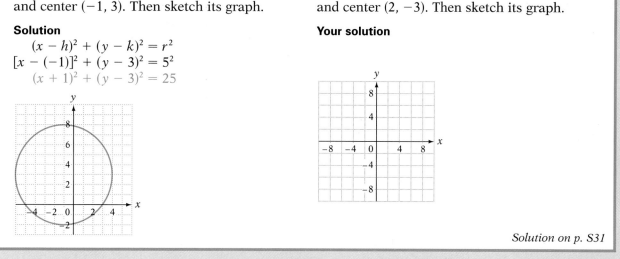

You Try It 2

Find the equation of the circle with radius 4 and center $(2, -3)$. Then sketch its graph.

Your solution

Solution on p. S31

Objective B   *To write the equation of a circle in standard form* .... 42 CT

The equation of a circle can also be expressed as $x^2 + y^2 + ax + by + c = 0$. This is called the **general form** of the equation of a circle. By completing the square, an equation in general form can be written in standard form.

➡ Find the center and the radius of a circle whose equation is given by $x^2 + y^2 + 4x + 2y + 1 = 0$. Then sketch its graph.

Write the equation in standard form by completing the square on x and y.

$$x^2 + y^2 + 4x + 2y + 1 = 0$$
$$x^2 + y^2 + 4x + 2y = -1$$

$$(x^2 + 4x) + (y^2 + 2y) = -1$$

$$(x^2 + 4x + 4) + (y^2 + 2y + 1) = -1 + 4 + 1$$

$$(x + 2)^2 + (y + 1)^2 = 4$$

- Subtract the constant term from each side of the equation.
- Rewrite the equation by grouping x terms and y terms.
- Complete the square on $x^2 + 4x$ and $y^2 + 2y$.
- Factor the trinomials.

The center is $(-2, -1)$; the radius is 2.

Example 3
Write the equation of the circle
$x^2 + y^2 - 4x + 2y + 4 = 0$ in standard form.
Then sketch its graph.

Solution

$$x^2 + y^2 - 4x + 2y + 4 = 0$$
$$(x^2 - 4x) + (y^2 + 2y) = -4$$
$$(x^2 - 4x + 4) + (y^2 + 2y + 1) = -4 + 4 + 1$$
$$(x - 2)^2 + (y + 1)^2 = 1$$

Center: $(2, -1)$ Radius: 1

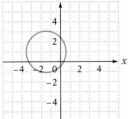

Example 4
Write the equation of the circle
$x^2 + y^2 + 3x - 2y = 1$ in standard form.
Then sketch its graph.

Solution

$$x^2 + y^2 + 3x - 2y = 1$$
$$(x^2 + 3x) + (y^2 - 2y) = 1$$
$$\left(x^2 + 3x + \frac{9}{4}\right) + (y^2 - 2y + 1) = 1 + \frac{9}{4} + 1$$
$$\left(x + \frac{3}{2}\right)^2 + (y - 1)^2 = \frac{17}{4}$$

Center: $\left(-\frac{3}{2}, 1\right)$ Radius: $\sqrt{\frac{17}{4}} = \frac{\sqrt{17}}{2}$

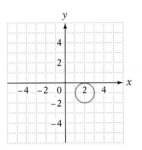

You Try It 3
Write the equation of the circle
$x^2 + y^2 - 2x - 15 = 0$ in standard form.
Then sketch its graph.

Your solution

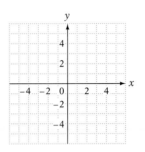

You Try It 4
Write the equation of the circle
$x^2 + y^2 - 4x + 8y + 15 = 0$ in standard
form. Then sketch its graph.

Your solution

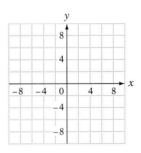

Solutions on pp. S31–S32

11.2 Exercises

· ·

Objective A

Sketch a graph of the circle given by each equation.

1. $(x - 2)^2 + (y + 2)^2 = 9$ **2.** $(x + 2)^2 + (y - 3)^2 = 16$ **3.** $(x + 3)^2 + (y - 1)^2 = 25$

4. $(x - 2)^2 + (y + 3)^2 = 4$ **5.** $(x + 2)^2 + (y + 2)^2 = 4$ **6.** $(x - 1)^2 + (y - 2)^2 = 25$

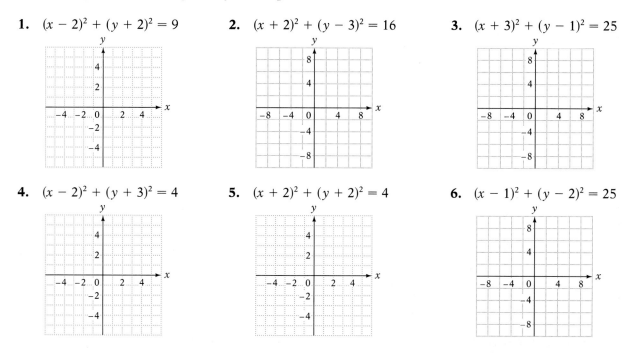

7. Find the equation of the circle with radius 2 and center $(2, -1)$. Then sketch its graph.

8. Find the equation of the circle with radius 3 and center $(-1, -2)$. Then sketch its graph.

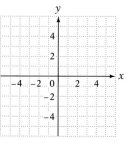

9. Find the equation of the circle that passes through the point $(1, 2)$ and whose center is $(-1, 1)$. Then sketch its graph.

10. Find the equation of the circle that passes through the point $(-1, 3)$ and whose center is $(-2, 1)$. Then sketch its graph.

Objective B

Write the equation of the circle in standard form. Then sketch its graph.

11. $x^2 + y^2 - 2x + 4y - 20 = 0$

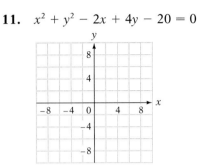

12. $x^2 + y^2 - 4x + 8y + 4 = 0$

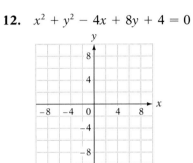

13. $x^2 + y^2 + 6x + 8y + 9 = 0$

14. $x^2 + y^2 - 6x + 10y + 25 = 0$

15. $x^2 + y^2 - 2x + 2y - 23 = 0$

16. $x^2 + y^2 - 6x + 4y + 9 = 0$

APPLYING THE CONCEPTS

17. Find the equation of a circle that has center $(4, 0)$ and passes through the origin.

18. Find the equation of a circle that has a diameter with endpoints $(-2, 4)$ and $(2, -2)$.

19. The radius of a sphere is 12 in. What is the radius of the circle that is formed by the intersection of a plane and the sphere at a point 6 in. from the center of the sphere?

20. Find the equation of the circle with center at $(3, 3)$ if the circle is tangent to the x-axis.

21. Is $x^2 + y^2 + 4x + 8y + 24 = 0$ the equation of a circle? If not, explain why. If it is, find the radius and the coordinates of the center.

11.3 The Ellipse and the Hyperbola

Objective A   To graph an ellipse with center at the origin ....

The orbits of the planets around the sun are "oval" shaped. This oval shape can be described as an **ellipse,** which is another of the conic sections.

There are two **axes of symmetry** for an ellipse. The intersection of these two axes is the **center** of the ellipse.

An ellipse with center at the origin is shown at the right. Note that there are two x-intercepts and two y-intercepts.

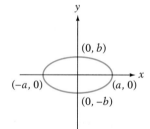

POINT OF INTEREST

The word *ellipse* comes from the Greek word *ellipsis*, which means "deficient." The method by which the early Greeks analyzed the conics caused a certain area in the construction of the ellipse to be less than another area (deficient). The word *ellipsis* in English, meaning "omission," has the same Greek root as the word *ellipse*.

> **The Standard Form of the Equation of an Ellipse with Center at the Origin**
>
> The equation of an ellipse with center at the origin is
> $$\frac{x^2}{a^2} + \frac{y^2}{b^2} = 1.$$
>
> The x-intercepts are $(a, 0)$ and $(-a, 0)$. The y-intercepts are $(0, b)$ and $(0, -b)$.

By finding the x- and y-intercepts for an ellipse and using the fact that the ellipse is oval-shaped, we can sketch a graph of an ellipse.

➡ Sketch the graph of the ellipse whose equation is $\dfrac{x^2}{9} + \dfrac{y^2}{4} = 1$.

The x-intercepts are $(3, 0)$ and $(-3, 0)$.
The y-intercepts are $(0, 2)$ and $(0, -2)$.

• $a^2 = 9, b^2 = 4$

• Use the intercepts and symmetry to sketch the graph of the ellipse.

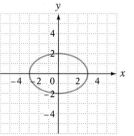

Using the vertical-line test, we find that the graph of an ellipse is not the graph of a function. The graph of an ellipse is the graph of a relation.

⇨ Sketch a graph of the ellipse whose equation is $\frac{x^2}{16} + \frac{y^2}{16} = 1$.

The x-intercepts are $(4, 0)$ and $(-4, 0)$.
The y-intercepts are $(0, 4)$ and $(0, -4)$.

• $a^2 = 16,\ b^2 = 16$

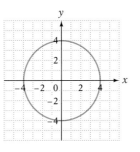

• Use the intercepts and symmetry to sketch the graph of the ellipse.

POINT OF INTEREST

For a circle, $a = b$ and thus $\frac{a}{b} = 1$. Early Greek astronomers thought that each planet had a circular orbit. Today, we know that the planets have elliptical orbits. However, in most cases, the ellipse is very nearly a circle.

For Earth, $\frac{a}{b} \approx 1.00014$. The most elliptical orbit is Pluto's, for which $\frac{a}{b} \approx 1.0328$.

The graph in this last example is the graph of a circle. A circle is a special case of an ellipse. It occurs when $a^2 = b^2$ in the equation $\frac{x^2}{a^2} + \frac{y^2}{b^2} = 1$.

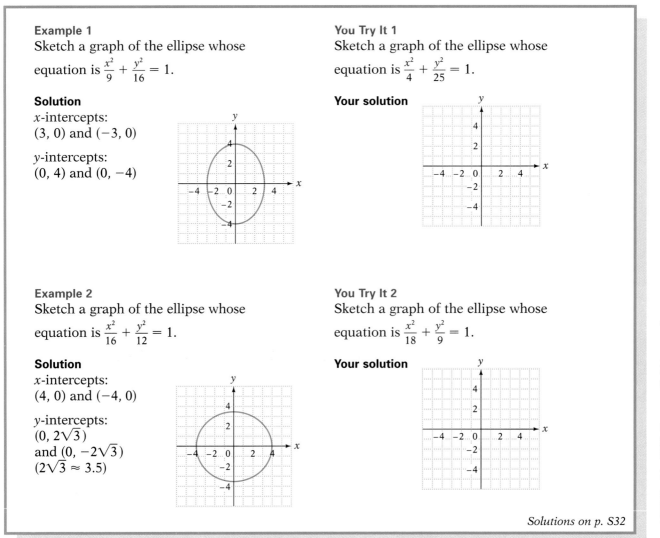

Example 1
Sketch a graph of the ellipse whose equation is $\frac{x^2}{9} + \frac{y^2}{16} = 1$.

Solution
x-intercepts:
$(3, 0)$ and $(-3, 0)$

y-intercepts:
$(0, 4)$ and $(0, -4)$

You Try It 1
Sketch a graph of the ellipse whose equation is $\frac{x^2}{4} + \frac{y^2}{25} = 1$.

Your solution

Example 2
Sketch a graph of the ellipse whose equation is $\frac{x^2}{16} + \frac{y^2}{12} = 1$.

Solution
x-intercepts:
$(4, 0)$ and $(-4, 0)$

y-intercepts:
$(0, 2\sqrt{3})$
and $(0, -2\sqrt{3})$
$(2\sqrt{3} \approx 3.5)$

You Try It 2
Sketch a graph of the ellipse whose equation is $\frac{x^2}{18} + \frac{y^2}{9} = 1$.

Your solution

Solutions on p. S32

Objective B   ***To graph a hyperbola with center at the origin*** ....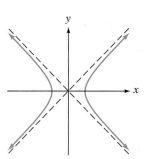

A **hyperbola** is a conic section that can be formed by the intersection of a cone and a plane perpendicular to the base of the cone.

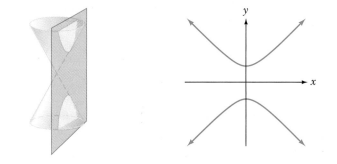

The hyperbola has two **vertices** and an **axis of symmetry** that passes through the vertices. The **center** of a hyperbola is the point halfway between the two vertices.

The graphs at the right show two possible graphs of a hyperbola with center at the origin.

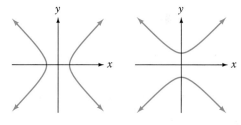

In the first graph, an axis of symmetry is the *x*-axis and the vertices are *x*-intercepts.

In the second graph, an axis of symmetry is the *y*-axis and the vertices are *y*-intercepts.

Note that in either case, the graph of a hyperbola is not the graph of a function. The graph of a hyperbola is the graph of a relation.

> **The Standard Form of the Equation of a Hyperbola with Center at the Origin**
>
> The equation of a hyperbola for which an axis of symmetry is the *x*-axis is $\dfrac{x^2}{a^2} - \dfrac{y^2}{b^2} = 1$. The vertices are $(a, 0)$ and $(-a, 0)$.
>
> The equation of a hyperbola for which an axis of symmetry is the *y*-axis is $\dfrac{y^2}{b^2} - \dfrac{x^2}{a^2} = 1$. The vertices are $(0, b)$ and $(0, -b)$.

To sketch a hyperbola, it is helpful to draw two lines that are "approached" by the hyperbola. These two lines are called **asymptotes.** As the hyperbola gets farther from the origin, the hyperbola "gets closer to" the asymptotes.

Because the asymptotes are straight lines, their equations are linear equations. The equations of the asymptotes for a hyperbola with center at the origin are $y = \dfrac{b}{a}x$ and $y = -\dfrac{b}{a}x$.

POINT OF INTEREST

Hyperbolas are used in LORAN (LOng RAnge Navigation) as a method for a ship's navigator to determine the position of the ship. They are also used as mirrors in some telescopes to focus incoming light as shown in the figure below.

➡ Sketch a graph of the hyperbola whose equation is $\frac{y^2}{9} - \frac{x^2}{4} = 1$.

An axis of symmetry is the y-axis.
The vertices are $(0, 3)$ and $(0, -3)$.

The asymptotes are $y = \frac{3}{2}x$ and $y = -\frac{3}{2}x$.

- $b^2 = 9$, $a^2 = 4$

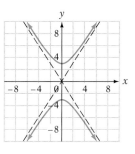

- Sketch the asymptotes. Use symmetry and the fact that the hyperbola will approach the asymptotes to sketch the graph.

Example 3
Sketch a graph of the hyperbola whose equation is $\frac{x^2}{16} - \frac{y^2}{4} = 1$.

Solution
Axis of symmetry:
x-axis

Vertices:
$(4, 0)$ and $(-4, 0)$

Asymptotes:
$y = \frac{1}{2}x$ and $y = -\frac{1}{2}x$

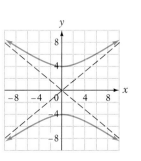

You Try It 3
Sketch a graph of the hyperbola whose equation is $\frac{x^2}{9} - \frac{y^2}{25} = 1$.

Your solution

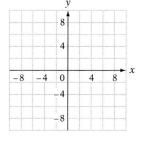

Example 4
Sketch a graph of the hyperbola whose equation is $\frac{y^2}{16} - \frac{x^2}{25} = 1$.

Solution
Axis of symmetry:
y-axis

Vertices:
$(0, 4)$ and $(0, -4)$

Asymptotes:
$y = \frac{4}{5}x$ and $y = -\frac{4}{5}x$

You Try It 4
Sketch a graph of the hyperbola whose equation is $\frac{y^2}{9} - \frac{x^2}{9} = 1$.

Your solution

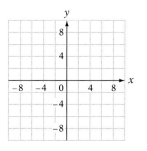

Solutions on p. S32

11.3 Exercises

Objective A

Sketch a graph of the ellipse given by each equation.

1. $\dfrac{x^2}{4} + \dfrac{y^2}{9} = 1$

2. $\dfrac{x^2}{25} + \dfrac{y^2}{16} = 1$

3. $\dfrac{x^2}{25} + \dfrac{y^2}{9} = 1$

4. $\dfrac{x^2}{16} + \dfrac{y^2}{9} = 1$

5. $\dfrac{x^2}{36} + \dfrac{y^2}{16} = 1$

6. $\dfrac{x^2}{49} + \dfrac{y^2}{64} = 1$

7. $\dfrac{x^2}{16} + \dfrac{y^2}{49} = 1$

8. $\dfrac{x^2}{25} + \dfrac{y^2}{36} = 1$

9. $\dfrac{x^2}{4} + \dfrac{y^2}{25} = 1$

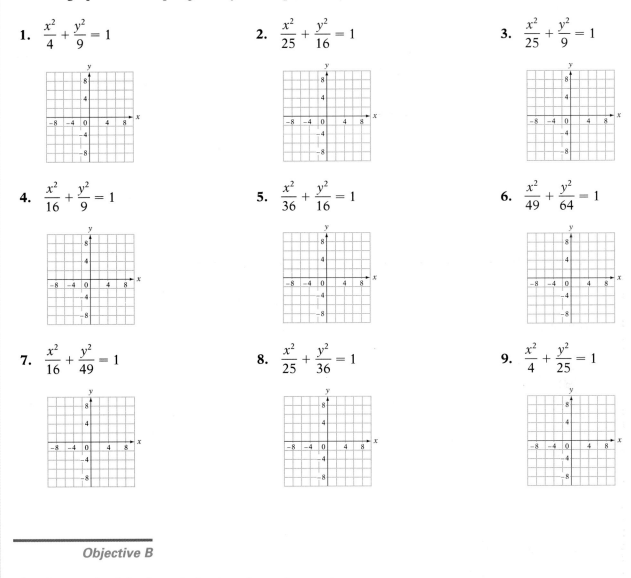

Objective B

Sketch a graph of the hyperbola given by each equation.

10. $\dfrac{x^2}{9} - \dfrac{y^2}{16} = 1$

11. $\dfrac{x^2}{25} - \dfrac{y^2}{4} = 1$

12. $\dfrac{y^2}{16} - \dfrac{x^2}{9} = 1$

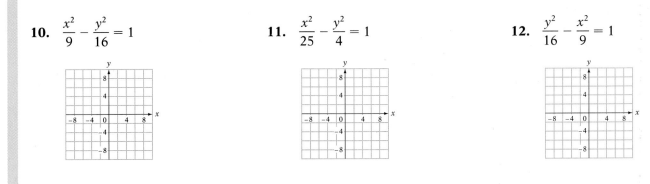

13. $\dfrac{y^2}{16} - \dfrac{x^2}{25} = 1$

14. $\dfrac{x^2}{16} - \dfrac{y^2}{4} = 1$

15. $\dfrac{x^2}{9} - \dfrac{y^2}{49} = 1$

16. $\dfrac{y^2}{25} - \dfrac{x^2}{9} = 1$

17. $\dfrac{y^2}{4} - \dfrac{x^2}{16} = 1$

18. $\dfrac{x^2}{4} - \dfrac{y^2}{25} = 1$

19. $\dfrac{x^2}{36} - \dfrac{y^2}{9} = 1$

20. $\dfrac{y^2}{9} - \dfrac{x^2}{36} = 1$

21. $\dfrac{y^2}{25} - \dfrac{x^2}{4} = 1$

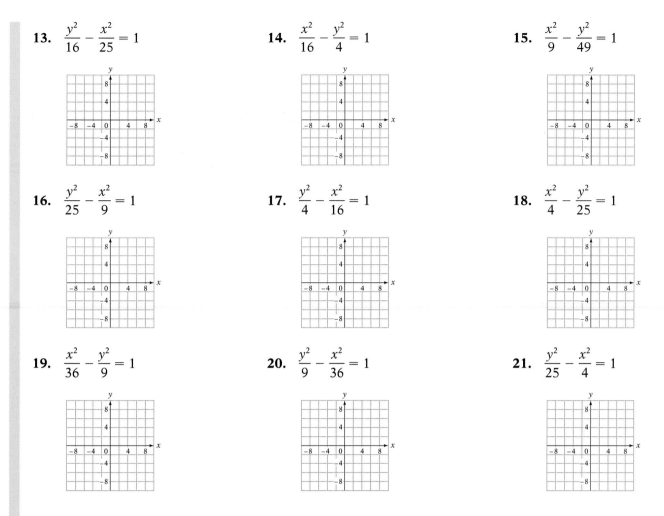

APPLYING THE CONCEPTS

For each of the following, write the equation in standard form. Identify the graph, and then graph the equation.

22. $4x^2 + 9y^2 = 36$

23. $16x^2 + 25y^2 = 400$

24. $9y^2 - 16x^2 = 144$

25. $25y^2 - 4x^2 = -100$

11.4 Solving Nonlinear Systems of Equations

Objective A   *To solve a nonlinear system of equations* .... CT

A **nonlinear system of equations** is one in which one or more of the equations are not linear equations. A nonlinear system of equations can be solved by using either a substitution method or an addition method.

⇒ Solve: $2x - y = 4$ (1)
$\quad\quad\quad y^2 = 4x$ (2)

When a nonlinear system of equations contains a linear equation, the substitution method is used.

Solve Equation (1) for y.

$2x - y = 4$
$\quad -y = -2x + 4$
$\quad\quad y = 2x - 4$

Substitute $2x - 4$ for y into equation (2).

$$y^2 = 4x$$
$$(2x - 4)^2 = 4x \quad\quad \bullet\ y = 2x - 4$$

$4x^2 - 16x + 16 = 4x \quad\quad \bullet\ \text{Solve for } x.$
$4x^2 - 20x + 16 = 0$

$\quad 4(x^2 - 5x + 4) = 0$
$4(x - 4)(x - 1) = 0$

$x - 4 = 0 \quad\quad x - 1 = 0$
$\quad x = 4 \quad\quad\quad\quad x = 1$

Substitute the values of x into the equation $y = 2x - 4$ and solve for y.

$y = 2x - 4 \quad\quad\quad\quad y = 2x - 4$
$y = 2(4) - 4 \quad \bullet\ x = 4 \quad\quad y = 2(1) - 4 \quad \bullet\ x = 1$
$y = 4 \quad\quad\quad\quad\quad\quad\quad y = -2$

The solutions are $(4, 4)$ and $(1, -2)$.

The graph of this system of equations is shown at the right. The graph of the line intersects the parabola at two points. The coordinates of these points are the solutions of the system of equations.

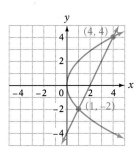

⇒ Solve: $x^2 + y^2 = 4$ (1)

            $y = x + 3$ (2)

Use the substitution method.

Substitute the expression for y into Equation (1).

$$x^2 + y^2 = 4$$
$$x^2 + (x + 3)^2 = 4 \qquad \bullet \; y = x + 3$$

$$x^2 + x^2 + 6x + 9 = 4 \qquad \bullet \; \text{Solve for } x.$$
$$2x^2 + 6x + 5 = 0$$

Consider the discriminant of $2x^2 + 6x + 5 = 0$.

$b^2 - 4ac$

$6^2 - 4 \cdot 2 \cdot 5 = 36 - 40 = -4 \qquad \bullet \; a = 2, b = 6, c = 5$

Because the discriminant is less than zero, the equation $2x^2 + 6x + 5 = 0$ has two complex number solutions. Therefore the system of equations has no real number solutions.

The graphs of the equations of this system are shown at the right. Note that the two graphs do not intersect.

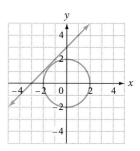

⇒ Solve: $4x^2 + y^2 = 16$ (1)

            $x^2 + y^2 = 4$ (2)

Use the addition method.

$$4x^2 + y^2 = 16$$
$$\underline{-x^2 - y^2 = -4} \qquad \bullet \; \text{Multiply Equation (2) by } -1.$$
$$3x^2 = 12 \qquad \bullet \; \text{Add the equations.}$$

Solve for x.

$$x^2 = 4$$
$$x = \pm 2$$

Substitute the values of x into Equation (2) and solve for y.

$$
\begin{array}{ll}
x^2 + y^2 = 4 & \qquad x^2 + y^2 = 4 \\
2^2 + y^2 = 4 \quad \bullet \; x = 2 & \qquad (-2)^2 + y^2 = 4 \quad \bullet \; x = -2 \\
y^2 = 0 & \qquad y^2 = 0 \\
y = 0 & \qquad y = 0
\end{array}
$$

The solutions are $(2, 0)$ and $(-2, 0)$.

The graphs of the equations in this system are shown at the right. Note that the graphs intersect at the points whose coordinates are $(2, 0)$ and $(-2, 0)$.

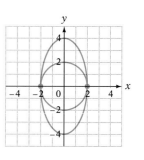

⇒ Solve: $2x^2 - y^2 = 1$ (1)
$\qquad\quad x^2 + 2y^2 = 18$ (2)

Use the addition method.

$$4x^2 - 2y^2 = 2$$
$$\underline{x^2 + 2y^2 = 18}$$

• **Multiply Equation (1) by 2.**

$$5x^2 = 20$$

• **Add the equations.**

$$x^2 = 4$$

• **Solve for x.**

$$x = \pm 2$$

Substitute the values of x into one of the equations and solve for y. Equation (2) is used here.

$$x^2 + 2y^2 = 18$$
$$2^2 + 2y^2 = 18$$

• **x = 2**

$$2y^2 = 14$$
$$y^2 = 7$$
$$y = \pm\sqrt{7}$$

$$x^2 + 2y^2 = 18$$
$$(-2)^2 + 2y^2 = 18$$

• **x = −2**

$$2y^2 = 14$$
$$y^2 = 7$$
$$y = \pm\sqrt{7}$$

The solutions are $(2, \sqrt{7})$, $(2, -\sqrt{7})$, $(-2, \sqrt{7})$, and $(-2, -\sqrt{7})$.

The graphs of the equations in this system are shown at the right. Note that there are four points of intersection.

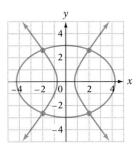

Note from the previous three examples that the number of points at which the graphs of the equations of the system intersect is the same as the number of real number solutions of the system of equations.

Example 1 Solve: (1) $y = 2x^2 - 3x - 1$
(2) $y = x^2 - 2x + 5$

Solution Use the substitution method.

$$y = x^2 - 2x + 5$$
$$2x^2 - 3x - 1 = x^2 - 2x + 5$$
$$x^2 - x - 6 = 0$$
$$(x - 3)(x + 2) = 0$$

$$x - 3 = 0 \qquad x + 2 = 0$$
$$x = 3 \qquad x = -2$$

Substitute each value of x into Equation (1).

$$y = 2x^2 - 3x - 1$$
$$y = 2(3)^2 - 3(3) - 1$$
$$y = 18 - 9 - 1$$
$$y = 8$$

$$y = 2x^2 - 3x - 1$$
$$y = 2(-2)^2 - 3(-2) - 1$$
$$y = 8 + 6 - 1$$
$$y = 13$$

The solutions are $(3, 8)$ and $(-2, 13)$.

You Try It 1 Solve: $y = 2x^2 + x - 3$
$y = 2x^2 - 2x + 9$

Your solution

Example 2 Solve: (1) $3x^2 - 2y^2 = 26$
(2) $x^2 - y^2 = 5$

Solution Use the addition method.
Multiply Equation (2) by -2.

$$-2x^2 + 2y^2 = -10$$
$$3x^2 - 2y^2 = 26$$
$$x^2 = 16$$
$$x = \pm\sqrt{16} = \pm 4$$

Substitute each value of x into Equation (2).

$$x^2 - y^2 = 5 \qquad\qquad x^2 - y^2 = 5$$
$$4^2 - y^2 = 5 \qquad\qquad (-4)^2 - y^2 = 5$$
$$16 - y^2 = 5 \qquad\qquad 16 - y^2 = 5$$
$$-y^2 = -11 \qquad\qquad -y^2 = -11$$
$$y^2 = 11 \qquad\qquad y^2 = 11$$
$$y = \pm\sqrt{11} \qquad\qquad y = \pm\sqrt{11}$$

The solutions are $(4, \sqrt{11})$, $(4, -\sqrt{11})$, $(-4, \sqrt{11})$, and $(-4, -\sqrt{11})$.

You Try It 2 Solve: $x^2 - y^2 = 10$
$x^2 + y^2 = 8$

Your solution

Solutions on p. S32

11.4 Exercises

· ·

Objective A

Solve.

1. $y = x^2 - x - 1$
$y = 2x + 9$

2. $y = x^2 - 3x + 1$
$y = x + 6$

3. $y^2 = -x + 3$
$x - y = 1$

4. $y^2 = 4x$
$x - y = -1$

5. $y^2 = 2x$
$x + 2y = -2$

6. $y^2 = 2x$
$x - y = 4$

7. $x^2 + 2y^2 = 12$
$2x - y = 2$

8. $x^2 + 4y^2 = 37$
$x - y = -4$

9. $x^2 + y^2 = 13$
$x + y = 5$

10. $x^2 + y^2 = 16$
$x - 2y = -4$

11. $4x^2 + y^2 = 12$
$y = 4x^2$

12. $2x^2 + y^2 = 6$
$y = 2x^2$

13. $y = x^2 - 2x - 3$
$y = x - 6$

14. $y = x^2 + 4x + 5$
$y = -x - 3$

15. $3x^2 - y^2 = -1$
$x^2 + 4y^2 = 17$

16. $x^2 + y^2 = 10$
$x^2 + 9y^2 = 18$

17. $2x^2 + 3y^2 = 30$
$x^2 + y^2 = 13$

18. $x^2 + y^2 = 61$
$x^2 - y^2 = 11$

19. $y = 2x^2 - x + 1$
$y = x^2 - x + 5$

20. $y = -x^2 + x - 1$
$y = x^2 + 2x - 2$

21. $2x^2 + 3y^2 = 24$
$x^2 - y^2 = 7$

22. $2x^2 + 3y^2 = 21$
$x^2 + 2y^2 = 12$

23. $x^2 + y^2 = 36$
$4x^2 + 9y^2 = 36$

24. $2x^2 + 3y^2 = 12$
$x^2 - y^2 = 25$

25. $11x^2 - 2y^2 = 4$
$3x^2 + y^2 = 15$

26. $x^2 + 4y^2 = 25$
$x^2 - y^2 = 5$

27. $2x^2 - y^2 = 7$
$2x - y = 5$

28. $3x^2 + 4y^2 = 7$
$x - 2y = -3$

29. $y = 3x^2 + x - 4$
$y = 3x^2 - 8x + 5$

30. $y = 2x^2 + 3x + 1$
$y = 2x^2 + 9x + 7$

31. $x = y + 3$
$x^2 + y^2 = 5$

32. $x - y = -6$
$x^2 + y^2 = 4$

33. $y = x^2 + 4x + 4$
$x + 2y = 4$

APPLYING THE CONCEPTS

34. Give the maximum number of points in which the following pairs of graphs can intersect.
a. A line and an ellipse.
b. A line and a parabola.
c. Two ellipses with centers at the origin.
d. Two different circles with centers at the origin.
e. Two hyperbolas with centers at the origin.

Solve by graphing. Approximate the solutions of the systems to the nearest thousandth.

35. $y = 2^x$
$x + y = 3$

36. $y = 3^{-x}$
$x^2 + y^2 = 9$

37. $y = \log_2 x$
$\dfrac{x^2}{9} + \dfrac{y^2}{1} = 1$

38. $y = \log_3 x$
$x^2 + y^2 = 4$

39. $y = -\log_3 x$
$x + y = 4$

40. $y = \left(\dfrac{1}{2}\right)^x$
$\dfrac{x^2}{9} + \dfrac{y^2}{4} = 1$

11.5 Quadratic Inequalities and Systems of Inequalities

Objective A   *To graph the solution set of a quadratic inequality in two variables* .... **CT**

The **graph of a quadratic inequality in two variables** is a region of the plane that is bounded by one of the conic sections (parabola, circle, ellipse, or hyperbola). When graphing an inequality of this type, first replace the inequality symbol with an equals sign. Graph the resulting conic using a dashed curve when the original inequality is less than (<) or greater than (>). Use a solid curve when the original inequality is $\leq$ or $\geq$. Use the point $(0, 0)$ to determine which region of the plane to shade. If $(0, 0)$ is a solution of the inequality, then shade the region of the plane containing $(0, 0)$. If not, shade the other portion of the plane.

➡ Graph the solution set: $x^2 + y^2 > 9$

Change the inequality to an equality.

$x^2 + y^2 = 9$

This is the equation of a circle with center $(0, 0)$ and radius 3.

The inequality is >, so the graph is drawn as a dotted circle.

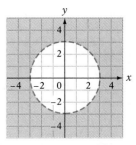

Substitute the point $(0, 0)$ in the inequality. Because $0^2 + 0^2 > 9$ is not true, the point $(0, 0)$ should not be in the shaded region.

Not all inequalities will result in shading a region of the plane. For example, the inequality

$$\frac{x^2}{9} + \frac{y^2}{4} < -1$$

has no ordered-pair solutions. The solution set is the empty set, and no region of the plane is shaded.

➡ Graph the solution set: $y \leq x^2 + 2x + 2$

Change the inequality to an equality.

$y = x^2 + 2x + 2$

This is the equation of a parabola that opens up. The vertex is $(-1, 1)$ and the axis of symmetry is the line $x = -1$.

The inequality is $\leq$, so the graph is drawn as a solid line.

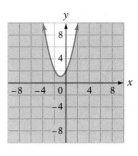

Substitute the point $(0, 0)$ into the inequality. Because $0 \leq 0^2 + 2(0) + 2$ is true, the point $(0, 0)$ should be in the shaded region.

➡ Graph the solution set: $\dfrac{y^2}{9} - \dfrac{x^2}{4} \geq 1$

Write the inequality as an equality.

$$\dfrac{y^2}{9} - \dfrac{x^2}{4} = 1$$

This is the equation of a hyperbola. The vertices are $(0, -3)$ and $(0, 3)$. The equations of the asymptotes are $y = \dfrac{3}{2}x$ and $y = -\dfrac{3}{2}x$.

The inequality is $\geq$, so the graph is drawn as a solid line.

Substitute the point $(0, 0)$ into the inequality. Because $\dfrac{0^2}{9} - \dfrac{0^2}{4} \geq 1$ is not true, the point $(0, 0)$ should not be in the shaded region.

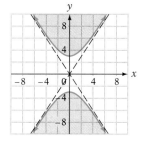

Example 1

Graph the solution set: $\dfrac{x^2}{9} + \dfrac{y^2}{16} \leq 1$

Solution
Graph the ellipse
$\dfrac{x^2}{9} + \dfrac{y^2}{16} = 1$ as a
solid line.

Shade the region
of the plane that
includes $(0, 0)$.

You Try It 1

Graph the solution set: $\dfrac{x^2}{9} - \dfrac{y^2}{16} \leq 1$

Your solution

Example 2
Graph the solution set: $x > y^2 - 4y + 2$

Solution
Graph the
parabola
$x = y^2 - 4y + 2$
as a dashed curve.

Shade the region
that does not
include $(0, 0)$.

You Try It 2

Graph the solution set: $\dfrac{x^2}{16} + \dfrac{y^2}{4} \geq 1$

Your solution

Solutions on p. S33

Objective B **To graph the solution set of a nonlinear system**
of inequalities ....

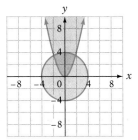

Recall that the solution set of a system of inequalities is the intersection of the solution sets of the individual inequalities. To graph the solution set of a system of inequalities, first graph the solution set for each inequality. The solution set of the system of inequalities is the region of the plane represented by the intersection of the two shaded regions.

⇒ Graph the solution set: $x^2 + y^2 \le 16$
$$y \ge x^2$$

Graph the solution set of each inequality.

$x^2 + y^2 = 16$ is the equation of a circle with a radius of 4. Because the inequality is ≤, use a solid line.

$y = x^2$ is the equation of a parabola that opens upward. Because the inequality is ≥, use a solid line.

Substitute the point (0, 0) into the inequality $x^2 + y^2 \le 16$. $0^2 + 0^2 \le 16$ is a true statement. Shade inside the circle.

Substitute (2, 0) into the inequality $y = x^2$. [We cannot use (0, 0), a point on the parabola.] $0 > 4$ is a false statement. Shade inside the parabola.

The solution is the intersection of the two shaded regions.

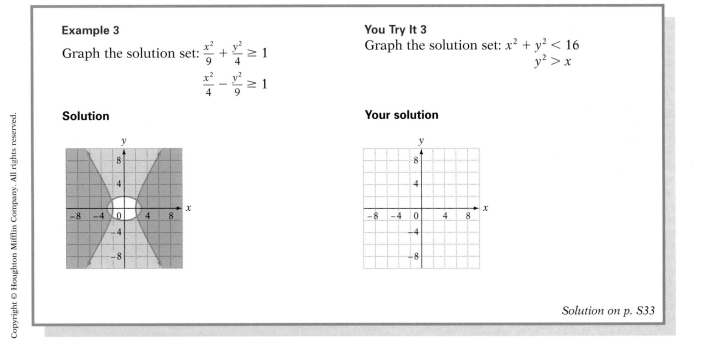

Example 3

Graph the solution set: $\dfrac{x^2}{9} + \dfrac{y^2}{4} \ge 1$

$$\dfrac{x^2}{4} - \dfrac{y^2}{9} \ge 1$$

Solution

You Try It 3

Graph the solution set: $x^2 + y^2 < 16$
$$y^2 > x$$

Your solution

Solution on p. S33

Example 4

Graph the solution set: $y \geq x^2$
$$y \leq x + 2$$

Solution

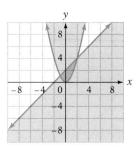

You Try It 4

Graph the solution set: $\dfrac{x^2}{4} + \dfrac{y^2}{9} \leq 1$
$$x > y^2 - 2$$

Your solution

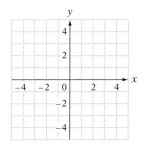

Example 5

Graph the solution set: $\dfrac{x^2}{9} - \dfrac{y^2}{16} \geq 1$
$$x^2 + y^2 \leq 4$$

Solution

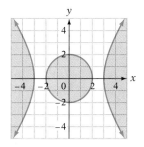

The solution sets of the two inequalities do not intersect. This system of inequalities has no real number solution.

You Try It 5

Graph the solution set: $\dfrac{x^2}{16} + \dfrac{y^2}{25} \geq 1$
$$x^2 + y^2 < 9$$

Your solution

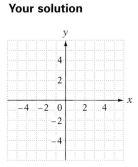

Solutions on p. S33

11.5 Exercises

Objective A

Graph the solution set.

1. $y \le x^2 - 4x + 3$

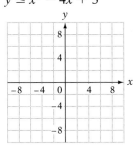

2. $y < x^2 - 2x - 3$

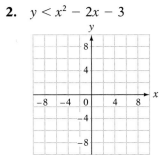

3. $(x - 1)^2 + (y + 2)^2 \le 9$

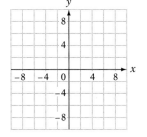

4. $(x + 2)^2 + (y - 3)^2 > 4$

5. $(x + 3)^2 + (y - 2)^2 \ge 9$

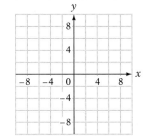

6. $(x - 2)^2 + (y + 1)^2 \le 16$

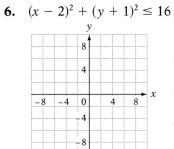

7. $\dfrac{x^2}{16} + \dfrac{y^2}{25} < 1$

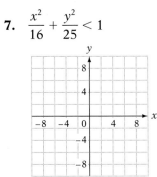

8. $\dfrac{x^2}{9} + \dfrac{y^2}{4} \ge 1$

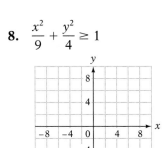

9. $\dfrac{x^2}{25} - \dfrac{y^2}{9} \le 1$

10. $\dfrac{y^2}{25} - \dfrac{x^2}{36} > 1$

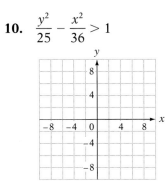

11. $\dfrac{x^2}{4} + \dfrac{y^2}{16} \ge 1$

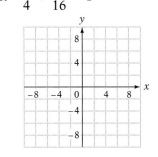

12. $\dfrac{x^2}{4} - \dfrac{y^2}{16} \le 1$

13. $y \le x^2 - 2x + 3$

14. $x \le y^2 + 2y + 1$

15. $\dfrac{y^2}{9} - \dfrac{x^2}{16} \le 1$

16. $\dfrac{x^2}{16} - \dfrac{y^2}{4} < 1$

17. $\dfrac{x^2}{9} + \dfrac{y^2}{1} \le 1$

18. $\dfrac{x^2}{16} + \dfrac{y^2}{4} > 1$

19. $(x - 1)^2 + (x + 3)^2 \le 25$

20. $(x + 1)^2 + (y - 2)^2 \ge 16$

21. $\dfrac{y^2}{25} - \dfrac{x^2}{4} \le 1$

22. $\dfrac{x^2}{9} - \dfrac{y^2}{25} \ge 1$

23. $\dfrac{x^2}{25} + \dfrac{y^2}{9} \le 1$

24. $\dfrac{x^2}{36} + \dfrac{y^2}{4} \le 1$

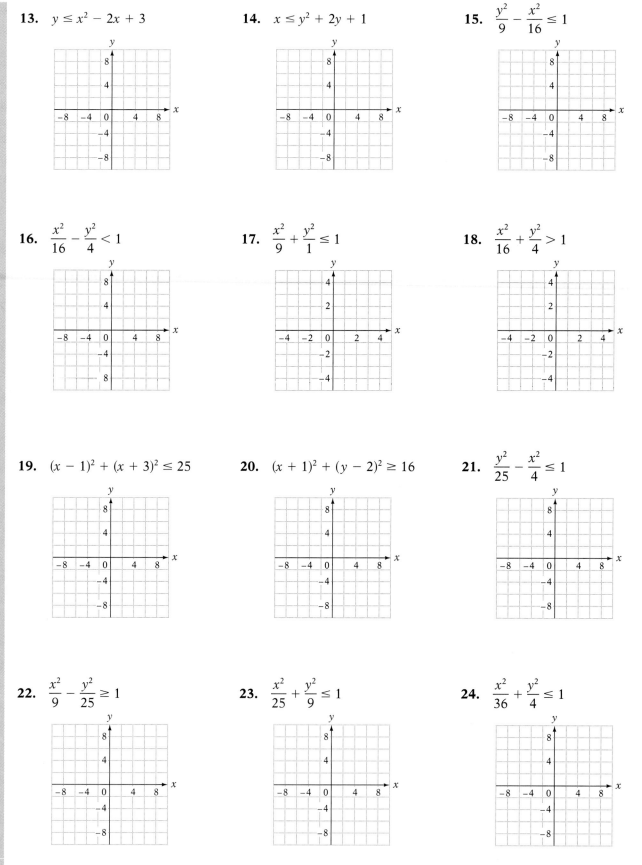

_____

Objective B

Graph the solution set.

25. $y \le (x - 2)^2$
$y + x > 4$

26. $x^2 + y^2 < 1$
$x + y \ge 4$

27. $x^2 + y^2 < 16$
$y > x + 1$

28. $y > x^2 - 4$
$y < x - 2$

29. $\dfrac{x^2}{4} + \dfrac{y^2}{16} \le 1$

$y \le -\dfrac{1}{2}x + 2$

30. $\dfrac{y^2}{4} - \dfrac{x^2}{25} \ge 1$

$y \le \dfrac{2}{3}x + 4$

31. $x \ge y^2 - 3y + 2$
$y \ge 2x - 2$

32. $x^2 + y^2 \le 25$

$y \le -\dfrac{1}{3}x + 2$

33. $x^2 + y^2 < 25$
$\dfrac{x^2}{9} + \dfrac{y^2}{36} < 1$

34. $\dfrac{x^2}{9} - \dfrac{y^2}{4} < 1$

$\dfrac{x^2}{25} + \dfrac{y^2}{9} < 1$

35. $x^2 + y^2 > 4$
$x^2 + y^2 < 25$

36. $\dfrac{x^2}{25} + \dfrac{y^2}{16} \le 1$

$\dfrac{x^2}{4} + \dfrac{y^2}{4} \ge 1$

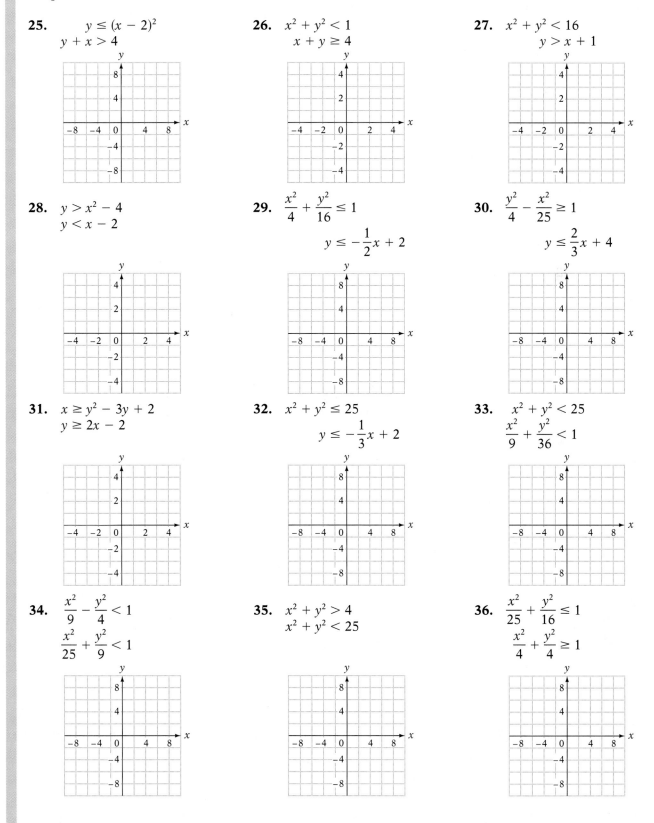

APPLYING THE CONCEPTS

Graph the solution set.

37. $y > x^2 - 3$
$y < x + 3$
$x \leq 0$

38. $x^2 + y^2 \leq 25$
$y > x + 1$
$x \geq 0$

39. $x^2 + y^2 < 3$
$x > y^2 - 1$
$y \geq 0$

40. $\dfrac{x^2}{4} - \dfrac{y^2}{25} \leq 1$
$\dfrac{x^2}{4} + \dfrac{y^2}{4} \leq 1$
$y \geq 0$

41. $\dfrac{x^2}{16} + \dfrac{y^2}{4} \leq 1$
$x^2 + y^2 \leq 4$
$x \geq 0$
$y \leq 0$

42. $\dfrac{x^2}{4} + \dfrac{y^2}{25} \leq 1$
$x > y^2 - 4$
$x \leq 0$
$y \geq 0$

43. $y > 2^x$
$x + y < 4$

44. $y < \left(\dfrac{1}{2}\right)^x$
$2x - y \geq 2$

45. $y \geq \log_2 x$
$x^2 + y^2 < 9$

46. $y \leq -\log_3 x$
$\dfrac{x^2}{9} + \dfrac{y^2}{4} < 1$

47. $y < 3^{-x}$
$\dfrac{x^2}{4} - \dfrac{y^2}{1} \geq 1$

48. $y \geq 2^{x-1}$
$2x + 3y > 6$

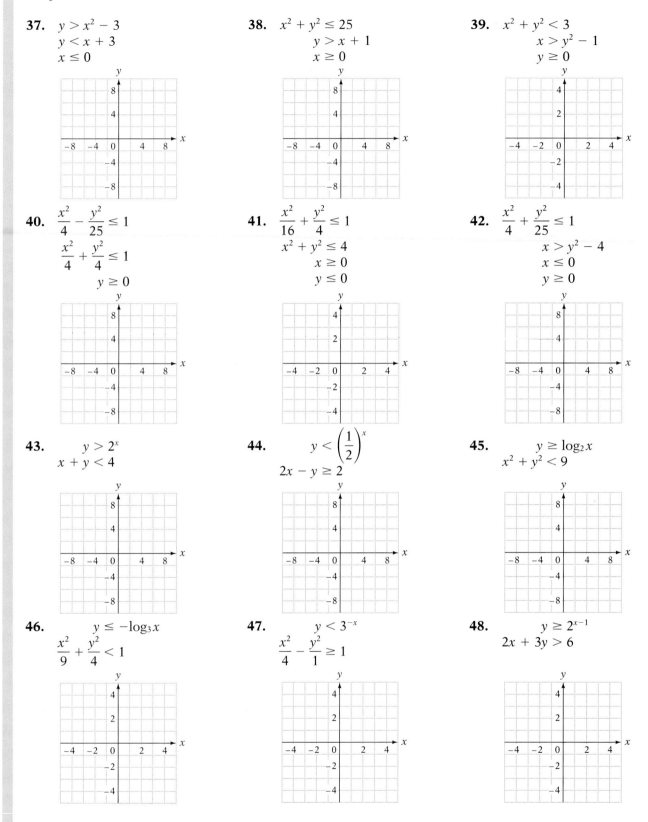

Focus on Problem Solving

Use a Variety of Problem-Solving Techniques

We have examined several problem-solving strategies throughout the text. See if you can apply those techniques to the following problems.

1. Eight coins look exactly alike, but one is lighter than the others. Explain how the different coin can be found in two weighings on a balance scale.

2. For the sequence of numbers 1, 1, 2, 3, 5, 8, 13, . . . , identify a possible pattern and then use that pattern to determine the next number in the sequence.

3. Arrange the numbers 1, 2, 3, 4, 5, 6, 7, 8, and 9 in the squares at the right so that the sum of any row, column, or diagonal is 15. (*Suggestion:* Note that 1, 5, 9; 2, 5, 8; 3, 5, 7; and 4, 5, 6 all add to 15. Because 5 is part of each sum, this suggests that 5 be placed in the center of the squares.)

4. A restaurant charges $10.00 for a pizza that has a diameter of 9 in. Determine the selling price of a pizza with a diameter of 18 in. so that the selling price per square inch is the same as for the 9-inch pizza.

5. You have a balance scale and weights of 1 g, 4 g, 8 g, and 16 g. Using only these weights, can you weigh something that weighs 7 g? 12 g? 14 g? 19 g?

6. Determine the number of possible paths from *A* to *B* for the grid at the right. A path consists of moves right or up along one of the grid lines.

7. Can the checkerboard at the right be covered with dominos (which look like ▢■) so that every square on the board is covered by a domino? Why or why not? (*Note:* The dominos cannot overlap.)

Projects and Group Activities

Finding the Proper Dosage

The elimination of a drug from the body usually occurs at a rate that is proportional to the amount of the drug in the body. This relationship, as a function of time, can be given by the formula

$$f(t) = Ae^{kt}$$

where A is the original dosage of the drug and $k = -\dfrac{\ln 2}{H}$, where H is the time for one-half of the drug to be eliminated.

The three graphs below show, respectively, one administration of a drug, repeated dosages in which the amount of the drug in the body remains relatively constant, and dosages in which the amount of the drug will increase with time.

The amount of a drug in the body after n time periods is given by

$$A + Ae^{kt} + Ae^{2kt} + \cdots + Ae^{nkt}$$

where t is the time between dosages.

The amount of a drug in the body at time t can be represented by

$$S = \frac{Ae^{kt}(1 - e^{nkt})}{1 - e^{kt}}$$

Over a period of time, with continuing dosages at periods of time t, the amount S may increase, decrease, or reach an equilibrium state, as shown in the diagram at the left.

To reach this equilibrium state, the original dosage A is reduced to some maintenance dosage M, given by the equation

$$M = A(1 - e^{nkt})$$

Solve.

1. Cancer cells have been exposed to x-rays. The number of surviving cells, $A(r)$, depends on the strength of the x-rays applied. Find the strength, r, of the x-rays (in roentgens) for 40% of the cancer cells to be destroyed. Use the equation $A(r) = A_0 e^{-0.2r}$.

2. Sodium pentobarbital is to be given to a patient for surgical anesthesia. The operation is assumed to last 0.5 h, and the half-life of the sodium pentobarbital is 2 h. The amount of anesthesia in the patient's system should not go below 500 mg. If only one dosage is to be given, find the initial dose of the sodium pentobarbital.

3. One dose of a drug increases the level of the drug in the blood by 0.5 mg/ml. The half-life of the drug is 8 h, and the dose is given every 4 h. Find the concentration of the drug just before the fourth dose.

4. A dosage of 50 mg of medication every 2 h for 8 h will achieve a desired level of medication.
   a. Find the level of medication after 8 h if the half-life of the medication is 5 h.
   b. Find the maintenance dose after 8 h.

Graphing Conic Sections Using a Graphing Utility

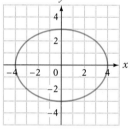

Consider the graph of the ellipse $\frac{x^2}{16} + \frac{y^2}{9} = 1$ shown at the left. Because a vertical line can intersect the graph at more than one point, the graph is not the graph of a function. And because the graph is not the graph of a function, the equation does not represent a function. Consequently, the equation cannot be entered into a graphing utility to be graphed. However, by solving the equation for y, we have

$$\frac{y^2}{9} = 1 - \frac{x^2}{16}$$

$$y^2 = 9\left(1 - \frac{x^2}{16}\right)$$

$$y = \pm 3\sqrt{1 - \frac{x^2}{16}}$$

There are two solutions for y, which can be written

$$y_1 = 3\sqrt{1 - \frac{x^2}{16}} \quad \text{and} \quad y_2 = -3\sqrt{1 - \frac{x^2}{16}}$$

Each of these equations is the equation of a function and therefore can be entered into a graphing utility. The graph of $y_1 = 3\sqrt{1 - \frac{x^2}{16}}$ is shown in blue at the left, and the graph of $y_2 = -3\sqrt{1 - \frac{x^2}{16}}$ is shown in red. Note that, together, the graphs are the graph of an ellipse.

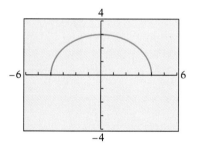

A similar technique can be used to graph a hyperbola. To graph $\frac{x^2}{16} - \frac{y^2}{4} = 1$, solve for y. Then graph each equation, $y_1 = 2\sqrt{\frac{x^2}{16} - 1}$ and $y_2 = -2\sqrt{\frac{x^2}{16} - 1}$.

Guidelines for using graphing calculators are found in the Appendix, page 647. In working through these examples or the exercises below, consult the Appendix or the user's manual for your particular calculator.

Solve each equation for y. Then graph using a graphing utility.

1. $\frac{x^2}{25} + \frac{y^2}{49} = 1$ **2.** $\frac{x^2}{4} + \frac{y^2}{64} = 1$ **3.** $\frac{x^2}{16} - \frac{y^2}{4} = 1$ **4.** $\frac{x^2}{9} - \frac{y^2}{36} = 1$

Chapter Summary

Key Words The graph of a *conic section* can be represented by the intersection of a plane and a cone. The four conic sections are the *parabola, ellipse, hyperbola,* and *circle*.

A *circle* is the set of all points (x, y) in the plane that are a fixed distance from a given point (h, k), called the *center*. The fixed distance is the *radius* of the circle.

The *asymptotes* of a hyperbola are the two straight lines that are "approached" by the hyperbola. As the graph of the hyperbola gets farther from the origin, the hyperbola gets "closer to" the asymptotes.

A *nonlinear system of equations* is one in which one or more of the equations are not linear equations.

The *graph of a quadratic inequality in two variables* is a region of the plane that is bounded by one of the conic sections.

Essential Rules *Equation of a Parabola* $y = ax^2 + bx + c$
When $a > 0$, the parabola opens up.
When $a < 0$, the parabola opens down.
The x-coordinate of the vertex is $-\dfrac{b}{2a}$.
The axis of symmetry is the line $x = -\dfrac{b}{2a}$.

$x = ay^2 + by + c$
When $a > 0$, the parabola opens to the right.
When $a < 0$, the parabola opens to the left.
The y-coordinate of the vertex is $-\dfrac{b}{2a}$.
The axis of symmetry is the line $y = -\dfrac{b}{2a}$.

Equation of a Circle $(x - h)^2 + (y - k)^2 = r^2$
The center is (h, k) and the radius is r.

Equation of an Ellipse $\dfrac{x^2}{a^2} + \dfrac{y^2}{b^2} = 1$
The x-intercepts are $(a, 0)$ and $(-a, 0)$.
The y-intercepts are $(0, b)$ and $(0, -b)$.

Equation of a Hyperbola $\dfrac{x^2}{a^2} - \dfrac{y^2}{b^2} = 1$
An axis of symmetry is the x-axis.
The vertices are $(a, 0)$ and $(-a, 0)$.
The equations of the asymptotes are $y = \pm\dfrac{b}{a}x$.
$\dfrac{y^2}{b^2} - \dfrac{x^2}{a^2} = 1$
An axis of symmetry is the y-axis.
The vertices are $(0, b)$ and $(0, -b)$.
The equations of the asymptotes are $y = \pm\dfrac{b}{a}x$.

Chapter Review

1. Sketch a graph of
$y = -2x^2 + x - 2$.

2. Sketch a graph of
$\dfrac{x^2}{1} + \dfrac{y^2}{9} = 1$.

3. Graph the solution set:
$\dfrac{x^2}{9} - \dfrac{y^2}{16} < 1$

4. Sketch a graph of
$(x + 3)^2 + (y + 1)^2 = 1$.

5. Find the vertex and axis of symmetry of the parabola $y = x^2 - 4x + 8$.

6. Solve: $y^2 = 2x^2 - 3x + 6$
$y^2 = 2x^2 + 5x - 2$

7. Graph the solution set:
$\dfrac{x^2}{25} + \dfrac{y^2}{16} \le 1$
$\dfrac{y^2}{4} - \dfrac{x^2}{4} \ge 1$

8. Sketch a graph of
$\dfrac{x^2}{25} - \dfrac{y^2}{1} = 1$.

9. Find the equation of the circle that passes through the point whose coordinates are $(2, -1)$ and whose center is $(-1, 2)$.

10. Find the vertex and axis of symmetry of the parabola $y = -x^2 + 7x - 8$.

11. Solve: $x = 2y^2 - 3y + 1$
$3x - 2y = 0$

12. Find the equation of the circle that passes through the point $(4, 6)$ and whose center is $(0, -3)$.

13. Find the equation of the circle with radius 6 and center $(-1, 5)$.

14. Solve: $2x^2 + y^2 = 19$
$3x^2 - y^2 = 6$

15. Write the equation $x^2 + y^2 + 4x - 2y = 4$ in standard form.

16. Solve: $y = x^2 + 5x - 6$
$y = x - 10$

17. Graph the solution set:
$\dfrac{x^2}{16} + \dfrac{y^2}{4} > 1$

18. Sketch a graph of
$\dfrac{y^2}{16} - \dfrac{x^2}{9} = 1.$

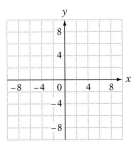

19. Graph the solution set:
$(x - 2)^2 + (y + 1)^2 \le 16$

20. Sketch a graph of
$x^2 + (y - 2)^2 = 9.$

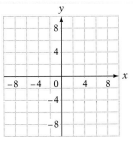

21. Sketch a graph of
$\dfrac{x^2}{25} + \dfrac{y^2}{9} = 1.$

22. Graph the solution set:
$y \ge -x^2 - 2x + 3$

23. Graph the solution set:
$\dfrac{x^2}{16} + \dfrac{y^2}{4} < 1$
$x^2 + y^2 > 9$

24. Graph the solution set:
$y \ge x^2 - 4x + 2$
$y \le \dfrac{1}{3}x - 1$

25. Sketch a graph of
$x = 2y^2 - 6y + 5.$

26. Graph the solution set:
$\dfrac{x^2}{9} + \dfrac{y^2}{1} \ge 1$
$\dfrac{x^2}{4} - \dfrac{y^2}{1} \le 1$

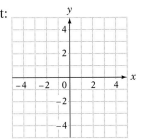

Chapter Test

1. Find the equation of the circle with radius 4 and center $(-3, -3)$.

2. Find the equation of the circle that passes through the point $(2, 5)$ and whose center is $(-2, 1)$.

3. Sketch a graph of $\dfrac{y^2}{25} - \dfrac{x^2}{16} = 1$.

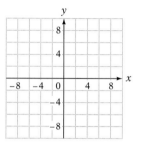

4. Graph the solution set: $x^2 + y^2 < 36$
   $\quad\quad\quad\quad\quad\quad\quad\quad x + y > 4$

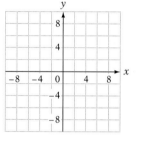

5. Find the axis of symmetry of the parabola $y = -x^2 + 6x - 5$.

6. Solve: $x^2 - y^2 = 24$
   $\quad\quad\quad 2x^2 + 5y^2 = 55$

7. Find the vertex of the parabola $y = -x^2 + 3x - 2$.

8. Sketch a graph of $x = y^2 - y - 2$.

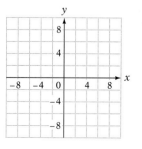

9. Sketch a graph of $\dfrac{x^2}{16} + \dfrac{y^2}{4} = 1$.

10. Graph the solution set: $\dfrac{x^2}{25} + \dfrac{y^2}{4} \le 1$

11. Find the equation of the circle with radius 3 and center $(-2, 4)$.

12. Solve: $x = 3y^2 + 2y - 4$
$x = y^2 - 5y$

13. Solve: $x^2 + 2y^2 = 4$
$x + y = 2$

14. Find the equation of the circle that passes through the point $(2, 4)$ and whose center is $(-1, -3)$.

15. Graph the solution set: $\dfrac{x^2}{25} - \dfrac{y^2}{16} \geq 1$
$x^2 + y^2 \leq 9$

16. Write the equation
$x^2 + y^2 - 4x + 2y + 1 = 0$ in standard form and then sketch its graph.

17. Sketch a graph of
$y = \dfrac{1}{2}x^2 + x - 4$.

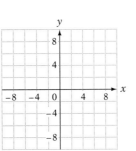

18. Sketch a graph of
$(x - 2)^2 + (y + 1)^2 = 9$.

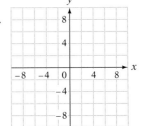

19. Sketch a graph of $\dfrac{x^2}{9} - \dfrac{y^2}{4} = 1$.

20. Graph the solution set: $\dfrac{x^2}{16} - \dfrac{y^2}{25} < 1$

Cumulative Review

1. Graph the solution set:
   $\{x \mid x < 4\} \cap \{x \mid x > 2\}$

   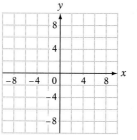
   $$-5\ -4\ -3\ -2\ -1\ \ 0\ \ 1\ \ 2\ \ 3\ \ 4\ \ 5$$

2. Solve: $\dfrac{5x - 2}{3} - \dfrac{1 - x}{5} = \dfrac{x + 4}{10}$

3. Solve: $4 + |3x + 2| < 6$

4. Find the equation of the line that contains the point $(2, -3)$ and has slope $-\dfrac{3}{2}$.

5. Find the equation of the line that contains the point $(4, -2)$ and is perpendicular to the line $y = -x + 5$.

6. Simplify: $x^{2n}(x^{2n} + 2x^n - 3x)$

7. Factor: $(x - 1)^3 - y^3$

8. Solve: $\dfrac{3x - 2}{x + 4} \le 1$

9. Simplify: $\dfrac{ax - bx}{ax + ay - bx - by}$

10. Simplify: $\dfrac{x - 4}{3x - 2} - \dfrac{1 + x}{3x^2 + x - 2}$

11. Solve: $\dfrac{6x}{2x - 3} - \dfrac{1}{2x - 3} = 7$

12. Graph the solution set: $5x + 2y > 10$

13. Simplify: $\left(\dfrac{12a^2b^2}{a^{-3}b^{-4}}\right)^{-1}\left(\dfrac{ab}{4^{-1}a^{-2}b^4}\right)^2$

14. Write $2\sqrt[4]{x^3}$ as an exponential expression.

15. Simplify: $\sqrt{18} - \sqrt{-25}$

16. Solve: $2x^2 + 2x - 3 = 0$

17. Solve: $x^2 + y^2 = 20$
    $\quad\quad\ x^2 - y^2 = 12$

18. Solve: $x - \sqrt{2x - 3} = 3$

19. Evaluate the function $f(x) = -x^2 + 3x - 2$ at $x = -3$.

20. Find the inverse of the function $f(x) = 4x + 8$.

21. Find the maximum value of the function $f(x) = -2x^2 + 4x - 2$.

22. Find the maximum product of two numbers whose sum is 40.

23. Find the distance between the points $(2, 4)$ and $(-1, 0)$.

24. Find the equation of the circle that passes through the point $(3, 1)$ and whose center is $(-1, 2)$.

25. Graph: $x = y^2 - 2y + 3$

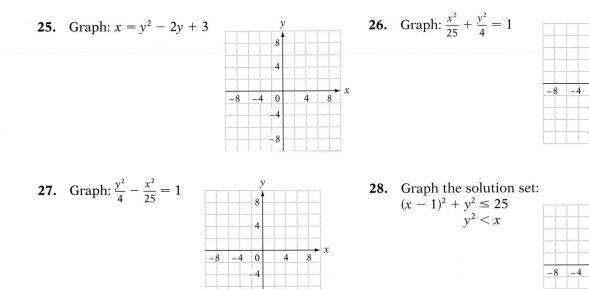

26. Graph: $\dfrac{x^2}{25} + \dfrac{y^2}{4} = 1$

27. Graph: $\dfrac{y^2}{4} - \dfrac{x^2}{25} = 1$

28. Graph the solution set:
$$(x - 1)^2 + y^2 \le 25$$
$$y^2 < x$$

29. Tickets for a school play sold for $4.00 for each adult and $1.50 for each child. The total receipts for the 192 tickets sold were $493. Find the number of adult tickets sold.

30. A motorcycle travels 180 mi in the same amount of time that a car travels 144 mi. The rate of the motorcycle is 12 mph faster than the rate of the car. Find the rate of the motorcycle.

31. The rate of a river's current is 1.5 mph. A rowing crew can row 12 mi down this river and 12 mi back in 6 h. Find the rowing rate of the crew in calm water.

32. The speed, v, of a gear varies inversely as the number of teeth, t. If a gear that has 36 teeth makes 30 revolutions per minute, how many revolutions per minute will a gear that has 60 teeth make?

CHAPTER

12

Sequences and Series

Objectives

Section 12.1
To write the terms of a sequence
To find the sum of a series

Section 12.2
To find the nth term of an arithmetic sequence
To find the sum of an arithmetic series
To solve application problems

Section 12.3
To find the nth term of a geometric sequence
To find the sum of a finite geometric series
To find the sum of an infinite geometric series
To solve application problems

Section 12.4
To expand $(a + b)^n$

As you will learn from studying this chapter, sequences are patterns of numbers. Discovering patterns is very important in the scientific community. It is by looking for patterns that geneticists have identified patterns in DNA, thereby enabling them to decipher the genetic codes carried by the DNA.

Tower of Hanoi

The Tower of Hanoi is a puzzle that has the following form.

Three pegs are placed in a board. A number of disks, graded in size, are stacked on one of the pegs with the largest disk on the bottom and the succeeding smaller disks placed on top.

The disks are moved according to the following rules:

1. Only one disk at a time may be moved.

2. A larger disk cannot be placed over a smaller disk.

The object of the puzzle is to transfer all the disks from one peg to one of the other two pegs. If initially there is only one disk, then only one move would be required. With two disks initially, three moves are required, and with three disks, seven moves are required.

You can try this puzzle using playing cards. Select five playing cards, in sequence, from a deck. The number of cards corresponds to the number of disks and the number on the card corresponds to the size of the disk. For example, an "ace" would correspond to the smallest disk, a "two" would correspond to the next largest disk, and so on for five cards. Place three coins on a table to be used as the pegs. Pile the cards on one of the coins (in order), and try to move the pile to a second coin. Now a numerically larger card cannot be placed on a numerically smaller card. Try this for five cards. The minimum number of moves is 31.

The chart below shows the minimum number of moves required for an initial number of disks. The difference between the number of moves for each succeeding disk is also given.

1	2	3	4	5	6	7	8
1	3	7	15	31	63	127	255
	2	4	8	16	32	64	128

For this last list of numbers, each succeeding number can be found by multiplying the preceding number by a constant (in this case 2). This list of numbers is a *geometric sequence*.

The formula for the minimum number of moves is given by $M = 2^n - 1$, where M is the number of moves and n is the number of disks. This equation is an exponential equation.

12.1 Introduction to Sequences and Series

Objective A *To write the terms of a sequence* .... [CT]

An investor deposits \$100 in an account that earns 10% interest compounded annually. The amount of interest earned each year can be determined by using the compound interest formula.

The amount of interest earned in each of the first four years of the investment is shown at the right.

Year	1	2	3	4
Interest Earned	\$10	\$11	\$12.10	\$13.31

The list of numbers 10, 11, 12.10, 13.31 is called a sequence. A **sequence** is an ordered list of numbers. The list 10, 11, 12.10, 13.31 is ordered because the position of a number in this list indicates the year in which that amount of interest was earned.

Each of the numbers of a sequence is called a **term** of the sequence.

For the sequence at the right, the first term is 2, the second term is 4, the third term is 6, and the fourth term is 8.

2, 4, 6, 8, ...

Examples of other sequences are shown at the right. These sequences are separated into two groups. A **finite sequence** contains a finite number of terms. An **infinite sequence** contains an infinite number of terms.

1, 1, 2, 3, 5, 8
1, 2, 3, 4, 5, 6, 7, 8   Finite Sequences
1, −1, 1, −1

1, 3, 5, 7, ...
$1, \dfrac{1}{2}, \dfrac{1}{4}, \dfrac{1}{8}, \ldots$ Infinite Sequences
1, 1, 2, 3, 5, 8, ...

A general sequence is shown at the right. The first term is a_1, the second term is a_2, the third term is a_3, and the nth term, also called the **general term** of the sequence, is a_n. Note that each term of the sequence is paired with a natural number.

$a_1, a_2, a_3, \ldots, a_n, \ldots$

Frequently a sequence has a definite pattern that can be expressed by a formula.

Each term of the sequence shown at the right is paired with a natural number by the formula $a_n = 3n$. The first term, a_1, is 3. The second term, a_2, is 6. The third term, a_3, is 9. The nth term, a_n, is $3n$.

$a_n = 3n$

$a_1, \quad a_2, \quad a_3, \ldots, \quad a_n, \ldots$

$3(1), 3(2), 3(3), \ldots, 3(n), \ldots$

$3, \quad 6, \quad 9, \ldots, \quad 3n, \ldots$

➡ Write the first three terms of the sequence whose nth term is given by the formula $a_n = 4n$.

$a_n = 4n$

$a_1 = 4(1) = 4$ • Replace *n* by 1.

$a_2 = 4(2) = 8$ • Replace *n* by 2.

$a_3 = 4(3) = 12$ • Replace *n* by 3.

The first term is 4, the second term is 8, and the third term is 12.

⇒ Find the fifth and seventh terms of the sequence whose nth term is given by the formula $a_n = \frac{1}{n^2}$.

$$a_n = \frac{1}{n^2}$$

$$a_5 = \frac{1}{5^2} = \frac{1}{25} \qquad \bullet \text{ Replace } n \text{ by 5.}$$

$$a_7 = \frac{1}{7^2} = \frac{1}{49} \qquad \bullet \text{ Replace } n \text{ by 7.}$$

The fifth term is $\frac{1}{25}$ and the seventh term is $\frac{1}{49}$.

Example 1
Write the first three terms of the sequence whose nth term is given by the formula $a_n = 2n - 1$.

Solution
$a_n = 2n - 1$
$a_1 = 2(1) - 1 = 1$ The first term is 1.
$a_2 = 2(2) - 1 = 3$ The second term is 3.
$a_3 = 2(3) - 1 = 5$ The third term is 5.

Example 2
Find the eighth and tenth terms of the sequence whose nth term is given by the formula $a_n = \frac{n}{n + 1}$.

Solution

$$a_n = \frac{n}{n + 1}$$

$$a_8 = \frac{8}{8 + 1} = \frac{8}{9} \qquad \text{The eighth term is } \frac{8}{9}.$$

$$a_{10} = \frac{10}{10 + 1} = \frac{10}{11} \qquad \text{The tenth term is } \frac{10}{11}.$$

You Try It 1
Write the first four terms of the sequence whose nth term is given by the formula $a_n = n(n + 1)$.

Your solution

You Try It 2
Find the sixth and ninth terms of the sequence whose nth term is given by the formula $a_n = \frac{1}{n(n + 2)}$.

Your solution

Solutions on p. S33

Objective B   *To find the sum of a series* ·· CT

In the last objective, the sequence 10, 11, 12.10, 13.31 was shown to represent the amount of interest earned in each of 4 years of an investment.

The sum of the terms of this sequence represents the total interest earned by the investment over the four-year period.

10, 11, 12.10, 13.31

$10 + 11 + 12.10 + 13.31 = 46.41$

The total interest earned over the four-year period is $46.41.

The indicated sum of the terms of a sequence is called a **series**. Given the sequence 10, 11, 12.10, 13.31, the series 10 + 11 + 12.10 + 13.31 can be written.

S_n is used to designate the sum of the first n terms of a sequence.

For the preceding example, the sums of the series S_1, S_2, S_3, and S_4 represent the total interest earned for 1, 2, 3, and 4 years, respectively.

$$S_1 = 10 \qquad\qquad\qquad = 10$$
$$S_2 = 10 + 11 \qquad\qquad = 21$$
$$S_3 = 10 + 11 + 12.10 \qquad = 33.10$$
$$S_4 = 10 + 11 + 12.10 + 13.31 = 46.41$$

For the general sequence a_1, a_2, a_3, ... , a_n, the series S_1, S_2, S_3, and S_n are shown at the right.

$$S_1 = a_1$$
$$S_2 = a_1 + a_2$$
$$S_3 = a_1 + a_2 + a_3$$
$$S_n = a_1 + a_2 + a_3 + \cdots + a_n$$

It is convenient to represent a series in a compact form called **summation notation**, or **sigma notation.** The Greek letter sigma, Σ, is used to indicate a sum.

The first four terms of the sequence whose nth term is given by the formula $a_n = 2n$ are 2, 4, 6, 8. The corresponding series is shown at the right written in summation notation; it is read "the sum from 1 to 4 of $2n$." The letter n is called the **index** of the summation.

$$\sum_{n=1}^{4} 2n$$

To write the terms of the series, replace n by the consecutive integers from 1 to 4.

$$\sum_{n=1}^{4} 2n = 2(1) + 2(2) + 2(3) + 2(4)$$

The series is 2 + 4 + 6 + 8.

$$= 2 + 4 + 6 + 8$$

The sum of the series is 20.

$$= 20$$

➡ Find the sum of the series $\displaystyle\sum_{n=1}^{6} n^2$.

$$\sum_{n=1}^{6} n^2 = 1^2 + 2^2 + 3^2 + 4^2 + 5^2 + 6^2$$ • Replace n by 1, 2, 3, 4, 5, and 6.

$$= 1 + 4 + 9 + 16 + 25 + 36$$ • Simplify.

$$= 91$$

The sum of the series is 91.

➡ Find the sum of the series $\displaystyle\sum_{i=1}^{3} (2i - 1)$.

$$\sum_{i=1}^{3} (2i - 1) = [2(1) - 1] + [2(2) - 1] + [2(3) - 1]$$ • Replace i by 1, 2, and 3.

$$= 1 + 3 + 5$$ • Simplify.

$$= 9$$

The sum of the series is 9.

TAKE NOTE

The placement of the parentheses in this example is important. For instance,

$$\sum_{i=1}^{3} 2i - 1$$
$$= 2(1) + 2(2) + 2(3) - 1$$
$$= 2 + 4 + 6 - 1 = 11$$

This is *not* the same result as for $\displaystyle\sum_{i=1}^{3} (2i - 1)$.

➡ Find the sum of the series $\sum\limits_{n=3}^{6}\frac{1}{2}n$.

$$\sum_{n=3}^{6}\frac{1}{2}n = \frac{1}{2}(3) + \frac{1}{2}(4) + \frac{1}{2}(5) + \frac{1}{2}(6)$$
• Replace n by 3, 4, 5, and 6.

$$= \frac{3}{2} + 2 + \frac{5}{2} + 3$$
• Simplify.

$$= 9$$

The sum of the series is 9.

➡ Write $\sum\limits_{i=1}^{5}x^i$ in expanded form.

This is a variable series.

$$\sum_{i=1}^{5}x^i = x + x^2 + x^3 + x^4 + x^5$$
• Replace i by 1, 2, 3, 4, and 5.

Example 3

Find the sum of the series $\sum\limits_{n=1}^{4}(7 - n)$.

Solution

$\sum\limits_{n=1}^{4}(7 - n)$

$= (7 - 1) + (7 - 2) + (7 - 3) + (7 - 4)$

$= 6 + 5 + 4 + 3 = 18$

You Try It 3

Find the sum of the series $\sum\limits_{i=3}^{6}(i^2 - 2)$.

Your solution

Example 4

Write $\sum\limits_{i=1}^{5}ix$ in expanded form.

Solution

$\sum\limits_{i=1}^{5}ix = 1 \cdot x + 2 \cdot x + 3 \cdot x + 4 \cdot x + 5 \cdot x$

$= x + 2x + 3x + 4x + 5x$

You Try It 4

Write $\sum\limits_{n=1}^{4}\frac{x}{n}$ in expanded form.

Your solution

Solutions on p. S33

12.1 Exercises

Objective A

Write the first four terms of the sequence whose nth term is given by the formula.

1. $a_n = n + 1$

2. $a_n = n - 1$

3. $a_n = 2n + 1$

4. $a_n = 3n - 1$

5. $a_n = 2 - 2n$

6. $a_n = 1 - 2n$

7. $a_n = 2^n$

8. $a_n = 3^n$

9. $a_n = n^2 + 1$

10. $a_n = n - \dfrac{1}{n}$

11. $a_n = n^2 - \dfrac{1}{n}$

12. $a_n = (-1)^{n+1}n$

Find the indicated term of the sequence whose nth term is given by the formula.

13. $a_n = 3n + 4;\ a_{12}$

14. $a_n = 2n - 5;\ a_{10}$

15. $a_n = n(n - 1);\ a_{11}$

16. $a_n = \dfrac{n}{n + 1};\ a_{12}$

17. $a_n = (-1)^{n-1}n^2;\ a_{15}$

18. $a_n = (-1)^{n-1}(n - 1);\ a_{25}$

19. $a_n = \left(\dfrac{1}{2}\right)^n;\ a_8$

20. $a_n = \left(\dfrac{2}{3}\right)^n;\ a_5$

21. $a_n = (n + 2)(n + 3);\ a_{17}$

22. $a_n = (n + 4)(n + 1);\ a_7$

23. $a_n = \dfrac{(-1)^{2n-1}}{n^2};\ a_6$

24. $a_n = \dfrac{(-1)^{2n}}{n + 4};\ a_{16}$

Objective B

Find the sum of the series.

25. $\displaystyle\sum_{n=1}^{5} (2n + 3)$

26. $\displaystyle\sum_{i=1}^{7} (i + 2)$

27. $\displaystyle\sum_{i=1}^{4} 2i$

28. $\displaystyle\sum_{n=1}^{7} n$

29. $\displaystyle\sum_{i=1}^{6} i^2$

30. $\displaystyle\sum_{i=1}^{5} (i^2 + 1)$

31. $\displaystyle\sum_{n=1}^{6} (-1)^n$

32. $\displaystyle\sum_{n=1}^{4} \frac{1}{2n}$

33. $\displaystyle\sum_{i=3}^{6} i^3$

34. $\displaystyle\sum_{i=1}^{4} (-1)^{i-1}(i+1)$

35. $\displaystyle\sum_{n=3}^{5} \frac{(-1)^{n-1}}{n-2}$

36. $\displaystyle\sum_{n=4}^{7} \frac{(-1)^{n-1}}{n-3}$

Write the series in expanded form.

37. $\displaystyle\sum_{n=1}^{5} 2x^n$

38. $\displaystyle\sum_{n=1}^{4} \frac{2n}{x}$

39. $\displaystyle\sum_{i=1}^{5} \frac{x^i}{i}$

40. $\displaystyle\sum_{i=1}^{4} \frac{x^i}{i+1}$

41. $\displaystyle\sum_{i=3}^{5} \frac{x^i}{2i}$

42. $\displaystyle\sum_{i=2}^{4} \frac{x^i}{2i-1}$

43. $\displaystyle\sum_{n=1}^{5} x^{2n}$

44. $\displaystyle\sum_{n=1}^{4} x^{2n-1}$

45. $\displaystyle\sum_{i=1}^{4} \frac{x^i}{i^2}$

46. $\displaystyle\sum_{n=1}^{4} (2n)x^n$

47. $\displaystyle\sum_{n=1}^{4} nx^{n-1}$

48. $\displaystyle\sum_{i=1}^{5} x^{-i}$

APPLYING THE CONCEPTS

49. In the first box below, $\frac{1}{2}$ of the box is shaded. In successive boxes the sums $\frac{1}{2}+\frac{1}{4}$, $\frac{1}{2}+\frac{1}{4}+\frac{1}{8}$, and so on are shown. Can you identify the infinite sum $\frac{1}{2}+\frac{1}{4}+\frac{1}{8}+\frac{1}{16}+\cdots$?

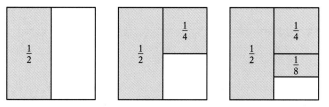

50. Rewrite $1+\frac{1}{2}+\frac{1}{3}+\cdots+\frac{1}{n}$ using sigma notation.

51. Indicate whether the following statements are true or false.
  a. No two terms of a sequence can be equal.
  b. The sum of an infinite number of terms is an infinite number.

52. Write a paragraph about the history of the sigma notation used for summation.

53. Write a paragraph explaining the Fibonacci Sequence.

12.2 Arithmetic Sequences and Series

Objective A **To find the nth term of an arithmetic sequence** ....

A company's expenses for training a new employee are quite high. To encourage employees to continue their employment with the company, a company that has a six-month training program offers a starting salary of $1600 a month and then a $200-per-month pay increase each month during the training period.

The sequence at the right shows the employee's monthly salaries during the training period. Each term of the sequence is found by adding $200 to the previous term.

Month	1	2	3	4	5	6
Salary	1600	1800	2000	2200	2400	2600

The sequence 1600, 1800, 2000, 2200, 2400, 2600 is called an arithmetic sequence. An **arithmetic sequence,** or **arithmetic progression,** is one in which the difference between any two consecutive terms is constant. The difference between consecutive terms is called the **common difference** of the sequence.

Each of the sequences shown at the right is an arithmetic sequence. To find the common difference of an arithmetic sequence, subtract the first term from the second term.

2, 7, 12, 17, 22, ... Common difference: 5

3, 1, −1, −3, −5, ... Common difference: −2

$1, \dfrac{3}{2}, 2, \dfrac{5}{2}, 3, \dfrac{7}{2}$ Common difference: $\dfrac{1}{2}$

Consider an arithmetic sequence in which the first term is a_1 and the common difference is d. Adding the common difference to each successive term of the arithmetic sequence yields a formula for the nth term.

The first term is a_1.

$$a_1 = a_1$$

To find the second term, add the common difference d to the first term.

$$a_2 = a_1 + d$$

To find the third term, add the common difference d to the second term.

$$a_3 = a_2 + d = (a_1 + d) + d$$
$$a_3 = a_1 + 2d$$

To find the fourth term, add the common difference d to the third term.

$$a_4 = a_3 + d = (a_1 + 2d) + d$$
$$a_4 = a_1 + 3d$$

Note the relationship between the term number and the number that multiplies d. The multiplier of d is 1 less than the term number.

$$a_n = a_1 + (n - 1)d$$

> **The Formula for the *n*th Term of an Arithmetic Sequence**
>
> The nth term of an arithmetic sequence with a common difference of d is given by $a_n = a_1 + (n - 1)d$.

⇒ Find the 27th term of the arithmetic sequence $-4, -1, 2, 5, 8, \ldots$.

$d = a_2 - a_1 = -1 - (-4) = 3$ • Find the common difference.

Use the Formula for the nth Term of an Arithmetic Sequence to find the 27th term.

$a_n = a_1 + (n-1)d$
$a_{27} = -4 + (27-1)3 = -4 + (26)3 = -4 + 78$ • $n = 27, a_1 = -4, d = 3$
$a_{27} = 74$

⇒ Find the formula for the nth term of the arithmetic sequence $-5, -2, 1, 4, \ldots$.

$d = a_2 - a_1 = -2 - (-5) = 3$ • Find the common difference.

Use the Formula for the nth Term of an Arithmetic Sequence.

$a_n = a_1 + (n-1)d$
$a_n = -5 + (n-1)3$ • $a_1 = -5, d = 3$
$a_n = -5 + 3n - 3$
$a_n = 3n - 8$

⇒ Find the formula for the nth term of the arithmetic sequence $2, -3, -8, -13, \ldots$.

$d = a_2 - a_1 = -3 - 2 = -5$ • Find the common difference.

Now use the Formula for the nth Term of an Arithmetic Sequence.

$a_n = a_1 + (n-1)d$
$a_n = 2 + (n-1)(-5)$ • $a_1 = 2, d = -5$
$a_n = 2 - 5n + 5$
$a_n = 7 - 5n$

Example 1
Find the 10th term of the arithmetic sequence $1, 6, 11, 16, \ldots$.

Solution
$d = a_2 - a_1 = 6 - 1 = 5$
$a_n = a_1 + (n-1)d$
$a_{10} = 1 + (10-1)5 = 1 + (9)5 = 1 + 45$
$a_{10} = 46$

You Try It 1
Find the 15th term of the arithmetic sequence $9, 3, -3, -9, \ldots$.

Your solution

Example 2
Find the number of terms in the finite arithmetic sequence $-3, 1, 5, \ldots, 41$.

Solution
$d = a_2 - a_1 = 1 - (-3) = 4$
$a_n = a_1 + (n-1)d$
$41 = -3 + (n-1)4$
$41 = -3 + 4n - 4$
$41 = -7 + 4n$
$48 = 4n$
$12 = n$

There are 12 terms in the sequence.

You Try It 2
Find the number of terms in the finite arithmetic sequence $7, 9, 11, \ldots, 59$.

Your solution

Solutions on p. S33

Objective B   *To find the sum of an arithmetic series* .... CT

The indicated sum of the terms of an arithmetic sequence is called an **arithmetic series.** The sum of an arithmetic series can be found by using a formula. A proof of this formula appears in the Appendix.

POINT OF INTEREST

This formula was proven in *Aryabhatiya,* which was written by Aryabhata around 499. The book is the earliest known Indian mathematical work by an identifiable author. Although the proof of the formula appears in that text, the formula was known before Aryabhata's time.

> **The Formula for the Sum of *n* Terms of an Arithmetic Series**
>
> Let a_1 be the first term of a finite arithmetic sequence, let n be the number of terms, and let a_n be the last term of the sequence.
>
> Then the sum of the series S_n is given by $S_n = \dfrac{n}{2}(a_1 + a_n)$.

➡ Find the sum of the first 10 terms of the arithmetic sequence 2, 4, 6, 8, ...

$d = a_2 - a_1 = 4 - 2 = 2$ • Find the common difference.

$a_n = a_1 + (n - 1)d$ • Find the 10th term.
$a_{10} = 2 + (10 - 1)2 = 2 + (9)2 = 2 + 18 = 20$

Use the Formula for the Sum of *n* Terms of an Arithmetic Series.

$S_n = \dfrac{n}{2}(a_1 + a_n)$

$S_{10} = \dfrac{10}{2}(2 + 20) = 5(22) = 110$ • $n = 10, a_1 = 2, a_n = 20$

➡ Find the sum of the arithmetic series $\displaystyle\sum_{n=1}^{25}(3n + 1)$.

$a_n = 3n + 1$
$a_1 = 3(1) + 1 = 4$ • Find the 1st term.
$a_{25} = 3(25) + 1 = 76$ • Find the 25th term.

Use the Formula for the Sum of *n* Terms of an Arithmetic Series.

$S_n = \dfrac{n}{2}(a_1 + a_n)$

$S_{25} = \dfrac{25}{2}(4 + 76) = \dfrac{25}{2}(80) = 1000$ • $n = 25, a_1 = 4, a_{25} = 76$

Example 3
Find the sum of the first 20 terms of the arithmetic sequence 3, 8, 13, 18, ...

Solution
$d = a_2 - a_1 = 8 - 3 = 5$

$a_n = a_1 + (n - 1)d$
$a_{20} = 3 + (20 - 1)5 = 3 + (19)5$
$\quad = 3 + 95 = 98$

$S_n = \dfrac{n}{2}(a_1 + a_n)$

$S_{20} = \dfrac{20}{2}(3 + 98) = 10(101) = 1010$

You Try It 3
Find the sum of the first 25 terms of the arithmetic sequence −4, −2, 0, 2, 4, ...

Your solution

Solution on p. S34

Example 4

Find the sum of the arithmetic series

$$\sum_{n=1}^{15}(2n + 3).$$

Solution

$a_n = 2n + 3$

$a_1 = 2(1) + 3 = 5$

$a_{15} = 2(15) + 3 = 33$

$S_n = \dfrac{n}{2}(a_1 + a_n)$

$S_{15} = \dfrac{15}{2}(5 + 33) = \dfrac{15}{2}(38) = 285$

You Try It 4

Find the sum of the arithmetic series

$$\sum_{n=1}^{18}(3n - 2).$$

Your solution

Solution on p. S34

Objective C   *To solve application problems* ··· CT

Example 5

The distance a ball rolls down a ramp each second is given by an arithmetic sequence. The distance in feet traveled by the ball during the nth second is given by $2n - 1$. Find the distance the ball will travel during the 10th second.

Strategy

To find the distance:

- Find the common difference of the arithmetic sequence.
- Use the Formula for the nth Term of an Arithmetic Sequence.

Solution

$a_n = 2n - 1$

$a_1 = 2(1) - 1 = 1$

$a_2 = 2(2) - 1 = 3$

$d = a_2 - a_1 = 3 - 1 = 2$

$a_n = a_1 + (n - 1)d$

$a_{10} = 1 + (10 - 1)2 = 1 + (9)2$

$\phantom{a_{10}} = 1 + 18 = 19$

The ball will travel 19 ft during the 10th second.

You Try It 5

A contest offers 20 prizes. The first prize is $10,000, and each successive prize is $300 less than the preceding prize. What is the value of the 20th-place prize? What is the total amount of prize money being awarded?

Your strategy

Your solution

Solution on p. S34

12.2 Exercises

· ·

Objective A

Find the indicated term of the arithmetic sequence.

1. 1, 11, 21, ...; a_{15}

2. 3, 8, 13, ...; a_{20}

3. −6, −2, 2, ...; a_{15}

4. −7, −2, 3, ...; a_{14}

5. 2, $\frac{5}{2}$, 3, ...; a_{31}

6. 1, $\frac{5}{4}$, $\frac{3}{2}$, ...; a_{17}

7. −4, −$\frac{5}{2}$, −1, ...; a_{12}

8. −$\frac{5}{3}$, −1, −$\frac{1}{3}$, ...; a_{22}

9. 8, 5, 2, ...; a_{40}

Find the formula for the *n*th term of the arithmetic sequence.

10. 1, 2, 3, ...

11. 1, 4, 7, ...

12. 6, 2, −2, ...

13. 3, 0, −3, ...

14. 2, $\frac{7}{2}$, 5, ...

15. 7, 4.5, 2, ...

Find the number of terms in the finite arithmetic sequence.

16. 1, 5, 9, ..., 81

17. 3, 8, 13, ..., 98

18. 2, 0, −2, ..., −56

19. 1, −3, −7, ..., −75

20. $\frac{5}{2}$, 3, $\frac{7}{2}$, ..., 13

21. $\frac{7}{3}$, $\frac{13}{3}$, $\frac{19}{3}$, ..., $\frac{79}{3}$

22. 1, 0.75, 0.50, ..., −4

23. 3.5, 2, 0.5, ..., −25

24. −3.4, −2.8, −2.2, ..., 11

Objective B

Find the sum of the indicated number of terms of the arithmetic sequence.

25. 1, 3, 5, ...; $n = 50$

26. 2, 4, 6, ...; $n = 25$

27. 20, 18, 16, ...; $n = 40$

28. 25, 20, 15, ...; $n = 22$

29. $\frac{1}{2}$, 1, $\frac{3}{2}$, ...; $n = 27$

30. 2, $\frac{11}{4}$, $\frac{7}{2}$, ...; $n = 10$

Find the sum of the arithmetic series.

31. $\displaystyle\sum_{i=1}^{15} (3i - 1)$

32. $\displaystyle\sum_{i=1}^{15} (3i + 4)$

33. $\displaystyle\sum_{n=1}^{17} \left(\frac{1}{2}n + 1\right)$

34. $\displaystyle\sum_{n=1}^{10} (1 - 4n)$

35. $\displaystyle\sum_{i=1}^{15} (4 - 2i)$

36. $\displaystyle\sum_{n=1}^{10} (5 - n)$

Objective C   *Application Problems*

37. An exercise program calls for walking 10 min each day for a week. Each week thereafter, the amount of time spent walking increases by 5 min per day. In how many weeks will a person be walking 60 min each day?

38. A display of cans in a grocery store consists of 24 cans in the bottom row, 21 cans in the next row, and so on in an arithmetic sequence. The top row has 3 cans. Find the number of cans in the display.

39. An object that is dropped from a low-flying airplane will fall 16 ft the first second, 48 ft the next second, 80 ft the third second, and so on in an arithmetic sequence. Find the distance that the object will fall during the fifth second. (Assume that air resistance is negligible.)

40. The loge seating section in a concert hall consists of 27 rows of chairs. There are 73 seats in the first row, 79 seats in the second row, 85 seats in the third row, and so on in an arithmetic sequence. How many seats are in the loge seating section?

41. The salary schedule for a software engineer apprentice program is $1500 for the first month and a $300-per-month salary increase for the next 7 months. Find the monthly salary during the eighth month. Find the total salary for the eight-month period.

APPLYING THE CONCEPTS

42. State whether the following statements are true or false.
   a. The sum of the successive terms of an arithmetic sequence always increases in value.
   b. Each successive term in an arithmetic series is found by adding a fixed number.
   c. $a_1 = 4$, $a_{n+1} = a_n - 2$ defines an arithmetic series.

43. Write $\displaystyle\sum_{i=1}^{2} \log 2i$ as a single logarithm with a coefficient of 1.

44. Write a formula for the *n*th term of the sequence of the odd natural numbers.

12.3 Geometric Sequences and Series

Objective A   *To find the nth term of a geometric sequence* .... CT

An ore sample contains 20 mg of a radioactive material with a half-life of one week. The amount of the radioactive material that the sample contains at the beginning of each week can be determined by using an exponential decay equation.

The sequence at the right represents the amount in the sample at the beginning of each week. Each term of the sequence is found by multiplying the preceding term by $\frac{1}{2}$.

Week	1	2	3	4	5
Amount	20	10	5	2.5	1.25

The sequence 20, 10, 5, 2.5, 1.25 is called a geometric sequence. A **geometric sequence,** or **geometric progression,** is one in which each successive term of the sequence is the same nonzero constant multiple of the preceding term. The common multiple is called the **common ratio** of the sequence.

Each of the sequences shown at the right is a geometric sequence. To find the common ratio of a geometric sequence, divide the second term of the sequence by the first term.

3, 6, 12, 24, 48, ...   Common ratio: 2

4, −12, 36, −108, 324, ...   Common ratio: −3

$6, 4, \frac{8}{3}, \frac{16}{9}, \frac{32}{27}, \ldots$ Common ratio: $\frac{2}{3}$

Consider a geometric sequence in which the first term is a_1 and the common ratio is r. Multiplying each successive term of the geometric sequence by the common ratio yields a formula for the nth term.

The first term is a_1.

$$a_1 = a_1$$

To find the second term, multiply the first term by the common ratio r.

$$a_2 = a_1 r$$

To find the third term, multiply the second term by the common ratio r.

$$a_3 = (a_1 r)r$$
$$a_3 = a_1 r^2$$

To find the fourth term, multiply the third term by the common ratio r.

$$a_4 = (a_1 r^2)r$$
$$a_4 = a_1 r^3$$

Note the relationship between the term number and the number that is the exponent on r. The exponent on r is 1 less than the term number.

$$a_n = a_1 r^{n-1}$$

The Formula for the nth Term of a Geometric Sequence

The nth term of a geometric sequence with first term a_1 and common ratio r is given by $a_n = a_1 r^{n-1}$.

➡ Find the 6th term of the geometric sequence 3, 6, 12, ...

$$r = \frac{a_2}{a_1} = \frac{6}{3} = 2 \qquad \bullet \text{ Find the common ratio.}$$

Use the Formula for the nth Term of a Geometric Sequence to find the 6th term.

$$a_n = a_1 r^{n-1}$$
$$a_6 = 3(2)^{6-1} \qquad \bullet \ n = 6, \ a_1 = 3, \ r = 2$$
$$= 3(2)^5 = 3 \cdot 32$$
$$a_6 = 96$$

➡ Find a_3 for the geometric sequence 8, a_2, a_3, -27, ...

Use the Formula for the nth Term of a Geometric Sequence to find the common ratio.

$$a_n = a_1 r^{n-1}$$
$$a_4 = a_1 r^{4-1} \qquad \bullet \text{ The 1st and 4th terms of the sequence are known.}$$
$$\qquad\qquad\qquad\qquad \text{ Substitute } n = 4.$$
$$-27 = 8r^3 \qquad \bullet \ a_4 = -27, \ a_1 = 8$$
$$-\frac{27}{8} = r^3 \qquad \bullet \text{ Solve for } r^3.$$
$$-\frac{3}{2} = r \qquad \bullet \text{ Take the cube root of each side of the equation.}$$

Use the Formula for the nth Term of a Geometric Sequence again, this time to find a_3.

$$a_n = a_1 r^{n-1}$$
$$a_3 = 8\left(-\frac{3}{2}\right)^{3-1} = 8\left(-\frac{3}{2}\right)^2 = 8\left(\frac{9}{4}\right) \qquad \bullet \ a_1 = 8, \ r = -\frac{3}{2}, \ n = 3$$
$$a_3 = 18$$

Example 1

Find the 7th term of the geometric sequence 3, -6, 12, ...

Solution

$$r = \frac{a_2}{a_1} = \frac{-6}{3} = -2$$
$$a_n = a_1 r^{n-1}$$
$$a_7 = 3(-2)^{7-1} = 3(-2)^6 = 3(64)$$
$$a_7 = 192$$

You Try It 1

Find the 5th term of the geometric sequence 5, 2, $\frac{4}{5}$, ...

Your solution

Solution on p. S34

Example 2

Find a_2 for the geometric sequence 2, a_2, a_3, 54, ...

Solution

$a_n = a_1 r^{n-1}$

$a_4 = 2r^{4-1}$ • $n = 4, a_1 = 2$

$54 = 2r^{4-1}$ • $a_4 = 54$

$54 = 2r^3$

$27 = r^3$

$3 = r$ • The common ratio is 3.

$a_n = a_1 r^{n-1}$

$a_2 = 2(3)^{2-1} = 2(3)$ • $n = 2, r = 3$

$a_2 = 6$

You Try It 2

Find a_3 for the geometric sequence 3, a_2, a_3, −192, ...

Your solution

Solution on p. S34

Objective B **To find the sum of a finite geometric series** ....

The indicated sum of the terms of a geometric sequence is called a **geometric series.** The sum of a geometric series can be found by a formula. A proof of this formula appears in the Appendix.

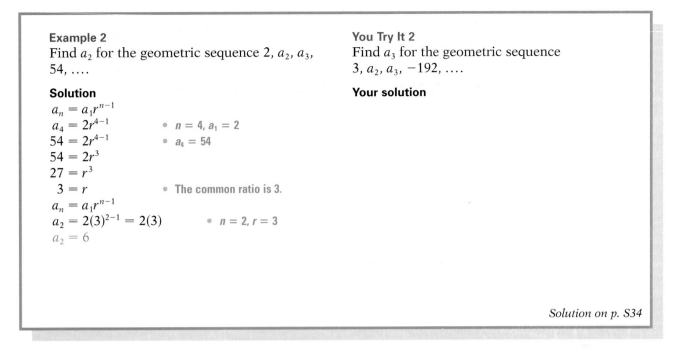

> **The Formula for the Sum of n Terms of a Finite Geometric Series**
>
> Let a_1 be the first term of a finite geometric sequence, let n be the number of terms, and let r be the common ratio. Then the sum of the series S_n is given by $S_n = \dfrac{a_1(1 - r^n)}{1 - r}$.

➡ Find the sum of the geometric sequence 2, 8, 32, 128, 512.

$r = \dfrac{a_2}{a_1} = \dfrac{8}{2} = 4$ • Find the common ratio.

Use the Formula for the sum of n Terms of a Finite Geometric Series.

$S_n = \dfrac{a_1(1 - r^n)}{1 - r}$

$S_5 = \dfrac{2(1 - 4^5)}{1 - 4}$ • $n = 5, a_1 = 2, r = 4$

$= \dfrac{2(1 - 1024)}{-3} = \dfrac{2(-1023)}{-3}$

$= \dfrac{-2046}{-3} = 682$

⇒ Find the sum of the geometric series $\sum\limits_{n=1}^{10}(-20)(-2)^{n-1}$.

$$a_n = (-20)(-2)^{n-1}$$

Find the 1st term.

$$a_1 = (-20)(-2)^{1-1} = (-20)(-2)^0 = (-20)(1) = -20$$

Find the 2nd term.

$$a_2 = (-20)(-2)^{2-1} = (-20)(-2)^1 = (-20)(-2) = 40$$

Find the common ratio.

$$r = \frac{a_2}{a_1} = \frac{40}{-20} = -2$$

Use the Formula for the Sum of n Terms of a Finite Geometric Series.

$$S_n = \frac{a_1(1-r^n)}{1-r}$$

$$S_{10} = \frac{-20[1-(-2)^{10}]}{1-(-2)}$$

• $n = 10, a_1 = -20, r = -2$

$$= \frac{-20(1-1024)}{3}$$

$$= \frac{-20(-1023)}{3} = \frac{20{,}460}{3} = 6820$$

Example 3

Find the sum of the geometric sequence
3, 6, 12, 24, 48, 96.

Solution

$$r = \frac{a_2}{a_1} = \frac{6}{3} = 2$$

$$S_n = \frac{a_1(1-r^n)}{1-r}$$

$$S_6 = \frac{3(1-2^6)}{1-2} = \frac{3(1-64)}{-1} = -3(-63) = 189$$

Example 4

Find the sum of the geometric series $\sum\limits_{n=1}^{4}4^n$.

Solution

$$a_n = 4^n$$
$$a_1 = 4^1 = 4$$
$$a_2 = 4^2 = 16$$

$$r = \frac{a_2}{a_1} = \frac{16}{4} = 4$$

$$S_n = \frac{a_1(1-r^n)}{1-r}$$

$$S_4 = \frac{4(1-4^4)}{1-4} = \frac{4(1-256)}{-3} = \frac{4(-255)}{-3} = \frac{-1020}{-3}$$

$$= 340$$

You Try It 3

Find the sum of the geometric sequence
$1, -\dfrac{1}{3}, \dfrac{1}{9}, -\dfrac{1}{27}$.

Your solution

You Try It 4

Find the sum of the geometric series $\sum\limits_{n=1}^{5}\left(\dfrac{1}{2}\right)^n$.

Your solution

Solutions on pp. S34–S35

Objective C   *To find the sum of an infinite geometric series* .... [CT]

When the absolute value of the common ratio of a geometric sequence is less than 1, $|r| < 1$, then as n becomes larger, r^n becomes closer to zero.

Examples of geometric sequences for which $|r| < 1$ are shown at the right. Note that as the number of terms increases, the value of the last term listed gets closer to zero.

$$1, \frac{1}{3}, \frac{1}{9}, \frac{1}{27}, \frac{1}{81}, \frac{1}{243}, \cdots$$

$$1, -\frac{1}{2}, \frac{1}{4}, -\frac{1}{8}, \frac{1}{16}, -\frac{1}{32}, \cdots$$

The indicated sum of the terms of an infinite geometric sequence is called an **infinite geometric series.**

An example of an infinite geometric series is shown at the right. The first term is 1. The common ratio is $\frac{1}{3}$.

$$1 + \frac{1}{3} + \frac{1}{9} + \frac{1}{27} + \frac{1}{81} + \frac{1}{243} + \cdots$$

The sums of the first 5, 7, 12, and 15 terms, along with the values of r^n, are shown at the right. Note that as n increases, the sum of the terms gets closer to 1.5 and the value of r^n gets closer to zero.

n	S_n	r^n
5	1.4938272	0.0041152
7	1.4993141	0.0004572
12	1.4999972	0.0000019
15	1.4999999	0.0000001

Using the Formula for the Sum of n Terms of a Geometric Sequence and the fact that r^n approaches zero when $|r| < 1$ and n increases, we can find a formula for an infinite geometric series.

The sum of the first n terms of a geometric series is shown at the right. If $|r| < 1$, then r^n can be made very close to zero by using larger and larger values of n. Therefore, the sum of the first n terms is approximately $\frac{a_1}{1 - r}$.

approximately zero

$$S_n = \frac{a_1(1 - r^n)}{1 - r}$$

$$S_n \approx \frac{a_1(1 - 0)}{1 - r} = \frac{a_1}{1 - r}$$

The Formula for the Sum of an Infinite Geometric Series

The sum of an infinite geometric series in which $|r| < 1$ is

$$S = \frac{a_1}{1 - r}.$$

When $|r| > 1$, the infinite geometric series does not have a sum. For example, the sum of the infinite geometric series $1 + 2 + 4 + 8 + \cdots$ increases without limit.

➡ Find the sum of the infinite geometric sequence $1, -\dfrac{1}{2}, \dfrac{1}{4}, -\dfrac{1}{8}, \ldots$.

The common ratio is $-\dfrac{1}{2}$. $\left| -\dfrac{1}{2} \right| < 1$.

$$S = \frac{a_1}{1 - r} = \frac{1}{1 - \left(-\dfrac{1}{2} \right)} = \frac{1}{\dfrac{3}{2}} = \frac{2}{3}$$

• Use the Formula for the Sum of an Infinite Geometric Series.

The sum of an infinite geometric series can be applied to nonterminating, repeating decimals.

The repeating decimal shown below has been rewritten as an infinite geometric series, with first term $\dfrac{3}{10}$ and common ratio $\dfrac{1}{10}$.

$$0.33\overline{3} = 0.3 + 0.03 + 0.003 + \cdots$$
$$= \frac{3}{10} + \frac{3}{100} + \frac{3}{1000} + \cdots$$

The sum of the series can be calculated by using the Formula for the Sum of an Infinite Geometric Series.

$$S = \frac{a_1}{1 - r} = \frac{\dfrac{3}{10}}{1 - \dfrac{1}{10}} = \frac{\dfrac{3}{10}}{\dfrac{9}{10}} = \frac{3}{9} = \frac{1}{3}$$

• $a_1 = \dfrac{3}{10}, r = \dfrac{1}{10}$

This method can be used to find an equivalent numerical fraction for any repeating decimal.

➡ Find an equivalent fraction for $0.12\overline{2}$.

Write the decimal as an infinite geometric series. Note that the geometric series does not begin with the first term. It begins with $\dfrac{2}{100}$. The common ratio is $\dfrac{1}{10}$.

$$0.12\overline{2} = 0.1 + 0.02 + 0.002 + 0.0002 + \cdots$$
$$= \frac{1}{10} + \underbrace{\frac{2}{100} + \frac{2}{1000} + \frac{2}{10,000} + \cdots}_{\text{Geometric Series}}$$

Use the Formula for the Sum of an Infinite Geometric Series.

$$S = \frac{a_1}{1 - r} = \frac{\dfrac{2}{100}}{1 - \dfrac{1}{10}} = \frac{\dfrac{2}{100}}{\dfrac{9}{10}} = \frac{2}{90}$$

• $a_1 = \dfrac{2}{100}, r = \dfrac{1}{10}$

Add $\dfrac{1}{10}$ to the sum of the geometric series.

$$0.12\overline{2} = \frac{1}{10} + \frac{2}{90} = \frac{11}{90}$$

An equivalent fraction for $0.12\overline{2}$ is $\dfrac{11}{90}$.

Example 5
Find the sum of the infinite geometric sequence $2, \frac{1}{2}, \frac{1}{8}, \ldots$.

Solution

$$r = \frac{a_2}{a_1} = \frac{\frac{1}{2}}{2} = \frac{1}{4}$$

$$S = \frac{a_1}{1-r} = \frac{2}{1-\frac{1}{4}} = \frac{2}{\frac{3}{4}} = \frac{8}{3}$$

You Try It 5
Find the sum of the infinite geometric sequence $3, -2, \frac{4}{3}, -\frac{8}{9}, \ldots$.

Your solution

Example 6
Find an equivalent fraction for $0.36\overline{36}$.

Solution
$$0.36\overline{36} = 0.36 + 0.0036 + 0.000036 + \cdots$$
$$= \frac{36}{100} + \frac{36}{10,000} + \frac{36}{1,000,000} + \cdots$$

$$S = \frac{a_1}{1-r} = \frac{\frac{36}{100}}{1-\frac{1}{100}} = \frac{\frac{36}{100}}{\frac{99}{100}} = \frac{36}{99} = \frac{4}{11}$$

An equivalent fraction is $\frac{4}{11}$.

You Try It 6
Find an equivalent fraction for $0.6\overline{6}$.

Your solution

Example 7
Find an equivalent fraction for $0.23\overline{45}$.

Solution
$$0.23\overline{45} = 0.23 + 0.0045 + 0.000045 + \cdots$$
$$= \frac{23}{100} + \frac{45}{10,000} + \frac{45}{1,000,000} + \cdots$$

$$S_n = \frac{a_1}{1-r} = \frac{\frac{45}{10,000}}{1-\frac{1}{100}} = \frac{\frac{45}{10,000}}{\frac{99}{100}} = \frac{45}{9900}$$

$$0.23\overline{45} = \frac{23}{100} + \frac{45}{9900} = \frac{2277}{9900} + \frac{45}{9900}$$
$$= \frac{2322}{9900} = \frac{129}{550}$$

An equivalent fraction is $\frac{129}{550}$.

You Try It 7
Find an equivalent fraction for $0.34\overline{21}$.

Your solution

Solutions on p. S35

Objective D   To solve application problems .... CT

Example 8

On the first swing, the length of the arc through which a pendulum swings is 16 in. The length of each successive swing is $\frac{7}{8}$ of the length of the preceding swing. Find the length of the arc on the fifth swing. Round to the nearest tenth.

Strategy

To find the length of the arc on the fifth swing, use the Formula for the nth Term of a Geometric Sequence.

Solution

$n = 5, a_1 = 16, r = \frac{7}{8}$

$a_n = a_1 r^{n-1}$

$a_5 = 16\left(\frac{7}{8}\right)^{5-1} = 16\left(\frac{7}{8}\right)^4 = 16\left(\frac{2401}{4096}\right)$

$\quad = \frac{38,416}{4096} \approx 9.4$

The length of the arc on the fifth swing is 9.4 in.

Example 9

Assume that a mutual fund will increase at a rate of 7% per year. If $25,000 is invested on January 1, 1997, find the value of the mutual fund on December 31, 2006.

Strategy

To find the value of the investment, use the Formula for the nth Term of a Geometric Sequence.

Solution

$n = 11, a_1 = 25,000, r = 1.07$

$a_{11} = 25,000(1.07)^{11-1} = 25,000(1.07)^{10}$

$\quad \approx 49,178.78$

The value of the investment after 10 years is $49,178.78.

You Try It 8

You start a chain letter and send it to three friends. Each of the three friends sends the letter to three other friends, and the sequence is repeated. Assuming that no one breaks the chain, find how many letters will have been mailed from the first through the sixth mailings.

Your strategy

Your solution

You Try It 9

Assume that a mutual fund will increase at a rate of 12% per year. If $25,000 is invested on January 1, 1997, find the value of the mutual fund on December 31, 2006.

Your strategy

Your solution

Solutions on p. S35

12.3 Exercises

Objective A

Find the indicated term of the geometric sequence.

1. $2, 8, 32, \ldots; a_9$

2. $4, 3, \dfrac{9}{4}, \ldots; a_8$

3. $6, -4, \dfrac{8}{3}, \ldots; a_7$

4. $-5, 15, -45, \ldots; a_7$

5. $-\dfrac{1}{16}, \dfrac{1}{8}, -\dfrac{1}{4}, \ldots; a_{10}$

6. $\dfrac{1}{27}, \dfrac{1}{9}, \dfrac{1}{3}, \ldots; a_7$

Find a_2 and a_3 for the geometric sequence.

7. $9, a_2, a_3, \dfrac{8}{3}, \ldots$

8. $8, a_2, a_3, \dfrac{27}{8}, \ldots$

9. $3, a_2, a_3, -\dfrac{8}{9}, \ldots$

10. $6, a_2, a_3, -48, \ldots$

11. $-3, a_2, a_3, 192, \ldots$

12. $5, a_2, a_3, 625, \ldots$

Objective B

Find the sum of the indicated number of terms of the geometric sequence.

13. $2, 6, 18, \ldots; n = 7$

14. $-4, 12, -36, \ldots; n = 7$

15. $12, 9, \dfrac{27}{4}, \ldots; n = 5$

16. $3, 3\sqrt{2}, 6, \ldots; n = 12$

Find the sum of the geometric series.

17. $\displaystyle\sum_{i=1}^{5} (2)^i$

18. $\displaystyle\sum_{n=1}^{6} \left(\dfrac{3}{2}\right)^n$

19. $\displaystyle\sum_{i=1}^{5} \left(\dfrac{1}{3}\right)^i$

20. $\displaystyle\sum_{n=1}^{6} \left(\dfrac{2}{3}\right)^n$

Objective C

Find the sum of the infinite geometric series.

21. $3 + 2 + \dfrac{4}{3} + \cdots$

22. $2 - \dfrac{1}{4} + \dfrac{1}{32} + \cdots$

23. $\dfrac{7}{10} + \dfrac{7}{100} + \dfrac{7}{1000} + \cdots$

24. $\dfrac{5}{100} + \dfrac{5}{10,000} + \dfrac{5}{1,000,000} + \cdots$

Find an equivalent fraction for the repeating decimal.

25. $0.88\overline{8}$ **26.** $0.55\overline{5}$ **27.** $0.22\overline{2}$ **28.** $0.99\overline{9}$

29. $0.45\overline{45}$ **30.** $0.18\overline{18}$ **31.** $0.166\overline{6}$ **32.** $0.833\overline{3}$

Objective D   *Application Problems*

33. A laboratory ore sample contains 400 mg of a radioactive material with a half-life of 1 h. Find the amount of radioactive material in the sample at the beginning of the fourth hour.

34. On the first swing, the length of the arc through which a pendulum swings is 20 in. The length of each successive swing is $\frac{4}{5}$ of the length of the preceding swing. What is the total distance the pendulum has traveled during four swings? Round to the nearest tenth of an inch.

35. To test the "bounce" of a tennis ball, the ball is dropped from a height of 10 ft. The ball bounces to 75% of its previous height with each bounce. How high does the ball bounce on the sixth bounce? Round to the nearest tenth of a foot.

36. A real estate broker estimates that a certain piece of land will increase in value at a rate of 15% each year. If the original value of the land is $25,000, what will be its value in 10 years?

37. Suppose an employee receives a wage of 1¢ for the first day of work, 2¢ the second day, 4¢ the third day, and so on in a geometric sequence. Find the total amount of money earned for working 30 days.

APPLYING THE CONCEPTS

38. State whether the following statements are true or false.
   a. The sum of an infinite geometric series is infinity.
   b. The sum of a geometric series always increases in value.
   c. $1, 8, 27, \ldots, k^3, \ldots$ is a geometric sequence.
   d. $\sqrt{1}, \sqrt{2}, \sqrt{3}, \sqrt{4}, \ldots, \sqrt{n}, \ldots$ is a geometric sequence.

39. The third term of a geometric sequence is 3, and the sixth term is $\frac{1}{9}$. Find the first term.

40. Given $a_n = 162, r = -3$, and $S_n = 122$ for a geometric sequence, find a_1 and n.

41. Explain the difference between an arithmetic sequence and a geometric sequence.

12.4   Binomial Expansions

Objective A   *To expand* $(a + b)^n$ .... CT

By carefully observing the series for each expansion of the binomial $(a + b)^n$ shown below, it is possible to identify some interesting patterns.

$(a + b)^1 = a + b$
$(a + b)^2 = a^2 + 2ab + b^2$
$(a + b)^3 = a^3 + 3a^2b + 3ab^2 + b^3$
$(a + b)^4 = a^4 + 4a^3b + 6a^2b^2 + 4ab^3 + b^4$
$(a + b)^5 = a^5 + 5a^4b + 10a^3b^2 + 10a^2b^3 + 5ab^4 + b^5$

PATTERNS FOR THE VARIABLE PART

1. The first term is a^n. The exponent on a decreases by 1 for each successive term.

2. The exponent on b increases by 1 for each successive term. The last term is b^n.

3. The degree of each term is n.

➡ Write the variable parts of the terms of the expansion of $(a + b)^6$.

$a^6, a^5b, a^4b^2, a^3b^3, a^2b^4, ab^5, b^6$ • The first term is a^6. For each successive term, the exponent on a decreases by 1, and the exponent on b increases by 1. The last term is b^6.

The variable parts of the general expansion of $(a + b)^n$ are

$a^n, a^{n-1}b, a^{n-2}b^2, ..., a^{n-r}b^r, ..., ab^{n-1}, b^n$

A pattern for the coefficients of the terms of the expanded binomial can be found by writing the coefficients in a triangular array known as **Pascal's Triangle.**

Each row begins and ends with the number 1. Any other number in a row is the sum of the two closest numbers above it. For example, $4 + 6 = 10$.

For $(a + b)^1$:   1   1
For $(a + b)^2$:   1   2   1
For $(a + b)^3$:   1   3   3   1
For $(a + b)^4$:   1   4   6   4   1
For $(a + b)^5$: 1   5   10   10   5   1

➡ Write the sixth row of Pascal's Triangle.

To write the sixth row, first write the numbers of the fifth row. The first and last numbers of the sixth row are 1. Each of the other numbers of the sixth row can be obtained by finding the sum of the two closest numbers above it in the fifth row.

1   5   10   10   5   1
1   6   15   20   15   6   1

These numbers will be the coefficients of the terms of the expansion of $(a + b)^6$.

POINT OF INTEREST

Blaise Pascal (1623–1662) is given credit for this triangle, which he first published in 1654. In that publication, the triangle looked like

1	2	3	4	5...
1	1	1	1	1...
2	1	2	3	4...
3	1	3	6...	
4	1	4...		
5	1			

Thus the triangle was rotated 45° from the way it is shown today.

The first European publication of the triangle is attributed to Peter Apianus in 1527. However, there are versions of it in a Chinese text by Yang Hui that dates from 1250. In that text, Hui demonstrated how to find the third, fourth, fifth, and sixth roots of a number by using the triangle.

Using the numbers of the sixth row of Pascal's Triangle for the coefficients and using the pattern for the variable part of each term, we can write the expanded form of $(a + b)^6$ as follows:

$$(a + b)^6 = a^6 + 6a^5b + 15a^4b^2 + 20a^3b^3 + 15a^2b^4 + 6ab^5 + b^6$$

Although Pascal's Triangle can be used to find the coefficients for the expanded form of the power of any binomial, this method is inconvenient when the power of the binomial is large. An alternative method for determining these coefficients is based on the concept of **factorial.**

POINT OF INTEREST

The exclamation point was first used as a notation for factorial in 1808 in the book *Elements d'Arithmetique Universelle,* for the convenience of the printer of the book. Some English textbooks suggested using the phrase "*n*-admiration" for *n*!.

> **n Factorial**
>
> $n!$ (which is read "n factorial") is the product of the first n consecutive natural numbers. $0!$ is defined to be 1.
>
> $$n! = n(n - 1)(n - 2) \cdots 3 \cdot 2 \cdot 1$$

$1!$, $5!$, and $7!$ are shown at the right.

$$1! = 1$$
$$5! = 5 \cdot 4 \cdot 3 \cdot 2 \cdot 1 = 120$$
$$7! = 7 \cdot 6 \cdot 5 \cdot 4 \cdot 3 \cdot 2 \cdot 1 = 5040$$

➡ Evaluate: $6!$

$$6! = 6 \cdot 5 \cdot 4 \cdot 3 \cdot 2 \cdot 1 = 720$$

• Write the factorial as a product. Then simplify.

➡ Evaluate: $\dfrac{7!}{4!\,3!}$

$$\frac{7!}{4!\,3!} = \frac{7 \cdot 6 \cdot 5 \cdot 4 \cdot 3 \cdot 2 \cdot 1}{(4 \cdot 3 \cdot 2 \cdot 1)(3 \cdot 2 \cdot 1)} = 35$$

• Write each factorial as a product. Then simplify.

The coefficients in a binomial expansion can be given in terms of factorials.

Note that in the expansion of $(a + b)^5$, the coefficient of a^2b^3 can be given by $\dfrac{5!}{2!\,3!}$. The numerator is the factorial of the power of the binomial. The denominator is the product of the factorials of the exponents on a and b.

$$(a + b)^5 =$$
$$a^5 + 5a^4b + 10a^3b^2 + 10a^2b^3 + 5ab^4 + b^5$$

$$\frac{5!}{2!\,3!} = \frac{5 \cdot 4 \cdot 3 \cdot 2 \cdot 1}{(2 \cdot 1)(3 \cdot 2 \cdot 1)} = 10$$

POINT OF INTEREST

Leonhard Euler (1707–1783) used the notation $\left(\dfrac{n}{r}\right)$ and $\left[\dfrac{n}{r}\right]$ for binomial coefficients around 1784. The notation $\binom{n}{r}$ appeared in the late 1820s.

> **Binomial Coefficients**
>
> The coefficients of $a^{n-r}b^r$ in the expansion of $(a + b)^n$ are given by $\dfrac{n!}{(n - r)!\,r!}$. The symbol $\binom{n}{r}$ is used to express this quotient.
>
> $$\binom{n}{r} = \frac{n!}{(n - r)!\,r!}$$

➡ Evaluate: $\dbinom{8}{5}$

$$\binom{8}{5} = \frac{8!}{(8 - 5)!\,5!} = \frac{8!}{3!\,5!}$$

• Write the quotient of the factorials.

$$= \frac{8 \cdot 7 \cdot 6 \cdot 5 \cdot 4 \cdot 3 \cdot 2 \cdot 1}{(3 \cdot 2 \cdot 1)(5 \cdot 4 \cdot 3 \cdot 2 \cdot 1)} = 56$$

• Simplify.

⇒ Evaluate: $\dbinom{7}{0}$

$$\dbinom{7}{0} = \dfrac{7!}{(7-0)!\,0!} = \dfrac{7!}{7!\,0!}$$ • Write the quotient of the factorials.

$$= \dfrac{7 \cdot 6 \cdot 5 \cdot 4 \cdot 3 \cdot 2 \cdot 1}{(7 \cdot 6 \cdot 5 \cdot 4 \cdot 3 \cdot 2 \cdot 1)(1)} = 1$$ • Recall that $0! = 1$.

Using factorials and the pattern for the variable part of each term, we can write a formula for any natural number power of a binomial.

The Binomial Expansion Formula

$$(a + b)^n = \dbinom{n}{0}a^n + \dbinom{n}{1}a^{n-1}b + \dbinom{n}{2}a^{n-2}b^2 + \cdots +$$
$$\dbinom{n}{r}a^{n-r}b^r + \cdots + \dbinom{n}{n}b^n$$

The Binomial Expansion Formula is used below to expand $(a + b)^5$.

$(a + b)^5$
$$= \dbinom{5}{0}a^5 + \dbinom{5}{1}a^4b + \dbinom{5}{2}a^3b^2 + \dbinom{5}{3}a^2b^3 + \dbinom{5}{4}ab^4 + \dbinom{5}{5}b^5$$
$$= a^5 + 5a^4b + 10a^3b^2 + 10a^2b^3 + 5ab^4 + b^5$$

⇒ Write $(x - 2)^4$ in expanded form.

Use the Binomial Expansion Formula. Then simplify each term.

$(x - 2)^4$
$$= \dbinom{4}{0}x^4 + \dbinom{4}{1}x^3(-2) + \dbinom{4}{2}x^2(-2)^2 + \dbinom{4}{3}x(-2)^3 + \dbinom{4}{4}(-2)^4$$
$$= x^4 + 4x^3(-2) + 6x^2(-2)^2 + 4x(-2)^3 + (-2)^4$$
$$= x^4 - 8x^3 + 24x^2 - 32x + 16$$

⇒ Write $(4x + 3y)^3$ in expanded form.

Use the Binomial Expansion Formula. Then simplify each term.

$$(4x + 3y)^3 = \dbinom{3}{0}(4x)^3 + \dbinom{3}{1}(4x)^2(3y) + \dbinom{3}{2}(4x)(3y)^2 + \dbinom{3}{3}(3y)^3$$
$$= 1(64x^3) + 3(16x^2)(3y) + 3(4x)(9y^2) + 1(27y^3)$$
$$= 64x^3 + 144x^2y + 108xy^2 + 27y^3$$

The Binomial Theorem can also be used to write any term of a binomial expansion.

Note below that in the expansion of $(a + b)^5$, the exponent on b is 1 less than the term number.

$$(a + b)^5 = a^5 + 5a^4b + 10a^3b^2 + 10a^2b^3 + 5ab^4 + b^5$$

The Formula for the rth Term in a Binomial Expansion

The rth term of $(a + b)^n$ is $\dbinom{n}{r-1}a^{n-r+1}b^{r-1}$.

⇒ Find the 4th term in the expansion of $(x + 3)^7$.

Use the Formula for the rth Term in a Binomial Expansion. $r = 4$

$$\binom{n}{r-1}a^{n-r+1}b^{r-1}$$

$$\binom{7}{4-1}x^{7-4+1}(3)^{4-1} = \binom{7}{3}x^4(3)^3 = 35x^4(27)$$

$$= 945x^4$$

⇒ Find the 12th term in the expansion of $(2x - 1)^{14}$.

Use the Formula for the rth Term in a Binomial Expansion. $r = 12$

$$\binom{14}{12-1}(2x)^{14-12+1}(-1)^{12-1} = \binom{14}{11}(2x)^3(-1)^{11} = 364(8x^3)(-1)$$

$$= -2912x^3$$

Example 1
Write $(2x + y)^3$ in expanded form.

Solution
$(2x + y)^3$

$$= \binom{3}{0}(2x)^3 + \binom{3}{1}(2x)^2(y) + \binom{3}{2}(2x)(y)^2$$

$$+ \binom{3}{3}(y)^3$$

$$= 1(8x^3) + 3(4x^2)(y) + 3(2x)(y^2) + 1(y^3)$$

$$= 8x^3 + 12x^2y + 6xy^2 + y^3$$

You Try It 1
Write $(3m - n)^4$ in expanded form.

Your solution

Example 2
Find the first three terms in the expansion of $(x + 3)^{15}$.

Solution
$(x + 3)^{15}$

$$= \binom{15}{0}x^{15} + \binom{15}{1}x^{14}(3) + \binom{15}{2}x^{13}(3)^2 + \cdots$$

$$= 1(x^{15}) + 15x^{14}(3) + 105x^{13}(9) + \cdots$$

$$= x^{15} + 45x^{14} + 945x^{13} + \cdots$$

You Try It 2
Find the first three terms in the expansion of $(y - 2)^{10}$.

Your solution

Example 3
Find the 4th term in the expansion of $(5x - y)^6$.

Solution
$n = 6, a = 5x, b = -y, r = 4$

$$\binom{6}{4-1}(5x)^{6-4+1}(-y)^{4-1}$$

$$= \binom{6}{3}(5x)^3(-y)^3$$

$$= 20(125x^3)(-y^3)$$

$$= -2500x^3y^3$$

You Try It 3
Find the 3rd term in the expansion of $(t - 2s)^7$.

Your solution

Solutions on p.S35

12.4 Exercises

Objective A

Evaluate.

1. $3!$

2. $4!$

3. $8!$

4. $9!$

5. $0!$

6. $1!$

7. $\dfrac{5!}{2!\,3!}$

8. $\dfrac{8!}{5!\,3!}$

9. $\dfrac{6!}{6!\,0!}$

10. $\dfrac{10!}{10!\,0!}$

11. $\dfrac{9!}{6!\,3!}$

12. $\dfrac{10!}{2!\,8!}$

Evaluate.

13. $\dbinom{7}{2}$

14. $\dbinom{8}{6}$

15. $\dbinom{10}{2}$

16. $\dbinom{9}{6}$

17. $\dbinom{9}{0}$

18. $\dbinom{10}{10}$

19. $\dbinom{6}{3}$

20. $\dbinom{7}{6}$

21. $\dbinom{11}{1}$

22. $\dbinom{13}{1}$

23. $\dbinom{4}{2}$

24. $\dbinom{8}{4}$

Write in expanded form.

25. $(x + y)^4$

26. $(r - s)^3$

27. $(x - y)^5$

28. $(y - 3)^4$

29. $(2m + 1)^4$

30. $(2x + 3y)^3$

31. $(2r - 3)^5$

32. $(x + 3y)^4$

Find the first three terms in the expansion.

33. $(a + b)^{10}$ | **34.** $(a + b)^9$

35. $(a - b)^{11}$ | **36.** $(a - b)^{12}$

37. $(2x + y)^8$ | **38.** $(x + 3y)^9$

39. $(4x - 3y)^8$ | **40.** $(2x - 5)^7$

41. $\left(x + \dfrac{1}{x}\right)^7$ | **42.** $\left(x - \dfrac{1}{x}\right)^8$

Find the indicated term in the expansion.

43. $(2x - 1)^7$; 4th term | **44.** $(x + 4)^5$; 3rd term

45. $(x^2 - y^2)^6$; 2nd term | **46.** $(x^2 + y^2)^7$; 6th term

47. $(y - 1)^9$; 5th term | **48.** $(x - 2)^8$; 8th term

49. $\left(n + \dfrac{1}{n}\right)^5$; 2nd term | **50.** $\left(x + \dfrac{1}{2}\right)^6$; 3rd term

APPLYING THE CONCEPTS

51. State whether the following statements are true or false.
   a. $0! \cdot 4! = 0$
   b. $\dfrac{4!}{0!}$ is undefined.
   c. In the expansion $(a + b)^8$, the exponent on a for the fifth term is 5.
   d. $n!$ is the sum of the first n positive numbers.
   e. There are n terms in the expansion of $(a + b)^n$.
   f. The sum of the exponents in each term of the expansion of $(a + b)^n$ is n.

52. Write a summary of the history of the development of Pascal's Triangle. Include some of the properties of the triangle.

Focus on Problem Solving

Forming Negations
Problem solving sometimes requires that you form the **negation** of a statement. If a statement is true, its negation must be false. If a statement is false, its negation must be true. For instance,

> "Henry Aaron broke Babe Ruth's home run record" is a true sentence. Accordingly, the sentence "Henry Aaron did not break Babe Ruth's home run record" is false.

> "Dogs have twelve paws" is a false sentence, so the sentence "Dogs do not have twelve paws" is a true sentence.

To form the negation of a statement requires a precise understanding of the statement being negated. Here are some phrases that demand special attention.

Statement	Meaning
At least seven	Greater than or equal to seven
More than seven	More than seven (does not include 7)
At most seven	Less than or equal to seven
Less than (or *fewer than*) seven	Less than seven (does not include 7)

Consider the sentence "At least three people scored over 90 on the last test." The negation of that sentence is "Fewer than three people scored over 90 on the last test."

For each of the following, write the negation of the given sentence.

1. There was at least one error on the test.
2. The temperature was less than 30 degrees.
3. The mountain is more than 5000 ft tall.
4. There are at most five vacancies for the field trip to New York.

When the word *all*, *no* (or *none*), or *some* occurs in a sentence, forming the negation requires careful thought. Consider the sentence "All roads are paved with cement." This sentence is not true because there are some roads—dirt roads, for example—that are not paved with cement. Because the sentence is false, its negation must be true. You might be tempted to write "All roads are not paved with cement" as the negation, but that sentence is not true because some roads are paved with cement. The correct negation is "*Some* roads are *not* paved with cement."

Now consider the sentence "Some fish live in aquariums." Because this sentence is true, the negation must be false. Writing "Some fish do not live in aquariums" as the negation is not correct because that sentence is true. The correct negation is "*All* fish do *not* live in aquariums."

The sentence "No houses have basements" is false because there is at least one house with a basement. Because this sentence is false, its negation must be true. The negation is "Some houses do have basements."

Statement	Negation
All *A* are *B*.	Some *A* are not *B*.
No *A* are *B*.	Some *A* are *B*.
Some *A* are *B*.	All *A* are not *B*.
Some *A* are not *B*.	All *A* are *B*.

Write the negation of each sentence.

5. All trees are tall.

6. All cats chase mice.

7. Some flowers have red blooms.

8. No golfers like tennis.

9. Some students do not like math.

10. No honest people are politicians.

11. All cars have power steering.

12. Some televisions are black and white.

Projects and Group Activities

ISBN and UPC Numbers

Every book that is cataloged for the Library of Congress must have an ISBN (International Standard Book Number). An ISBN is a 10-digit number of the form a_1-$a_2a_3a_4$-$a_5a_6a_7a_8a_9$-c. For instance, the ISBN for the Windows version of the CD-ROM containing the *American Heritage Children's Dictionary* is 0-395-73580-7. The first number, 0, indicates that the book is written in English. The next three numbers, 395, indicate the publisher (Houghton Mifflin Company). The next five numbers, 73580, identify the book (*American Heritage Children's Dictionary*), and the last digit, c, is called a *check digit*. This digit is chosen such that the following sum is divisible by 11.

$$a_1(10) + a_2(9) + a_3(8) + a_4(7) + a_5(6) + a_6(5) + a_7(4) + a_8(3) + a_9(2) + c$$

For the *American Heritage Children's Dictionary*,

$$0(10) + 3(9) + 9(8) + 5(7) + 7(6) + 3(5) + 5(4) + 8(3) + 0(2) + c$$
$$= 235 + c$$

The last digit of the ISBN is chosen as 7 because $235 + 7 = 242$ and $242 \div 11 = 22$. The value of c could be any number from 0 to 10. The number 10 is coded as an X.

One purpose of the ISBN method of coding books is to ensure that orders placed for books are accurately filled. For instance, suppose a clerk sends an order for the *American Heritage Children's Dictionary* and inadvertently enters the number 0-395-75380-7 (the 3 and 5 have been transposed). Now

$$0(10) + 3(9) + 9(8) + 5(7) + 7(6) + 5(5) + 3(4) + 8(3) + 0(2) + 7 = 244$$

and 244 is not divisible by 11. Thus an error in the ISBN has been made.

1. Determine the check digit for the book *Reader's Digest Book of Facts*. The first nine digits of the ISBN are 0-895-77692-?

2. Is 0-395-12370-4 a possible ISBN?

The UPC (Universal Product Code) is another coding scheme. This number is particularly useful in grocery stores. A checkout clerk passes the number by a scanner that reads the number and records the price on the cash register.

The UPC is a 12-digit number of the form a_1-$a_2a_3a_4a_5$-$a_6a_7a_8a_9a_{10}a_{11}$-c. The last digit is the check digit and is chosen such that the following sum ends in zero.

$$a_1(3) + a_2 + a_3(3) + a_4 + a_5(3) + a_6 + a_7(3) + a_8 + a_9(3) + a_{10} + a_{11}(3) + c$$

The UPC for the *Consumer Guide, 1997 Cars* is 0-71162-00699-5. Using the expression above,

$$0(3) + 7 + 1(3) + 1 + 6(3) + 2 + 0(3) + 0 + 6(3) + 9 + 9(3) + c$$
$$= 85 + c$$

Because $85 + 5 = 90$, which ends in zero, the check digit is 5.

Unlike the ISBN, the UPC coding scheme does not detect all transpositions. If the 6 and 1 are transposed for the *Consumer Guide, 1997 Cars*, then

$$0(3) + 7 + 1(3) + 6 + 1(3) + 2 + 0(3) + 0 + 6(3) + 9 + 9(3) + 5 = 80$$

The number still ends in zero, but the UPC is incorrect.

3. Check the UPC code of a product in your home.

4. Check the ISBN of the intermediate algebra text that you are now using.

Chapter Summary

Key Words   A *sequence* is an ordered list of numbers.

Each of the numbers of a sequence is called a *term* of the sequence.

A *finite sequence* contains a finite number of terms.

An *infinite sequence* contains an infinite number of terms.

The indicated sum of the terms of a sequence is a *series*.

An *arithmetic sequence*, or arithmetic progression, is one in which the difference between any two consecutive terms is constant. The difference between consecutive terms is called the *common difference* of the sequence.

A *geometric sequence*, or geometric progression, is one in which each successive term of the sequence is the same nonzero constant multiple of the preceding term. The common multiple is called the *common ratio* of the sequence.

An *arithmetic series* is the indicated sum of the terms of an arithmetic sequence.

A *geometric series* is the indicated sum of the terms of a geometric sequence.

n factorial, written *n*!, is the product of the first *n* natural numbers.

Essential Rules   *Formula for the nth Term of an Arithmetic Sequence*
The *n*th term of an arithmetic sequence with a common difference of d is given by $a_n = a_1 + (n - 1)d$.

Formula for the Sum of n Terms of an Arithmetic Sequence
Let a_1 be the first term of a finite arithmetic sequence, let n be the number of terms, and let a_n be the last term of the sequence. Then the sum of the series S_n is given by $S_n = \frac{n}{2}(a_1 + a_n)$.

Formula for the nth Term of a Geometric Sequence
The *n*th term of a geometric sequence with first term a_1 and common ratio r is given by $a_n = a_1 r^{n-1}$.

Formula for the Sum of n Terms of a Geometric Series
Let a_1 be the first term of a finite geometric sequence, let n be the number of terms, and let r be the common ratio. Then the sum of the series S_n is given by $S_n = \frac{a_1(1 - r^n)}{1 - r}$.

Formula for the Sum of an Infinite Geometric Series
The sum of an infinite geometric series in which $|r| < 1$ and a_1 is the first term is given by $S = \frac{a_1}{1 - r}$.

The Binomial Formula
$$(a + b)^n = \binom{n}{0}a^n + \binom{n}{1}a^{n-1}b + \binom{n}{2}a^{n-2}b^2 + \cdots + \binom{n}{n-1}ab^{n-1} + \binom{n}{n}b^n$$

Formula for the rth Term in a Binomial Expansion
The *r*th term of $(a + b)^n$ is $\binom{n}{r-1}a^{n-r+1}b^{r-1}$.

Chapter Review

1. Write $\sum_{i=1}^{4} 2x^{i-1}$ in expanded form.

2. Write the 10th term of the sequence whose nth term is given by the formula $a_n = 3n - 2$.

3. Find an equivalent fraction for $0.63\overline{3}$.

4. Find the sum of the infinite geometric series $\frac{3}{10} + \frac{3}{100} + \frac{3}{1000} + \cdots$.

5. Find the sum of the arithmetic series $\sum_{i=1}^{30} (4i - 1)$.

6. Find the sum of the series $\sum_{n=1}^{5} (3n - 2)$.

7. Find an equivalent fraction for $0.23\overline{23}$.

8. Evaluate: $\binom{9}{3}$

9. Find the sum of the geometric series $\sum_{n=1}^{5} 2(3)^n$.

10. Find the number of terms in the finite arithmetic sequence 8, 2, -4, ..., -118.

11. Find the sum of the geometric series $\sum_{n=1}^{8} \left(\frac{1}{2}\right)^n$. Round to the nearest thousandth.

12. Find the 5th term in the expansion of $(3x - y)^8$.

13. Write the 5th term of the sequence whose nth term is given by the formula $a_n = \frac{(-1)^{2n-1}n}{n^2 + 2}$.

14. Find the sum of the first seven terms of the geometric sequence 5, $5\sqrt{5}$, 25, ... Round to the nearest whole number.

15. Find the formula for the nth term of the arithmetic sequence -7, -2, 3, ...

16. Find the 8th term in the expansion of $(x - 2y)^{11}$.

17. Find the 12th term of the geometric sequence 1, $\sqrt{3}$, 3, ….

18. Find the sum of the first 40 terms of the arithmetic sequence 11, 13, 15, ….

19. Evaluate: $\dbinom{12}{9}$

20. Find the sum of the series $\displaystyle\sum_{n=1}^{4} \frac{(-1)^{n-1}n}{n+1}$.

21. Write $\displaystyle\sum_{i=1}^{5} \frac{(2x)^i}{i}$ in expanded form.

22. Find the 8th term of the geometric sequence 3, 1, $\frac{1}{3}$, ….

23. Write $(x - 3y^2)^5$ in expanded form.

24. Find the sum of the infinite geometric series $4 - 1 + \frac{1}{4} - \cdots$.

25. Find the sum of the infinite geometric series $2 + \frac{4}{3} + \frac{8}{9} + \cdots$.

26. Evaluate: $\dfrac{12!}{5!\,8!}$

27. Find the 20th term of the arithmetic sequence 1, 5, 9, ….

28. The temperature of a hot water spa is 102°F. Each hour the temperature is 5% lower than during the previous hour. Find the temperature of the spa after 8 h. Round to the nearest tenth.

29. The salary schedule for an apprentice electrician is $1200 for the first month and a $40-per-month salary increase for the next eight months. Find the total salary for the nine-month period.

30. A laboratory radioactive sample contains 200 mg of a material with a half-life of 1 h. Find the amount of radioactive material in the sample at the beginning of the seventh hour.

Chapter Test

1. Find the sum of the series $\displaystyle\sum_{n=1}^{4}(3n + 1)$.

2. Evaluate: $\dbinom{9}{6}$

3. Find the 7th term of the geometric sequence $4, 4\sqrt{2}, 8, \ldots$.

4. Write the 14th term of the sequence whose nth term is given by the formula $a_n = \dfrac{8}{n + 2}$.

5. Write in expanded form: $\displaystyle\sum_{i=1}^{4} 3x^i$

6. Find the sum of the first 18 terms of the arithmetic sequence $-25, -19, -13, \ldots$.

7. Find the sum of the infinite geometric sequence $4, 3, \dfrac{9}{4}, \ldots$.

8. Find the number of terms in the finite arithmetic sequence $-5, -8, -11, \ldots, -50$.

9. Find an equivalent fraction for $0.23\overline{3}$.

10. Evaluate: $\dfrac{8!}{4!\,4!}$

11. Find the 5th term of the geometric sequence $6, 2, \dfrac{2}{3}, \ldots$.

12. Find the 4th term in the expansion of $(x - 2y)^7$.

13. Find the 35th term of the arithmetic sequence $-13, -16, -19, \ldots$.

14. Find the formula for the nth term of the arithmetic sequence 12, 9, 6, ….

15. Find the sum of the first 5 terms of the geometric sequence $-6, 12, -24, \ldots$.

16. Find the 6th and 7th terms of the sequence whose nth term is given by the formula $a_n = \dfrac{n + 1}{n}$.

17. Find the sum of the first 6 terms of the geometric sequence $1, \dfrac{3}{2}, \dfrac{9}{4}, \ldots$.

18. Find the sum of the first 21 terms of the arithmetic sequence 5, 12, 19, ….

19. An inventory of supplies for a fabric manufacturer indicated that 7500 yd of material were in stock on January 1. On February 1, and on the first of the month for each successive month, the manufacturer sent 550 yd of material to retail outlets. How much material was in stock after the shipment on October 1?

20. An ore sample contains 320 mg of a radioactive substance with a half-life of one day. Find the amount of radioactive material in the sample at the beginning of the fifth day.

Cumulative Review

1. Graph: $3x - 2y = -4$

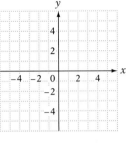

2. Factor: $2x^6 + 16$

3. Simplify: $\dfrac{4x^2}{x^2 + x - 2} - \dfrac{3x - 2}{x + 2}$

4. Given $f(x) = 2x^2 - 3x$, find $f(-2)$.

5. Simplify: $\sqrt{2y}(\sqrt{8xy} - \sqrt{y})$

6. Solve by using the quadratic formula: $2x^2 - x + 7 = 0$

7. Solve: $5 - \sqrt{x} = \sqrt{x + 5}$

8. Find the equation of the circle that passes through the point $(4, 2)$ and whose center is $(-1, -1)$.

9. Solve by the addition method:
$3x - 3y = 2$
$6x - 4y = 5$

10. Evaluate the determinant:
$\begin{vmatrix} -3 & 1 \\ 4 & 2 \end{vmatrix}$

11. Solve: $2x - 1 > 3$ or $1 - 3x > 7$

12. Graph: $2x - 3y < 9$

13. Write $\log_5 \sqrt{\dfrac{x}{y}}$ in expanded form.

14. Solve for x: $4^x = 8^{x-1}$

15. Write the 5th and 6th terms of the sequence whose nth term is given by the formula $a_n = n(n - 1)$.

16. Find the sum of the series $\displaystyle\sum_{n=1}^{7} (-1)^{n-1}(n + 2)$.

17. Find the 33rd term of the arithmetic sequence $-7, -10, -13, \ldots$.

18. Find the sum of the infinite geometric sequence $3, -2, \frac{4}{3}, \ldots$.

19. Find an equivalent fraction for $0.4\overline{6}$.

20. Find the 6th term in the expansion of $(2x + y)^6$.

21. How many ounces of pure water must be added to 200 oz of an 8% salt solution to make a 5% salt solution?

22. A new computer can complete a payroll in 16 min less time than it takes an older computer to complete the same payroll. Working together, both computers can complete the payroll in 15 min. How long would it take each computer working alone to complete the payroll?

23. A boat traveling with the current went 15 mi in 2 h. Against the current it took 3 h to travel the same distance. Find the rate of the boat in calm water and the rate of the current.

24. An 80-milligram sample of a radioactive material decays to 55 mg in 30 days. Use the exponential decay equation $A = A_0 \left(\frac{1}{2}\right)^{t/k}$, where A is the amount of radioactive material present after time t, k is the half-life, and A_0 is the original amount of radioactive material, to find the half-life of the 80-milligram sample. Round to the nearest whole number.

25. A "theater in the round" has 62 seats in the first row, 74 seats in the second row, 86 seats in the third row, and so on in an arithmetic sequence. Find the total number of seats in the theater if there are 12 rows of seats.

26. To test the "bounce" of a ball, the ball is dropped from a height of 8 ft. The ball bounces to 80% of its previous height with each bounce. How high does the ball bounce on the fifth bounce? Round to the nearest tenth.

Final Exam

1. Simplify: $12 - 8[3 - (-2)]^2 \div 5 - 3$

2. Evaluate $\dfrac{a^2 - b^2}{a - b}$ when $a = 3$ and $b = -4$.

3. Simplify: $5 - 2[3x - 7(2 - x) - 5x]$

4. Solve: $\dfrac{3}{4}x - 2 = 4$

5. Solve: $\dfrac{2 - 4x}{3} - \dfrac{x - 6}{12} = \dfrac{5x - 2}{6}$

6. Solve: $8 - |5 - 3x| = 1$

7. Graph $2x - 3y = 9$ using the x- and y-intercepts.

8. Find the equation of the line containing the points $(3, -2)$ and $(1, 4)$.

9. Find the equation of the line that contains the point $(-2, 1)$ and is perpendicular to the line $3x - 2y = 6$.

10. Simplify: $2a[5 - a(2 - 3a) - 2a] + 3a^2$

11. Factor: $8 - x^3y^3$

12. Factor: $x - y - x^3 + x^2y$

13. Simplify: $(2x^3 - 7x^2 + 4) \div (2x - 3)$

14. Simplify: $\dfrac{x^2 - 3x}{2x^2 - 3x - 5} \div \dfrac{4x - 12}{4x^2 - 4}$

15. Simplify: $\dfrac{x - 2}{x + 2} - \dfrac{x + 3}{x - 3}$

16. Simplify: $\dfrac{\dfrac{3}{x} + \dfrac{1}{x + 4}}{\dfrac{1}{x} + \dfrac{3}{x + 4}}$

17. Solve: $\dfrac{5}{x - 2} - \dfrac{5}{x^2 - 4} = \dfrac{1}{x + 2}$

18. Solve $a_n = a_1 + (n - 1)d$ for d.

19. Simplify: $\left(\dfrac{4x^2y^{-1}}{3x^{-1}y}\right)^{-2}\left(\dfrac{2x^{-1}y^2}{9x^{-2}y^2}\right)^3$

20. Simplify: $\left(\dfrac{3x^{2/3}y^{1/2}}{6x^2y^{4/3}}\right)^6$

21. Simplify: $x\sqrt{18x^2y^3} - y\sqrt{50x^4y}$

22. Simplify: $\dfrac{\sqrt{16x^5y^4}}{\sqrt{32xy^7}}$

23. Simplify: $\dfrac{3}{2 + i}$

24. Write a quadratic equation that has integer coefficients and has solutions $-\dfrac{1}{2}$ and 2.

25. Solve by using the quadratic formula: $2x^2 - 3x - 1 = 0$

26. Solve: $x^{2/3} - x^{1/3} - 6 = 0$

27. Solve: $\dfrac{2}{x} - \dfrac{2}{2x + 3} = 1$

28. Graph: $f(x) = -x^2 + 4$

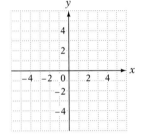

29. Graph: $\dfrac{x^2}{16} + \dfrac{y^2}{4} = 1$

30. Find the inverse of the function $f(x) = \dfrac{2}{3}x - 4.$

31. Solve by the addition method:
$3x - 2y = 1$
$5x - 3y = 3$

32. Evaluate the determinant:
$\begin{vmatrix} 3 & 4 \\ -1 & 2 \end{vmatrix}$

33. Solve: $x^2 - y^2 = 4$
$\qquad x + y = 1$

34. Solve: $2 - 3x < 6$ and $2x + 1 > 4$

35. Solve: $|2x + 5| < 3$

36. Graph the solution set: $3x + 2y > 6$

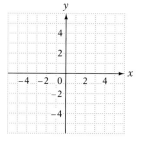

37. Graph: $f(x) = \log_2(x + 1)$

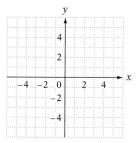

38. Write $2(\log_2 a - \log_2 b)$ as a single logarithm with a coefficient of 1.

39. Solve for x: $\log_3 x - \log_3(x - 3) = \log_3 2$

40. Write $\displaystyle\sum_{i=1}^{5} 2y^i$ in expanded form.

41. Find an equivalent fraction $0.5\overline{1}$.

42. Find the 3rd term in the expansion of $(x - 2y)^9$.

43. An average score of 70–79 in a history class receives a C grade. A student has grades of 64, 58, 82, and 77 on four history tests. Find the range of scores on the fifth test that will give the student a C grade for the course.

44. A jogger and a cyclist set out at 8 A.M. from the same point headed in the same direction. The average speed of the cyclist is two and a half times the average speed of the jogger. In 2 h, the cyclist is 24 mi ahead of the jogger. How far did the cyclist ride in that time?

45. You have a total of $12,000 invested in two simple interest accounts. On one account, a money market fund, the annual simple interest rate is 8.5%. On the other account, a tax free bond fund, the annual simple interest rate is 6.4%. The total annual interest earned by the two accounts is $936. How much do you have invested in each account?

46. The length of a rectangle is 1 ft less than three times the width. The area of the rectangle is 140 ft². Find the length and width of the rectangle.

47. Three hundred shares of a utility stock earn a yearly dividend of $486. How many additional shares of the utility stock would give a total dividend income of $810?

48. An account executive traveled 45 mi by car and then an additional 1050 mi by plane. The rate of the plane was seven times the rate of the car. The total time for the trip was $3\frac{1}{4}$ h. Find the rate of the plane.

49. An object is dropped from the top of a building. Find the distance the object has fallen when the speed reaches 75 ft/s. Use the equation $v = \sqrt{64d}$, where v is the speed of the object and d is the distance. Round to the nearest whole number.

50. A small plane made a trip of 660 mi in 5 h. The plane traveled the first 360 mi at a constant rate before increasing its speed by 30 mph. Then it traveled another 300 mi at the increased speed. Find the rate of the plane for the first 360 mi.

51. The intensity, L, of a light source is inversely proportional to the square of the distance, d, from the source. If the intensity is 8 foot-candles at a distance of 20 ft, what is the intensity when the distance is 4 ft?

52. A motorboat traveling with the current can go 30 mi in 2 h. Against the current, it takes 3 h to go the same distance. Find the rate of the motorboat in calm water and the rate of the current.

53. An investor deposits $4000 into an account that earns 9% annual interest compounded monthly. Use the compound interest formula $P = A(1 + i)^n$, where A is the original value of the investment, i is the interest rate per compounding period, n is the total number of compounding periods, and P is the value of the investment after n periods, to find the value of the investment after two years. Round to the nearest cent.

54. Assume that the average value of a home increases 6% per year. How much will a house costing $80,000 be worth in 20 years? Round to the nearest dollar.

Appendix: Guidelines for Using Graphing Calculators

TEXAS INSTRUMENTS TI-83

To evaluate an expression

a. Press the $\boxed{\text{Y=}}$ key. A menu showing $\backslash Y_1 =$ through $\backslash Y_7 =$ will be displayed vertically with a blinking cursor to the right of $\backslash Y_1 =$. Press $\boxed{\text{CLEAR}}$, if necessary, to delete an unwanted expression.

b. Input the expression to be evaluated. For example, to input the expression $-3a^2b - 4c$, use the following keystrokes:

$\boxed{(-)}$ 3 $\boxed{\text{ALPHA}}$ A $\boxed{\wedge}$ 2 $\boxed{\text{ALPHA}}$ B $\boxed{-}$ 4 $\boxed{\text{ALPHA}}$ C $\boxed{\text{2nd}}$ QUIT

Note the difference between the keys for a negative sign $\boxed{(-)}$ and a *minus* sign $\boxed{-}$.

c. Store the value of each variable that will be used in the expression. For example, to evaluate the expression above when $a = 3$, $b = -2$, and $c = -4$, use the following keystrokes:

3 $\boxed{\text{STO}\triangleright}$ $\boxed{\text{ALPHA}}$ A $\boxed{\text{ENTER}}$ $\boxed{(-)}$ 2 $\boxed{\text{STO}\triangleright}$ $\boxed{\text{ALPHA}}$ B $\boxed{\text{ENTER}}$ $\boxed{(-)}$ 4 $\boxed{\text{STO}\triangleright}$ $\boxed{\text{ALPHA}}$ C $\boxed{\text{ENTER}}$

These steps store the value of each variable.

d. Press $\boxed{\text{VARS}}$ $\boxed{\triangleright}$ $\boxed{1}$ $\boxed{1}$ $\boxed{\text{ENTER}}$. The value for the expression, Y_1, for the given values is displayed; in this case, $Y_1 = 70$.

To graph a function

a. Press the $\boxed{\text{Y=}}$ key. A menu showing $\backslash Y_1 =$ through $\backslash Y_7 =$ will be displayed vertically with a blinking cursor to the right of $\backslash Y_1 =$. Press $\boxed{\text{CLEAR}}$, if necessary, to delete an unwanted expression.

b. Input the expression for each function that is to be graphed. Press $\boxed{\text{X,T,}\theta,n}$ to input x. For example, to input $y = x^3 + 2x^2 - 5x - 6$, use the following keystrokes:

$\boxed{\text{X,T,}\theta,n}$ $\boxed{\wedge}$ 3 $\boxed{+}$ 2 $\boxed{\text{X,T,}\theta,n}$ $\boxed{\wedge}$ 2 $\boxed{-}$ 5 $\boxed{\text{X,T,}\theta,n}$ $\boxed{-}$ 6

c. Set the domain and range by pressing $\boxed{\text{WINDOW}}$. Enter the values for the minimum x-value (Xmin), the maximum x-value (Xmax), the distance between tick marks on the x-axis (Xscl), the minimum y-value (Ymin), the maximum y-value (Ymax), and the distance between tick marks on the y-axis (Yscl). Now press $\boxed{\text{GRAPH}}$. For the graph shown at the left, Xmin = -10, Xmax = 10, Xscl = 1, Ymin = -10, Ymax = 10, and Yscl = 1. This is called the standard viewing rectangle. Pressing $\boxed{\text{ZOOM}}$ $\boxed{6}$ is a quick way to set the calculator to the standard viewing rectangle. *Note:* This will also immediately graph the function in that window.

d. Press the $\boxed{\text{Y=}}$ key. The equal sign has a black rectangle around it. This indicates that the function is active and will be graphed when the $\boxed{\text{GRAPH}}$ key is pressed. A function is deactivated by using the arrow keys. Move the cursor over the equal sign and press $\boxed{\text{ENTER}}$. When the cursor is moved to the right, the black rectangle will not be present and that equation will not be active.

e. Graphing some radical equations requires special care. To graph the function $y = \sqrt{2x + 3}$, enter the following keystrokes:

$\boxed{\text{Y=}}$ $\boxed{\text{2nd}}$ $\boxed{\sqrt{}}$ 2 $\boxed{\text{X,T,}\theta,n}$ $\boxed{+}$ 3 $\boxed{)}$

The graph is shown below.

To display the *x*-coordinates of rectangular coordinates as integers

a. Set the viewing window as follows: Xmin = −47, Xmax = 47, Xscl = 10, Ymin = −31, Ymax = 31, Yscl = 10.

b. Graph the function and use the TRACE feature. Press ⌈TRACE⌉ and then move the cursor with the ⌈◁⌉ and ⌈▷⌉ keys. The values of *x* and *y* = *f*(*x*) displayed on the bottom of the screen are the coordinates of a point on the graph.

To display the *x*-coordinates of rectangular coordinates in tenths

a. Set the viewing window as follows: ⌈ZOOM⌉ ⌈4⌉

b. Graph the function and use the TRACE feature. Press ⌈TRACE⌉ and then move the cursor with the ⌈◁⌉ and ⌈▷⌉ keys. The values of *x* and *y* = *f*(*x*) displayed on the bottom of the screen are the coordinates of a point on the graph.

To evaluate a function for a given value of *x*, or to produce ordered pairs of a function

a. Input the equation; for example, input $y_1 = 2x^3 - 3x + 2$.

b. Press ⌈2nd⌉ QUIT.

c. Input a value for *x*; for example, to input 3 press 3 ⌈STO▷⌉ ⌈X,T,θ,*n*⌉ ⌈ENTER⌉.

d. Press ⌈VARS⌉ ⌈▷⌉ ⌈1⌉ ⌈1⌉ ⌈ENTER⌉. The value for the expression, Y₁, for the given *x*-value is displayed, in this case, Y₁ = 47. An ordered pair of the function is (3, 47).

e. Repeat steps **c.** and **d.** to produce as many pairs as desired. The TABLE feature of the *TI-83* can also be used to determine pairs.

ZOOM FEATURES

To zoom in or out on a graph

a. Here are two methods of using ZOOM. The first method uses the built-in features of the calculator. Move the cursor to a point on the graph that is of interest. Press ⌈ZOOM⌉. The ZOOM menu will appear. Press ⌈2⌉ ⌈ENTER⌉ to zoom in on the graph by the amount shown under the SET FACTORS menu. The center of the new graph is the location at which you placed the cursor. Press ⌈ZOOM⌉ ⌈3⌉ ⌈ENTER⌉ to zoom out on the graph by the amount under the SET FACTORS menu. (The SET FACTORS menu is accessed by pressing ⌈ZOOM⌉ ⌈▷⌉ ⌈4⌉.)

b. The second method uses the ZBOX option under the ZOOM menu. To use this method, press ⌈ZOOM⌉ ⌈1⌉. A cursor will appear on the graph. Use the arrow keys to move the cursor to a portion of the graph that is of interest. Press ⌈ENTER⌉. Now use the arrow keys to draw a box around the portion of the graph you wish to see. Press ⌈ENTER⌉. The portion of the graph defined by the box will be drawn.

c. Pressing ⌈ZOOM⌉ ⌈6⌉ resets the window to the standard 10 × 10 viewing window.

SOLVING EQUATIONS

This discussion is based on the fact that the solution of an equation can be related to the x-intercepts of a graph. For instance, the real solutions of the equation $x^2 = x + 1$ are the x-intercepts of the graph of $f(x) = x^2 - x - 1$, which are the zeros of f.

To solve $x^2 = x + 1$, rewrite the equation with all terms on one side. The equation is now $x^2 - x - 1 = 0$. Think of this equation as $Y_1 = x^2 - x - 1$. The x-intercepts of the graph of Y_1 are the solutions of the equation $x^2 = x + 1$.

a. Enter $x^2 - x - 1$ into Y_1.

b. Graph the equation. You may need to adjust the viewing window so that the x-intercepts are visible.

c. Press ⎡2nd⎤ CALC ⎡2⎤.

d. Move the cursor to a point on the curve that is to the left of an x-intercept. Press ⎡ENTER⎤.

e. Move the cursor to a point on the curve that is to the right of an x-intercept. Press ⎡ENTER⎤.

f. Press ⎡ENTER⎤.

g. The root is shown as the x-coordinate on the bottom of the screen; in this case, the root is approximately -0.618034. To find the next intercept, repeat steps **c.** through **f.** The SOLVER feature under the MATH menu can also be used to find solutions of equations.

SOLVING SYSTEMS OF EQUATIONS IN TWO VARIABLES

To solve a system of equations

To solve $\quad \begin{array}{l} y = x^2 - 1 \\ \frac{1}{2}x + y = 1 \end{array}\quad$,

a. Solve each equation for y.

b. Enter the first equation as Y_1. For instance, $Y_1 = x^2 - 1$.

c. Enter the second equation as Y_2. For instance, $Y_2 = 1 - \frac{1}{2}x$.

d. Graph both equations. (*Note:* The point of intersection must appear on the screen. It may be necessary to adjust the viewing window so that the point(s) of intersection are displayed.)

e. Press ⎡2nd⎤ CALC ⎡5⎤.

f. Move the cursor to the left of the first point of intersection. Press ⎡ENTER⎤.

g. Move the cursor to the right of the first point of intersection. Press ⎡ENTER⎤.

h. Press ⎡ENTER⎤.

i. The first point of intersection is $(-1.686141, 1.8430703)$.

j. Repeat steps **e.** through **h.** for each point of intersection.

FINDING MINIMUM OR MAXIMUM VALUES OF A FUNCTION

a. Enter the function into Y_1. The equation $y = x^2 - x - 1$ is used here.

b. Graph the equation. You may need to adjust the viewing window so that the maximum or minimum points are visible.

c. Press ⎡2nd⎤ CALC ⎡3⎤ to determine a minimum value or press ⎡2nd⎤ CALC ⎡4⎤ to determine a maximum value.

d. Move the cursor to a point on the curve that is to the left of the minimum (maximum). Press ⎡ENTER⎤.

e. Move the cursor to a point on the curve that is to the right of the minimum (maximum). Press ENTER.

f. Press ENTER.

g. The minimum (maximum) is shown as the *y*-coordinate on the bottom of the screen; in this case the minimum value is -1.25.

SHARP EL-9600

To evaluate an expression

a. The SOLVER mode of the calculator is used to evaluate expressions. To enter SOLVER mode, press 2ndF SOLVER CL. The expression $-3a^2b - 4c$ must be entered as the equation $-3a^2b - 4c = t$. The letter t can be any letter other than one used in the expression. Use the following keystrokes to input $-3a^2b - 4c = t$:

(−) 3 ALPHA A a^b 2 ▷ ALPHA B − 4 ALPHA C ALPHA = ALPHA T ENTER

Note the difference between the keys for a *negative* sign (−) and a *minus* sign.

b. After you press ENTER, variables used in the equation will be displayed on the screen. To evaluate the expression for $a = 3$, $b = -2$, and $c = -4$, input each value, pressing ENTER after each number. When the cursor moves to T, press 2ndF EXE. T = 70 will appear on the screen. This is the value of the expression. To evaluate the expression again for different values of *a*, *b*, and *c*, press 2ndF QUIT and then 2ndF SOLVER.

c. Press [±/×÷] to return to normal operation.

To graph a function

a. Press the Y= key. The screen will show Y_1 through Y_8.

b. Input the expression for a function that is to be graphed. Press X/T/θ/*n* to enter an *x*. For example, to input $y = \frac{1}{2}x - 3$, use the following keystrokes:

Y= CL (1 ÷ 2) X/T/θ/*n* − 3 ENTER

c. Set the viewing window by pressing WINDOW. Enter the values for the minimum x-value (Xmin), the maximum x-value (Xmax), the distance between tick marks on the x-axis (Xscl), the minimum y-value (Ymin), the maximum y-value (Ymax), and the distance between tick marks on the y-axis (Yscl). Press ENTER after each entry. Press GRAPH. For the graph shown at the left, enter Xmin = −10, Xmax = 10, Ymin = −10, Ymax = 10. Press GRAPH.

d. Press Y= to return to the equation. The equal sign has a black rectangle around it. This indicates that the function is active and will be graphed when the GRAPH key is pressed. A function is deactivated by using the arrow keys. Move the cursor over the equal sign and press ENTER. When the cursor is moved to the right, the black rectangle will not be present and that equation will not be active.

e. Graphing some radical equations requires special care. To graph the function $y = \sqrt{2x + 3}$, enter the following keystrokes:

Y= CL 2ndF √ 2 X/T/θ/*n* + 3 ▷ GRAPH

The graph is shown at the left.

To display the *xy*-coordinates as integers

a. Press ZOOM ▷ 8.

b. Graph the function. Press TRACE. Use the left and right arrow keys to trace

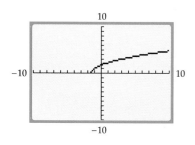

along the graph of the function. The x- and y-coordinates of the function are shown on the bottom of the screen.

To display the xy-coordinates in tenths

a. Press ZOOM ▷ 7.

b. Graph the function. Press TRACE .Use the left and right arrow keys to trace along the graph of the function. The x- and y-coordinates of the function are shown on the bottom of the screen.

To evaluate a function for a given value of x, or to produce ordered pairs of the function

a. Press Y= . Input the expression. For instance, input
   Y= CL 2 X/T/θ/n ∧ 3 − 3 X/T/θ/n + 2. Press ENTER .

b. Press ⊞⊟⊠÷ . Store the x-coordinate of the ordered pair you want in X/T/θ/n .
   For instance, enter 3 STO X/T/θ/n ENTER .

c. Press VARS ENTER 1 ENTER . The value of y, 47, will be displayed on the screen. The ordered pair is (3, 47). The TABLE feature of the calculator can also be used to find many ordered pairs for a function.

ZOOM FEATURES OF THE SHARP EL-9600

To zoom in or out on a graph

a. Here are two methods of using ZOOM. The first method uses the built-in features of the calculator. Move the cursor to a point on the graph that is of interest. Press ZOOM . The ZOOM menu will appear. Press 3 to zoom in on the graph by the amount shown by FACTOR. The center of the new graph is the location at which you placed the cursor. Press ZOOM 4 to zoom out on the graph by the amount shown in FACTOR.

b. The second method uses the BOX option under the ZOOM menu. To use this method, press ZOOM 2. A cursor will appear on the screen. Use the arrow keys to move the cursor to a portion of the graph that is of interest. Press ENTER . Use the arrow keys to draw a box around the portion of the graph you wish to see. Press ENTER .

SOLVING EQUATIONS OR SYSTEMS OF EQUATIONS IN TWO VARIABLES

This discussion is based on the fact that the real solutions of an equation can be related to the x-intercepts of a graph. For instance, the real solutions of $x^2 = x + 1$ are the x-intercepts of the graph of $f(x) = x^2 - x - 1$, which are the zeros of f.

To solve $x^2 = x + 1$, rewrite the equation with all terms on one side of the equation. The equation is now $x^2 - x - 1 = 0$. Think of this equation as $Y_1 = x^2 - x - 1$. The x-intercepts of the graph of Y_1 are the solutions of the equation $x^2 = x + 1$.

a. Enter $x^2 - x - 1$ into Y_1.

b. Graph the equation. You may need to adjust the viewing window so that the x-intercepts are visible.

c. Press 2ndF CALC 5

d. A solution is shown as the x-coordinate at the bottom of the screen. To find the next intercept, move the cursor to the right of the first x-intercept. Then press 2ndF CALC 5.

SOLVING SYSTEMS OF EQUATIONS

To solve a system of equations

a. Solve each equation for y.

b. Press [Y=] and then enter both equations.

c. Graph the equations. You may need to adjust the viewing window so that the point of intersection is visible.

d. Press [2ndF] CALC 2 to find the point of intersection. Pressing [2ndF] CALC 2 again will find the next point of intersection.

e. The x- and y-coordinates at the bottom of the screen are the coordinates for the point of intersection.

FINDING MAXIMUM AND MINIMUM VALUES OF A FUNCTION

a. Press [Y=] and then enter the function.

b. Graph the equation. You may need to adjust the viewing window so that the maximum (minimum) are visible.

c. Press [2ndF] CALC 3 for the minimum value of the function or [2ndF] CALC 4 for the maximum value of the fuction.

d. The y-coordinate at the bottom of the screen is the maximum (minimum).

CASIO *CFX-9850G*

To evaluate an expression

a. Press [MENU] [5]. Use the arrow keys to highlight Y_1.

b. Input the expression to be evaluated. For example, to input the expression $-3A^2B - 4C$, use the following keystrokes:

[(-)] 3 [ALPHA] A [x^2] [ALPHA] B [−] 4 [ALPHA] C [EXE]

Note the difference between the keys for a *negative* sign [(-)] and a *minus* sign [−].

c. Press [MENU] 1. Store the value of each variable that will be used in the expression. For example, to evaluate the expression above when $A = 3$, $B = -2$, and $C = -4$, use the following keystrokes:

3 → [ALPHA] A [EXE] [(-)] 2 → [ALPHA] B [EXE] [(-)] 4 → [ALPHA] C [EXE]

These steps store the value of each variable.

d. Press [VARS] [F4] [F1] 1 [EXE].

The value of the expression, Y_1, for the given values is displayed; in this case, $Y_1 = 70$.

To graph a function

a. Press Menu [5] to obtain the GRAPH FUNCTION Menu.

b. Input the function that you desire to graph. Press [X,θ,T] to input the variable x. For example, to input $y = x^3 + 2x^2 - 5x - 6$, use the following keystrokes:

[X,θ,T] [∧] 3 [+] 2 [X,θ,T] [x^2] [−] 5 [X,θ,T] [−] 6 [EXE]

c. Set the viewing window by pressing [SHIFT] [F3] and the Range Parameter Menu will appear. Enter the values for the minimum x-value (Xmin), maximum x-value (Xmax), units between tick marks on the x-axis (Xscl), minimum y-value (Ymin), maximum y-value (Ymax), and the units between tick marks on the y-axis (Yscl). Press [EXE] after each of the 6 entries above. Press [EXIT], or [SHIFT] [QUIT], to leave the Range Parameter Menu.

d. Press [F6] to draw the graph. For the graph shown at the left, Xmin $= -10$, Xmax $= 10$, Xscl $= 1$, Ymin $= -10$, Ymax $= 10$, Yscl $= 1$.

e. In the equation for Y₁, there is a rectangle around the equal sign. This indicates that this function is *active* and will be graphed when the F6 key is pressed. A function is deactivated by using the F1 key. After using this key once, the rectangle around the equal sign will not be present and that function will not be graphed.

To display the x-coordinates of rectangular coordinates as integers

a. Set the Range as follows: For example, set Xmin = −63, Xmax = 63, Xscl = 10, Ymin = −32, Ymax = 32, Yscl = 10.

b. Graph a function and use the Trace feature. Press F1 and then move the cursor with the ◁ and the ▷ keys. The values of x and $y = f(x)$ displayed on the bottom of the screen are the coordinates of a point on the graph. Observe that the x-value is given as an integer.

To display the x-coordinates of rectangular coordinates in tenths

a. Set the Range as follows: For example, set Xmin = −6.3, Xmax = 6.3. A quick way to choose these range parameter settings is to press F1 from the V-Window Menu.

b. Graph a function and use the Trace feature. Press F1 and then move the cursor with the ◁ and the ▷ keys. The values of x and $y = f(x)$ displayed on the bottom of the screen are the coordinates of a point on the graph. Observe that the x-value is given as a decimal that terminates in the first decimal place (tenths).

To evaluate a function for a given value of x, or to produce ordered pairs of the function

a. Press MENU 5.

b. Input the function to be evaluated. For example, input $2x^3 − 3x + 2$ into Y₁.

c. Press MENU 1.

d. Input a value for x; for example, to input 3 press

$3 \rightarrow$ X,θ,T EXE

e. Press VARS F4 F1 1 EXE.

The value of Y₁ for the given value $x = 3$ is displayed. In this case, Y₁ = 47.

ZOOM FEATURES

To zoom in or out on a graph

a. After drawing a graph, press SHIFT Zoom to display the Zoom/Auto Range menu. To zoom in on a graph by a factor of 2 on the x-axis and a factor of 1.5 on the y-axis:
Press F2 to display the Factor Input Screen. Input the zoom factors for each axis: 2 EXE 1 · 5 EXE EXIT. Press F3 to redraw the graph according to the factors specified above. To specify the center point of the enlarged (reduced) display after pressing SHIFT Zoom use the arrow keys to move the pointer to the position you wish to become the center of the next display. You can repeat the zoom procedures as needed. If you wish to see the original graph, press F6 F1. This procedure resets the range parameters to their original values and redraws the graph.

b. A second method of zooming makes use of the Box Zoom Function. To use this method, first draw a graph. Then press SHIFT Zoom F1. Now use the arrow (cursor) keys to move the pointer. Once the pointer is located at a portion of the graph that is of interest, press EXE. Now use the arrow keys to draw a box around the portion of the graph you wish to see. Press EXE. The portion of the graph defined by the box will be drawn.

SOLVING EQUATIONS

This discussion is based on the fact that the real solutions of an equation can be related to the x-intercepts of a graph. For instance, the real solutions of $x^2 = x + 1$ are the x-intercepts of the graph of $f(x) = x^2 - x - 1$, which are the zeros of f.

To solve $x^2 = x + 1$, rewrite the equation with all terms on one side. The equation is now $x^2 - x - 1 = 0$. Think of this equation as $Y_1 = x^2 - x - 1$. The x-intercepts of the graph of Y_1 are the solutions of the equation $x^2 = x + 1$.

a. Enter $x^2 - x - 1$ into Y_1.

b. Graph the equation. You may need to adjust the viewing window so that the x-intercept is visible.

c. Press $\boxed{\text{SHIFT}}$ G-SOLV $\boxed{\text{F1}}$.

d. The root is shown as the x-coordinate on the bottom of the screen; in this case, the root is approximately -0.618034. To find the next x-intercept, press the right arrow key.

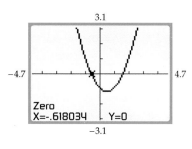

The EQUA Mode (Press $\boxed{\text{MENU}}$ $\boxed{\text{ALPHA}}$ A) can also be used to find solutions of linear, quadratic, and cubic equations.

SOLVING SYSTEMS OF TWO EQUATIONS IN TWO VARIABLES

The following discussion is based on the concept that the solutions of a system of two equations are represented by the point(s) of intersections of the graphs.

The system of equations $\begin{aligned} y &= x^2 - 1 \\ \tfrac{1}{2}x + y &= 1 \end{aligned}$ will be solved.

a. Solve each equation for y.

b. Enter the first equation in the Graph Menu as Y_1. For instance, let $Y_1 = x^2 - 1$.

c. Enter the second equation as Y_2. For instance, let $Y_2 = 1 - \frac{1}{2}x$.

d. Graph both equations. (*Note:* The point of intersection must appear on the screen. It may be necessary to adjust the viewing window so that the point of intersection that is of interest is the only intersection point that is displayed.)

e. Press $\boxed{\text{SHIFT}}$ G-SOL $\boxed{\text{F5}}$ $\boxed{\text{EXE}}$.

f. The display will show that the graphs intersect at $(-1.686141, 1.8430703)$. To find the next intersect, repeat step **e**.

FINDING MINIMUM OR MAXIMUM VALUES OF A FUNCTION

a. Enter the function into the graphing menu. For this example we have used $y = x^2 - x - 1$.

b. Graph the function. Adjust the viewing window so that the maximum or minimum is visible.

c. Press $\boxed{\text{SHIFT}}$ G-SOL $\boxed{\text{F2}}$ $\boxed{\text{EXE}}$ for a maximum and $\boxed{\text{F3}}$ $\boxed{\text{EXE}}$ for a minimum.

d. The local maximum (minimum) is shown as the y-coordinate on the bottom of the screen; in this case, the minimum value is -1.25.

Proof of the Formula for the Sum of n Terms of an Arithmetic Series

Each term of the arithmetic sequence shown at the right was found by adding 3 to the previous term.

$2, 5, 8, \ldots, 17, 20$

Each term of the reverse arithmetic sequence can be found by subtracting 3 from the previous term.

$20, 17, 14, \ldots, 5, 2$

This idea is used in the following proof.

Theorem: The sum of the first n terms of an arithmetic sequence for which a_1 is the first term, n is the number of terms, a_n is the last term, and d is the common difference is given by $S_n = \dfrac{n}{2}(a_1 + a_n)$.

Proof: Let S_n represent the sum of the sequence.

$$S_n = a_1 + (a_1 + d) + (a_1 + 2d) + \cdots + a_n$$

Write the terms of the sum of the sequence in reverse order. The sum will be the same.

$$S_n = a_n + (a_n - d) + (a_n - 2d) + \cdots + a_1$$

Add the two equations.

$$2S_n = (a_1 + a_n) + (a_1 + a_n) + (a_1 + a_n) + \cdots + (a_1 + a_n)$$

Simplify the right side of the equation by using the fact that there are n terms in the sequence.

$$2S_n = n(a_1 + a_n)$$

Solve for S_n.

$$S_n = \frac{n}{2}(a_1 + a_n)$$

Table of Symbols

$+$	add	$<$	is less than
$-$	subtract	$\leq$	is less than or equal to
$\cdot, \times, (a)(b)$	multiply	$>$	is greater than
$\dfrac{a}{b}, \div$	divide	$\geq$	is greater than or equal to
		(a, b)	an ordered pair whose first component is a and whose second component is b
$(\ )$	parentheses, a grouping symbol		
$[\ ]$	brackets, a grouping symbol	$^\circ$	degree (for angles)
		$\sqrt{a}$	the principal square root of a
π	pi, a number approximately equal to $\dfrac{22}{7}$ or 3.14	$\varnothing, \{\}$	the empty set
		$|a|$	the absolute value of a
$-a$	the opposite, or additive inverse, of a	$\cup$	union of two sets
$\dfrac{1}{a}$	the reciprocal, or multiplicative inverse, of a	$\cap$	intersection of two sets
		$\in$	is an element of (for sets)
$=$	is equal to	$\notin$	is not an element of (for sets)
$\approx$	is approximately equal to		
$\neq$	is not equal to		

Proofs of Logarithmic Properties

In each of the following proofs of logarithmic properties, it is assumed that the Properties of Exponents are true for all real number exponents.

The Logarithm Property of the Product of Two Numbers

For any positive real numbers x, y, and b, $b \neq 1$, $\log_b xy = \log_b x + \log_b y$.

Proof: Let $\log_b x = m$ and $\log_b y = n$.

Write each equation in its equivalent exponential form.	$x = b^m \qquad y = b^n$
Use substitution and the Properties of Exponents.	$xy = b^m b^n$
	$xy = b^{m+n}$
Write the equation in its equivalent logarithmic form.	$\log_b xy = m + n$
Substitute $\log_b x$ for m and $\log_b y$ for n.	$\log_b xy = \log_b x + \log_b y$

The Logarithm Property of the Quotient of Two Numbers

For any positive real numbers x, y, and b, $b \neq 1$, $\log_b \dfrac{x}{y} = \log_b x - \log_b y$.

Proof: Let $\log_b x = m$ and $\log_b y = n$.

Write each equation in its equivalent exponential form.	$x = b^m \qquad y = b^n$
Use substitution and the Properties of Exponents.	$\dfrac{x}{y} = \dfrac{b^m}{b^n}$
	$\dfrac{x}{y} = b^{m-n}$
Write the equation in its equivalent logarithmic form.	$\log_b \dfrac{x}{y} = m - n$
Substitute $\log_b x$ for m and $\log_b y$ for n.	$\log_b \dfrac{x}{y} = \log_b x - \log_b y$

The Logarithm Property of the Power of a Number

For any real numbers x, r, and b, $b \neq 1$, $\log_b x^r = r \log_b x$.

Proof: Let $\log_b x = m$.

Write the equation in its equivalent exponential form.	$x = b^m$
Raise both sides to the r power.	$x^r = (b^m)^r$
	$x^r = b^{mr}$
Write the equation in its equivalent logarithmic form.	$\log_b x^r = mr$
Substitute $\log_b x$ for m.	$\log_b x^r = r \log_b x$

Proof of the Formula for the Sum of n Terms of a Geometric Series

Theorem: The sum of the first n terms of a geometric sequence whose nth term is ar^{n-1} is given by $S_n = \dfrac{a(1 - r^n)}{1 - r}$.

Proof:

Let S_n represent the sum of n terms of the sequence.	$S_n = a + ar + ar^2 + \cdots + ar^{n-2} + ar^{n-1}$
Multiply each side of the equation by r.	$rS_n = ar + ar^2 + ar^3 + \cdots + ar^{n-1} + ar^n$
Subtract the two equations.	$S_n - rS_n = a - ar^n$
Assuming $r \neq 1$, solve for S_n.	$(1 - r)S_n = a(1 - r^n)$
	$S_n = \dfrac{a(1 - r^n)}{1 - r}$

Table of Measurement Abbreviations

U.S. Customary System

Length		**Capacity**		**Weight**		**Area**	
in.	inches	oz	fluid ounces	oz	ounces	in²	square inches
ft	feet	c	cups	lb	pounds	ft²	square feet
yd	yards	qt	quarts				
mi	miles	gal	gallons				

Metric System

Length		**Capacity**		**Weight/Mass**		**Area**	
mm	millimeter (0.001 m)	ml	milliliter (0.001 L)	mg	milligram (0.001 g)	cm²	square centimeters
cm	centimeter (0.01 m)	cl	centiliter (0.01 L)	cg	centigram (0.01 g)	m²	square meters
dm	decimeter (0.1 m)	dl	deciliter (0.1 L)	dg	decigram (0.1 g)		
m	meter	L	liter	g	gram		
dam	decameter (10 m)	dal	decaliter (10 L)	dag	decagram (10 g)		
hm	hectometer (100 m)	hl	hectoliter (100 L)	hg	hectogram (100 g)		
km	kilometer (1000 m)	kl	kiloliter (1000 L)	kg	kilogram (1000 g)		

Time

h	hours	min	minutes	s	seconds

Solutions to Chapter 1 "You Try It"

SECTION 1.1

You Try It 1   Replace z by each of the elements of the set and determine whether the inequality is true.
$$z > -5$$
$$-10 > -5 \quad \text{False}$$
$$-5 > -5 \quad \text{False}$$
$$6 > -5 \quad \text{True}$$
The inequality is true for 6.

You Try It 2   **a.** Replace d in $-d$ by each element of the set and determine the value of the expression.
$$-d$$
$$-(-11) = 11$$
$$-(0) = 0$$
$$-(8) = -8$$
b. Replace d in $|d|$ by each element of the set and determine the value of the expression.
$$|d|$$
$$|-11| = 11$$
$$|0| = 0$$
$$|8| = 8$$

You Try It 3 $\{-5, -4, -3, -2, -1\}$

You Try It 4 $\{x \mid x \geq 15, x \in \text{whole numbers}\}$

You Try It 5 $C \cup D = \{1, 3, 5, 7, 9, 11, 13, 17\}$

You Try It 6 $E \cap F = \varnothing$

You Try It 7   Draw a parenthesis at 0 to indicate that 0 is not in the set. Draw a solid line to the left of 0.

You Try It 8   This is the set of real numbers less than -2 *or* greater than -1.

You Try It 9   This is the set of real numbers less than 1 *and* greater than -3.

You Try It 10   **a.** The set $\{x \mid x < -1\}$ is the numbers less than -1. In interval notation, this is written $(-\infty, -1)$.
b. The set $\{x \mid -2 \leq x < 4\}$ is the numbers greater than or equal to -2 and less than 4. In interval notation, this is written $[-2, 4)$.

You Try It 11   **a.** The ∞ symbol indicates that the interval extends forever. Therefore, $(3, \infty)$ is the numbers greater than 3. In set-builder notation, this is written $\{x \mid x > 3\}$.
b. $(-4, 1]$ is the numbers greater than -4 and less than or equal to 1. In set-builder notation, this is written $\{x \mid -4 < x \leq 1\}$.

You Try It 12   Draw a bracket at -2 to show that it is in the set. The ∞ symbol indicates that the set extends forever. Draw a solid line to the right of -2.

SECTION 1.2

You Try It 1
$$6 - (-8) - 10 = 6 + 8 + (-10)$$
$$= 14 + (-10)$$
$$= 4$$

You Try It 2
$$12(-3)|-6| = 12(-3)(6)$$
$$= (-36)(6)$$
$$= -216$$

You Try It 3
$$-\frac{28}{|-14|} = -\frac{28}{14}$$
$$= -2$$

You Try It 4
$$\frac{5}{6} - \frac{3}{8} - \frac{7}{9} = \frac{5}{6} + \frac{-3}{8} + \frac{-7}{9}$$
$$= \frac{5}{6} \cdot \frac{12}{12} + \frac{-3}{8} \cdot \frac{9}{9} + \frac{-7}{9} \cdot \frac{8}{8}$$
$$= \frac{60}{72} + \frac{-27}{72} + \frac{-56}{72}$$
$$= \frac{60 + (-27) + (-56)}{72} = \frac{-23}{72}$$
$$= -\frac{23}{72}$$

You Try It 5 $\dfrac{5}{8} \div \left(-\dfrac{15}{40}\right) = -\dfrac{5}{8} \cdot \dfrac{40}{15}$

$$= -\dfrac{5 \cdot 40}{8 \cdot 15} = -\dfrac{5}{3}$$

You Try It 6 $-2^5 = -(2 \cdot 2 \cdot 2 \cdot 2 \cdot 2) = -32$
$(-5)^2 = (-5)(-5) = 25$

You Try It 7 $\left(\dfrac{2}{3}\right)^4 = \left(\dfrac{2}{3}\right)\left(\dfrac{2}{3}\right)\left(\dfrac{2}{3}\right)\left(\dfrac{2}{3}\right)$

$$= \dfrac{2 \cdot 2 \cdot 2 \cdot 2}{3 \cdot 3 \cdot 3 \cdot 3}$$

$$= \dfrac{16}{81}$$

You Try It 8
$$-2\left[3 - 3^3 + \dfrac{16 + 2}{1 - 10}\right] = -2\left[3 - 3^3 + \dfrac{18}{-9}\right]$$
$$= -2[3 - 3^3 + (-2)]$$
$$= -2[3 - 27 + (-2)]$$
$$= -2[-24 + (-2)]$$
$$= -2[-26]$$
$$= 52$$

You Try It 9
$$\dfrac{1}{3} + \dfrac{5}{8} \div \dfrac{15}{16} - \dfrac{7}{12} = \dfrac{1}{3} + \dfrac{5}{8} \cdot \dfrac{16}{15} - \dfrac{7}{12}$$
$$= \dfrac{1}{3} + \dfrac{2}{3} - \dfrac{7}{12}$$
$$= 1 - \dfrac{7}{12}$$
$$= \dfrac{5}{12}$$

You Try It 10
$$\dfrac{11}{12} - \dfrac{\frac{5}{4}}{2 - \frac{7}{2}} \cdot \dfrac{3}{4} = \dfrac{11}{12} - \dfrac{\frac{5}{4}}{-\frac{3}{2}} \cdot \dfrac{3}{4}$$
$$= \dfrac{11}{12} - \left[\dfrac{5}{4} \cdot \left(-\dfrac{2}{3}\right)\right] \cdot \dfrac{3}{4}$$
$$= \dfrac{11}{12} - \left(-\dfrac{5}{6}\right) \cdot \dfrac{3}{4}$$
$$= \dfrac{11}{12} - \left(-\dfrac{5}{8}\right)$$
$$= \dfrac{37}{24}$$

SECTION 1.3

You Try It 1 $3x + (-3x) = 0$

You Try It 2 The Associative Property of Addition

You Try It 3
$-2x^2 + 3(4xy - z)$
$-2(-3)^2 + 3[4(-3)(-1) - 2]$
$$= -2(-3)^2 + 3[12 - 2]$$
$$= -2(-3)^2 + 3(10)$$
$$= -2(9) + 3(10)$$
$$= -18 + 30$$
$$= 12$$

You Try It 4
$2x - y|4x^2 - y^2|$
$2(-2) - (-6)|4(-2)^2 - (-6)^2|$
$$= 2(-2) - (-6)|4 \cdot 4 - 36|$$
$$= 2(-2) - (-6)|16 - 36|$$
$$= 2(-2) - (-6)|-20|$$
$$= 2(-2) - (-6)(20)$$
$$= -4 - (-120)$$
$$= -4 + 120$$
$$= 116$$

You Try It 5
$9 - 2(3y - 4) + 5y = 9 - 6y + 8 + 5y$
$$= -y + 17$$

You Try It 6
$6z - 3(5 - 3z) + 5(2z - 3)$
$$= 6z - 15 + 9z + 10z - 15$$
$$= 25z - 30$$

SECTION 1.4

You Try It 1 twice x divided by the difference between x and 7
$$\dfrac{2x}{x - 7}$$

You Try It 2 the product of negative 3 and the square of d
$-3d^2$

You Try It 3 The smaller number is x.
The larger number is $16 - x$.
the difference between twice the smaller number and the larger number
$2x - (16 - x) = 2x - 16 + x$
$$= 3x - 16$$

You Try It 4 Let the number be x.
the difference between 14 and the sum of a number and 7
$14 - (x + 7) = 14 - x - 7$
$$= -x + 7$$

You Try It 5   the height of the Empire State Building: x
the length of *Destiny*: $x + 56$

You Try It 6   the depth of the shallow end: x
the depth of the deep end: $2x + 2$

You Try It 7   the total credit card bill: x
the cost of restaurant meals: $\dfrac{1}{4}x$

Solutions to Chapter 2 "You Try It"

SECTION 2.1

You Try It 1
$$x + 4 = -3$$
$$x + 4 - 4 = -3 - 4$$
$$x = -7$$

The solution is -7.

You Try It 2
$$-3x = 18$$
$$\frac{-3x}{-3} = \frac{18}{-3}$$
$$x = -6$$

The solution is -6.

You Try It 3
$$6x - 5 - 3x = 14 - 5x$$
$$3x - 5 = 14 - 5x$$
$$3x - 5 + 5x = 14 - 5x + 5x$$
$$8x - 5 = 14$$
$$8x - 5 + 5 = 14 + 5$$
$$8x = 19$$
$$\frac{8x}{8} = \frac{19}{8}$$
$$x = \frac{19}{8}$$

The solution is $\dfrac{19}{8}$.

You Try It 4
$$6(5 - x) - 12 = 2x - 3(4 + x)$$
$$30 - 6x - 12 = 2x - 12 - 3x$$
$$18 - 6x = -x - 12$$
$$18 - 6x + x = -x - 12 + x$$
$$18 - 5x = -12$$
$$18 - 5x - 18 = -12 - 18$$
$$-5x = -30$$
$$\frac{-5x}{-5} = \frac{-30}{-5}$$
$$x = 6$$

The solution is 6.

You Try It 5
$$S = C - rC$$
$$S - C = -rC$$
$$\frac{S - C}{-C} = r$$
$$r = -\frac{S - C}{C} = \frac{C - S}{C}$$

SECTION 2.2

You Try It 1

Strategy   • The first number: n
The second number: $2n$
The third number: $4n - 3$
• The sum of the numbers is 81.
$n + 2n + (4n - 3) = 81$

Solution
$$n + 2n + (4n - 3) = 81$$
$$7n - 3 = 81$$
$$7n = 84$$
$$n = 12$$
$$2n = 2(12) = 24$$
$$4n - 3 = 4(12) - 3 = 48 - 3 = 45$$

The numbers are 12, 24, and 45.

You Try It 2

Strategy   • First odd integer: n
Second odd integer: $n + 2$
Third odd integer: $n + 4$
• Three times the sum of the first two integers is ten more than the product of the third integer and four.
$3[n + (n + 2)] = (n + 4)4 + 10$

Solution
$$3[n + (n + 2)] = (n + 4)4 + 10$$
$$3[2n + 2] = 4n + 16 + 10$$
$$6n + 6 = 4n + 26$$
$$2n + 6 = 26$$
$$2n = 20$$
$$n = 10$$

Because 10 is not an odd integer, there is no solution.

You Try It 3

Strategy   • Number of 3¢ stamps: x
Number of 10¢ stamps: $2x + 2$
Number of 15¢ stamps: $3x$

Stamps	Number	Value	Total Value
3¢	x	3	$3x$
10¢	$2x + 2$	10	$10(2x + 2)$
15¢	$3x$	15	$45x$

• The sum of the total values of each type of stamp equals the total value of all the stamps (156 cents).
$3x + 10(2x + 2) + 45x = 156$

Solution
$$3x + 10(2x + 2) + 45x = 156$$
$$3x + 20x + 20 + 45x = 156$$
$$68x + 20 = 156$$
$$68x = 136$$
$$x = 2$$
$$3x = 3(2) = 6$$

There are six 15¢ stamps in the collection.

SECTION 2.3

You Try It 1

Strategy   • Pounds of $3.00 hamburger: x
Pounds of $1.80 hamburger: $75 - x$
Pounds of the $2.20 mixture: 75

	Amount	Cost	Value
$3.00 hamburger	x	3.00	$3.00x$
$1.80 hamburger	$75 - x$	1.80	$1.80(75 - x)$
Mixture	75	2.20	$75(2.20)$

• The sum of the values before mixing equals the value after mixing.
$3.00x + 1.80(75 - x) = 75(2.20)$

Solution
$$3.00x + 1.80(75 - x) = 75(2.20)$$
$$3x + 135 - 1.80x = 165$$
$$1.2x + 135 = 165$$
$$1.2x = 30$$
$$x = 25$$
$$75 - x = 75 - 25 = 50$$

The mixture must contain 25 lb of the $3.00 hamburger and 50 lb of the $1.80 hamburger.

You Try It 2

Strategy   • Pounds of 22% hamburger: x
Pounds of 12% hamburger: $80 - x$
Pounds of 18% hamburger: 80

	Amount	Percent	Quantity
22%	x	0.22	$0.22x$
12%	$80 - x$	0.12	$0.12(80 - x)$
18%	80	0.18	$0.18(80)$

• The sum of the quantities before mixing is equal to the quantity after mixing.
$0.22x + 0.12(80 - x) = 0.18(80)$

Solution
$$0.22x + 0.12(80 - x) = 0.18(80)$$
$$0.22x + 9.6 - 0.12x = 14.4$$
$$0.10x + 9.6 = 14.4$$
$$0.10x = 4.8$$
$$x = 48$$
$$80 - x = 80 - 48 = 32$$

The butcher needs 48 lb of the hamburger that is 22% fat and 32 lb of the hamburger that is 12% fat.

You Try It 3

Strategy   • Rate of the second plane: r
Rate of the first plane: $r + 30$

	Rate	Time	Distance
1st plane	$r + 30$	4	$4(r + 30)$
2nd plane	r	4	$4r$

• The total distance traveled by the two planes is 1160 mi.
$4(r + 30) + 4r = 1160$

Solution
$$4(r + 30) + 4r = 1160$$
$$4r + 120 + 4r = 1160$$
$$8r + 120 = 1160$$
$$8r = 1040$$
$$r = 130$$
$$r + 30 = 130 + 30 = 160$$

The first plane is traveling 160 mph. The second plane is traveling 130 mph.

SECTION 2.4

You Try It 1
$$2x - 1 < 6x + 7$$
$$-4x - 1 < 7$$
$$-4x < 8$$
$$\frac{-4x}{-4} > \frac{8}{-4}$$
$$x > -2$$
$$\{x \mid x > -2\}$$

You Try It 2
$$5x - 2 \le 4 - 3(x - 2)$$
$$5x - 2 \le 4 - 3x + 6$$
$$5x - 2 \le 10 - 3x$$
$$8x - 2 \le 10$$
$$8x \le 12$$
$$\frac{8x}{8} \le \frac{12}{8}$$
$$x \le \frac{3}{2}$$
$$\left\{x \mid x \le \frac{3}{2}\right\}$$

You Try It 3
$$-2 \le 5x + 3 \le 13$$
$$-2 - 3 \le 5x + 3 - 3 \le 13 - 3$$
$$-5 \le 5x \le 10$$
$$\frac{-5}{5} \le \frac{5x}{5} \le \frac{10}{5}$$
$$-1 \le x \le 2$$
$$\{x \mid -1 \le x \le 2\}$$

You Try It 4
$$2 - 3x > 11 \quad \text{or} \quad 5 + 2x > 7$$
$$-3x > 9 \qquad\qquad 2x > 2$$
$$x < -3 \qquad\qquad x > 1$$
$$\{x \mid x < -3\} \qquad \{x \mid x > 1\}$$
$$\{x \mid x < -3\} \cup \{x \mid x > 1\}$$
$$= \{x \mid x < -3 \text{ or } x > 1\}$$

You Try It 5

Strategy To find the maximum height, substitute the given values in the inequality $\frac{1}{2}bh < A$ and solve.

Solution
$$\frac{1}{2}bh < A$$
$$\frac{1}{2}(12)(x + 2) < 50$$
$$6(x + 2) < 50$$
$$6x + 12 < 50$$
$$6x < 38$$
$$x < \frac{19}{3}$$

The largest integer less than $\frac{19}{3}$ is 6.
$$x + 2 = 6 + 2 = 8$$

The maximum height of the triangle is 8 in.

You Try It 6

Strategy To find the range of scores, write and solve an inequality using N to represent the score on the last test.

Solution
$$80 \le \frac{72 + 94 + 83 + 70 + N}{5} \le 89$$
$$80 \le \frac{319 + N}{5} \le 89$$
$$5 \cdot 80 \le 5\left(\frac{319 + N}{5}\right) \le 5 \cdot 89$$
$$400 \le 319 + N \le 445$$
$$400 - 319 \le 319 + N - 319 \le 445 - 319$$
$$81 \le N \le 126$$

Since 100 is a maximum score, the range of scores to receive a B grade is $81 \le N \le 100$.

SECTION 2.5

You Try It 1 $|2x - 3| = 5$
$$2x - 3 = 5 \qquad 2x - 3 = -5$$
$$2x = 8 \qquad\quad 2x = -2$$
$$x = 4 \qquad\qquad x = -1$$

The solutions are 4 and -1.

You Try It 2 $|x - 3| = -2$

There is no solution to this equation because the absolute value of a number must be nonnegative.

You Try It 3
$$5 - |3x + 5| = 3$$
$$-|3x + 5| = -2$$
$$|3x + 5| = 2$$
$$3x + 5 = 2 \qquad 3x + 5 = -2$$
$$3x = -3 \qquad\quad 3x = -7$$
$$x = -1 \qquad\quad x = -\frac{7}{3}$$

The solutions are -1 and $-\frac{7}{3}$.

You Try It 4 $|3x + 2| < 8$

$$-8 < 3x + 2 < 8$$

$$-8 - 2 < 3x + 2 - 2 < 8 - 2$$

$$-10 < 3x < 6$$

$$\frac{-10}{3} < \frac{3x}{3} < \frac{6}{3}$$

$$-\frac{10}{3} < x < 2$$

$$\left\{ x \,\middle|\, -\frac{10}{3} < x < 2 \right\}$$

You Try It 5 $|3x - 7| < 0$

The absolute value of a number must be nonnegative.

The solution set is the empty set.

You Try It 6 $|2x + 7| \geq -1$

The absolute value of a number must be nonnegative.

The solution set is the set of real numbers.

You Try It 7
$$|5x + 3| > 8$$

$$5x + 3 < -8 \quad \text{or} \quad 5x + 3 > 8$$
$$5x < -11 \qquad\qquad 5x > 5$$
$$x < -\frac{11}{5} \qquad\qquad x > 1$$

$$\left\{ x \,\middle|\, x < -\frac{11}{5} \right\} \qquad \{x \mid x > 1\}$$

$$\left\{ x \,\middle|\, x < -\frac{11}{5} \right\} \cup \{x \mid x > 1\}$$

$$= \left\{ x \,\middle|\, x < -\frac{11}{5} \text{ or } x > 1 \right\}$$

You Try It 8

Strategy

Let b represent the diameter of the bushing, T the tolerance, and d the lower and upper limits of the diameter. Solve the absolute-value inequality $|d - b| \leq T$ for d.

Solution
$$|d - b| \leq T$$
$$|d - 2.55| \leq 0.003$$
$$-0.003 \leq d - 2.55 \leq 0.003$$
$$-0.003 + 2.55 \leq d - 2.55 + 2.55 \leq 0.003 + 2.55$$
$$2.547 \leq d \leq 2.553$$

The lower and upper limits of the diameter of the bushing are 2.547 in. and 2.553 in.

Solutions to Chapter 3 "You Try It"

SECTION 3.1

You Try It 1 $y = \dfrac{3x}{x + 1}$

Replace x by -2 and solve for y.

$$y = \frac{3(-2)}{-2 + 1} = \frac{-6}{-1} = 6$$

The ordered-pair solution is $(-2, 6)$.

You Try It 2

x	y
-3	2
-2	1
-1	0
0	1
1	2

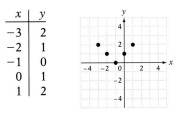

You Try It 3 $(x_1, y_1) = (5, -2)$ $(x_2, y_2) = (-4, 3)$

$$d = \sqrt{(x_1 - x_2)^2 + (y_1 - y_2)^2}$$
$$= \sqrt{[5 - (-4)]^2 + (-2 - 3)^2}$$
$$= \sqrt{9^2 + (-5)^2}$$
$$= \sqrt{81 + 25}$$
$$= \sqrt{106} \approx 10.30$$

You Try It 4 $(x_1, y_1) = (-3, -5)$ $(x_2, y_2) = (-2, 3)$

$$x_m = \frac{x_1 + x_2}{2} \qquad y_m = \frac{y_1 + y_2}{2}$$
$$= \frac{-3 + (-2)}{2} \qquad = \frac{-5 + 3}{2}$$
$$= -\frac{5}{2} \qquad\qquad = -1$$

The midpoint is $\left(-\dfrac{5}{2}, -1 \right)$.

You Try It 5

Strategy   To find the number of points scored by Green Bay, read the scatter diagram.

Solution   The ordered pair (275, 30) means that Green Bay scored 30 points when they gained 275 yd.

SECTION 3.2

You Try It 1 $G(x) = \dfrac{3x}{x + 1}$

$G(-2) = \dfrac{3(-2)}{-2 + 1} = \dfrac{-6}{-1} = 6$

You Try It 2   Domain: $\{-1, 3, 4, 6\}$
Range: $\{5\}$

You Try It 3 $h(z) = 3z + 1$

$h(0) = 3(0) + 1 = 1$

$h\left(\dfrac{1}{3}\right) = 3\left(\dfrac{1}{3}\right) + 1 = 2$

$h\left(\dfrac{2}{3}\right) = 3\left(\dfrac{2}{3}\right) + 1 = 3$

$h(1) = 3(1) + 1 = 4$

The range is $\{1, 2, 3, 4\}$.

You Try It 4 $f(x) = \dfrac{2}{x - 5}$

For $x = 5, 5 - 5 = 0$.

$f(5) = \dfrac{2}{5 - 5} = \dfrac{2}{0}$, which is not a real number.

5 is excluded from the domain of the function.

SECTION 3.3

You Try It 1

You Try It 2

You Try It 3 $-3x + 2y = 4$

$2y = 3x + 4$

$y = \dfrac{3}{2}x + 2$

You Try It 4 $y - 3 = 0$

$y = 3$

You Try It 5 x-intercept: y-intercept:

$3x - y = 2$ $3x - y = 2$

$3x - 0 = 2$ $3(0) - y = 2$

$3x = 2$ $-y = 2$

$x = \dfrac{2}{3}$ $y = -2$

$\left(\dfrac{2}{3}, 0\right)$ $(0, -2)$

You Try It 6 x-intercept: y-intercept:

$y = \dfrac{1}{4}x + 1$ $(0, b)$

$b = 1$

$0 = \dfrac{1}{4}x + 1$ $(0, 1)$

$-\dfrac{1}{4}x = 1$

$x = -4$

$(-4, 0)$

You Try It 7

The ordered pair (32, 74) means that a person with a stride of 32 in. is 74 in. tall.

SECTION 3.4

You Try It 1   Let $P_1 = (4, -3)$ and $P_2 = (2, 7)$.

$$m = \frac{y_2 - y_1}{x_2 - x_1} = \frac{7 - (-3)}{2 - 4} = \frac{10}{-2} = -5$$

The slope is -5.

You Try It 2   Let $P_1 = (6, -1)$ and $P_2 = (6, 7)$.

$$m = \frac{y_2 - y_1}{x_2 - x_1} = \frac{7 - (-1)}{6 - 6} = \frac{8}{0}$$

Division by zero is not defined.

The slope of the line is undefined.

You Try It 3

$$m = \frac{55,000 - 25,000}{2 - 5}$$
$$= \frac{30,000}{-3}$$
$$= -10,000$$

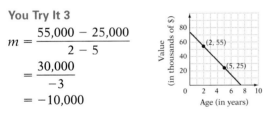

A slope of $-10,000$ means that the value of the printing press is decreasing by $10,000 per year.

You Try It 4

$$2x + 3y = 6$$
$$3y = -2x + 6$$
$$y = -\frac{2}{3}x + 2$$
$$m = -\frac{2}{3} = \frac{-2}{3}$$

y-intercept $= (0, 2)$

You Try It 5 $(x_1, y_1) = (-3, -2)$
$m = 3$

SECTION 3.5

You Try It 1 $m = -\dfrac{1}{3}$ $(x_1, y_1) = (-3, -2)$

$$y - y_1 = m(x - x_1)$$
$$y - (-2) = -\frac{1}{3}[x - (-3)]$$
$$y + 2 = -\frac{1}{3}(x + 3)$$
$$y + 2 = -\frac{1}{3}x - 1$$
$$y = -\frac{1}{3}x - 1 - 2$$
$$y = -\frac{1}{3}x - 3$$

The equation of the line is
$y = -\dfrac{1}{3}x - 3$.

You Try It 2 $m = -3$ $(x_1, y_1) = (4, -3)$

$$y - y_1 = m(x - x_1)$$
$$y - (-3) = -3(x - 4)$$
$$y + 3 = -3(x - 4)$$
$$y + 3 = -3x + 12$$
$$y = -3x + 12 - 3$$
$$y = -3x + 9$$

The equation of the line is
$y = -3x + 9$.

You Try It 3   Let $(x_1, y_1) = (2, 0)$ and $(x_2, y_2) = (5, 3)$.

$$m = \frac{y_2 - y_1}{x_2 - x_1} = \frac{3 - 0}{5 - 2} = \frac{3}{3} = 1$$
$$y - y_1 = m(x - x_1)$$
$$y - 0 = 1(x - 2)$$
$$y = 1(x - 2)$$
$$y = x - 2$$

The equation of the line is $y = x - 2$.

You Try It 4   Let $(x_1, y_1) = (2, 3)$ and $(x_2, y_2) = (-5, 3)$.

$$m = \frac{y_2 - y_1}{x_2 - x_1} = \frac{3 - 3}{-5 - 2} = \frac{0}{-7} = 0$$

The line has zero slope.

The line is a horizontal line.
All points on the line have an
ordinate of 3.
The equation of the line is $y = 3$.

You Try It 5

Strategy
- Select the independent and dependent variables. The function is to predict the Celsius temperature, so that quantity is the dependent variable, y. The Fahrenheit temperature is the independent variable x.
- From the given data, two ordered pairs are (212, 100) and (32, 0). Use these ordered pairs to determine the linear function.

Solution
Let $(x_1, y_1) = (32, 0)$ and
$(x_2, y_2) = (212, 100)$.

$$m = \frac{y_2 - y_1}{x_2 - x_1} = \frac{100 - 0}{212 - 32} = \frac{100}{180} = \frac{5}{9}$$

$$y - y_1 = m(x - x_1)$$

$$y - 0 = \frac{5}{9}(x - 32)$$

$$y = \frac{5}{9}(x - 32), \text{ or } C = \frac{5}{9}(F - 32).$$

The linear function is

$$f(F) = \frac{5}{9}(F - 32).$$

SECTION 3.6

You Try It 1

$$m_1 = \frac{1 - (-3)}{7 - (-2)} = \frac{4}{9}$$

$$m_2 = \frac{-5 - 1}{6 - 4} = \frac{-6}{2} = -3$$

$$m_1 \cdot m_2 = \frac{4}{9} \cdot -3 = -\frac{4}{3}$$

No, the lines are not perpendicular.

You Try It 2
$$5x + 2y = 2$$
$$2y = -5x + 2$$
$$y = -\frac{5}{2}x + 1$$

$$m_1 = -\frac{5}{2}$$

$$5x + 2y = -6$$
$$2y = -5x - 6$$
$$y = -\frac{5}{2}x - 3$$

$$m_2 = -\frac{5}{2}$$

$$m_1 = m_2 = -\frac{5}{2}$$

Yes, the lines are parallel.

You Try It 3
$$x - 4y = 3$$
$$-4y = -x + 3$$
$$y = \frac{1}{4}x - \frac{3}{4}$$

$$m_1 = \frac{1}{4}$$

$$m_1 \cdot m_2 = -1$$
$$\frac{1}{4} \cdot m_2 = -1$$
$$m_2 = -4$$
$$y - y_1 = m(x - x_1)$$
$$y - 2 = -4[x - (-2)]$$
$$y - 2 = -4(x + 2)$$
$$y - 2 = -4x - 8$$
$$y = -4x - 6$$

The equation of the line is
$y = -4x - 6$.

SECTION 3.7

You Try It 1
$$x + 3y > 6$$
$$3y > -x + 6$$
$$y > -\frac{1}{3}x + 2$$

You Try It 2 $y < 2$

Solutions to Chapter 4 "You Try It"

SECTION 4.1

You Try It 1

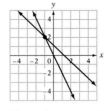

The solution is $(-1, 2)$.

You Try It 2

The two equations represent the same line. The system of equations is dependent. The solutions are the ordered pairs $\left(x, \dfrac{3}{4}x - 3\right)$.

You Try It 3

(1) $3x - y = 3$
(2) $6x + 3y = -4$

Solve Equation (1) for y.

$$3x - y = 3$$
$$-y = -3x + 3$$
$$y = 3x - 3$$

Substitute into Equation (2).

$$6x + 3y = -4$$
$$6x + 3(3x - 3) = -4$$
$$6x + 9x - 9 = -4$$
$$15x - 9 = -4$$
$$15x = 5$$
$$x = \frac{5}{15} = \frac{1}{3}$$

Substitute the value of x into Equation (1).

$$3x - y = 3$$
$$3\left(\frac{1}{3}\right) - y = 3$$
$$1 - y = 3$$
$$-y = 2$$
$$y = -2$$

The solution is $\left(\dfrac{1}{3}, -2\right)$.

You Try It 4

(1) $y = 2x - 3$
(2) $2x - 4y = 5$

$$2x - 4y = 5$$
$$2x - 4(2x - 3) = 5$$
$$2x - 8x + 12 = 5$$
$$-6x + 12 = 5$$
$$-6x = -7$$
$$x = \frac{-7}{-6} = \frac{7}{6}$$

Substitute the value of x into Equation (1).

$$y = 2x - 3$$
$$y = 2\left(\frac{7}{6}\right) - 3$$
$$y = \frac{7}{3} - 3$$
$$y = -\frac{2}{3}$$

The solution is $\left(\dfrac{7}{6}, -\dfrac{2}{3}\right)$.

You Try It 5

(1) $6x - 3y = 6$
(2) $2x - y = 2$

Solve Equation (2) for y.

$$2x - y = 2$$
$$-y = -2x + 2$$
$$y = 2x - 2$$

Substitute into Equation (1).

$$6x - 3y = 6$$
$$6x - 3(2x - 2) = 6$$
$$6x - 6x + 6 = 6$$
$$6 = 6$$

The system of equations is dependent. The solutions are the ordered pairs $(x, 2x - 2)$.

You Try It 6

Strategy • Amount invested at 4.2%: x
Amount invested at 6%: y

	Principal	Rate	Interest
Amount at 4.2%	x	0.042	0.042x
Amount at 6%	y	0.06	0.06y

• The total investment is $13,600. The two accounts earn the same interest.

Solution $x + y = 13,600$
$0.042x = 0.06y$

$$x = \frac{10}{7}y$$

Substitute $\frac{10}{7}y$ for x in
$x + y = 13,600$ and solve for y.

$$\frac{10}{7}y + y = 13,600$$

$$\frac{17}{7}y = 13,600$$

$$y = 5600$$

$$x + 5600 = 13,600$$
$$x = 8000$$

$8000 must be invested at 4.2% and $5600 invested at 6%.

SECTION 4.2

You Try It 1 (1) $2x + 5y = 6$
(2) $3x - 2y = 6x + 2$

Write Equation (2) in the form
$Ax + By = C$.

$3x - 2y = 6x + 2$
$-3x - 2y = 2$

Solve the system: $2x + 5y = 6$
$-3x - 2y = 2$

Eliminate y.

$2(2x + 5y) = 2(6)$
$5(-3x - 2y) = 5(2)$

$4x + 10y = 12$
$-15x - 10y = 10$

Add the equations.
$-11x = 22$
$x = -2$

Replace x in Equation (1).

$2x + 5y = 6$
$2(-2) + 5y = 6$
$-4 + 5y = 6$
$5y = 10$
$y = 2$

The solution is $(-2, 2)$.

You Try It 2 $2x + y = 5$
$4x + 2y = 6$

Eliminate y.

$-2(2x + y) = -2(5)$
$4x + 2y = 6$

$-4x - 2y = -10$
$4x + 2y = 6$

Add the equations.

$0x + 0y = -4$
$0 = -4$

This is not a true equation. The system is inconsistent and therefore has no solution.

You Try It 3 (1) $x - y + z = 6$
(2) $2x + 3y - z = 1$
(3) $x + 2y + 2z = 5$

Eliminate z. Add Equations (1) and (2).

$x - y + z = 6$
$2x + 3y - z = 1$
(4) $3x + 2y = 7$

Multiply Equation (2) by 2 and add to Equation (3).

$4x + 6y - 2z = 2$
$x + 2y + 2z = 5$
(5) $5x + 8y = 7$

Solve the system of two equations.

(4) $3x + 2y = 7$
(5) $5x + 8y = 7$

Multiply Equation (4) by -4 and add to Equation (5).

$-12x - 8y = -28$
$5x + 8y = 7$
$-7x = -21$
$x = 3$

Replace x by 3 in Equation (4).

$3x + 2y = 7$
$3(3) + 2y = 7$
$9 + 2y = 7$
$2y = -2$
$y = -1$

(Continued on page S12)

Replace x by 3 and y by -1 in Equation (1).

$$x - y + z = 6$$
$$3 - (-1) + z = 6$$
$$4 + z = 6$$
$$z = 2$$

The solution is $(3, -1, 2)$.

SECTION 4.3

You Try It 1
$$\begin{vmatrix} -1 & -4 \\ 3 & -5 \end{vmatrix} = -1(-5) - (-4)(3)$$
$$= 5 + 12 = 17$$

The value of the determinant is 17.

You Try It 2 Expand by cofactors of the first row.
$$\begin{vmatrix} 1 & 4 & -2 \\ 3 & 1 & 1 \\ 0 & -2 & 2 \end{vmatrix}$$
$$= 1\begin{vmatrix} 1 & 1 \\ -2 & 2 \end{vmatrix} - 4\begin{vmatrix} 3 & 1 \\ 0 & 2 \end{vmatrix} + (-2)\begin{vmatrix} 3 & 1 \\ 0 & -2 \end{vmatrix}$$
$$= 1(2 + 2) - 4(6 - 0) - 2(-6 - 0)$$
$$= 4 - 24 + 12$$
$$= -8$$

The value of the determinant is -8.

You Try It 3
$$\begin{vmatrix} 3 & -2 & 0 \\ 1 & 4 & 2 \\ -2 & 1 & 3 \end{vmatrix}$$
$$= 3\begin{vmatrix} 4 & 2 \\ 1 & 3 \end{vmatrix} - (-2)\begin{vmatrix} 1 & 2 \\ -2 & 3 \end{vmatrix} + 0\begin{vmatrix} 1 & 4 \\ -2 & 1 \end{vmatrix}$$
$$= 3(12 - 2) + 2(3 + 4) + 0$$
$$= 3(10) + 2(7)$$
$$= 30 + 14$$
$$= 44$$

The value of the determinant is 44.

You Try It 4
$$3x - y = 4$$
$$6x - 2y = 5$$
$$D = \begin{vmatrix} 3 & -1 \\ 6 & -2 \end{vmatrix} = 0$$

Because $D = 0$, $\dfrac{D_x}{D}$ is undefined.

Therefore, the system of equations is dependent or inconsistent.

You Try It 5
$$2x - y + z = -1$$
$$3x + 2y - z = 3$$
$$x + 3y + z = -2$$

$$D = \begin{vmatrix} 2 & -1 & 1 \\ 3 & 2 & -1 \\ 1 & 3 & 1 \end{vmatrix} = 21$$

$$D_x = \begin{vmatrix} -1 & -1 & 1 \\ 3 & 2 & -1 \\ -2 & 3 & 1 \end{vmatrix} = 9$$

$$D_y = \begin{vmatrix} 2 & -1 & 1 \\ 3 & 3 & -1 \\ 1 & -2 & 1 \end{vmatrix} = -3$$

$$D_z = \begin{vmatrix} 2 & -1 & -1 \\ 3 & 2 & 3 \\ 1 & 3 & -2 \end{vmatrix} = -42$$

$$x = \frac{D_x}{D} = \frac{9}{21} = \frac{3}{7}$$

$$y = \frac{D_y}{D} = \frac{-3}{21} = -\frac{1}{7}$$

$$z = \frac{D_z}{D} = \frac{-42}{21} = -2$$

The solution is $\left(\dfrac{3}{7}, -\dfrac{1}{7}, -2\right)$.

SECTION 4.4

You Try It 1

Strategy
- Rate of the rowing team in calm water: t
  Rate of the current: c

	Rate	Time	Distance
With current	$t + c$	2	$2(t + c)$
Against current	$t - c$	2	$2(t - c)$

- The distance traveled with the current is 18 mi.
  The distance traveled against the current is 10 mi.

$$2(t + c) = 18$$
$$2(t - c) = 10$$

Solution

$$2(t + c) = 18 \qquad \frac{1}{2} \cdot 2(t + c) = \frac{1}{2} \cdot 18$$

$$2(t - c) = 10 \qquad \frac{1}{2} \cdot 2(t - c) = \frac{1}{2} \cdot 10$$

$$t + c = 9$$
$$t - c = 5$$
$$2t = 14$$
$$t = 7$$

$$t + c = 9$$
$$7 + c = 9$$
$$c = 2$$

The rate of the rowing team in calm water is 7 mph.
The rate of the current is 2 mph.

You Try It 2

Strategy • Number of dimes: d
Number of nickels: n
Number of quarters: q
• There are 19 coins in a bank that
contains only nickels, dimes, and
quarters. ($n + d + q = 19$)
The value of the coins is $2.
($5n + 10d + 25q = 200$)
There are twice as many nickels as
dimes. ($n = 2d$)

Solution (1) $n + d + q = 19$
(2) $n = 2d$
(3) $5n + 10d + 25q = 200$

Solve the system of equations.
Substitute $2d$ for n in Equation (1)
and Equation (3).

$$2d + d + q = 19$$
$$5(2d) + 10d + 25q = 200$$

(4) $3d + q = 19$
(5) $20d + 25q = 200$

Solve the system of equations in two
variables by multiplying Equation (4)
by -25 and then adding it to
Equation (5).

$$-75d - 25q = -475$$
$$\underline{20d + 25q = 200}$$
$$-55d = -275$$
$$d = 5$$

Substituting the value of d into
Equation (2), we have $n = 10$.
Substituting the values of d and n
into Equation (1), we have $q = 4$.

There are 5 dimes, 10 nickels, and
4 quarters in the bank.

You Try It 1   Shade above the solid line
$y = 2x - 3$.
Shade above the dotted line $y = -3x$.

The solution set of the system is the
intersection of the solution sets of the
individual inequalities.

You Try It 2 $3x + 4y > 12$
$$4y > -3x + 12$$
$$y > -\frac{3}{4}x + 3$$

Shade above the dotted line

$$y = -\frac{3}{4}x + 3.$$

Shade below the dotted line

$$y = \frac{3}{4}x - 1.$$

The solution set of the system is the
intersection of the solution sets of the
individual inequalities.

Solutions to Chapter 5 "You Try It"

SECTION 5.1

You Try It 1
$(-3a^2b^4)(-2ab^3)^4 = (-3a^2b^4)[(-2)^4a^4b^{12}]$
$$= (-3a^2b^4)(16a^4b^{12})$$
$$= -48a^6b^{16}$$

You Try It 2 $(y^{n-3})^2 = y^{(n-3)2}$
$$= y^{2n-6}$$

You Try It 3 $[(ab^3)^3]^4 = [a^3b^9]^4$
$$= a^{12}b^{36}$$

You Try It 4 $\dfrac{20r^{-2}t^{-5}}{-16r^{-3}s^{-2}} = -\dfrac{4 \cdot 5r^{-2-(-3)}s^2t^{-5}}{4 \cdot 4}$
$$= -\dfrac{5rs^2}{4t^5}$$

You Try It 5 $\dfrac{(9u^{-6}v^4)^{-1}}{(6u^{-3}v^{-2})^{-2}} = \dfrac{9^{-1}u^6v^{-4}}{6^{-2}u^6v^4}$
$$= 9^{-1} \cdot 6^2u^0v^{-8}$$
$$= \dfrac{36}{9v^8}$$
$$= \dfrac{4}{v^8}$$

You Try It 6
$$\frac{a^{2n+1}}{a^{n+3}} = a^{2n+1-(n+3)}$$
$$= a^{2n+1-n-3}$$
$$= a^{n-2}$$

You Try It 7 $942,000,000 = 9.42 \times 10^8$

You Try It 8 $2.7 \times 10^{-5} = 0.000027$

You Try It 9
$$\frac{5,600,000 \times 0.000000081}{900 \times 0.000000028}$$
$$= \frac{5.6 \times 10^6 \times 8.1 \times 10^{-8}}{9 \times 10^2 \times 2.8 \times 10^{-8}}$$
$$= \frac{(5.6)(8.1) \times 10^{6+(-8)-2-(-8)}}{(9)(2.8)}$$
$$= 1.8 \times 10^4 = 18,000$$

You Try It 10

Strategy   To find the number of arithmetic operations:
• Find the reciprocal of 1×10^{-7}, which is the number of operations performed in one second.
• Write the number of seconds in one minute (60) in scientific notation.
• Multiply the number of arithmetic operations per second by the number of seconds in one minute.

Solution
$$\frac{1}{1 \times 10^{-7}} = 10^7$$
$$60 = 6 \times 10$$

$$6 \times 10 \times 10^7$$
$$6 \times 10^8$$

The computer can perform 6×10^8 operations in one minute.

SECTION 5.2

You Try It 1
$R(x) = -2x^4 - 5x^3 + 2x - 8$
$R(2) = -2(2^4) - 5(2^3) + 2(2) - 8$
$\quad = -2(16) - 5(8) + 4 - 8$
$\quad = -32 - 40 + 4 - 8$
$\quad = -76$

You Try It 2   The leading coefficient is -3; the constant term is -12; and the degree is 4.

You Try It 3
a. This is a polynomial function.
b. This is not a polynomial function. A polynomial function does not have a variable expression raised to a negative power.

c. This is not a polynomial function. A polynomial function does not have a variable expression within a radical.

You Try It 4

x	y
-3	-25
-2	-6
-1	1
0	2
1	3
2	10
3	29

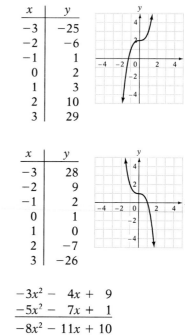

You Try It 5

x	y
-3	28
-2	9
-1	2
0	1
1	0
2	-7
3	-26

You Try It 6
$$\begin{array}{r} -3x^2 - 4x + 9 \\ -5x^2 - 7x + 1 \\ \hline -8x^2 - 11x + 10 \end{array}$$

You Try It 7   Add the additive inverse of $6x^2 + 3x - 7$ to $-5x^2 + 2x - 3$.
$$\begin{array}{r} -5x^2 + 2x - 3 \\ -6x^2 - 3x + 7 \\ \hline -11x^2 - x + 4 \end{array}$$

You Try It 8
$S(x) = (4x^3 - 3x^2 + 2) + (-2x^2 + 2x - 3)$
$\quad = 4x^3 - 5x^2 + 2x - 1$

$S(-1) = 4(-1)^3 - 5(-1)^2 + 2(-1) - 1$
$\quad = 4(-1) - 5(1) - 2 - 1$
$\quad = -4 - 5 - 2 - 1$
$\quad = -12$

You Try It 9
$D(x) = P(x) - R(x)$

$D(x) = (5x^{2n} - 3x^n - 7) - (-2x^{2n} - 5x^n + 8)$
$\quad = (5x^{2n} - 3x^n - 7) + (2x^{2n} + 5x^n - 8)$
$\quad = 7x^{2n} + 2x^n - 15$

SECTION 5.3

You Try It 1
$(2b^2 - 7b - 8)(-5b) = -10b^3 + 35b^2 + 40b$

You Try It 2
$$x^2 - 2x[x - x(4x - 5) + x^2]$$
$$= x^2 - 2x[x - 4x^2 + 5x + x^2]$$
$$= x^2 - 2x[6x - 3x^2]$$
$$= x^2 - 12x^2 + 6x^3$$
$$= 6x^3 - 11x^2$$

You Try It 3
$$y^{n+3}(y^{n-2} - 3y^2 + 2)$$
$$= y^{n+3}(y^{n-2}) - (y^{n+3})(3y^2) + (y^{n+3})(2)$$
$$= y^{n+3+(n-2)} - 3y^{n+3+2} + 2y^{n+3}$$
$$= y^{2n+1} - 3y^{n+5} + 2y^{n+3}$$

You Try It 4
$$\begin{array}{r} -2b^2 + 5b - 4 \\ -3b + 2 \\ \hline -4b^2 + 10b - 8 \\ 6b^3 - 15b^2 + 12b \\ \hline 6b^3 - 19b^2 + 22b - 8 \end{array}$$

You Try It 5
$$(3x - 4)(2x - 3) = 6x^2 - 9x - 8x + 12$$
$$= 6x^2 - 17x + 12$$

You Try It 6
$$(2x^n + y^n)(x^n - 4y^n)$$
$$= 2x^{2n} - 8x^n y^n + x^n y^n - 4y^{2n}$$
$$= 2x^{2n} - 7x^n y^n - 4y^{2n}$$

You Try It 7
$$(3x - 7)(3x + 7) = 9x^2 - 49$$

You Try It 8
$$(2x^n + 3)(2x^n - 3) = 4x^{2n} - 9$$

You Try It 9
$$(3x - 4y)^2 = 9x^2 - 24xy + 16y^2$$

You Try It 10
$$(2x^n - 8)^2 = 4x^{2n} - 32x^n + 64$$

You Try It 11

Strategy   To find the area, replace the variables b and h in the equation $A = \frac{1}{2}bh$ by the given values and solve for A.

Solution $A = \frac{1}{2}bh$

$A = \frac{1}{2}(2x + 6)(x - 4)$

$A = (x + 3)(x - 4)$

$A = x^2 - 4x + 3x - 12$

$A = x^2 - x - 12$

The area is $(x^2 - x - 12)$ ft².

You Try It 12

Strategy   To find the volume, subtract the volume of the small rectangular solid from the volume of the large rectangular solid.

Large rectangular solid:
Length = $L_1 = 12x$
Width = $W_1 = 7x + 2$
Height = $H_1 = 5x - 4$
Small rectangular solid:
Length = $L_2 = 12x$
Width = $W_2 = x$
Height = $H_2 = 2x$

Solution
V = Volume of large rectangular solid − volume of small rectangular solid
$V = (L_1 \cdot W_1 \cdot H_1) - (L_2 \cdot W_2 \cdot H_2)$
$V = (12x)(7x + 2)(5x - 4) - (12x)(x)(2x)$
$= (84x^2 + 24x)(5x - 4) - (12x^2)(2x)$
$= (420x^3 - 336x^2 + 120x^2 - 96x) - 24x^3$
$= 396x^3 - 216x^2 - 96x$

The volume is $(396x^3 - 216x^2 - 96x)$ ft³.

You Try It 13

Strategy   To find the area, replace the variable r in the equation $A = \pi r^2$ by the given value and solve for A.

Solution $A = \pi r^2$
$A = 3.14(2x + 3)^2$
$= 3.14(4x^2 + 12x + 9)$
$= 12.56x^2 + 37.68x + 28.26$

The area is $(12.56x^2 + 37.68x + 28.26)$ cm².

SECTION 5.4

You Try It 1
$$\begin{array}{r} 5x - 1 \\ 3x + 4 \overline{)15x^2 + 17x - 20} \\ \underline{15x^2 + 20x} \\ -3x - 20 \\ \underline{-3x - 4} \\ -16 \end{array}$$

$$\frac{15x^2 + 17x - 20}{3x + 4} = 5x - 1 - \frac{16}{3x + 4}$$

You Try It 2
$$\begin{array}{r} x^2 + 3x - 1 \\ 3x - 1 \overline{)3x^3 + 8x^2 - 6x + 2} \\ \underline{3x^3 - x^2} \\ 9x^2 - 6x \\ \underline{9x^2 - 3x} \\ -3x + 2 \\ \underline{-3x + 1} \\ 1 \end{array}$$

$$\frac{3x^3 + 8x^2 - 6x + 2}{3x - 1} = x^2 + 3x - 1 + \frac{1}{3x - 1}$$

You Try It 3

$$\begin{array}{r} 3x^2 - 2x + 4 \\ x^2 - 3x + 2\overline{)3x^4 - 11x^3 + 16x^2 - 16x + 8} \\ \underline{3x^4 - 9x^3 + 6x^2} \\ -2x^3 + 10x^2 - 16x \\ \underline{-2x^3 + 6x^2 - 4x} \\ 4x^2 - 12x + 8 \\ \underline{4x^2 - 12x + 8} \\ 0 \end{array}$$

$$\frac{3x^4 - 11x^3 + 16x^2 - 16x + 8}{x^2 - 3x + 2} = 3x^2 - 2x + 4$$

You Try It 4

$$\begin{array}{r|rrr} -2 & 6 & 8 & -5 \\ & & -12 & 8 \\ \hline & 6 & -4 & 3 \end{array}$$

$$(6x^2 + 8x - 5) \div (x + 2) = 6x - 4 + \frac{3}{x + 2}$$

You Try It 5

$$\begin{array}{r|rrrr} 2 & 5 & -12 & -8 & 16 \\ & & 10 & -4 & -24 \\ \hline & 5 & -2 & -12 & -8 \end{array}$$

$$(5x^3 - 12x^2 - 8x + 16) \div (x - 2)$$

$$= 5x^2 - 2x - 12 - \frac{8}{x - 2}$$

You Try It 6

$$\begin{array}{r|rrrrr} 3 & 2 & -3 & -8 & 0 & -2 \\ & & 6 & 9 & 3 & 9 \\ \hline & 2 & 3 & 1 & 3 & 7 \end{array}$$

$$(2x^4 - 3x^3 - 8x^2 - 2) \div (x - 3)$$

$$= 2x^3 + 3x^2 + x + 3 + \frac{7}{x - 3}$$

You Try It 7

$$\begin{array}{r|rrr} 2 & 2 & -3 & -5 \\ & & 4 & 2 \\ \hline & 2 & 1 & -3 \end{array}$$

$$P(2) = -3$$

You Try It 8

$$\begin{array}{r|rrrr} -3 & 2 & -5 & 0 & 7 \\ & & -6 & 33 & -99 \\ \hline & 2 & -11 & 33 & -92 \end{array}$$

$$P(-3) = -92$$

SECTION 5.5

You Try It 1   The GCF of $3x^3y$, $6x^2y^2$, and $3xy^3$ is $3xy$.

$$3x^3y - 6x^2y^2 - 3xy^3 = 3xy(x^2 - 2xy - y^2)$$

You Try It 2   The GCF of $6t^{2n}$ and $9t^n$ is $3t^n$.

$$6t^{2n} - 9t^n = 3t^n(2t^n - 3)$$

You Try It 3 $3(6x - 7y) - 2x^2(6x - 7y)$
$$= (6x - 7y)(3 - 2x^2)$$

You Try It 4 $4a^2 - 6a - 6ax + 9x$
$$= (4a^2 - 6a) - (6ax - 9x)$$
$$= 2a(2a - 3) - 3x(2a - 3)$$
$$= (2a - 3)(2a - 3x)$$

You Try It 5 $x^2 - x - 20 = (x + 4)(x - 5)$

You Try It 6 $x^2 + 5xy + 6y^2 = (x + 2y)(x + 3y)$

You Try It 7 $4x^2 + 15x - 4 = (x + 4)(4x - 1)$

You Try It 8 $10x^2 + 39x + 14 = (2x + 7)(5x + 2)$

You Try It 9
The GCF of $3a^3b^3$, $3a^2b^2$, and $60ab$ is $3ab$.

$$3a^3b^3 + 3a^2b^2 - 60ab = 3ab(a^2b^2 + ab - 20)$$
$$= 3ab(ab + 5)(ab - 4)$$

SECTION 5.6

You Try It 1 $x^2 - 36y^4 = x^2 - (6y^2)^2$
$$= (x + 6y^2)(x - 6y^2)$$

You Try It 2 $9x^2 + 12x + 4 = (3x + 2)^2$

You Try It 3
$(a + b)^2 - (a - b)^2$
$$= [(a + b) + (a - b)][(a + b) - (a - b)]$$
$$= (a + b + a - b)(a + b - a + b)$$
$$= (2a)(2b) = 4ab$$

You Try It 4 $a^3b^3 - 27 = (ab)^3 - 3^3$
$$= (ab - 3)(a^2b^2 + 3ab + 9)$$

You Try It 5 $8x^3 + y^3z^3 = (2x)^3 + (yz)^3$
$$= (2x + yz)(4x^2 - 2xyz + y^2z^2)$$

You Try It 6
$(x - y)^3 + (x + y)^3$
$$= [(x - y) + (x + y)]$$
$$\times [(x - y)^2 - (x - y)(x + y) + (x + y)^2]$$
$$= 2x[x^2 - 2xy + y^2 - (x^2 - y^2)$$
$$+ x^2 + 2xy + y^2]$$
$$= 2x(x^2 - 2xy + y^2 - x^2 + y^2 + x^2$$
$$+ 2xy + y^2)$$
$$= 2x(x^2 + 3y^2)$$

You Try It 7   Let $u = x^2$.

$$3x^4 + 4x^2 - 4 = 3u^2 + 4u - 4$$
$$= (u + 2)(3u - 2)$$
$$= (x^2 + 2)(3x^2 - 2)$$

You Try It 8 $18x^3 - 6x^2 - 60x = 6x(3x^2 - x - 10)$
$$= 6x(3x + 5)(x - 2)$$

You Try It 9 $4x - 4y - x^3 + x^2y$
$$= (4x - 4y) - (x^3 - x^2y)$$
$$= 4(x - y) - x^2(x - y)$$
$$= (x - y)(4 - x^2)$$
$$= (x - y)(2 + x)(2 - x)$$

You Try It 10 $x^{4n} - x^{2n}y^{2n} = x^{2n+2n} - x^{2n}y^{2n}$
$$= x^{2n}(x^{2n} - y^{2n})$$
$$= x^{2n}[(x^n)^2 - (y^n)^2]$$
$$= x^{2n}(x^n + y^n)(x^n - y^n)$$

You Try It 11 $ax^5 - ax^2y^6 = ax^2(x^3 - y^6)$
$$= ax^2(x - y^2)(x^2 + xy^2 + y^4)$$

SECTION 5.7

You Try It 1 $(x + 4)(x - 1) = 14$
$$x^2 + 3x - 4 = 14$$
$$x^2 + 3x - 18 = 0$$
$$(x + 6)(x - 3) = 0$$
$$x + 6 = 0 \qquad x - 3 = 0$$
$$x = -6 \qquad x = 3$$

The solutions are -6 and 3.

You Try It 2

$$A = \frac{1}{2}bh$$

$$54 = \frac{1}{2}x(x + 3)$$

$$108 = x(x + 3)$$
$$0 = x^2 + 3x - 108$$
$$0 = (x - 9)(x + 12)$$

$$x - 9 = 0 \qquad x + 12 = 0$$
$$x = 9 \qquad x = -12$$

$$x + 3 = 12$$

The base is 9 cm; the height is 12 cm.

Solutions to Chapter 6 "You Try It"

SECTION 6.1

You Try It 1 $f(x) = \dfrac{3 - 5x}{x^2 + 5x + 6}$

$$f(2) = \frac{3 - 5(2)}{2^2 + 5(2) + 6}$$

$$= \frac{3 - 10}{4 + 10 + 6}$$

$$= \frac{-7}{20}$$

$$= -\frac{7}{20}$$

You Try It 2   Set the denominator equal to zero.

Then solve for x.

$$2x^2 - 7x + 3 = 0$$
$$(2x - 1)(x - 3) = 0$$
$$2x - 1 = 0 \qquad x - 3 = 0$$
$$x = \frac{1}{2} \qquad x = 3$$

The domain is $\left\{ x \mid x \neq \dfrac{1}{2}, 3 \right\}$.

You Try It 3 $\dfrac{6x^4 - 24x^3}{12x^3 - 48x^2} = \dfrac{6x^3(x - 4)}{12x^2(x - 4)}$

$$= \frac{6x^3\overset{1}{\cancel{(x - 4)}}}{12x^2\underset{1}{\cancel{(x - 4)}}} = \frac{x}{2}$$

You Try It 4 $\dfrac{21a^3b - 14a^3b^2}{7a^2b} = \dfrac{7a^3b(3 - 2b)}{7a^2b}$

$$= a(3 - 2b)$$

You Try It 5

$$\frac{20x - 15x^2}{15x^3 - 5x^2 - 20x} = \frac{5x(4 - 3x)}{5x(3x^2 - x - 4)}$$

$$= \frac{5x(4 - 3x)}{5x(3x - 4)(x + 1)}$$

$$= \frac{\overset{-1}{5x(4 - 3x)}}{\underset{1}{5x(3x - 4)}(x + 1)}$$

$$= -\frac{1}{x + 1}$$

You Try It 6

$$\frac{x^{2n} + x^n - 12}{x^{2n} - 3x^n} = \frac{(x^n + 4)(x^n - 3)}{x^n(x^n - 3)}$$

$$= \frac{(x^n + 4)\overset{1}{(x^n - 3)}}{x^n\underset{1}{(x^n - 3)}}$$

$$= \frac{x^n + 4}{x^n}$$

You Try It 7

$$\frac{12 + 5x - 3x^2}{x^2 + 2x - 15} \cdot \frac{2x^2 + x - 45}{3x^2 + 4x}$$

$$= \frac{(4 + 3x)(3 - x)}{(x + 5)(x - 3)} \cdot \frac{(2x - 9)(x + 5)}{x(3x + 4)}$$

$$= \frac{(4 + 3x)(3 - x)(2x - 9)(x + 5)}{(x + 5)(x - 3) \cdot x(3x + 4)}$$

$$= \frac{\overset{1}{(4 + 3x)}\overset{-1}{(3 - x)}(2x - 9)\overset{1}{(x + 5)}}{\underset{1}{(x + 5)}\underset{1}{(x - 3)} \cdot x\underset{1}{(3x + 4)}} = -\frac{2x - 9}{x}$$

You Try It 8

$$\frac{2x^2 - 13x + 20}{x^2 - 16} \cdot \frac{2x^2 + 9x + 4}{6x^2 - 7x - 5}$$

$$= \frac{(2x - 5)(x - 4)}{(x - 4)(x + 4)} \cdot \frac{(2x + 1)(x + 4)}{(3x - 5)(2x + 1)}$$

$$= \frac{(2x - 5)(x - 4) \cdot (2x + 1)(x + 4)}{(x - 4)(x + 4) \cdot (3x - 5)(2x + 1)}$$

$$= \frac{(2x - 5)\overset{1}{(x - 4)}\overset{1}{(2x + 1)}\overset{1}{(x + 4)}}{\underset{1}{(x - 4)}\underset{1}{(x + 4)}(3x - 5)\underset{1}{(2x + 1)}} = \frac{2x - 5}{3x - 5}$$

You Try It 9

$$\frac{7a^3b^7}{15x^2y^3} \div \frac{21a^5b^2}{20x^4y}$$

$$= \frac{7a^3b^7}{15x^2y^3} \cdot \frac{20x^4y}{21a^5b^2}$$

$$= \frac{7a^3b^7 \cdot 20x^4y}{15x^2y^3 \cdot 21a^5b^2}$$

$$= \frac{4b^5x^2}{9a^2y^2}$$

You Try It 10

$$\frac{6x^2 - 3xy}{10ab^4} \div \frac{16x^2y^2 - 8xy^3}{15a^2b^2}$$

$$= \frac{6x^2 - 3xy}{10ab^4} \cdot \frac{15a^2b^2}{16x^2y^2 - 8xy^3}$$

$$= \frac{3x(2x - y)}{10ab^4} \cdot \frac{15a^2b^2}{8xy^2(2x - y)}$$

$$= \frac{3x(2x - y) \cdot 15a^2b^2}{10ab^4 \cdot 8xy^2(2x - y)}$$

$$= \frac{3x\overset{1}{(2x - y)} \cdot 15a^2b^2}{10ab^4 \cdot 8xy^2\underset{1}{(2x - y)}} = \frac{9a}{16b^2y^2}$$

You Try It 11

$$\frac{6x^2 - 7x + 2}{3x^2 + x - 2} \div \frac{4x^2 - 8x + 3}{5x^2 + x - 4}$$

$$= \frac{6x^2 - 7x + 2}{3x^2 + x - 2} \cdot \frac{5x^2 + x - 4}{4x^2 - 8x + 3}$$

$$= \frac{(2x - 1)(3x - 2)}{(x + 1)(3x - 2)} \cdot \frac{(x + 1)(5x - 4)}{(2x - 1)(2x - 3)}$$

$$= \frac{(2x - 1)(3x - 2)(x + 1)(5x - 4)}{(x + 1)(3x - 2)(2x - 1)(2x - 3)}$$

$$= \frac{\overset{1}{(2x - 1)}\overset{1}{(3x - 2)}\overset{1}{(x + 1)}(5x - 4)}{\underset{1}{(x + 1)}\underset{1}{(3x - 2)}\underset{1}{(2x - 1)}(2x - 3)} = \frac{5x - 4}{2x - 3}$$

SECTION 6.2

You Try It 1
The LCM is $(2x - 5)(x + 4)$.

$$\frac{2x}{2x - 5} = \frac{2x}{2x - 5} \cdot \frac{x + 4}{x + 4} = \frac{2x^2 + 8x}{(2x - 5)(x + 4)}$$

$$\frac{3}{x + 4} = \frac{3}{x + 4} \cdot \frac{2x - 5}{2x - 5} = \frac{6x - 15}{(2x - 5)(x + 4)}$$

You Try It 2
$2x^2 - 11x + 15 = (x - 3)(2x - 5); \; x^2 - 3x = x(x - 3)$

The LCM is $x(x - 3)(2x - 5)$.

$$\frac{3x}{2x^2 - 11x + 15} = \frac{3x}{(x - 3)(2x - 5)} \cdot \frac{x}{x} = \frac{3x^2}{x(x - 3)(2x - 5)}$$

$$\frac{x - 2}{x^2 - 3x} = \frac{x - 2}{x(x - 3)} \cdot \frac{2x - 5}{2x - 5} = \frac{2x^2 - 9x + 10}{x(x - 3)(2x - 5)}$$

You Try It 3
$2x - x^2 = x(2 - x) = -x(x - 2);$
$3x^2 - 5x - 2 = (x - 2)(3x + 1)$

The LCM is $x(x - 2)(3x + 1)$.

$$\frac{2x - 7}{2x - x^2} = -\frac{2x - 7}{x(x - 2)} \cdot \frac{3x + 1}{3x + 1} = -\frac{6x^2 - 19x - 7}{x(x - 2)(3x + 1)}$$

$$\frac{3x - 2}{3x^2 - 5x - 2} = \frac{3x - 2}{(x - 2)(3x + 1)} \cdot \frac{x}{x} = \frac{3x^2 - 2x}{x(x - 2)(3x + 1)}$$

You Try It 4

The LCM is ab.

$$\frac{2}{b} - \frac{1}{a} + \frac{4}{ab} = \frac{2}{b} \cdot \frac{a}{a} - \frac{1}{a} \cdot \frac{b}{b} + \frac{4}{ab}$$

$$= \frac{2a}{ab} - \frac{b}{ab} + \frac{4}{ab} = \frac{2a - b + 4}{ab}$$

You Try It 5

The LCM is $a(a - 5)(a + 5)$.

$$\frac{a - 3}{a^2 - 5a} + \frac{a - 9}{a^2 - 25}$$

$$= \frac{a - 3}{a(a - 5)} \cdot \frac{a + 5}{a + 5} + \frac{a - 9}{(a - 5)(a + 5)} \cdot \frac{a}{a}$$

$$= \frac{(a - 3)(a + 5) + a(a - 9)}{a(a - 5)(a + 5)}$$

$$= \frac{(a^2 + 2a - 15) + (a^2 - 9a)}{a(a - 5)(a + 5)}$$

$$= \frac{a^2 + 2a - 15 + a^2 - 9a}{a(a - 5)(a + 5)}$$

$$= \frac{2a^2 - 7a - 15}{a(a - 5)(a + 5)} = \frac{(2a + 3)(a - 5)}{a(a - 5)(a + 5)}$$

$$= \frac{(2a + 3)\overset{1}{\cancel{(a - 5)}}}{a\underset{1}{\cancel{(a - 5)}}(a + 5)} = \frac{2a + 3}{a(a + 5)}$$

You Try It 6

The LCM is $(x - 4)(x + 1)$.

$$\frac{2x}{x - 4} - \frac{x - 1}{x + 1} + \frac{2}{x^2 - 3x - 4}$$

$$= \frac{2x}{x - 4} \cdot \frac{x + 1}{x + 1} - \frac{x - 1}{x + 1} \cdot \frac{x - 4}{x - 4} + \frac{2}{(x - 4)(x + 1)}$$

$$= \frac{2x(x + 1) - (x - 1)(x - 4) + 2}{(x - 4)(x + 1)}$$

$$= \frac{(2x^2 + 2x) - (x^2 - 5x + 4) + 2}{(x - 4)(x + 1)}$$

$$= \frac{x^2 + 7x - 2}{(x - 4)(x + 1)}$$

SECTION 6.3

You Try It 1

The LCM of $x + 3$ and $x + 2$ is $(x + 3)(x + 2)$.

$$\frac{1 - \dfrac{2}{x + 3}}{1 - \dfrac{1}{x + 2}} = \frac{1 - \dfrac{2}{x + 3}}{1 - \dfrac{1}{x + 2}} \cdot \frac{(x + 3)(x + 2)}{(x + 3)(x + 2)}$$

$$= \frac{(x + 3)(x + 2) - \dfrac{2}{x + 3}(x + 3)(x + 2)}{(x + 3)(x + 2) - \dfrac{1}{x + 2}(x + 3)(x + 2)}$$

$$= \frac{x^2 + 5x + 6 - 2x - 4}{x^2 + 5x + 6 - x - 3}$$

$$= \frac{x^2 + 3x + 2}{x^2 + 4x + 3} = \frac{(x + 2)\overset{1}{\cancel{(x + 1)}}}{(x + 3)\underset{1}{\cancel{(x + 1)}}} = \frac{x + 2}{x + 3}$$

You Try It 2

The LCM is $x - 3$.

$$\frac{2x + 5 + \dfrac{14}{x - 3}}{4x + 16 + \dfrac{49}{x - 3}} = \frac{2x + 5 + \dfrac{14}{x - 3}}{4x + 16 + \dfrac{49}{x - 3}} \cdot \frac{x - 3}{x - 3}$$

$$= \frac{(2x + 5)(x - 3) + \dfrac{14}{x - 3}(x - 3)}{(4x + 16)(x - 3) + \dfrac{49}{x - 3}(x - 3)}$$

$$= \frac{2x^2 - x - 15 + 14}{4x^2 + 4x - 48 + 49} = \frac{2x^2 - x - 1}{4x^2 + 4x + 1}$$

$$= \frac{(2x + 1)(x - 1)}{(2x + 1)(2x + 1)} = \frac{\overset{1}{\cancel{(2x + 1)}}(x - 1)}{\underset{1}{\cancel{(2x + 1)}}(2x + 1)} = \frac{x - 1}{2x + 1}$$

You Try It 3

The LCM of the denominators is x.

$$2 - \frac{1}{2 - \dfrac{1}{x}} = 2 - \frac{1}{2 - \dfrac{1}{x}} \cdot \frac{x}{x}$$

$$= 2 - \frac{1 \cdot x}{2 \cdot x - \dfrac{1}{x} \cdot x} = 2 - \frac{x}{2x - 1}$$

The LCM of the denominators is $2x - 1$.

$$2 - \frac{x}{2x - 1} = 2 \cdot \frac{(2x - 1)}{(2x - 1)} - \frac{x}{2x - 1}$$

$$= \frac{4x - 2}{2x - 1} - \frac{x}{2x - 1}$$

$$= \frac{4x - 2 - x}{2x - 1} = \frac{3x - 2}{2x - 1}$$

SECTION 6.4

You Try It 1

$$\frac{5}{x - 2} = \frac{3}{4}$$

$$\frac{5}{x - 2} \cdot 4(x - 2) = \frac{3}{4} \cdot 4(x - 2)$$

$$5 \cdot 4 = 3(x - 2)$$

$$20 = 3x - 6$$

$$26 = 3x$$

$$\frac{26}{3} = x$$

The solution is $\dfrac{26}{3}$.

You Try It 2

$$\frac{5}{2x - 3} = \frac{-2}{x + 1}$$

$$\frac{5}{2x - 3}(x + 1)(2x - 3) = \frac{-2}{x + 1}(x + 1)(2x - 3)$$

$$5(x + 1) = -2(2x - 3)$$

$$5x + 5 = -4x + 6$$

$$9x + 5 = 6$$

$$9x = 1$$

$$x = \frac{1}{9}$$

The solution is $\frac{1}{9}$.

You Try It 3

Strategy To find the cost, write and solve a proportion using x to represent the cost.

Solution

$$\frac{2}{3.10} = \frac{15}{x}$$

$$\frac{2}{3.10} \cdot x(3.10) = \frac{15}{x} \cdot x(3.10)$$

$$2x = 15(3.10)$$

$$2x = 46.50$$

$$x = 23.25$$

The cost of 15 lb of cashews is $23.25.

SECTION 6.5

You Try It 1

$$\frac{x}{x - 2} + x = \frac{6}{x - 2}$$

$$(x - 2)\left(\frac{x}{x - 2} + x\right) = (x - 2)\left(\frac{6}{x - 2}\right)$$

$$(x - 2)\left(\frac{x}{x - 2}\right) + (x - 2)x = (x - 2)\left(\frac{6}{x - 2}\right)$$

$$x + x^2 - 2x = 6$$

$$x^2 - x = 6$$

$$x^2 - x - 6 = 0$$

$$(x - 3)(x + 2) = 0$$

$$x = 3 \qquad x = -2$$

-2 and 3 check as solutions.

The solutions are -2 and 3.

You Try It 2

$$\frac{5}{x - 2} = 2x + \frac{3x - 1}{x - 2}$$

$$(x - 2)\left(\frac{5}{x - 2}\right) = (x - 2)\left(2x + \frac{3x - 1}{x - 2}\right)$$

$$5 = (x - 2)(2x) + 3x - 1$$

$$5 = 2x^2 - 4x + 3x - 1$$

$$0 = 2x^2 - x - 6$$

$$0 = (2x + 3)(x - 2)$$

$$2x + 3 = 0 \qquad x - 2 = 0$$

$$x = -\frac{3}{2} \qquad x = 2$$

2 does not check as a solution.

The solution is $-\frac{3}{2}$.

You Try It 3

$$\frac{P_1 V_1}{T_1} = \frac{P_2 V_2}{T_2}$$

$$T_1 T_2 \left(\frac{P_1 V_1}{T_1}\right) = T_1 T_2 \left(\frac{P_2 V_2}{T_2}\right)$$

$$T_2 P_1 V_1 = T_1 P_2 V_2$$

$$\frac{T_2 P_1 V_1}{P_2 V_2} = \frac{T_1 P_2 V_2}{P_2 V_2}$$

$$\frac{T_2 P_1 V_1}{P_2 V_2} = T_1$$

You Try It 4

Strategy • Time required for the small pipe to fill the tank: x

	Rate	Time	Part
Large pipe	$\frac{1}{9}$	6	$\frac{6}{9}$
Small pipe	$\frac{1}{x}$	6	$\frac{6}{x}$

• The sum of the part of the task completed by the large pipe and the part of the task completed by the small pipe is 1.

Solution

$$\frac{6}{9} + \frac{6}{x} = 1$$

$$\frac{2}{3} + \frac{6}{x} = 1$$

$$3x\left(\frac{2}{3} + \frac{6}{x}\right) = 3x \cdot 1$$

$$2x + 18 = 3x$$

$$18 = x$$

The small pipe working alone will fill the tank in 18 h.

You Try It 5

Strategy

• Rate of the wind: r

	Distance	Rate	Time
With wind	700	$150 + r$	$\dfrac{700}{150 + r}$
Against wind	500	$150 - r$	$\dfrac{500}{150 - r}$

• The time flying with the wind equals the time flying against the wind.

Solution

$$\frac{700}{150 + r} = \frac{500}{150 - r}$$

$$(150 + r)(150 - r)\left(\frac{700}{150 + r}\right) = (150 + r)(150 - r)\left(\frac{500}{150 - r}\right)$$

$$(150 - r)700 = (150 + r)500$$

$$105{,}000 - 700r = 75{,}000 + 500r$$

$$30{,}000 = 1200r$$

$$25 = r$$

The rate of the wind is 25 mph.

SECTION 6.6

You Try It 1

Strategy   To find the distance:

• Write the basic direct variation equation, replace the variables by the given values, and solve for k.
• Write the direct variation equation, replacing k by its value. Substitute 5 for t and solve for s.

Solution

$$s = kt^2$$

$$64 = k(2)^2$$

$$64 = k \cdot 4$$

$$16 = k$$

$$s = 16t^2 = 16(5)^2 = 400$$

The object will fall 400 ft in 5 s.

You Try It 2

Strategy   To find the resistance:

• Write the basic inverse variation equation, replace the variables by the given values, and solve for k.
• Write the inverse variation equation, replacing k by its value. Substitute 0.02 for d and solve for R.

Solution

$$R = \frac{k}{d^2}$$

$$0.5 = \frac{k}{(0.01)^2}$$

$$0.5 = \frac{k}{0.0001}$$

$$0.00005 = k$$

$$R = \frac{0.00005}{d^2} = \frac{0.00005}{(0.02)^2} = 0.125$$

The resistance is 0.125 ohm.

You Try It 3

Strategy

• Write the basic combined variation equation, replace the variables by the given values, and solve for k.
• Write the combined variation equation, replacing k by its value and substituting 4 for W, 8 for d, and 16 for L. Solve for s.

Solution

$$s = \frac{kWd^2}{L}$$ • Combined variation equation.

$$1200 = \frac{k(2)(12)^2}{12}$$ • Replace s by 1200, W by 2, d by 12, and L by 12.

$$1200 = 24k$$

$$50 = k$$

$$s = \frac{50Wd^2}{L}$$ • Replace k by 50 in the combined variation equation.

$$= \frac{50(4)8^2}{16}$$ • Replace W by 4, d by 8, and L by 16.

$$= 800$$

The strength of the beam is 800 lb.

Solutions to Chapter 7 "You Try It"

SECTION 7.1

You Try It 1
$$16^{-3/4} = (2^4)^{-3/4}$$
$$= 2^{-3}$$
$$= \frac{1}{2^3} = \frac{1}{8}$$

You Try It 2
$(-81)^{3/4}$
The base of the exponential expression is negative, and the denominator of the exponent is a positive even number.

Therefore, $(-81)^{3/4}$ is not a real number.

You Try It 3
$(x^{3/4}y^{1/2}z^{-2/3})^{-4/3} = x^{-1}y^{-2/3}z^{8/9}$
$$= \frac{z^{8/9}}{xy^{2/3}}$$

You Try It 4
$$\left(\frac{16a^{-2}b^{4/3}}{9a^4b^{-2/3}}\right)^{-1/2} = \left(\frac{2^4a^{-6}b^2}{3^2}\right)^{-1/2}$$
$$= \frac{2^{-2}a^3b^{-1}}{3^{-1}}$$
$$= \frac{3a^3}{2^2b} = \frac{3a^3}{4b}$$

You Try It 5
$(2x^3)^{3/4} = \sqrt[4]{(2x^3)^3}$
$$= \sqrt[4]{8x^9}$$

You Try It 6
$-5a^{5/6} = -5(a^5)^{1/6}$
$$= -5\sqrt[6]{a^5}$$

You Try It 7
$\sqrt[3]{3ab} = (3ab)^{1/3}$

You Try It 8
$\sqrt[4]{x^4 + y^4} = (x^4 + y^4)^{1/4}$

You Try It 9
$\sqrt{121x^{10}y^4} = \sqrt{11^2x^{10}y^4}$
$$= (11^2x^{10}y^4)^{1/2}$$
$$= 11x^5y^2$$

You Try It 10
$\sqrt[3]{-8x^{12}y^3} = \sqrt[3]{(-2)^3x^{12}y^3}$
$$= [(-2)^3x^{12}y^3]^{1/3}$$
$$= -2x^4y$$

You Try It 11
$-\sqrt[4]{81x^{12}y^8} = -\sqrt[4]{3^4x^{12}y^8}$
$$= -(3^4x^{12}y^8)^{1/4}$$
$$= -3x^3y^2$$

SECTION 7.2

You Try It 1
$\sqrt[5]{x^7} = \sqrt[5]{x^5 \cdot x^2}$
$$= \sqrt[5]{x^5}\sqrt[5]{x^2}$$
$$= x\sqrt[5]{x^2}$$

You Try It 2
$\sqrt[3]{-64x^8y^{18}} = \sqrt[3]{(-4)^3x^8y^{18}}$
$$= \sqrt[3]{(-4)^3x^6y^{18}(x^2)}$$
$$= \sqrt[3]{(-4)^3x^6y^{18}}\sqrt[3]{x^2}$$
$$= -4x^2y^6\sqrt[3]{x^2}$$

You Try It 3
$3xy\sqrt[3]{81x^5y} - \sqrt[3]{192x^8y^4}$
$$= 3xy\sqrt[3]{3^4x^5y} - \sqrt[3]{2^6 \cdot 3x^8y^4}$$
$$= 3xy\sqrt[3]{3^3x^3}\sqrt[3]{3x^2y} - \sqrt[3]{2^6x^6y^3}\sqrt[3]{3x^2y}$$
$$= 3xy \cdot 3x\sqrt[3]{3x^2y} - 2^2x^2y\sqrt[3]{3x^2y}$$
$$= 9x^2y\sqrt[3]{3x^2y} - 4x^2y\sqrt[3]{3x^2y} = 5x^2y\sqrt[3]{3x^2y}$$

You Try It 4
$\sqrt{5b}(\sqrt{3b} - \sqrt{10})$
$$= \sqrt{15b^2} - \sqrt{50b}$$
$$= \sqrt{3 \cdot 5b^2} - \sqrt{2 \cdot 5^2b}$$
$$= \sqrt{b^2}\sqrt{3 \cdot 5} - \sqrt{5^2}\sqrt{2b}$$
$$= b\sqrt{15} - 5\sqrt{2b}$$

You Try It 5
$(2\sqrt[3]{2x} - 3)(\sqrt[3]{2x} - 5)$
$$= 2\sqrt[3]{4x^2} - 10\sqrt[3]{2x} - 3\sqrt[3]{2x} + 15$$
$$= 2\sqrt[3]{4x^2} - 13\sqrt[3]{2x} + 15$$

You Try It 6
$(\sqrt{a} - 3\sqrt{y})(\sqrt{a} + 3\sqrt{y})$
$$= (\sqrt{a})^2 - (3\sqrt{y})^2$$
$$= a - 9y$$

You Try It 7
$$\frac{y}{\sqrt{3y}} = \frac{y}{\sqrt{3y}} \cdot \frac{\sqrt{3y}}{\sqrt{3y}} = \frac{y\sqrt{3y}}{\sqrt{3^2y^2}} = \frac{y\sqrt{3y}}{3y} = \frac{\sqrt{3y}}{3}$$

You Try It 8
$$\frac{3}{\sqrt[3]{3x^2}} = \frac{3}{\sqrt[3]{3x^2}} \cdot \frac{\sqrt[3]{3^2x}}{\sqrt[3]{3^2x}} = \frac{3\sqrt[3]{9x}}{\sqrt[3]{3^3x^3}}$$
$$= \frac{3\sqrt[3]{9x}}{3x} = \frac{\sqrt[3]{9x}}{x}$$

You Try It 9
$$\frac{3 + \sqrt{6}}{2 - \sqrt{6}} = \frac{3 + \sqrt{6}}{2 - \sqrt{6}} \cdot \frac{2 + \sqrt{6}}{2 + \sqrt{6}}$$

$$= \frac{6 + 3\sqrt{6} + 2\sqrt{6} + (\sqrt{6})^2}{2^2 - (\sqrt{6})^2}$$

$$= \frac{6 + 5\sqrt{6} + 6}{4 - 6} = \frac{12 + 5\sqrt{6}}{-2}$$

$$= -\frac{12 + 5\sqrt{6}}{2}$$

SECTION 7.3

You Try It 1 $\sqrt{-45} = i\sqrt{45} = i\sqrt{3^2 \cdot 5} = 3i\sqrt{5}$

You Try It 2 $\sqrt{98} - \sqrt{-60} = \sqrt{98} - i\sqrt{60}$
$$= \sqrt{2 \cdot 7^2} - i\sqrt{2^2 \cdot 3 \cdot 5}$$
$$= 7\sqrt{2} - 2i\sqrt{15}$$

You Try It 3 $(-4 + 2i) - (6 - 8i) = -10 + 10i$

You Try It 4 $(16 - \sqrt{-45}) - (3 + \sqrt{-20})$
$$= (16 - i\sqrt{45}) - (3 + i\sqrt{20})$$
$$= (16 - i\sqrt{3^2 \cdot 5}) - (3 + i\sqrt{2^2 \cdot 5})$$
$$= (16 - 3i\sqrt{5}) - (3 + 2i\sqrt{5})$$
$$= 13 - 5i\sqrt{5}$$

You Try It 5 $(3 - 2i) + (-3 + 2i) = 0 + 0i = 0$

You Try It 6 $(-3i)(-10i) = 30i^2 = 30(-1) = -30$

You Try It 7
$-\sqrt{-8} \cdot \sqrt{-5} = -i\sqrt{8} \cdot i\sqrt{5} = -i^2\sqrt{40}$
$$= -(-1)\sqrt{40} = \sqrt{2^3 \cdot 5} = 2\sqrt{10}$$

You Try It 8
$-6i(3 + 4i) = -18i - 24i^2$
$$= -18i - 24(-1) = 24 - 18i$$

You Try It 9
$\sqrt{-3}(\sqrt{27} - \sqrt{-6}) = i\sqrt{3}(\sqrt{27} - i\sqrt{6})$
$$= i\sqrt{81} - i^2\sqrt{18}$$
$$= i\sqrt{3^4} - (-1)\sqrt{2 \cdot 3^2}$$
$$= 9i + 3\sqrt{2}$$
$$= 3\sqrt{2} + 9i$$

You Try It 10 $(4 - 3i)(2 - i) = 8 - 4i - 6i + 3i^2$
$$= 8 - 10i + 3i^2$$
$$= 8 - 10i + 3(-1)$$
$$= 5 - 10i$$

You Try It 11 $(3 + 6i)(3 - 6i) = 3^2 + 6^2$
$$= 9 + 36$$
$$= 45$$

You Try It 12 $\dfrac{2 - 3i}{4i} = \dfrac{2 - 3i}{4i} \cdot \dfrac{i}{i}$
$$= \frac{2i - 3i^2}{4i^2}$$
$$= \frac{2i - 3(-1)}{4(-1)}$$
$$= \frac{3 + 2i}{-4} = -\frac{3}{4} - \frac{1}{2}i$$

You Try It 13
$$\frac{2 + 5i}{3 - 2i} = \frac{2 + 5i}{3 - 2i} \cdot \frac{3 + 2i}{3 + 2i} = \frac{6 + 4i + 15i + 10i^2}{3^2 + 2^2}$$
$$= \frac{6 + 19i + 10(-1)}{13} = \frac{-4 + 19i}{13}$$
$$= -\frac{4}{13} + \frac{19}{13}i$$

SECTION 7.4

You Try It 1
$\sqrt{x} - \sqrt{x + 5} = 1$
$$\sqrt{x} = 1 + \sqrt{x + 5}$$
$$(\sqrt{x})^2 = (1 + \sqrt{x + 5})^2$$
$$x = 1 + 2\sqrt{x + 5} + x + 5$$
$$-6 = 2\sqrt{x + 5}$$
$$-3 = \sqrt{x + 5}$$
$$(-3)^2 = (\sqrt{x + 5})^2$$
$$9 = x + 5$$
$$4 = x$$

4 does not check as a solution. The equation has no solution.

You Try It 2 $\sqrt[4]{x - 8} = 3$ *Check:*
$$(\sqrt[4]{x - 8})^4 = 3^4 \qquad \sqrt[4]{x - 8} = 3$$
$$x - 8 = 81 \qquad \sqrt[4]{89 - 8} \mid 3$$
$$x = 89 \qquad\quad \sqrt[4]{81} \mid 3$$
$$\qquad\qquad\qquad\qquad 3 = 3$$

The solution is 89.

You Try It 3

Strategy   To find the diagonal, use the Pythagorean Theorem. One leg is the length of the rectangle. The second leg is the width of the rectangle. The hypotenuse is the diagonal of the rectangle.

Solution $c^2 = a^2 + b^2$
$$c^2 = (6)^2 + (3)^2$$
$$c^2 = 36 + 9$$
$$c^2 = 45$$
$$(c^2)^{1/2} = (45)^{1/2}$$
$$c = \sqrt{45}$$
$$c \approx 6.7$$

The diagonal is 6.7 cm.

You Try It 4

Strategy To find the height, replace d in the equation with the given value and solve for h.

Solution
$$d = \sqrt{1.5h}$$
$$5.5 = \sqrt{1.5h}$$
$$(5.5)^2 = (\sqrt{1.5h})^2$$
$$30.25 = 1.5h$$
$$20.17 \approx h$$

The periscope must be approximately 20.17 ft above the water.

You Try It 5

Strategy To find the distance, replace the variables v and a in the equation by their given values and solve for s.

Solution
$$v = \sqrt{2as}$$
$$88 = \sqrt{2 \cdot 22s}$$
$$88 = \sqrt{44s}$$
$$(88)^2 = (\sqrt{44s})^2$$
$$7744 = 44s$$
$$176 = s$$

The distance required is 176 ft.

Solutions to Chapter 8 "You Try It"

SECTION 8.1

You Try It 1
$$2x^2 = 7x - 3$$
$$2x^2 - 7x + 3 = 0$$
$$(2x - 1)(x - 3) = 0$$

$$2x - 1 = 0 \qquad x - 3 = 0$$
$$2x = 1 \qquad\quad x = 3$$
$$x = \frac{1}{2}$$

The solutions are $\frac{1}{2}$ and 3.

You Try It 2
$$x^2 - 3ax - 4a^2 = 0$$
$$(x + a)(x - 4a) = 0$$

$$x + a = 0 \qquad x - 4a = 0$$
$$x = -a \qquad\quad x = 4a$$

The solutions are $-a$ and $4a$.

You Try It 3
$$(x - r_1)(x - r_2) = 0$$
$$(x - 3)\left[x - \left(-\frac{1}{2}\right)\right] = 0$$
$$(x - 3)\left(x + \frac{1}{2}\right) = 0$$
$$x^2 - \frac{5}{2}x - \frac{3}{2} = 0$$
$$2\left(x^2 - \frac{5}{2}x - \frac{3}{2}\right) = 2 \cdot 0$$
$$2x^2 - 5x - 3 = 0$$

You Try It 4
$$2(x + 1)^2 - 24 = 0$$
$$2(x + 1)^2 = 24$$
$$(x + 1)^2 = 12$$

$$\sqrt{(x + 1)^2} = \sqrt{12}$$
$$x + 1 = \pm\sqrt{12} = \pm 2\sqrt{3}$$

$$x + 1 = 2\sqrt{3} \qquad x + 1 = -2\sqrt{3}$$
$$x = -1 + 2\sqrt{3} \qquad x = -1 - 2\sqrt{3}$$

The solutions are $-1 + 2\sqrt{3}$ and $-1 - 2\sqrt{3}$.

SECTION 8.2

You Try It 1
$$4x^2 - 4x - 1 = 0$$
$$4x^2 - 4x = 1$$
$$\frac{1}{4}(4x^2 - 4x) = \frac{1}{4} \cdot 1$$
$$x^2 - x = \frac{1}{4}$$

Complete the square.

$$x^2 - x + \frac{1}{4} = \frac{1}{4} + \frac{1}{4}$$
$$\left(x - \frac{1}{2}\right)^2 = \frac{2}{4}$$
$$\sqrt{\left(x - \frac{1}{2}\right)^2} = \sqrt{\frac{2}{4}}$$
$$x - \frac{1}{2} = \pm\frac{\sqrt{2}}{2}$$

$$x - \frac{1}{2} = \frac{\sqrt{2}}{2} \qquad x - \frac{1}{2} = -\frac{\sqrt{2}}{2}$$
$$x = \frac{1}{2} + \frac{\sqrt{2}}{2} \qquad x = \frac{1}{2} - \frac{\sqrt{2}}{2}$$

The solutions are $\dfrac{1 + \sqrt{2}}{2}$ and $\dfrac{1 - \sqrt{2}}{2}$.

You Try It 2

$2x^2 + x - 5 = 0$

$2x^2 + x = 5$

$\dfrac{1}{2}(2x^2 + x) = \dfrac{1}{2} \cdot 5$

$x^2 + \dfrac{1}{2}x = \dfrac{5}{2}$

Complete the square.

$x^2 + \dfrac{1}{2}x + \dfrac{1}{16} = \dfrac{5}{2} + \dfrac{1}{16}$

$\left(x + \dfrac{1}{4}\right)^2 = \dfrac{41}{16}$

$\sqrt{\left(x + \dfrac{1}{4}\right)^2} = \sqrt{\dfrac{41}{16}}$

$x + \dfrac{1}{4} = \pm\dfrac{\sqrt{41}}{4}$

$x + \dfrac{1}{4} = \dfrac{\sqrt{41}}{4}$ $x + \dfrac{1}{4} = -\dfrac{\sqrt{41}}{4}$

$x = -\dfrac{1}{4} + \dfrac{\sqrt{41}}{4}$ $x = -\dfrac{1}{4} - \dfrac{\sqrt{41}}{4}$

The solutions are $\dfrac{-1 + \sqrt{41}}{4}$ and $\dfrac{-1 - \sqrt{41}}{4}$.

SECTION 8.3

You Try It 1 $x^2 - 2x + 10 = 0$

$a = 1, b = -2, c = 10$

$x = \dfrac{-b \pm \sqrt{b^2 - 4ac}}{2a}$

$= \dfrac{-(-2) \pm \sqrt{(-2)^2 - 4(1)(10)}}{2 \cdot 1}$

$= \dfrac{2 \pm \sqrt{4 - 40}}{2} = \dfrac{2 \pm \sqrt{-36}}{2}$

$= \dfrac{2 \pm 6i}{2} = 1 \pm 3i$

The solutions are $1 + 3i$ and $1 - 3i$.

You Try It 2 $4x^2 = 4x - 1$

$4x^2 - 4x + 1 = 0$

$a = 4, b = -4, c = 1$

$x = \dfrac{-b \pm \sqrt{b^2 - 4ac}}{2a}$

$= \dfrac{-(-4) \pm \sqrt{(-4)^2 - 4(4)(1)}}{2 \cdot 4}$

$= \dfrac{4 \pm \sqrt{16 - 16}}{8} = \dfrac{4 \pm \sqrt{0}}{8}$

$= \dfrac{4}{8} = \dfrac{1}{2}$

The solution is $\dfrac{1}{2}$.

You Try It 3 $3x^2 - x - 1 = 0$

$a = 3, b = -1, c = -1$

$b^2 - 4ac =$

$(-1)^2 - 4(3)(-1) = 1 + 12 = 13$

$13 > 0$

Because the discriminant is greater than zero, the equation has two real number solutions.

SECTION 8.4

You Try It 1 $x - 5x^{1/2} + 6 = 0$

$(x^{1/2})^2 - 5(x^{1/2}) + 6 = 0$

$u^2 - 5u + 6 = 0$

$(u - 2)(u - 3) = 0$

$u - 2 = 0$ $u - 3 = 0$

$u = 2$ $u = 3$

Replace u by $x^{1/2}$.

$x^{1/2} = 2$ $x^{1/2} = 3$

$\sqrt{x} = 2$ $\sqrt{x} = 3$

$(\sqrt{x})^2 = 2^2$ $(\sqrt{x})^2 = 3^2$

$x = 4$ $x = 9$

The solutions are 4 and 9.

You Try It 2 $\sqrt{2x + 1} + x = 7$

$\sqrt{2x + 1} = 7 - x$

$(\sqrt{2x + 1})^2 = (7 - x)^2$

$2x + 1 = 49 - 14x + x^2$

$0 = x^2 - 16x + 48$

$0 = (x - 4)(x - 12)$

$x - 4 = 0$ $x - 12 = 0$

$x = 4$ $x = 12$

4 checks as a solution.
12 does not check as a solution.

The solution is 4.

You Try It 3 $\sqrt{2x - 1} + \sqrt{x} = 2$

Solve for one of the radical expressions.

$\sqrt{2x - 1} = 2 - \sqrt{x}$

$(\sqrt{2x - 1})^2 = (2 - \sqrt{x})^2$

$2x - 1 = 4 - 4\sqrt{x} + x$

$x - 5 = -4\sqrt{x}$

Square each side of the equation.

$(x - 5)^2 = (-4\sqrt{x})^2$

$x^2 - 10x + 25 = 16x$

$x^2 - 26x + 25 = 0$

$(x - 1)(x - 25) = 0$

$$x - 1 = 0 \qquad x - 25 = 0$$
$$x = 1 \qquad x = 25$$

1 checks as a solution.
25 does not check as a solution.

The solution is 1.

You Try It 4

$$3y + \frac{25}{3y - 2} = -8$$

$$(3y - 2)\left(3y + \frac{25}{3y - 2}\right) = (3y - 2)(-8)$$

$$(3y - 2)(3y) + (3y - 2)\left(\frac{25}{3y - 2}\right) = (3y - 2)(-8)$$

$$9y^2 - 6y + 25 = -24y + 16$$
$$9y^2 + 18y + 9 = 0$$
$$9(y^2 + 2y + 1) = 0$$
$$9(y + 1)(y + 1) = 0$$

$$y + 1 = 0 \qquad y + 1 = 0$$
$$y = -1 \qquad y = -1$$

The solution is -1.

SECTION 8.5

You Try It 1

$$2x^2 - x - 10 \le 0$$
$$(2x - 5)(x + 2) \le 0$$

$$\left\{x \mid -2 \le x \le \frac{5}{2}\right\}$$

SECTION 8.6

You Try It 1

Strategy
- This is a geometry problem.
- Width of the rectangle: w
  Length of the rectangle: $w + 3$
- Use the equation $A = L \cdot w$.

Solution
$$A = L \cdot w$$
$$54 = (w + 3)(w)$$
$$54 = w^2 + 3w$$
$$0 = w^2 + 3w - 54$$
$$0 = (w + 9)(w - 6)$$

$$w + 9 = 0 \qquad w - 6 = 0$$
$$w = -9 \qquad w = 6$$

The solution -9 is not possible.

$$w + 3 = 6 + 3 = 9$$

The length is 9 m.

Solutions to Chapter 9 "You Try It"

SECTION 9.1

You Try It 1
x-coordinate of vertex:

$$-\frac{b}{2a} = -\frac{4}{2(4)} = -\frac{1}{2}$$

y-coordinate of vertex:

$$y = 4x^2 + 4x + 1$$
$$= 4\left(-\frac{1}{2}\right)^2 + 4\left(-\frac{1}{2}\right) + 1$$
$$= 1 - 2 + 1$$
$$= 0$$

Vertex: $\left(-\frac{1}{2}, 0\right)$

Axis of symmetry: $x = -\frac{1}{2}$

You Try It 2
x-coordinate of vertex:

$$-\frac{b}{2a} = -\frac{-2}{2(-1)} = -1$$

y-coordinate of vertex:

$$f(x) = -x^2 - 2x - 1$$
$$f(-1) = -(-1)^2 - 2(-1) - 1$$
$$= -1 + 2 - 1$$
$$= 0$$

Vertex: $(-1, 0)$

The domain is all real numbers. The range is $\{y \mid y \le 0\}$.

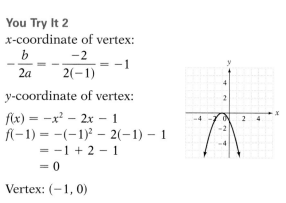

You Try It 3
$$y = x^2 + 3x + 4$$
$$0 = x^2 + 3x + 4$$

$$x = \frac{-b \pm \sqrt{b^2 - 4ac}}{2a}$$

$$= \frac{-3 \pm \sqrt{3^2 - 4(1)(4)}}{2 \cdot 1} \qquad \bullet \, a = 1, \, b = 3, \, c = 4$$

$$= \frac{-3 \pm \sqrt{-7}}{2}$$

$$= \frac{-3 \pm i\sqrt{7}}{2}$$

The equation has no real number solutions. There are no x-intercepts.

You Try It 4

$$g(x) = x^2 - x + 6$$
$$0 = x^2 - x + 6$$

$$x = \frac{-b \pm \sqrt{b^2 - 4ac}}{2a}$$

$$= \frac{-(-1) \pm \sqrt{(-1)^2 - 4(1)(6)}}{2(1)} \qquad \bullet \, a = 1, \, b = -1, \, c = 6$$

$$= \frac{1 \pm \sqrt{1 - 24}}{2}$$

$$= \frac{1 \pm \sqrt{-23}}{2} = \frac{1 \pm i\sqrt{23}}{2}$$

The zeros of the function are $\frac{1}{2} + \frac{\sqrt{23}}{2}i$ and $\frac{1}{2} - \frac{\sqrt{23}}{2}i$.

You Try It 5

$$y = x^2 - x - 6$$
$$a = 1, \, b = -1, \, c = -6$$

$$b^2 - 4ac$$
$$(-1)^2 - 4(1)(-6) = 1 + 24 = 25$$

Because the discriminant is greater than zero, the parabola has two x-intercepts.

You Try It 6

$$f(x) = -3x^2 + 4x - 1$$

$$x = -\frac{b}{2a} = -\frac{4}{2(-3)} = \frac{2}{3}$$

$$f(x) = -3x^2 + 4x - 1$$

$$f\left(\frac{2}{3}\right) = -3\left(\frac{2}{3}\right)^2 + 4\left(\frac{2}{3}\right) - 1$$

$$= -\frac{4}{3} + \frac{8}{3} - 1 = \frac{1}{3}$$

Because a is negative, the function has a maximum value.

The maximum value of the function is $\frac{1}{3}$.

You Try It 7

Strategy   • To find the time it takes the ball to reach its maximum height, find the t-coordinate of the vertex.

• To find the maximum height, evaluate the function at the t-coordinate of the vertex.

Solution

$$t = -\frac{b}{2a} = -\frac{64}{2(-16)} = 2$$

The ball reaches its maximum height in 2 s.

$$s(t) = -16t^2 + 64t$$
$$s(2) = -16(2)^2 + 64(2) = -64 + 128 = 64$$

The maximum height is 64 ft.

You Try It 8

Strategy
$$P = 2x + y$$
$$100 = 2x + y \qquad \bullet \, P = 100$$
$$100 - 2x = y \qquad \bullet \, \text{Solve for } y.$$

Express the area of the rectangle in terms of x.

$$A = xy$$
$$A = x(100 - 2x) \qquad \bullet \, y = 100 - 2x$$
$$A = -2x^2 + 100x$$

• To find the width, find the x-coordinate of the vertex of $f(x) = -2x^2 + 100x$.
• To find the length, replace x in $100 - 2x = y$ by the x-coordinate of the vertex.

Solution $x = -\dfrac{b}{2a} = -\dfrac{100}{2(-2)} = 25$

The width is 25 ft.

$$100 - 2x = 100 - 2(25)$$
$$= 100 - 50 = 50$$

The length is 50 ft.

SECTION 9.2

You Try It 1   Any vertical line intersects the graph at most once. The graph is the graph of a function.

You Try It 2   Domain: $(-\infty, \infty)$
Range: $(-\infty, \infty)$

You Try It 3   Domain: $\{x \mid x \text{ is a real number}\}$
Range: $\{y \mid y \geq 0\}$

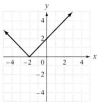

You Try It 4   Domain: $[1, \infty)$
Range: $(-\infty, 0]$

SECTION 9.3

You Try It 1
$$(f + g)(-2) = f(-2) + g(-2)$$
$$= [(-2)^2 + 2(-2)] + [5(-2) - 2]$$
$$= (4 - 4) + (-10 - 2)$$
$$= -12$$

$(f + g)(-2) = -12$

You Try It 2 $(f \cdot g)(3) = f(3) \cdot g(3)$
$$= (4 - 3^2) \cdot [3(3) - 4]$$
$$= (4 - 9) \cdot (9 - 4)$$
$$= (-5)(5)$$
$$= -25$$

$(f \cdot g)(3) = -25$

You Try It 3 $\left(\dfrac{f}{g}\right)(4) = \dfrac{f(4)}{g(4)}$
$$= \dfrac{4^2 - 4}{4^2 + 2 \cdot 4 + 1}$$
$$= \dfrac{16 - 4}{16 + 8 + 1}$$
$$= \dfrac{12}{25}$$

$\left(\dfrac{f}{g}\right)(4) = \dfrac{12}{25}$

You Try It 4 $g(x) = x^2$
$g(-1) = (-1)^2 = 1$

$f(x) = 1 - 2x$
$f[g(-1)] = f(1) = 1 - 2(1) = -1$

You Try It 5 $f(x) = 3x - 1$
$f(1) = 3(1) - 1 = 2$

$g(x) = \dfrac{x}{x^2 - 2}$

$g[f(1)] = g(2) = \dfrac{2}{2^2 - 2} = \dfrac{2}{2} = 1$

You Try It 6 $M(s) = s^3 + 1$

$M[L(s)] = (s + 1)^3 + 1$
$$= s^3 + 3s^2 + 3s + 1 + 1$$
$$= s^3 + 3s^2 + 3s + 2$$

You Try It 7 $V(x) = x^2 + 1$

$V[W(x)] = (-\sqrt{x - 1})^2 + 1$
$$= x - 1 + 1$$
$$= x$$

SECTION 9.4

You Try It 1   Because any horizontal line intersects the graph at most once, the graph is the graph of a 1–1 function.

You Try It 2 $f(x) = \dfrac{1}{2}x + 4$

$y = \dfrac{1}{2}x + 4$

$x = \dfrac{1}{2}y + 4$

$x - 4 = \dfrac{1}{2}y$

$2x - 8 = y$
$f^{-1}(x) = 2x - 8$

The inverse of the function is given by $f^{-1}(x) = 2x - 8$.

You Try It 3 $f[g(x)] = 2\left(\dfrac{1}{2}x - 3\right) - 6$
$$= x - 6 - 6 = x - 12$$

No, $g(x)$ is not the inverse of $f(x)$.

Solutions to Chapter 10 "You Try It"

SECTION 10.1

You Try It 1 $f(x) = \left(\dfrac{2}{3}\right)^x$

$$f(3) = \left(\dfrac{2}{3}\right)^3 = \dfrac{8}{27}$$

$$f(-2) = \left(\dfrac{2}{3}\right)^{-2} = \left(\dfrac{3}{2}\right)^2 = \dfrac{9}{4}$$

You Try It 2 $f(x) = 2^{2x+1}$
$f(0) = 2^{2(0)+1} = 2^1 = 2$

$$f(-2) = 2^{2(-2)+1} = 2^{-3} = \dfrac{1}{2^3} = \dfrac{1}{8}$$

You Try It 3 $f(x) = e^{2x-1}$
$f(2) = e^{2 \cdot 2 - 1} = e^3 \approx 20.0855$
$f(-2) = e^{2(-2)-1} = e^{-5} \approx 0.0067$

You Try It 4

x	y
-4	4
-2	2
0	1
2	$\dfrac{1}{2}$
4	$\dfrac{1}{4}$

You Try It 5

x	y
-2	$\dfrac{5}{4}$
-1	$\dfrac{3}{2}$
0	2
1	3
2	5

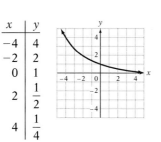

You Try It 6

x	y
-2	6
-1	4
0	3
1	$\dfrac{5}{2}$
2	$\dfrac{9}{4}$

You Try It 7

x	y
-4	$\dfrac{9}{4}$
-2	$\dfrac{5}{2}$
0	3
2	4
4	6

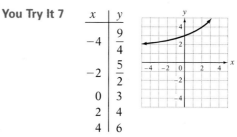

SECTION 10.2

You Try It 1 $\log_4 64 = x$
$64 = 4^x$
$4^3 = 4^x$
$3 = x$

$\log_4 64 = 3$

You Try It 2 $\log_2 x = -4$
$2^{-4} = x$

$\dfrac{1}{2^4} = x$

$\dfrac{1}{16} = x$

The solution is $\dfrac{1}{16}$.

You Try It 3 $\ln x = 3$
$e^3 = x$
$20.0855 \approx x$

You Try It 4 $\log_8 \sqrt[3]{xy^2} = \log_8(xy^2)^{1/3} = \dfrac{1}{3}\log_8(xy^2)$

$$= \dfrac{1}{3}(\log_8 x + \log_8 y^2)$$

$$= \dfrac{1}{3}(\log_8 x + 2\log_8 y)$$

$$= \dfrac{1}{3}\log_8 x + \dfrac{2}{3}\log_8 y$$

You Try It 5

$\dfrac{1}{3}(\log_4 x - 2\log_4 y + \log_4 z)$

$$= \dfrac{1}{3}(\log_4 x - \log_4 y^2 + \log_4 z)$$

$$= \dfrac{1}{3}\left(\log_4 \dfrac{x}{y^2} + \log_4 z\right) = \dfrac{1}{3}\left(\log_4 \dfrac{xz}{y^2}\right)$$

$$= \log_4\left(\dfrac{xz}{y^2}\right)^{1/3} = \log_4 \sqrt[3]{\dfrac{xz}{y^2}}$$

You Try It 6   Because $\log_b 1 = 0$, $\log_9 1 = 0$

You Try It 7 $\log_7 6.45 = \dfrac{\log 6.45}{\log 7} \approx 0.95795$

You Try It 8 $\log_3 0.834 = \dfrac{\ln 0.834}{\ln 3} \approx -0.16523$

SECTION 10.3

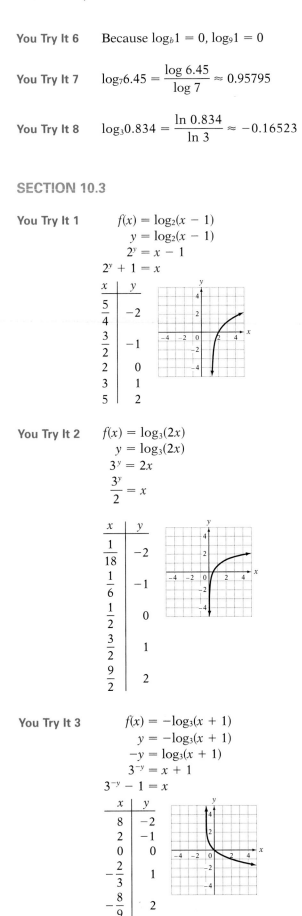

You Try It 1
$$f(x) = \log_2(x - 1)$$
$$y = \log_2(x - 1)$$
$$2^y = x - 1$$
$$2^y + 1 = x$$

x	y
$\dfrac{5}{4}$	-2
$\dfrac{3}{2}$	-1
2	0
3	1
5	2

You Try It 2
$$f(x) = \log_3(2x)$$
$$y = \log_3(2x)$$
$$3^y = 2x$$
$$\dfrac{3^y}{2} = x$$

x	y
$\dfrac{1}{18}$	-2
$\dfrac{1}{6}$	-1
$\dfrac{1}{2}$	0
$\dfrac{3}{2}$	1
$\dfrac{9}{2}$	2

You Try It 3
$$f(x) = -\log_3(x + 1)$$
$$y = -\log_3(x + 1)$$
$$-y = \log_3(x + 1)$$
$$3^{-y} = x + 1$$
$$3^{-y} - 1 = x$$

x	y
8	-2
2	-1
0	0
$-\dfrac{2}{3}$	1
$-\dfrac{8}{9}$	2

SECTION 10.4

You Try It 1
$$4^{3x} = 25$$
$$\log 4^{3x} = \log 25$$
$$3x \log 4 = \log 25$$
$$3x = \dfrac{\log 25}{\log 4}$$
$$3x \approx 2.3219$$
$$x \approx 0.7740$$

The solution is 0.7740.

You Try It 2
$$(1.06)^n = 1.5$$
$$\log(1.06)^n = \log 1.5$$
$$n \log 1.06 = \log 1.5$$
$$n = \dfrac{\log 1.5}{\log 1.06}$$
$$n \approx 6.9585$$

The solution is 6.9585.

You Try It 3 $\log_4(x^2 - 3x) = 1$

Rewrite in exponential form.

$$4^1 = x^2 - 3x$$
$$4 = x^2 - 3x$$
$$0 = x^2 - 3x - 4$$
$$0 = (x + 1)(x - 4)$$

$$x + 1 = 0 \qquad x - 4 = 0$$
$$x = -1 \qquad x = 4$$

The solutions are -1 and 4.

You Try It 4
$$\log_3 x + \log_3(x + 3) = \log_3 4$$
$$\log_3[x(x + 3)] = \log_3 4$$

Use the fact that if $\log_b u = \log_b v$, then $u = v$.

$$x(x + 3) = 4$$
$$x^2 + 3x = 4$$
$$x^2 + 3x - 4 = 0$$
$$(x + 4)(x - 1) = 0$$

$$x + 4 = 0 \qquad x - 1 = 0$$
$$x = -4 \qquad x = 1$$

-4 does not check as a solution. The solution is 1.

You Try It 5
$$\log_3 x + \log_3(x + 6) = 3$$
$$\log_3[x(x + 6)] = 3$$

$$x(x + 6) = 3^3$$
$$x^2 + 6x - 27 = 0$$
$$(x + 9)(x - 3) = 0$$

$$x + 9 = 0 \qquad x - 3 = 0$$
$$x = -9 \qquad x = 3$$

-9 does not check as a solution. The solution is 3.

SECTION 10.5

You Try It 1

Strategy To find the hydrogen ion concentration, replace pH by 2.9 in the equation $pH = -\log(H^+)$ and solve for H^+.

Solution
$$pH = -\log(H^+)$$
$$2.9 = -\log(H^+)$$
$$-2.9 = \log(H^+)$$
$$10^{-2.9} = H^+$$
$$0.00126 \approx H^+$$

The hydrogen ion concentration is approximately 0.00126.

You Try It 2

Strategy To find how many times stronger the San Francisco earthquake was, use the Richter equation to write a system of equations. Solve the system of equations for the ratio $\dfrac{I_1}{I_2}$.

Solution
$$7.8 = \log \frac{I_1}{I_0}$$
$$5 = \log \frac{I_2}{I_0}$$
$$7.8 = \log I_1 - \log I_0$$
$$5 = \log I_2 - \log I_0$$
$$2.8 = \log I_1 - \log I_2$$
$$2.8 = \log \frac{I_1}{I_2}$$

$$\frac{I_1}{I_{2+}} = 10^{2.8} \approx 630.957$$

The San Francisco earthquake was 631 times stronger than one that can cause serious damage.

Solutions to Chapter 11 "You Try It"

SECTION 11.1

You Try It 1
$$y = x^2 + 2x + 1$$
$$-\frac{b}{2a} = -\frac{2}{2(1)} = -1$$
$$y = (-1)^2 + 2(-1) + 1$$
$$= 0$$

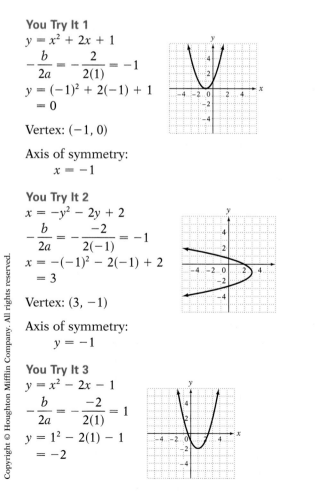

Vertex: $(-1, 0)$

Axis of symmetry:
  $x = -1$

You Try It 2
$$x = -y^2 - 2y + 2$$
$$-\frac{b}{2a} = -\frac{-2}{2(-1)} = -1$$
$$x = -(-1)^2 - 2(-1) + 2$$
$$= 3$$

Vertex: $(3, -1)$

Axis of symmetry:
  $y = -1$

You Try It 3
$$y = x^2 - 2x - 1$$
$$-\frac{b}{2a} = -\frac{-2}{2(1)} = 1$$
$$y = 1^2 - 2(1) - 1$$
$$= -2$$

Vertex: $(1, -2)$

Axis of symmetry:
  $x = 1$

SECTION 11.2

You Try It 1

You Try It 2 $(x - h)^2 + (y - k)^2 = r^2$
$(x - 2)^2 + [y - (-3)]^2 = 4^2$
$(x - 2)^2 + (y + 3)^2 = 16$

You Try It 3 $x^2 + y^2 - 2x - 15 = 0$
$(x^2 - 2x) + y^2 = 15$
$(x^2 - 2x + 1) + y^2 = 15 + 1$
$(x - 1)^2 + y^2 = 16$

Center: (1, 0)
Radius: 4

You Try It 4
$$x^2 + y^2 - 4x + 8y + 15 = 0$$
$$(x^2 - 4x) + (y^2 + 8y) = -15$$
$$(x^2 - 4x + 4) + (y^2 + 8y + 16) = -15 + 4 + 16$$
$$(x - 2)^2 + (y + 4)^2 = 5$$

Center: (2, −4)
Radius: $\sqrt{5}$

SECTION 11.3

You Try It 1
x-intercepts:
(2, 0) and (−2, 0)

y-intercepts:
(0, 5) and (0, −5)

You Try It 2
x-intercepts:
$(3\sqrt{2}, 0)$ and $(-3\sqrt{2}, 0)$

y-intercepts:
(0, 3) and (0, −3)

$\left(3\sqrt{2} \approx 4\frac{1}{4}\right)$

You Try It 3
Vertices:
(3, 0) and (−3, 0)

Asymptotes:
$y = \frac{5}{3}x$ and $y = -\frac{5}{3}x$

You Try It 4
Vertices:
(0, 3) and (0, −3)

Asymptotes:
$y = x$ and $y = -x$

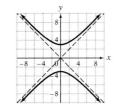

SECTION 11.4

You Try It 1   (1) $y = 2x^2 + x - 3$
(2) $y = 2x^2 - 2x + 9$

Use the substitution method.

$$y = 2x^2 + x - 3$$
$$2x^2 - 2x + 9 = 2x^2 + x - 3$$
$$-3x + 9 = -3$$
$$-3x = -12$$
$$x = 4$$

Substitute into Equation (1).

$$y = 2x^2 + x - 3$$
$$y = 2(4)^2 + 4 - 3$$
$$y = 32 + 4 - 3$$
$$y = 33$$

The solution is (4, 33).

You Try It 2
(1) $x^2 - y^2 = 10$
(2) $x^2 + y^2 = 8$

Use the addition method.

$$2x^2 = 18$$
$$x^2 = 9$$
$$x = \pm\sqrt{9} = \pm 3$$

Substitute into Equation (2).

$$x^2 + y^2 = 8 \qquad\qquad x^2 + y^2 = 8$$
$$3^2 + y^2 = 8 \qquad\qquad (-3)^2 + y^2 = 8$$
$$9 + y^2 = 8 \qquad\qquad 9 + y^2 = 8$$
$$y^2 = -1 \qquad\qquad y^2 = -1$$
$$y = \pm\sqrt{-1} \qquad\qquad y = \pm\sqrt{-1}$$

Because y is not a real number, the system of equations has no real number solution. The graphs do not intersect.

SECTION 11.5

You Try It 1 $\dfrac{x^2}{9} - \dfrac{y^2}{16} \le 1$

You Try It 2 $\dfrac{x^2}{16} + \dfrac{y^2}{4} \ge 1$

You Try It 3 $x^2 + y^2 < 16$
$y^2 > x$

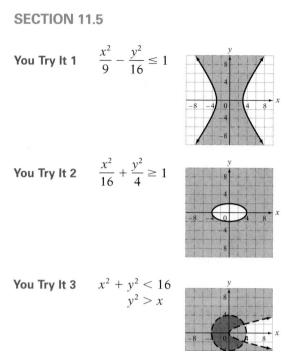

You Try It 4 $\dfrac{x^2}{4} + \dfrac{y^2}{9} \le 1$
$x > y^2 - 2$

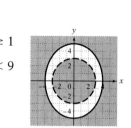

You Try It 5 $\dfrac{x^2}{16} + \dfrac{y^2}{25} \ge 1$
$x^2 + y^2 < 9$

The solution sets of the two inequalities do not intersect. This system of inequalities has no real number solution.

Solutions to Chapter 12 "You Try It"

SECTION 12.1

You Try It 1
$a_n = n(n + 1)$
$a_1 = 1(1 + 1) = 2$ The first term is 2.
$a_2 = 2(2 + 1) = 6$ The second term is 6.
$a_3 = 3(3 + 1) = 12$ The third term is 12.
$a_4 = 4(4 + 1) = 20$ The fourth term is 20.

You Try It 2
$a_n = \dfrac{1}{n(n + 2)}$

$a_6 = \dfrac{1}{6(6 + 2)} = \dfrac{1}{48}$ The sixth term is $\dfrac{1}{48}$.

$a_9 = \dfrac{1}{9(9 + 2)} = \dfrac{1}{99}$ The ninth term is $\dfrac{1}{99}$.

You Try It 3
$\displaystyle\sum_{i=3}^{6} (i^2 - 2) = (3^2 - 2) + (4^2 - 2) + (5^2 - 2)$
$+ (6^2 - 2)$
$= 7 + 14 + 23 + 34 = 78$

You Try It 4 $\displaystyle\sum_{n=1}^{4} \dfrac{x}{n} = \dfrac{x}{1} + \dfrac{x}{2} + \dfrac{x}{3} + \dfrac{x}{4}$
$= x + \dfrac{x}{2} + \dfrac{x}{3} + \dfrac{x}{4}$

SECTION 12.2

You Try It 1 $9, 3, -3, -9, \ldots$
$d = a_2 - a_1 = 3 - 9 = -6$
$a_n = a_1 + (n - 1)d$
$a_{15} = 9 + (15 - 1)(-6) = 9 + (14)(-6)$
$= 9 - 84$
$a_{15} = -75$

You Try It 2 $7, 9, 11, \ldots, 59$
$d = a_2 - a_1 = 9 - 7 = 2$
$a_n = a_1 + (n - 1)d$
$59 = 7 + (n - 1)2$
$59 = 7 + 2n - 2$
$59 = 5 + 2n$
$54 = 2n$
$27 = n$

There are 27 terms in the sequence.

You Try It 3 $-4, -2, 0, 2, 4, \ldots$

$$d = a_2 - a_1 = -2 - (-4) = 2$$

$$a_n = a_1 + (n - 1)d$$
$$a_{25} = -4 + (25 - 1)2 = -4 + (24)2$$
$$= -4 + 48$$
$$a_{25} = 44$$

$$S_n = \frac{n}{2}(a_1 + a_n)$$

$$S_{25} = \frac{25}{2}(-4 + 44) = \frac{25}{2}(40) = 25(20)$$

$$S_{25} = 500$$

You Try It 4 $\displaystyle\sum_{n=1}^{18} (3n - 2)$

$$a_n = 3n - 2$$
$$a_1 = 3(1) - 2 = 1$$
$$a_{18} = 3(18) - 2 = 52$$

$$S_n = \frac{n}{2}(a_1 + a_n)$$

$$S_{18} = \frac{18}{2}(1 + 52) = 9(53) = 477$$

You Try It 5

Strategy   To find the value of the 20th-place prize:

• Write the equation for the nth-place prize.
• Find the 20th term of the sequence.

To find the total amount of prize money being awarded, use the Formula for the Sum of n Terms of an Arithmetic Sequence.

Solution
$10,000, 9700, \ldots$

$$d = a_2 - a_1 = 9700 - 10,000 = -300$$

$$a_n = a_1 + (n - 1)d$$
$$= 10,000 + (n - 1)(-300)$$
$$= 10,000 - 300n + 300$$
$$= -300n + 10,300$$

$$a_{20} = -300(20) + 10,300 = -6000 + 10,300$$
$$= 4300$$

$$S_n = \frac{n}{2}(a_1 + a_n)$$

$$S_{20} = \frac{20}{2}(10,000 + 4300) = 10(14,300)$$
$$= 143,000$$

The value of the 20th-place prize is $4300.

The total amount of prize money being awarded is $143,000.

SECTION 12.3

You Try It 1 $5, 2, \dfrac{4}{5}, \ldots$

$$r = \frac{a_2}{a_1} = \frac{2}{5}$$

$$a_n = a_1 r^{n-1}$$

$$a_5 = 5\left(\frac{2}{5}\right)^{5-1} = 5\left(\frac{2}{5}\right)^4 = 5\left(\frac{16}{625}\right)$$

$$a_5 = \frac{16}{125}$$

You Try It 2 $3, a_2, a_3, -192, \ldots$

$$a_n = a_1 r^{n-1}$$
$$a_4 = 3r^{4-1}$$
$$-192 = 3r^{4-1}$$
$$-192 = 3r^3$$
$$-64 = r^3$$
$$-4 = r$$

$$a_n = a_1 r^{n-1}$$
$$a_3 = 3(-4)^{3-1} = 3(-4)^2 = 3(16) = 48$$

You Try It 3 $1, -\dfrac{1}{3}, \dfrac{1}{9}, -\dfrac{1}{27}$

$$r = \frac{a_2}{a_1} = \frac{-\dfrac{1}{3}}{1} = -\frac{1}{3}$$

$$S_n = \frac{a_1(1 - r^n)}{1 - r}$$

$$S_4 = \frac{1\left[1 - \left(-\dfrac{1}{3}\right)^4\right]}{1 - \left(-\dfrac{1}{3}\right)} = \frac{1 - \dfrac{1}{81}}{\dfrac{4}{3}} = \frac{\dfrac{80}{81}}{\dfrac{4}{3}}$$

$$= \frac{80}{81} \cdot \frac{3}{4} = \frac{20}{27}$$

You Try It 4 $\displaystyle\sum_{n=1}^{5} \left(\frac{1}{2}\right)^n$

$$a_n = \left(\frac{1}{2}\right)^n$$

$$a_1 = \left(\frac{1}{2}\right)^1 = \frac{1}{2}$$

$$a_2 = \left(\frac{1}{2}\right)^2 = \frac{1}{4}$$

$$r = \frac{a_2}{a_1} = \frac{\dfrac{1}{4}}{\dfrac{1}{2}} = \frac{1}{4} \cdot \frac{2}{1} = \frac{1}{2}$$

$$S_n = \frac{a_1(1 - r^n)}{1 - r}$$

$$S_5 = \frac{\frac{1}{2}\left[1 - \left(\frac{1}{2}\right)^5\right]}{1 - \frac{1}{2}} = \frac{\frac{1}{2}\left(1 - \frac{1}{32}\right)}{\frac{1}{2}} = \frac{\frac{1}{2}\left(\frac{31}{32}\right)}{\frac{1}{2}}$$

$$= \frac{\frac{31}{64}}{\frac{1}{2}} = \frac{31}{64} \cdot \frac{2}{1} = \frac{31}{32}$$

You Try It 5 $3, -2, \frac{4}{3}, -\frac{8}{9}, \ldots$

$$r = \frac{a_2}{a_1} = \frac{-2}{3} = -\frac{2}{3}$$

$$S = \frac{a_1}{1 - r} = \frac{3}{1 - \left(-\frac{2}{3}\right)} = \frac{3}{1 + \frac{2}{3}}$$

$$= \frac{3}{\frac{5}{3}} = \frac{9}{5}$$

You Try It 6 $0.66\overline{6} = 0.6 + 0.06 + 0.006 + \cdots$

$$= \frac{6}{10} + \frac{6}{100} + \frac{6}{1000} + \cdots$$

$$S = \frac{a_1}{1 - r} = \frac{\frac{6}{10}}{1 - \frac{1}{10}} = \frac{\frac{6}{10}}{\frac{9}{10}} = \frac{6}{9} = \frac{2}{3}$$

An equivalent fraction is $\frac{2}{3}$.

You Try It 7
$0.3\overline{421} = 0.34 + 0.0021 + 0.000021 + \cdots$

$$= \frac{34}{100} + \frac{21}{10,000} + \frac{21}{1,000,000} + \cdots$$

$$S_n = \frac{a_1}{1 - r} = \frac{\frac{21}{10,000}}{1 - \frac{1}{100}} = \frac{\frac{21}{10,000}}{\frac{99}{100}} = \frac{21}{9900}$$

$$0.3\overline{421} = \frac{34}{100} + \frac{21}{9900} = \frac{3366}{9900} + \frac{21}{9900}$$

$$= \frac{3387}{9900} = \frac{1129}{3300}$$

An equivalent fraction is $\frac{1129}{3300}$.

You Try It 8

Strategy   To find the total number of letters mailed, use the Formula for the Sum of n Terms of a Finite Geometric Series.

Solution $n = 6, a_1 = 3, r = 3$

$$S_n = \frac{a_1(1 - r^n)}{1 - r}$$

$$S_6 = \frac{3(1 - 3^6)}{1 - 3} = \frac{3(1 - 729)}{1 - 3}$$

$$= \frac{3(-728)}{-2} = \frac{-2184}{-2} = 1092$$

From the first through the sixth mailings, 1092 letters will have been mailed.

You Try It 9

Strategy   To find the value of the investment, use the Formula for the nth Term of a Geometric Sequence.

Solution $n = 11, a_1 = 25,000, r_1 = 1.12$

$$a_{11} = 25,000(1.12)^{11-1} = 25,000(1.12)^{10}$$
$$\approx 77,646.21$$

The value of the investment after 10 years is $77,646.21.

SECTION 12.4

You Try It 1
$$(3m - n)^4 = \binom{4}{0}(3m)^4 + \binom{4}{1}(3m)^3(-n)$$

$$+ \binom{4}{2}(3m)^2(-n)^2 + \binom{4}{3}(3m)(-n)^3$$

$$+ \binom{4}{4}(-n)^4$$

$$= 1(81m^4) + 4(27m^3)(-n) + 6(9m^2)(n^2)$$
$$+ 4(3m)(-n^3) + 1(n^4)$$
$$= 81m^4 - 108m^3n + 54m^2n^2$$
$$- 12mn^3 + n^4$$

You Try It 2 $(y - 2)^{10} = \binom{10}{0}y^{10} + \binom{10}{1}y^9(-2)$

$$+ \binom{10}{2}y^8(-2)^2 + \cdots$$

$$= 1(y^{10}) + 10y^9(-2) + 45y^8(4)$$
$$= y^{10} - 20y^9 + 180y^8$$

You Try It 3
$(t - 2s)^7$

$n = 7, a = t, b = -2s, r = 3$

$$\binom{7}{3 - 1}(t)^{7-3+1}(-2s)^{3-1} = \binom{7}{2}(t)^5(-2s)^2$$

$$= 21t^5(4s^2) = 84t^5s^2$$

Answers to Chapter 1 Odd-Numbered Exercises

SECTION 1.1

1a. Integers: $0, -3$ **b.** Rational numbers: $-\dfrac{15}{2}, 0, -3, 2.\overline{33}$ **c.** Irrational numbers: $\pi, 4.232232223..., \dfrac{\sqrt{5}}{4}, \sqrt{7}$

d. Real numbers: all   **3.** -27 **5.** $-\dfrac{3}{4}$ **7.** 0 **9.** $\sqrt{33}$ **11.** 91 **13.** $-3, 0$ **15.** 7 **17.** $-2, -1$

19. $9, 0, -9$ **21.** $4, 0, 4$ **23.** $-6, -2, 0, -1, -4$ **25.** $\{-2, -1, 0, 1, 2, 3, 4\}$ **27.** $\{2, 4, 6, 8, 10, 12\}$

29. $\{3, 6, 9, 12, 15, 18, 21, 24, 27, 30\}$ **31.** $\{-35, -30, -25, -20, -15, -10, -5\}$ **33.** $\{x \,|\, x > 4, x \in \text{integers}\}$

35. $\{x \,|\, x \geq -2\}$ **37.** $\{x \,|\, 0 < x < 1\}$ **39.** $\{x \,|\, 1 \leq x \leq 4\}$ **41.** $A \cup B = \{1, 2, 4, 6, 9\}$ **43.** $A \cup B = \{2, 3, 5, 8, 9, 10\}$

45. $A \cup B = \{-4, -2, 0, 2, 4, 8\}$ **47.** $A \cup B = \{1, 2, 3, 4, 5\}$ **49.** $A \cap B = \{6\}$ **51.** $A \cap B = \{5, 10, 20\}$

53. $A \cap B = \varnothing$ **55.** $A \cap B = \{4, 6\}$ **57.**   **59.**

61.   **63.**   **65.**

67.   **69.**   **71.**

73. $\{x \,|\, 0 < x < 8\}$ **75.** $\{x \,|\, -5 \leq x \leq 7\}$ **77.** $\{x \,|\, -3 \leq x < 6\}$ **79.** $\{x \,|\, x \leq 4\}$ **81.** $\{x \,|\, x > 5\}$ **83.** $(-2, 4)$

85. $[-1, 5]$ **87.** $(-\infty, 1)$ **89.** $[-2, \infty)$ **91.**   **93.**

95.   **97.**   **99.** A **101.** B **103.** A **105.** R

107. R **109.** 0

SECTION 1.2

1. -30 **3.** -17 **5.** -96 **7.** -6 **9.** 5 **11.** $11{,}200$ **13.** $98{,}915$ **15.** 96 **17.** 23 **19.** 7 **21.** 17

23. -4 **25.** -62 **27.** -25 **29.** 7 **31.** 368 **33.** 26 **35.** -83 **37.** $\dfrac{43}{48}$ **39.** $-\dfrac{67}{45}$ **41.** $-\dfrac{13}{36}$

43. $\dfrac{11}{24}$ **45.** $\dfrac{13}{24}$ **47.** $-\dfrac{3}{56}$ **49.** $-\dfrac{2}{3}$ **51.** $-\dfrac{11}{14}$ **53.** $-\dfrac{1}{24}$ **55.** -12.974 **57.** -6.008 **59.** 1.9215

61. -6.02 **63.** -6.7 **65.** -1.11 **67.** -2030.44 **69.** 125 **71.** -8 **73.** -125 **75.** 324 **77.** -36

79. -72 **81.** 864 **83.** -160 **85.** -6480 **87.** $2{,}654{,}208$ **89.** -7 **91.** $\dfrac{177}{11}$ **93.** $\dfrac{16}{3}$ **95.** -40

97. 32 **99.** 24 **101.** $\dfrac{2}{15}$ **103.** $-\dfrac{1}{2}$ **105.** $-\dfrac{97}{72}$ **107.** 6.284 **109.** 5.4375 **111.** 1.891878 **113.** Zero

115. No, zero does not have a multiplicative inverse.   **117.** 9 **119.** 625 **121.** Find b^c first, then $a^{(b^c)}$.

SECTION 1.3

1. 3 **3.** 3 **5.** 0 **7.** 6 **9.** 0 **11.** 1 **13.** $(2 \cdot 3)$ **15.** Division Property of Zero   **17.** Inverse Property of Multiplication   **19.** Addition Property of Zero   **21.** Division Property of Zero   **23.** Distributive Property

25. Associative Property of Multiplication   **27.** 10 **29.** 4 **31.** 0 **33.** $-\dfrac{1}{7}$ **35.** $\dfrac{9}{2}$ **37.** $\dfrac{1}{2}$ **39.** 2

41. 3 **43.** -12 **45.** 2 **47.** 6 **49.** -2 **51.** -14 **53.** 56 **55.** 256 **57.** $12x$ **59.** $-13ab$ **61.** $7x$

63. $-8a - 7b$ **65.** y **67.** $-5x + 45$ **69.** $-x - y$ **71.** $3a - 15$ **73.** $4x - 6y + 15$ **75.** $-7x + 14$

77. $48a - 75$ **79.** $-3x - 12y$ **81.** $-12x + 12y$ **83.** $33a - 25b$ **85.** $31x + 34y$ **87.** $4 - 8x - 5y$

89. $2x + 9$ **91.** Distributive Property   **93.** Incorrect use of the Distributive Property. $2 + 3x = 2 + 3x$

95. Incorrect use of the Associative Property of Multiplication. $2(3y) = (2 \cdot 3)y = 6y$ **97.** Commutative Property of Addition

SECTION 1.4

1. $n - (n + 2)$; -2 **3.** $5(8n)$; $40n$ **5.** $17n - 2n$; $15n$ **7.** $n^2 - (12 + n^2)$; -12 **9.** $15n + (5n + 12)$; $20n + 12$

11. $(15 - x + 2) + 2x$; $x + 17$ **13.** $\dfrac{5(34 - x)}{x - 3}$ **15.** $390d$ **17.** $c + 3$ **19.** $2L$ **21.** $10{,}000 - x$

23. Measure of angle B: x; measure of angle A: $2x$; measure of angle C: $4x$ **25.** The sum of twice x and 3

27. Twice the sum of x and 3 **29a.** $\dfrac{1}{2}gt^2$ **b.** ma **c.** Av^2 **d.** $\sqrt{\dfrac{k}{m}}$

CHAPTER REVIEW

1. $\{-2, -1, 0, 1, 2, 3\}$ [1.1B] **2.** $A \cap B = \{2, 3\}$ [1.1C] **3.** [1.1C] **4.** The

Associative Property of Multiplication [1.3A] **5.** -2.84 [1.2B] **6.** $\dfrac{7}{6}$ [1.3B] **7.** -288 [1.2C]

8. $16y - 15x + 18$ [1.3C] **9.** $\dfrac{3}{4}$ [1.1A] **10.** $\{x \mid x < -3\}$ [1.1B] **11.** [1.1C]

12. -15 [1.2A] **13.** $-\dfrac{7}{30}$ [1.2B] **14.** $3 + (4 + y) = (3 + 4) + y$ [1.3A] **15.** $-\dfrac{5}{8}$ [1.2B] **16.** $0, 2$ [1.1A]

17. 20 [1.3B] **18.** 14 [1.2A] **19.** 52 [1.2D] **20.** [1.1C]

21. $A \cup B = \{1, 2, 3, 4, 5, 6, 7, 8\}$ [1.1C] **22.** 12 [1.2A] **23.** $\{x \mid -2 \le x \le 3\}$ [1.1C] **24.** $\dfrac{2}{15}$ [1.2B]

25. $6x - 21y = 3(2x - 7y)$ [1.3A] **26.** [1.1C] **27.** $-6x + 14$ [1.3C]

28. $-4, 0, -7$ [1.1A] **29.** The Inverse Property of Addition [1.3A] **30.** 3.1 [1.2B]

31. $12 - \dfrac{x + 3}{x}$; $\dfrac{11x - 3}{x}$ [1.4A] **32.** $2x + (40 - x) + 5$; $x + 45$ [1.4A] **33.** $3w - 3$ [1.4B]

34. $x - 341{,}602$ [1.4B]

CHAPTER TEST

1. -30 [1.2A] **2.** $A \cap B = \{5, 7\}$ [1.1C] **3.** -72 [1.2C] **4.** [1.1C]

5. $A \cap B = \{-1, 0, 1\}$ [1.1C] **6.** -5 [1.3B] **7.** 2 [1.2A] **8.** $14x + 48y$ [1.3C] **9.** 12 [1.1A]

10. -100 [1.2C] **11.** [1.1C] **12.** 12 [1.2A] **13.** $\dfrac{25}{36}$ [1.2B]

14. $(3 + 4) + 2 = (4 + 3) + 2$ [1.3A] **15.** $-\dfrac{4}{27}$ [1.2B] **16.** -5 [1.1A] **17.** 2 [1.3B] **18.** -15 [1.2A]

19. 10 [1.2D] **20.** [1.1C] **21.** $A \cup B = \{1, 2, 3, 4, 5, 7\}$ [1.1C] **22.** $13x - y$ [1.3C]

23. 6 [1.2D] **24.** $\dfrac{2}{15}$ [1.2B] **25.** The Distributive Property [1.3A] **26.** [1.1C]

27. -1.41 [1.2B] **28.** $A \cup B = \{-2, -1, 0, 1, 2, 3\}$ [1.1C] **29.** $13 - (n - 3)(9)$; $40 - 9n$ [1.4A]

30. $(x + 1) - 2(9 - x)$; $3x - 17$ [1.4A]

Answers to Chapter 2 Odd-Numbered Exercises

SECTION 2.1

1. 9 **3.** -10 **5.** -2 **7.** -15 **9.** 4 **11.** $-\dfrac{2}{3}$ **13.** $\dfrac{17}{6}$ **15.** $\dfrac{1}{6}$ **17.** $\dfrac{15}{2}$ **19.** $-\dfrac{32}{25}$ **21.** 1

23. $\dfrac{15}{16}$ **25.** -64 **27.** $\dfrac{5}{6}$ **29.** $\dfrac{3}{2}$ **31.** 8 **33.** 0 **35.** 6 **37.** 6 **39.** The equation has no solution.

41. -3 **43.** 1 **45.** $\dfrac{4}{3}$ **47.** 1 **49.** $-\dfrac{4}{3}$ **51.** 6 **53.** $\dfrac{1}{2}$ **55.** -6 **57.** $\dfrac{5}{6}$ **59.** $-\dfrac{31}{7}$ **61.** $\dfrac{2}{3}$

63. $\dfrac{35}{12}$ **65.** -22 **67.** 6 **69.** 6 **71.** $\dfrac{25}{14}$ **73.** $\dfrac{11}{2}$ **75.** $-\dfrac{4}{29}$ **77.** -12 **79.** $\dfrac{17}{8}$ **81.** 0 **83.** $r = \dfrac{C}{2\pi}$

85. $h = \dfrac{2A}{b}$ **87.** $M = \dfrac{IC}{100}$ **89.** $r = \dfrac{A - P}{Pt}$ **91.** $c = 2s - a - b$ **93.** $h = \dfrac{S - 2\pi r^2}{2\pi r}$ **95.** $R = Pn + C$

97. $H = \dfrac{S - 2WL}{2W + 2L}$ **99.** The solution is not correct. The correct solution is 0. Therefore, in the next-to-last step, each side of the equation is divided by zero, and division by zero is not defined. **101.** Answers will vary.

SECTION 2.2

1. The number is 5. **3.** The integers are 3 and 7. **5.** The integers are 21 and 29. **7.** The three numbers are 21, 44, and 58. **9.** The integers are -20, -19, and -18. **11.** There is no solution. **13.** The integers are 5, 7, and 9. **15.** There are 21 dimes in the collection. **17.** There are 12 dimes in the bank. **19.** There are eight 20¢ stamps and sixteen 15¢ stamps in the collection. **21.** There are five 3¢ stamps in the collection. **23.** There are seven 18¢ stamps in the collection. **25.** No solution

SECTION 2.3

1. The cost is $2.95 per pound. **3.** There were 320 adult tickets sold. **5.** The cook must use 22.5 L of imitation maple syrup. **7.** The goldsmith used 20 oz of pure gold and 30 oz of the gold alloy. **9.** The cost of the tea mixture is $4.11 per pound. **11.** 23.8 gal of cranberry juice was used. **13.** 200 lb of the 15% aluminum alloy must be used. **15.** You should combine 2.25 oz of 70% rubbing alcohol and 1.25 oz of water. **17.** 45 oz of pure water must be added. **19.** 300 ml of alcohol must be added. **21.** The result is 6% fruit juice. **23.** 4 qt will have to be replaced with pure antifreeze. **25.** The helicopter overtakes the car 104 mi from the starting point. **27.** The first car is traveling 58 mph. The second car is traveling 66 mph. **29.** The distance between the two airports is 375 mi. **31.** The freight train is traveling 30 mph. The passenger train is traveling 48 mph. **33.** The cyclist rode 44 mi. **35.** 15 oz of 12 karat gold should be mixed with the 24 karat gold. **37.** They are $3\dfrac{1}{3}$ mi apart. **39.** The grass seed is 18 ft from the base of the 40-foot tower.

SECTION 2.4

1. $\{x \mid x < 5\}$ **3.** $\{x \mid x \le 2\}$ **5.** $\{x \mid x < -4\}$ **7.** $\{x \mid x > 3\}$ **9.** $\{x \mid x > 4\}$ **11.** $\{x \mid x \le 2\}$ **13.** $\{x \mid x > -2\}$ **15.** $\{x \mid x \ge 2\}$ **17.** $\{x \mid x > -2\}$ **19.** $\{x \mid x \le 3\}$ **21.** $\{x \mid x < 2\}$ **23.** $\{x \mid x < -3\}$ **25.** $\{x \mid x \le 5\}$ **27.** $\left\{x \mid x \ge -\dfrac{1}{2}\right\}$ **29.** $\left\{x \mid x < \dfrac{23}{16}\right\}$ **31.** $\left\{x \mid x < \dfrac{8}{3}\right\}$ **33.** $\{x \mid x > 1\}$ **35.** $\left\{x \mid x > \dfrac{14}{11}\right\}$ **37.** $\{x \mid x \le 1\}$ **39.** $\left\{x \mid x \le \dfrac{3}{8}\right\}$ **41.** $\left\{x \mid x \le \dfrac{7}{4}\right\}$ **43.** $\left\{x \mid x \ge -\dfrac{5}{4}\right\}$ **45.** $\{x \mid x \le 2\}$ **47.** $\{x \mid -2 \le x \le 4\}$ **49.** $\{x \mid x < 3 \text{ or } x > 5\}$ **51.** $\{x \mid -4 < x < 2\}$ **53.** $\{x \mid x > 6 \text{ or } x < -4\}$ **55.** $\{x \mid x < -3\}$ **57.** $\{x \mid -3 < x < 2\}$ **59.** $\{x \mid -2 < x < 1\}$ **61.** $\{x \mid x < -2 \text{ or } x > 2\}$ **63.** $\{x \mid 2 < x < 6\}$ **65.** $\{x \mid -3 < x < -2\}$ **67.** $\left\{x \mid x > 5 \text{ or } x < -\dfrac{5}{3}\right\}$ **69.** $\{x \mid x < 3\}$ **71.** The solution set is the empty set. **73.** The solution set is the set of real numbers. **75.** $\left\{x \mid \dfrac{17}{7} \le x \le \dfrac{45}{7}\right\}$ **77.** $\left\{x \mid -5 < x < \dfrac{17}{3}\right\}$ **79.** The solution set is the set of real numbers. **81.** The solution set is the empty set. **83.** The smallest number is -12. **85.** The maximum width as an integer is 11 cm. **87.** The TopPage plan is less expensive for more than 460 pages per month. **89.** A call must last 7 min or less. **91.** The temperature range is $32° < F < 86°$. **93.** The amount of sales is $44,000 or more. **95.** The business writes more than 200 checks per month.   **97.** The range of scores is $58 \le x \le 100$.   **99.** The three consecutive even integers can be 10, 12, 14, or 12, 14, 16, or 14, 16, 18.   **101.** The solution is correct.

SECTION 2.5

1. 7 and -7 **3.** 4 and -4 **5.** 6 and -6 **7.** 7 and -7 **9.** There is no solution.   **11.** There is no solution.

13. -5 and 1   **15.** 2 and 8   **17.** 2   **19.** There is no solution.   **21.** 3 and $-\dfrac{3}{2}$ **23.** $\dfrac{3}{2}$ **25.** There is no solution.

27. -3 and 7   **29.** $-\dfrac{10}{3}$ and 2   **31.** 3 and 1   **33.** $\dfrac{3}{2}$ **35.** There is no solution.   **37.** $-\dfrac{1}{6}$ and $\dfrac{11}{6}$

39. -1 and $-\dfrac{1}{3}$ **41.** There is no solution.   **43.** 0 and 3   **45.** There is no solution.   **47.** $\dfrac{13}{3}$ and 1

49. There is no solution.   **51.** $\dfrac{1}{3}$ and $\dfrac{7}{3}$ **53.** $-\dfrac{1}{2}$ **55.** $-\dfrac{7}{2}$ and $-\dfrac{1}{2}$ **57.** $\dfrac{10}{3}$ and $-\dfrac{8}{3}$ **59.** There is no solution.

61. $\{x \mid x > 3 \text{ or } x < -3\}$ **63.** $\{x \mid x > 1 \text{ or } x < -3\}$ **65.** $\{x \mid 4 \le x \le 6\}$ **67.** $\{x \mid x \ge 5 \text{ or } x \le -1\}$

69. $\{x \mid -3 < x < 2\}$ **71.** $\left\{x \mid x > 2 \text{ or } x < -\dfrac{14}{5}\right\}$ **73.** The solution set is the empty set.   **75.** The solution set

is the set of real numbers.   **77.** $\left\{x \mid x \le -\dfrac{1}{3} \text{ or } x \ge 3\right\}$ **79.** $\left\{x \mid -2 \le x \le \dfrac{9}{2}\right\}$ **81.** $\{x \mid x = 2\}$

83. $\left\{x \mid x < -2 \text{ or } x > \dfrac{22}{9}\right\}$ **85.** $\left\{x \mid -\dfrac{3}{2} < x < \dfrac{9}{2}\right\}$ **87.** $\left\{x \mid x < 0 \text{ or } x > \dfrac{4}{5}\right\}$ **89.** $\{x \mid x > 5 \text{ or } x < 0\}$

91. Lower limit: 1.742 in.; upper limit: 1.758 in.   **93.** Lower limit: 195 volts; upper limit: 245 volts   **95.** Lower limit:

$9\dfrac{19}{32}$ in.; upper limit: $9\dfrac{21}{32}$ in.   **97.** Lower limit: 28,420 ohms; upper limit: 29,580 ohms   **99.** Lower limit: 23,750 ohms;

upper limit: 26,250 ohms   **101a.** $\{x \mid x \ge -3\}$ **b.** $\{a \mid a \le 4\}$ **103a.** $\le$ **b.** $\ge$ **c.** $\ge$ **d.** $=$ **e.** $=$

CHAPTER REVIEW

1. 6 [2.1B]   **2.** $\left\{x \mid x > \dfrac{5}{3}\right\}$ [2.4A]   **3.** $L = \dfrac{P - 2W}{2}$ [2.1D]   **4.** -9 [2.1A]   **5.** $\left\{x \mid -3 < x < \dfrac{4}{3}\right\}$ [2.4B]

6. $-\dfrac{40}{7}$ [2.1B]   **7.** $-\dfrac{2}{3}$ [2.1A]   **8.** -1 and 9 [2.5A]   **9.** $\{x \mid 1 < x < 4\}$ [2.5B]   **10.** $-\dfrac{9}{19}$ [2.1C]

11. $\dfrac{26}{17}$ [2.1C]   **12.** $\{x \mid x > 2 \text{ or } x < -2\}$ [2.4B]   **13.** $\left\{x \mid x \ge 2 \text{ or } x \le \dfrac{1}{2}\right\}$ [2.5B]   **14.** $C = R - Pn$ [2.1D]

15. $-\dfrac{17}{2}$ [2.1C]   **16.** No solution [2.5A]   **17.** The set of real numbers [2.4B]   **18.** $\dfrac{5}{2}$ [2.1C]

19. 52 gal of apple juice were used. [2.3A]   **20.** The amount of sales must be $55,000 or more. [2.4C]   **21.** There are seven quarters in the collection. [2.2B]   **22.** Lower limit: 2.747 in.; upper limit: 2.753 in. [2.5C]   **23.** The integers are 6 and 14. [2.2A]   **24.** The range of scores is $82 \le x \le 100$. [2.4C]   **25.** The speed of the faster plane is 520 mph. The speed of the slower plane is 440 mph. [2.3C]   **26.** 375 lb of 30% tin and 125 lb of 70% tin were used. [2.3B]

27. Lower limit: $10\dfrac{11}{32}$ in.; upper limit: $10\dfrac{13}{32}$ in. [2.5C]

CHAPTER TEST

1. -2 [2.1A]   **2.** $-\dfrac{1}{8}$ [2.1A]   **3.** $\dfrac{5}{6}$ [2.1A]   **4.** 4 [2.1B]   **5.** $\dfrac{32}{3}$ [2.1B]   **6.** $-\dfrac{1}{5}$ [2.1B]   **7.** 1 [2.1C]

8. $R = \dfrac{E - Ir}{I}$ [2.1D]   **9.** $\dfrac{12}{7}$ [2.1C]   **10.** $\{x \mid x \le -3\}$ [2.4A]   **11.** $\{x \mid x > -1\}$ [2.4A]   **12.** $\{x \mid x > 2\}$ [2.4B]

13. ∅ [2.4B]   **14.** 3 and $-\dfrac{9}{5}$ [2.5A]   **15.** 7 and -2 [2.5A]   **16.** $\left\{x \,\middle|\, \dfrac{1}{3} < x \le 3\right\}$ [2.5B]

17. $\left\{x \,\middle|\, x > 2 \text{ or } x < -\dfrac{1}{2}\right\}$ [2.5B]   **18.** You can drive less than 120 mi. [2.4C]   **19.** Lower limit: 2.648 in.; upper limit:

2.652 in. [2.5C]   **20.** The integers are 4 and 11. [2.2A]   **21.** There are six 24¢ stamps in the collection. [2.2B]

22. The cost of the hamburger mixture is $2.20 per pound. [2.3A]   **23.** The total distance the jogger ran was

12 mi. [2.3C]   **24.** The speed of the slower train is 60 mph. The speed of the faster train is 65 mph. [2.3C]

25. 100 oz of pure water must be added. [2.3B]

CUMULATIVE REVIEW

1. -11 [1.2A]   **2.** -108 [1.2C]   **3.** 3 [1.2D]   **4.** -64 [1.2D]   **5.** -8 [1.3B]   **6.** 1 [1.3B]

7. Commutative Property of Addition [1.3A]   **8.** $(3n + 6) + 3n$; $6n + 6$ [1.4A]   **9.** $B = \dfrac{Fc}{ev}$ [2.1D]

10. $25y$ [1.3C]   **11.** $\{-4, 0\}$ [1.1C]   **12.** 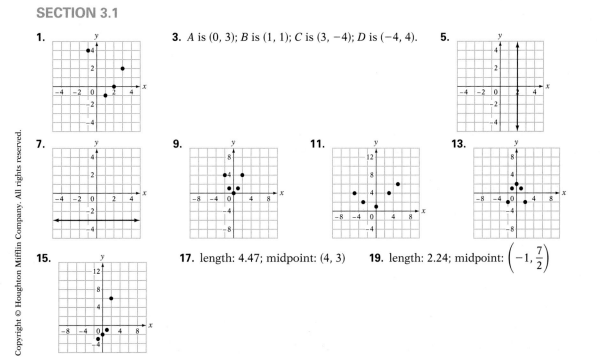 [1.1C]   **13.** $y = \dfrac{-Ax - C}{B}$ [2.1D]

14. $\dfrac{1}{2}$ [2.1A]   **15.** 1 [2.1B]   **16.** 24 [2.1B]   **17.** 2 [2.1C]   **18.** 2 [2.1C]   **19.** 1 [2.1C]

20. $-\dfrac{13}{5}$ [2.1C]   **21.** $\{x \,|\, x \le 1\}$ [2.4A]   **22.** $\{x \,|\, -4 < x \le 1\}$ [2.4B]   **23.** -1 and 4 [2.5A]

24. 7 and -4 [2.5A]   **25.** $\left\{x \,\middle|\, x < -\dfrac{4}{3} \text{ or } x > 2\right\}$ [2.5B]   **26.** $\{x \,|\, -2 < x < 6\}$ [2.5B]   **27.** The customer can write

fewer than 50 checks. [2.4C]   **28.** The first integer is -3. [2.2A]   **29.** There are 15 dimes in the coin purse. [2.2B]

30. 80 oz of pure silver were used. [2.3A]   **31.** The speed of the slower plane is 220 mph. [2.3C]   **32.** Lower limit:

2.449 in.; upper limit: 2.451 in. [2.5C]   **33.** 3 L of 12% acid solution must be used. [2.3B]

Answers to Chapter 3 Odd-Numbered Exercises

SECTION 3.1

1. 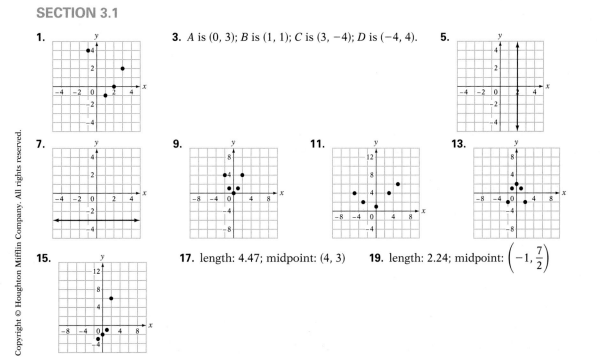   **3.** A is $(0, 3)$; B is $(1, 1)$; C is $(3, -4)$; D is $(-4, 4)$.   **5.**

7.   **9.**   **11.**   **13.**

15.   **17.** length: 4.47; midpoint: $(4, 3)$ **19.** length: 2.24; midpoint: $\left(-1, \dfrac{7}{2}\right)$

21. length: 5.10; midpoint: $\left(-\frac{1}{2}, -\frac{9}{2}\right)$ **23.** length: 9.90; midpoint: $\left(\frac{3}{2}, \frac{3}{2}\right)$ **25.** length: 3; midpoint: $\left(\frac{7}{2}, -5\right)$

27. length: 4.18; midpoint: $\left(\frac{1}{2}, \frac{1}{2}\right)$ **29a.** The temperature of the reaction after 20 min was 280°F.

b. The temperature was 160°F in 50 min. **31.**   **33.**

35. The graph is a circle of radius 5 centered at the origin. **37.**

SECTION 3.2

1. function **3.** function **5.** function **7.** not a function **9.** Yes. $22.25 **11.** $f(3) = 11$ **13.** $f(0) = -4$

15. $G(0) = 4$ **17.** $G(-2) = 10$ **19.** $q(3) = 5$ **21.** $q(-2) = 0$ **23.** $F(4) = 24$ **25.** $F(-3) = -4$

27. $H(1) = 1$ **29.** $H(t) = \frac{3t}{t+2}$ **31.** $s(-1) = 6$ **33.** $s(a) = a^3 - 3a + 4$ **35.** $P(-2 + h) - P(-2) = 4h$

37. $f(-3 + h) - f(-3) = -3h$ **39a.** The packaging cost is $4.75 per game. **b.** The packaging cost is $4.00 per game.

41a. The appraiser's fee is $3000. **b.** The appraiser's fee is $950. **43.** Domain: {1, 2, 3, 4, 5}; range: {1, 4, 7, 10, 13}

45. Domain: {0, 2, 4, 6}; range: {1, 2, 3, 4} **47.** Domain: {1, 3, 5, 7, 9}; range: {0} **49.** Domain: {-2, -1, 0, 1, 2};

range: {0, 1, 2} **51.** Domain: {-2, -1, 0, 1, 2}; range: {-3, 3, 6, 7, 9} **53.** 1 **55.** -8 **57.** None **59.** None

61. 0 **63.** None **65.** None **67.** -2 **69.** None **71.** Range: {-3, 1, 5, 9} **73.** Range: {-23, -13, -8, -3, 7}

75. Range: {0, 1, 4} **77.** Range: {2, 14, 26, 42} **79.** Range: $\left\{-5, \frac{5}{3}, 5\right\}$ **81.** Range: $\left\{-1, -\frac{1}{2}, -\frac{1}{3}, 1\right\}$

83. Range: {-38, -8, 2} **85.** Answers will vary. **87.** {(-2, -8), (-1, -1), (0, 0), (1, 1), (2, 8)}. Yes, the set defines a

function. **89.** The car will skid 61.2 ft. **91a.** After 5 s the parachutist is falling at a rate of 25 ft/s. **b.** After 15 s the

parachutist is falling at a rate of 30 ft/s. **93a.** After 5 h the temperature will be 64°F. **b.** After 15 h the temperature

will be 52°F.

SECTION 3.3

17.

19. x-intercept: $(-4, 0)$; y-intercept: $(0, 2)$ **21.** x-intercept: $\left(\dfrac{9}{2}, 0\right)$; y-intercept: $(0, -3)$

23. x-intercept: $(2, 0)$; y-intercept: $(0, -4)$ **25.** x-intercept: $\left(\dfrac{5}{3}, 0\right)$; y-intercept: $\left(0, \dfrac{5}{2}\right)$

27. x-intercept: $\left(\dfrac{4}{3}, 0\right)$; y-intercept: $(0, 2)$ **29.** x-intercept: $(3, 0)$; y-intercept: $\left(0, -\dfrac{9}{5}\right)$

31. Marlys received \$165 for tutoring 15 h.

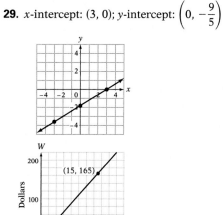

33. The roller coaster travels 550 ft in 5 s.

35. The cost of manufacturing 6000 compact disks is \$33,000.

37. Answers will vary.　　**39.** Answers will vary.　　**41.**　　　　　**43.**

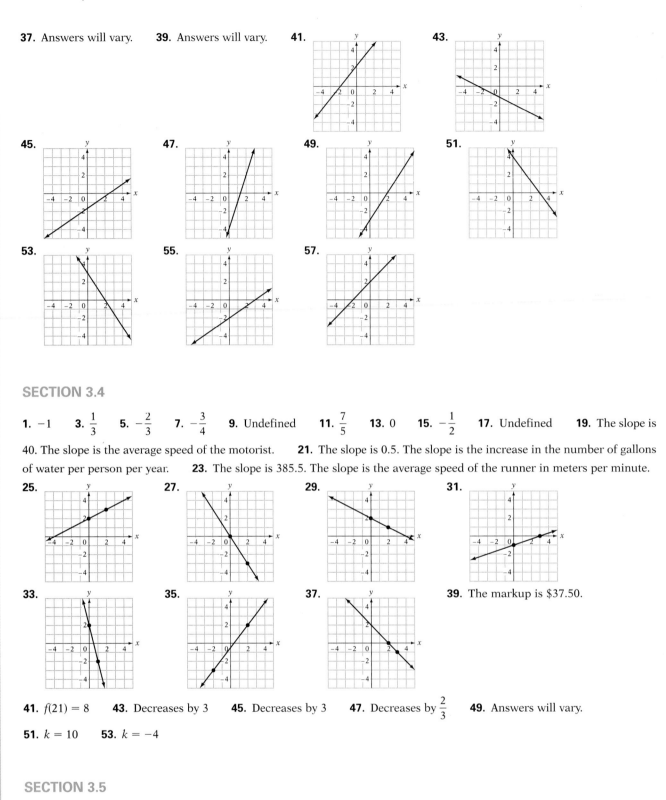

SECTION 3.4

1. -1　**3.** $\dfrac{1}{3}$　**5.** $-\dfrac{2}{3}$　**7.** $-\dfrac{3}{4}$　**9.** Undefined　**11.** $\dfrac{7}{5}$　**13.** 0　**15.** $-\dfrac{1}{2}$　**17.** Undefined　**19.** The slope is

40. The slope is the average speed of the motorist.　**21.** The slope is 0.5. The slope is the increase in the number of gallons

of water per person per year.　**23.** The slope is 385.5. The slope is the average speed of the runner in meters per minute.

25.　　　　　**27.**　　　　　**29.**　　　　　**31.**

33.　　　　　**35.**　　　　　**37.**　　　　　**39.** The markup is $37.50.

41. $f(21) = 8$　**43.** Decreases by 3　**45.** Decreases by 3　**47.** Decreases by $\dfrac{2}{3}$　**49.** Answers will vary.

51. $k = 10$　**53.** $k = -4$

SECTION 3.5

1. $y = 2x + 5$　**3.** $y = \dfrac{1}{2}x + 2$　**5.** $y = \dfrac{5}{4}x + \dfrac{21}{4}$　**7.** $y = -\dfrac{5}{3}x + 5$　**9.** $y = -3x + 9$　**11.** $y = -3x + 4$

13. $y = \dfrac{2}{3}x - \dfrac{7}{3}$　**15.** $y = \dfrac{1}{2}x$　**17.** $y = 3x - 9$　**19.** $y = -\dfrac{2}{3}x + 7$　**21.** $y = -x - 3$　**23.** $y = \dfrac{7}{5}x - \dfrac{27}{5}$

25. $y = -\dfrac{2}{5}x + \dfrac{3}{5}$　**27.** $x = 3$　**29.** $y = -\dfrac{5}{4}x - \dfrac{15}{2}$　**31.** $y = -3$　**33.** $y = -2x + 3$　**35.** $x = -5$

37. $y = x + 2$　**39.** $y = -2x - 3$　**41.** $y = \dfrac{2}{3}x + \dfrac{5}{3}$　**43.** $y = \dfrac{1}{3}x + \dfrac{10}{3}$　**45.** $y = \dfrac{3}{2}x - \dfrac{1}{2}$　**47.** $y = -\dfrac{3}{2}x + 3$

49. $y = -1$ **51.** $y = x - 1$ **53.** $y = -x + 1$ **55.** $y = -\dfrac{8}{3}x + \dfrac{25}{3}$ **57.** $y = \dfrac{1}{2}x - 1$ **59.** $y = -4$ **61.** $y = \dfrac{3}{4}x$

63. $y = -\dfrac{4}{3}x + \dfrac{5}{3}$ **65.** $x = -2$ **67.** $y = x - 1$ **69.** $y = \dfrac{4}{3}x + \dfrac{7}{3}$ **71.** $y = -x + 3$ **73.** $y = 0.5875x - 1161.325.$

This model predicts an hourly wage of \$10.74 in 1995.   **75.** $y = 45{,}455x - 90{,}037{,}270.$ This model predicts 872,730

health care jobs in the year 2000.   **79a.** The slope is the rate at which the number of CD players sold decreases per dollar

increase in price.   **b.** The y-intercept represents the number of CD players that would be given away if the price were \$0.

c. The x-intercept represents the price at which no CD players would be sold.   **81.** $\left(-\dfrac{b}{m}, 0\right)$ **83.** $\{(0, 3), (1, 2), (3, 0)\}$.

Other answers are possible.   **85.** $f(0) = 5$

SECTION 3.6

1. Yes   **3.** No   **5.** No   **7.** Yes   **9.** Yes   **11.** Yes   **13.** No   **15.** Yes   **17.** Yes   **19.** $y = \dfrac{2}{3}x - \dfrac{8}{3}$

21. $y = \dfrac{1}{3}x - \dfrac{1}{3}$ **23.** $y = -\dfrac{5}{3}x - \dfrac{14}{3}$ **25.** Answers will vary.   **27.** $\dfrac{A_1}{B_1} = -\dfrac{B_2}{A_2}$ **29.** Any equation of the form

$y = 2x + b, b \neq -13,$ or $y = -\dfrac{3}{2}x + c, c \neq 8.$ **31.** x-intercept: $(9, 0)$; y-intercept: $(0, 9)$

SECTION 3.7

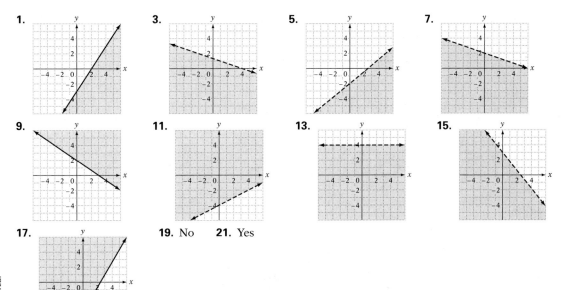

17.   **19.** No   **21.** Yes

CHAPTER REVIEW

1. $(4, 2)$ [3.1A]   **2.** $-2; 3a + 4$ [3.2A]   **3.**   [3.1A]   **4.**   [3.1A]

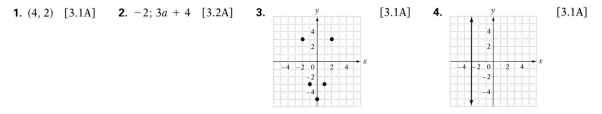

5. $\{-1, 1, 5\}$ [3.2A]   **6.** Domain = $\{-1, 0, 1, 5\}$; range = $\{0, 2, 4\}$ [3.2A]   **7.** $\left(\dfrac{1}{2}, \dfrac{9}{2}\right)$; 5.10 [3.1B]   **8.** -4 [3.2A]

9. $(-3, 0)$; $(0, -2)$ [3.3C]   **10.** $(-2, 0)$; $(0, -3)$ [3.3C]

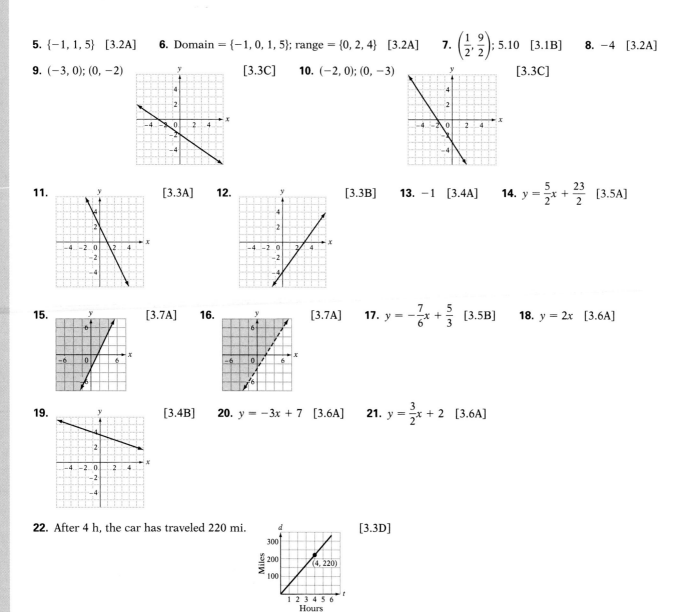

11. [3.3A]   **12.** [3.3B]   **13.** -1 [3.4A]   **14.** $y = \dfrac{5}{2}x + \dfrac{23}{2}$ [3.5A]

15. [3.7A]   **16.** [3.7A]   **17.** $y = -\dfrac{7}{6}x + \dfrac{5}{3}$ [3.5B]   **18.** $y = 2x$ [3.6A]

19. [3.4B]   **20.** $y = -3x + 7$ [3.6A]   **21.** $y = \dfrac{3}{2}x + 2$ [3.6A]

22. After 4 h, the car has traveled 220 mi. [3.3D]

23. $m = 20$; The slope is the cost of manufacturing one calculator. [3.4A]

24. $y = 80x + 25{,}000$; The cost to build a 2000-square-foot house is \$185,000. [3.5C]

CHAPTER TEST

1. [3.1A]   **2.** $(-3, 0)$ [3.1A]   **3.** [3.3A]   **4.** [3.3B]

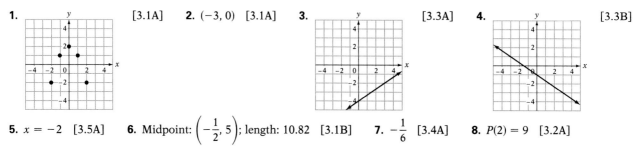

5. $x = -2$ [3.5A]   **6.** Midpoint: $\left(-\dfrac{1}{2}, 5\right)$; length: 10.82 [3.1B]   **7.** $-\dfrac{1}{6}$ [3.4A]   **8.** $P(2) = 9$ [3.2A]

9. 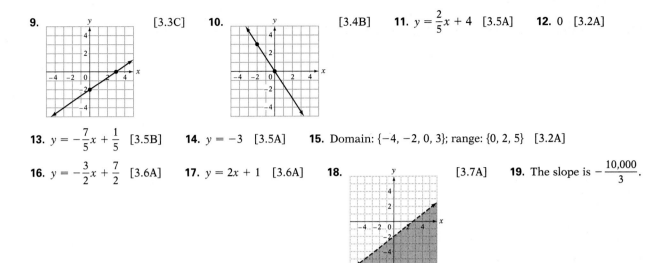 [3.3C]   **10.** [3.4B]   **11.** $y = \frac{2}{5}x + 4$ [3.5A]   **12.** 0 [3.2A]

13. $y = -\frac{7}{5}x + \frac{1}{5}$ [3.5B]   **14.** $y = -3$ [3.5A]   **15.** Domain: $\{-4, -2, 0, 3\}$; range: $\{0, 2, 5\}$ [3.2A]

16. $y = -\frac{3}{2}x + \frac{7}{2}$ [3.6A]   **17.** $y = 2x + 1$ [3.6A]   **18.** [3.7A]   **19.** The slope is $-\frac{10,000}{3}$.

The value of the house decreases by $\$\frac{10,000}{3}$ each year. [3.4A]   **20.** $y = -\frac{3}{10}x + 175$. The model predicts that 85 students will enroll when the tuition is $300. [3.5C]

CUMULATIVE REVIEW

1. Commutative Property of Multiplication [1.3A]   **2.** $\frac{9}{2}$ [2.1B]   **3.** $\frac{8}{9}$ [2.1C]   **4.** $-\frac{1}{14}$ [2.1C]

5. $\left\{x \,|\, x < -1 \text{ or } x > \frac{1}{2}\right\}$ [2.4B]   **6.** $\frac{5}{2}$ and $-\frac{3}{2}$ [2.5A]   **7.** $\left\{x \,|\, 0 < x < \frac{10}{3}\right\}$ [2.5B]   **8.** 8 [1.2D]

9. -4.5 [1.3B]   **10.** [1.1C]   **11.** $C = R - Pn$ [2.1D]   **12.** $x = 3 - \frac{3}{2}y$ [2.1D]

13. $\varnothing$ [2.4B]   **14.** $P(-3) = 14$ [3.2A]   **15.** $(-8, 13)$ [3.1A]   **16.** $-\frac{7}{4}$ [3.4A]   **17.** $y = \frac{3}{2}x + \frac{13}{2}$ [3.5A]

18. $y = -\frac{5}{4}x + 3$ [3.5B]   **19.** $y = -\frac{3}{2}x + 7$ [3.6A]   **20.** $y = -\frac{2}{3}x + \frac{8}{3}$ [3.6A]   **21.** There are 7 dimes in the purse. [2.2B]   **22.** The speed of the first plane is 200 mph. The speed of the second plane is 400 mph. [2.3B]

23. 20 lb of $6 coffee and 40 lb of $9 coffee should be used. [2.3A]   **24.** [3.3C]

25. [3.4B]   **26.** [3.7A]

27. $y = -2500x + 15,000$. The value of the truck decreases by $2500 each year. [3.5C]

Answers to Chapter 4 Odd-Numbered Exercises

SECTION 4.1

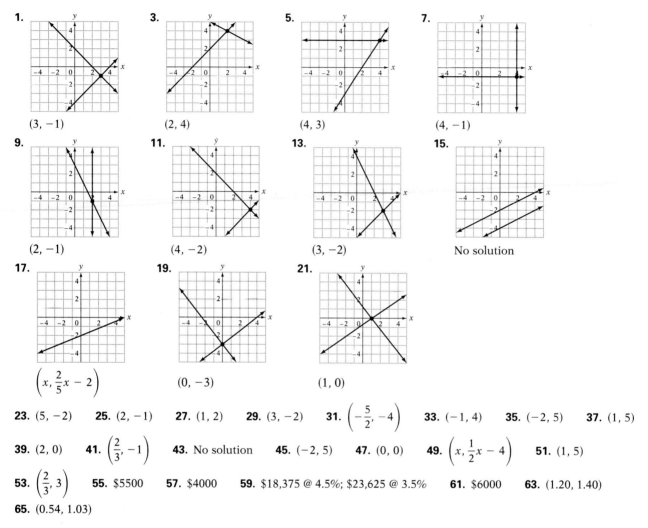

1. (3, −1) **3.** (2, 4) **5.** (4, 3) **7.** (4, −1)

9. (2, −1) **11.** (4, −2) **13.** (3, −2) **15.** No solution

17. $\left(x, \dfrac{2}{5}x - 2\right)$ **19.** (0, −3) **21.** (1, 0)

23. (5, −2) **25.** (2, −1) **27.** (1, 2) **29.** (3, −2) **31.** $\left(-\dfrac{5}{2}, -4\right)$ **33.** (−1, 4) **35.** (−2, 5) **37.** (1, 5)

39. (2, 0) **41.** $\left(\dfrac{2}{3}, -1\right)$ **43.** No solution **45.** (−2, 5) **47.** (0, 0) **49.** $\left(x, \dfrac{1}{2}x - 4\right)$ **51.** (1, 5)

53. $\left(\dfrac{2}{3}, 3\right)$ **55.** $5500 **57.** $4000 **59.** $18,375 @ 4.5%; $23,625 @ 3.5% **61.** $6000 **63.** (1.20, 1.40)

65. (0.54, 1.03)

SECTION 4.2

1. (6, 1) **3.** (1, 1) **5.** (2, 1) **7.** (−2, 1) **9.** The equations are dependent. The solutions are (x, 3x − 4).

11. $\left(-\dfrac{1}{2}, 2\right)$ **13.** No solution **15.** (−1, −2) **17.** (−5, 4) **19.** (2, 5) **21.** $\left(\dfrac{1}{2}, \dfrac{3}{4}\right)$ **23.** (0, 0) **25.** (−1, 3)

27. $\left(\dfrac{2}{3}, -\dfrac{2}{3}\right)$ **29.** (2, −3) **31.** (2, −1) **33.** (10, −5) **35.** $\left(-\dfrac{1}{2}, \dfrac{2}{3}\right)$ **37.** $\left(\dfrac{5}{3}, \dfrac{1}{3}\right)$ **39.** No solution

41. (1, −1) **43.** (2, 1, 3) **45.** (1, −1, 2) **47.** (1, 2, 4) **49.** (2, −1, −2) **51.** (−2, −1, 3) **53.** No solution

55. (1, 4, 1) **57.** (1, 3, 2) **59.** (1, −1, 3) **61.** (0, 2, 0) **63.** (1, 5, 2) **65.** (−2, 1, 1) **67.** Answers will vary.

69. (1, −1) **71.** (1, −1) **73.** $y = \dfrac{2x}{1 - 3x}, \ y = \dfrac{-3x}{x + 2}$

SECTION 4.3

1. 11 **3.** 18 **5.** 0 **7.** 15 **9.** −30 **11.** 0 **13.** (3, −4) **15.** (4, −1) **17.** $\left(\dfrac{11}{14}, \dfrac{17}{21}\right)$ **19.** $\left(\dfrac{1}{2}, 1\right)$

21. Not independent   **23.** $(-1, 0)$ **25.** $(1, -1, 2)$ **27.** $(2, -2, 3)$ **29.** Not independent   **31a.** Sometimes true
b. Always true   **c.** Sometimes true   **33.** $\left(-\dfrac{13}{32}, -\dfrac{7}{16}, \dfrac{5}{32}\right)$ **35.** Not independent

SECTION 4.4

1. The rate of the boat is 15 mph. The rate of the current is 3 mph.   **3.** The rate of the plane is 502.5 mph. The rate of the wind is 47.5 mph.   **5.** The rate of the team is 8 km/h. The rate of the current is 2 km/h.   **7.** The rate of the plane is 180 mph. The rate of the wind is 20 mph.   **9.** The rate of the plane is 110 mph. The rate of the wind is 10 mph.
11. There are 30 nickels in the bank.   **13.** The cost of the pine was $.15 per foot; the cost of the redwood was $.25 per foot.   **15.** The cost of the wool carpet is $26 per yard.   **17.** The company plans to manufacture twenty-five 10-speed bicycles.   **19.** There are 480 g of the first alloy and 40 g of the second alloy.   **21.** The cost of a Model VI computer is $4000.   **23.** The science museum sold 190 regular tickets, 210 student tickets, and 350 member discount tickets.   **25.** The investor placed $10,400 in the 8% account, $5200 in the 6% account, and $9400 in the 4% account.
27. The angles are 35° and 145°.   **29.** The oil painting is 85 years old and the watercolor is 50 years old.

SECTION 4.5

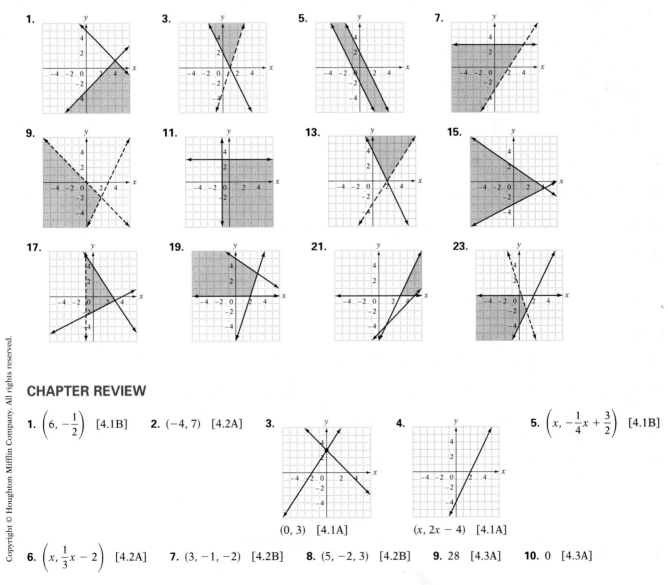

1.   **3.**   **5.**   **7.**

9.   **11.**   **13.**   **15.**

17.   **19.**   **21.**   **23.**

CHAPTER REVIEW

1. $\left(6, -\dfrac{1}{2}\right)$ [4.1B]   **2.** $(-4, 7)$ [4.2A]   **3.**   **4.**   **5.** $\left(x, -\dfrac{1}{4}x + \dfrac{3}{2}\right)$ [4.1B]

$(0, 3)$ [4.1A] $(x, 2x - 4)$ [4.1A]

6. $\left(x, \dfrac{1}{3}x - 2\right)$ [4.2A]   **7.** $(3, -1, -2)$ [4.2B]   **8.** $(5, -2, 3)$ [4.2B]   **9.** 28 [4.3A]   **10.** 0 [4.3A]

11. $(3, -1)$ [4.3B]   **12.** $\left(\dfrac{110}{23}, \dfrac{25}{23}\right)$ [4.3B]   **13.** $(-1, -3, 4)$ [4.3B]   **14.** $(2, 3, -5)$ [4.3B]

15. [4.5A]   **16.** [4.5A]

17. The rate of the cabin cruiser is 16 mph; the rate of the current is 4 mph. [4.4A]   **18.** The rate of the plane is 175 mph; the rate of the wind is 25 mph. [4.4A]   **19.** There were 100 children who attended the movie. [4.4B]
20. There was $5000 invested at 3%, and $15,000 invested at 7%. [4.1C]

CHAPTER TEST

1. $(3, 4)$ [4.1A]   **2.** $(-5, 0)$ [4.1A]

3. [4.5A]   **4.** [4.5A]   **5.** $\left(\dfrac{3}{4}, \dfrac{7}{8}\right)$ [4.1B]

6. $(-3, -4)$ [4.1B]   **7.** $(2, -1)$ [4.1B]   **8.** $(-2, 1)$ [4.2A]   **9.** No solution [4.2A]   **10.** $(1, 1)$ [4.2A]

11. No solution [4.2B]   **12.** $(2, -1, -2)$ [4.2B]   **13.** 10 [4.3A]   **14.** -32 [4.3A]   **15.** $\left(-\dfrac{1}{3}, -\dfrac{10}{3}\right)$ [4.3B]

16. $\left(\dfrac{59}{19}, -\dfrac{62}{19}\right)$ [4.3B]   **17.** $\left(\dfrac{1}{5}, -\dfrac{6}{5}, \dfrac{3}{5}\right)$ [4.3B]   **18.** The rate of the plane is 150 mph. The rate of the wind is 25 mph. [4.4A]   **19.** The cost of the cotton is $4.50 per yard. The cost of the wool is $7 per yard. [4.4B]   **20.** $9000 is invested at 2.7%; $6000 is invested at 5.1%. [4.1C]

CUMULATIVE REVIEW

1. $-\dfrac{11}{28}$ [2.1C]   **2.** $y = 5x - 11$ [3.5B]   **3.** $3x - 24$ [1.3C]   **4.** -4 [1.3B]   **5.** $\{x \mid x < 6\}$ [2.4B]

6. $\{x \mid -4 < x < 8\}$ [2.5B]   **7.** $\{x \mid x > 4 \text{ or } x < -1\}$ [2.5B]   **8.** $f(-3) = -98$ [3.2A]

9. Range: $\{0, 1, 5, 8, 16\}$ [3.2A]   **10.** $F(2) = 1$ [3.2A]   **11.** $f(2 + h) - f(2) = 3h$ [3.2A]

12. [1.1C]   **13.** $y = -\dfrac{2}{3}x + \dfrac{5}{3}$ [3.5A]   **14.** $y = -\dfrac{3}{2}x + \dfrac{1}{2}$ [3.6A]   **15.** 6.32 [3.1B]

16. $\left(-\dfrac{1}{2}, 4\right)$ [3.1B]   **17.** [3.4B]   **18.** [3.7A]

19. $(2, 0)$　[4.1A]　**20.**　[4.5A]　**21.** $(1, 0, -1)$　[4.2A]　**22.** 3　[4.3A]

23. $(2, -3)$　[4.3B]　**24.** $(-5, -11)$　[4.1B]　**25.** There are 16 nickels in the coin purse.　[2.2B]　**26.** 60 ml of pure water must be used.　[2.3B]　**27.** The rate of the wind is 12.5 mph.　[4.4A]　**28.** One pound of steak costs $3.　[4.4B]　**29.** The lower limit is 10,200 ohms. The upper limit is 13,800 ohms.　[2.5C]　**30.** The slope is 40. The slope is the commission rate of the executive.　[3.4A]

Answers to Chapter 5 Odd-Numbered Exercises

SECTION 5.1

1. a^4b^4　**3.** $-18x^3y^4$　**5.** x^8y^{16}　**7.** $81x^8y^{12}$　**9.** $729a^{10}b^6$　**11.** x^5y^{11}　**13.** $729x^6$　**15.** $a^{18}b^{18}$　**17.** $4096x^{12}y^{12}$　**19.** $64a^{24}b^{18}$　**21.** x^{2n+1}　**23.** y^{6n-2}　**25.** a^{2n^2-6n}　**27.** x^{15n+10}　**29.** $-6x^5y^5z^4$　**31.** $-12a^2b^9c^2$　**33.** $-6x^4y^4z^5$　**35.** $-432a^7b^{11}$　**37.** $54a^{13}b^{17}$　**39.** 243　**41.** y^3　**43.** $\dfrac{a^3b^2}{4}$　**45.** $\dfrac{x}{y^4}$　**47.** $\dfrac{1}{2}$　**49.** $-\dfrac{1}{9}$　**51.** $\dfrac{1}{y^8}$　**53.** $\dfrac{1}{x^6y^{10}}$　**55.** x^5y^5　**57.** $\dfrac{a^8}{b^9}$　**59.** $\dfrac{1}{2187a}$　**61.** $\dfrac{y^6}{x^3}$　**63.** $\dfrac{y^4}{x^3}$　**65.** $-\dfrac{1}{2x^2}$　**67.** $-\dfrac{1}{243a^5b^{10}}$　**69.** $\dfrac{16x^8}{81y^4z^{12}}$　**71.** $\dfrac{3a^4}{4b^3}$　**73.** $-\dfrac{9a}{8b^6}$　**75.** $\dfrac{16x^2}{y^6}$　**77.** $\dfrac{1}{b^{4n}}$　**79.** $-\dfrac{1}{y^{6n}}$　**81.** y^{n-2}　**83.** $\dfrac{1}{y^{2n}}$　**85.** $\dfrac{x^{n-5}}{y^6}$　**87.** $\dfrac{8b^{15}}{3a^{18}}$　**89.** 4.67×10^{-6}　**91.** 1.7×10^{-10}　**93.** 2×10^{11}　**95.** 0.000000123　**97.** 8,200,000,000,000,000　**99.** 0.039　**101.** 150,000　**103.** 20,800,000　**105.** 0.000000015　**107.** 0.0000000000178　**109.** 140,000,000　**111.** 11,456,790　**113.** 0.000008　**115.** Light travels 2.592×10^{10} km in one day.　**117.** The signals traveled at a speed of $1.08\overline{1} \times 10^7$ mi/min.　**119.** The centrifuge makes one revolution in 6.6×10^{-7} s.　**121.** The sun is 3.38983×10^5 times heavier.　**123.** The weight of one orchid seed is 3.225806×10^{-8} oz.　**125.** The distance from the Coma cluster to Earth is 1.6423949×10^{21} mi.　**127a.** $\dfrac{8}{5}$　**b.** $\dfrac{5}{4}$

SECTION 5.2

1. $P(3) = 13$　**3.** $R(2) = 10$　**5.** $f(-1) = -11$　**7a.** The leading coefficient is -1.　**b.** The constant term is 8.　**c.** The degree is 2.　**9.** The expression is not a polynomial.　**11.** The expression is not a polynomial.　**13a.** The leading coefficient is 3.　**b.** The constant term is π.　**c.** The degree is 5.　**15a.** The leading coefficient is -5.　**b.** The constant term is 2.　**c.** The degree is 3.　**17a.** The leading coefficient is 14.　**b.** The constant term is 14.　**c.** The degree is 0.　**19.**　**21.**　**23.**　**25.** $6x^2 - 6x + 5$

27. $-x^2 + 1$　**29.** $5y^2 - 15y + 2$　**31.** $7a^2 - a + 2$　**33.** $P(x) + R(x) = 3x^2 - 3xy - 2y^2$　**35.** $P(x) - R(x) = 8x^2 - 2xy + 5y^2$　**37.** $S(x) = 3x^4 - 8x^2 + 2x$;　$S(2) = 20$　**39a.** $k = 8$　**b.** $k = -4$　**41.** $P(x) - Q(x)$ is a fifth-degree polynomial.

SECTION 5.3

1. $2x^2 - 6x$ **3.** $6x^4 - 3x^3$ **5.** $6x^2y - 9xy^2$ **7.** $x^{n+1} + x^n$ **9.** $x^{2n} + x^ny^n$ **11.** $-4b^2 + 10b$

13. $-6a^4 + 4a^3 - 6a^2$ **15.** $9b^5 - 9b^3 + 24b$ **17.** $-3y^4 - 4y^3 + 2y^2$ **19.** $-20x^2 + 15x^3 - 15x^4 - 20x^5$

21. $-2x^4y + 6x^3y^2 - 4x^2y^3$ **23.** $x^{3n} + x^{2n} + x^{n+1}$ **25.** $a^{2n+1} - 3a^{n+2} + 2a^{n+1}$ **27.** $5y^2 - 11y$ **29.** $6y^2 - 31y$

31. $x^2 + 5x - 14$ **33.** $8y^2 + 2y - 21$ **35.** $8x^2 + 8xy - 30y^2$ **37.** $x^2y^2 + xy - 12$ **39.** $2x^4 - 15x^2 + 25$

41. $10x^4 - 15x^2y + 5y^2$ **43.** $x^{2n} - x^n - 6$ **45.** $6a^{2n} + a^n - 15$ **47.** $6a^{2n} + a^nb^n - 2b^{2n}$

49. $x^4 + 5x^3 - 3x^2 - 11x + 20$ **51.** $10a^3 - 27a^2b + 26ab^2 - 12b^3$ **53.** $2y^5 - 10y^4 - y^3 - y^2 + 3$

55. $4x^5 - 16x^4 + 15x^3 - 4x^2 + 28x - 45$ **57.** $x^4 - 3x^3 - 6x^2 + 29x - 21$ **59.** $2a^3 + 7a^2 - 43a + 42$

61. $x^{3n} + 2x^{2n} + 2x^n + 1$ **63.** $x^{2n} - 2x^{2n}y^n + 4x^ny^n - 2x^ny^{2n} + 3y^{2n}$ **65.** $9x^2 - 4$ **67.** $36 - x^2$ **69.** $4a^2 - 9b^2$

71. $x^4 - 1$ **73.** $x^{2n} - 9$ **75.** $x^2 - 10x + 25$ **77.** $9a^2 + 30ab + 25b^2$ **79.** $x^4 - 6x^2 + 9$ **81.** $4x^4 - 12x^2y^2 + 9y^4$

83. $a^{2n} - 2a^nb^n + b^{2n}$ **85.** $-x^2 + 2xy$ **87.** $-4xy$ **89.** $(3x^2 + 10x - 8)$ ft^2 **91.** $(x^2 + 3x)$ m^2

93. $(x^3 + 9x^2 + 27x + 27)$ cm^3 **95.** $(2x^3)$ in^3 **97.** $(78.5x^2 + 125.6x + 50.24)$ in^2 **99a.** $a^3 - b^3$ **b.** $x^3 + y^3$

101a. $k = 5$ **b.** $k = 1$ **103.** $a^2 + b^2$

SECTION 5.4

1. $x + 8$ **3.** $x^2 + 3x + 6 + \dfrac{20}{x - 3}$ **5.** $3x + 5 + \dfrac{3}{2x + 1}$ **7.** $5x + 7 + \dfrac{2}{2x - 1}$ **9.** $4x^2 + 6x + 9 + \dfrac{18}{2x - 3}$

11. $3x^2 + 1 + \dfrac{1}{2x^2 - 5}$ **13.** $x^2 - 3x - 10$ **15.** $x^2 - 2x + 1 - \dfrac{1}{x - 3}$ **17.** $2x^3 - 3x^2 + x - 4$ **19.** $2x + \dfrac{x + 2}{x^2 + 2x - 1}$

21. $x^2 + 4x + 6 + \dfrac{10x + 8}{x^2 - 2x - 1}$ **23.** $x^2 - 2x + 4 + \dfrac{-6x - 7}{x^2 + 2x + 3}$ **25.** $2x - 8$ **27.** $3x - 8$ **29.** $3x + 3 - \dfrac{1}{x - 1}$

31. $2x^2 - 3x + 9$ **33.** $4x^2 + 8x + 15 + \dfrac{12}{x - 2}$ **35.** $2x^2 - 3x + 7 - \dfrac{8}{x + 4}$ **37.** $3x^3 + 2x^2 + 12x + 19 + \dfrac{33}{x - 2}$

39. $3x^3 - x + 4 - \dfrac{2}{x + 1}$ **41.** $2x^3 + 6x^2 + 17x + 51 + \dfrac{155}{x - 3}$ **43.** $P(3) = 8$ **45.** $R(4) = 43$ **47.** $P(-2) = -39$

49. $Z(-3) = -60$ **51.** $Q(2) = 31$ **53.** $F(-3) = 178$ **55.** $P(5) = 122$ **57.** $R(-3) = 302$ **59.** $Q(2) = 0$

61. $R(-2) = -65$ **63a.** $a^2 - ab + b^2$ **b.** $x^4 - x^3y + x^2y^2 - xy^3 + y^4$ **c.** $x^5 - x^4y + x^3y^2 - x^2y^3 + xy^4 - y^5$

65a. $\dfrac{1}{2}x^2 + \dfrac{3}{4}x - 1$ **b.** $\dfrac{2}{3}x^2 + \dfrac{7}{2}x + \dfrac{10}{3} + \dfrac{64}{6x - 12}$ **c.** $2x^2 - x + 1 + \dfrac{3x - 11}{x^2 - x + 1}$ **d.** $x^2 + 6x + 17 + \dfrac{51x + 56}{x^2 - 2x - 3}$

SECTION 5.5

1. $3a(2a - 5)$ **3.** $x^2(4x - 3)$ **5.** Nonfactorable over the integers   **7.** $x(x^4 - x^2 - 1)$ **9.** $4(4x^2 - 3x + 6)$

11. $5b^2(1 - 2b + 5b^2)$ **13.** $x^n(x^n - 1)$ **15.** $x^{2n}(x^n - 1)$ **17.** $a^2(a^{2n} + 1)$ **19.** $6x^2y(2y - 3x + 4)$

21. $4a^2b^2(6a - 1 - 4b^2)$ **23.** $y^2(y^{2n} + y^n - 1)$ **25.** $(a + 2)(x - 2)$ **27.** $(x - 2)(a + b)$ **29.** $(a - 2b)(x - y)$

31. $(x + 4)(y - 2)$ **33.** $(a + b)(x - y)$ **35.** $(y - 3)(x^2 - 2)$ **37.** $(3 + y)(2 + x^2)$ **39.** $(2a + b)(x^2 - 2y)$

41. $(2b + a)(3x - 2y)$ **43.** $(y - 5)(x^n + 1)$ **45.** $(2x - 1)(x^2 + 2)$ **47.** $(x + 10)(x + 2)$ **49.** $(a + 9)(a - 8)$

51. $(a + 6)(a + 1)$ **53.** $(y - 6)(y - 12)$ **55.** $(x + 12)(x - 11)$ **57.** $(x + 10)(x + 5)$ **59.** $(b + 2)(b - 8)$

61. $(a - b)(a - 2b)$ **63.** $(a + 11b)(a - 3b)$ **65.** $(x + 3y)(x + 2y)$ **67.** $(1 + x)(2 - x)$ **69.** $(1 + x)(5 - x)$

71. $(x - 3)(x - 2)$ **73.** $(2x + 1)(x + 3)$ **75.** $(2y + 3)(3y - 2)$ **77.** $(3b + 7)(2b - 5)$ **79.** $(3y - 13)(y - 3)$

81. Nonfactorable over the integers   **83.** $(a + 1)(4a - 5)$ **85.** $(5x - 2)(2x - 5)$ **87.** Nonfactorable over the integers

89. $(6x - y)(x + 7y)$ **91.** $(7a - 3b)(a + 7b)$ **93.** $(6x + 5y)(3x + 2y)$ **95.** $(2 + x)(3 - 5x)$

97. Nonfactorable over the integers   **99.** $(5 + 2b)(7 - 4b)$ **101.** $y^2(5y - 4)(y - 5)$ **103.** $-2x^2(5x - 2)(3x + 5)$

105. $a^2b^2(ab + 2)(ab - 5)$ **107.** $5(18a^2b^2 + 9ab + 2)$ **109.** Nonfactorable over the integers   **111.** $2a(a^2 + 5)(a^2 + 2)$

113. $3y^2(x^2 - 5)(x^2 - 8)$ **115.** $3xy(xy - 2)(xy + 4)$ **117.** $y(y^2 - 3)(y^2 - 5)$ **119.** $y(4y - 3)(4y - 1)$

121. $3(y^n - 3)(4y^n - 5)$ **123.** $x^n(x^n + 2)(x^n + 8)$ **125a.** $-9, -6, 6, 9$ **b.** $-5, -1, 1, 5$ **c.** $-7, -5, 5, 7$

d. $-9, -3, 3, 9$ **e.** $-16, -8, 8, 16$ **f.** $-5, -1, 1, 5$

SECTION 5.6

1. $(x + 4)(x - 4)$ **3.** $(2x + 1)(2x - 1)$ **5.** $(4x + 11)(4x - 11)$ **7.** $(1 + 3a)(1 - 3a)$ **9.** $(xy + 10)(xy - 10)$

11. Nonfactorable over the integers   **13.** $(5 + ab)(5 - ab)$ **15.** $(a^n + 1)(a^n - 1)$ **17.** $(x - 6)^2$ **19.** $(b - 1)^2$

21. $(4x - 5)^2$ **23.** Nonfactorable over the integers   **25.** Nonfactorable over the integers   **27.** $(x + 3y)^2$

29. $(5a - 4b)^2$ **31.** $(x^n + 3)^2$ **33.** $(x - 7)(x - 1)$ **35.** $(x - y + a + b)(x - y - a - b)$ **37.** $(x - 3)(x^2 + 3x + 9)$

39. $(2x - 1)(4x^2 + 2x + 1)$ **41.** $(x - y)(x^2 + xy + y^2)$ **43.** $(m + n)(m^2 - mn + n^2)$ **45.** $(4x + 1)(16x^2 - 4x + 1)$

47. $(3x - 2y)(9x^2 + 6xy + 4y^2)$ **49.** $(xy + 4)(x^2y^2 - 4xy + 16)$ **51.** Nonfactorable over the integers

53. Nonfactorable over the integers   **55.** $(a - 2b)(a^2 - ab + b^2)$ **57.** $(x^{2n} + y^n)(x^{4n} - x^{2n}y^n + y^{2n})$

59. $(x^n + 2)(x^{2n} - 2x^n + 4)$ **61.** $(xy - 3)(xy - 5)$ **63.** $(xy - 5)(xy - 12)$ **65.** $(x^2 - 3)(x^2 - 6)$

67. $(b^2 + 5)(b^2 - 18)$ **69.** $(x^2y^2 - 2)(x^2y^2 - 6)$ **71.** $(x^n + 1)(x^n + 2)$ **73.** $(3xy - 5)(xy - 3)$

75. $(2ab - 3)(3ab - 7)$ **77.** $(2x^2 - 15)(x^2 + 1)$ **79.** $(2x^n - 1)(x^n - 3)$ **81.** $(2a^n + 5)(3a^n + 2)$ **83.** $3(2x - 3)^2$

85. $a(3a - 1)(9a^2 + 3a + 1)$ **87.** $5(2x + 1)(2x - 1)$ **89.** $y^3(y + 11)(y - 5)$ **91.** $(4x^2 + 9)(2x + 3)(2x - 3)$

93. $2a(2 - a)(4 + 2a + a^2)$ **95.** $b^3(ab - 1)(a^2b^2 + ab + 1)$ **97.** $2x^2(2x - 5)^2$ **99.** $(x^2 + y^2)(x + y)(x - y)$

101. $(x^2 + y^2)(x^4 - x^2y^2 + y^4)$ **103.** Nonfactorable over the integers   **105.** $2a(2a - 1)(4a^2 + 2a + 1)$

107. $a^2b^2(a + 4b)(a - 12b)$ **109.** $2b^2(3a + 5b)(4a - 9b)$ **111.** $(x - 2)^2(x + 2)$ **113.** $(x + y)(x - y)(2x + 1)(2x - 1)$

115. $(x - 1)(x^2 + x + 1)(xy + 1)(x^2y^2 - xy + 1)$ **117.** $x(x^n + 1)^2$ **119.** $b^n(3b - 2)(b + 2)$

121. $(x - 3)(x - 2)(x - 1)$ **123.** $(x^2 + xy + y^2)(x^2 - xy + y^2)$ **125.** Answers will vary. For example, divide $x^3 + 6x^2 - 7x - 60$ by $x - 3$. The quotient will be a trinomial. Factor the trinomial. One factor is $x + 4$. The other factor is $x + 5$, a third first-degree factor of $x^3 + 6x^2 - 7x - 60$.

SECTION 5.7

1. -3 and 5 **3.** -7 and 8 **5.** $-4, 0,$ and $\frac{2}{3}$ **7.** -5 and 3 **9.** 1 and 3 **11.** -2 and 5 **13.** $-\frac{1}{2}$ and $\frac{3}{2}$

15. $\frac{1}{2}$ **17.** -3 and 3 **19.** $-\frac{1}{2}$ and $\frac{1}{2}$ **21.** -3 and 5 **23.** -1 and $\frac{13}{2}$ **25.** -2 and $\frac{4}{3}$ **27.** $-5, 0,$ and 2

29. -2 and 2 **31.** $-3, -1,$ and 3 **33.** $-2, -\frac{2}{3},$ and 2 **35.** $-2, -\frac{2}{5},$ and 2 **37.** The number is 14 or -15.

39. The length is 38 cm. The width is 10 cm.   **41.** The hypotenuse is 13 ft.   **43.** The stone will hit the bottom of the well in 2 s.   **45.** The length of the cardboard is 18 in. The width of the cardboard is 8 in.

CHAPTER REVIEW

1. $6a^2b(3a^3b - 2ab^2 + 5)$ [5.5A]   **2.** $5x + 4 + \dfrac{6}{3x - 2}$ [5.4A]   **3.** $144x^2y^{10}z^{14}$ [5.1B]

4. $(a + 2b)(2x - 3y)$ [5.5B]   **5.** $-(x - 4)(x + 3)$ [5.5C]   **6.** 1 [5.4C]   **7.** $4x^2 - 8xy + 5y^2$ [5.2B]

8. $(6x + 5)(4x + 3)$ [5.5D]   **9.** $(2x + 3y)^2$ [5.6A]   **10.** $-6a^3b^6$ [5.1A]   **11.** $(4a - 3b)(16a^2 + 12ab + 9b^2)$ [5.6B]

12. $4x^2 + 3x - 8 + \dfrac{50}{x + 6}$ [5.4A/5.4B]   **13.** -7 [5.2A]   **14.** $(x - 8)(x + 5)$ [5.5C]   **15.** $(xy + 3)(xy - 3)$ [5.6A]

16. $12x^5y^3 + 8x^3y^2 - 28x^2y^4$ [5.3A]   **17.** $(x^n - 6)^2$ [5.6A]   **18.** $\dfrac{5}{2}$ and 4 [5.7A]   **19.** $33x^2 + 24x$ [5.3A]

20. $3a^2(a^2 + 1)(a^2 - 6)$ [5.6D]   **21.** $16x^2 - 24xy + 9y^2$ [5.3C]   **22.** $x^3 + 4x^2 + 16x + 64 + \dfrac{252}{x - 4}$ [5.4A/5.4B]

23. $(3x^2 + 2)(5x^2 - 3)$ [5.6C]   **24.** $\dfrac{c^{10}}{2b^{17}}$ [5.1B]   **25.** $6x^3 - 29x^2 + 14x + 24$ [5.3B]

26. $(7x^2y^2 + 3)(3x^2y^2 + 2)$ [5.6C]   **27.** $1, 4,$ and -4 [5.7A]   **28.** $25a^2 - 4b^2$ [5.3C]   **29.** 0.00254 [5.1C]

30. $(3x - 2)(2x - 9)$ [5.5D]   **31.** [5.2A]   **32a.** 3   **b.** 8   **c.** 5 [5.2A]

33. The mass of the moon is 8.103×10^{19} tons. [5.1D]   **34.** The number is -8 or 7. [5.7B]   **35.** The Great Galaxy of Andromeda is 1.291224×10^{19} mi from Earth. [5.1D]   **36.** The area of the rectangle is $(10x^2 - 29x - 21)$ cm². [5.3D]

CHAPTER TEST

1. $(4t + 3)^2$ [5.6A]   **2.** $-18r^2s^2 + 12rs^3 + 18rs^2$ [5.3A]   **3.** -3 [5.2A]   **4.** $(3x - 2)(9x^2 + 6x + 4)$ [5.6B]
5. $(4x - 5)(4x + 5)$ [5.6A]   **6.** $6t^5 - 8t^4 - 15t^3 + 22t^2 - 5$ [5.3B]   **7.** $35x^2 - 55x$ [5.3A]

8. $3x(2x - 3)(2x + 5)$ [5.6D]   **9.** $-1, -\dfrac{1}{6}$, and 1 [5.7A]   **10.** $2x^3 - 4x^2 + 6x - 14$ [5.2B]

11. 5.01×10^{-7} [5.1C]   **12.** $2x + 1 + \dfrac{4}{7x - 3}$ [5.4A]   **13.** $49 - 25x^2$ [5.3C]   **14.** $(2a^2 - 5)(3a^2 + 1)$ [5.6C]

15. $6a^2 - 13ab - 28b^2$ [5.3B]   **16.** $(3x^2 + 4)(x - 3)(x + 3)$ [5.6D]   **17.** $64a^7b^7$ [5.1A]   **18.** $-\dfrac{1}{3}$ and $\dfrac{1}{2}$ [5.7A]

19. -8 [5.4C]   **20.** $\dfrac{2b^7}{a^{10}}$ [5.1B]   **21.** $x^2 - 5x + 10 - \dfrac{23}{x + 3}$ [5.4A/5.4B]   **22.** $(3x - 4)(2x - 3)$ [5.5D]

23. $(3x - 2)(2x - a)$ [5.5B]   **24.** There are 6.048×10^5 s in one week. [5.1D]   **25.** The arrow will be 64 ft above the ground after 1 s and after 2 s. [5.7B]   **26.** The area is $(10x^2 - 3x - 1)$ ft². [5.3D]

CUMULATIVE REVIEW

1. 4 [1.2D]   **2.** $-\dfrac{5}{4}$ [1.3B]   **3.** Inverse Property of Addition [1.3A]   **4.** $-18x + 8$ [1.3C]   **5.** $-\dfrac{1}{6}$ [2.1A]

6. $-\dfrac{11}{4}$ [2.1B]   **7.** $x^2 + 3x + 9 + \dfrac{24}{x - 3}$ [5.4B]   **8.** -1 and $\dfrac{7}{3}$ [2.5A]   **9.** $P(-2) = 18$ [3.2A]

10. -2 is excluded from the domain. [3.2A]   **11.** Range: $\{-4, -1, 8\}$ [3.2A]   **12.** The slope is $-\dfrac{1}{6}$. [3.4A]

13. The equation of the line is $y = -\dfrac{3}{2}x + \dfrac{1}{2}$. [3.5A]   **14.** The equation of the line is $y = \dfrac{2}{3}x + \dfrac{16}{3}$. [3.6A]

15. $\left(-\dfrac{7}{5}, -\dfrac{8}{5}\right)$ [4.3B]   **16.** $\left(-\dfrac{9}{7}, \dfrac{2}{7}, \dfrac{11}{7}\right)$ [4.2B]   **17.** [3.3C]   **18.** [3.7A]

19. $(1, -1)$ [4.1A]   **20.** [4.5A]   **21.** $\dfrac{b^5}{a^8}$ [5.1B]   **22.** $\dfrac{y^2}{25x^6}$ [5.1B]

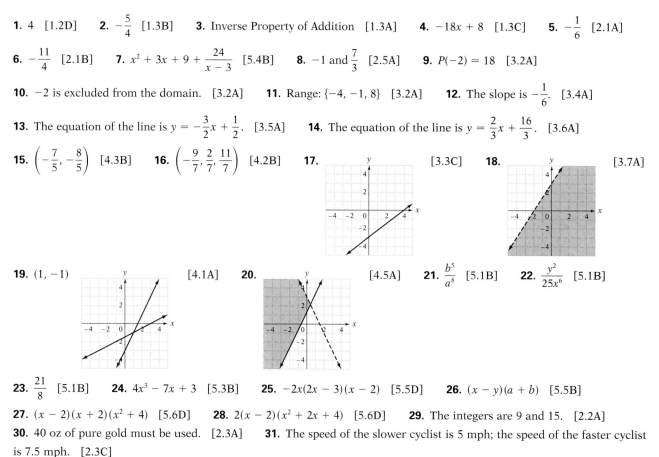

23. $\dfrac{21}{8}$ [5.1B]   **24.** $4x^3 - 7x + 3$ [5.3B]   **25.** $-2x(2x - 3)(x - 2)$ [5.5D]   **26.** $(x - y)(a + b)$ [5.5B]

27. $(x - 2)(x + 2)(x^2 + 4)$ [5.6D]   **28.** $2(x - 2)(x^2 + 2x + 4)$ [5.6D]   **29.** The integers are 9 and 15. [2.2A]
30. 40 oz of pure gold must be used. [2.3A]   **31.** The speed of the slower cyclist is 5 mph; the speed of the faster cyclist is 7.5 mph. [2.3C]

32. It takes the vehicle 12 h to reach the moon. [5.1D]   **33.** The slope is 50. The slope represents the average speed in miles per hour. [3.4A]

Answers to Chapter 6 Odd-Numbered Exercises

SECTION 6.1

1. $f(4) = 2$ **3.** $f(-2) = -2$ **5.** $f(-2) = \dfrac{1}{9}$ **7.** $f(3) = \dfrac{1}{35}$ **9.** $f(-1) = \dfrac{3}{4}$ **11.** The domain is $\{x \mid x \neq 3\}$.

13. The domain is $\{x \mid x \neq -4\}$.   **15.** The domain is $\{x \mid x \neq -3\}$.   **17.** The domain is $\left\{x \mid x \neq \dfrac{2}{3}, 4\right\}$.

19. The domain is $\{x \mid x \neq -3, 2\}$.   **21.** The domain is $\{x \mid x \in \text{real numbers}\}$.   **23.** $1 - 2x$ **25.** $3x - 1$ **27.** $2x$

29. $-\dfrac{2}{a}$ **31.** The expression is in simplest form.   **33.** $x^2y^2 - 4xy + 5$ **35.** $\dfrac{x^n}{x^n - y^n}$ **37.** $\dfrac{x-3}{x-5}$ **39.** $\dfrac{x+4}{x-4}$

41. $\dfrac{a-b}{a^2 - ab + b^2}$ **43.** $\dfrac{4x^2 + 2xy + y^2}{2x + y}$ **45.** $\dfrac{(a-2)(x+1)}{ax}$ **47.** $\dfrac{x^2 - 3}{x^2 + 1}$ **49.** $\dfrac{2xy + 1}{3xy - 1}$ **51.** $\dfrac{a^n + 4}{a^n + 1}$ **53.** $\dfrac{a^n + b^n}{a^n - b^n}$

55. $\dfrac{a+b}{(x+1)(x-1)}$ **57.** $\dfrac{abx}{2}$ **59.** $\dfrac{x}{2}$ **61.** $\dfrac{y(x-1)}{x^2(x+1)}$ **63.** $-\dfrac{x+5}{x-2}$ **65.** 1 **67.** $\dfrac{x^n + 4}{x^n - 1}$

69. $\dfrac{(x+1)(x-1)(x-4)}{x-2}$ **71.** $\dfrac{x+y}{3}$ **73.** $\dfrac{4by}{3ax}$ **75.** $\dfrac{4(x-y)^2}{9x^2y}$ **77.** $\dfrac{2x-3y}{4y^2}$ **79.** $-\dfrac{2x+5}{2x-5}$ **81.** $x(x-3)$

83. -1 **85.** $(x^n + 1)^2$ **87.** $\dfrac{(x+y)(x-y)}{x^3}$ **89.** $\dfrac{x+3}{x-3}$ **91a.** $\dfrac{5(x-4)(x+4)}{2(x-2)(x+2)(x-3)}$ **b.** $\dfrac{5(3y^2 + 2)}{y^2}$ **93.** OK

95. $\dfrac{5b^2 + 3b}{b^2} = \dfrac{\cancel{b}(5b+3)}{\cancel{b} \cdot b} = \dfrac{5b+3}{b}$ **97.** $\dfrac{(x-1)(x+4)}{x^2 + 3x + 4}$ is in simplest form.

SECTION 6.2

1. $\dfrac{9y^3}{12x^2y^4}, \dfrac{17x}{12x^2y^4}$ **3.** $\dfrac{2x^2 - 4x}{6x^2(x-2)}, \dfrac{3x - 6}{6x^2(x-2)}$ **5.** $\dfrac{3x-1}{2x(x-5)}, -\dfrac{6x^3 - 30x^2}{2x(x-5)}$ **7.** $\dfrac{6x^2 + 9x}{(2x-3)(2x+3)}, \dfrac{10x^2 - 15x}{(2x-3)(2x+3)}$

9. $\dfrac{2x}{(x+3)(x-3)}, \dfrac{x^2 + 4x + 3}{(x+3)(x-3)}$ **11.** $\dfrac{6}{6(x+2y)(x-2y)}, \dfrac{5x + 10y}{6(x+2y)(x-2y)}$ **13.** $\dfrac{3x^2 - 3x}{(x+1)(x-1)^2}, \dfrac{5x^2 + 5x}{(x+1)(x-1)^2}$

15. $-\dfrac{x-3}{(x-2)(x^2 + 2x + 4)}, \dfrac{2x-4}{(x-2)(x^2 + 2x + 4)}$ **17.** $\dfrac{2x^2 + 6x}{(x-1)(x+3)^2}, -\dfrac{x^2 - x}{(x-1)(x+3)^2}$

19. $-\dfrac{12x^2 - 8x}{(2x-3)(2x-5)(3x-2)}, \dfrac{6x^2 - 9x}{(2x-3)(2x-5)(3x-2)}$ **21.** $\dfrac{5}{(3x-4)(2x-3)}, -\dfrac{4x^2 - 6x}{(3x-4)(2x-3)}, \dfrac{3x^2 - x - 4}{(3x-4)(2x-3)}$

23. $\dfrac{2x^2 + 10x}{(x-3)(x+5)}, -\dfrac{2x-6}{(x-3)(x+5)}, -\dfrac{x-1}{(x-3)(x+5)}$ **25.** $\dfrac{x-5}{(x^n + 1)(x^n + 2)}, \dfrac{2x^{n+1} + 2x}{(x^n + 1)(x^n + 2)}$ **27.** $\dfrac{1}{2x^2}$ **29.** $\dfrac{1}{x+2}$

31. $\dfrac{12ab - 9b + 8a}{30a^2b^2}$ **33.** $\dfrac{5 - 16b + 12a}{40ab}$ **35.** $\dfrac{7}{12x}$ **37.** $\dfrac{2xy - 8x + 3y}{10x^2y^2}$ **39.** $-\dfrac{a(2a - 13)}{(a-2)(a+1)}$ **41.** $\dfrac{5x^2 - 6x + 10}{(2x-5)(5x-2)}$

43. $\dfrac{a}{b(a-b)}$ **45.** $\dfrac{a^2 + 18a - 9}{a(a-3)}$ **47.** $\dfrac{17x^2 + 20x - 25}{x(6x-5)}$ **49.** $\dfrac{6}{(x+3)(x-3)^2}$ **51.** $-\dfrac{2(x-1)}{(x+2)^2}$ **53.** $-\dfrac{5x^2 - 17x + 8}{(x+4)(x-2)}$

55. $\dfrac{3x^n + 2}{(x^n + 1)(x^n - 1)}$ **57.** 1 **59.** $\dfrac{x^2 - 52x + 160}{4(x+3)(x-3)}$ **61.** $\dfrac{3x-1}{4x+1}$ **63.** $\dfrac{2(5x-3)}{(x+3)(x+4)(x-3)}$ **65.** $\dfrac{x-2}{x+3}$

67. 1 **69.** $\dfrac{x+1}{2x-1}$ **71.** $\dfrac{1}{2x-1}$ **73.** $\dfrac{1}{x^2 + 4}$ **75.** $\dfrac{3-a}{3a}$ **77.** $-\dfrac{2x^2 + 5x - 2}{(x+2)(x+1)}$ **79.** $\dfrac{b-a}{b+2a}$ **81.** $\dfrac{2}{x+2}$

83a. $\dfrac{4x + 15}{20}$ **b.** $\dfrac{4x + 5}{4}$ **c.** $\dfrac{x+y}{xy}$ **85a.** $\dfrac{3}{y} + \dfrac{6}{x}$ **b.** $\dfrac{4}{b^2} + \dfrac{3}{ab}$ **c.** $\dfrac{1}{4mn} + \dfrac{1}{6m^2}$

SECTION 6.3

1. $\dfrac{5}{23}$ **3.** $\dfrac{2}{5}$ **5.** $\dfrac{x}{x-1}$ **7.** $-\dfrac{a}{a+2}$ **9.** $-\dfrac{a-1}{a+1}$ **11.** $\dfrac{2}{5}$ **13.** $-\dfrac{1}{2}$ **15.** $\dfrac{x^2-x-1}{x^2+x+1}$ **17.** $\dfrac{x+2}{x-1}$

19. $-\dfrac{x+4}{2x+3}$ **21.** $\dfrac{a(a^2+a+1)}{a^2+1}$ **23.** $\dfrac{x+1}{x-4}$ **25.** $\dfrac{(x-1)(x+1)}{x^2+1}$ **27.** $-\dfrac{1}{x(x+h)}$ **29.** $\dfrac{x-2}{x-3}$ **31.** $\dfrac{x-3}{x+4}$

33. $\dfrac{3x+1}{x-5}$ **35.** $-\dfrac{2a+2}{7a-4}$ **37.** $\dfrac{x+y}{x-y}$ **39.** $-\dfrac{2x}{x^2+1}$ **41.** $-\dfrac{a^2}{1-2a}$ **43.** $-\dfrac{3x+2}{x-2}$ **45.** $\dfrac{3n^2+12n+8}{n(n+2)(n+4)}$

47a. $\dfrac{2}{2+x}$ **b.** -1 **c.** $\dfrac{x-3}{x-2}$

SECTION 6.4

1. 9   **3.** $\dfrac{15}{2}$ **5.** 3   **7.** $\dfrac{10}{3}$ **9.** -2 **11.** $\dfrac{2}{5}$ **13.** -4 **15.** $\dfrac{3}{4}$ **17.** $-\dfrac{6}{5}$ **19.** -2 **21.** 6600 of the

dentists would recommend Trident.   **23.** There would be approximately 60,000 squawfish in the area.   **25.** You would expect 504 of the computers to have defective CD-ROM drives.   **27.** The dimensions of the room are 18 ft by 24 ft.   **29.** The 210-pound adult would require 0.75 additional ounces of medication.   **31.** The Postal Service would handle 175 billion pieces of mail in a year.   **33.** The complete solution is in the Solutions Manual.   **35.** The first person's share of the winnings is $1.2 million.

SECTION 6.5

1. -5 **3.** $\dfrac{5}{2}$ **5.** -1 **7.** 8   **9.** -3 **11.** -4 **13.** The equation has no solution.   **15.** -1 and $-\dfrac{5}{3}$

17. $-\dfrac{1}{3}$ and 5   **19.** $-\dfrac{11}{3}$ **21.** The equation has no solution.   **23.** $P_2 = \dfrac{P_1 V_1 T_2}{T_1 V_2}$ **25.** $b = \dfrac{af}{a-f}$ **27.** It would take the experienced bricklayer 14 h to do the job.   **29.** It would have taken the slower machine 160 min to send the fax.   **31.** With all three machines working, it would take 4 h to fill the bottles.   **33.** With both pipes open, it would take 90 min to empty the tank.   **35.** With both clowns working, it would take 120 min to have 76 balloons.   **37.** With both clerks working, it would take 2400 s to address the envelopes.   **39.** The rate of the runner is 8 mph.   **41.** The tortoise was running at 0.4 ft/s. The hare was running at 72 ft/s.   **43.** The rate of the cyclist is 10 mph.   **45.** The rate of the current is 2 mph.   **47.** The rate of the wind is 75 mph.   **49.** The rate of the wind is 60.80 mph.   **51.** The rate of the current is 2 mph.   **53a.** 3   **b.** 0 and y **c.** $3y$ and $\dfrac{3}{2}y$ **55.** The bus usually travels 60 mph.

SECTION 6.6

1. The profit is $80,000.   **3.** The pressure is 6.75 lb/in².   **5.** The object will fall 1600 ft.   **7.** The ball will roll 54 ft in 3 s.   **9.** The length is 10 ft when the width is 4 ft.   **11.** The gear will make 30 revolutions/min.   **13.** The current will be 7.5 amps.   **15.** The intensity of light will be 48 foot-candles.   **17.** y is doubled.   **19.** inversely   **21.** inversely

CHAPTER REVIEW

1. $\dfrac{1}{a-1}$ [6.1B]   **2.** $-\dfrac{5x^2-17x-9}{(x-3)(x+2)}$ [6.2B]   **3.** 4   [6.1A]   **4.** 4   [6.4A]   **5.** $-\dfrac{9x^2+16}{24x}$ [6.3A]

6. $\dfrac{16x^2+4x}{(4x-1)(4x+1)},\ \dfrac{12x^2-7x+1}{(4x-1)(4x+1)}$ [6.2A]   **7.** $r = \dfrac{S-a}{S}$ [6.5A]   **8.** $\dfrac{2}{21}$ [6.1A]   **9.** $\dfrac{2}{5}$ [6.4A]

10. The domain is $\{x \mid x \neq -3, x \neq 2\}$.   [6.1A]   **11.** $\dfrac{3x^2-1}{3x^2+1}$ [6.1A]   **12.** The domain is $\{x \mid x \neq 3\}$.   [6.1A]

13. x [6.1B]   **14.** $\dfrac{4x-1}{x+2}$ [6.2B]   **15.** $N = \dfrac{S}{1-Q}$ [6.5A]   **16.** The equation has no solution.   [6.5A]

17. $\dfrac{x}{x-3}$ [6.3A]   **18.** $\dfrac{x^2-7x+12}{(x-5)(x-4)};\ \dfrac{x}{(x-5)(x-4)};\ -\dfrac{x-5}{(x-5)(x-4)}$ [6.2A]   **19.** 10 [6.5A]   **20.** $\dfrac{1}{x}$ [6.1C]

21. $\dfrac{3x+2}{x}$ [6.1C]   **22.** $\dfrac{9x^2+x+4}{(3x-1)(x-2)}$ [6.2B]   **23.** $\dfrac{x^2+3x+9}{x+3}$ [6.1A]   **24.** $\dfrac{21a+40b}{24a^2b^4}$ [6.2B]   **25.** The rate of the helicopter is 180 mph. [6.5C]   **26.** It will take 375 min to read 150 pages. [6.4B]   **27.** The current in the circuit is 2 amps. [6.6A]   **28.** 48 mi would be represented by 12 in. [6.4B]   **29.** The stopping distance of the car is 61.2 ft. [6.6A]   **30.** It would take the apprentice 104 min working alone. [6.5B]

CHAPTER TEST

1. 2 [6.4A]   **2.** $\dfrac{x+2}{x-1}$ [6.1C]   **3.** $\dfrac{x^2-9x+3}{(x+2)(x-3)}$ [6.2B]   **4.** $\dfrac{x^2-2x-3}{(x+3)(x-3)(x-2)};\ \dfrac{2x^2-4x}{(x+3)(x-3)(x-2)}$ [6.2A]

5. No solution [6.5A]   **6.** $\dfrac{v(v+2)}{2v-1}$ [6.1A]   **7.** $\dfrac{6(x-2)}{5}$ [6.1B]   **8.** The domain is $\{x\,|\,x\neq-3,3\}$. [6.1A]

9. $\dfrac{x-4}{x+3}$ [6.3A]   **10.** $\dfrac{x+4}{x+2}$ [6.3A]   **11.** $\dfrac{x+1}{3x-4}$ [6.1C]   **12.** 1 and 2 [6.5A]   **13.** $-\dfrac{2(a-2)}{3a+2}$ [6.1A]

14. $t=\dfrac{4r}{r-2}$ [6.5A]   **15.** $f(-1)=2$ [6.1A]   **16.** $\dfrac{-x^2-5x+2}{(x+1)(x+4)(x-1)}$ [6.2B]   **17.** The rate of the cyclist is 10 mph. [6.5C]   **18.** The resistance of the cable is 0.4 ohm. [6.6A]   **19.** The designer needs 14 rolls of wallpaper. [6.4B]   **20.** It would take both landscapers 10 min to till the soil. [6.5B]

CUMULATIVE REVIEW

1. $\dfrac{36}{5}$ [1.2D]   **2.** $\dfrac{15}{2}$ [2.1C]   **3.** 7 and 1 [2.5A]   **4.** The domain is $\{x\,|\,x\neq3\}$. [6.1A]   **5.** $P(-2)=\dfrac{3}{7}$ [6.1A]

6. 3.5×10^{-8} [5.1C]   **7.** $\dfrac{a^5}{b^6}$ [5.1B]   **8.** $\{x\,|\,x\le4\}$ [2.4A]   **9.** $-4a^4+6a^3-2a^2$ [5.3A]

10. $(2x^n-1)(x^n+2)$ [5.6C]   **11.** $(xy-3)(x^2y^2+3xy+9)$ [5.6B]   **12.** $x+3y$ [6.1A]   **13.** The equation of the line is $y=\dfrac{3}{2}x+2$. [3.6A]   **14.** $\dfrac{3}{2}$ and $-\dfrac{3}{4}$ [5.7A]   **15.** $4x^2+10x+10+\dfrac{21}{x-2}$ [5.4B]   **16.** $\dfrac{3xy}{x-y}$ [6.1C]

17. $\dfrac{x^3y-2x^2y}{2x^2(x+1)(x-2)};\ \dfrac{2}{2x^2(x+1)(x-2)}$ [6.2A]   **18.** $-\dfrac{x}{(3x+2)(x+1)}$ [6.2B]   **19.**

[3.3C]

20.

[4.5A]   **21.** The value of the determinant is -28. [4.3A]   **22.** $\dfrac{x-3}{x+3}$ [6.3A]

23. $(1,1,1)$ [4.3B]   **24.** $\left\{x\,\middle|\,x<-\dfrac{2}{3}\text{ or }x>2\right\}$ [2.5B]   **25.** 9 [6.4A]   **26.** 13 [6.5A]   **27.** $r=\dfrac{E-IR}{I}$ [2.1D]

28. $\dfrac{x}{x-1}$ [5.1B]   **29.** The integers are 5 and 10. [2.2A]   **30.** The mixture must contain 50 lb of almonds. [2.3A]

31. The number of people expected to vote is 75,000. [6.4B]   **32.** The new computer would complete the job in 14 min. [6.5B]   **33.** The rate of the wind is 60 mph. [6.5C]   **34.** The second person has made 12 laps and is at the starting point. The first person has made 20 laps and is at the starting point. [2.3C]

Answers to Chapter 7 Odd-Numbered Exercises

SECTION 7.1

1. 2   **3.** 27   **5.** $\dfrac{1}{9}$ **7.** 4   **9.** $(-25)^{5/2}$ is not a real number.   **11.** $\dfrac{343}{125}$ **13.** x **15.** $y^{1/2}$ **17.** $x^{1/12}$

19. $a^{7/12}$ **21.** $\dfrac{1}{a}$ **23.** $\dfrac{1}{y}$ **25.** $y^{3/2}$ **27.** $\dfrac{1}{x}$ **29.** $\dfrac{1}{x^4}$ **31.** a **33.** $x^{3/10}$ **35.** a^3 **37.** $\dfrac{1}{x^{1/2}}$ **39.** $y^{1/9}$

41. $x^4 y$ **43.** $x^6 y^3 z^9$ **45.** $\dfrac{x}{y^2}$ **47.** $\dfrac{x^{3/2}}{y^{1/4}}$ **49.** $\dfrac{x^2}{y^8}$ **51.** $\dfrac{1}{x^{11/12}}$ **53.** $\dfrac{1}{y^{5/2}}$ **55.** $\dfrac{1}{b^{7/8}}$ **57.** $a^5 b^{13}$ **59.** $\dfrac{m^2}{4n^{3/2}}$

61. $\dfrac{y^{17/2}}{x^3}$ **63.** $\dfrac{16b^2}{a^{1/3}}$ **65.** $y^2 - y$ **67.** $a - a^2$ **69.** x^{4n} **71.** $x^{3n/2}$ **73.** $y^{3n/2}$ **75.** x^{2n^2} **77.** $x^{2n} y^n$

79. $x^{4n} y^{2n}$ **81.** $\sqrt[4]{3}$ **83.** $\sqrt{a^3}$ **85.** $\sqrt{32t^5}$ **87.** $-2\sqrt[3]{x^2}$ **89.** $\sqrt[3]{a^4 b^2}$ **91.** $\sqrt[5]{a^6 b^{12}}$ **93.** $\sqrt[4]{(4x-3)^3}$

95. $\dfrac{1}{\sqrt[3]{x^2}}$ **97.** $14^{1/2}$ **99.** $x^{1/3}$ **101.** $x^{4/3}$ **103.** $b^{3/5}$ **105.** $(2x^2)^{1/3}$ **107.** $-(3x^5)^{1/2}$ **109.** $3xy^{2/3}$

111. $(a^2 - 2)^{1/2}$ **113.** x^8 **115.** $-x^4$ **117.** xy^3 **119.** $-x^5 y$ **121.** $4a^2 b^6$ **123.** $\sqrt{-16x^4 y^2}$ is not a real number.
125. $3x^3$ **127.** $-4x^3 y^4$ **129.** $-x^2 y^3$ **131.** $x^4 y^2$ **133.** $3xy^5$ **135.** $2ab^2$ **137a.** False; 2   **b.** True   **c.** True
d. False; $(a^n + b^n)^{1/n}$ **e.** False; $a + 2a^{1/2} b^{1/2} + b$ **f.** False; $a^{n/m}$

SECTION 7.2

1. $x^2 yz^2 \sqrt{yz}$ **3.** $2ab^4 \sqrt{2a}$ **5.** $3xyz^2 \sqrt{5yz}$ **7.** $\sqrt{-9x^3}$ is not a real number.   **9.** $a^5 b^2 \sqrt[3]{ab^2}$ **11.** $-5y\sqrt[3]{x^2 y}$
13. $abc^2 \sqrt[3]{ab^2}$ **15.** $2x^2 y \sqrt[4]{xy}$ **17.** $-6\sqrt{x}$ **19.** $-2\sqrt{2}$ **21.** $3\sqrt{2b} + 5\sqrt{3b}$ **23.** $-2xy\sqrt{2y}$
25. $6ab^2\sqrt{3ab} + 3ab\sqrt{3ab}$ **27.** $-\sqrt[3]{2}$ **29.** $8b\sqrt[3]{2b^2}$ **31.** $3a\sqrt[4]{2a}$ **33.** $17\sqrt{2} - 15\sqrt{5}$ **35.** $5b\sqrt{b}$
37. $-8xy\sqrt{2x} + 2xy\sqrt{xy}$ **39.** $2y\sqrt[3]{2x}$ **41.** $-4ab\sqrt[4]{2b}$ **43.** 16   **45.** $2\sqrt[3]{4}$ **47.** $xy^3 \sqrt{x}$ **49.** $8xy\sqrt{x}$
51. $2x^2 y\sqrt[3]{2}$ **53.** $2ab\sqrt[3]{3a^2 b}$ **55.** 6   **57.** $x - \sqrt{2x}$ **59.** $4x - 8\sqrt{x}$ **61.** $x - 6\sqrt{x} + 9$ **63.** $84 + 16\sqrt{5}$
65. $672x^2 y^2$ **67.** $4a^3 b^3 \sqrt[3]{a}$ **69.** $-8\sqrt{5}$ **71.** $x - y^2$ **73.** $12x - y$ **75.** $y\sqrt{5y}$ **77.** $b\sqrt{13b}$ **79.** $\dfrac{\sqrt{2}}{2}$

81. $\dfrac{2\sqrt{3y}}{3y}$ **83.** $\dfrac{3\sqrt{3a}}{a}$ **85.** $\dfrac{\sqrt{2y}}{2}$ **87.** $\dfrac{5\sqrt[3]{3}}{3}$ **89.** $\dfrac{5\sqrt[3]{9y^2}}{3y}$ **91.** $\dfrac{b\sqrt{2a}}{2a^2}$ **93.** $\dfrac{\sqrt{15x}}{5x}$ **95.** $2 + 2\sqrt{2}$

97. $-\dfrac{12 + 4\sqrt{2}}{7}$ **99.** $-\dfrac{10 + 5\sqrt{7}}{3}$ **101.** $-\dfrac{7\sqrt{x} + 21}{x - 9}$ **103.** $-\sqrt{6} + 3 - 2\sqrt{2} + 2\sqrt{3}$ **105.** $-\dfrac{17 + 5\sqrt{5}}{4}$

107. $\dfrac{8a - 10\sqrt{ab} + 3b}{16a - 9b}$ **109.** $\dfrac{3 - 7\sqrt{y} + 2y}{1 - 4y}$ **111a.** False; $\sqrt[6]{432}$ **b.** True   **c.** False; $\sqrt[3]{x} \cdot \sqrt[3]{x} = x^{2/3}$

d. False; $\sqrt{x} + \sqrt{y}$ **e.** False; $\sqrt[2]{2} + \sqrt[3]{3}$ **f.** True   **113a.** $14\sqrt{2} - 20$ **b.** $\dfrac{2\sqrt{x+4} - 4}{x}$ **c.** $\dfrac{b + 18 - 6\sqrt{b+9}}{b}$

SECTION 7.3

1. $2i$ **3.** $7i\sqrt{2}$ **5.** $3i\sqrt{3}$ **7.** $4 + 2i$ **9.** $2\sqrt{3} - 3i\sqrt{2}$ **11.** $4\sqrt{10} - 7i\sqrt{3}$ **13.** $8 - i$ **15.** $-8 + 4i$
17. $6 - 6i$ **19.** $19 - 7i\sqrt{2}$ **21.** $6\sqrt{2} - 3i\sqrt{2}$ **23.** 63   **25.** -4 **27.** $-3\sqrt{2}$ **29.** $-4 + 12i$ **31.** $-2 + 4i$

33. $17 - i$ **35.** $8 + 27i$ **37.** 1   **39.** 1   **41.** $-3i$ **43.** $\dfrac{3}{4} + \dfrac{1}{2}i$ **45.** $\dfrac{10}{13} - \dfrac{2}{13}i$ **47.** $\dfrac{4}{5} + \dfrac{2}{5}i$ **49.** $-i$

51. $-\dfrac{\sqrt{5}}{5} + \dfrac{2\sqrt{5}}{5}i$ **53.** $\dfrac{3}{10} - \dfrac{11}{10}i$ **55.** $\dfrac{6}{5} + \dfrac{7}{5}i$ **57a.** $(y + i)(y - i)$ **b.** $(7x + 4i)(7x - 4i)$

c. $(3a + 8i)(3a - 8i)$ **59.** $-\dfrac{\sqrt{2}}{2} + \dfrac{\sqrt{2}}{2}i$

SECTION 7.4

1. -2 **3.** 9 **5.** 7 **7.** $\dfrac{13}{3}$ **9.** 35 **11.** -7 **13.** -12 **15.** 9 **17.** 2 **19.** 2 **21.** 1 **23.** The object will fall 576 ft.   **25.** The HDTV screen is 7.15 in. wider.   **27.** The length of the pendulum is 7.30 ft.   **29.** 2
31a. $A = \dfrac{s^2 + s^2\sqrt{5}}{2}$ **b.** $\dfrac{1 + \sqrt{5}}{2}$ **33.** The length of the side labeled x is $\sqrt{6}$.

CHAPTER REVIEW

1. $20x^2y^2$ [7.1A]   **2.** 7 [7.4A]   **3.** $39 - 2i$ [7.3C]   **4.** $7x^{2/3}y$ [7.1B]   **5.** $6\sqrt{3} - 13$ [7.2C]   **6.** -2 [7.4A]
7. $\dfrac{1}{x^5}$ [7.1A]   **8.** $\dfrac{8\sqrt{3y}}{3y}$ [7.2D]   **9.** $-2a^2b^4$ [7.1C]   **10.** $2a^2b\sqrt{2b}$ [7.2B]
11. $\dfrac{x\sqrt{x} - x\sqrt{2} + 2\sqrt{x} - 2\sqrt{2}}{x - 2}$ [7.2D]   **12.** $\dfrac{2}{3} - \dfrac{5}{3}i$ [7.3D]   **13.** $3ab^3\sqrt{2a}$ [7.2A]   **14.** $-4\sqrt{2} + 8i\sqrt{2}$ [7.3B]
15. $5x^3y^3\sqrt[3]{2x^2y}$ [7.2B]   **16.** $4xy^2\sqrt[3]{x^2}$ [7.2C]   **17.** $7 + 3i$ [7.3C]   **18.** $3\sqrt[4]{x^3}$ [7.1B]   **19.** $-2ab^2\sqrt[5]{2a^3b^2}$ [7.2A]
20. $-2 + 7i$ [7.3D]   **21.** $-6\sqrt{2}$ [7.3C]   **22.** 30 [7.4A]   **23.** $3a^2b^3$ [7.1C]   **24.** $5i\sqrt{2}$ [7.3A]
25. $-12 + 10i$ [7.3B]   **26.** $31 - 10\sqrt{6}$ [7.2C]   **27.** $6x^2\sqrt{3y}$ [7.2B]   **28.** The amount of power generated is 120 watts. [7.4B]   **29.** The distance required to reach a velocity of 88 ft/s is 242 ft. [7.4B]   **30.** The bottom of the ladder is 6.63 ft from the building. [7.4B]

CHAPTER TEST

1. $\dfrac{1}{2}x^{3/4}$ [7.1B]   **2.** $-2x^2y\sqrt[3]{2x}$ [7.2B]   **3.** $3\sqrt[5]{y^2}$ [7.1B]   **4.** $18 + 16i$ [7.3C]   **5.** $4x + 4\sqrt{xy} + y$ [7.2C]
6. $r^{1/6}$ [7.1A]   **7.** 4 [7.4A]   **8.** $2xy^2$ [7.1C]   **9.** $-4x\sqrt{3}$ [7.2C]   **10.** $-3 + 2i$ [7.3B]   **11.** $4x^2y^3\sqrt{2y}$ [7.2A]
12. $14 + 10\sqrt{3}$ [7.2C]   **13.** $10 + 2i$ [7.3C]   **14.** 2 [7.2D]   **15.** $8a\sqrt{2a}$ [7.2B]   **16.** $2a - \sqrt{ab} - 15b$ [7.2C]
17. $\dfrac{64x^3}{y^6}$ [7.1A]   **18.** $\dfrac{x + \sqrt{xy}}{x - y}$ [7.2D]   **19.** $-\dfrac{4}{5} + \dfrac{7}{5}i$ [7.3D]   **20.** -3 [7.4A]   **21.** $\dfrac{b^3}{8a^6}$ [7.1A]
22. $3abc^2\sqrt[3]{ac}$ [7.2A]   **23.** $\dfrac{4x^2}{y}$ [7.2D]   **24.** -4 [7.3C]   **25.** The object has fallen 576 ft. [7.4B]

CUMULATIVE REVIEW

1. Distributive Property [1.3A]   **2.** 34 [3.2A]   **3.** $\dfrac{3}{2}$ [2.1B]   **4.** $\dfrac{2}{3}$ [2.1C]   **5.** $\dfrac{1}{3}$ and $\dfrac{7}{3}$ [2.5A]
6. $\{x \mid x > 1\}$ [2.4A]   **7.** $\{x \mid -6 \le x \le 3\}$ [2.5B]   **8.** $(9x + y)(9x - y)$ [5.6A]   **9.** $x(x^2 + 3)(x + 1)(x - 1)$ [5.6D]
10. The equation of the line is $y = \dfrac{1}{3}x + \dfrac{7}{3}$. [3.5B]   **11.** The value of the determinant is 3. [4.3A]
12. $C = R - nP$ [2.1D]   **13.** $2x^2y^2$ [5.1B]   **14.** $\dfrac{x(2x - 3)}{y(x + 4)}$ [6.1B]   **15.** $-x\sqrt{10x}$ [7.2B]   **16.** $-\dfrac{1}{2}$ and 3 [6.5A]
17. $m = \dfrac{3}{2}$, $b = 3$ [3.4B]   **18.**   [3.7A]   **19.** $-\dfrac{1}{5} + \dfrac{3}{5}i$ [7.3D]

20. -20 [7.4A]   **21.** $\dfrac{x^2 + 12x - 12}{(2x - 3)(x + 4)}$ [6.2B]   **22.** $\left(\dfrac{17}{4}, \dfrac{9}{2}\right)$ [4.3B]   **23.** There are nineteen 18¢ stamps in the collection.   [2.2B]   **24.** The rate of the plane was 250 mph.   [2.3C]   **25.** Light travels to the earth from the moon in 1.25 s. [5.1D]   **26.** The periscope would have to be 32.7 ft above the surface of the water. [7.4B]   **27.** The slope is 0.08. The slope indicates that the annual income is 8% of the investment. [3.4A]

Answers to Chapter 8 Odd-Numbered Exercises

SECTION 8.1

1. 0 and 4   **3.** 5 and -5 **5.** 3 and -2 **7.** 3   **9.** 0 and 2   **11.** 5 and -2 **13.** 2 and 5   **15.** 6 and $-\dfrac{3}{2}$

17. 2 and $\dfrac{1}{4}$ **19.** $\dfrac{1}{3}$ and -4 **21.** $\dfrac{9}{2}$ and $-\dfrac{2}{3}$ **23.** $\dfrac{1}{4}$ and -4 **25.** 9 and -2 **27.** -2 and $-\dfrac{3}{4}$ **29.** 2 and -5

31. -4 and $-\dfrac{3}{2}$ **33.** $2b$ and $7b$ **35.** $7c$ and $-c$ **37.** $-\dfrac{b}{2}$ and $-b$ **39.** $4a$ and $\dfrac{2a}{3}$ **41.** $-\dfrac{a}{3}$ and $3a$

43. $-\dfrac{3y}{2}$ and $-\dfrac{y}{2}$ **45.** $-\dfrac{a}{2}$ and $-\dfrac{4a}{3}$ **47.** $x^2 - 7x + 10 = 0$ **49.** $x^2 + 6x + 8 = 0$ **51.** $x^2 - 5x - 6 = 0$

53. $x^2 - 9 = 0$ **55.** $x^2 - 8x + 16 = 0$ **57.** $x^2 - 5x = 0$ **59.** $x^2 - 3x = 0$ **61.** $2x^2 - 7x + 3 = 0$

63. $4x^2 - 5x - 6 = 0$ **65.** $3x^2 + 11x + 10 = 0$ **67.** $9x^2 - 4 = 0$ **69.** $6x^2 - 5x + 1 = 0$ **71.** $10x^2 - 7x - 6 = 0$

73. $8x^2 + 6x + 1 = 0$ **75.** $50x^2 - 25x - 3 = 0$ **77.** 7 and -7 **79.** $2i$ and $-2i$ **81.** 2 and -2 **83.** $\dfrac{9}{2}$ and $-\dfrac{9}{2}$

85. $7i$ and $-7i$ **87.** $4\sqrt{3}$ and $-4\sqrt{3}$ **89.** $5\sqrt{3}$ and $-5\sqrt{3}$ **91.** $3i\sqrt{2}$ and $-3i\sqrt{2}$ **93.** 7 and -5

95. 0 and -6 **97.** -7 and 3   **99.** 1 and 0   **101.** $-5 + \sqrt{6}$ and $-5 - \sqrt{6}$ **103.** $3 + 3i\sqrt{5}$ and $3 - 3i\sqrt{5}$

105. $-\dfrac{2 - 9\sqrt{2}}{3}$ and $-\dfrac{2 + 9\sqrt{2}}{3}$ **107.** $x^2 - 2 = 0$ **109.** $x^2 + 1 = 0$ **111.** $x^2 - 8 = 0$ **113.** $x^2 + 2 = 0$

115. $\dfrac{3b}{a}$ and $-\dfrac{3b}{a}$ **117.** $-a + 2$ and $-a - 2$ **119.** $-\dfrac{1}{2}$

SECTION 8.2

1. 5 and -1 **3.** -9 and 1   **5.** 3   **7.** $-2 + \sqrt{11}$ and $-2 - \sqrt{11}$ **9.** $3 + \sqrt{2}$ and $3 - \sqrt{2}$ **11.** $1 + i$ and $1 - i$

13. 8 and -3 **15.** 4 and -9 **17.** $\dfrac{3 + \sqrt{5}}{2}$ and $\dfrac{3 - \sqrt{5}}{2}$ **19.** $\dfrac{1 + \sqrt{5}}{2}$ and $\dfrac{1 - \sqrt{5}}{2}$ **21.** $3 + \sqrt{13}$ and $3 - \sqrt{13}$

23. 5 and 3   **25.** $2 + 3i$ and $2 - 3i$ **27.** $-3 + 2i$ and $-3 - 2i$ **29.** $1 + 3\sqrt{2}$ and $1 - 3\sqrt{2}$

31. $\dfrac{1 + \sqrt{17}}{2}$ and $\dfrac{1 - \sqrt{17}}{2}$ **33.** $1 + 2i\sqrt{3}$ and $1 - 2i\sqrt{3}$ **35.** $\dfrac{1}{2} + i$ and $\dfrac{1}{2} - i$ **37.** $\dfrac{1}{3} + \dfrac{1}{3}i$ and $\dfrac{1}{3} - \dfrac{1}{3}i$

39. $\dfrac{2 + \sqrt{14}}{2}$ and $\dfrac{2 - \sqrt{14}}{2}$ **41.** 1 and $-\dfrac{3}{2}$ **43.** $1 + \sqrt{5}$ and $1 - \sqrt{5}$ **45.** $\dfrac{1}{2}$ and 5   **47.** $2 + \sqrt{5}$ and $2 - \sqrt{5}$

53. 5.317 and -1.317 **55.** $-a$ and $2a$ **57.** $-5a$ and $2a$ **59.** No. The ball will have gone only 197.2 ft when it hits the ground.

SECTION 8.3

1. 5 and -2 **3.** 4 and -9 **5.** $4 + 2\sqrt{22}$ and $4 - 2\sqrt{22}$ **7.** 3 and -8 **9.** -3 and $\dfrac{1}{2}$ **11.** $\dfrac{3}{2}$ and $-\dfrac{1}{4}$

13. 2 and 12   **15.** $\dfrac{1 + \sqrt{3}}{2}$ and $\dfrac{1 - \sqrt{3}}{2}$ **17.** $-1 + i$ and $-1 - i$ **19.** $1 + 2i$ and $1 - 2i$ **21.** $2 + 3i$ and $2 - 3i$

23. $\dfrac{1}{2} + \dfrac{3}{2}i$ and $\dfrac{1}{2} - \dfrac{3}{2}i$ **25.** $-\dfrac{3}{2} + \dfrac{1}{2}i$ and $-\dfrac{3}{2} - \dfrac{1}{2}i$ **27.** $\dfrac{3}{4} + \dfrac{3\sqrt{3}}{4}i$ and $\dfrac{3}{4} - \dfrac{3\sqrt{3}}{4}i$ **29.** Two complex number solutions

31. One real number solution   **33.** Two real number solutions   **35.** $\{p \mid p < 9\}$ **37.** $\{p \mid p > 1\}$ **41.** Yes

43a. $x = 1.05$; will increase   **b.** $x = 0.96$; will decrease

SECTION 8.4

1. 3, −3, 2, and −2   **3.** $\sqrt{2}$, $-\sqrt{2}$, 2, and −2   **5.** 1 and 4   **7.** 16   **9.** $2i$, $-2i$, 1, and −1   **11.** $4i$, $-4i$, 2, and −2

13. 16   **15.** 1 and 512   **17.** $\frac{2}{3}$, $-\frac{2}{3}$, 1, and −1   **19.** 3   **21.** 9   **23.** 2 and −1   **25.** 0 and 2   **27.** 2 and $-\frac{1}{2}$

29. −2   **31.** 1   **33.** 1   **35.** −3   **37.** 10 and −1   **39.** $-\frac{1}{2}+\frac{\sqrt{7}}{2}i$ and $-\frac{1}{2}-\frac{\sqrt{7}}{2}i$ **41.** 1 and −3

43. 0 and −1   **45.** $\frac{1}{2}$ and $-\frac{1}{3}$ **47.** $-\frac{2}{3}$ and 6   **49.** $\frac{4}{3}$ and 3   **51.** $-\frac{1}{4}$ and 3   **53.** 0 and 36

SECTION 8.5

1. $\{x \mid x < -2 \text{ or } x > 4\}$ **3.** $\{x \mid x \le 1 \text{ or } x \ge 2\}$

5. $\{x \mid -3 < x < 4\}$ **7.** $\{x \mid x < -2 \text{ or } 1 < x < 3\}$

9. $\{x \mid -4 \le x \le 1 \text{ or } x \ge 2\}$ **11.** $\{x \mid x < -2 \text{ or } x > 4\}$

13. $\{x \mid -1 < x \le 3\}$ **15.** $\{x \mid x \le -2 \text{ or } 1 \le x < 3\}$

17. $\{x \mid x > 4 \text{ or } x < -4\}$ **19.** $\{x \mid -3 \le x \le 12\}$ **21.** $\left\{x \mid \frac{1}{2} < x < \frac{3}{2}\right\}$ **23.** $\left\{x \mid x < 1 \text{ or } x > \frac{5}{2}\right\}$

25. $\{x \mid x < -1 \text{ or } 1 < x \le 2\}$ **27.** $\left\{x \mid \frac{1}{2} < x \le 1\right\}$ **29.** $\{x \mid 2 < x \le 3\}$ **31.** $\{x \mid x > 5 \text{ or } -4 < x < -1\}$

33.   **35.**   **37.**

39.

SECTION 8.6

1. The height is 3 cm; the base is 14 cm.   **3.** The length is 13 ft; the width is 5 ft.   **5.** The dimensions of Colorado are approximately 272 mi by 383 mi.   **7.** The cardboard is 90 cm by 90 cm.   **9.** The projectile is 64 ft above the ground in 0.54 s or in 7.46 s.   **11.** The smaller pipe requires 12 min. The larger pipe requires 6 min.   **13.** The rate of the wind is 108 mph.   **15.** The rowing rate of the guide is 6 mph.   **17.** The Internet revenue will be $200 billion in the year 2001. A negative value of t would produce a year that is not in the domain of the equation.

CHAPTER REVIEW

1. 0 and $\frac{3}{2}$ [8.1A]   **2.** $\frac{c}{2}$ and $-2c$ [8.1A]   **3.** $4\sqrt{3}$ and $-4\sqrt{3}$ [8.1C]   **4.** $-\frac{1}{2}+2i$ and $-\frac{1}{2}-2i$ [8.1C]

5. −3 and −1   [8.2A]   **6.** $\frac{7+2\sqrt{7}}{7}$ and $\frac{7-2\sqrt{7}}{7}$ [8.2A]   **7.** $\frac{3}{4}$ and $\frac{4}{3}$ [8.3A]   **8.** $\frac{1}{2}+\frac{\sqrt{31}}{2}i$ and $\frac{1}{2}-\frac{\sqrt{31}}{2}i$ [8.3A]

9. $x^2+3x=0$ [8.1B]   **10.** $12x^2-x-6=0$ [8.1B]   **11.** $1+i\sqrt{7}$ and $1-i\sqrt{7}$ [8.2A]   **12.** $2i$ and $-2i$ [8.2A]

13. $\frac{11+\sqrt{73}}{6}$ and $\frac{11-\sqrt{73}}{6}$ [8.3A]   **14.** Two real number solutions   [8.3A]   **15.** $\left\{x \mid -3 < x < \frac{5}{2}\right\}$ [8.5A]

16. $\left\{x \mid x \le -4 \text{ or } -\frac{3}{2} \le x \le 2\right\}$ [8.5A]   **17.** 27 and −64   [8.4A]   **18.** $\frac{5}{4}$ [8.4B]   **19.** −1 and 3   [8.4C]

20. −1   [8.4C]   **21.**   [8.5A]   **22.**   [8.5A]   **23.** 4   [8.4B]

$\left\{x \mid x < \frac{3}{2} \text{ or } x \ge 2\right\}$ $\left\{x \mid x \le -3 \text{ or } \frac{1}{2} \le x < 4\right\}$

24. 5   [8.4B]   **25.** $\frac{-3+\sqrt{249}}{10}$ and $\frac{-3-\sqrt{249}}{10}$ [8.4C]   **26.** $\frac{-11+\sqrt{129}}{2}$ and $\frac{-11-\sqrt{129}}{2}$ [8.4C]   **27.** The length is 12 cm; the width is 5 cm. [8.6A] **28.** The integers are 2, 4, and 6 or -6, -4, and -2. [8.6A] **29.** It takes the computer 12 min. [8.6A] **30.** The first car is traveling 40 mph; the second car is traveling 50 mph. [8.6A]

CHAPTER TEST

1. $\frac{2}{3}$ and -4 [8.1A] **2.** $\frac{3}{2}$ and $-\frac{2}{3}$ [8.1A] **3.** $x^2 - 9 = 0$ [8.1B] **4.** $2x^2 + 7x - 4 = 0$ [8.1B]

5. $2 + 2\sqrt{2}$ and $2 - 2\sqrt{2}$ [8.1C] **6.** $3 + \sqrt{11}$ and $3 - \sqrt{11}$ [8.2A] **7.** $\frac{3 + \sqrt{15}}{3}$ and $\frac{3 - \sqrt{15}}{3}$ [8.2A]

8. $\frac{1 + \sqrt{3}}{2}$ and $\frac{1 - \sqrt{3}}{2}$ [8.3A] **9.** $-2 + 2i\sqrt{2}$ and $-2 - 2i\sqrt{2}$ [8.3A] **10.** Two real number solutions [8.3A]

11. Two complex number solutions [8.3A] **12.** $\frac{1}{4}$ [8.4A] **13.** $1, -1, \sqrt{3}$, and $-\sqrt{3}$ [8.4A] **14.** 4 [8.4B]

15. No solution [8.4B] **16.** 2 and -9 [8.4C] **17.** $\{x \mid x < -4 \text{ or } 2 < x < 4\}$ [8.5A]

18. $\left\{x \mid -4 < x \leq \frac{3}{2}\right\}$ [8.5A] **19.** The base is 15 ft. The height is 4 ft. [8.6A] **20.** The rowing rate of the canoe in calm water is 4 mph. [8.6A]

CUMULATIVE REVIEW

1. 14 [1.3B] **2.** -28 [2.1C] **3.** $-\frac{3}{2}$ [3.4A] **4.** $y = x + 1$ [3.6A] **5.** $-3xy(x^2 - 2xy + 3y^2)$ [5.5A]

6. $(2x - 5)(3x + 4)$ [5.5D] **7.** $(x + y)(a^n - 2)$ [5.5B] **8.** $x^2 - 3x - 4 - \frac{6}{3x - 4}$ [5.4A] **9.** $\frac{x}{2}$ [6.1B]

10. $2\sqrt{5}$ [3.1B] **11.** $b = \frac{2S - an}{n}$ [2.1D] **12.** $-8 - 14i$ [7.3C] **13.** $1 - a$ [7.1A] **14.** $\frac{x\sqrt[3]{4y^2}}{2y}$ [7.2D]

15. $-\frac{3}{2}$ and -1 [8.4C] **16.** $-\frac{1}{2}$ [6.5A] **17.** $2, -2, \sqrt{2}$, and $-\sqrt{2}$ [8.4A] **18.** 0 and 1 [8.4B]

19. $\left\{x \mid -2 < x < \frac{10}{3}\right\}$ [2.5B] **20.** $\left(\frac{5}{2}, 0\right)$; $(0, -3)$ [3.3C] **21.** [4.5A] **22.** $(1, -1, 2)$ [4.2B]

23. $f(-2) = -\frac{7}{3}$ [6.1A] **24.** $\{x \mid x \neq -3, 5\}$ [6.1A] **25.** $\{x \mid x < -3 \text{ or } 0 < x < 2\}$ [8.5A]

26. $\{x \mid -3 < x \leq 1 \text{ or } x \geq 5\}$ [8.5A] **27.** Lower limit: $9\frac{23}{64}$ in.; upper limit: $9\frac{25}{64}$ in. [2.5C]

28. The area of the triangle is $(x^2 + 6x - 16)$ ft^2. [5.3D] **29.** Two complex number solutions [8.3A]

30. The slope is $-\frac{25{,}000}{3}$. The slope indicates that the building decreases $\frac{\$25{,}000}{3}$ in value each year. [3.4A]

Answers to Chapter 9 Odd-Numbered Exercises

SECTION 9.1

1.
Vertex: $(1, -5)$
Axis of symmetry: $x = 1$

3.
Vertex: $(1, -2)$
Axis of symmetry: $x = 1$

5.
Vertex: $(-3, -4)$
Axis of symmetry: $x = -3$

7.
Vertex: $\left(\dfrac{1}{2}, -\dfrac{9}{4}\right)$
Axis of symmetry: $x = \dfrac{1}{2}$

9.
Vertex: $(1, -1)$
Axis of symmetry: $x = 1$

11.
Vertex: $(-2, 1)$
Axis of symmetry: $x = -2$

13.
Vertex: $(0, 4)$
Axis of symmetry: $x = 0$

15.
Vertex: $\left(1, \dfrac{1}{2}\right)$
Axis of symmetry: $x = 1$

17.
Vertex: $(-2, -8)$
Axis of symmetry: $x = -2$

19. $(2, 0)$ and $(-2, 0)$ **21.** $(0, 0)$ and $(2, 0)$ **23.** $(2, 0)$ and $(-1, 0)$ **25.** $\left(-\dfrac{1}{2}, 0\right)$ and $(1, 0)$

27. $(-1 + \sqrt{2}, 0)$ and $(-1 - \sqrt{2}, 0)$ **29.** No x-intercepts   **31.** $(1 + \sqrt{3}, 0)$ and $(1 - \sqrt{3}, 0)$

33. $(2 + \sqrt{5}, 0)$ and $(2 - \sqrt{5}, 0)$ **35.** 3   **37.** $\dfrac{3 + \sqrt{41}}{2}$ and $\dfrac{3 - \sqrt{41}}{2}$ **39.** 0 and $\dfrac{4}{3}$ **41.** $i\sqrt{2}$ and $-i\sqrt{2}$

43. $\dfrac{1}{6} + \dfrac{\sqrt{47}}{6}i$ and $\dfrac{1}{6} - \dfrac{\sqrt{47}}{6}i$ **45.** $\dfrac{1 + \sqrt{41}}{4}$ and $\dfrac{1 - \sqrt{41}}{4}$ **47.** Two x-intercepts   **49.** Two x-intercepts

51. One x-intercept   **53.** No x-intercepts   **55.** No x-intercepts   **57.** No x-intercepts   **59.** No x-intercepts

61. minimum, 2   **63.** maximum, -1 **65.** minimum, -2 **67.** maximum, -3 **69.** minimum, $-\dfrac{73}{8}$

71. minimum, $-\dfrac{11}{4}$ **73.** maximum, $-\dfrac{2}{3}$ **75.** minimum, $-\dfrac{1}{12}$ **77.** The maximum height is 13.1 m.

79. The minimum height of the cable is 24.36 ft.   **81.** The minimum thickness is 20.21 in.   **83.** No. The ball will not

clear the fence.   **85.** The dimensions are $1\dfrac{3}{4}$ ft by $2\dfrac{1}{3}$ ft.   **89.**

93a. $y = (x - 2)^2 + 3$; $(2, 3)$ **b.** $y = (x - 1)^2 - 3$; $(1, -3)$ **c.** $y = (x - 3)^2 - 6$; $(3, -6)$

d. $y = (x + 2)^2 - 5$; $(-2, -5)$ **e.** $y = \left(x + \dfrac{1}{2}\right)^2 + \dfrac{7}{4}$; $\left(-\dfrac{1}{2}, \dfrac{7}{4}\right)$ **f.** $y = \left(x - \dfrac{1}{2}\right)^2 - \dfrac{13}{4}$; $\left(\dfrac{1}{2}, -\dfrac{13}{4}\right)$

SECTION 9.2

1. Yes   **3.** No   **5.** Yes   **7.** Domain: $\{x \mid x \text{ is a real number}\}$; range: $\{y \mid y \geq 0\}$

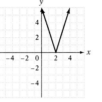

9. Domain: $\{x \mid x \text{ is a real number}\}$; range: $\{y \mid y \text{ is a real number}\}$ **11.** Domain: $\{x \mid x \leq 4\}$; range: $\{y \mid y \geq 0\}$

13. Domain: $\{x \mid x \text{ is a real number}\}$; range: $\{y \mid y \text{ is a real number}\}$ **15.** Domain: $\{x \mid x \geq -2\}$; range: $\{y \mid y \leq 0\}$

17. Domain: $\{x \mid x \text{ is a real number}\}$; range: $\{y \mid y \geq 0\}$ **19.** $a = 18$ **21.** $f(2, 5) + g(2, 5) = 17$ **23.** $f(14) = 8$

25. $\{x \mid -2 < x < 2\}$ **27.** $x = 1$

SECTION 9.3

1. $f(2) - g(2) = 5$ **3.** $f(0) + g(0) = 1$ **5.** $(f \cdot g)(2) = 0$ **7.** $\left(\dfrac{f}{g}\right)(4) = -\dfrac{29}{4}$ **9.** $\left(\dfrac{g}{f}\right)(-3) = \dfrac{2}{3}$ **11.** $f(1) + g(1) = 2$

13. $f(4) - g(4) = 39$ **15.** $(f \cdot g)(1) = -8$ **17.** $\left(\dfrac{f}{g}\right)(-3) = -\dfrac{4}{5}$ **19.** $f(2) - g(2) = -2$ **21.** $\left(\dfrac{f}{g}\right)(-2) = 7$

23. $g[f(0)] = -13$ **25.** $g[f(-2)] = -29$ **27.** $g[f(x)] = 8x - 13$ **29.** $f[h(0)] = 4$ **31.** $f[h(-1)] = 3$

33. $f[h(x)] = x + 4$ **35.** $h[g(0)] = 1$ **37.** $h[g(-2)] = 5$ **39.** $h[g(x)] = x^2 + 1$ **41.** $h[f(0)] = 5$

43. $h[f(-2)] = 11$ **45.** $h[f(x)] = 3x^2 + 3x + 5$ **47.** $f[g(-1)] = -3$ **49.** $g[f(-1)] = -27$

51. $g[f(x)] = x^3 - 6x^2 + 12x - 8$ **53.** $g(3 + h) - g(3) = 6h + h^2$ **55.** $\dfrac{g(1 + h) - g(1)}{h} = 2 + h$

57. $\dfrac{g(a + h) - g(a)}{h} = 2a + h$ **59.** $g(h[f(1)]) = -1$ **61.** $f(h[g(0)]) = -6$ **63.** $g(f[h(x)]) = 6x - 13$

SECTION 9.4

1. Yes   **3.** No   **5.** Yes   **7.** No   **9.** No   **11.** No   **13.** $\{(0, 1), (3, 2), (8, 3), (15, 4)\}$ **15.** No inverse

17. $\{(-2, 0), (5, -1), (3, 3), (6, -4)\}$ **19.** No inverse   **21.** $f^{-1}(x) = \frac{1}{4}x + 2$ **23.** $f^{-1}(x) = \frac{1}{2}x - 2$

25. $f^{-1}(x) = 2x + 2$ **27.** $f^{-1}(x) = -\frac{1}{2}x + 1$ **29.** $f^{-1}(x) = \frac{3}{2}x - 6$ **31.** $f^{-1}(x) = -3x + 3$ **33.** $f^{-1}(x) = \frac{1}{2}x + \frac{5}{2}$

35. $f^{-1}(x) = \frac{1}{5}x + \frac{2}{5}$ **37.** $f^{-1}(x) = \frac{1}{6}x + \frac{1}{2}$ **39.** $f^{-1}(x) = -\frac{1}{6}x + \frac{1}{3}$ **41.** $f^{-1}(x) = \frac{1}{3}x + \frac{4}{3}$ **43.** $f^{-1}(x) = -\frac{3}{2}x + 6$

45. $f^{-1}(x) = \frac{1}{3}x + \frac{2}{3}$ **47.** $f^{-1}(x) = -\frac{4}{3}x - \frac{8}{3}$ **49.** Yes   **51.** No   **53.** Yes   **55.** No   **57.** No   **59.** Yes

61. Yes   **63.**   **65.**   **67.**   **69.** No   **71.** $f^{-1}(-1) = 3$

73. $f^{-1}(3) = -3$ **75.** $f^{-1}(8) = 0$ **77.** Yes

CHAPTER REVIEW

1. Yes   [9.2A]   **2.** Yes   [9.4A]   **3.**   **4.**

Domain: $\{x \mid x \text{ is a real number}\}$
Range: $\{y \mid y \text{ is a real number}\}$ [9.2A]

Domain: $\{x \mid x \geq -4\}$
Range: $\{y \mid y \geq 0\}$ [9.2A]

5. Two x-intercepts   [9.1B]   **6.** $(0, 0)$ and $(-3, 0)$ [9.1B]   **7.** $-\frac{1}{3} + \frac{\sqrt{5}}{3}i$ and $-\frac{1}{3} - \frac{\sqrt{5}}{3}i$ [9.1B]   **8.** 3   [9.1C]

9. $-\frac{17}{4}$ [9.1C]   **10.** 5   [9.3B]   **11.** 10   [9.3B]   **12.** $12x^2 + 12x - 1$ [9.3B]   **13.** Yes   [9.4B]

14.   **15.**   **16.**

Domain: $\{x \mid x \text{ is a real number}\}$
Range: $\{y \mid y \geq -5\}$ [9.1A]

Vertex: $(1, 2)$
Axis of symmetry: $x = 1$ [9.1A]

Domain: $\{x \mid x \text{ is a real number}\}$
Range: $\{y \mid y \geq -3\}$ [9.2A]

17. No   [9.4A]   **18.** 7   [9.3A]   **19.** -9 [9.3A]   **20.** 70   [9.3A]   **21.** $\frac{12}{7}$ [9.3A]   **22.** $6x^2 + 3x - 16$ [9.3B]

23. $f^{-1}(x) = -\frac{1}{6}x + \frac{2}{3}$ [9.4B]   **24.** $f^{-1}(x) = \frac{3}{2}x + 18$ [9.4B]   **25.** $f^{-1}(x) = 2x - 16$ [9.4B]   **26.** The dimensions

of the rectangle are 7 ft by 7 ft.   [9.1D]

CHAPTER TEST

1. The x-intercepts are $\frac{3}{4} + \frac{\sqrt{23}}{4}i$ and $\frac{3}{4} - \frac{\sqrt{23}}{4}i$.   [9.1B]

2. The zeros of the function are $\dfrac{-3 + \sqrt{41}}{2}$ and $\dfrac{-3 - \sqrt{41}}{2}$. [9.1B]   **3.** The parabola has two real zeros. [9.1B]

4. $(f - g)(2) = -2$ [9.3A]   **5.** $(f \cdot g)(-3) = 234$ [9.3A]   **6.** $\left(\dfrac{f}{g}\right)(-2) = -\dfrac{13}{2}$ [9.3A]   **7.** $(f - g)(-4) = -5$ [9.3A]

8. $f[g(3)] = 5$ [9.3B]   **9.** $f[g(x)] = 2x^2 - 4x - 5$ [9.3B]   **10.** The maximum value of the function is 9. [9.1C]

11. $f^{-1}(x) = \dfrac{1}{4}x + \dfrac{1}{2}$ [9.4B]   **12.** $f^{-1}(x) = 4x + 16$ [9.4B]   **13.** $\{(6, 2), (5, 3), (4, 4), (3, 5)\}$ [9.4B]   **14.** Yes [9.4B]

15. The maximum product is 100. [9.1D]   **16.** Domain: $\{x \mid x \le 3\}$; range: $\{y \mid y \le 0\}$ [9.2A]

17. Domain: $\{x \mid x \text{ is a real number}\}$; range: $\{y \mid y \ge -2\}$ [9.2A]

18. Domain: $\{x \mid x \text{ is a real number}\}$; range: $\{y \mid y \text{ is a real number}\}$ [9.2A]

19. No [9.4A]   **20.** The dimensions are 50 cm by 50 cm. The maximum area is 2500 cm². [9.1D]

CUMULATIVE REVIEW

1. $-\dfrac{23}{4}$ [1.3B]   **2.** [1.1C]   **3.** 3 [2.1C]   **4.** $\{x \mid x < -2 \text{ or } x > 3\}$ [2.4B]   **5.** The set of all

real numbers [2.5B]   **6.** $-\dfrac{a^{10}}{12b^4}$ [5.1B]   **7.** $2x^3 - 4x^2 - 17x + 4$ [5.3B]   **8.** $(a + 2)(a - 2)(a^2 + 2)$ [5.6D]

9. $xy(x - 2y)(x + 3y)$ [5.6D]   **10.** -3 and 8 [5.7A]   **11.** $\{x \mid x < -3 \text{ or } x > 5\}$ [8.5A]   **12.** $\dfrac{5}{2x - 1}$ [6.2B]

13. -2 [6.5A]   **14.** $-3 - 2i$ [7.3D]   **15.** Vertex: $(0, 0)$; axis of symmetry: $x = 0$ [9.1A]

16. [3.7A]   **17.** $y = -2x - 2$ [3.5B]   **18.** $y = -\dfrac{3}{2}x - \dfrac{7}{2}$ [3.6A]

19. $\dfrac{1}{2} + \dfrac{\sqrt{3}}{6}i$ and $\dfrac{1}{2} - \dfrac{\sqrt{3}}{6}i$ [8.3A]   **20.** 3 [8.4B]   **21.** -3 [9.1C]   **22.** $\{1, 2, 4, 5\}$ [3.2A]   **23.** Yes [3.2A]

24. 2 [7.4A]   **25.** $g[h(2)] = 10$ [9.3B]   **26.** $f^{-1}(x) = -\dfrac{1}{3}x + 3$ [9.4B]   **27.** The cost per pound is $3.96. [2.3A]

28. There must be 25 lb of 80% copper alloy.   [2.3B]   **29.** There must be an additional 4.5 oz.   [6.4B]   **30.** It would take the larger pipe 4 min.   [8.6A]   **31.** The spring will stretch 24 in.   [6.6A]   **32.** The frequency in the pipe is 80 vibrations/min.   [6.6A]

Answers to Chapter 10 Odd-Numbered Exercises

SECTION 10.1

1a. $f(2) = 9$ **b.** $f(0) = 1$ **c.** $f(-2) = \dfrac{1}{9}$ **3a.** $g(3) = 16$ **b.** $g(1) = 4$ **c.** $g(-3) = \dfrac{1}{4}$

5a. $P(0) = 1$ **b.** $P\!\left(\dfrac{3}{2}\right) = \dfrac{1}{8}$ **c.** $P(-2) = 16$ **7a.** $G(4) = 7.3891$ **b.** $G(-2) = 0.3679$ **c.** $G\!\left(\dfrac{1}{2}\right) = 1.2840$

9a. $H(-1) = 54.5982$ **b.** $H(3) = 1$ **c.** $H(5) = 0.1353$ **11a.** $F(2) = 16$ **b.** $F(-2) = 16$ **c.** $F\!\left(\dfrac{3}{4}\right) = 1.4768$

13a. $f(-2) = 0.1353$ **b.** $f(2) = 0.1353$ **c.** $f(-3) = 0.0111$ **15.**   **17.**

19.   **21.**   **23.**   **25.**

27.   **29.**   **31.**   **33.**

35.   **37.**   **39a.**   **b.** The point (5, 1.242) means that in the year 1998, the Chinese population will be approximately 1.242 billion.

41a.   **b.** The point (2, 27.7) means that after 2 s, the object is dropping at a speed of 27.7 ft/s.   **43a.** Always true   **b.** Always true   **45.** e

SECTION 10.2

1. $\log_5 25 = 2$ **3.** $\log_4 \dfrac{1}{16} = -2$ **5.** $\log_{10} x = y$ **7.** $\log_a w = x$ **9.** $3^2 = 9$ **11.** $10^{-2} = 0.01$ **13.** $e^y = x$

15. $b^v = u$ **17.** $\log_3 81 = 4$ **19.** $\log_2 128 = 7$ **21.** $\log 100 = 2$ **23.** $\ln e^3 = 3$ **25.** $\log_8 1 = 0$

27. $\log_5 625 = 4$ **29.** 9   **31.** 64   **33.** $\dfrac{1}{7}$ **35.** 1   **37.** 316.23   **39.** 0.02   **41.** 7.39   **43.** 0.61

45. $\log_3(x^3 y^2)$ **47.** $\ln\left(\dfrac{x^4}{y^2}\right)$ **49.** $\log_7 x^3$ **51.** $\ln(x^3 y^4)$ **53.** $\log_4(x^2 y^2)$ **55.** $\log_3\left(\dfrac{x^2 z^2}{y}\right)$ **57.** $\ln\left(\dfrac{x}{y^2 z}\right)$

59. $\log_6 \sqrt{\dfrac{x}{y}}$ **61.** $\log_4 \dfrac{s^2 r^2}{t^4}$ **63.** $\ln\left(\dfrac{x}{y^2 z^2}\right)$ **65.** $\log_2\left(\dfrac{t^3 v^2}{r^2}\right)$ **67.** $\log_4 \sqrt{\dfrac{x^3 z}{y^2}}$ **69.** $\ln \sqrt{\dfrac{x}{y^3}}$ **71.** $\log_2 \dfrac{\sqrt{xz}}{\sqrt[3]{y^2}}$

73. $\log_8 x + \log_8 z$ **75.** $5\log_3 x$ **77.** $\log_b r - \log_b s$ **79.** $2\log_3 x + 6\log_3 y$ **81.** $3\log_7 u - 4\log_7 v$

83. $2\log_2 r + 2\log_2 s$ **85.** $2\ln x + \ln y + \ln z$ **87.** $\log_5 x + 2\log_5 y - 4\log_5 z$ **89.** $2\log_8 x - \log_8 y - 2\log_8 z$

91. $\dfrac{3}{2}\log_4 x + \dfrac{1}{2}\log_4 y$ **93.** $\dfrac{3}{2}\log_7 x - \dfrac{1}{2}\log_7 y$ **95.** $\ln x + \dfrac{1}{2}\ln y - \dfrac{1}{2}\ln z$ **97.** $\log_3 t - \dfrac{1}{2}\log_3 x$

99. $\dfrac{1}{2}\log_7 u + \dfrac{1}{2}\log_7 v - \log_7 x$ **101.** 0.8451   **103.** -0.2218 **105.** 1.3863   **107.** 1.0415   **109.** 0.8617

111. 2.1133   **113.** -0.6309 **115.** 0.2727   **117.** 1.6826   **119.** 1.9266   **121.** 0.6752   **123.** 2.6125

125a. False   **b.** True   **c.** False   **d.** False   **e.** False   **f.** True   **g.** False   **h.** True

SECTION 10.3

1.   **3.**   **5.**   **7.**

9.   **11.**   **13.**   **15.**

17.   **19.**   **21.**

23a.   **b.** The point (25.1, 2) means that a star that is 25.1 parsecs from Earth has a distance modulus of 2.

SECTION 10.4

1. $-\dfrac{1}{3}$ **3.** -3 **5.** 1   **7.** 6   **9.** $\dfrac{4}{7}$ **11.** $\dfrac{9}{8}$ **13.** 1.1133   **15.** 1.0986   **17.** 1.3222   **19.** -2.8074

21. 3.5850   **23.** 1.1309   **25.** $\dfrac{11}{2}$ **27.** -4 and 2   **29.** $\dfrac{5}{3}$ **31.** $\dfrac{1}{2}$ **33.** $\dfrac{9}{2}$ **35.** 17.5327   **37.** 3   **39.** 2

41. No solution   **43.** -0.55 **45.** 1.38   **47.** No solution   **49.** 0.09   **51a.**

b. It will take the object approximately 2.64 s to fall 100 ft.

SECTION 10.5

1. The value of the investment is $5982 after two years.   **3.** The company must deposit $16,786.   **5.** It will take 3.5 h to decay to 20 mg.   **7.** The half-life of the material is 2.5 years.   **9.** It will take 6 weeks of practice to make 80% of the welds correctly.   **11.** The pH of the solution is 1.35.   **13.** At a depth of 2.5 m, the light intensity will be 75% of the intensity at the surface.   **15.** The earthquake in China was 20 times stronger.   **17.** The magnitude of the earthquake is 5.2.   **19.** There are 65 decibels in normal conversation.   **21.** The star is 150.7 parsecs from Earth.   **23.** No, Antares is 3.5 times farther.   **25.** 742.9 billion barrels will last 20 years.   **27.** The value of the investment will be $3210.06 in 5 years.   **29.** $r = 243.31(e^{T/14.29} - 1)$ **31.** $r_1 = \sqrt{10}r_2$

CHAPTER REVIEW

1. 1 [10.1A]   **2.** $5^2 = 25$ [10.2A]   **3.** [10.1B]   **4.** [10.3A]

5. $\frac{2}{5}\log_3 x + \frac{4}{5}\log_3 y$ [10.2B]   **6.** $\log_3 \frac{x^2}{y^5}$ [10.2B]   **7.** -12 [10.4A]   **8.** $\frac{1}{4}$ [10.4B]   **9.** 1.7251 [10.2C]

10. 32 [10.2A]   **11.** 79 [10.4B]   **12.** 1000 [10.2A]   **13.** $\log_7 \sqrt[3]{xy^4}$ [10.2B]   **14.** $\frac{1}{2}(5\log_8 x - 3\log_8 y)$ [10.2B]

15. $\log_2 32 = 5$ [10.2A]   **16.** 0.4278 [10.2C]   **17.** -0.535 [10.4A]   **18.** $\frac{3}{2}$ [10.1A]   **19.** $\frac{2}{3}$ [10.4B]

20. 2 [10.4B]   **21.** [10.1B]   **22.** [10.3A]

23. The investment is worth $4692 after 2 years. [10.5A]   **24.** The magnitude is 1000 times stronger. [10.5A]   **25.** The half-life is 27 days. [10.5A]   **26.** The sound at a busy street corner is 107 decibels. [10.5A]

CHAPTER TEST

1. $f(0) = 1$ [10.1A]   **2.** $f(-2) = \frac{1}{3}$ [10.1A]   **3.** [10.1B]   **4.** [10.1B]

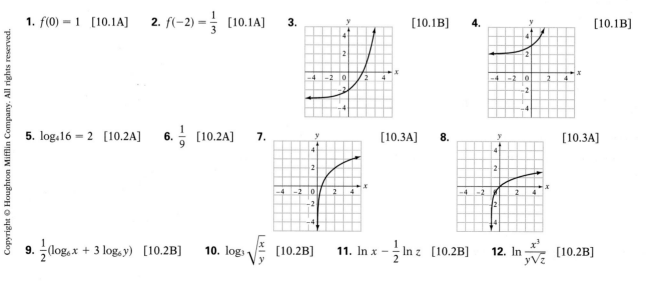

5. $\log_4 16 = 2$ [10.2A]   **6.** $\frac{1}{9}$ [10.2A]   **7.** [10.3A]   **8.** [10.3A]

9. $\frac{1}{2}(\log_6 x + 3\log_6 y)$ [10.2B]   **10.** $\log_3 \sqrt{\frac{x}{y}}$ [10.2B]   **11.** $\ln x - \frac{1}{2}\ln z$ [10.2B]   **12.** $\ln \frac{x^3}{y\sqrt{z}}$ [10.2B]

13. -2 [10.4A]   **14.** -3 [10.4A]   **15.** 2.5789   [10.4A]   **16.** 6   [10.4B]   **17.** 3   [10.4B]

18. $\log_5 9 = 1.3652$ [10.2C]   **19.** $\log_3 19 = 2.6801$ [10.2C]   **20.** The half-life is 33 h.   [10.5A]

CUMULATIVE REVIEW

1. $\dfrac{8}{7}$ [2.1C]   **2.** $y = 2x - 6$ [3.6A]   **3.** $(4x^n + 3)(x^n + 1)$ [5.6C]   **4.** $\dfrac{x - 3}{x + 3}$ [6.3A]   **5.** $\dfrac{x\sqrt{y} + y\sqrt{x}}{x - y}$ [7.2D]

6. $2 + \sqrt{10}$ and $2 - \sqrt{10}$ [8.2A]   **7.** $3x^2 + 8x - 3 = 0$ [8.1B]   **8.**   [4.5A]

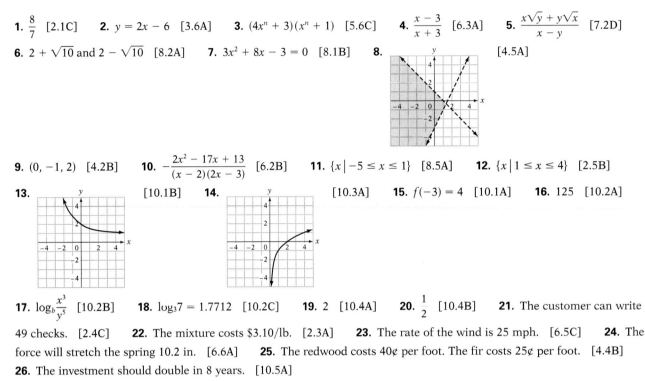

9. $(0, -1, 2)$ [4.2B]   **10.** $-\dfrac{2x^2 - 17x + 13}{(x - 2)(2x - 3)}$ [6.2B]   **11.** $\{x \mid -5 \le x \le 1\}$ [8.5A]   **12.** $\{x \mid 1 \le x \le 4\}$ [2.5B]

13.   [10.1B]   **14.**   [10.3A]   **15.** $f(-3) = 4$ [10.1A]   **16.** 125   [10.2A]

17. $\log_b \dfrac{x^3}{y^5}$ [10.2B]   **18.** $\log_3 7 = 1.7712$ [10.2C]   **19.** 2   [10.4A]   **20.** $\dfrac{1}{2}$ [10.4B]   **21.** The customer can write 49 checks.   [2.4C]   **22.** The mixture costs \$3.10/lb.   [2.3A]   **23.** The rate of the wind is 25 mph.   [6.5C]   **24.** The force will stretch the spring 10.2 in.   [6.6A]   **25.** The redwood costs 40¢ per foot. The fir costs 25¢ per foot.   [4.4B]   **26.** The investment should double in 8 years.   [10.5A]

Answers to Chapter 11 Odd-Numbered Exercises

SECTION 11.1

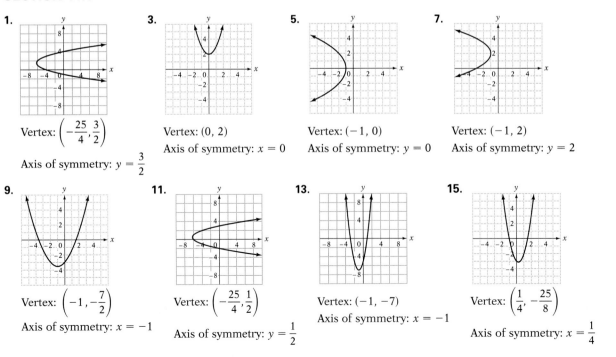

1. Vertex: $\left(-\dfrac{25}{4}, \dfrac{3}{2}\right)$ Axis of symmetry: $y = \dfrac{3}{2}$

3. Vertex: $(0, 2)$ Axis of symmetry: $x = 0$

5. Vertex: $(-1, 0)$ Axis of symmetry: $y = 0$

7. Vertex: $(-1, 2)$ Axis of symmetry: $y = 2$

9. Vertex: $\left(-1, -\dfrac{7}{2}\right)$ Axis of symmetry: $x = -1$

11. Vertex: $\left(-\dfrac{25}{4}, \dfrac{1}{2}\right)$ Axis of symmetry: $y = \dfrac{1}{2}$

13. Vertex: $(-1, -7)$ Axis of symmetry: $x = -1$

15. Vertex: $\left(\dfrac{1}{4}, -\dfrac{25}{8}\right)$ Axis of symmetry: $x = \dfrac{1}{4}$

17.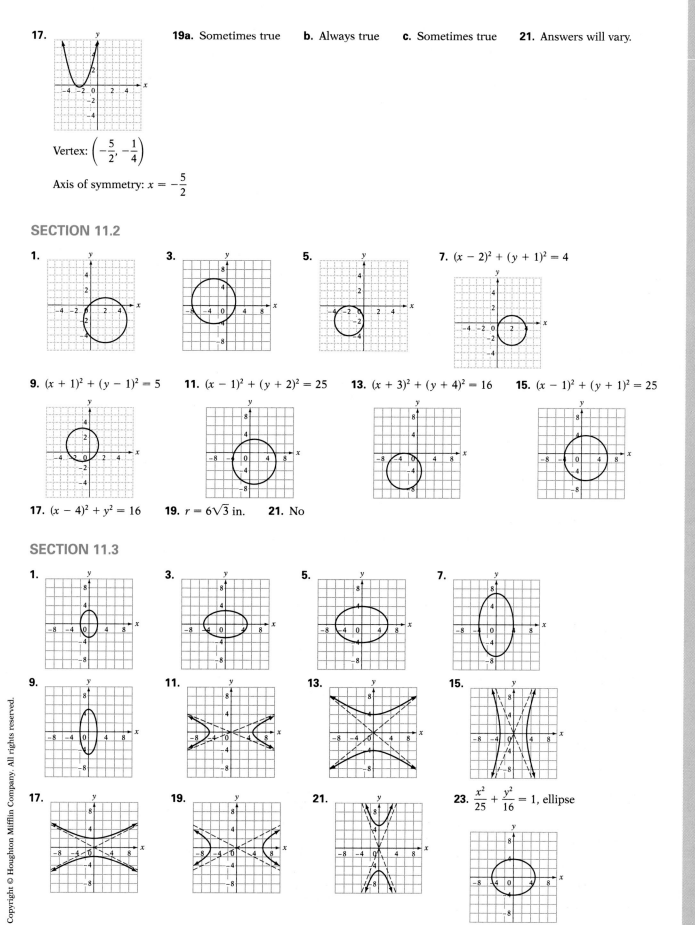

Vertex: $\left(-\dfrac{5}{2}, -\dfrac{1}{4}\right)$

Axis of symmetry: $x = -\dfrac{5}{2}$

19a. Sometimes true   **b.** Always true   **c.** Sometimes true   **21.** Answers will vary.

SECTION 11.2

1.   **3.**   **5.**   **7.** $(x - 2)^2 + (y + 1)^2 = 4$

9. $(x + 1)^2 + (y - 1)^2 = 5$ **11.** $(x - 1)^2 + (y + 2)^2 = 25$ **13.** $(x + 3)^2 + (y + 4)^2 = 16$ **15.** $(x - 1)^2 + (y + 1)^2 = 25$

17. $(x - 4)^2 + y^2 = 16$ **19.** $r = 6\sqrt{3}$ in.   **21.** No

SECTION 11.3

1.   **3.**   **5.**   **7.**

9.   **11.**   **13.**   **15.**

17.   **19.**   **21.**   **23.** $\dfrac{x^2}{25} + \dfrac{y^2}{16} = 1$, ellipse

25. $\dfrac{x^2}{25} - \dfrac{y^2}{4} = 1$, hyperbola

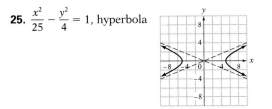

SECTION 11.4

1. $(-2, 5)$ and $(5, 19)$ **3.** $(-1, -2)$ and $(2, 1)$ **5.** $(2, -2)$ **7.** $(2, 2)$ and $\left(-\dfrac{2}{9}, -\dfrac{22}{9}\right)$ **9.** $(3, 2)$ and $(2, 3)$

11. $\left(\dfrac{\sqrt{3}}{2}, 3\right)$ and $\left(-\dfrac{\sqrt{3}}{2}, 3\right)$ **13.** The system of equations has no real number solution.

15. $(1, 2), (1, -2), (-1, 2)$, and $(-1, -2)$ **17.** $(3, 2), (3, -2), (-3, 2)$, and $(-3, -2)$ **19.** $(2, 7)$ and $(-2, 11)$

21. $(3, \sqrt{2}), (3, -\sqrt{2}), (-3, \sqrt{2})$, and $(-3, -\sqrt{2})$ **23.** The system of equations has no real number solution.

25. $(\sqrt{2}, 3), (\sqrt{2}, -3), (-\sqrt{2}, 3)$, and $(-\sqrt{2}, -3)$ **27.** $(2, -1)$ and $(8, 11)$ **29.** $(1, 0)$ **31.** $(2, -1)$ and $(1, -2)$

33. $\left(-\dfrac{1}{2}, \dfrac{9}{4}\right)$ and $(-4, 4)$ **35.** $(1.000, 2.000)$ **37.** $(1.755, 0.811), (0.505, -0.986)$ **39.** $(5.562, -1.562), (0.013, 3.987)$

SECTION 11.5

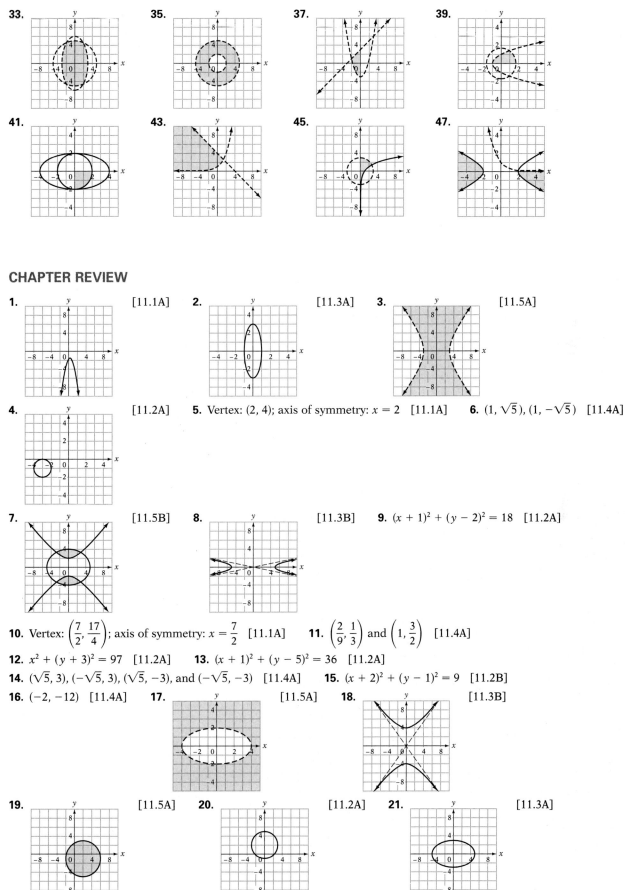

33. [11.1A] **35.** **37.** **39.**

41. **43.** **45.** **47.**

CHAPTER REVIEW

1. [11.1A] **2.** [11.3A] **3.** [11.5A]

4. [11.2A] **5.** Vertex: (2, 4); axis of symmetry: $x = 2$ [11.1A] **6.** $(1, \sqrt{5})$, $(1, -\sqrt{5})$ [11.4A]

7. [11.5B] **8.** [11.3B] **9.** $(x + 1)^2 + (y - 2)^2 = 18$ [11.2A]

10. Vertex: $\left(\dfrac{7}{2}, \dfrac{17}{4}\right)$; axis of symmetry: $x = \dfrac{7}{2}$ [11.1A] **11.** $\left(\dfrac{2}{9}, \dfrac{1}{3}\right)$ and $\left(1, \dfrac{3}{2}\right)$ [11.4A]

12. $x^2 + (y + 3)^2 = 97$ [11.2A] **13.** $(x + 1)^2 + (y - 5)^2 = 36$ [11.2A]

14. $(\sqrt{5}, 3)$, $(-\sqrt{5}, 3)$, $(\sqrt{5}, -3)$, and $(-\sqrt{5}, -3)$ [11.4A] **15.** $(x + 2)^2 + (y - 1)^2 = 9$ [11.2B]

16. $(-2, -12)$ [11.4A] **17.** [11.5A] **18.** [11.3B]

19. [11.5A] **20.** [11.2A] **21.** [11.3A]

22. 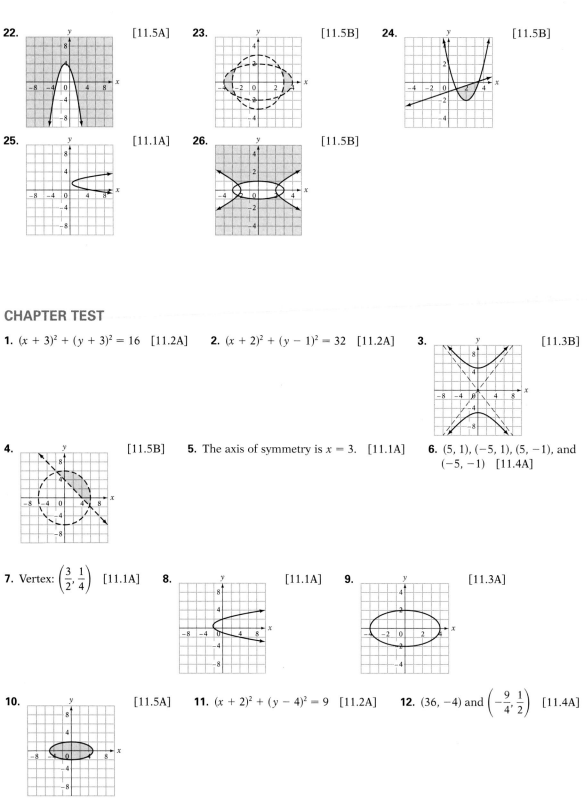 [11.5A]

23. [11.5B]

24. [11.5B]

25. [11.1A]

26. [11.5B]

CHAPTER TEST

1. $(x + 3)^2 + (y + 3)^2 = 16$ [11.2A]

2. $(x + 2)^2 + (y - 1)^2 = 32$ [11.2A]

3. [11.3B]

4. [11.5B]

5. The axis of symmetry is $x = 3$. [11.1A]

6. $(5, 1), (-5, 1), (5, -1)$, and $(-5, -1)$ [11.4A]

7. Vertex: $\left(\dfrac{3}{2}, \dfrac{1}{4}\right)$ [11.1A]

8. [11.1A]

9. [11.3A]

10. [11.5A]

11. $(x + 2)^2 + (y - 4)^2 = 9$ [11.2A]

12. $(36, -4)$ and $\left(-\dfrac{9}{4}, \dfrac{1}{2}\right)$ [11.4A]

13. $(2, 0)$ and $\left(\dfrac{2}{3}, \dfrac{4}{3}\right)$ [11.4A]

14. $(x + 1)^2 + (y + 3)^2 = 58$ [11.2A]

15. [11.5B]

16. $(x - 2)^2 + (y + 1)^2 = 4$ [11.2B]   **17.**   [11.1A]

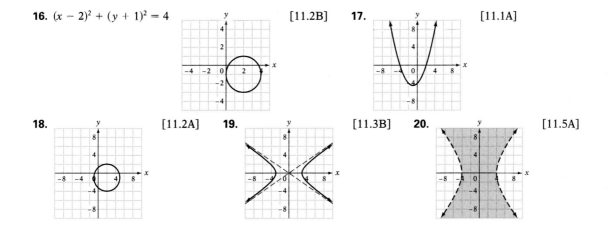

18.   [11.2A]   **19.**   [11.3B]   **20.**   [11.5A]

CUMULATIVE REVIEW

1.   [1.1C]   **2.** $\dfrac{38}{53}$ [2.1C]   **3.** $\left\{ x \,\middle|\, -\dfrac{4}{3} < x < 0 \right\}$ [2.5B]   **4.** $y = -\dfrac{3}{2}x$ [3.5A]

5. $y = x - 6$ [3.6A]   **6.** $x^{4n} + 2x^{3n} - 3x^{2n+1}$ [5.3A]   **7.** $(x - y - 1)(x^2 - 2x + 1 + xy - y + y^2)$ [5.6B]

8. $\{x \mid -4 < x \le 3\}$ [8.5A]   **9.** $\dfrac{x}{x + y}$ [6.1A]   **10.** $\dfrac{x - 5}{3x - 2}$ [6.2B]   **11.** $\dfrac{5}{2}$ [6.5A]

12.   [3.7A]   **13.** $\dfrac{4a}{3b^{12}}$ [5.1B]   **14.** $2x^{3/4}$ [7.1B]   **15.** $3\sqrt{2} - 5i$ [7.3A]

16. $\dfrac{-1 + \sqrt{7}}{2}$ and $\dfrac{-1 - \sqrt{7}}{2}$ [8.3A]   **17.** $(4, 2), (-4, 2), (4, -2),$ and $(-4, -2)$ [11.4A]   **18.** 6 [8.4B]

19. $f(-3) = -20$ [3.2A]   **20.** $f^{-1}(x) = \dfrac{1}{4}x - 2$ [9.4B]   **21.** Maximum value: 0 [9.1C]

22. The maximum product is 400. [9.1D]   **23.** The distance is 5. [3.1B]   **24.** $(x + 1)^2 + (y - 2)^2 = 17$ [11.2A]

25.   [11.1A]   **26.**   [11.3A]   **27.**   [11.3B]

28.   [11.5B]   **29.** The number of adult tickets sold was 82. [2.3A]

30. The rate of the motorcycle is 60 mph. [6.5C]   **31.** The rowing rate in calm water is 4.5 mph. [6.5C]

32. The gear will make 18 revolutions/min. [6.6A]

Answers to Chapter 12 Odd-Numbered Exercises

SECTION 12.1

1. 2, 3, 4, 5 **3.** 3, 5, 7, 9 **5.** 0, -2, -4, -6 **7.** 2, 4, 8, 16 **9.** 2, 5, 10, 17 **11.** 0, $\dfrac{7}{2}$, $\dfrac{26}{3}$, $\dfrac{63}{4}$ **13.** 40

15. 110 **17.** 225 **19.** $\dfrac{1}{256}$ **21.** 380 **23.** $-\dfrac{1}{36}$ **25.** 45 **27.** 20 **29.** 91 **31.** 0 **33.** 432 **35.** $\dfrac{5}{6}$

37. $2x + 2x^2 + 2x^3 + 2x^4 + 2x^5$ **39.** $x + \dfrac{x^2}{2} + \dfrac{x^3}{3} + \dfrac{x^4}{4} + \dfrac{x^5}{5}$ **41.** $\dfrac{x^3}{6} + \dfrac{x^4}{8} + \dfrac{x^5}{10}$ **43.** $x^2 + x^4 + x^6 + x^8 + x^{10}$

45. $x + \dfrac{x^2}{4} + \dfrac{x^3}{9} + \dfrac{x^4}{16}$ **47.** $1 + 2x + 3x^2 + 4x^3$ **49.** 1 **51a.** False **b.** False

SECTION 12.2

1. $a_{15} = 141$ **3.** $a_{15} = 50$ **5.** $a_{31} = 17$ **7.** $a_{12} = 12\dfrac{1}{2}$ **9.** $a_{40} = -109$ **11.** $a_n = 3n - 2$ **13.** $a_n = -3n + 6$

15. $a_n = -2.5n + 9.5$ **17.** 20 **19.** 20 **21.** 13 **23.** 20 **25.** 2500 **27.** -760 **29.** 189 **31.** 345

33. $\dfrac{187}{2}$ **35.** -180 **37.** It will take 11 weeks. **39.** The object will fall 144 ft during the fifth second.

41. The apprentice will receive $3600 during the eighth month. The apprentice will receive $20,400 for the eight months.
43. log 8

SECTION 12.3

1. $a_9 = 131,072$ **3.** $a_7 = \dfrac{128}{243}$ **5.** $a_{10} = 32$ **7.** $a_2 = 6, a_3 = 4$ **9.** $a_2 = -2, a_3 = \dfrac{4}{3}$ **11.** $a_2 = 12, a_3 = -48$

13. 2186 **15.** $\dfrac{2343}{64}$ **17.** 62 **19.** $\dfrac{121}{243}$ **21.** 9 **23.** $\dfrac{7}{9}$ **25.** $\dfrac{8}{9}$ **27.** $\dfrac{2}{9}$ **29.** $\dfrac{5}{11}$ **31.** $\dfrac{1}{6}$ **33.** The

amount of radioactive material is 50 mg. **35.** The ball will bounce 1.8 ft. **37.** The total amount earned is
$10,737,418.23. **39.** 27

SECTION 12.4

1. 6 **3.** 40,320 **5.** 1 **7.** 10 **9.** 1 **11.** 84 **13.** 21 **15.** 45 **17.** 1 **19.** 20 **21.** 11 **23.** 6
25. $x^4 + 4x^3y + 6x^2y^2 + 4xy^3 + y^4$ **27.** $x^5 - 5x^4y + 10x^3y^2 - 10x^2y^3 + 5xy^4 - y^5$ **29.** $16m^4 + 32m^3 + 24m^2 + 8m + 1$
31. $32r^5 - 240r^4 + 720r^3 - 1080r^2 + 810r - 243$ **33.** $a^{10} + 10a^9b + 45a^8b^2$ **35.** $a^{11} - 11a^{10}b + 55a^9b^2$
37. $256x^8 + 1024x^7y + 1792x^6y^2$ **39.** $65,536x^8 - 393,216x^7y + 1,032,192x^6y^2$ **41.** $x^7 + 7x^5 + 21x^3$ **43.** $-560x^4$
45. $-6x^{10}y^2$ **47.** $126y^5$ **49.** $5n^3$ **51a.** False **b.** False **c.** False **d.** False **e.** False **f.** True

CHAPTER REVIEW

1. $2 + 2x + 2x^2 + 2x^3$ [12.1B] **2.** 28 [12.1A] **3.** $\dfrac{19}{30}$ [12.3C] **4.** $\dfrac{1}{3}$ [12.3C] **5.** 1830 [12.2B]

6. 35 [12.1B] **7.** $\dfrac{23}{99}$ [12.3C] **8.** 84 [12.4A] **9.** 726 [12.3B] **10.** 22 terms [12.2A] **11.** 0.996 [12.3B]

12. $5670x^4y^4$ [12.4A] **13.** $-\dfrac{5}{27}$ [12.1A] **14.** 1127 [12.3B] **15.** $5n - 12$ [12.2A] **16.** $-42,240x^4y^7$ [12.4A]

17. $243\sqrt{3}$ [12.3A]   **18.** 2000 [12.2B]   **19.** 220 [12.4A]   **20.** $-\dfrac{13}{60}$ [12.1B]

21. $2x + 2x^2 + \dfrac{8x^3}{3} + 4x^4 + \dfrac{32x^5}{5}$ [12.1B]   **22.** $\dfrac{1}{729}$ [12.3A]

23. $x^5 - 15x^4y^2 + 90x^3y^4 - 270x^2y^6 + 405xy^8 - 243y^{10}$ [12.4A]   **24.** $\dfrac{16}{5}$ [12.3C]   **25.** 6 [12.3C]   **26.** 99 [12.4A]

27. 77 [12.2A]   **28.** The temperature of the spa is 67.7°F. [12.3D]   **29.** The total salary is $12,240. [12.2C]
30. The amount of radioactive material is 3.125 mg. [12.3D]

CHAPTER TEST

1. 34 [12.1B]   **2.** 84 [12.4A]   **3.** 32 [12.3A]   **4.** $\dfrac{1}{2}$ [12.1A]   **5.** $3x + 3x^2 + 3x^3 + 3x^4$ [12.1B]

6. 468 [12.2B]   **7.** 16 [12.3C]   **8.** 16 [12.2A]   **9.** $\dfrac{7}{30}$ [12.3C]   **10.** 70 [12.4A]   **11.** $\dfrac{2}{27}$ [12.3A]

12. $-280x^4y^3$ [12.4A]   **13.** -115 [12.2A]   **14.** $a_n = -3n + 15$ [12.2A]   **15.** -66 [12.3B]   **16.** $\dfrac{7}{6}; \dfrac{8}{7}$ [12.1A]

17. $\dfrac{665}{32}$ [12.3B]   **18.** 1575 [12.2B]   **19.** There were 2550 yd of material in stock after the shipment on October 1.
[12.2C]   **20.** There will be 20 mg of radioactive material in the sample at the beginning of the fifth day. [12.3D]

CUMULATIVE REVIEW

1.   [3.3B]   **2.** $2(x^2 + 2)(x^4 - 2x^2 + 4)$ [5.6D]   **3.** $\dfrac{x^2 + 5x - 2}{(x + 2)(x - 1)}$ [6.2B]   **4.** 14 [3.2A]

5. $4y\sqrt{x} - y\sqrt{2}$ [7.2C]   **6.** $\dfrac{1}{4} + \dfrac{\sqrt{55}}{4}i$ and $\dfrac{1}{4} - \dfrac{\sqrt{55}}{4}i$ [8.3A]   **7.** 4 [7.4A]   **8.** $(x + 1)^2 + (y + 1)^2 = 34$ [11.2A]

9. $\left(\dfrac{7}{6}, \dfrac{1}{2}\right)$ [4.2A]   **10.** -10 [4.3A]   **11.** $\{x \mid x < -2 \text{ or } x > 2\}$ [2.4B]   **12.**   [3.7A]

13. $\dfrac{1}{2}\log_5 x - \dfrac{1}{2}\log_5 y$ [10.2B]   **14.** 3 [10.4A]   **15.** 20, 30 [12.1A]   **16.** 6 [12.1B]   **17.** -103 [12.2A]

18. $\dfrac{9}{5}$ [12.3C]   **19.** $\dfrac{7}{15}$ [12.3C]   **20.** $12xy^5$ [12.4A]   **21.** There must be 120 oz of pure water added. [2.3B]

22. The new computer takes 24 min. The old computer takes 40 min. [6.5B]   **23.** The rate of the boat is 6.25 mph. The
rate of the current is 1.25 mph. [6.5C]   **24.** The half-life of the sample is 55 days. [10.5A]   **25.** There are
1536 seats. [12.2C]   **26.** The ball bounces 2.6 ft on the fifth bounce. [12.3D]

FINAL EXAM

1. -31 [1.2D]   **2.** -1 [1.3B]   **3.** $33 - 10x$ [1.3C]   **4.** 8 [2.1B]   **5.** $\dfrac{2}{3}$ [2.1C]   **6.** 4 and $-\dfrac{2}{3}$ [2.5A]

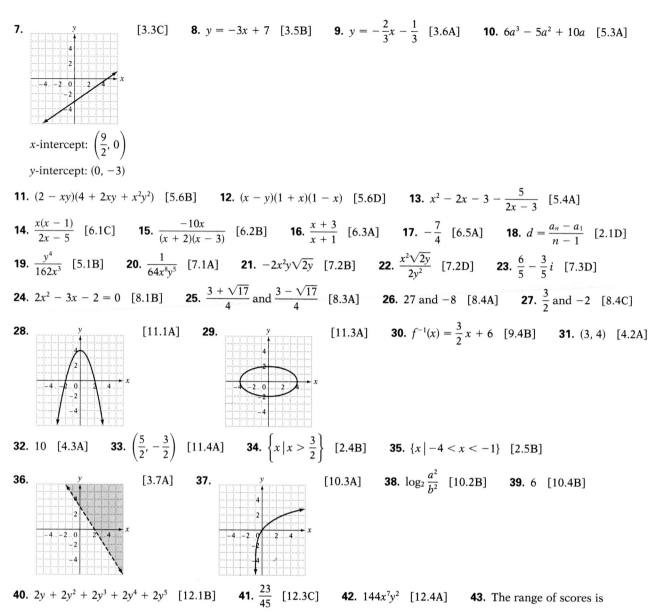

7.   [3.3C]   **8.** $y = -3x + 7$ [3.5B]   **9.** $y = -\frac{2}{3}x - \frac{1}{3}$ [3.6A]   **10.** $6a^3 - 5a^2 + 10a$ [5.3A]

x-intercept: $\left(\frac{9}{2}, 0\right)$

y-intercept: $(0, -3)$

11. $(2 - xy)(4 + 2xy + x^2y^2)$ [5.6B]   **12.** $(x - y)(1 + x)(1 - x)$ [5.6D]   **13.** $x^2 - 2x - 3 - \frac{5}{2x - 3}$ [5.4A]

14. $\frac{x(x - 1)}{2x - 5}$ [6.1C]   **15.** $\frac{-10x}{(x + 2)(x - 3)}$ [6.2B]   **16.** $\frac{x + 3}{x + 1}$ [6.3A]   **17.** $-\frac{7}{4}$ [6.5A]   **18.** $d = \frac{a_n - a_1}{n - 1}$ [2.1D]

19. $\frac{y^4}{162x^3}$ [5.1B]   **20.** $\frac{1}{64x^8y^5}$ [7.1A]   **21.** $-2x^2y\sqrt{2y}$ [7.2B]   **22.** $\frac{x^2\sqrt{2y}}{2y^2}$ [7.2D]   **23.** $\frac{6}{5} - \frac{3}{5}i$ [7.3D]

24. $2x^2 - 3x - 2 = 0$ [8.1B]   **25.** $\frac{3 + \sqrt{17}}{4}$ and $\frac{3 - \sqrt{17}}{4}$ [8.3A]   **26.** 27 and -8 [8.4A]   **27.** $\frac{3}{2}$ and -2 [8.4C]

28.   [11.1A]   **29.**   [11.3A]   **30.** $f^{-1}(x) = \frac{3}{2}x + 6$ [9.4B]   **31.** $(3, 4)$ [4.2A]

32. 10 [4.3A]   **33.** $\left(\frac{5}{2}, -\frac{3}{2}\right)$ [11.4A]   **34.** $\left\{x \mid x > \frac{3}{2}\right\}$ [2.4B]   **35.** $\{x \mid -4 < x < -1\}$ [2.5B]

36.   [3.7A]   **37.**   [10.3A]   **38.** $\log_2 \frac{a^2}{b^2}$ [10.2B]   **39.** 6 [10.4B]

40. $2y + 2y^2 + 2y^3 + 2y^4 + 2y^5$ [12.1B]   **41.** $\frac{23}{45}$ [12.3C]   **42.** $144x^7y^2$ [12.4A]   **43.** The range of scores is $69 \le x \le 100$. [2.4C]   **44.** The cyclist rode 40 mi. [2.3C]   **45.** There is $8000 invested at 8.5% and $4000 invested at 6.4%. [4.1C]   **46.** The length is 20 ft. The width is 7 ft. [8.6A]   **47.** An additional 200 shares are needed. [6.4A]   **48.** The rate of the plane was 420 mph. [4.4B]   **49.** The object has fallen 88 ft when the speed reaches 75 ft/s. [7.4B]   **50.** The rate of the plane for the first 360 mi was 120 mph. [8.6A]   **51.** The intensity is 200 foot-candles. [6.6A]   **52.** The rate of the boat is 12.5 mph. The rate of the current is 2.5 mph. [4.4A]   **53.** The value of the investment after two years would be $4785.65. [10.5A]   **54.** The house would be worth $256,571 in 20 years. [12.3D]

17. $243\sqrt{3}$ [12.3A]   **18.** 2000 [12.2B]   **19.** 220 [12.4A]   **20.** $-\dfrac{13}{60}$ [12.1B]

21. $2x + 2x^2 + \dfrac{8x^3}{3} + 4x^4 + \dfrac{32x^5}{5}$ [12.1B]   **22.** $\dfrac{1}{729}$ [12.3A]

23. $x^5 - 15x^4y^2 + 90x^3y^4 - 270x^2y^6 + 405xy^8 - 243y^{10}$ [12.4A]   **24.** $\dfrac{16}{5}$ [12.3C]   **25.** 6 [12.3C]   **26.** 99 [12.4A]

27. 77 [12.2A]   **28.** The temperature of the spa is 67.7°F. [12.3D]   **29.** The total salary is $12,240. [12.2C]

30. The amount of radioactive material is 3.125 mg. [12.3D]

CHAPTER TEST

1. 34 [12.1B]   **2.** 84 [12.4A]   **3.** 32 [12.3A]   **4.** $\dfrac{1}{2}$ [12.1A]   **5.** $3x + 3x^2 + 3x^3 + 3x^4$ [12.1B]

6. 468 [12.2B]   **7.** 16 [12.3C]   **8.** 16 [12.2A]   **9.** $\dfrac{7}{30}$ [12.3C]   **10.** 70 [12.4A]   **11.** $\dfrac{2}{27}$ [12.3A]

12. $-280x^4y^3$ [12.4A]   **13.** -115 [12.2A]   **14.** $a_n = -3n + 15$ [12.2A]   **15.** -66 [12.3B]   **16.** $\dfrac{7}{6}$; $\dfrac{8}{7}$ [12.1A]

17. $\dfrac{665}{32}$ [12.3B]   **18.** 1575 [12.2B]   **19.** There were 2550 yd of material in stock after the shipment on October 1.

[12.2C]   **20.** There will be 20 mg of radioactive material in the sample at the beginning of the fifth day. [12.3D]

CUMULATIVE REVIEW

1.   [3.3B]   **2.** $2(x^2 + 2)(x^4 - 2x^2 + 4)$ [5.6D]   **3.** $\dfrac{x^2 + 5x - 2}{(x + 2)(x - 1)}$ [6.2B]   **4.** 14 [3.2A]

5. $4y\sqrt{x} - y\sqrt{2}$ [7.2C]   **6.** $\dfrac{1}{4} + \dfrac{\sqrt{55}}{4}i$ and $\dfrac{1}{4} - \dfrac{\sqrt{55}}{4}i$ [8.3A]   **7.** 4 [7.4A]   **8.** $(x + 1)^2 + (y + 1)^2 = 34$ [11.2A]

9. $\left(\dfrac{7}{6}, \dfrac{1}{2}\right)$ [4.2A]   **10.** -10 [4.3A]   **11.** $\{x \mid x < -2 \text{ or } x > 2\}$ [2.4B]   **12.**   [3.7A]

13. $\dfrac{1}{2}\log_5 x - \dfrac{1}{2}\log_5 y$ [10.2B]   **14.** 3 [10.4A]   **15.** 20, 30 [12.1A]   **16.** 6 [12.1B]   **17.** -103 [12.2A]

18. $\dfrac{9}{5}$ [12.3C]   **19.** $\dfrac{7}{15}$ [12.3C]   **20.** $12xy^5$ [12.4A]   **21.** There must be 120 oz of pure water added. [2.3B]

22. The new computer takes 24 min. The old computer takes 40 min. [6.5B]   **23.** The rate of the boat is 6.25 mph. The rate of the current is 1.25 mph. [6.5C]   **24.** The half-life of the sample is 55 days. [10.5A]   **25.** There are 1536 seats. [12.2C]   **26.** The ball bounces 2.6 ft on the fifth bounce. [12.3D]

FINAL EXAM

1. -31 [1.2D]   **2.** -1 [1.3B]   **3.** $33 - 10x$ [1.3C]   **4.** 8 [2.1B]   **5.** $\dfrac{2}{3}$ [2.1C]   **6.** 4 and $-\dfrac{2}{3}$ [2.5A]

7. 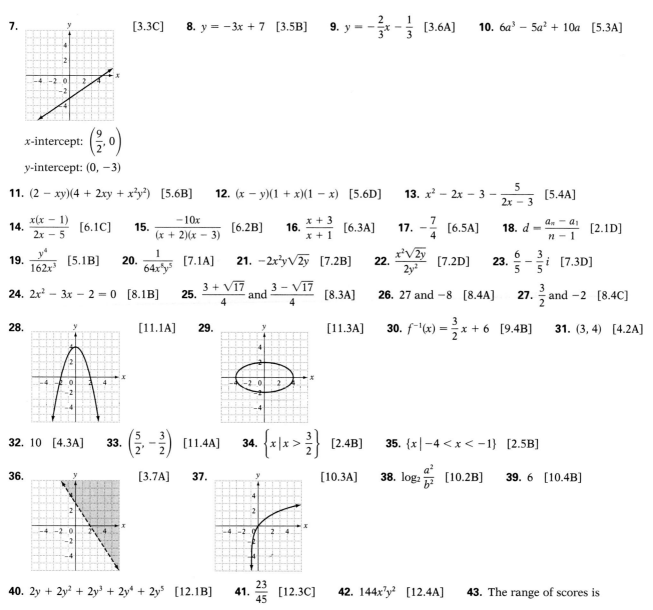 [3.3C] **8.** $y = -3x + 7$ [3.5B] **9.** $y = -\frac{2}{3}x - \frac{1}{3}$ [3.6A] **10.** $6a^3 - 5a^2 + 10a$ [5.3A]

x-intercept: $\left(\frac{9}{2}, 0\right)$

y-intercept: $(0, -3)$

11. $(2 - xy)(4 + 2xy + x^2y^2)$ [5.6B] **12.** $(x - y)(1 + x)(1 - x)$ [5.6D] **13.** $x^2 - 2x - 3 - \dfrac{5}{2x - 3}$ [5.4A]

14. $\dfrac{x(x - 1)}{2x - 5}$ [6.1C] **15.** $\dfrac{-10x}{(x + 2)(x - 3)}$ [6.2B] **16.** $\dfrac{x + 3}{x + 1}$ [6.3A] **17.** $-\dfrac{7}{4}$ [6.5A] **18.** $d = \dfrac{a_n - a_1}{n - 1}$ [2.1D]

19. $\dfrac{y^4}{162x^3}$ [5.1B] **20.** $\dfrac{1}{64x^8y^5}$ [7.1A] **21.** $-2x^2y\sqrt{2y}$ [7.2B] **22.** $\dfrac{x^2\sqrt{2y}}{2y^2}$ [7.2D] **23.** $\dfrac{6}{5} - \dfrac{3}{5}i$ [7.3D]

24. $2x^2 - 3x - 2 = 0$ [8.1B] **25.** $\dfrac{3 + \sqrt{17}}{4}$ and $\dfrac{3 - \sqrt{17}}{4}$ [8.3A] **26.** 27 and -8 [8.4A] **27.** $\dfrac{3}{2}$ and -2 [8.4C]

28. [11.1A] **29.** [11.3A] **30.** $f^{-1}(x) = \dfrac{3}{2}x + 6$ [9.4B] **31.** $(3, 4)$ [4.2A]

32. 10 [4.3A] **33.** $\left(\dfrac{5}{2}, -\dfrac{3}{2}\right)$ [11.4A] **34.** $\left\{x \mid x > \dfrac{3}{2}\right\}$ [2.4B] **35.** $\{x \mid -4 < x < -1\}$ [2.5B]

36. [3.7A] **37.** [10.3A] **38.** $\log_2 \dfrac{a^2}{b^2}$ [10.2B] **39.** 6 [10.4B]

40. $2y + 2y^2 + 2y^3 + 2y^4 + 2y^5$ [12.1B] **41.** $\dfrac{23}{45}$ [12.3C] **42.** $144x^7y^2$ [12.4A] **43.** The range of scores is $69 \le x \le 100$. [2.4C] **44.** The cyclist rode 40 mi. [2.3C] **45.** There is $8000 invested at 8.5% and $4000 invested at 6.4%. [4.1C] **46.** The length is 20 ft. The width is 7 ft. [8.6A] **47.** An additional 200 shares are needed. [6.4A] **48.** The rate of the plane was 420 mph. [4.4B] **49.** The object has fallen 88 ft when the speed reaches 75 ft/s. [7.4B] **50.** The rate of the plane for the first 360 mi was 120 mph. [8.6A] **51.** The intensity is 200 foot-candles. [6.6A] **52.** The rate of the boat is 12.5 mph. The rate of the current is 2.5 mph. [4.4A] **53.** The value of the investment after two years would be $4785.65. [10.5A] **54.** The house would be worth $256,571 in 20 years. [12.3D]

Glossary

abscissa The first number of an ordered pair; it measures a horizontal distance and is also called the first coordinate of an ordered pair. (Sec. 3.1)

absolute value of a number The distance of the number from zero on the number line. (Sec. 1.1, 2.5)

absolute-value equation An equation containing the absolute-value symbol. (Sec. 2.5)

addition method An algebraic method of finding an exact solution of a system of linear equations. (Sec. 4.2)

additive inverses Numbers that are the same distance from zero on the number line but lie on different sides of zero; also called opposites. (Sec. 1.1)

analytic geometry Geometry in which a coordinate system is used to study relationships between variables. (Sec. 3.1)

antilogarithm If $\log_b M = N$, then the antilogarithm, base b, of N is M. (Sec. 10.2)

arithmetic progression A sequence in which the difference between any two consecutive terms is constant; also called an arithmetic sequence. (Sec. 12.2)

arithmetic sequence A sequence in which the difference between any two consecutive terms is constant; also called an arithmetic progression. (Sec. 12.2)

arithmetic series The indicated sum of the terms of an arithmetic sequence. (Sec. 12.2)

asymptotes The two straight lines that a hyperbola "approaches." (Sec. 11.3)

axes The two number lines that form a rectangular coordinate system; also called coordinate axes. (Sec. 3.1)

axis of symmetry of a parabola A line of symmetry that passes through the vertex of the parabola and is parallel to the y-axis for an equation of the form $y = ax^2 + bx + c$ or parallel to the x-axis for an equation of the form $x = ay^2 + by + c$. (Sec. 9.1, 11.1)

base In an exponential expression, the number that is taken as a factor as many times as indicated by the exponent. (Sec. 1.2)

binomial A polynomial of two terms. (Sec. 5.2)

center of a circle The central point that is equidistant from all the points that make up a circle. (Sec. 11.2)

center of an ellipse The intersection of the two axes of symmetry of the ellipse. (Sec. 11.3)

characteristic The integer part of a common logarithm. (Sec. 10.2)

circle The set of all points (x, y) in the plane that are a fixed distance from a given point (h, k) called the center. (Sec. 11.2)

clearing denominators Removing denominators from an equation that contains fractions by multiplying each side of the equation by the LCM of the denominators. (Sec. 6.5)

closed interval In set-builder notation, an interval that contains its endpoints. (Sec. 1.1)

coefficient The number part of a variable term. (Sec. 1.3)

cofactor of an element of a matrix $(-1)^{i+j}$ times the minor of that element, where i is the row number of the element and j is its column number. (Sec. 4.3)

combined variation A variation in which two or more types of variation occur at the same time. (Sec. 6.6)

combining like terms Using the Distributive Property to add the coefficients of like variable terms; adding like terms of a variable expression. (Sec. 1.3)

common difference of a sequence The difference between any two consecutive terms in an arithmetic sequence. (Sec. 12.2)

common logarithms Logarithms to the base 10. (Sec. 10.2)

common ratio of a sequence In a geometric sequence, each successive term of the sequence is the same nonzero constant multiple of the preceding term. This common multiple is called the common ratio of the sequence. (Sec. 12.3)

completing the square Adding to a binomial the constant term that makes it a perfect-square trinomial. (Sec. 8.2)

complex fraction A fraction whose numerator or denominator contains one or more fractions. (Sec. 1.2, 6.3)

complex number A number of the form $a + bi$, where a and b are real numbers and $i = \sqrt{-1}$. (Sec. 7.3)

composite number A number that has whole-number factors besides 1 and itself. For example, 12 is a composite number. (Sec. 1.1)

composition of functions The operation on two functions f and g denoted by $f \circ g$. The value of the composition of f and g is given by $(f \circ g)(x) = f[g(x)]$. (Sec. 9.3)

compound inequality Two inequalities joined with a connective word such as "and" or "or." (Sec. 2.4)

compound interest Interest that is computed not only on the original principal but also on the interest already earned. (Sec. 10.5)

conditional equation An equation that is true if the variable it contains is replaced by the proper value. $x + 2 = 5$ is a conditional equation. (Sec. 2.1)

conic section A curve that can be constructed from the intersection of a plane and a right circular cone. The four conic sections are the parabola, hyperbola, ellipse, and circle. (Sec. 11.1)

conjugates Binomial expressions that differ only in the sign of a term. The expressions $a + b$ and $a - b$ are conjugates. (Sec. 7.2)

consecutive even integers Even integers that follow one another in order. (Sec. 2.2)

consecutive integers Integers that follow one another in order. (Sec. 2.2)

consecutive odd integers Odd integers that follow one another in order. (Sec. 2.2)

constant function A function given by $f(x) = b$, where b is a constant. Its graph is a horizontal line passing through $(0, b)$. (Sec. 3.3)

constant of proportionality k in a variation equation; also called the constant of variation. (Sec. 6.6)

constant of variation k in a variation equation; also called the constant of proportionality. (Sec. 6.6)

constant term A term that contains no variable part. (Sec. 1.3)

contradiction An equation in which any replacement for the variable will result in a false equation. $x = x + 1$ is a contradiction. (Sec. 2.1)

coordinate axes The two number lines that form a rectangular coordinate system; also called axes. (Sec. 3.1)

coordinates of a point The numbers in the ordered pair that is associated with the point. (Sec. 3.1)

cube root of a perfect cube One of the three equal factors of the perfect cube. (Sec. 5.6)

cubic function A third-degree polynomial function. (Sec. 5.2)

degree of a monomial The sum of the exponents of the variables. (Sec. 5.1)

degree of a polynomial The greatest of the degrees of any of its terms. (Sec. 5.2)

dependent system of equations A system of equations whose graphs coincide. (Sec. 4.1)

dependent variable A variable whose value depends on that of another variable known as the independent variable. (Sec. 3.2)

descending order The terms of a polynomial in one variable are arranged in descending order when the exponents of the variable decrease from left to right. (Sec. 5.2)

determinant A number associated with a square matrix. (Sec. 4.3)

direct variation A special function that can be expressed as the equation $y = kx$, where k is a constant called the constant of variation or the constant of proportionality. (Sec. 6.6)

discriminant For an equation of the form $ax^2 + bx + c = 0$, the quantity $b^2 - 4ac$ is called the discriminant. (Sec. 8.3)

domain The set of the first coordinates of all the ordered pairs of a function. (Sec. 1.1, 3.2)

double root When a quadratic equation has two solutions that are the same number, the solution is called a double root of the equation. (Sec. 8.1)

element of a matrix A number in a matrix. (Sec. 4.3)

elements of a set The objects in the set. (Sec. 1.1)

ellipse An oval shape that is one of the conic sections. (Sec. 11.3)

empty set The set that contains no elements. (Sec. 1.1)

equation A statement of the equality of two mathematical expressions. (Sec. 2.1)

equivalent equations Equations that have the same solution. (Sec. 2.1)

evaluating a function Determining $f(x)$ for a given value of x. (Sec. 3.2)

even integer An integer that is divisible by 2. (Sec. 2.2)

expanding by cofactors A technique for finding the value of a 3×3 or larger determinant. (Sec. 4.3)

exponent In an exponential expression, the raised number that indicates how many times the factor, or base, occurs in the multiplication. (Sec. 1.2)

exponential equation An equation in which the variable occurs in the exponent. (Sec. 10.4)

exponential form The expression 2^6 is in exponential form. Compare *factored form*. (Sec. 1.2)

exponential function The exponential function with base b is defined by $f(x) = b^x$, where b is a positive real number not equal to one. (Sec. 10.1)

extraneous solution When each side of an equation is raised to an even power, the resulting equation may have a solution that is not a solution of the original equation. Such a solution is called an extraneous solution. (Sec. 7.4)

factored form The multiplication $2 \cdot 2 \cdot 2 \cdot 2 \cdot 2 \cdot 2$ is in factored form. Compare *exponential form*. (Sec. 1.2)

factoring a polynomial Writing the polynomial as a product of other polynomials. (Sec. 5.5)

factoring a quadratic trinomial Expressing the trinomial as the product of two binomials. (Sec. 5.5)

finite sequence A sequence that contains a finite number of terms. (Sec. 12.1)

finite set A set for which all the elements can be listed. (Sec. 1.1)

first coordinate of an ordered pair The first number of the ordered pair; it measures a horizontal distance and is also called the abscissa. (Sec. 3.1)

first-degree equation An equation in which all variables have an exponent of 1. (Sec. 2.1)

FOIL A method of finding the product of two binomials. The letters stand for First, Outer, Inner, and Last. (Sec. 5.3)

formula A literal equation that states rules about measurement. (Sec. 2.1)

function A relation in which no two ordered pairs that have the same first coordinate have different second coordinates. (Sec. 3.2)

functional notation Notation used for those equations that define functions. The letter f is commonly used to name a function. (Sec. 3.2)

general term of a sequence In the sequence $a_1, a_2, a_3, \ldots, a_n, \ldots$ the general term of the sequence is a_n. (Sec. 12.1)

geometric progression A sequence in which each successive term of the sequence is the same nonzero constant multiple of the preceding term; also called a geometric sequence. (Sec. 12.3)

geometric sequence A sequence in which each successive term of the sequence is the same nonzero constant multiple of the preceding term; also called a geometric progression. (Sec. 12.3)

geometric series The indicated sum of the terms of a geometric sequence. (Sec. 12.3)

graph of a function A graph of the ordered pairs that belong to the function. (Sec. 3.3)

graph of a quadratic inequality in two variables A region of the plane that is bounded by one of the conic sections. (Sec. 11.5)

graph of a real number A heavy dot placed directly above the number on the number line. (Sec. 1.1)

graph of an ordered pair The dot drawn at the coordinates of the point in the plane. (Sec. 3.1)

graphing a point in the plane Placing a dot at the location given by the ordered pair; also called plotting a point in the plane. (Sec. 3.1)

greater than A number that lies to the right of another number on the number line is said to be greater than that number. (Sec. 1.1)

greatest common factor (GCF) The GCF of two or more numbers is the largest integer that divides evenly into all of them. (Sec. 1.2)

half-open interval In set-builder notation, an interval that contains one of its endpoints. (Sec. 1.1)

half-plane The solution set of a linear inequality in two variables. (Sec. 3.7)

hyperbola A conic section formed by the intersection of a cone and a plane perpendicular to the base of the cone. (Sec. 11.3)

hypotenuse In a right triangle, the side opposite the 90° angle. (Sec. 7.4)

identity An equation in which any replacement for the variable will result in a true equation. $x + 2 = x + 2$ is an identity. (Sec. 2.1)

imaginary number A number of the form ai, where a is a real number and $i = \sqrt{-1}$. (Sec. 7.3)

imaginary part of a complex number For the complex number $a + bi$, b is the imaginary part. (Sec. 7.3)

inconsistent system of equations A system of equations that has no solution. (Sec. 4.1)

independent system of equations A system of equations whose graphs intersect at only one point. (Sec. 4.1)

independent variable A variable whose value determines that of another variable known as the dependent variable. (Sec. 3.2)

index In the expression $\sqrt[n]{a}$, n is the index of the radical. (Sec. 7.1)

infinite geometric series The indicated sum of the terms of an infinite geometric sequence. (Sec. 12.3)

infinite sequence A sequence that contains an infinite number of terms. (Sec. 12.1)

infinite set A set in which the list of elements continues without end. (Sec. 1.1)

integers The numbers $\ldots, -3, -2, -1, 0, 1, 2, 3, \ldots$. (Sec. 1.1)

intersection of two sets The set that contains all elements that are common to both of the sets. (Sec. 1.1)

interval notation A type of set-builder notation in which the property that distinguishes the elements of the set is their location within a specified interval. (Sec. 1.1)

inverse of a function The set of ordered pairs formed by reversing the coordinates of each ordered pair of the function. (Sec. 9.4)

inverse variation A function that can be expressed as the equation $y = k/x$, where k is a constant. (Sec. 6.6)

irrational number The decimal representation of an irrational number never terminates or repeats and can only be approximated. (Sec. 1.1)

joint variation A variation in which a variable varies directly as the product of two or more variables. A joint variation can be expressed as the equation $z = kxy$, where k is a constant. (Sec. 6.6)

leading coefficient In a polynomial, the coefficient of the variable with the largest exponent. (Sec. 5.2)

least common multiple (LCM) The LCM of two or more numbers is the smallest number that is a multiple of each of those numbers. (Sec. 1.2)

least common multiple of two polynomials The simplest polynomial of least degree that contains the factors of each polynomial. (Sec. 6.2)

leg In a right triangle, one of the two sides that are not opposite the 90° angle. (Sec. 7.4)

less than A number that lies to the left of another number on the number line is said to be less than that number. (Sec. 1.1)

like terms Terms of a variable expression that have the same variable part. Having no variable part, constant terms are like terms. (Sec. 1.3)

linear equation in three variables An equation of the form $Ax + By + Cz = D$, where A, B, C, and D are constants. (Sec. 4.2)

linear equation in two variables An equation of the form $y = mx + b$ or $Ax + By = C$. (Sec. 3.3)

linear function A function that can be expressed in the form $f(x) = mx + b$. Its graph is a straight line. (Sec. 3.3)

linear inequality in two variables An inequality of the form $y > mx + b$ or $Ax + By > C$. (The symbol $>$ could be replaced by $\geq$, $<$, or $\leq$.) (Sec. 3.7)

literal equation An equation that contains more than one variable. (Sec. 2.1)

logarithm For b greater than zero and not equal to 1, the statement $y = \log_b x$ (the logarithm of x to the base b) is equivalent to $x = b^y$. (Sec. 10.2)

mantissa The decimal part of a common logarithm. (Sec. 10.2)

matrix A rectangular array of numbers. (Sec. 4.3)

minor of an element The minor of an element in a 3×3 determinant is the 2×2 determinant obtained by eliminating the row and column that contain that element. (Sec. 4.3)

monomial A number, a variable, or a product of a number and variables; a polynomial of one term. (Sec. 5.1, 5.2)

more than A number that lies to the right of another number on the number line is said to be greater than that number. (Sec. 1.1)

multiplicative inverse The multiplicative inverse of a nonzero real number a is $1/a$; also called the reciprocal. (Sec. 1.2)

n factorial The product of the first n natural numbers; n factorial is written $n!$ (Sec. 12.4)

natural exponential function The function defined by $f(x) = e^x$, where $e \approx 2.71828$. (Sec. 10.1)

natural logarithm When e (the base of the natural exponential function) is used as the base of a logarithm, the logarithm is referred to as the natural logarithm and is abbreviated $\ln x$. (Sec. 10.2)

natural numbers The numbers $1, 2, 3, \ldots$; also called the positive integers. (Sec. 1.1)

negative integers The numbers $\ldots, -3, -2, -1$. (Sec. 1.1)

negative slope The slope of a line that slants downward to the right. (Sec. 3.4)

nonfactorable over the integers A polynomial is nonfactorable over the integers if it does not factor using only integers. (Sec. 5.5)

nonlinear system of equations A system of equations in which one or more of the equations are not linear equations. (Sec. 11.4)

nth root of a A number b such that $b^n = a$. The nth root of a can be written $a^{1/n}$ or $\sqrt[n]{a}$. (Sec. 7.1)

null set The set that contains no elements. (Sec. 1.1)

numerical coefficient The number part of a variable term. (Sec. 1.3)

odd integer An integer that is not divisible by 2. (Sec. 2.2)

one-to-one function In a one-to-one function, given any y, there is only one x that can be paired with the given y. (Sec. 9.4)

open interval In set-builder notation, an interval that does not contain its endpoints. (Sec. 1.1)

opposites Numbers that are the same distance from zero on the number line but lie on different sides of zero; also called additive inverses. (Sec. 1.1)

order $m \times n$ A matrix of m rows and n columns is of order $m \times n$. (Sec. 4.3)

Order of Operations Agreement Rules that specify the order in which we perform operations in simplifying numerical expressions. (Sec. 1.2)

ordered pair Pair of numbers expressed in the form (a, b) and used to locate a point in the plane determined by a rectangular coordinate system. (Sec. 3.1)

ordinate The second number of an ordered pair; it measures a vertical distance and is also called the second coordinate of an ordered pair. (Sec. 3.1)

origin The point of intersection of the two number lines that form a rectangular coordinate system. (Sec. 3.1)

parabola The graph of a quadratic function is called a parabola. (Sec. 9.1)

parallel lines Lines that have the same slope and thus do not intersect. (Sec. 3.6)

Pascal's Triangle A pattern for the coefficients of the terms of the expansion of the binomial $(a + b)^n$ can be formed by writing the coefficients in a triangular array known as Pascal's Triangle. (Sec. 12.4)

perfect cube The product of the same three factors. (Sec. 5.6)

perfect square The product of a term and itself. (Sec. 5.6)

perpendicular lines Lines that intersect at right angles. The slopes of perpendicular lines are negative reciprocals of each other. (Sec. 3.6)

plotting a point in the plane Placing a dot at the location given by the ordered pair; also called graphing a point in the plane. (Sec. 3.1)

point-slope formula The equation $y - y_1 = m(x - x_1)$, where m is the slope of a line and (x_1, y_1) is a point on the line. (Sec. 3.5)

polynomial A variable expression in which the terms are monomials. (Sec. 5.2)

positive integers The numbers $1, 2, 3, \ldots$; also called the natural numbers. (Sec. 1.1)

positive slope The slope of a line that slants upward to the right. (Sec. 3.4)

prime number A number whose only whole-number factors are 1 and itself. For example, 17 is a prime number. (Sec. 1.1)

prime polynomial A polynomial that is nonfactorable over the integers. (Sec. 5.5)

principal square root The positive square root of a number. (Sec. 7.1)

proportion An equation that states the equality of two ratios or rates. (Sec. 6.4)

Pythagorean Theorem The square of the hypotenuse of a right triangle is equal to the sum of the squares of the two legs. (Sec. 7.4)

quadrant One of the four regions into which a rectangular coordinate system divides the plane. (Sec. 3.1)

quadratic equation An equation of the form $ax^2 + bx + c = 0$, where a, b, and c are constants and a is not equal to zero; also called a second-degree equation. (Sec. 5.7, 8.1)

quadratic formula A general formula, derived by applying the method of completing the square to the standard form of a quadratic equation, used to solve quadratic equations. (Sec. 8.3)

quadratic function A function that can be expressed by the equation $f(x) = ax^2 + bx + c$, where a is not equal to zero. (Sec. 5.2, 9.1)

quadratic inequality An inequality that can be written in the form $ax^2 + bx + c < 0$ or $ax^2 + bx + c > 0$, where a is not equal to zero. The symbols $\leq$ and $\geq$ can also be used. (Sec. 8.5)

quadratic trinomial A trinomial of the form $ax^2 + bx + c$, where a, b, and c are nonzero constants. (Sec. 5.5)

radical In a radical expression, the symbol $\sqrt{}$. (Sec. 7.1)

radical equation An equation that contains a variable expression in a radicand. (Sec. 7.4)

radicand In a radical expression, the number within the radical. (Sec. 7.1)

radius The fixed distance, from the center of a circle, of all points that make up the circle. (Sec. 11.2)

range The set of the second coordinates of all the ordered pairs of a function. (Sec. 3.2)

rate The quotient of two quantities that have different units. (Sec. 6.4)

rate of work That part of a task that is completed in one unit of time. (Sec. 6.5)

ratio The quotient of two quantities that have the same unit. (Sec. 6.4)

rational expression A fraction in which the numerator or denominator is a polynomial. (Sec. 6.1)

rational function A function that is written in terms of a rational expression. (Sec. 6.1)

rational number A number of the form a/b, where a and b are integers and b is not equal to zero. (Sec. 1.1)

rationalizing the denominator The procedure used to remove a radical from the denominator of a fraction. (Sec. 7.2)

real numbers The rational numbers and the irrational numbers taken together. (Sec. 1.1)

real part of a complex number For the complex number $a + bi$, a is the real part. (Sec. 7.3)

reciprocal The reciprocal of a nonzero real number a is $1/a$; also called the multiplicative inverse. (Sec. 1.2)

reciprocal of a rational expression The rational expression with the numerator and denominator interchanged. (Sec. 6.1)

rectangular coordinate system A coordinate system formed by two number lines, one horizontal and one vertical, that intersect at the zero point of each line. (Sec. 3.1)

relation A set of ordered pairs. (Sec. 3.2)

repeating decimal Decimal formed when dividing the numerator of its fractional counterpart by the denominator results in a decimal part wherein one or more digits repeat infinitely. (Sec. 1.1)

root(s) of an equation The replacement value(s) of the variable that will make the equation true; also called the solution(s) of the equation. (Sec. 2.1)

roster method A method of designating a set by enclosing a list of its elements in braces. (Sec. 1.1)

scatter diagram A graph of ordered-pair data. (Sec. 3.1)

scientific notation Notation in which a number is expressed as the product of a number between 1 and 10 and a power of 10. (Sec. 5.1)

second coordinate of an ordered pair The second number of the ordered pair; it measures a vertical distance and is also called the ordinate. (Sec. 3.1)

second-degree equation An equation of the form $ax^2 + bx + c = 0$, where a, b, and c are constants and a is not equal to zero; also called a quadratic equation. (Sec. 8.1)

sequence An ordered list of numbers. (Sec. 12.1)

series The indicated sum of the terms of a sequence. (Sec. 12.1)

set A collection of objects. (Sec. 1.1)

set-builder notation A method of designating a set that makes use of a variable and a certain property that only elements of that set possess. (Sec. 1.1)

sigma notation Notation used to represent a series in a compact form; also called summation notation. (Sec. 12.1)

simplest form of a rational expression A rational expression is in simplest form when the numerator and denominator have no common factors. (Sec. 6.1)

slope A measure of the slant, or tilt, of a line. The symbol for slope is m. (Sec. 3.4)

slope-intercept form of a straight line The equation $y = mx + b$, where m is the slope of the line and $(0, b)$ is the y-intercept. (Sec. 3.4)

solution of a system of equations in three variables An ordered triple that is a solution of each equation of the system. (Sec. 4.2)

solution of a system of equations in two variables An ordered pair that is a solution of each equation of the system. (Sec. 4.1)

solution of an equation in three variables An ordered triple (x, y, z) whose coordinates make the equation a true statement. (Sec. 4.2)

solution of an equation in two variables An ordered pair whose coordinates make the equation a true statement. (Sec. 3.1)

solution set of a system of inequalities The intersection of the solution sets of the individual inequalities. (Sec. 4.5)

solution set of an inequality A set of numbers, each element of which, when substituted for the variable, results in a true inequality. (Sec. 2.4)

solution(s) of an equation The replacement value(s) of the variable that will make the equation true; also called the root(s) of the equation. (Sec. 2.1)

solving an equation Finding a root, or solution, of the equation. (Sec. 2.1)

square matrix A matrix that has the same number of rows as columns. (Sec. 4.3)

square root of a perfect square One of the two equal factors of the perfect square. (Sec. 5.6)

standard form of a quadratic equation A quadratic equation is in standard form when the polynomial is in descending order and equal to zero. (Sec. 8.1)

substitution method An algebraic method of finding an exact solution of a system of linear equations. (Sec. 4.1)

summation notation Notation used to represent a series in a compact form; also called sigma notation. (Sec. 12.1)

synthetic division A shorter method of dividing a polynomial by a binomial of the form $x - a$. This method uses only the coefficients of the variable terms. (Sec. 5.4)

system of equations Two or more equations considered together. (Sec. 4.1)

system of inequalities Two or more inequalities considered together. (Sec. 4.5)

term of a sequence A number in a sequence. (Sec. 12.1)

terminating decimal Decimal formed when dividing the numerator of its fractional counterpart by the denominator results in a remainder of zero. (Sec. 1.1)

terms of a variable expression The addends of the expression. (Sec. 1.3)

tolerance of a component The acceptable amount by which the component may vary from a given measurement. (Sec. 2.5)

trinomial A polynomial of three terms. (Sec. 5.2)

undefined slope The slope of a vertical line is undefined. (Sec. 3.4)

uniform motion The motion of an object whose speed and direction do not change. (Sec. 2.3, 6.5)

union of two sets The set that contains all elements that belong to either of the sets. (Sec. 1.1)

value mixture problem A problem that involves combining two ingredients that have different prices into a single blend. (Sec. 2.3)

value of a function The value of the dependent variable for a given value of the independent variable. (Sec. 3.2)

variable A letter used to stand for a quantity that is unknown or that can change. (Sec. 1.1)

variable expression An expression that contains one or more variables. (Sec. 1.3)

variable term A term composed of a numerical coefficient and a variable part. When the numerical coefficient is 1 or -1, the 1 is not usually written. (Sec. 1.3)

vertex of a parabola The point on the parabola with the smallest y-coordinate or the largest y-coordinate. (Sec. 9.1)

whole numbers The numbers 0, 1, 2, 3, 4, 5, ... (Sec. 1.1)

x-coordinate The abscissa in an xy-coordinate system. (Sec. 3.1)

x-intercept The point at which a graph crosses the x-axis. (Sec. 3.3)

xy-coordinate system A rectangular coordinate system in which the horizontal axis is labeled x and the vertical axis is labeled y. (Sec. 3.1)

y-coordinate The ordinate in an xy-coordinate system. (Sec. 3.1)

y-intercept The point at which a graph crosses the y-axis. (Sec. 3.3)

zero slope The slope of a horizontal line. (Sec. 3.4)

Index

Abacus, 318
Abscissa, 113
Absolute value, 5, 91
  applications of, 95
  and distance, 91
  equations with, 91–92
  inequalities with, 93–94
  of numbers, 5
Absolute-value equations, 91–92
Absolute-value function, graph of, 480
Absolute-value inequality, 93–94
  applications of, 95
Addition
  of additive inverses, 30
  Associative Property of, 29
  Commutative Property of, 29
  of complex numbers, 394–395
  Distributive Property, 30
  of functions, 485
  Inverse Property of, 30
  of polynomials, 256
  of radical expressions, 384
  of rational expressions, 331
  of rational numbers, 19–20
  of real numbers, 17
  verbal phrases for, 37
Addition method of solving systems of equations
  linear systems, 197–198, 202–203
  nonlinear systems, 578–579
Addition Property of Equations, 53
Addition Property of Inequalities, 79
Addition Property of Zero, 29
Additive inverse, 5
  of polynomials, 256
  of real numbers, 5, 30
Algebra, origins of, 240
Algebraic fraction(s), see Rational expression(s)
Algorithm, 240
al-Khowarizmi, 240
Analytic geometry, 113, 186
Antecedent, 361
Antilogarithm, 520
Aphelion, 558
Apollonius, 558
Application problems
  absolute value, 95
  carbon dating, 540
  coins, 65
  compound interest, 539
  current or rate of wind, 217
  distance (rate, time), 73, 349, 450
  distance modulus, 532
  dosage, 592
  exponential decay, 540
  exponential functions, 539–540
  exponential growth, 539
  functions, 140, 160, 472

geometry, 304, 450
  inequalities, 84
  integer, 63
  investment, 191
  linear equations, 140, 160
  logarithms, 540–541
  minimum and maximum of a function, 472
  mixture, 69, 71
  motion, 73, 349, 450
  multiplication of polynomials, 265–266
  percent mixture, 71
  percent-of-light, 541
  pH, 540
  proportions, 342
  Pythagorean Theorem, 403
  quadratic equations, 449
  quadratic functions, 472
  rate of wind or current, 217
  Richter scale, 541
  scientific notation, 248
  sequences and series, 612, 622
  slope, 149
  solving equations by factoring, 304
  solving equations containing radicals, 403–404
  solving first-degree equations in one variable, 63, 65, 69, 71, 73
  stamps, 65
  systems of equations, 191, 217–219
  tolerance, 95
  translating into equations and solving, 40
  two-variable, 140, 160
  uniform motion, 73, 349, 450
  unit price, 44
  value mixture, 69
  variation, 357
  water displacement, 45
  work, 347, 449
Argand diagram, 408
Aristotle, 499
Arithmetic progression, 609
Arithmetic sequence, 609
Arithmetic series, 611
Associative Property of Addition, 29
Associative Property of Multiplication, 29
Asymptotes, 363
  of a hyperbola, 573
Axes, 113
Axis of symmetry
  ellipse, 571
  hyperbola, 573
  parabola, 466, 559, 561

Babylonian mathematics, 52
Base
  of exponential expression, 21, 241

of exponential function, 511
  of logarithmic expression, 519
Binomial expansion, 625–628
Binomial Expansion Formula, 627
Binomial factor, 281
Binomial(s), 253
  expanding powers of, 625–628
  product of, 263
  square of a, 264
Brachistochrone problem, 112

Carbon dating, 540
Cardano, Hieronimo, 408
Center
  of circle, 565
  of ellipse, 571
  of hyperbola, 573
Change-of-Base Formula, 524
Chapter Review, 47, 105, 179, 233, 311, 365, 411, 457, 503, 551, 595, 635
Chapter Summary, 46, 103, 177, 232, 309, 364, 410, 456, 502, 550, 594, 634
Chapter Test, 49, 107, 181, 235, 313, 367, 413, 459, 505, 553, 597, 637
Characteristic of common logarithm, 520
Chord, 175
Circle, 565–567
Clearing denominators, 57, 345
Closed interval, 10
Coefficient, 31
  leading, 253
  of expanded binomial terms, 626
Coefficient determinant, 212
Cofactor, 210
Cofactor expansion of a determinant, 210–211
Coin problems, 65
Combined variation, 356
Combining like terms, 32
Common denominator, 20
  rewrite rational expressions in terms of a, 329
Common difference, in arithmetic sequence, 609
Common logarithm(s), see Logarithm(s)
Common monomial factor, 281
Common ratio, in geometric sequence, 615
Commutative Property of Addition, 29
Commutative Property of Multiplication, 29
Complementary angles, 224
Completing the square, 427–429
  finding equation of circle, 567
  finding vertex of parabola, 487
  geometric method, 454
Complex fraction(s), 23, 337

Complex number(s), 393, 418
    addition and subtraction of, 394–395
    conjugate of, 396
    division of, 398
    geometric description, 408
    multiplication of, 395–396
Composite function, 487
Composite number, 3
Composition, 487
    of inverse function, 494
Compound inequality, 82
Compound interest formula, 539
    continuous, 546
Conditional equation, 53
Conic sections, 558, 559
    circle, 565–567
    ellipse, 571–572
    graphing using a graphing calculator, 593
    hyperbola, 573–574
    parabola, 559–561
Conjugate, 386
    of a complex number, 396
Consecutive integers, 63
Consequent, 361
Constant function, 136
Constant of proportionality, 355
Constant of variation, 355
Constant term, 31
    degree of, 241
    of a perfect-square trinomial, 427
Continued fraction, 362
Contradiction, 53
    proof by, 547
Contrapositive, 361
Convergent, 362
Converse, 361
Coordinate axes, 113
Coordinates, 113
Coordinate system, rectangular, 113
Counterexample, 307
Cramer's Rule, 212–213
Cube, of a variable, 37
Cube root(s), 295, 377
Cubes, sum and difference of, factoring, 295
Cubic function, 253
    graphing, 254, 479
Cumulative Review, 109, 183, 237, 315, 369, 415, 461, 507, 555, 599, 639
Current or rate-of-wind problems, 217
Cycloid, 112

Decimal(s)
    and fractions, 4
    repeating, 4
        writing as fractions, 620
    representing irrational numbers, 4
    representing rational numbers, 4
    and scientific notation, 247
    terminating, 4
Deductive proof, 499
Deductive reasoning, 453
Degree

of a constant term, 241
of a monomial, 241
of a polynomial, 253
of a quadratic equation, 419
of a quadratic trinomial, 283
Denominator(s)
    clearing, 57, 345
    least common multiple of, 20
    of rational expressions, 319
    rationalization of, 387
Dependent system, 188
Dependent variable, 124
Descartes, 113
Descending order, 253
Determinant(s), 209
    cofactor expansion of, 210
    and Cramer's Rule, 212–213
    and solving systems, 212–213
Difference
    common, in arithmetic sequence, 609
    of two cubes, 295
    of two squares, 293
Direct variation, 355
Discriminant, 435, 469–470
Distance
    and absolute value, 5, 91
    motion problems, 73, 349, 450
    between two points in the plane, 116
    between two points on the number line, 91
Distance formula, 116
Distance modulus, 532
Distributive Property, 30
    factoring and, 282
    use in simplifying expressions, 32
    use in solving equations, 57
    use in solving inequalities, 81
Dividend, 271
Division
    of complex numbers, 398
    exponential expressions and, 243–246
    of functions, 485–486
    of polynomials, 271–274
    of radical expressions, 387–388
    of rational expressions, 323
    of rational numbers, 20–21
    of real numbers, 18
    and reciprocals, 18, 21
    synthetic, 273–274
    verbal phrases for, 37
    and zero, 18–19
Domain, 4, 125
    determining from a graph, 481
    of inverse function, 492
    of quadratic function, 465
    of radical function, 480
    of rational function, 319
Dosage, 592
Double root, 419

Egyptian number system, 2

Element
    of a matrix, 209
    of a set, 3
Ellipse, 558, 571–572
Empty set, 7
Endpoint, 10
Equals sign, 464
Equation(s), 53
    with absolute value, 91–92
    Addition Property of, 53
    of circle, 565, 567
    conditional, 53
    dependent, 188
    of ellipse, 571
    exponential, 533–534
    first-degree, 53
    formulas, see Formula(s)
    fractional, 57, 345
    of hyperbola, 573
    identity, 53
    inconsistent, 187
    independent, 187
    linear, see Linear equations
    literal, 58
    logarithmic, 520, 535
    Multiplication Property of, 54
    of parabola, 465–466, 559, 561
    containing parentheses, 57
    quadratic, see Quadratic equation(s)
    radical, 401–402
    rational, 345
    reducible to quadratic, 439–442
    root of, 53
    second-degree, 419
    solution of, 53
    solving, see Solving equations
    systems, see Systems of equations
    in three variables, 200
    in two variables, 114
    of variation, 355–357
Equivalent equations, 53
Euclid, 186
Evaluating determinants, 209–211
Evaluating expressions
    absolute value, 5
    exponential, 21–22
    polynomials, 252, 275–276
    rational, 319
    variable, 31
Evaluating functions, 125, 176, 511
Even integer, 63
Expanding by cofactors, 210
Exponent(s), 21
    base of, 21, 241
    in division, 243–246
    fractional, 373–376
    integers as, 243–244
    irrational, 511
    in multiplication, 241
    negative, 244
    of perfect cubes, 295
    of perfect squares, 293
    raising a power to a power, 242
    rational, 373–376

rules of, 245
zero as, 243
Exponential decay, 540
Exponential equations, 533–534
Exponential expression(s), 21
  division of, 243–246
  evaluating, 21–22
  factored form of, 21
  multiplication of, 241
  and radical expressions, 375–376
  as repeated multiplication, 21
  simplifying, 22, 241–246, 373–374
  writing equivalent logarithmic
    expressions, 519
Exponential form, 21
Exponential function, 511
  applications of, 539–540
  evaluating, 511
  graph of, 513
  inverse of, 519
  natural, 512
  one-to-one property of, 519
  properties of, 513
Exponential growth, 539
Expression(s)
  evaluating, 31
  exponential, 21–22, 241–246,
    373–376
  like terms of, 32
  logarithmic, 519–520
  radical, 375–378, 383–388
  rational, 319
  terms of, 31
  variable, 31
  verbal, 37
Extraneous solution, 402

Factor
  binomial, 281
  common binomial, 282
  common monomial, 281
  greatest common, 281
Factored form of an exponential
  expression, 21
Factorial, 626
Factoring
  applications of, 303
  binomial factor, 281
  common monomial factor, 281
  completely, 297
  difference of two squares, 293–294
  by grouping, 282–283
  perfect square trinomial, 293–294
  solving equations by, 303–304, 419
  solving inequalities by, 445
  sum or difference of two cubes, 295
  trinomials, 283–288
  trinomials that are quadratic in
    form, 296–297
Figurate number, 175
Final exam, 641
Finite sequence, 603
Finite series, geometric, 617–618
Finite set, 7

First-degree equations, solving, 53–57,
  231
First-degree inequalities, 79
  in two-variables, 171
Focus on Problem Solving, 43, 101,
  175, 229, 307, 361, 407, 453, 499,
  547, 591, 631
FOIL method, 263
Formula(s), 58
  for arithmetic sequences and series,
    609, 611
  Binomial Expansion, 627
  Change of Base, for logarithms, 524
  compound interest, 539, 546
  distance, 116
  for distance (rate, time), 73
  for distance between two points on
    the number line, 91
  for geometric sequences and series,
    616, 617, 619
  midpoint, 117
  point-slope, 157
  quadratic, 433
  for the rth term in a Binomial
    Expansion, 627
  simple interest, 191
  slope, 147
  slope-intercept, 151
Fractals, 186, 548
Fraction(s)
  algebraic, see Rational expression(s)
  complex, 23, 337
  continued, 362
  and decimals, 4, 620
  negative exponents on, 245
  reciprocals of, 18
Fractional equations, 57, 345
  reducible to quadratic, 442
Fractional exponents, 373–376
Fractional inequality, 446
Function(s), 124
  applications of, 140
  composite, 487
  composition of polynomial, 487
  constant, 136
  cubic, 253, 479
  domain of, 125
  evaluating, 125, 176, 253
  exponential, 511
  graph of, 132, 254, 479–481; see also
    Graphing Calculator
  greatest-integer, 500
  horizontal line test for, 492
  inverse, 492–494
  linear, 133
  logarithmic, 529, 549
  minimum and maximum of, 471, 501
  one-to-one, 491
  operations on, 485
  polynomial, 253–254, 479
  quadratic, 253, 465
  radical, 480
  ramp, 501
  range of, 125

rational, 319
step, 500
vertical line test for, 480
zeros of, 468
Functional notation, 124

General form of the equation of a
  circle, 567
General term, 603
Geometric progression, 615
Geometric sequence, 615
Geometric series, 617
Golden rectangle, 362, 372
Graph(s)
  of absolute value function, 480
  applications of, 117–118
  with calculator, see Graphing
    calculator
  of circles, 565–566
  of constant functions, 136
  of cubic functions, 254
  of ellipses, 571–572, 593
  of exponential functions, 513
  of functions, 132, 133–139, 363
  of greatest-integer function, 500
  of hyperbolas, 573–574, 593
  of inequalities
    in one variable, 9–10
    in two variables, 171–172
  of linear equation in three variables,
    200–201
  of linear equation in two variables,
    133–139, 151–152
  of linear functions, 133–139,
    151–152
  of logarithmic functions, 529, 549
  of Mandelbrot set, 186
  of nonlinear systems of equations,
    577–579
  of one-to-one functions, 492
  of ordered pair, 113
  of ordered triple, 200
  of parabolas, 465–467, 559–561
  of polynomial functions, 254, 479,
    500
  of quadratic inequalities, 445,
    583–584
  of quadratic functions, 254, 465–467
  of radical functions, 480
  of rational functions, 319, 363
  of rational inequality, 446
  of real numbers, 4
  of scatter diagram, 117–118
  of solution sets of system of
    inequalities, 225, 585
  of systems of linear equations,
    187–188
  of variations, 363
  using x- and y-intercepts, 139
Graphing calculator
  evaluating functions, 176
  finding maximum or minimum of a
    function, 501–502
  graphing conic sections, 593

graphing functions, 145, 176–177, 363, 500–501, 516–518, 532, 538, 459
graphing variation expressions, 303
solving equations, 231, 409, 455
solving inequalities, 456
solving systems, 196, 208, 230, 582
Graph of a function, 133
Greater than, 5
Greatest common factor (GCF), 20, 281
Greatest-integer function, 500
Grouping, factoring by, 282–283
Grouping symbols, 22

Half-open interval, 10
Half-plane, 171
Hieroglyphics, 2
Horizontal axis, 113
Horizontal line test, 492
Hypatia, 559
Hyperbola, 558, 573–574
Hypotenuse, 115, 403

Identity, 53
If-then statements, 361
Imaginary number (*i*), 393, 418
Implication, 361
Inconsistent system, 187
Independent system, 187
Independent variable, 124
Index
of a radical expression, 375
in summation notation, 605
Inductive reasoning, 453
Inequality(ies)
with absolute value, 93–94
Addition Property of, 79
applications of, 84
compound, 82
fractional, 446, 456
graphs of
in one variable, 9–10
in two variables, 171–172, 583–585
linear, 171
Multiplication Property of, 80
nonlinear, 445–446, 583–585
quadratic, 445, 456, 583–584
rational, 446
solution set of
in one variable, 79
in a system of, 225, 585
in two variables, 171, 583
systems of, 225, 585
Inequality symbols, 5
Infinite sequence, 603
Infinite series, geometric, 619
Infinite set, 6
Infinity symbol, 10
Integer problems, 63
Integer(s), 3
consecutive, 63
as exponents, 243–246
negative, 3
positive, 3

Intercepts
of an ellipse, 571
graphing using, 139
of a parabola, 468
x- and *y*-, 138
Interest, 191, 539
Interest rate, 191
International Standard Book Numbers, 632–633
Intersection
point of, 187
of sets, 8
Interval notation, 10
Inverse
additive, 30
of a polynomial, 256
of exponential function, 519
of functions, 492
composition of, 494
condition for, 493
multiplicative, 18, 30
Inverse Property of Addition, 30
Inverse Property of Multiplication, 30
Inverse function, 492
Inverse variation, 356
Investment problems, 191
Irrational number, 4, 383
ISBN, 362–363

Joint variation, 356

Khayyam, Omar, 240

Leading coefficient, 253
Least common multiple (LCM), 20
of polynomials, 329
Legs of a right triangle, 115, 403
Less than, 5
Like terms, 32
Line(s)
equations of, *see* Linear equations
horizontal, 136
parallel, 165
perpendicular, 166
slope of, 147
vertical, 137
Line segment, midpoint of, 116
Linear equation(s), 133
applications of, 140, 160
graphing, 133–139, 151–152, 176–177
slope, 147
slope-intercept form, 151
solution of, 114
systems of, *see* Systems of Equations
in three variables, 200
in two variables, 114, 133
writing, given the slope and a point on the line, 157–158
writing, given two points, 159
x- and *y*-intercepts of, 138
Linear function, 133, 465
applications of, 140
see also Linear equation(s)

Linear inequality, 171
Literal equation, 58, 345
Logarithm(s), 519
antilogarithm, 520
Change of Base Formula for, 524
characteristic of, 520
common, 520
equations, solving, 520, 535
mantissa of, 520
natural, 520
Properties of, 521–523
use in solving exponential equations, 534
Logarithmic equation(s), 519
converting to exponential equations, 519–520
solving, 520
Logarithmic function(s), graphs of, 529, 549
Lower limit, 95

Mandelbrot set, 186
Mantissa of a common logarithm, 520
Matrix, 209–210
Maximum value of a quadratic function, 471
Midpoint formula, 117
Midpoint of a line segment, 116
Minimum value of a quadratic function, 471
Minor of an element of a matrix, 209
Mixture problems, 69, 71
Monomial(s), 241, 253
common factor, 281
degree of, 241
products of, 241
quotients of, 243–246
simplifying powers of, 242
Moscow Papyrus, 52
Motion problems, 73, 349, 450
Multiple, least common, 20
Multiplication
Associative Property of, 29
of binomials, 263
Commutative Property of, 29
of complex numbers, 395–396
Distributive Property, 30
of exponential expressions, 241
FOIL method, 263
of functions, 485
Inverse Property of, 30
of monomials, 241
by one, 30
of polynomials, 261–264
of radical expressions, 385–386
of rational expressions, 322
of rational numbers, 20
of real numbers, 18
verbal phrases for, 37
by zero, 29
Multiplication Property of Equations, 54
Multiplication Property of Inequalities, 80

Multiplication Property of One, 30
Multiplication Property of Zero, 29
Multiplicative inverse, 18, 30

Napier Rods, 510
Natural exponential function, 512
Natural logarithm, 520
Natural number, 3
Negation, 631–632
Negative exponent, 244
Negative infinity symbol, 10
Negative integer, 3
  cube root of, 377
  as an exponent, 244
  square root of, 377
Negative reciprocal, 166
Negative square root, 377
Nonlinear inequalities, 445–446, 456
Nonlinear system of equations,
  577–579
Nonlinear system of inequalities, 585
nth root, 373
Null set, 7
Number line
  distance between two points, 91
  graph of a real number on, 4
Number(s)
  absolute value of, 5
  complex, 393
  composite, 3
  figurative, 175
  imaginary, 393
  integer, 3
  irrational, 4, 383
  natural, 3
  prime, 3
  rational, 3
  real, 4
  triangular, 175
  whole, 3
Numerator determinant, 212
Numerical coefficient, 31

Odd integer, 63
One
  in division, 19
  Multiplication Property of, 30
One-to-one function, 491
One-to-One Property of Exponential
  Functions, 519, 533
One-to-One Property of Logarithms,
  522
Open interval, 10
Opposite, 5
Ordered pair, 113
Ordered triple, 200
Order of a matrix, 209
Order of Operations Agreement, 22–23
Ordinate, 113
Origin, 113

Parabola, 465, 558, 559–561
  axis of symmetry, 466, 559, 561
  equation of, 465–466, 559, 561
  focus of, 558

graphs of, 465–467, 559–561
  intercepts of, 468
  vertex of, 466, 559, 561
Parallel lines, 165
Pascal, Blaise, 625
Pascal's Triangle, 625
Percent mixture problems, 71
Percent-of-light equation, 541
Perfect cube, 295
Perfect square, 293
Perfect-square trinomial, 293
Perihelion, 558
Perpendicular lines, 166
pH equation, 540
Plane, 113
Plot an ordered pair, 113
Point-slope formula, 157
Polya, George, 43
Polya's four-step process, 43–44,
  101–102, 175, 407
Polynomial function(s), 253
  evaluating, 253, 275–276
  graph of, 254, 479, 500
Polynomial(s), 253
  addition and subtraction of, 256–257
  additive inverse of, 256
  binomial, 253
  degree of, 253
  descending order, 253
  division of, 271–274
  factoring, *see* Factoring
  greatest common factor of the terms
    of, 281
  least common multiple of, 329
  monomial, 241, 253
  multiplication of, 261–264
  nonfactorable over the integers, 285
  trinomial, 253
Positive integer, 3
Power(s)
  of exponential expressions, 21–22,
    242
  of products, 242
  verbal phrases for, 37
Power property of logarithms, 522
Prime number, 3
Prime polynomial, 285
Principal, 191
Principal square root, 377
Principle of Zero Products, 303, 419
Product Property of Radicals, 383
Product(s)
  of complex numbers, 395–396
  of conjugates, 386, 396
  expressing trinomials as, 283–288
  of multiplicative inverses, 30
  of polynomials, 261–264
  of radical expressions, 385–386
  simplifying powers of, 242
  of the square of a binomial, 264
  of the sum and difference of two
    terms, 264
  of two binomials, 263
  of two rational expressions, 322

Progression
  arithmetic, 609
  geometric, 615
Projects and Group Activities, 45, 102,
  176, 230, 308, 362, 408, 454, 500,
  548, 592, 632
Proof by contradiction, 547
Proof in mathematics, 499
Property(ies)
  Associative
    of Addition, 29
    of Multiplication, 29
  Commutative
    of Addition, 29
    of Multiplication, 29
  Composition of Inverse Functions,
    494
  Distributive, 30
  of Equations
    Addition, 53
    Multiplication, 54
  of Inequalities
    of Addition, 79
    of Multiplication, 80
  Inverse, of Addition, 30
  Inverse, of Multiplication, 30
  of logarithms, 521–523
  of One, Multiplication, 30
  one-to-one, of exponential functions,
    519
  one-to-one, of logarithms, 522
  Product, of Radicals, 383
  Quotient, of Radicals, 387
  of Raising Both Sides of an Equation
    to a Power, 401
  of Zero, Addition, 29
  of Zero, Multiplication, 29
Proportion, 341
Proportionality, constant of, 355
Pythagorean Theorem, 115, 403
Pythagorean triple, 309

Quadrant, 113
Quadratic equation(s), 303
  applications of, 304
  degree, 419
  discriminant of, 435
  reducible to, 439–442
  solving
    by completing the square,
      427–429
    by factoring, 303–304, 419
    using a graphing calculator, 455
    by quadratic formula, 434–435
    by taking square roots, 421–422
  standard form, 303, 419
  writing, given solutions, 420–421
Quadratic formula, 433
Quadratic function, 253
  graph of, 254, 465–467
  maximum and minimum of, 471
  zeros of, 468
Quadratic inequality, 445, 585–586
Quadratic trinomial, 283

Quotient Property of Radicals, 387
Quotient, Simplifying Powers of, 244

Radical, 375
Radical equation, 401
    graphing, 409
    reducible to quadratic, 440
Radical expression(s)
    addition and subtraction of, 384
    division of, 387–388
    exponential form of, 375–376
    index of, 375
    multiplication of, 385–386
    radicand of, 375
    simplest form of, 383, 387
    simplifying, 377–378, 383–384
Radical function, 480
Radicand, 375
Radius, 565
Ramp function, 501
Range, 125
    determining from a graph, 481
    of quadratic function, 465
Rate
    interest, 191
    motion problems, 73, 349
    in proportions, 341
    in work problems, 347
Rate-of-wind or current problems, 217
Ratio, 341
    common, in geometric sequence, 615
Rational equation, 345
    reducible to quadratic, 442
Rational exponents, 373–376
Rational expression(s), 319
    addition and subtraction of, 331
    division of, 323
    multiplication of, 322
    simplifying, 320
Rational function, 319
    domain of, 319
    graph of, 319, 363
Rational inequality, 446
Rationalizing a denominator, 387–388
Rational number(s), 3
    decimal notation for, 4
    as exponents, 373–376
    operations on, 19–21
Real number(s), 4
    as complex numbers, 394
    graph on the number line, 4
    operations on, 17–18
    Properties of, 29–30
Reciprocal(s), 18
    and division, 18, 21
    negative, 166
    of rational expressions, 323
Recorde, Robert, 464
Rectangle, golden, 362, 372
Rectangular coordinate system, 113
Regression analysis, 118
Relation, 123
Remainder Theorem, 276
Repeating decimal, 4

Reverse Polish Notation, 308
Richter scale, 541
Right triangle, 115, 403
Root(s)
    cube, 295, 377
    double, 419
    of an equation, 53
    nth, 373
    of powers, 377–378
    square, 293, 377
Roster method, 6
Rule for Dividing Exponential
    Expressions, 245
Rule for Multiplying Exponential
    Expressions, 241
Rule of Negative Exponents on
    Fractional Expressions, 245
Rule for Rational Exponents, 373
Rule for Simplifying the Power of an
    Exponential Expression, 242
Rule for Simplifying Powers of
    Products, 242
Rule for Simplifying Powers of
    Quotients, 244
Rule for Writing Exponential
    Expressions as Radical Expressions,
    375
Rules of exponents, 245

Scatter diagrams, 117–118
Scientific notation, 247
    applications of, 248
Second-degree equation, 419
Seismogram, 541
Sequence(s), 603
    applications of, 612
    arithmetic, 609
    finite, 603
    general term of, 603
    geometric, 615
    infinite, 603
    term of, 603
Series, 605
    applications of, 612
    arithmetic, 611
    geometric, 617
    infinite, 619
    variable, 606
Set(s), 2
    empty, 7
    finite, 7
    graphs of, see Graph(s)
    infinite, 6
    intersection of, 8–9
    null, 7
    solution, 79
    union of, 8–10
    Venn diagrams of, 102–103
    writing
        using interval notation, 10
        using roster method, 6
        using set-builder notation, 7
Set-builder notation, 7
Sigma notation, 605

Simple interest, 191
Simplest form
    of an exponential expression, 245
    of a radical expression, 383, 387
    of a rate, 341
    of a ratio, 341
    of a rational expression, 320, 398
Simplifying
    complex fractions, 23, 337
    complex numbers, 383–384
    exponential expressions, 22, 241–246
    expressions with rational exponents,
        373–374
    radical expressions, 377–378,
        383–384
    rational expressions, 320
    variable expressions, 32
Slope-intercept form of linear
    equation, 151
Slope of a line, 147
    applications of, 149
    of parallel lines, 165
    of perpendicular lines, 166
Solution(s)
    of equations, 53
    extraneous, 402
    of inequalities, see Solution set of an
        inequality
    of linear equation in three variables,
        202
    of linear equation in two variables,
        114
    of quadratic equation, see Quadratic
        equation(s)
    repeated, 304
    of system of equations, 187, 202
        approximations of, 230
Solution set of an inequality, 79
    linear, 171
    quadratic, 445, 583
    rational, 446
    system, 585
Solving equations
    with absolute value, 91–92
    using the Addition Property, 53–54,
        56
    exponential, 533–534
    by factoring, 303–304
    first-degree, 53–57, 231
    fractional, 57
    literal, 58
    logarithmic, 535
    using the Multiplication Property,
        54–56
    containing parentheses, 57
    proportions, 341
    quadratic, see Quadratic equation(s)
    containing radical expressions,
        401–402
    rational, 345
    reducible to quadratic, 439–442
    systems of, see Systems of equations
Solving inequalities
    with absolute value, 93–94

using the Addition Property, 79–80
applications of, 84
compound, 82–83
by factoring, 445
fractional, 446, 456
using a graphing calculator, 456
using the Multiplication Property,
80–81
in one variable, 79–83
containing parentheses, 81
quadratic, 445
rational, 446
systems, 585
in two variables, 171–172, 583–584
Solving proportions, 341
Square
of a binomial, 264
perfect, trinomial, 293
of a variable, 37
Square matrix, 209
Square root(s), 377
approximations of, 383
of negative numbers, 377
of a perfect square, 293
principal, 377
taking, in solving equations, 421–422
Stamp problems, 65
Standard form of the equation of a
circle, 565
Standard form of the equation of an
ellipse with center at the origin, 571
Standard form of the equation of a
hyperbola with center at the origin,
573
Standard form of a quadratic equation,
303, 419
Step function, 500
Substitution method
for solving nonlinear systems,
577–578
for solving systems of linear
equations, 189
Subtraction
of complex numbers, 394
of functions, 485
of polynomials, 257
of radical expressions, 384
of rational expressions, 331
of rational numbers, 20
of real numbers, 17
verbal phrases for, 37
Sum
of additive inverses, 30
of *n* terms of
arithmetic series, 611
geometric series, 617
Sum and difference of two terms, 264
Summation notation, 605
Sum or difference of two cubes, 295

Supplementary angles, 224
Symbols
element of, 5
i, 393
inequality, 5
infinity, 10
intersection, 8
m, 147
union, 8
Symmetry, axis of, *see* Axis of
symmetry
Synthetic division, 273–274
Systems of equations, 187
applications of, 191, 217–219
dependent, 188
graphing, 187–188, 230
inconsistent, 187
independent, 187
nonlinear, 577–579
solution of, 187, 202
solving
by addition method, 197–198,
202–203
by using Cramer's Rule, 212–213
by graphing, 187–188, 230
by substitution method, 189
in three variables, 201–202
in two variables, 187
Systems of inequalities, 225, 585

Tangent, 170, 468
Term(s), 31
coefficient of, 31
combining like, 32
constant, 31
degree of, 241
like, 32
of a sequence, 603
Terminating decimal, 4
Tolerance, 95
Tower of Hanoi, 602
Translating verbal expressions into
variable expressions, 37–40
Triangle, right, 115, 403
Triangular number, 175
Trinomial, 253
factoring, 283–288
perfect square, 293
quadratic, 283
quadratic in form, 296
Turning point, 500

Uniform motion problems, 73, 349,
450
Union, of sets, 8
Universal Product Code, 633
UPC numbers, 633
Upper limit, 95

Value of a function, 124

Value mixture problems, 69
Variable, 4
dependent, 124
independent, 124
Variable expression(s), 31
evaluating, 31
like terms of, 32
simplifying, 32
translating into, from verbal
expressions, 37–40
Variable part of a variable term, 31
Variable series, 606
Variable term, 31
Variation, 355–357
Venn diagrams, 102–103
Verbal expressions, translating into
variable expressions, 37–40
Vertex
of a hyperbola, 573
of a parabola, 466, 559, 561
Vertical axis, 113
Vertical line test, 480

Whole numbers, 3
Wind and current problems, 217
Work problems, 347, 449

x-axis, 114
x-coordinate, 114
x-coordinate of the vertex, 466,
559–560, 561
x-intercept(s)
discriminant and, 469–470
of an ellipse, 571
of a line, 138
of a parabola, 468
xy-coordinate system, 114
xyz-coordinate system, 200

y-axis, 114
y-coordinate, 114
y-coordinate of the vertex, 466,
559–560, 561
y-intercept(s)
of an ellipse, 571
of a line, 138

z-axis, 200
Zero of a function, 468
Zero(s)
absolute value of, 5
Addition Property of, 29
in the denominator of a rational
expression, 319
division and, 18–19
as an exponent, 243
Multiplication Property of, 29
Products, Principle of, 303, 419
square root of, 377